W9-BZT-862

Weiss Ratings' Guide to Life and Annuity Insurers

Weiss Ratings'
Guide to
Life and Annuity Insurers

A Quarterly Compilation of Insurance
Company Ratings and Analyses

Winter 2016-17

GREY HOUSE PUBLISHING

Weiss Ratings
4400 Northcorp Parkway
Palm Beach Gardens, FL 33410
561-627-3300

Published by Grey House Publishing, Inc., located at 4919 Route 22, Amenia, NY 12501; telephone 518-789-8700. Grey House Publishing neither guarantees the accuracy of the data contained herein nor assumes any responsibility for errors, omissions or discrepancies. Grey House Publishing accepts no payment for listing; inclusion in the publication of any organization, agency, institution, publication, service or individual does not imply endorsement of the publisher.

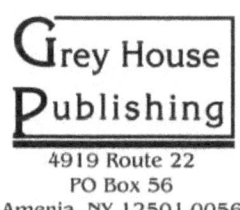

4919 Route 22
PO Box 56
Amenia, NY 12501-0056

Edition No. 106, Winter 2016-17

ISBN: 978-1-68217-422-7
ISSN: 2158-527X

Contents

Terms and Conditions

This document is prepared strictly for the confidential use of our customer(s). It has been provided to you at your specific request. It is not directed to, or intended for distribution to or use by, any person or entity who is a citizen or resident of or located in any locality, state, country or other jurisdiction where such distribution, publication, availability or use would be contrary to law or regulation or which would subject Weiss Ratings or its affiliates to any registration or licensing requirement within such jurisdiction.

No part of the analysts' compensation was, is, or will be, directly or indirectly, related to the specific recommendations or views expressed in this research report.

This document is not intended for the direct or indirect solicitation of business. Weiss Ratings, LLC., and its affiliates disclaims any and all liability to any person or entity for any loss or damage caused, in whole or in part, by any error (negligent or otherwise) or other circumstances involved in, resulting from or relating to the procurement, compilation, analysis, interpretation, editing, transcribing, publishing and/or dissemination or transmittal of any information contained herein.

Weiss Ratings has not taken any steps to ensure that the securities or investment vehicle referred to in this report are suitable for any particular investor. The investment or services contained or referred to in this report may not be suitable for you and it is recommended that you consult an independent investment advisor if you are in doubt about such investments or investment services. Nothing in this report constitutes investment, legal, accounting or tax advice or a representation that any investment or strategy is suitable or appropriate to your individual circumstances or otherwise constitutes a personal recommendation to you.

The ratings and other opinions contained in this document must be construed solely as statements of opinion from Weiss Ratings, LLC., and not statements of fact. Each rating or opinion must be weighed solely as a factor in your choice of an institution and should not be construed as a recommendation to buy, sell or otherwise act with respect to the particular product or company involved.

Past performance should not be taken as an indication or guarantee of future performance, and no representation or warranty, expressed or implied, is made regarding future performance. Information, opinions and estimates contained in this report reflect a judgment at its original date of publication and are subject to change without notice. Weiss Ratings offers a notification service for rating changes on companies you specify. For more information visit WeissRatings.com or call 1-877-934-7778. The price, value and income from any of the securities or financial instruments mentioned in this report can fall as well as rise.

This document and the information contained herein is copyrighted by Weiss Ratings, LLC. Any copying, displaying, selling, distributing or otherwise reproducing or delivering this information or any part of this document to any other person or entity is prohibited without the express written consent of Weiss Ratings, LLC, with the exception of a reviewer or editor who may quote brief passages in connection with a review or a news story.

Message To Insurers

All survey data received on or before October 4, 2016 has been considered or incorporated into this edition of the Directory. If there are particular circumstances which you believe could affect your rating, please use the online survey **(http://weissratings.com/survey/)** or e-mail Weiss Ratings, LLC **(insurancesurvey@weissinc.com)** with documentation to support your request. If warranted, we will make every effort to incorporate the changes in our next edition.

Welcome to Weiss Ratings'
Guide to Life and Annuity Insurers

Most people automatically assume their insurance company will survive, year after year. However, prudent consumers and professionals realize that in this world of shifting risks, the solvency of insurance companies can't be taken for granted.

If you are looking for accurate, unbiased ratings and data to help you choose life and annuity insurance for yourself, your family, your company or your clients, *Weiss Ratings' Guide to Life and Annuity Insurers* gives you precisely what you need.

In fact, it's the only source that currently provides ratings and analyses on 1,000 life and annuity insurers.

Weiss Ratings' Mission Statement

Weiss Ratings' mission is to empower consumers, professionals, and institutions with high quality advisory information for selecting or monitoring a financial services company or financial investment.

In doing so, Weiss Ratings will adhere to the highest ethical standards by maintaining our independent, unbiased outlook and approach to advising our customers.

Why rely on Weiss Ratings?

Weiss Ratings provides fair, objective ratings to help professionals and consumers alike make educated purchasing decisions.

At Weiss Ratings, integrity is number one. Weiss Ratings never takes a penny from insurance companies for its ratings. And, we publish Weiss Safety Ratings without regard for insurers' preferences. However, other rating agencies like A.M. Best, Fitch, Moody's and Standard & Poor's are paid by insurance companies for their ratings and may even suppress unfavorable ratings at an insurer's request.

Our ratings are more frequently reviewed and updated than any other ratings. You can be sure that the information you receive is accurate and current – providing you with advance warning of financial vulnerability early enough to do something about it.

Other rating agencies focus primarily on a company's current claims paying ability and consider only mild economic adversity. Weiss Ratings also considers these issues, but in addition, our analysis covers a company's ability to deal with severe economic adversity and a sharp increase in claims.

Our use of more rigorous standards stems from the viewpoint that an insurance company's obligations to its policyholders should not depend on favorable business conditions. An insurer must be able to honor its policy commitments in bad times as well as good.

Our rating scale, from A to F, is easy to understand. Only a few outstanding companies receive an A (Excellent) rating, although there are many to choose from within the B (Good) category. An even larger group falls into the broad average range which receives C (Fair) ratings. Companies that demonstrate marked vulnerabilities receive either D (Weak) or E (Very Weak) ratings.

How to Use This Guide

The purpose of the *Guide to Life and Annuity Insurers* is to provide policyholders and prospective policy purchasers with a reliable source of insurance company ratings and analyses on a timely basis. We realize that the financial stength of an insurer is an important factor to consider when making the decision to purchase a policy or change companies. The ratings and analyses in this Guide can make that evaluation easier when you are considering:

- Life insurance
- Annuities
- Health insurance
- Guaranteed Investment Contracts (GICs) and other pension products

This Guide also includes ratings for some Blue Cross Blue Shield plans.

The rating for a particular company indicates our opinion regarding that company's ability to meet its commitments to the policyholder – not only under current economic conditions, but also during a declining economy or in an environment of increased liquidity demands.

To use this Guide most effectively, we recommend you follow the steps outlined below:

Step 1 To ensure you evaluate the correct company, verify the company's exact name and state of domicile as it was given to you or appears on your policy. Many companies have similar names but are not related to one another, so you want to make sure the company you look up is really the one you are interested in evaluating.

Step 2 Turn to Section I, the Index of Companies, and locate the company you are evaluating. This section contains all companies analyzed by Weiss Ratings including those that did not receive a Safety Rating. It is sorted alphabetically by the name of the company and shows the state of domicile following the name for additional verification. Once you have located your specific company, the first column after the state of domicile shows its Weiss Safety Rating. Turn to *About Weiss Safety Ratings* for information about what this rating means. If the rating has changed since the last issue of this Guide, a downgrade will be indicated with a down triangle ▼ to the left of the company name; an upgrade will be indicated with an up triangle ▲.

Step 3 Following Weiss Safety Rating are some of the various indexes that our analysts used in rating the company. Refer to the Critical Ranges In Our Indexes table for an interpretation of which index values are considered strong, good, fair or weak. You can also turn to the introduction of Section I to see what each of these factors measures. In most cases, lower rated companies will have a low index value in one or more of the factors shown. Bear in mind, however, that Weiss Safety Rating is the result of a complex qualitative and quantitative analysis which cannot be reproduced using only the data provided here.

Step 4 The quality of a company's investment portfolio – bonds, mortgages and other investments – is an integral part of our analysis. So, the right hand page of Section I shows you where the company has invested its premiums. Again, refer to the introduction of Section I for a description of each investment category.

Step 5 Some insurers have a bullet ● preceding the company name on the right hand page of Section I. If the company you are evaluating is identified with a bullet, turn to Section II, the Analysis of Largest Companies, and locate it there (otherwise skip to step 8). Section II contains the largest insurers rated by Weiss Ratings, regardless of rating. It too is sorted alphabetically by the name of the company.

Step 6 Once you have identified your company in Section II, you will find its Safety Rating and a description of the rating immediately to the right of the company name. Then, below the company name is a description of the various rating factors that were considered in assigning the company's rating. These factors and the information below them are designed to give you a better feel for the company and its strengths and weaknesses. See the Section II introduction, to get a better understanding of what each of these factors means.

Step 7 To the right, you will find a five-year summary of the company's Safety Rating, capitialization and income. Look for positive or negative trends in this data. Below the five-year summary, we have included a graphic illustration of the most critical factor or factors impacting the company's rating. Again, the Section II introduction provides an overview of the content of each graph or table.

Step 8 If the company you are evaluating is not highly rated and you want to find an insurer with a higher rating, turn to the page in Section IV that has your state's name at the top. This section contains those Recommended Companies (rating of A+, A, A- or B+) that are licensed to underwrite insurance in your state, sorted by rating. From here you can select a company and then refer back to Sections I and II to analyze it.

Step 9 If you decide that you would like to contact one of Weiss Recommended Companies about obtaining a policy or for additional information, refer to Section III. Following each company's name is its address and phone number to assist you in making contact.

Step 10 In order to use Weiss Safety Ratings most effectively, we strongly recommend you consult the Important Warnings and Cautions listed. These are more than just "standard disclaimers"; they are very important factors you should be aware of before using this Guide. If you have any questions regarding the precise meaning of specific terms used in the Guide, refer to the Glossary.

Step 11 The Appendix contains information about State Guaranty Associations and the types of coverage they provide to policyholders when an insurance company fails. Keep in mind that while guaranty funds have now been established in all states, many do not cover all types of insurance. Furthermore, all of these funds have limits on their amount of coverage. Use the table to determine whether the level of coverage is applicable to your policy and the limits are adequate for your needs. You should pay particular attention to the notes regarding whether the coverage is for residents of the state or companies domiciled in the state.

Step 12 If you want more information on your state's guaranty fund, call the State Commissioner's Office directly.

Step 13 Keep in mind that good coverage from a state guaranty association is no substitute for dealing with a financially strong company. Weiss Ratings only recommends those companies which we feel are most able to stand on their own, without regard to what might happen in case the company does fail.

Step 14   Make sure you stay up to date with the latest information available since the publication of this Guide.   For information on how to set up a rating change notification service, acquire follow-up reports or receive a more in-depth analysis of an individual company, call 1-877-934-7778 or visit www.weissratings.com.

Data Sources: Annual and quarterly statutory statements filed with state insurance commissioners and data provided by the insurance companies being rated. The National Association of Insurance Commissioners has provided some of the raw data. Any analyses or conclusions are not provided or endorsed by the NAIC.

Date of data analyzed: June 30, 2016 unless otherwise noted.

About Weiss Safety Ratings

The Weiss Ratings of insurers are based upon the annual and quarterly financial statements obtained from state insurance commissioners. This data may be supplemented by information that we request from the insurance companies themselves. However, if a company chooses not to provide supplemental data, we reserve the right to rate the company based exclusively on publicly available data.

The Weiss Ratings are based on a complex analysis of hundreds of factors that are synthesized into a series of indexes: capitalization, investment safety (life, health and annuity companies only), reserve adequacy (property and casualty companies only), profitability, liquidity, and stability. These indexes are then used to arrive at a letter grade rating. A weak score on any one index can result in a low rating, as financial problems can be caused by any one of a number of factors, such as inadequate capital, unpredictable claims experience, poor liquidity, speculative investments, inadequate reserving, or consistent operating losses.

Our **Capital Index** gauges capital adequacy in terms of each insurer's ability to handle a variety of business and economic scenarios as they may impact investment performance, claims experience, persistency, and market position. The index combines two Risk-Adjusted Capital ratios as well as a leverage test that examines pricing risk.

Our **Investment Safety Index** measures the exposure of the company's investment portfolio to loss of principal and/or income due to default and market risks. Each investment area is rated by a factor that takes into consideration both quality and liquidity. (This factor is measured as a separate index only for life, health, and annuity insurers.)

Our **Profitability Index** measures the soundness of the company's operations and the contribution of profits to the company's financial strength. The profitability index is a composite of five sub-factors: 1) gain or loss on operations; 2) consistency of operating results; 3) impact of operating results on surplus; 4) adequacy of investment income as compared to the needs of policy reserves (life, health and annuity companies only); and 5) expenses in relation to industry norms for the types of policies that the company offers.

Our **Liquidity Index** evaluates a company's ability to raise the necessary cash to settle claims and honor cash withdrawal obligations. We model various cash flow scenarios, applying liquidity tests to determine how the company might fare in the event of an unexpected spike in claims and/or a run on policy surrenders.

Our **Stability Index** integrates a number of sub-factors that affect consistency (or lack thereof) in maintaining financial strength over time. These sub-factors will vary depending on the type of insurance company being evaluated but may include such things as 1) risk diversification in terms of company size, group size, number of policies in force, types of policies written, and use of reinsurance; 2) deterioration of operations as reported in critical asset, liability, income and expense items, such as surrender rates and premium volume; 3) years in operation; 4) former problem areas where, despite recent improvement, the company has yet to establish a record of stable performance over a suitable period of time; 5) a substantial shift in the company's operations; 6) potential instabilities such as reinsurance quality, asset/liability matching, and sources of capital; and 7) relationships with holding companies and affiliates.

In order to help guarantee our objectivity, we reserve the right to publish ratings expressing our opinion of a company's financial stability based exclusively on publicly available data and our own proprietary standards for safety.

Each of these indexes is measured according to the following range of values.

What Our Ratings Mean

A   **Excellent.** The company offers excellent financial security. It has maintained a conservative stance in its investment strategies, business operations and underwriting commitments. While the financial position of any company is subject to change, we believe that this company has the resources necessary to deal with severe economic conditions.

B   **Good.** The company offers good financial security and has the resources to deal with a variety of adverse economic conditions. It comfortably exceeds the minimum levels for all of our rating criteria, and is likely to remain healthy for the near future. However, in the event of a severe recession or major financial crisis, we feel that this assessment should be reviewed to make sure that the firm is still maintaining adequate financial strength.

C   **Fair.** The company offers fair financial security and is currently stable. But during an economic downturn or other financial pressures, we feel it may encounter difficulties in maintaining its financial stability.

D   **Weak.** The company currently demonstrates what, in our opinion, we consider to be significant weaknesses which could negatively impact policyholders. In an unfavorable economic environment, these weaknesses could be magnified.

E   **Very Weak.** The company currently demonstrates what we consider to be significant weaknesses and has also failed some of the basic tests that we use to identify fiscal stability. Therefore, even in a favorable economic environment, it is our opinion that policyholders could incur significant risks.

F   **Failed.** The company is deemed failed if it is either 1) under supervision of an insurance regulatory authority; 2) in the process of rehabilitation; 3) in the process of liquidation; or 4) voluntarily dissolved after disciplinary or other regulatory action by an insurance regulatory authority.

+   The **plus sign** is an indication that the company is in the upper third of the letter grade.

-   The **minus sign** is an indication that the company is in the lower third of the letter grade.

U   **Unrated.** The company is unrated for one or more of the following reasons: (1) total assets are less than $1 million; (2) premium income for the current year was less than $100,000; or (3) the company functions almost exclusively as a holding company rather than as an underwriter; or, (4) in our opinion, we do not have enough information to reliably issue a rating.

How Our Ratings Differ From Those of Other Services

Weiss Safety Ratings are conservative and consumer-oriented. We use tougher standards than other rating agencies because our system is specifically designed to inform risk-averse consumers about the financial strength of life and annuity insurers.

Our rating scale (A to F) is easy to understand by the general public. Users can intuitively understand that an A+ rating is at the top of the scale rather than in the middle like some of the other rating agencies.

Other rating agencies give top ratings more generously so that most companies receive excellent ratings.

More importantly, other rating agencies focus primarily on a company's *current* claims paying ability or consider only relatively mild economic adversity. We also consider these scenarios but extend our analysis to cover a company's ability to deal with severe economic adversity and potential liquidity problems. This stems from the viewpoint that an insurance company's obligations to its policyholders should not be contingent upon a healthy economy. The company must be capable of honoring its policy commitments in bad times as well.

Looking at the insurance industry as a whole, we note that several major rating firms have poor historical track records in identifying troubled companies. The 1980s saw a persistent decline in capital ratios, increased holdings of risky investments in the life and health industry as well as recurring long-term claims liabilities in the property and casualty industry. Despite these clear signs that insolvency risk was rising, other rating firms failed to downgrade at-risk insurance companies. Instead, they often rated companies by shades of excellence, understating the gravity of potential problems.

They have not issued clear warnings that the ordinary consumer can understand. Few, if any, companies receive "weak" or "poor" ratings. Surely, weak companies do exist. However, the other rating agencies apparently do not view themselves as consumer advocates with the responsibility of warning the public about the risks involved in doing business with such companies.

Additionally, these firms will at times agree *not* to issue a rating if a company denies them permission to do so. In short, too often insurance rating agencies work hand-in-glove with the companies they rate.

At Weiss Ratings, although we seek to maintain good relationships with the firms, we owe our primary obligation to the consumer, not the industry. We reserve the right to rate companies based on publicly available data and make the necessary conservative assumptions when companies choose not to provide the additional data we request.

Comparison of Insurance Company Rating Agency Scales

Weiss Ratings [a]	Best [a,b]	S&P [c]	Moody's	Fitch [d]
A+, A, A-	A++, A+	AAA	Aaa	AAA
B+, B, B-	A, A-	AA+, AA AA-	Aa1, Aa2, Aa3	AA+, AA, AA-
C+, C, C-	B++, B+,	A+, A, A-, BBB+, BBB, BBB-	A1, A2, A3, Baa1, Baa2, Baa3	A+, A, A-, BBB+, BBB, BBB-
D+, D, D-	B, B- C++, C+, C, C-	BB+, BB, BB-, B+, B, B-	Ba1, Ba2, Ba3, B1, B2, B3	BB+, BB, BB-, B+, B, B-
E+, E, E- F	D E, F	CCC R	Caa, Ca, C	CCC+, CCC, CCC- DD

[a] Weiss Ratings and Best use additional symbols to designate that they recognize an insurer's existence but do not provide a rating. These symbols are not included in this table.

[b] Best added the A++, B++ and C++ ratings in 1992. In 1994, Best classified its ratings into "secure" and "vulnerable" categories, changed the definition of its "B" and "B-" ratings from "good" to "adequate" and assigned these ratings to the "vulnerable" category. This table contains GAO's assignment of Best's ratings to bands based on our interpretation of their rating descriptions prior to 1994.

[c] S&P discontinued CCC "+" and "-" signs, CC, C and D ratings and added the R rating in 1992.
Source: 1994 GAO *Insurance Ratings* study.

[d] Duff & Phelps Credit Rating Co. merged with Fitch IBCA in 2000, and minor changes were made to the rating scale at that time. These changes were not reflected in the GAO's 1994 study, but *are* reflected in the chart.

Rate of Insurance Company Failures

Weiss Ratings provides quarterly Safety Ratings for thousands of insurance companies each year. Weiss Ratings strives for fairness and objectivity in its ratings and analyses, ensuring that each company receives the rating that most accurately depicts its current financial status, and more importantly, its ability to deal with severe economic adversity and a sharp increase in claims. Weiss Ratings has every confidence that its Safety Ratings provide an accurate representation of a company's stability.

In order for these ratings to be of any true value, it is important that they prove accurate over time. One way to determine the accuracy of a rating is to examine those insurance companies that have failed, and their respective Weiss Safety Ratings. A high percentage of failed companies with "A" ratings would indicate that Weiss Ratings is not being conservative enough with its "secure" ratings, while conversely, a low percentage of failures with "vulnerable" ratings would show that Weiss Ratings is overly conservative.

Over the past 27 years (1989–2015) Weiss Ratings has rated 615 insurance companies, for all industries, that subsequently failed. The chart below shows the number of failed companies in each rating category, the average number of companies rated in each category per year, and the percentage of annual failures for each letter grade.

	Safety Rating	Number of Failed Companies	Average Number of Companies Rated per year	Percentage of Failed Companies per year (by ratings category)*
Secure	A	1	155	0.02%
	B	6	1,102	0.02%
	C	69	1,615	0.16%
Vulnerable	D	268	756	1.31%
	E	271	217	4.62%

A=Excellent, B=Good, C=Fair, D=Weak, E=Very Weak

On average, only 0.10% of the companies Weiss Ratings rates as "secure" fail each year. On the other hand, an average of 2.05% of the companies Weiss Ratings rates as "vulnerable" fail annually. That means that a company rated by Weiss Ratings as "Vulnerable" is 20.9 times more likely to fail than a company rated as "Secure".

When considering a Weiss safety rating, one can be sure that they are getting the most fair, objective, and accurate financial rating available anywhere.

*Percentage of Failed Companies per year = (Number of Failed Companies) / [(Average Number of Companies Rated per year) x (years in study)]

Data as of December 2015 for Life & Annuity Insurers, Property & Casualty Insurers and Health Insurers.

What Does Average Mean?

At Weiss Ratings, we consider the words average and fair to mean just that – average and fair. So when we assign our ratings to insurers, a large percentage of companies receive an average C rating. That way, you can be sure that a company receiving Weiss B or A rating is truly above average. Likewise, you can feel confident that companies with D or E ratings are truly below average. In recent years, life and health insurers have experienced consistent, solid performance resulting in a shift in the rating distribution so that more insurers than ever are rated B or better.

Current Weiss Ratings Distribution for Life and Annuity Insurers

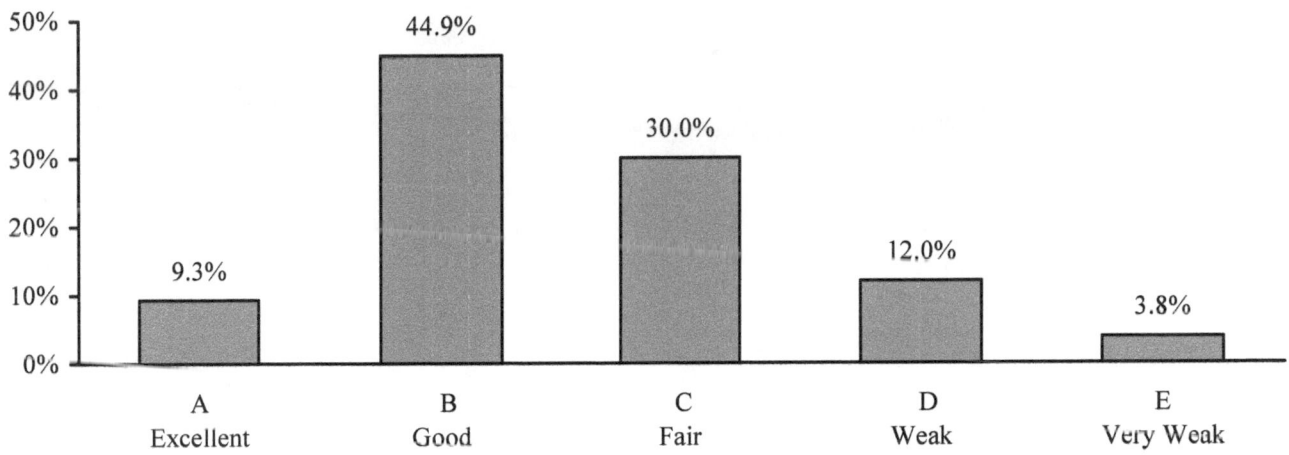

Important Warnings and Cautions

1. A rating alone cannot tell the whole story. Please read the explanatory information contained in this publication. It is provided in order to give you an understanding of our rating philosophy, as well as paint a more complete picture of how we arrive at our opinion of a company's strengths and weaknesses.

2. Weiss Safety Ratings represent our opinion of a company's insolvency risk. As such, a high rating means we feel that the company has less chance of running into financial difficulties. A high rating is not a guarantee of solvency nor is a low rating a prediction of insolvency. Weiss Safety Ratings are not deemed to be a recommendation concerning the purchase or sale of the securities of any insurance company that is publicly owned.

3. Company performance is only one factor in determining a rating. Conditions in the marketplace and overall economic conditions are additional factors that may affect the company's financial strength. Therefore, a rating upgrade or downgrade does not necessarily reflect changes in the company's profits, capital or other financial measures, but may be due to external factors. Likewise, changes in Weiss indexes may reflect changes in our risk assessment of business or economic conditions as well as changes in company performance.

4. All firms that have the same Safety Rating should be considered to be essentially equal in strength. This is true regardless of any differences in the underlying numbers which might appear to indicate greater strengths. Weiss Safety Rating already takes into account a number of lesser factors which, due to space limitations, cannot be included in this publication.

5. A good rating requires consistency. If a company is excellent on four indicators and fair on one, the company may receive a fair rating. This requirement is necessary due to the fact that fiscal problems can arise from any *one* of several causes including speculative investments, inadequate capital resources or operating losses.

6. We are an independent rating agency and do not depend on the cooperation of the companies we rate. Our data are derived, for the most part, from annual and quarterly financial statements that we obtain from federal banking regulators and state insurance commissioners. The latter may be supplemented by information insurance companies voluntarily provide upon request. Although we seek to maintain an open line of communication with the companies, we do not grant them the right to stop or influence publication of the ratings. This policy stems from the fact that this publication is designed for the protection of the consumer.

7. Affiliated companies do not automatically receive the same rating. We recognize that a troubled company may expect financial support from its parent or affiliates. Weiss Safety Ratings reflect our opinion of the measure of support that may become available to a subsidiary , if the subsidiary were to experience serious financial difficulties. In the case of a strong parent and a weaker subsidiary, the affiliate relationship will generally result in a higher rating for the subsidiary than it would have on a stand-alone basis. Seldom, however, would the rating be brought up to the level of the parent. This treatment is appropriate because we do not assume the parent would have either the resources or the will to "bail out" a troubled subsidiary during a severe economic crisis. Even when there is a binding legal obligation for a parent corporation to honor the policy obligations of its subsidiaries, the possibility exists that the subsidiary could be sold and lose its parental support. Therefore, it is quite common for one affiliate to have a higher rating than another. This is another reason why it is especially important that you have the precise name of the company you are evaluating.

Section I

Index of Companies

An analysis of all rated and unrated

U.S. Life and Annuity Insurers.

Companies are listed in alphabetical order.

Section I Contents

This section contains the key rating factors and investment portfolio analysis for all rated and unrated insurers analyzed by Weiss Ratings. An explanation of each of the footnotes and stability factors appears at the end of this section.

Left Pages

1. **Insurance Company Name**

    The legally registered name, which can sometimes differ from the name that the company uses for advertising. If you cannot find the company you are interested in, or if you have any doubts regarding the precise name, verify the information with the company before looking the name up in this Guide. Also, determine the domicile state for confirmation. (See column 2.)

2. **Domicile State**

    The state which has primary regulatory responsibility for the company. It may differ from the location of the company's corporate headquarters. You do not have to be living in the domicile state to purchase insurance from this firm, provided it is licensed to do business in your state.

    Also use this column to confirm that you have located the correct company. It is possible for two unrelated companies to have the same name if they are domiciled in different states.

3. **Safety Rating**

    Our rating is measured on a scale from A to F and considers a wide range of factors. Please see What Our Ratings Mean for specific descriptions of each letter grade. Also, refer to how our ratings differ from those of other rating agencies. Most important, when using this rating, please be sure to consider the warnings regarding the ratings' limitations and the underlying assumptions. Notes in this column refer to the date of the data included in the rating evaluation and are explained.

4. **Total Assets**

    All assets admitted by state insurance regulators in millions of dollars. This includes investments, current business assets, and separate accounts. The year-end figure is used to correspond with the figures on the right-hand pages, some of which are only available on an annual basis.

    The overall size is an important factor which affects the ability of a company to manage risk. Mortality, morbidity (sickness) and investment risks can be more effectively diversified by large companies. Because the insurance business is based on probability, the number of policies must be large enough so that actuarial statistics are valid. Life insurance policies, for example, are based on mortality tables containing the expected number of deaths per thousand at various ages.

    The larger the number of policyholders, the more reliable the actuarial projections will be. A large company with a correspondingly large policy base can spread its risk and minimize the effects of claims experience that exceeds actuarial expectations.

5. Capital and Surplus

The company's statutory net worth in millions of dollars. Consumers may wish to limit the size of any policy so that the policyholder's maximum benefits do not exceed approximately 1% of the company's capital and surplus. For example, when buying a policy from a company with capital and surplus of $10,000,000, the 1% limit would be $100,000. (When performing this calculation, do not forget that figures in this column are expressed in millions of dollars.)

Critical Ranges In Our Indexes and Ratios

Indicators	Strong	Good	Fair	Weak
Risk-Adjusted Capital Ratio #1	—	1.0 or more	0.75 - 0.99	0.74 or less
Risk-Adjusted Capital Ratio #2	1.0 or more	0.75 - 0.99	0.5 - 0.74	0.49 or less
Capitalization Index	6.9 – 10	4.9 - 6.8	2.9 - 4.8	Less than 2.9
5 Year Profitability Index	6.9 – 10	4.9 - 6.8	2.9 - 4.8	Less than 2.9
Liquidity Index	6.9 – 10	4.9 - 6.8	2.9 - 4.8	Less than 2.9
Investment Safety Index	6.9 – 10	4.9 - 6.8	2.9 - 4.8	Less than 2.9
Stability Index	6.9 – 10	4.9 - 6.8	2.9 - 4.8	Less than 2.9

6. Risk-Adjusted Capital Ratio #1

This ratio examines the adequacy of the company's capital base and whether the company has sufficient capital resources to cover potential losses which might occur in an average recession or other moderate loss scenario. Specifically, the figure cited in the table answers the question: For every dollar of capital that we feel would be needed, how many dollars in capital resources does the company actually have? (See the table above for the levels which we believe are critical.) You may find that some companies have unusually high levels of capital. This often reflects special circumstances related to the small size or unusual operations of the company.

7. Risk-Adjusted Capital Ratio #2

This is similar to item 6. But in this case, the question relates to whether the company has enough capital cushion to withstand a *severe* recession or other severe loss scenario.

8. Capitalization Index

An index that measures the adequacy of the company's capital resources to deal with a variety of business and economic scenarios. It combines Risk-Adjusted Capital Ratios #1 and #2 as well as a leverage test that examines pricing risk. (See the table above for the levels which we believe are critical.)

9. Investment Safety Index

An index that measures the exposure of the company's investment portfolio to a loss of principal and/or income due to default and market risks. It is the composite of a series of elements, some of which are shown on the right pages. Each investment area is rated by a factor that takes into consideration both quality and liquidity. (See the table on the next page for the levels which we believe are critical.)

10. 5-Year Profitability Index

An index that measures the soundness of the company's operations and the contribution of profits to the company's fiscal strength. The Profitability Index is a composite of five factors: (1) gain or loss on operations; (2) consistency of operating results; (3) impact of operating results on surplus; (4) adequacy of investment income as compared to the needs of policy reserves; and (5) expenses in relation to industry averages for the types of policies that the company offers.

This factor is especially important among health insurers including Blue Cross Blue Shield companies that rely more heavily on current earnings than do life and annuity writers. After factoring out the normal cycle, companies with stable earnings and capital growth are viewed more favorably than those whose results are erratic from year to year. (See the table for the levels which we believe are critical.)

11. Liquidity Index

An index which measures the company's ability to raise the necessary cash to meet policyholder obligations. This index includes a stress test which considers the consequences of a spike in claims or a run on policy surrenders. Sometimes a company may appear to have the necessary resources, but may be unable to sell its investments at the prices at which they are valued in the company's financial statements. (See the table for the levels which we believe are critical.)

12. Stability Index

An index which integrates a number of factors such as: (1) risk diversification in terms of company size, number of policies in force, use of reinsurance and other items related to spread of risk; (2) deterioration of operations as reported in critical asset, liability, income or expense items such as surrender rates and premium volume; (3) former problem areas where, despite recent improvement, the company has yet to establish a record of stable performance over a suitable period of time; (4) a substantial shift in the company's operations; (5) potential instabilities such as reinsurance quality, asset/liability matching and sources of capital; plus (6) relationships to holding companies and affiliates. (See the table for the levels which we believe are critical.)

| 13. Stability Factors | Indicates those specific areas that have negatively impacted the company's Stability Index. |

Right Pages

| 1. Net Premiums | The amount of insurance premiums received from policyholders less any premiums that have been transferred to other companies through reinsurance agreements. Generally speaking, companies with large net premium volume generally have more predictable claims experience. |

| 2. Invested Assets | The value of the firm's total investment portfolio, measured in millions of dollars. The year-end figure is used to correspond with the following figures, some of which are only available on an annual basis. Use the figure in this column to determine the actual dollar amounts invested in each asset category shown in columns 3 through 11 on the right-side pages. For example, if the firm has $500 million in invested assets and column 3 shows that 10% of its portfolio is in cash, the company has $50 million in cash. |
| | Looking at the right-side pages, columns 3 through 11 will, unless otherwise noted, add up to approximately 100%. Column 12 (investments in affiliates) is already included in other columns (usually 4, 5 or 6) depending upon the specific investment vehicle. |

| 3. Cash | Cash on hand and demand deposits. A negative cash position implies checks outstanding exceed cash balances, a situation not unusual for insurance companies. |

| 4. CMOs (Collateralized Mortgage Obligations) and Other Structured Securities | Mortgage-backed bonds that split the payments from mortgage pools into different classes, called tranches. The split may be based on maturity dates or a variety of other factors. For example, the owner of one type of CMO, called a PAC, receives principal and interest payments made by the mortgage holders between specific dates. The large majority of CMOs held by insurance companies are those issued by government agencies and carry very little risk of default. Virtually all of the CMOs included here are investment grade. However, they all carry some measure of risk based on the payment speed of the underlying mortgages. |

5. **Other Investment Grade Bonds**

All investment grade bonds other than the CMOs included in column 4. Specifically, this includes: (1) issues guaranteed by U.S. and foreign governments which are rated as "highest quality" (Class 1) by state insurance commissioners; (2) nonguaranteed obligations of governments, such as Fannie Maes, which do not carry full faith and credit guarantees; (3) obligations of governments rated as "high quality" (Class 2) by state insurance commissioners; (4) state and municipal bonds; plus (5) investment-grade corporate bonds as defined by the state insurance commissioners. The data shown in this column are based exclusively on the definition used by state insurance commissioners. However, on the companies for which a more detailed breakdown of bond ratings is available, the actual bond ratings - and not the data shown in this column - are used in our rating process to calculate the Investment Safety Index.

6. **Noninvestment Grade Bonds**

Low-rated issues – commonly known as "junk bonds" – which carry a high risk as defined by the state insurance commissioners. In an unfavorable economic environment, we generally assume that these will be far more subject to default than other categories of corporate bonds.

7. **Common and Preferred Stock**

Common and preferred equities. Although a certain amount is acceptable for the sake of diversification, excessive investment in this area is viewed as a factor that can increase the company's overall vulnerability to market declines.

8. **Mortgages In Good Standing**

Mortgages which are current in their payments. Mortgage-backed securities are excluded.

9. **Non-performing Mortgages**

Mortgages which are (a) 90 days or more past due; or (b) in process of foreclosure. If the mortgages have already been foreclosed, the asset is transferred to the next category - real estate. Clearly, a high level of nonperforming mortgages is a negative, reflecting on the quality of the entire mortgage portfolio.

10. **Real Estate**

Direct real estate investments including (a) property occupied by the company; and (b) properties acquired through foreclosure. A certain amount of real estate investment is considered acceptable for portfolio diversification. However, excessive amounts may subject the company to losses during a recessionary period.

11. **Other Investments**

Items such as premium notes, collateral loans, short-term investments, policy loans and a long list of miscellaneous items.

12. Investments in Affiliates   Bonds, preferred and common stocks, as well as other vehicles which many insurance companies use to invest in - and establish a corporate link with - affiliated companies. Since these can often be non-income-producing paper assets, they are considered less desirable than the equivalent securities of publicly traded companies. Investments in affiliates are also included in other columns (usually 4, 5 or 6). Therefore, the percentage shown here represents a duplication of some of the amounts shown in the other columns.

Footnotes:

(1)   Data items shown are from the company's 2015 annual statutory statement except for Risk-Adjusted Capital Indexes 1 and 2, Profitability Index, Investment Safety Index, Liquidity Index and Stability Index which have been updated using the company's March 2016 quarterly statutory statement. Other more recent data may have been factored into the rating when available.

(2)   Data items shown are from the company's 2015 annual statutory statement. Other more recent data may have been factored into the rating when available.

(3)   Data items shown are from the company's 2014 annual statutory statement except for Risk-Adjusted Capital Indexes 1 and 2, Profitability Index, Investment Safety Index, Liquidity Index and Stability Index which have been updated using the company's September 2015 quarterly statutory statement. Other more recent data may have been factored into the rating when available.

(4)   Data items shown are from the company's 2014 annual statutory statement except for Risk-Adjusted Capital Indexes 1 and 2, Profitability Index, Investment Safety Index, Liquidity Index and Stability Index which have been updated using the company's June 2015 quarterly statutory statement. Other more recent data may have been factored into the rating when available.

(5)   These companies have data items that are older than March 31, 2015. They will be unrated (U) if they are not failed companies (F).

(*)   Breakdown of the company's investment portfolio, shown in percentages in columns 3-11 on the right hand page, does not total to 100% due to the inclusion of non–admitted assets in the bond or mortgage figures, or due to other accounting adjustments.

Stability Factors

(A)   Stability Index was negatively impacted by the financial problems or weaknesses of a parent or **affiliate** company.

(C)   Stability Index was negatively impacted by past results on our Risk-Adjusted **Capital** tests. In general, the Stability Index of any company can be affected by past results even if current results show improvement. While such improvement is a plus, the improved results must be maintained for a period of time to assure that the improvement is not a temporary fluctuation. During a five-year period, the impact of poor past results on the Stability Index gradually diminishes.

(D)   Stability Index was negatively impacted by limited **diversification** of general business, policy, and/or investment risk. This factor especially affects smaller companies that do not issue as many policies as larger firms. It can also affect firms that specialize in only one line of business.

(E)   Stability Index was negatively impacted due to a lack of operating **experience**. The company has been in operation for less than five years. Consequently, it has not been able to establish the kind of stable track record that we believe is needed to demonstrate financial permanence and strength.

(F)   Stability Index was negatively impacted by negative cash **flow**. In other words, the company paid out more in claims and expenses than it received in premiums and investment income.

(G)   Stability Index was negatively impacted by fast asset or premium **growth**. Fast growth can pose a serious problem for insurers. It is generally achieved by offering policies with premiums that are too low, benefits that are too costly, or agents commissions that are too high. Due to the highly competitive nature of the insurance marketplace, rapid growth has been a factor in many insurance insolvencies.

(I)   Stability Index was negatively impacted by past results on our **Investment** Safety Index. This can pose a problem for insurers even after risky investments have been sold off. To illustrate, consider those companies that have sold off their junk bonds and now carry much smaller junk bond risk. For a period of time the company that had the junk bonds incorporated the expectation of higher yields into its policy design and marketing strategy. Only time will tell how the company's investment income margins and future sales will be affected by the junk bond sell off. So, while the Investment Safety Index would improve right away, the Stability Index would improve only gradually over a period of three years, if the transition to lower yielding investments is handled smoothly.

(L)   Stability Index was negatively impacted by past results on our **liquidity** tests. In general, the Stability Index of any company can be affected by past results even if current results show improvement. While such improvement is a plus, the improved results must be maintained for a period of time to assure that the improvement is not a temporary fluctuation. During a five-year period, the impact of poor past results on the Stability Index gradually diminishes.

(O)   Stability Index was negatively impacted by significant changes in the company's business **operations**. These changes can include shifts in the kinds of insurance offered by the company, a temporary or permanent freeze on the sale of new policies, or recent release from conservatorship. In these circumstances, past performance cannot be a reliable indicator of future financial strength.

(R)   Stability Index was negatively impacted by concerns about the financial strength of its **reinsurers**.

(T)   Stability Index was negatively impacted by significant **trends** in critical asset, liability, income or expense items. Examples include increasing surrender rates, increasing mortgage defaults, and shrinking premium volume.

(Z)   This company is unrated due to data, as received by Weiss Ratings, that are either incomplete in substantial ways or contain items that, in the opinion of Weiss Ratings analysts, may not be reliable.

INSURANCE COMPANY NAME	DOM. STATE	RATING		TOTAL ASSETS ($MIL)	CAPITAL & SURPLUS ($MIL)	RISK ADJUSTED CAPITAL RATIO 1	RISK ADJUSTED CAPITAL RATIO 2	CAPITAL- IZATION INDEX (PTS)	INVEST. SAFETY INDEX (PTS)	PROFIT- ABILITY INDEX (PTS)	LIQUIDITY INDEX (PTS)	STAB. INDEX (PTS)	STABILITY FACTORS
4 EVER LIFE INS CO	IL	A		211.4	93.5	5.60	3.68	10.0	5.9	7.4	6.9	6.1	ADIT
AAA LIFE INS CO	MI	B		612.8	142.8	2.90	1.71	8.1	6.5	6.5	6.7	6.1	T
▲ AAA LIFE INS CO OF NY	NY	B		7.9	6.6	3.20	2.88	9.8	5.2	2.0	6.9	4.8	ADEGI
ABILITY INS CO	NE	D-		1299.9	21.7	0.56	0.27	1.5	0.5	1.5	9.1	1.3	CFIT
ACADEME INC	WA	U	(2)	5.7	5.6	3.40	3.06	8.0	9.3	3.9	10.0	4.1	DT
ACCORDIA LIFE & ANNUITY CO	IA	C		7633.4	681.8	1.27	0.88	4.0	5.3	4.3	5.8	3.7	CFT
▲ ACE LIFE INS CO	CT	B		46.0	8.6	1.40	1.01	7.0	9.2	2.0	7.8	5.5	AFT
ADVANCE INS CO OF KS	KS	B+		54.9	46.0	3.93	2.61	9.4	4.9	8.4	7.2	6.8	AI
AETNA HEALTH & LIFE INS CO	CT	B+		2349.9	279.5	2.25	1.38	7.6	6.0	6.1	7.4	6.8	AI
AETNA LIFE INS CO	CT	B		22194.2	3130.1	1.34	0.99	5.8	6.2	8.4	6.6	6.0	AIT
AGC LIFE INS CO	MO	C		15561.0	8882.2	0.74	0.66	4.3	2.1	6.3	7.5	3.9	CIT
ALABAMA LIFE REINS CO INC	AL	E+		25.9	9.2	2.15	1.93	8.4	7.8	1.6	9.3	0.8	DFT
ALFA LIFE INS CORP	AL	B-		1412.5	236.6	2.70	1.52	7.8	5.3	2.9	6.6	5.2	IT
ALL SAVERS INS CO	IN	C		1437.0	821.5	5.43	4.23	10.0	8.8	1.9	7.3	3.7	FGT
ALL SAVERS LIFE INS CO OF CA	CA	C+		6.8	6.2	3.37	3.03	10.0	9.8	2.5	10.0	4.6	ADFG
ALLIANZ LIFE & ANNUITY CO	MN	U	(2)	9.4	6.1	2.87	2.59	8.0	9.5	2.7	10.0	4.1	DFT
ALLIANZ LIFE INS CO OF NORTH AMERICA	MN	B		125342.0	6059.1	2.84	1.60	7.9	5.2	6.0	6.4	5.4	I
ALLIANZ LIFE INS CO OF NY	NY	A-		3131.2	248.6	7.33	4.84	10.0	7.6	7.2	9.5	7.1	AF
ALLIED FINANCIAL INS CO	TX	U	(5)	--	--	--	--	--	--	--	--	--	Z
ALLSTATE ASR CO	IL	C+		654.6	123.1	3.63	2.00	8.5	6.7	1.8	6.0	4.7	DFGT
ALLSTATE LIFE INS CO	IL	B		32095.1	2902.1	1.68	0.97	6.8	4.5	3.5	6.6	4.0	FGIT
ALLSTATE LIFE INS CO OF NEW YORK	NY	C+		6366.6	489.2	1.97	1.03	7.0	4.9	2.5	6.3	4.7	FI
AMALGAMATED LIFE & HEALTH INS CO	IL	C		5.8	3.8	2.29	2.06	8.6	8.8	4.5	7.1	4.0	DF
AMALGAMATED LIFE INS CO	NY	A-		122.5	56.3	4.28	3.40	10.0	8.1	8.0	6.4	7.0	
AMERICAN BANKERS LIFE ASR CO OF FL	FL	C+		392.8	49.4	6.55	3.25	10.0	6.6	7.4	7.3	3.3	AFT
AMERICAN BENEFIT LIFE INS CO	OK	C-		117.9	15.7	2.21	1.59	7.9	4.9	8.5	6.2	3.2	AD
AMERICAN CENTURY LIFE INS CO	OK	C	(3)	71.9	8.3	1.13	0.99	6.9	2.1	8.4	2.1	2.8	CDIL
AMERICAN CENTURY LIFE INS CO TX	TX	U	(5)	--	--	--	--	--	--	--	--	--	Z
AMERICAN COMMUNITY MUT INS CO	MI	F	(5)	--	--	--	--	--	--	--	--	--	Z
AMERICAN CONTINENTAL INS CO	TN	B-		208.7	75.0	1.34	1.02	5.6	7.8	1.8	5.3	4.9	D
AMERICAN CREDITORS LIFE INS CO	DE	U	(2)	12.0	9.7	3.71	3.34	8.0	8.2	1.5	10.0	1.7	DF
AMERICAN EQUITY INVEST LIFE INS CO	IA	B		44851.9	2431.5	2.26	1.18	7.3	6.0	6.2	5.3	6.3	GIL
AMERICAN EQUITY INVESTMENT LIFE NY	NY	B-		215.2	31.1	3.16	1.90	8.4	6.3	5.6	5.3	4.5	DFGT
AMERICAN FAMILY LIFE ASR CO OF COLUM	NE	B+		117278.0	11448.6	2.54	1.78	8.2	6.8	7.2	7.1	6.7	IT
AMERICAN FAMILY LIFE ASR CO OF NY	NY	A-		885.2	280.2	5.50	3.70	10.0	8.0	9.0	7.7	7.3	AD
AMERICAN FAMILY LIFE INS CO	WI	A+		5407.4	969.6	4.72	2.48	9.2	6.4	6.6	6.4	7.9	AI
AMERICAN FARM LIFE INS CO	TX	B		3.9	1.9	1.53	1.38	7.6	8.1	7.9	6.9	4.1	ADT
AMERICAN FARMERS & RANCHERS LIFE INS	OK	C		27.2	2.4	0.61	0.55	3.4	7.4	2.9	5.1	3.4	ACD
AMERICAN FEDERATED LIFE INS CO	MS	B-		32.1	8.8	1.84	1.65	8.0	8.5	5.3	8.7	5.0	A
AMERICAN FIDELITY ASR CO	OK	B+		5305.5	412.9	1.96	1.10	7.2	6.0	8.6	6.4	6.8	I
AMERICAN FIDELITY LIFE INS CO	FL	B-		421.6	64.7	1.97	1.35	7.5	6.0	5.7	5.8	5.3	D
AMERICAN FINANCIAL SECURITY L I C	MO	D		7.5	5.5	2.91	2.62	9.4	7.6	3.0	7.4	2.3	DFT
AMERICAN GENERAL LIFE INS CO	TX	B		171739.0	9155.3	3.07	1.49	7.7	4.9	6.1	5.9	5.8	AI
AMERICAN HEALTH & LIFE INS CO	TX	A-		907.2	177.0	3.98	2.32	9.0	6.3	6.9	7.9	6.5	AIT
AMERICAN HERITAGE LIFE INS CO	FL	B		1846.7	303.0	1.09	0.88	6.0	6.3	5.8	6.5	6.0	ACI
AMERICAN HOME LIFE INS CO	KS	C-		250.5	20.9	2.12	1.16	7.2	5.8	3.3	4.6	3.2	DL
AMERICAN HOME LIFE INS CO	AR	E		19.9	0.5	0.19	0.17	0.0	0.0	2.4	1.0	0.0	CIL
AMERICAN INCOME LIFE INS CO	IN	B-		3234.8	222.8	1.25	0.75	5.4	4.2	5.2	2.6	4.6	CIL
AMERICAN INDEPENDENT NETWORK INS CO	NY	E-		24.4	-12.4	-1.45	-1.30	0.0	5.8	0.5	2.0	0.0	CDFILT
AMERICAN INTEGRITY LIFE INS CO	AR	U	(2)	0.9	0.8	1.98	1.78	8.2	7.8	2.8	9.4	3.0	DGT
AMERICAN LABOR LIFE INS CO	AZ	D		9.4	7.2	3.24	2.91	9.9	7.0	9.0	9.9	1.4	D
AMERICAN LIFE & ACC INS CO OF KY	KY	C		207.9	112.1	3.29	1.89	8.3	2.3	6.8	6.0	3.9	DFGIT

See Page 27 for explanation of footnotes and Page 28 for explanation of stability factors.
Arrows denote recent upgrades ▲ or downgrades▼ (see Section VI for explanations)

30

www.weissratings.com

NET PREMIUM ($MIL)	IN-VESTED ASSETS ($MIL)	% OF INVESTED ASSETS IN:										INSURANCE COMPANY NAME
		CASH	CMO & STRUCT. SECS.	OTH.INV. GRADE BONDS	NON-INV. GRADE BONDS	CMMON & PREF. STOCK	MORT IN GOOD STAND.	NON-PERF. MORT.	REAL ESTATE	OTHER INVEST-MENTS	INVEST. IN AFFIL	
49.5	177.3	4.8	27.0	50.1	6.8	6.2	0.0	0.0	0.0	5.1	0.0	● 4 EVER LIFE INS CO
57.5	539.2	2.0	17.3	68.4	8.0	3.3	0.0	0.0	0.0	1.1	1.4	● AAA LIFE INS CO
1.1	7.6	0.7	0.0	88.5	10.8	0.0	0.0	0.0	0.0	0.0	0.0	AAA LIFE INS CO OF NY
7.0	1,170.2	-0.2	29.8	37.2	8.8	0.9	6.8	0.6	0.3	15.9	0.0	ABILITY INS CO
0.0	5.7	1.8	27.3	70.9	0.0	0.0	0.0	0.0	0.0	0.0	0.0	ACADEME INC
180.9	7,099.4 (*)	2.0	28.3	45.7	1.4	5.4	8.9	0.0	0.0	7.2	6.1	● ACCORDIA LIFE & ANNUITY CO
3.0	41.6	0.2	0.0	99.8	0.0	0.0	0.0	0.0	0.0	0.0	0.0	ACE LIFE INS CO
5.4	53.2	0.6	22.7	46.1	0.0	29.7	0.0	0.0	0.0	0.0	2.4	● ADVANCE INS CO OF KS
391.7	2,232.7	0.1	12.5	62.0	5.5	0.2	11.5	0.0	0.0	8.1	4.3	● AETNA HEALTH & LIFE INS CO
9,212.2	12,939.0	0.0	12.1	60.5	6.2	0.4	10.0	0.0	2.3	9.2	4.4	● AETNA LIFE INS CO
627.1	14,653.5	0.0	2.8	3.6	0.0	93.6	0.0	0.0	0.0	0.0	93.6	● AGC LIFE INS CO
0.3	26.7	75.1	0.0	18.7	0.0	6.2	0.0	0.0	0.0	0.0	0.0	ALABAMA LIFE REINS CO INC
77.9	1,348.6	0.8	5.2	68.2	6.0	9.4	0.0	0.0	0.0	10.4	0.0	● ALFA LIFE INS CORP
800.3	784.2	6.4	3.6	90.0	0.0	0.0	0.0	0.0	0.0	0.0	0.0	● ALL SAVERS INS CO
0.1	6.6	76.6	0.0	23.4	0.0	0.0	0.0	0.0	0.0	0.0	0.0	ALL SAVERS LIFE INS CO OF CA
0.0	7.4	1.3	0.0	98.6	0.0	0.0	0.0	0.0	0.0	0.1	0.0	ALLIANZ LIFE & ANNUITY CO
7,080.3	92,602.6 (*)	-0.1	14.2	68.4	2.3	1.5	9.5	0.0	0.1	1.0	1.5	● ALLIANZ LIFE INS CO OF NORTH AMERICA
136.0	650.0 (*)	0.0	21.1	74.9	1.0	0.0	0.0	0.0	0.0	0.8	0.0	● ALLIANZ LIFE INS CO OF NY
--	--	--	--	--	--	--	--	--	--	--	--	ALLIED FINANCIAL INS CO
58.4	622.0	0.1	4.0	70.0	3.1	0.0	16.1	0.0	0.0	6.7	0.0	● ALLSTATE ASR CO
602.6	27,954.8	0.0	10.9	47.1	10.8	6.7	11.0	0.0	0.2	13.1	4.6	● ALLSTATE LIFE INS CO
79.8	5,743.5	0.1	9.0	66.4	4.6	3.7	10.2	0.0	0.0	5.8	0.1	● ALLSTATE LIFE INS CO OF NEW YORK
1.7	5.7	6.7	25.4	63.7	0.0	0.0	0.0	0.0	0.0	4.3	0.0	AMALGAMATED LIFE & HEALTH INS CO
39.8	103.7	0.4	31.8	67.7	0.0	0.0	0.0	0.0	0.0	0.1	0.0	● AMALGAMATED LIFE INS CO
18.8	337.7	7.0	10.5	58.9	1.5	0.9	7.5	0.0	11.7	2.0	0.0	● AMERICAN BANKERS LIFE ASR CO OF FL
12.6	98.7	1.0	3.9	68.2	2.4	1.7	18.6	1.6	0.0	2.7	0.0	AMERICAN BENEFIT LIFE INS CO
8.4	67.8	5.7	0.0	81.1	8.1	3.3	1.1	0.0	0.6	0.0	0.0	AMERICAN CENTURY LIFE INS CO
--	--	--	--	--	--	--	--	--	--	--	--	AMERICAN CENTURY LIFE INS CO TX
--	--	--	--	--	--	--	--	--	--	--	--	AMERICAN COMMUNITY MUT INS CO
234.5	180.7 (*)	0.0	31.2	72.2	0.0	0.0	0.0	0.0	0.0	0.1	0.0	● AMERICAN CONTINENTAL INS CO
0.0	12.0	10.2	0.0	83.8	0.0	5.9	0.0	0.0	0.0	0.0	0.0	AMERICAN CREDITORS LIFE INS CO
3,013.1	40,842.0	0.0	18.9	69.4	2.7	0.3	6.9	0.0	0.0	1.2	0.3	● AMERICAN EQUITY INVEST LIFE INS CO
0.2	215.6	0.7	15.2	81.4	1.6	0.0	0.0	0.0	0.0	1.2	0.0	● AMERICAN EQUITY INVESTMENT LIFE NY
9,356.4	100,093.4	0.6	3.5	88.8	3.6	2.2	0.0	0.0	0.2	0.5	2.2	● AMERICAN FAMILY LIFE ASR CO OF COLUM
157.1	754.5	2.1	0.7	95.6	1.2	0.0	0.0	0.0	0.0	0.3	0.0	● AMERICAN FAMILY LIFE ASR CO OF NY
177.6	4,919.3	0.8	19.8	57.0	4.4	3.0	10.7	0.0	0.0	4.3	0.0	● AMERICAN FAMILY LIFE INS CO
0.2	3.6	6.1	2.8	86.7	2.8	0.0	0.0	0.0	0.0	1.6	0.0	AMERICAN FARM LIFE INS CO
1.1	25.7	1.6	7.6	90.5	0.0	0.0	0.0	0.0	0.0	0.3	0.0	AMERICAN FARMERS & RANCHERS LIFE INS
5.7	28.8	9.5	2.5	88.0	0.0	0.0	0.0	0.0	0.0	0.0	0.0	AMERICAN FEDERATED LIFE INS CO
452.8	4,403.6	4.0	17.2	65.1	2.2	0.7	8.9	0.0	0.2	1.7	0.3	● AMERICAN FIDELITY ASR CO
5.7	419.8	1.4	0.0	73.4	0.3	6.9	8.7	0.0	6.7	2.7	12.4	● AMERICAN FIDELITY LIFE INS CO
2.3	5.2	0.3	0.0	87.6	0.0	1.1	0.0	0.0	10.9	0.0	0.0	AMERICAN FINANCIAL SECURITY L I C
6,864.8	119,484.1 (*)	-0.1	30.0	47.0	5.2	0.3	8.3	0.1	0.2	7.6	6.6	● AMERICAN GENERAL LIFE INS CO
84.9	862.7	2.0	18.3	74.2	4.6	0.7	0.0	0.0	0.0	0.2	0.0	● AMERICAN HEALTH & LIFE INS CO
432.2	1,633.3 (*)	0.0	3.4	53.7	0.6	13.3	10.1	0.0	2.2	17.8	9.8	● AMERICAN HERITAGE LIFE INS CO
13.3	236.8	0.5	26.2	62.4	1.8	1.7	1.7	0.0	0.4	5.3	0.0	AMERICAN HOME LIFE INS CO
1.1	19.4	1.9	0.0	70.1	3.9	10.7	4.9	0.0	7.7	0.8	0.0	AMERICAN HOME LIFE INS CO
380.3	2,762.1	1.2	2.5	79.8	5.0	2.9	0.0	0.0	0.0	8.6	3.6	● AMERICAN INCOME LIFE INS CO
1.2	25.1	0.9	14.9	71.5	5.2	5.6	0.0	0.0	0.0	2.0	0.0	AMERICAN INDEPENDENT NETWORK INS CO
0.2	0.8	18.0	4.6	71.5	0.0	5.9	0.0	0.0	0.0	0.0	0.0	AMERICAN INTEGRITY LIFE INS CO
1.3	8.9	52.9	0.0	29.3	0.0	13.1	3.9	0.0	0.0	0.9	3.9	AMERICAN LABOR LIFE INS CO
101.9	213.7	1.7	2.4	21.6	0.0	61.0	0.0	0.0	8.2	5.2	0.0	● AMERICAN LIFE & ACC INS CO OF KY

● Bullets denote a more detailed analysis is available in Section II.
(*) Asset category percentages do not add up to 100%

INSURANCE COMPANY NAME	DOM. STATE	RATING	TOTAL ASSETS ($MIL)	CAPITAL & SURPLUS ($MIL)	RISK ADJUSTED CAPITAL RATIO 1	RISK ADJUSTED CAPITAL RATIO 2	CAPITAL-IZATION INDEX (PTS)	INVEST. SAFETY INDEX (PTS)	PROFIT-ABILITY INDEX (PTS)	LIQUIDITY INDEX (PTS)	STAB. INDEX (PTS)	STABILITY FACTORS
AMERICAN LIFE & ANNUITY CO	AR	C-	51.1	4.3	0.73	0.65	4.2	3.7	3.7	5.3	2.9	CDI
AMERICAN LIFE & SECURITY CORP	NE	E+	20.1	1.9	0.47	0.34	1.1	1.2	1.6	0.0	0.8	CDILT
AMERICAN LIFE INS CO	DE	C	11974.0	6284.6	1.13	1.07	7.1	3.1	5.3	7.5	3.4	GIT
AMERICAN MATURITY LIFE INS CO	CT	B	60.5	47.9	6.66	6.00	10.0	9.5	4.2	7.0	5.8	A
AMERICAN MEDICAL & LIFE INS CO	NY	U (2)	4.4	0.9	1.20	1.08	7.1	9.6	0.6	7.8	0.0	CDT
AMERICAN MEMORIAL LIFE INS CO	SD	B-	2876.1	129.1	1.49	0.74	5.7	3.3	7.1	5.6	4.9	CI
AMERICAN MODERN LIFE INS CO	OH	B	45.9	29.5	2.23	2.10	8.7	8.0	7.5	8.3	5.7	DFT
AMERICAN NATIONAL INS CO	TX	B	18521.1	2920.3	1.20	0.99	6.9	5.3	7.9	6.5	6.1	I
AMERICAN NATIONAL LIFE INS CO OF NY	NY	B	401.1	30.1	2.72	1.32	7.5	4.9	2.0	7.1	4.4	DGIT
AMERICAN NATIONAL LIFE INS CO OF TX	TX	B-	123.5	34.0	3.80	3.11	10.0	7.1	3.0	5.9	5.0	F
AMERICAN PHOENIX LIFE & REASSUR CO	CT	U (2)	6.4	5.5	3.13	2.82	8.0	8.7	2.7	9.4	3.4	DFT
AMERICAN PROGRESSIVE L&H I C OF NY	NY	C	222.7	102.5	1.21	0.97	6.0	7.4	3.2	0.6	2.7	DFL
AMERICAN PUBLIC LIFE INS CO	OK	B	91.4	25.9	2.00	1.48	7.7	8.0	8.2	7.1	5.6	T
AMERICAN REPUBLIC CORP INS CO	NE	B	23.5	8.8	2.14	1.92	8.0	8.6	5.3	6.7	5.4	F
AMERICAN REPUBLIC INS CO	IA	A-	909.7	488.4	5.00	3.51	10.0	6.9	9.3	6.9	6.9	I
AMERICAN RETIREMENT LIFE INS CO	OH	C+	77.1	42.6	1.09	0.84	5.7	7.9	1.6	0.9	3.3	DFGLT
AMERICAN SAVINGS LIFE INS CO	AZ	C	57.8	14.8	1.42	0.86	5.9	2.6	8.0	6.6	3.6	DGIT
AMERICAN SERVICE LIFE INS CO	AR	U (2)	0.9	0.9	2.22	1.99	8.5	9.8	9.2	9.4	8.5	D
AMERICAN UNDERWRITERS LIFE INS CO	AZ	D	70.6	8.2	0.52	0.37	1.4	2.2	1.2	3.2	1.4	CDFILT
AMERICAN UNITED LIFE INS CO	IN	B+	23906.8	927.2	2.75	1.38	7.6	5.8	6.1	7.4	6.6	I
AMERICAN-AMICABLE LIFE INS CO OF TX	TX	C	292.4	74.3	1.21	1.07	7.1	6.4	5.4	6.4	4.3	AD
AMERICO FINANCIAL LIFE & ANNUITY INS	TX	B-	4250.1	423.4	1.67	0.97	6.8	4.6	7.1	6.1	5.3	AIT
AMERITAS LIFE INS CORP	NE	B	18307.1	1532.6	2.41	1.44	7.7	4.9	6.0	6.2	4.8	GIT
AMERITAS LIFE INS CORP OF NY	NY	B-	1188.8	77.3	1.81	0.98	6.8	5.6	1.8	4.4	3.6	LT
AMICA LIFE INS CO	RI	B	1239.5	281.1	5.05	2.93	9.9	7.2	4.9	6.5	5.6	
▲ ANNUITY INVESTORS LIFE INS CO	OH	A-	3041.6	256.8	2.93	1.48	7.7	6.4	8.7	5.8	6.9	AI
ANTHEM LIFE & DISABILITY INS CO	NY	B	25.1	19.1	3.99	2.98	10.0	8.9	3.4	9.3	5.5	
ANTHEM LIFE INS CO	IN	A-	630.6	94.7	1.98	1.38	7.6	7.6	6.7	6.2	7.1	A
ARKANSAS BANKERS LIFE INS CO	AR	D (1)	3.1	1.7	1.66	1.49	7.7	9.8	2.2	9.8	2.1	FT
ASSOCIATED MUTUAL	MI	D	8.6	7.5	2.39	2.15	8.7	7.0	1.1	9.2	1.4	DFT
ASSURED LIFE ASSOCIATION	CO	U	--	--	--	--	--	--	--	--	--	Z
ASSURITY LIFE INS CO	NE	B+	2550.8	309.3	2.58	1.44	7.7	5.5	6.5	5.8	6.6	IL
ATHENE ANNUITY & LIFE ASR CO	DE	C	10581.5	1252.7	0.88	0.70	4.6	3.6	4.4	6.2	3.7	CFIT
ATHENE ANNUITY & LIFE ASR CO OF NY	NY	C	3274.1	213.1	1.42	0.68	5.6	2.4	6.8	9.1	3.7	CGIT
ATHENE ANNUITY & LIFE CO	IA	C+	45056.3	1104.4	1.01	0.53	5.0	2.3	5.1	5.5	4.5	CGIT
ATHENE LIFE INS CO	DE	U (2)	227.8	77.2	7.62	6.86	8.0	7.9	4.3	8.3	6.2	DFT
ATHENE LIFE INS CO OF NEW YORK	NY	C	944.2	75.2	2.68	1.25	7.4	4.9	4.7	7.8	3.3	CIT
ATLANTA LIFE INS CO	GA	D	47.1	13.8	1.83	1.28	7.4	8.2	2.6	6.8	2.1	DFT
ATLANTIC COAST LIFE INS CO	SC	B-	205.2	20.1	1.93	1.13	4.0	3.7	7.3	7.9	3.8	AFGIT
AURIGEN REINS CO OF AMERICA	AR	C-	42.5	21.0	2.23	1.53	7.8	8.9	1.8	6.9	2.9	GT
AURORA NATIONAL LIFE ASR CO	CA	B	2899.3	310.7	3.83	1.91	8.4	6.7	5.4	6.9	5.5	AFG
AUTO CLUB LIFE INS CO	MI	C+	681.0	78.2	1.16	0.83	5.6	6.0	2.0	5.8	4.4	
AUTO-OWNERS LIFE INS CO	MI	A-	3832.7	400.9	2.72	1.45	7.7	5.9	5.4	6.4	6.9	IT
AUTOMOBILE CLUB OF SOUTHERN CA INS	CA	B-	1031.3	77.3	1.54	0.87	6.0	4.7	1.9	5.2	5.1	I
▲ AXA CORPORATE SOLUTIONS LIFE REINS	DE	B	258.3	173.1	2.06	1.79	8.2	4.9	3.6	9.5	4.4	IT
▲ AXA EQUITABLE LIFE & ANNUITY CO	CO	B	448.0	22.2	0.99	0.51	4.9	7.5	3.3	2.3	4.2	CFLT
AXA EQUITABLE LIFE INS CO	NY	B+	171038.0	5853.1	2.41	1.45	7.7	7.1	7.4	6.8	6.8	
BALTIMORE LIFE INS CO	MD	B	1216.4	80.1	1.77	0.91	6.3	4.3	5.9	3.3	5.3	CIL
BANKERS CONSECO LIFE INS CO	NY	D	226.5	51.6	5.24	3.18	10.0	7.1	4.9	5.6	1.8	DT
BANKERS FIDELITY ASR CO	GA	B-	9.7	9.3	3.98	3.59	8.0	3.8	8.4	10.0	4.8	AIT
BANKERS FIDELITY LIFE INS CO	GA	B	141.3	34.2	1.22	0.91	6.3	3.7	8.1	5.7	5.7	CDI
BANKERS LIFE & CAS CO	IL	D+	17123.8	1253.0	2.13	1.11	7.2	4.7	9.0	5.5	2.7	AI

See Page 27 for explanation of footnotes and Page 28 for explanation of stability factors.
Arrows denote recent upgrades ▲ or downgrades▼ (see Section VI for explanations)

32

www.weissratings.com

NET PREMIUM ($MIL)	IN-VESTED ASSETS ($MIL)	CASH	CMO & STRUCT. SECS.	OTH.INV. GRADE BONDS	NON-INV. GRADE BONDS	CMMON & PREF. STOCK	MORT IN GOOD STAND.	NON-PERF. MORT.	REAL ESTATE	OTHER INVEST-MENTS	INVEST. IN AFFIL	INSURANCE COMPANY NAME
2.4	50.0	1.0	48.2	43.3	2.9	4.1	0.0	0.0	0.4	0.1	0.0	AMERICAN LIFE & ANNUITY CO
1.8	18.2	2.8	0.0	74.8	0.0	17.2	0.0	0.0	2.9	2.2	25.9	AMERICAN LIFE & SECURITY CORP
652.6	9,094.7	6.8	1.5	14.8	12.6	61.9	0.0	0.0	0.1	2.3	62.7	● AMERICAN LIFE INS CO
0.0	48.7	0.1	0.0	99.9	0.0	0.0	0.0	0.0	0.0	0.0	0.0	● AMERICAN MATURITY LIFE INS CO
0.0	2.8	22.1	0.0	77.9	0.0	0.0	0.0	0.0	0.0	0.0	0.0	AMERICAN MEDICAL & LIFE INS CO
264.0	2,650.4	-0.1	9.1	71.3	7.6	1.0	8.0	0.0	0.0	3.2	0.0	● AMERICAN MEMORIAL LIFE INS CO
2.0	44.9	2.1	8.0	62.4	0.0	27.4	0.0	0.0	0.0	0.1	27.4	AMERICAN MODERN LIFE INS CO
946.6	16,956.1	0.0	1.6	54.0	1.8	13.0	20.0	0.0	2.1	7.2	19.7	● AMERICAN NATIONAL INS CO
135.6	269.3	0.2	0.0	94.1	1.7	0.0	3.9	0.0	0.0	0.0	0.0	● AMERICAN NATIONAL LIFE INS CO OF NY
14.0	120.8	-0.4	0.7	94.5	1.7	0.0	0.0	0.0	0.0	3.6	0.0	● AMERICAN NATIONAL LIFE INS CO OF TX
0.0	6.3	7.3	14.6	78.1	0.0	0.0	0.0	0.0	0.0	0.0	0.0	AMERICAN PHOENIX LIFE & REASSUR CO
258.4	173.0	-5.4	22.3	72.8	0.0	2.3	0.0	0.0	0.0	8.0	0.0	● AMERICAN PROGRESSIVE L&H I C OF NY
36.2	82.5	5.7	23.5	58.2	0.0	1.5	9.1	0.0	1.1	1.0	0.0	AMERICAN PUBLIC LIFE INS CO
0.0	11.9	8.6	19.7	71.7	0.0	0.0	0.0	0.0	0.0	0.0	0.0	AMERICAN REPUBLIC CORP INS CO
191.6	721.6	0.7	22.3	58.7	3.3	5.7	3.2	0.0	4.8	1.4	4.2	● AMERICAN REPUBLIC INS CO
122.1	76.6	-6.1	0.0	106.1	0.0	0.0	0.0	0.0	0.0	0.0	0.0	● AMERICAN RETIREMENT LIFE INS CO
1.2	55.0	14.5	0.0	5.7	0.6	1.1	65.9	4.6	5.9	1.7	0.8	AMERICAN SAVINGS LIFE INS CO
0.4	0.8	64.8	0.0	29.6	0.0	5.7	0.0	0.0	0.0	0.0	5.7	AMERICAN SERVICE LIFE INS CO
3.3	69.7	2.6	1.5	62.5	7.0	14.9	5.9	0.0	0.9	4.8	11.6	AMERICAN UNDERWRITERS LIFE INS CO
1,652.5	10,936.3	-0.3	16.7	62.0	3.0	0.9	13.9	0.0	0.6	3.3	0.0	● AMERICAN UNITED LIFE INS CO
29.9	267.4	0.0	1.5	66.7	0.2	20.0	5.4	0.0	1.1	5.4	19.6	● AMERICAN-AMICABLE LIFE INS CO OF TX
240.2	3,680.9	0.0	34.7	39.5	3.2	11.8	7.4	0.0	0.0	2.9	3.1	● AMERICO FINANCIAL LIFE & ANNUITY INS
1,122.4	11,399.5	-0.3	15.5	57.1	2.5	5.0	12.8	0.0	0.5	6.6	1.4	● AMERITAS LIFE INS CORP
65.7	1,076.2	0.2	16.9	64.9	1.9	0.0	13.7	0.0	0.0	2.3	0.0	● AMERITAS LIFE INS CORP OF NY
35.7	1,150.2	0.1	32.6	58.0	1.4	4.2	0.4	0.0	0.0	3.2	0.0	● AMICA LIFE INS CO
101.8	2,380.8	-0.2	29.6	65.8	1.8	0.2	0.0	0.0	0.0	2.5	0.0	● ANNUITY INVESTORS LIFE INS CO
3.6	23.7	45.3	0.0	54.7	0.0	0.0	0.0	0.0	0.0	0.0	0.0	ANTHEM LIFE & DISABILITY INS CO
184.9	573.7 (*)	5.0	16.6	62.4	0.5	1.4	0.0	0.0	0.0	2.5	0.0	● ANTHEM LIFE INS CO
0.2	3.1 (*)	88.7	0.0	8.2	0.0	0.0	0.0	0.0	0.0	0.0	0.0	ARKANSAS BANKERS LIFE INS CO
0.0	9.2	27.4	0.0	63.8	4.7	4.2	0.0	0.0	0.0	0.0	4.2	ASSOCIATED MUTUAL
--	--	--	--	--	--	--	--	--	--	--	--	ASSURED LIFE ASSOCIATION
99.2	2,380.0	0.1	12.5	57.5	2.0	3.9	14.3	0.0	2.5	7.3	0.8	● ASSURITY LIFE INS CO
12.9	7,622.7	2.1	32.5	18.2	4.5	16.8	9.8	0.0	0.0	15.7	31.1	● ATHENE ANNUITY & LIFE ASR CO
11.0	3,191.8	0.3	58.0	12.3	17.2	1.7	8.1	0.0	0.0	2.4	1.4	● ATHENE ANNUITY & LIFE ASR CO OF NY
549.6	42,231.3	0.1	28.6	51.9	3.8	1.0	10.2	0.1	0.0	3.4	3.4	● ATHENE ANNUITY & LIFE CO
0.0	224.8	17.1	34.4	44.8	0.0	2.0	0.0	0.0	0.0	1.2	0.0	ATHENE LIFE INS CO
0.4	806.0	-0.1	1.9	85.0	1.1	0.5	11.6	0.0	0.0	0.1	0.0	● ATHENE LIFE INS CO OF NEW YORK
5.7	16.3	11.8	1.9	80.9	0.0	4.9	0.0	0.0	0.0	0.6	0.0	ATLANTA LIFE INS CO
19.8	136.0	0.1	36.9	35.6	4.4	0.2	19.5	0.0	2.2	1.0	0.0	ATLANTIC COAST LIFE INS CO
2.1	35.6	11.5	7.6	81.0	0.0	0.0	0.0	0.0	0.0	0.0	0.0	AURIGEN REINS CO OF AMERICA
0.4	2,913.7	0.8	4.7	73.6	2.4	0.0	13.1	0.0	0.0	5.6	0.0	● AURORA NATIONAL LIFE ASR CO
89.6	576.1	0.0	17.7	64.7	8.3	6.3	0.0	0.0	0.0	3.0	6.3	● AUTO CLUB LIFE INS CO
133.5	3,199.1	1.3	20.3	62.3	1.2	2.6	4.6	0.0	4.2	3.5	0.0	● AUTO-OWNERS LIFE INS CO
148.9	865.3	0.0	18.0	74.2	6.8	0.3	0.0	0.0	0.0	0.7	0.0	● AUTOMOBILE CLUB OF SOUTHERN CA INS
2.6	240.4	9.7	1.9	55.2	2.6	29.8	0.0	0.0	0.0	0.8	29.8	● AXA CORPORATE SOLUTIONS LIFE REINS
-1.5	443.9	0.1	2.6	36.0	0.2	0.0	0.0	0.0	0.0	61.1	0.0	AXA EQUITABLE LIFE & ANNUITY CO
6,294.0	47,864.9	0.5	3.3	64.9	1.8	2.6	15.6	0.1	0.0	10.2	5.8	● AXA EQUITABLE LIFE INS CO
67.6	1,149.2 (*)	0.4	2.7	78.4	4.8	1.1	3.4	0.0	0.8	7.1	0.4	● BALTIMORE LIFE INS CO
27.8	207.3	0.7	21.8	71.4	2.8	1.1	0.0	0.0	0.0	2.3	0.0	● BANKERS CONSECO LIFE INS CO
0.0	9.6	1.9	0.0	84.8	13.3	0.0	0.0	0.0	0.0	0.0	0.0	BANKERS FIDELITY ASR CO
50.9	133.8	1.7	0.0	66.4	16.9	11.4	0.0	0.0	0.0	3.7	7.3	BANKERS FIDELITY LIFE INS CO
1,245.6	16,314.3	1.1	23.6	60.1	4.2	1.5	6.9	0.0	0.0	2.4	0.9	● BANKERS LIFE & CAS CO

  ● Bullets denote a more detailed analysis is available in Section II.
                                                 (*) Asset category percentages do not add up to 100%

INSURANCE COMPANY NAME	DOM. STATE	RATING	TOTAL ASSETS ($MIL)	CAPITAL & SURPLUS ($MIL)	RISK ADJUSTED CAPITAL RATIO 1	RISK ADJUSTED CAPITAL RATIO 2	CAPITAL-IZATION INDEX (PTS)	INVEST. SAFETY INDEX (PTS)	PROFIT-ABILITY INDEX (PTS)	LIQUIDITY INDEX (PTS)	STAB. INDEX (PTS)	STABILITY FACTORS
BANKERS LIFE INS CO	FL	C	426.3	22.0	1.48	0.70	5.7	1.6	4.8	7.0	3.7	DIT
BANKERS LIFE INS CO OF AMERICA	TX	D (3)	5.3	0.7	0.48	0.43	2.2	4.8	2.8	4.7	1.9	CDIL
BANKERS LIFE OF LOUISIANA	LA	C	14.0	5.6	1.97	1.77	8.2	8.6	2.9	7.4	4.2	A
▲ BANNER LIFE INS CO	MD	C+	2469.4	413.8	2.05	1.49	7.7	5.9	4.4	7.1	4.6	T
BENEFICIAL LIFE INS CO	UT	B	2339.7	187.5	1.92	1.06	7.1	5.3	6.8	6.8	5.3	FI
BENEVOLENT LIFE INS CO INC	LA	D (2)	2.1	0.5	0.66	0.60	3.8	8.8	2.6	10.0	1.6	CD
BERKLEY LIFE & HEALTH INS CO	IA	B	243.3	137.5	5.21	4.03	10.0	8.5	8.6	7.0	5.9	AD
BERKSHIRE HATHAWAY LIFE INS CO OF NE	NE	C+	16826.7	3587.5	1.55	1.30	7.5	6.4	6.6	9.6	3.0	GT
BERKSHIRE LIFE INS CO OF AMERICA	MA	B	3436.0	217.1	3.02	1.39	7.6	3.9	5.2	7.2	6.2	I
BEST LIFE & HEALTH INS CO	TX	B	18.4	14.3	1.95	1.56	7.8	8.3	8.1	7.1	5.5	T
BEST MERIDIAN INS CO	FL	B-	309.9	59.0	1.84	1.18	7.3	6.0	5.3	7.0	5.3	DT
BLUE CROSS BLUE SHIELD OF KANSAS INC	KS	B	1497.5	741.3	1.92	1.43	7.6	4.2	3.1	5.4	5.4	FILT
BLUE SHIELD OF CALIFORNIA L&H INS CO	CA	B	483.6	318.5	3.10	2.44	9.2	8.1	5.9	6.5	4.9	FT
BLUE SPIRIT INS CO	VT	U	--	--	--	--	--	--	--	--	--	Z
BLUEBONNET LIFE INS CO	MS	B+	58.9	54.3	7.72	6.95	10.0	8.1	9.2	9.8	6.5	AD
BOSTON MUTUAL LIFE INS CO	MA	B+	1317.6	166.6	2.01	1.31	7.5	6.4	6.1	4.7	6.4	IL
BROOKE LIFE INS CO	MI	C+	3935.4	3574.9	0.87	0.77	5.2	1.2	8.6	9.9	4.8	IT
CALPERS LONG-TERM CARE PROGRAM		U	--	--	--	--	--	--	--	--	--	Z
CANADA LIFE ASSURANCE CO-US BRANCH	MI	C	4463.0	151.5	1.17	0.61	5.3	5.7	3.1	5.1	4.0	CF
CANYON STATE LIFE INS CO	AZ	U (5)	--	--	--	--	--	--	--	--	--	Z
CAPITAL RESERVE LIFE INS CO	MO	E+	1.4	1.4	2.38	2.15	8.0	8.4	2.0	6.9	0.8	AF
CAPITOL LIFE INS CO	TX	C	229.5	23.9	2.58	1.62	7.9	4.7	5.4	7.0	3.5	ADGIT
CAPITOL SECURITY LIFE INS CO	TX	D-	4.5	1.4	1.00	0.90	6.2	9.4	2.5	6.4	1.0	ADF
CAREAMERICA LIFE INS CO	CA	U (2)	28.7	25.7	5.79	5.22	10.0	8.4	8.7	9.8	5.2	DT
CARIBBEAN AMERICAN LIFE ASR CO	PR	B	39.0	10.4	1.85	1.54	7.8	6.6	5.5	8.8	5.4	AT
CASS COUNTY LIFE INS CO	TX	U (2)	3.1	0.4	0.42	0.38	1.6	3.0	2.2	7.0	1.6	CDFI
CATERPILLAR LIFE INS CO	MO	U (2)	147.4	53.4	4.29	2.45	8.0	4.6	2.4	10.0	4.2	DFI
CATHOLIC FINANCIAL LIFE	WI	U	--	--	--	--	--	--	--	--	--	Z
CENTRAL RESERVE LIFE INS CO	OH	C+	29.2	27.7	1.53	1.47	7.7	4.3	8.1	7.8	4.6	DIT
CENTRAL SECURITY LIFE INS CO	TX	D	93.1	4.3	0.44	0.39	1.7	3.4	4.7	4.0	1.7	CDGL
CENTRAL STATES H & L CO OF OMAHA	NE	A-	421.1	127.1	4.09	2.92	9.9	5.8	7.5	8.3	6.9	I
CENTRAL UNITED LIFE INS CO	AR	C	381.6	92.6	0.62	0.57	3.6	5.2	2.4	6.8	3.6	C
CENTRE LIFE INS CO	MA	B-	1850.7	90.8	3.81	2.47	9.2	6.7	2.4	9.3	3.7	AFT
CENTURION LIFE INS CO	IA	D	1275.3	306.5	3.52	2.10	8.7	6.8	1.3	6.5	1.8	T
CENTURY LIFE ASR CO	OK	D	12.0	6.2	2.50	2.25	8.9	6.6	5.8	7.6	1.8	ADT
CHESAPEAKE LIFE INS CO	OK	C+	118.2	64.5	1.78	1.42	7.6	9.2	2.9	8.2	4.4	CDG
CHESTERFIELD REINS CO	MO	C	325.4	97.4	1.60	1.12	7.2	6.8	1.4	0.0	2.8	DEL
CHRISTIAN FIDELITY LIFE INS CO	TX	B	70.6	32.4	3.04	2.21	8.8	7.8	7.8	7.0	5.9	AD
CHURCH LIFE INS CORP	NY	B	298.1	54.6	3.88	2.10	8.7	6.3	7.4	6.1	5.7	DI
CICA LIFE INS CO OF AMERICA	CO	D	878.2	33.7	0.48	0.37	1.4	4.7	2.4	6.0	1.4	CD
CIGNA ARBOR LIFE INS CO	CT	U (2)	8.4	7.4	3.47	3.13	8.0	9.6	4.3	10.0	5.8	DFT
CIGNA HEALTH & LIFE INS CO	CT	B	6742.1	3124.0	1.74	1.38	6.9	3.7	9.8	1.8	4.2	AIL
CIGNA LIFE INS CO OF NEW YORK	NY	A-	380.3	96.0	2.65	1.74	8.1	6.5	6.8	7.3	7.0	ADI
CIGNA WORLDWIDE INS CO	DE	B	51.5	9.4	1.48	1.33	7.5	4.5	4.9	10.0	4.0	AIT
CINCINNATI EQUITABLE LIFE INS CO	OH	C-	113.7	8.1	0.96	0.70	4.7	4.3	2.7	4.1	3.1	DL
CINCINNATI LIFE INS CO	OH	B	4214.2	204.6	1.42	0.74	5.6	3.4	2.7	5.0	5.6	CIL
CITIZENS FIDELITY INS CO	AR	C+	70.0	11.7	1.74	1.16	7.2	3.2	8.2	7.1	4.5	DI
CITIZENS NATIONAL LIFE INS CO	TX	C	12.6	2.3	3.04	2.74	9.6	7.7	1.7	6.9	3.0	ADFT
CITIZENS SECURITY LIFE INS CO	KY	C	23.6	14.8	0.99	0.75	5.0	2.9	9.2	6.9	4.1	CI
CLEAR SPRING LIFE INS CO	TX	U (2)	283.7	52.8	4.96	4.47	3.0	7.2	6.5	7.0	5.0	EFT
CLOVER INS CO	TX	B- (1)	11.7	11.5	6.40	5.76	8.0	9.0	4.1	10.0	5.1	A
CM LIFE INS CO	CT	B	9489.1	1522.2	3.09	1.90	8.4	5.3	9.0	6.4	6.3	FI

See Page 27 for explanation of footnotes and Page 28 for explanation of stability factors.
Arrows denote recent upgrades ▲ or downgrades▼ (see Section VI for explanations)

34

www.weissratings.com

NET PREMIUM ($MIL)	IN-VESTED ASSETS ($MIL)	CASH	CMO & STRUCT. SECS.	OTH.INV. GRADE BONDS	NON-INV. GRADE BONDS	CMMON & PREF. STOCK	MORT IN GOOD STAND.	NON-PERF. MORT.	REAL ESTATE	OTHER INVEST-MENTS	INVEST. IN AFFIL	INSURANCE COMPANY NAME
						% OF INVESTED ASSETS IN:						
21.8	408.0	0.3	34.2	58.4	3.0	3.3	0.0	0.0	0.2	0.6	0.0	BANKERS LIFE INS CO
0.8	5.0	1.9	0.0	66.5	0.0	2.1	0.0	0.0	19.2	10.3	0.0	BANKERS LIFE INS CO OF AMERICA
5.8	13.2	0.1	4.6	89.0	0.0	5.3	0.0	0.0	0.0	0.0	0.0	BANKERS LIFE OF LOUISIANA
201.5	1,383.0	-1.6	7.3	60.0	5.7	10.3	16.7	0.0	0.0	1.9	10.3 ●	BANNER LIFE INS CO
18.2	2,721.2	0.8	21.3	67.5	1.8	4.6	0.0	0.0	0.0	4.0	0.0 ●	BENEFICIAL LIFE INS CO
0.3	2.1	75.4	4.9	16.5	0.0	2.1	0.0	0.0	1.2	0.0	0.0	BENEVOLENT LIFE INS CO INC
112.3	212.2 (*)	0.0	25.8	75.3	0.5	0.0	0.0	0.0	0.0	0.0	0.0 ●	BERKLEY LIFE & HEALTH INS CO
1,210.8	15,660.2	7.2	4.3	44.0	1.7	17.2	0.0	0.0	0.0	25.6	26.7 ●	BERKSHIRE HATHAWAY LIFE INS CO OF NE
61.7	3,253.0	0.2	0.9	93.8	4.4	0.0	0.0	0.0	0.6	0.2	0.0 ●	BERKSHIRE LIFE INS CO OF AMERICA
16.1	17.6	32.9	0.3	45.1	1.4	20.2	0.0	0.0	0.0	0.0	0.0	BEST LIFE & HEALTH INS CO
74.6	249.6	11.7	15.8	42.0	0.6	0.7	14.9	0.0	11.9	2.5	0.7 ●	BEST MERIDIAN INS CO
939.3	1,201.3	0.0	18.5	43.0	2.4	29.6	0.0	0.0	0.0	2.6	4.0	5.2 ● BLUE CROSS BLUE SHIELD OF KANSAS INC
157.9	594.4	1.7	47.5	50.8	0.0	0.0	0.0	0.0	0.0	0.0	0.0 ●	BLUE SHIELD OF CALIFORNIA L&H INS CO
--	--	--	--	--	--	--	--	--	--	--	--	BLUE SPIRIT INS CO
2.4	56.1	1.0	29.8	58.2	0.6	0.7	0.0	0.0	0.0	9.7	0.0 ●	BLUEBONNET LIFE INS CO
97.4	1,174.7	0.0	4.4	61.1	1.7	4.8	14.1	0.0	0.7	13.2	2.4 ●	BOSTON MUTUAL LIFE INS CO
5.0	5,125.9	0.0	1.5	6.4	0.1	92.1	0.0	0.0	0.0	0.0	92.1 ●	BROOKE LIFE INS CO
--	--	--	--	--	--	--	--	--	--	--	--	CALPERS LONG-TERM CARE PROGRAM
69.1	3,361.2	0.2	13.3	65.8	0.6	0.0	10.5	0.0	0.0	8.8	0.0 ●	CANADA LIFE ASSURANCE CO-US BRANCH
--	--	--	--	--	--	--	--	--	--	--	--	CANYON STATE LIFE INS CO
0.0	1.5	4.9	0.0	95.1	0.0	0.0	0.0	0.0	0.0	0.0	0.0	CAPITAL RESERVE LIFE INS CO
11.8	215.8	3.6	1.1	71.2	3.0	0.6	19.2	0.4	1.0	0.2	0.0	CAPITOL LIFE INS CO
0.3	4.2	6.9	0.0	93.1	0.0	0.0	0.0	0.0	0.0	0.0	0.0	CAPITOL SECURITY LIFE INS CO
0.1	28.2	5.4	54.1	40.4	0.0	0.0	0.0	0.0	0.0	0.1	0.0	CAREAMERICA LIFE INS CO
5.2	37.5	15.9	10.0	60.1	1.9	12.0	0.0	0.0	0.0	0.0	12.0	CARIBBEAN AMERICAN LIFE ASR CO
0.1	3.1	10.7	0.1	43.5	11.4	6.9	10.7	0.0	0.0	17.6	0.0	CASS COUNTY LIFE INS CO
0.0	144.6	0.4	24.6	53.6	1.2	20.2	0.0	0.0	0.0	0.0	25.0	CATERPILLAR LIFE INS CO
--	--	--	--	--	--	--	--	--	--	--	--	CATHOLIC FINANCIAL LIFE
2.0	27.5	1.1	0.0	39.5	0.0	59.5	0.0	0.0	0.0	0.0	59.5 ●	CENTRAL RESERVE LIFE INS CO
1.5	92.8	0.3	53.7	34.5	0.2	3.1	0.7	0.0	1.9	5.8	3.0	CENTRAL SECURITY LIFE INS CO
27.4	402.4	1.6	26.3	43.0	0.7	10.7	4.9	0.0	1.4	11.5	5.8 ●	CENTRAL STATES H & L CO OF OMAHA
50.7	283.1	4.6	1.0	41.4	0.0	42.1	1.2	0.0	8.0	1.7	42.1 ●	CENTRAL UNITED LIFE INS CO
0.7	1,858.5	0.4	15.7	83.9	0.0	0.0	0.0	0.0	0.0	0.1	0.0 ●	CENTRE LIFE INS CO
83.3	1,239.0	1.0	48.4	45.4	5.1	0.0	0.0	0.0	0.0	0.0	0.0 ●	CENTURION LIFE INS CO
0.5	11.9	13.9	2.7	76.4	7.0	0.0	0.0	0.0	0.0	0.0	0.0	CENTURY LIFE ASR CO
92.3	90.6	0.9	1.3	97.9	0.0	0.0	0.0	0.0	0.0	0.6	0.0 ●	CHESAPEAKE LIFE INS CO
99.2	84.9	0.4	16.3	83.4	0.0	0.0	0.0	0.0	0.0	0.0	0.0 ●	CHESTERFIELD REINS CO
17.6	64.5	-0.1	4.2	89.2	0.6	0.0	4.7	0.0	0.7	0.6	0.0 ●	CHRISTIAN FIDELITY LIFE INS CO
17.6	288.1	0.0	26.8	64.0	3.8	5.5	0.0	0.0	0.0	0.2	0.0 ●	CHURCH LIFE INS CORP
70.8	807.1	6.4	1.9	75.8	1.6	7.4	0.0	0.0	0.0	0.3	6.8	6.8 ● CICA LIFE INS CO OF AMERICA
0.0	8.3	0.6	0.0	99.4	0.0	0.0	0.0	0.0	0.0	0.0	0.0	CIGNA ARBOR LIFE INS CO
5,796.5	3,490.7 (*)	0.0	1.8	41.2	19.1	11.9	10.9	0.0	0.0	20.6	11.8 ●	CIGNA HEALTH & LIFE INS CO
82.4	341.4	0.0	4.2	88.0	8.1	0.0	0.0	0.0	0.0	0.0	0.0 ●	CIGNA LIFE INS CO OF NEW YORK
0.0	36.7	0.5	0.0	99.5	0.0	0.0	0.0	0.0	0.0	0.0	39.3	CIGNA WORLDWIDE INS CO
18.0	99.5	0.5	7.0	79.6	3.3	9.6	0.0	0.0	0.0	0.1	3.4	CINCINNATI EQUITABLE LIFE INS CO
140.3	3,141.0	1.4	7.0	81.0	8.0	0.2	0.0	0.0	0.0	2.4	0.0 ●	CINCINNATI LIFE INS CO
1.9	67.0	2.2	0.1	77.7	5.0	7.9	0.2	0.1	6.1	0.8	0.0	CITIZENS FIDELITY INS CO
0.6	12.4	15.5	2.3	76.5	0.0	4.7	0.0	0.0	0.0	1.0	0.0	CITIZENS NATIONAL LIFE INS CO
23.0	17.5	20.8	0.0	18.5	3.0	27.2	0.0	0.0	30.4	0.4	0.0	CITIZENS SECURITY LIFE INS CO
0.0	51.5	0.7	0.0	99.3	0.0	0.0	0.0	0.0	0.0	0.0	0.0	CLEAR SPRING LIFE INS CO
0.0	11.4	0.4	15.6	84.0	0.0	0.0	0.0	0.0	0.0	0.2	0.0	CLOVER INS CO
154.2	6,902.5 (*)	0.3	11.1	47.1	6.9	3.9	14.3	0.0	0.0	8.4	10.1 ●	CM LIFE INS CO

35   ● Bullets denote a more detailed analysis is available in Section II.
(*) Asset category percentages do not add up to 100%

INSURANCE COMPANY NAME	DOM. STATE	RATING	TOTAL ASSETS ($MIL)	CAPITAL & SURPLUS ($MIL)	RISK ADJUSTED CAPITAL RATIO 1	RISK ADJUSTED CAPITAL RATIO 2	CAPITAL-IZATION INDEX (PTS)	INVEST. SAFETY INDEX (PTS)	PROFIT-ABILITY INDEX (PTS)	LIQUIDITY INDEX (PTS)	STAB. INDEX (PTS)	STABILITY FACTORS
CMFG LIFE INS CO	IA	B-	15969.4	1941.0	1.53	1.20	7.3	4.8	8.2	6.9	5.0	I
COLONIAL LIFE & ACCIDENT INS CO	SC	C+	3091.7	567.4	2.59	1.60	7.9	5.9	8.3	6.9	4.7	A
COLONIAL LIFE INS CO OF TX	TX	C-	18.2	14.0	4.34	3.51	10.0	5.3	4.2	7.8	3.3	D
COLONIAL PENN LIFE INS CO	PA	D+	845.9	108.1	1.42	0.82	5.6	4.7	1.9	0.7	2.7	ACFILT
COLONIAL SECURITY LIFE INS CO	TX	D+	2.6	1.8	2.07	1.86	8.3	7.1	6.6	7.3	2.6	D
COLORADO BANKERS LIFE INS CO	NC	B	333.4	54.6	4.65	3.03	4.0	7.9	2.9	9.1	4.1	FT
COLUMBIAN LIFE INS CO	IL	C	318.3	31.2	1.72	1.13	7.2	7.3	2.2	5.3	4.3	R
COLUMBIAN MUTUAL LIFE INS CO	NY	B	1377.6	85.1	1.36	0.89	6.1	6.4	5.4	5.0	5.4	CIL
COLUMBUS LIFE INS CO	OH	C+	3642.9	263.7	1.96	1.02	7.0	4.9	2.0	4.8	4.4	IL
▲ COMBINED INS CO OF AMERICA	IL	C+	1364.1	91.7	0.88	0.59	4.0	4.2	2.9	6.5	4.0	CFIT
▲ COMBINED LIFE INS CO OF NEW YORK	NY	C+	407.6	29.2	0.83	0.59	3.7	6.8	1.5	7.1	3.7	C
COMMENCEMENT BAY LIFE INS CO	WA	U (2)	7.7	7.4	3.71	3.34	8.0	8.4	7.8	10.0	8.0	D
COMMERCIAL TRAVELERS MUTUAL INS CO	NY	D	15.4	5.8	1.09	0.98	6.8	8.3	1.9	8.7	1.5	DFT
COMMONWEALTH ANNUITY & LIFE INS CO	MA	B-	12253.5	2259.8	0.95	0.84	5.7	4.7	7.1	7.9	5.0	FIT
COMMONWEALTH DEALERS LIFE INS CO	VA	U (2)	6.0	4.8	2.84	2.56	9.3	6.9	1.3	10.0	1.5	DT
COMPANION LIFE INS CO	NY	C+	1037.2	43.3	1.38	0.72	5.6	3.5	2.0	4.0	4.6	CIL
COMPANION LIFE INS CO	SC	A-	329.6	180.4	3.26	2.47	9.2	5.4	8.6	6.9	7.2	AI
CONCERT HEALTH PLAN INS CO	IL	F (5)	--	--	--	--	--	--	--	--	--	Z
CONNECTICUT GENERAL LIFE INS CO	CT	B-	17491.2	3846.5	1.35	1.21	7.3	4.4	8.6	7.0	3.9	AIT
CONSECO LIFE INS CO OF TX	TX	U (2)	1264.6	1246.2	0.86	0.77	5.2	1.6	8.0	10.0	3.6	CI
CONSTITUTION LIFE INS CO	TX	C+	393.9	72.0	3.07	2.05	8.6	7.4	2.8	7.3	4.5	F
CONSUMERS LIFE INS CO	OH	B	41.7	23.9	2.32	1.78	8.2	9.4	3.8	7.1	4.7	T
CONTINENTAL AMERICAN INS CO	SC	B	582.5	158.8	1.94	1.43	7.6	8.2	4.3	7.1	4.5	GT
CONTINENTAL GENERAL INS CO	OH	C+	247.5	19.2	1.32	0.91	6.3	5.2	5.5	7.1	4.6	AF
CONTINENTAL LIFE INS CO	PA	D+	24.9	2.0	0.56	0.50	3.0	4.8	2.3	5.8	2.8	AC
CONTINENTAL LIFE INS CO OF BRENTWOOD	TN	B	283.3	147.0	1.10	0.98	6.8	5.5	4.1	6.5	5.5	DIT
COOPERATIVA DE SEGUROS DE VIDA DE PR	PR	C-	516.9	23.6	1.02	0.45	4.4	1.5	5.4	3.8	2.9	CIL
COOPERATIVE LIFE INS CO	AR	D (3)	6.6	2.5	1.52	1.37	7.6	5.4	8.3	6.9	2.2	DF
CORVESTA LIFE INS CO	AZ	U (2)	9.2	7.8	3.66	3.29	10.0	9.0	1.7	9.9	1.9	DFT
COTTON STATES LIFE INS CO	GA	A-	334.6	68.1	4.49	2.49	9.2	6.8	8.2	6.2	7.3	DI
COUNTRY INVESTORS LIFE ASR CO	IL	A-	297.1	186.5	12.42	6.06	8.0	8.2	7.9	8.5	7.1	
COUNTRY LIFE INS CO	IL	A+	10264.7	1133.6	2.07	1.35	7.5	5.8	7.5	5.8	7.5	I
CROWN GLOBAL INS CO OF AMERICA	DE	E	417.0	1.4	0.13	0.11	0.0	3.7	2.3	7.0	0.0	CDEGIT
CSA FRATERNAL LIFE	IL	U	--	--	--	--	--	--	--	--	--	Z
CSI LIFE INS CO	NE	B	18.9	14.2	4.31	3.68	10.0	8.2	6.4	8.3	4.6	AGT
DAKOTA CAPITAL LIFE INS CO	ND	D	4.1	1.4	1.47	1.32	7.5	3.9	0.9	6.7	1.5	DEGT
DEARBORN NATIONAL LIFE INS CO	IL	B+	1969.6	535.0	3.70	2.30	9.0	6.4	6.8	6.5	6.0	AFIT
DEARBORN NATIONAL LIFE INS CO OF NY	NY	B+	38.7	24.3	4.37	3.93	10.0	8.3	5.3	7.7	5.0	AFT
DELAWARE AMERICAN LIFE INS CO	DE	A-	145.9	65.2	3.55	2.61	9.4	7.6	6.8	6.8	7.2	A
DELAWARE LIFE INS CO	DE	C	40645.8	1485.7	1.40	0.88	6.0	4.7	5.8	8.5	3.9	GIT
DELAWARE LIFE INS CO OF NEW YORK	NY	C+	2815.6	411.4	7.39	3.58	10.0	6.4	7.0	7.1	3.6	AFT
▼ DELTA LIFE INS CO	GA	D-	62.6	8.7	0.49	0.30	0.9	1.1	2.0	4.9	0.9	CIL
DESERET MUTUAL INS CO	UT	B	39.6	8.4	2.18	1.72	8.1	6.7	3.8	7.2	5.5	AFT
DESTINY HEALTH INS CO	IL	U (2)	3.5	3.5	3.08	2.77	8.0	9.8	2.3	10.0	2.5	DF
DIRECT GENERAL LIFE INS CO	SC	C+	29.3	16.4	3.88	3.49	10.0	9.0	8.9	7.0	4.8	AD
DIRECTORS LIFE ASR CO	OK	E	32.2	1.8	0.29	0.26	0.1	0.8	2.4	0.4	0.1	CIL
DL REINSURANCE CO	DE	U (2)	1363.2	30.6	1.51	1.35	7.5	7.6	0.9	10.0	2.9	EGT
DLE LIFE INS CO	LA	F (5)	--	--	--	--	--	--	--	--	--	Z
DOCTORS LIFE INS CO	CA	U (2)	15.6	7.0	2.52	2.27	8.9	9.1	1.7	9.3	3.0	DFT
EAGLE LIFE INS CO	IA	B	393.4	64.7	4.24	2.09	8.6	6.8	3.0	6.9	5.8	G
EDUCATORS LIFE INS CO OF AMERICA	IL	U (2)	441.3	423.8	1.20	1.07	7.1	0.9	8.4	9.4	2.9	DI
ELCO MUTUAL LIFE & ANNUITY	IL	C-	680.2	47.5	1.46	0.70	5.7	3.6	2.8	7.7	3.0	DGT

See Page 27 for explanation of footnotes and Page 28 for explanation of stability factors.
Arrows denote recent upgrades ▲ or downgrades▼ (see Section VI for explanations)

36

www.weissratings.com

NET PREMIUM ($MIL)	IN-VESTED ASSETS ($MIL)	CASH	CMO & STRUCT. SECS.	OTH.INV. GRADE BONDS	NON-INV. GRADE BONDS	CMMON & PREF. STOCK	MORT IN GOOD STAND.	NON-PERF. MORT.	REAL ESTATE	OTHER INVEST-MENTS	INVEST. IN AFFIL	INSURANCE COMPANY NAME
						% OF INVESTED ASSETS IN:						
1,536.0	10,920.6	0.4	11.8	52.5	4.0	9.8	13.9	0.0	0.7	6.7	10.2 ●	CMFG LIFE INS CO
709.4	2,717.8	0.0	4.3	72.7	5.9	0.8	12.1	0.0	1.8	3.1	0.0 ●	COLONIAL LIFE & ACCIDENT INS CO
0.4	17.4	3.8	17.7	49.4	4.8	22.9	0.0	0.0	0.0	1.4	0.0	COLONIAL LIFE INS CO OF TX
188.1	745.4	1.8	16.5	69.3	3.2	1.5	2.9	0.0	0.0	3.9	0.2 ●	COLONIAL PENN LIFE INS CO
0.3	2.5	2.0	0.1	83.1	0.0	5.2	0.0	0.0	0.0	9.7	0.0	COLONIAL SECURITY LIFE INS CO
31.7	308.0	7.1	5.4	85.3	0.5	0.0	0.0	0.0	0.0	1.7	0.0 ●	COLORADO BANKERS LIFE INS CO
28.6	283.0	0.7	17.0	67.6	0.0	2.3	6.4	0.0	0.0	6.1	2.3 ●	COLUMBIAN LIFE INS CO
91.8	1,283.4	0.1	11.5	66.2	0.0	2.9	13.3	0.0	0.3	5.7	2.5 ●	COLUMBIAN MUTUAL LIFE INS CO
144.4	3,276.1	0.2	17.6	62.1	5.8	2.9	4.8	0.0	0.0	6.5	2.7 ●	COLUMBUS LIFE INS CO
222.0	1,175.2	2.3	19.8	62.8	10.0	1.9	0.0	0.0	0.0	3.2	1.9 ●	COMBINED INS CO OF AMERICA
77.5	374.6	-1.0	41.1	57.5	0.0	0.1	0.0	0.0	0.0	2.3	0.0 ●	COMBINED LIFE INS CO OF NEW YORK
0.0	7.6	0.0	45.0	55.0	0.0	0.0	0.0	0.0	0.0	0.0	0.0	COMMENCEMENT BAY LIFE INS CO
0.6	16.5	30.2	17.4	49.2	0.0	1.7	0.0	0.0	1.4	0.0	0.7	COMMERCIAL TRAVELERS MUTUAL INS CO
127.3	9,391.3 (*)	1.4	37.5	27.0	2.7	22.0	3.2	0.0	0.0	4.3	22.0 ●	COMMONWEALTH ANNUITY & LIFE INS CO
0.0	6.0	5.0	0.0	65.3	2.2	0.0	0.0	0.0	0.0	27.5	0.0	COMMONWEALTH DEALERS LIFE INS CO
52.0	898.3	2.5	22.4	61.9	2.1	0.2	7.5	0.0	0.0	3.4	0.0 ●	COMPANION LIFE INS CO
118.3	214.3	6.7	19.1	50.2	0.5	23.5	0.0	0.0	0.0	0.0	6.6 ●	COMPANION LIFE INS CO
--	--	--	--	--	--	--	--	--	--	--	--	CONCERT HEALTH PLAN INS CO
202.1	9,167.9	0.0	3.1	33.0	5.6	33.4	3.8	0.0	1.5	19.5	35.3 ●	CONNECTICUT GENERAL LIFE INS CO
0.2	1,246.2	2.1	0.0	1.1	0.0	96.7	0.0	0.0	0.0	0.0	96.7	CONSECO LIFE INS CO OF TX
56.8	367.4	-1.4	35.4	64.9	0.0	0.0	0.0	0.0	0.0	1.2	0.0 ●	CONSTITUTION LIFE INS CO
16.1	30.6	26.6	0.0	73.4	0.0	0.0	0.0	0.0	0.0	0.0	0.0	CONSUMERS LIFE INS CO
267.1	359.0	5.3	0.0	93.8	0.0	0.0	0.0	0.0	0.0	1.0	0.0 ●	CONTINENTAL AMERICAN INS CO
6.9	236.4	5.1	26.0	58.5	1.7	6.5	0.5	0.0	0.0	1.7	3.3	CONTINENTAL GENERAL INS CO
2.4	21.4	4.6	1.8	68.7	0.0	0.0	16.3	0.0	2.3	6.4	0.0	CONTINENTAL LIFE INS CO
209.6	248.1 (*)	0.0	26.9	42.9	0.2	32.1	0.0	0.0	0.0	0.4	32.1 ●	CONTINENTAL LIFE INS CO OF BRENTWOOD
39.4	355.2	6.0	0.0	61.0	17.7	1.5	0.6	1.0	11.0	1.2	0.0	COOPERATIVA DE SEGUROS DE VIDA DE PR
0.3	6.6	4.6	2.7	71.4	4.5	16.4	0.0	0.0	0.3	0.2	0.0	COOPERATIVE LIFE INS CO
0.0	9.2	11.2	26.7	62.1	0.0	0.0	0.0	0.0	0.0	0.0	0.0	CORVESTA LIFE INS CO
12.0	318.9	-0.1	17.6	71.6	1.9	3.8	0.0	0.0	0.0	5.2	0.0 ●	COTTON STATES LIFE INS CO
0.0	213.6	-0.2	18.2	80.5	1.2	0.0	0.0	0.0	0.0	0.2	0.0 ●	COUNTRY INVESTORS LIFE ASR CO
360.3	8,588.2 (*)	-0.1	20.0	58.6	3.7	7.0	3.4	0.0	0.4	4.7	3.9 ●	COUNTRY LIFE INS CO
36.8	1.6	6.4	0.0	74.7	18.9	0.0	0.0	0.0	0.0	0.0	0.0	CROWN GLOBAL INS CO OF AMERICA
--	--	--	--	--	--	--	--	--	--	--	--	CSA FRATERNAL LIFE
7.8	17.2	6.6	0.0	89.1	0.0	4.2	0.0	0.0	0.0	0.1	49.3	CSI LIFE INS CO
0.7	3.0	2.6	1.7	60.2	0.0	35.5	0.0	0.0	0.0	0.0	0.0	DAKOTA CAPITAL LIFE INS CO
202.2	1,914.5	0.3	24.0	64.2	8.2	1.2	1.4	0.0	0.0	0.5	1.2 ●	DEARBORN NATIONAL LIFE INS CO
1.0	38.7	2.4	20.4	71.2	0.0	0.0	0.0	0.0	0.0	0.0	0.0	DEARBORN NATIONAL LIFE INS CO OF NY
57.6	112.1	6.3	37.6	52.8	0.0	0.0	0.0	0.0	0.0	3.4	3.3 ●	DELAWARE AMERICAN LIFE INS CO
936.9	9,881.2 (*)	-0.1	26.7	32.8	3.9	5.9	5.0	0.0	0.0	19.1	9.2 ●	DELAWARE LIFE INS CO
10.0	1,157.3	0.1	33.1	61.5	1.7	1.5	1.6	0.0	0.0	0.4	0.0 ●	DELAWARE LIFE INS CO OF NEW YORK
7.4	62.2	4.3	0.0	23.3	4.3	36.5	0.0	0.0	22.3	9.3	18.5	DELTA LIFE INS CO
7.1	37.7	3.4	0.0	89.6	1.8	5.1	0.0	0.0	0.0	0.0	0.0	DESERET MUTUAL INS CO
0.0	3.5	57.1	0.0	42.9	0.0	0.0	0.0	0.0	0.0	0.0	0.0	DESTINY HEALTH INS CO
10.5	14.9	14.1	13.7	72.2	0.0	0.0	0.0	0.0	0.0	0.0	0.0	DIRECT GENERAL LIFE INS CO
3.3	29.8	2.4	0.7	93.4	2.2	0.0	0.0	0.0	0.0	1.4	0.0	DIRECTORS LIFE ASR CO
0.0	30.7	2.4	25.3	59.0	0.0	0.0	13.3	0.0	0.0	0.0	0.0	DL REINSURANCE CO
--	--	--	--	--	--	--	--	--	--	--	--	DLE LIFE INS CO
0.0	15.2	12.5	9.0	78.5	0.0	0.0	0.0	0.0	0.0	0.0	0.0	DOCTORS LIFE INS CO
75.6	310.8	2.2	19.8	72.5	0.9	0.0	4.2	0.0	0.0	0.0	0.0 ●	EAGLE LIFE INS CO
1.2	440.3	0.0	0.0	0.6	3.6	95.8	0.0	0.0	0.0	0.0	95.8	EDUCATORS LIFE INS CO OF AMERICA
99.2	614.6	4.5	0.0	91.8	2.5	0.0	0.7	0.0	0.5	0.0	0.0 ●	ELCO MUTUAL LIFE & ANNUITY

● Bullets denote a more detailed analysis is available in Section II.
(*) Asset category percentages do not add up to 100%

INSURANCE COMPANY NAME	DOM. STATE	RATING	TOTAL ASSETS ($MIL)	CAPITAL & SURPLUS ($MIL)	RISK ADJUSTED CAPITAL RATIO 1	RISK ADJUSTED CAPITAL RATIO 2	CAPITAL- IZATION INDEX (PTS)	INVEST. SAFETY INDEX (PTS)	PROFIT- ABILITY INDEX (PTS)	LIQUIDITY INDEX (PTS)	STAB. INDEX (PTS)	STABILITY FACTORS
EMC NATIONAL LIFE CO	IA	B	965.4	104.5	2.52	1.43	7.6	6.5	7.5	5.2	5.7	FL
EMPIRE FIDELITY INVESTMENTS L I C	NY	B+	2497.9	78.7	2.67	2.29	8.9	8.1	3.3	7.0	6.7	
EMPLOYERS REASSURANCE CORP	KS	C	10616.1	643.4	1.03	0.77	5.2	5.8	3.3	6.9	4.2	AF
▲ ENTERPRISE LIFE INS CO	TX	B-	30.3	21.5	0.96	0.85	5.8	5.7	8.5	7.1	5.1	ADGT
EPIC LIFE INSURANCE CO	WI	C	44.1	13.2	2.05	1.38	7.6	4.3	4.0	7.0	3.6	AFIT
EQUITABLE LIFE & CASUALTY INS CO	UT	B	317.1	51.3	3.29	2.16	8.7	7.6	5.9	7.0	5.7	D
EQUITRUST LIFE INS CO	IL	B-	16791.6	748.5	1.17	0.58	5.3	4.1	6.7	8.3	5.0	CI
ERIE FAMILY LIFE INS CO	PA	A-	2217.2	311.9	3.30	1.79	8.2	5.9	8.0	7.9	7.1	AI
EVERENCE ASSN INC	IN	U	--	--	--	--	--	--	--	--	--	Z
EVERENCE INS CO	IN	U (2)	22.5	13.3	3.56	3.20	10.0	7.4	6.6	9.4	5.7	DFT
EVERGREEN LIFE INS CO	TX	U (2)	1.6	1.6	2.60	2.34	8.0	9.8	3.1	10.0	3.3	DF
FAMILY BENEFIT LIFE INS CO	MO	C	104.3	10.0	1.19	1.07	7.1	4.1	5.4	6.4	2.9	ADGIT
FAMILY HERITAGE LIFE INS CO OF AMER	OH	A-	1004.9	77.5	1.81	1.18	7.3	6.6	9.5	7.9	7.3	AI
FAMILY LIBERTY LIFE INS CO	TX	D (2)	32.2	8.7	1.94	1.41	7.6	4.9	2.7	6.0	2.2	DI
FAMILY LIFE INS CO	TX	C	158.6	34.6	3.66	2.98	10.0	8.5	2.9	6.8	4.2	D
FAMILY SECURITY LIFE INS CO INC	MS	C	6.7	1.6	0.91	0.82	5.6	7.3	3.0	7.0	3.4	CF
FAMILY SERVICE LIFE INS CO	TX	U (2)	350.7	27.5	2.47	1.42	7.6	5.2	2.4	5.5	4.4	DFI
FARM BUREAU LIFE INS CO	IA	B+	8582.6	592.6	2.10	1.08	7.1	5.4	7.9	4.0	6.0	IL
FARM BUREAU LIFE INS CO OF MICHIGAN	MI	A-	2361.9	405.7	3.42	1.86	8.3	6.0	7.3	5.6	6.9	I
FARM BUREAU LIFE INS CO OF MISSOURI	MO	A-	558.9	61.4	1.77	1.15	7.2	5.2	5.6	5.5	6.9	I
FARM FAMILY LIFE INS CO	NY	B	1327.5	171.2	2.38	1.33	7.5	5.0	5.5	5.3	6.0	IL
FARMERS NEW WORLD LIFE INS CO	WA	B-	7148.3	512.7	1.41	0.84	5.7	4.6	3.0	4.7	4.9	AIL
FEDERAL LIFE INS CO	IL	C-	226.4	13.8	1.60	0.90	6.2	3.8	1.9	5.3	3.0	DI
FEDERATED LIFE INS CO	MN	A	1710.7	348.0	4.53	2.45	9.2	6.7	8.7	6.6	7.4	AI
FIDELITY & GUARANTY LIFE INS CO	IA	C+	20647.2	1251.5	1.30	0.71	5.5	3.4	8.2	5.6	4.6	ACI
FIDELITY & GUARANTY LIFE INS CO NY	NY	B-	526.8	61.9	3.37	1.64	8.0	5.2	6.4	6.4	5.1	ADFIT
FIDELITY INVESTMENTS LIFE INS CO	UT	A-	25080.7	792.6	3.39	2.06	8.6	6.6	8.9	7.0	6.9	IT
FIDELITY LIFE ASSN A LEGAL RESERVE	IL	C	405.4	126.6	6.18	3.31	10.0	6.3	3.0	6.9	4.0	D
FIDELITY MUTUAL LIFE INS CO	PA	F (5)	--	--	--	--	--	--	--	--	--	Z
FIDELITY SECURITY LIFE INS CO	MO	B	864.4	178.2	2.64	1.81	8.2	7.0	7.8	5.6	4.9	DGT
FIDELITY SECURITY LIFE INS CO OF NY	NY	B	39.4	10.2	2.17	1.95	8.4	5.5	7.0	6.7	5.8	AFI
FIDELITY STANDARD LIFE INS CO	AR	D	3.1	0.4	0.46	0.41	1.9	0.8	2.0	5.3	1.6	CDFI
▼ FINANCIAL AMERICAN LIFE INS CO	KS	D+	7.9	3.2	1.33	1.20	4.0	8.7	2.1	6.5	2.7	DFT
FINANCIAL ASSURANCE LIFE INS CO	TX	U (2)	11.3	10.4	4.05	3.65	10.0	7.8	8.2	10.0	8.3	D
FIRST ALLMERICA FINANCIAL LIFE INS	MA	C	3403.1	181.9	4.02	1.86	4.0	6.6	4.3	6.0	2.8	FT
FIRST ASR LIFE OF AMERICA	LA	B	39.4	33.7	3.25	3.06	10.0	8.8	8.2	8.2	5.7	A
FIRST BERKSHIRE HATHAWAY LIFE INS CO	NY	C	162.7	97.5	10.49	5.55	10.0	3.6	1.7	10.0	2.9	DIT
FIRST COMMAND LIFE INS CO	TX	B-	36.6	11.5	2.26	2.03	8.5	7.4	7.6	6.7	4.3	D
FIRST CONTINENTAL LIFE & ACC INS CO	TX	D (1)	8.0	5.8	2.14	1.81	8.2	6.6	3.9	7.3	1.8	DGT
FIRST DIMENSION LIFE INS CO INC	OK	U (2)	4.8	3.6	2.46	2.21	8.8	8.3	6.9	6.9	7.1	D
FIRST GUARANTY INS CO	LA	D (3)	55.4	4.1	0.65	0.59	3.7	2.8	2.3	5.4	2.2	CI
FIRST HEALTH LIFE & HEALTH INS CO	TX	B-	650.1	209.8	1.56	1.28	7.4	8.7	1.9	5.3	3.5	DT
FIRST LANDMARK LIFE INS CO	NE	U (2)	2.0	2.0	2.77	2.50	8.0	9.5	2.8	10.0	3.0	DFT
FIRST METLIFE INVESTORS INS CO	NY	C+	6131.2	322.9	4.23	2.10	8.7	6.3	3.0	7.3	3.7	T
FIRST NATIONAL LIFE INS CO OF USA	NE	C-	5.6	2.1	1.47	1.01	7.0	2.7	6.2	7.2	2.9	FGIT
FIRST PENN-PACIFIC LIFE INS CO	IN	B	1568.0	183.3	2.54	1.36	7.5	5.7	5.8	5.2	5.0	AFIT
FIRST RELIANCE STANDARD LIFE INS CO	NY	A	190.3	70.8	6.38	4.25	10.0	6.5	7.1	6.9	6.0	AI
FIRST SECURITY BENEFIT LIFE & ANN	NY	B	683.1	26.4	1.12	0.51	5.1	0.8	2.4	5.3	4.5	CDFIT
FIRST SYMETRA NATL LIFE INS CO OF NY	NY	A	1467.2	115.9	2.98	1.45	7.7	6.1	9.1	6.5	7.5	AGI
FIRST UNITED AMERICAN LIFE INS CO	NY	B+	219.9	37.0	2.26	1.42	7.6	5.0	7.5	5.0	6.7	ADIL
FIRST UNUM LIFE INS CO	NY	C+	3181.3	258.1	2.44	1.21	7.3	3.7	5.9	7.1	4.8	AI
FIRST WYOMING LIFE INS CO	NE	D-	4.2	2.6	2.06	1.86	8.3	7.4	1.7	6.7	0.9	ADFT

See Page 27 for explanation of footnotes and Page 28 for explanation of stability factors.
Arrows denote recent upgrades ▲ or downgrades▼ (see Section VI for explanations)

38

www.weissratings.com

NET PREMIUM ($MIL)	IN-VESTED ASSETS ($MIL)	% OF INVESTED ASSETS IN:										INSURANCE COMPANY NAME
		CASH	CMO & STRUCT. SECS.	OTH.INV. GRADE BONDS	NON-INV. GRADE BONDS	CMMON & PREF. STOCK	MORT IN GOOD STAND.	NON-PERF. MORT.	REAL ESTATE	OTHER INVEST-MENTS	INVEST. IN AFFIL	
34.0	930.1	-0.2	6.7	82.1	0.8	3.7	4.5	0.0	0.2	2.3	0.0 ●	EMC NATIONAL LIFE CO
92.2	145.1	-0.2	4.4	95.1	0.7	0.0	0.0	0.0	0.0	0.1	0.0 ●	EMPIRE FIDELITY INVESTMENTS L I C
152.7	10,381.4	0.1	17.7	69.9	0.8	4.2	5.1	0.0	0.0	2.0	5.1 ●	EMPLOYERS REASSURANCE CORP
28.4	26.2	7.6	0.3	28.4	1.0	62.8	0.0	0.0	0.0	0.0	62.8	ENTERPRISE LIFE INS CO
12.7	59.2	3.4	18.8	56.3	0.0	21.5	0.0	0.0	0.0	0.0	0.0	EPIC LIFE INSURANCE CO
32.7	266.5	0.6	18.4	75.7	0.1	0.0	4.9	0.0	0.1	0.3	0.0 ●	EQUITABLE LIFE & CASUALTY INS CO
942.5	14,158.3 (*)	0.5	30.8	41.1	2.8	2.1	9.8	0.0	0.1	11.7	0.0 ●	EQUITRUST LIFE INS CO
82.2	2,064.6	-0.2	1.7	92.6	1.7	2.9	0.0	0.0	0.1	1.3	0.0 ●	ERIE FAMILY LIFE INS CO
--	--	--	--	--	--	--	--	--	--	--	--	EVERENCE ASSN INC
0.0	22.1	6.0	4.3	82.8	4.0	0.1	2.4	0.4	0.0	0.0	4.4	EVERENCE INS CO
0.0	1.6	100.0	0.0	0.0	0.0	0.0	0.0	0.0	0.0	0.0	0.0	EVERGREEN LIFE INS CO
6.5	96.0	3.3	0.1	68.3	3.7	0.2	23.5	0.1	0.1	0.7	0.0	FAMILY BENEFIT LIFE INS CO
136.6	805.2	0.1	0.0	96.6	1.0	0.0	0.0	0.0	0.0	2.0	0.0 ●	FAMILY HERITAGE LIFE INS CO OF AMER
1.7	31.9	1.6	2.0	76.4	1.7	16.3	1.0	0.0	0.2	1.0	0.0	FAMILY LIBERTY LIFE INS CO
13.2	142.1	0.5	3.9	83.0	0.0	0.4	2.1	0.0	0.0	10.2	0.0 ●	FAMILY LIFE INS CO
0.5	0.4	19.1	0.0	72.9	1.5	2.3	0.0	0.0	4.2	0.0	0.0	FAMILY SECURITY LIFE INS CO INC
0.0	345.0	0.0	0.0	95.2	3.5	1.2	0.0	0.0	0.0	0.1	1.2	FAMILY SERVICE LIFE INS CO
356.7	7,515.0	0.0	22.5	58.0	3.3	2.0	9.2	0.0	0.0	5.0	0.1 ●	FARM BUREAU LIFE INS CO
63.7	2,195.5	0.0	1.6	67.3	2.6	6.8	18.8	0.0	0.5	2.5	0.5 ●	FARM BUREAU LIFE INS CO OF MICHIGAN
23.3	526.6	0.2	16.6	64.9	0.1	12.3	0.0	0.0	0.0	5.9	2.2 ●	FARM BUREAU LIFE INS CO OF MISSOURI
37.7	1,282.5	0.7	2.1	74.6	3.1	9.2	5.8	0.2	0.4	4.0	0.0 ●	FARM FAMILY LIFE INS CO
304.1	6,091.4	-0.2	18.0	62.1	2.0	2.1	8.8	0.0	2.3	4.8	1.8 ●	FARMERS NEW WORLD LIFE INS CO
11.4	197.1	0.4	22.3	61.2	4.6	5.4	0.0	0.0	1.0	5.2	0.3	FEDERAL LIFE INS CO
97.3	1,601.5	0.0	10.2	83.8	3.2	1.7	0.0	0.0	0.0	1.2	0.0 ●	FEDERATED LIFE INS CO
1,368.4	18,923.2	1.3	22.7	57.7	6.6	5.3	3.3	0.0	0.0	2.6	3.6 ●	FIDELITY & GUARANTY LIFE INS CO
5.7	518.8	0.2	17.3	70.4	4.1	4.3	0.0	0.0	0.0	3.6	0.0 ●	FIDELITY & GUARANTY LIFE INS CO NY
640.5	909.7	-0.7	3.1	82.1	6.9	8.5	0.0	0.0	0.0	0.2	8.5 ●	FIDELITY INVESTMENTS LIFE INS CO
32.4	405.2	3.4	29.2	51.7	4.7	1.2	7.3	0.0	0.0	2.6	0.0 ●	FIDELITY LIFE ASSN A LEGAL RESERVE
--	--	--	--	--	--	--	--	--	--	--	--	FIDELITY MUTUAL LIFE INS CO
62.5	820.7	3.7	40.2	46.9	2.6	2.8	0.5	0.0	0.0	3.1	1.7 ●	FIDELITY SECURITY LIFE INS CO
1.1	39.1	2.2	20.4	74.8	1.8	0.8	0.0	0.0	0.0	0.0	0.0	FIDELITY SECURITY LIFE INS CO OF NY
0.1	3.1	8.0	0.0	36.1	27.7	18.5	4.4	2.0	0.0	3.4	0.0	FIDELITY STANDARD LIFE INS CO
-0.4	9.0	3.5	25.3	71.2	0.0	0.0	0.0	0.0	0.0	0.0	0.0	FINANCIAL AMERICAN LIFE INS CO
0.1	11.2	0.0	54.9	36.0	0.0	9.0	0.0	0.0	0.0	0.2	0.0	FINANCIAL ASSURANCE LIFE INS CO
13.5	2,695.3	0.6	28.5	67.6	0.8	0.0	0.7	0.0	0.0	1.6	0.0 ●	FIRST ALLMERICA FINANCIAL LIFE INS
1.4	38.6 (*)	1.5	0.0	69.6	0.0	24.5	0.0	0.0	0.0	0.0	24.5 ●	FIRST ASR LIFE OF AMERICA
1.0	156.4 (*)	18.7	25.8	33.9	26.0	6.7	0.0	0.0	0.0	0.0	10.2 ●	FIRST BERKSHIRE HATHAWAY LIFE INS CO
1.2	34.7	0.1	18.8	77.7	3.0	0.0	0.0	0.0	0.0	0.4	0.0	FIRST COMMAND LIFE INS CO
0.6	8.1	65.0	0.0	17.8	0.0	13.7	0.0	0.0	3.4	0.0	13.7	FIRST CONTINENTAL LIFE & ACC INS CO
0.0	4.8	2.2	0.0	95.0	0.0	1.8	0.0	0.0	0.0	1.4	0.0	FIRST DIMENSION LIFE INS CO INC
4.4	53.1	1.4	10.6	71.0	1.4	1.1	11.3	0.0	2.9	0.3	0.0	FIRST GUARANTY INS CO
400.9	241.5	23.4	4.8	71.2	0.7	0.0	0.0	0.0	0.0	0.0	0.0 ●	FIRST HEALTH LIFE & HEALTH INS CO
0.0	2.0	0.1	0.0	99.9	0.0	0.0	0.0	0.0	0.0	0.0	623.2	FIRST LANDMARK LIFE INS CO
24.2	1,246.3	-0.1	22.7	60.6	5.0	0.0	11.4	0.0	0.0	0.0	0.0 ●	FIRST METLIFE INVESTORS INS CO
0.8	5.4	1.4	44.5	10.0	0.0	41.5	0.0	0.0	0.0	2.6	0.0	FIRST NATIONAL LIFE INS CO OF USA
62.5	1,424.7	0.0	11.3	71.5	5.2	0.2	10.0	0.0	0.0	2.3	0.0 ●	FIRST PENN-PACIFIC LIFE INS CO
30.9	175.7	-0.1	22.2	68.6	7.8	0.0	0.0	0.0	0.0	1.5	0.0 ●	FIRST RELIANCE STANDARD LIFE INS CO
6.3	548.8	1.5	45.9	41.8	9.8	0.0	0.0	0.0	0.0	1.0	0.0 ●	FIRST SECURITY BENEFIT LIFE & ANN
236.3	1,244.8	0.9	12.7	75.3	0.6	0.0	10.5	0.0	0.0	0.0	0.0 ●	FIRST SYMETRA NATL LIFE INS CO OF NY
40.2	180.2	0.7	4.3	83.0	6.4	0.0	0.0	0.0	0.0	5.2	0.0 ●	FIRST UNITED AMERICAN LIFE INS CO
186.2	3,039.2	0.0	7.2	75.0	12.4	0.0	4.9	0.0	0.0	0.6	0.0 ●	FIRST UNUM LIFE INS CO
0.4	4.0	2.2	0.0	97.8	0.0	0.0	0.0	0.0	0.0	0.0	0.0	FIRST WYOMING LIFE INS CO

● Bullets denote a more detailed analysis is available in Section II.
(*) Asset category percentages do not add up to 100%

INSURANCE COMPANY NAME	DOM. STATE	RATING	TOTAL ASSETS ($MIL)	CAPITAL & SURPLUS ($MIL)	RISK ADJUSTED CAPITAL RATIO 1	RISK ADJUSTED CAPITAL RATIO 2	CAPITAL-IZATION INDEX (PTS)	INVEST. SAFETY INDEX (PTS)	PROFIT-ABILITY INDEX (PTS)	LIQUIDITY INDEX (PTS)	STAB. INDEX (PTS)	STABILITY FACTORS
FIVE STAR LIFE INS CO	LA	C+	270.7	31.6	2.23	1.37	7.6	6.6	1.8	5.9	4.4	
FLORIDA COMBINED LIFE INS CO INC	FL	C	51.7	28.4	4.80	3.14	8.0	4.8	4.1	7.3	4.3	
FORESTERS LIFE INS & ANNUITY CO	NY	C+	2002.0	61.5	1.86	0.96	6.7	4.7	3.5	6.0	4.5	I
FORETHOUGHT LIFE INS CO	IN	B	22257.6	1319.6	2.64	1.27	7.4	5.6	8.1	7.4	6.2	AGI
FORETHOUGHT NATIONAL LIFE INS CO	TX	U (2)	199.4	21.8	2.20	1.79	8.2	9.1	2.1	0.0	3.5	DLT
FOUNDATION LIFE INS CO OF AR	AR	D	4.9	1.3	1.06	0.96	6.7	4.9	1.4	7.9	2.0	FI
FRANDISCO LIFE INS CO	GA	A	78.5	69.9	8.84	7.96	10.0	8.9	9.8	9.5	6.7	ADT
FREEDOM LIFE INS CO OF AMERICA	TX	C+	83.9	42.7	0.79	0.68	4.4	6.7	8.4	7.2	4.4	C
FREMONT LIFE INS CO	CA	F (5)	--	--	--	--	--	--	--	--	--	Z
FRINGE BENEFIT LIFE INS CO	TX	C-	42.0	28.1	5.13	2.78	9.7	4.3	7.1	6.9	3.3	DFIT
FUNERAL DIRECTORS LIFE INS CO	TX	B-	1199.9	103.5	2.25	1.21	7.3	6.2	8.0	2.6	4.6	L
FUTURAL LIFE CO	AZ	D+ (3)	6.3	5.0	3.29	2.96	9.9	4.0	3.9	10.0	2.4	DFIT
GARDEN STATE LIFE INS CO	TX	A-	126.5	65.6	7.22	6.50	10.0	6.7	8.6	6.9	7.2	ADI
GENERAL AMERICAN LIFE INS CO	MO	B	12497.0	1000.6	3.41	1.54	7.8	6.0	8.4	5.6	6.2	AI
GENERAL FIDELITY LIFE INS CO	SC	D+	25.3	16.5	4.06	3.65	10.0	9.6	2.8	10.0	2.6	DFT
GENERAL RE LIFE CORP	CT	B	3389.4	615.1	2.15	1.34	7.5	5.1	3.0	8.5	5.4	AI
GENERATION LIFE INS CO	AZ	B	32.9	29.6	6.18	5.56	10.0	7.8	2.0	10.0	5.8	DT
GENWORTH LIFE & ANNUITY INS CO	VA	B-	23144.6	1585.9	1.60	1.00	7.0	5.6	2.7	6.3	3.5	AT
GENWORTH LIFE INS CO	DE	B-	39497.6	2629.6	0.97	0.73	4.8	5.5	4.2	7.2	4.8	ACT
GENWORTH LIFE INS CO OF NEW YORK	NY	C+	8470.8	530.6	2.36	1.18	7.3	5.5	2.7	6.7	4.4	AT
GERBER LIFE INS CO	NY	B+	3240.4	299.7	1.88	1.13	7.2	6.1	6.4	5.6	6.8	IL
GERMANIA LIFE INS CO	TX	C	82.5	8.4	1.09	0.98	6.8	5.5	2.0	5.4	4.0	A
GERTRUDE GEDDES WILLIS LIFE INS CO	LA	F (5)	--	--	--	--	--	--	--	--	--	Z
GLOBE LIFE & ACCIDENT INS CO	NE	B-	3889.2	272.7	1.71	0.91	6.3	4.2	5.2	3.7	5.3	IL
GMHP HEALTH INS LMTD	GU	U (2)	0.5	0.3	1.72	1.55	7.8	3.0	0.7	9.1	0.9	DIT
GOLDEN RULE INS CO	IN	B	618.1	262.5	1.45	1.13	5.5	8.0	7.0	6.2	4.7	AT
GOVERNMENT PERSONNEL MUTUAL L I C	TX	B+	834.7	116.6	2.79	1.74	8.1	7.0	7.2	5.4	6.4	DL
GPM HEALTH & LIFE INS CO	WA	B	141.0	10.0	1.17	1.00	7.0	2.3	5.3	3.7	5.1	DFIL
GRANGE LIFE INS CO	OH	C+	401.8	36.6	1.50	1.00	7.0	6.4	2.3	6.6	4.6	D
GREAT AMERICAN LIFE INS CO	OH	B-	27716.3	1893.8	1.71	0.96	6.7	5.2	9.0	5.4	5.3	AI
GREAT CENTRAL LIFE INS CO	LA	C (5)	--	--	--	--	--	--	--	--	--	Z
GREAT FIDELITY LIFE INS CO	IN	D	3.2	2.6	2.16	1.94	8.4	7.1	2.1	7.7	1.8	ADFGT
GREAT PLAINS LIFE ASR CO	SD	E+	7.8	1.6	0.83	0.75	5.0	5.9	1.2	3.2	0.8	ADLT
GREAT REPUBLIC LIFE INS CO	WA	F (5)	--	--	--	--	--	--	--	--	--	Z
GREAT SOUTHERN LIFE INS CO	TX	B+	218.2	46.8	5.11	2.72	9.6	6.5	9.2	7.5	6.0	AGIT
GREAT WEST LIFE ASR CO	MI	C+	77.4	20.9	2.66	2.13	8.7	7.5	2.9	7.0	4.8	
GREAT WESTERN INS CO	UT	B	1149.2	73.6	1.94	1.00	7.0	4.9	6.2	7.2	5.5	IT
GREAT WESTERN LIFE INS CO	MT	U (5)	--	--	--	--	--	--	--	--	--	Z
GREAT-WEST LIFE & ANNUITY INS CO	CO	B-	58321.7	1028.1	1.15	0.62	5.2	5.3	6.1	6.4	5.0	CI
GREAT-WEST LIFE & ANNUITY INS OF NY	NY	B	1801.4	89.8	2.74	1.46	7.7	6.5	5.6	6.0	5.9	A
GREATER GEORGIA LIFE INS CO	GA	B+	58.6	22.4	1.51	1.12	7.2	8.4	3.6	7.1	6.4	A
GREENFIELDS LIFE INS CO	CO	B	8.9	4.5	2.22	1.99	8.5	8.8	2.0	8.7	5.5	DEGT
GRIFFIN LEGGETT BURIAL INS CO	AR	U (2)	0.1	0.1	1.88	1.69	8.0	9.8	1.9	10.0	2.1	DF
GUARANTEE TRUST LIFE INS CO	IL	B	515.0	73.6	1.84	1.23	7.3	6.6	8.2	7.6	6.0	T
GUARANTY INCOME LIFE INS CO	LA	C	491.3	41.3	2.57	1.26	7.4	3.9	8.2	5.1	4.4	DI
GUARDIAN INS & ANNUITY CO INC	DE	B	16278.3	190.4	1.25	0.63	5.4	5.5	3.6	9.2	5.4	CI
GUARDIAN LIFE INS CO OF AMERICA	NY	A	50389.3	6144.3	2.45	1.58	7.9	6.0	7.6	5.9	7.5	I
GUGGENHEIM LIFE & ANNUITY CO	DE	B-	13900.3	589.2	1.07	0.63	5.1	4.3	5.7	7.2	4.9	CIT
GULF GUARANTY LIFE INS CO	MS	C-	16.2	8.7	1.49	1.16	7.2	4.1	3.4	8.3	2.9	I
GULF STATES LIFE INS CO INC	LA	U (2)	2.7	2.5	2.91	2.62	4.0	4.5	4.7	10.0	4.9	DI
HALLMARK LIFE INS CO	AZ	C	18.4	12.0	3.45	3.10	10.0	9.8	6.9	5.7	3.5	ADFGT
HANNOVER LIFE REASSUR CO OF AMERICA	FL	B-	4177.5	239.6	1.50	0.83	5.8	6.6	7.9	7.2	4.4	CT

See Page 27 for explanation of footnotes and Page 28 for explanation of stability factors.
Arrows denote recent upgrades ▲ or downgrades▼ (see Section VI for explanations)

40

www.weissratings.com

NET PREMIUM ($MIL)	IN-VESTED ASSETS ($MIL)	CASH	CMO & STRUCT. SECS.	OTH.INV. GRADE BONDS	NON-INV. GRADE BONDS	CMMON & PREF. STOCK	MORT IN GOOD STAND.	NON-PERF. MORT.	REAL ESTATE	OTHER INVEST-MENTS	INVEST. IN AFFIL	INSURANCE COMPANY NAME
65.7	217.2	4.7	17.5	68.3	5.9	0.2	0.0	0.0	0.0	3.5	0.1	• FIVE STAR LIFE INS CO
0.0	39.9	7.8	3.4	19.0	0.1	0.0	0.0	0.0	0.0	69.7	69.7	• FLORIDA COMBINED LIFE INS CO INC
102.2	684.6 (*)	0.2	0.0	78.4	4.7	0.0	0.0	0.0	0.0	15.2	0.0	• FORESTERS LIFE INS & ANNUITY CO
3,385.5	15,902.6	0.7	51.1	34.7	2.0	0.2	10.2	0.0	0.0	1.0	0.0	• FORETHOUGHT LIFE INS CO
0.1	21.8	61.2	7.0	31.7	0.0	0.0	0.0	0.0	0.0	0.1	0.0	FORETHOUGHT NATIONAL LIFE INS CO
0.6	4.9	31.0	0.0	43.3	9.9	12.8	0.0	0.0	0.0	3.1	0.0	FOUNDATION LIFE INS CO OF AR
5.6	74.4	0.1	0.0	99.9	0.0	0.0	0.0	0.0	0.0	0.0	0.0	• FRANDISCO LIFE INS CO
90.4	64.1	-14.4	6.4	75.4	1.1	31.6	0.0	0.0	0.0	0.0	31.6	• FREEDOM LIFE INS CO OF AMERICA
--	--	--	--	--	--	--	--	--	--	--	--	FREMONT LIFE INS CO
0.0	41.3 (*)	1.2	0.8	16.3	6.5	19.2	45.0	0.0	0.0	16.1	0.0	• FRINGE BENEFIT LIFE INS CO
110.2	1,129.2	0.1	1.2	87.0	1.0	0.5	8.1	0.0	1.7	0.5	1.0	• FUNERAL DIRECTORS LIFE INS CO
0.1	5.5 (*)	3.5	0.0	55.5	0.0	31.2	0.0	0.0	0.0	0.0	0.0	FUTURAL LIFE CO
11.0	111.7	-0.6	1.1	96.6	0.0	0.0	0.0	0.0	0.0	2.8	0.0	• GARDEN STATE LIFE INS CO
410.0	10,798.7 (*)	0.2	14.6	50.1	5.1	0.5	8.4	0.0	0.1	19.9	2.7	• GENERAL AMERICAN LIFE INS CO
0.2	25.3	32.0	5.6	62.4	0.0	0.0	0.0	0.0	0.0	0.0	0.0	GENERAL FIDELITY LIFE INS CO
491.0	3,138.6	0.3	0.2	67.4	6.6	9.6	0.0	0.0	0.0	15.9	16.4	• GENERAL RE LIFE CORP
2.0	32.1	61.1	0.0	34.8	0.0	4.1	0.0	0.0	0.0	0.0	0.0	• GENERATION LIFE INS CO
-2,349.4	14,681.2	-0.5	22.9	53.5	4.3	3.4	11.4	0.0	0.2	4.1	3.0	• GENWORTH LIFE & ANNUITY INS CO
659.2	36,968.1 (*)	-0.2	14.5	60.4	3.9	5.8	10.0	0.0	0.0	3.9	6.5	• GENWORTH LIFE INS CO
145.6	7,218.3	-0.1	22.2	60.0	3.9	0.7	10.6	0.0	0.0	1.7	0.0	• GENWORTH LIFE INS CO OF NEW YORK
354.1	2,846.6	0.1	18.4	72.1	1.5	3.2	0.0	0.0	0.0	4.7	0.0	• GERBER LIFE INS CO
3.6	70.5	0.4	26.3	66.8	5.1	0.1	0.0	0.0	0.0	1.3	0.0	GERMANIA LIFE INS CO
--	--	--	--	--	--	--	--	--	--	--	--	GERTRUDE GEDDES WILLIS LIFE INS CO
364.8	3,320.7	0.0	2.9	86.4	6.1	0.0	0.0	0.0	0.0	4.6	2.5	• GLOBE LIFE & ACCIDENT INS CO
0.0	0.4	22.2	0.0	0.0	0.0	0.0	0.0	0.0	77.8	0.0	0.0	GMHP HEALTH INS LMTD
669.9	527.7	-0.7	21.8	75.1	0.0	0.0	0.0	0.0	0.6	3.3	0.0	• GOLDEN RULE INS CO
23.0	804.7	1.4	0.0	68.6	2.4	2.8	14.9	0.0	1.3	8.7	2.0	• GOVERNMENT PERSONNEL MUTUAL L I C
2.2	136.9	1.6	0.7	82.3	3.7	1.1	0.0	0.0	0.0	10.7	0.0	GPM HEALTH & LIFE INS CO
29.6	342.8 (*)	6.8	35.7	45.2	4.4	2.9	0.0	0.0	0.0	3.2	2.9	• GRANGE LIFE INS CO
2,283.4	25,287.0	0.0	30.4	57.2	2.8	3.3	3.5	0.0	0.3	1.5	1.1	• GREAT AMERICAN LIFE INS CO
--	--	--	--	--	--	--	--	--	--	--	--	GREAT CENTRAL LIFE INS CO
0.1	3.1	4.0	1.9	76.9	4.1	0.7	9.0	0.0	3.4	0.0	0.0	GREAT FIDELITY LIFE INS CO
1.0	7.2	3.7	0.0	96.1	0.0	0.0	0.0	0.0	0.0	0.2	0.0	GREAT PLAINS LIFE ASR CO
--	--	--	--	--	--	--	--	--	--	--	--	GREAT REPUBLIC LIFE INS CO
0.1	212.9	-0.8	28.5	59.8	2.0	10.2	0.3	0.0	0.0	0.2	0.0	• GREAT SOUTHERN LIFE INS CO
1.3	69.7 (*)	0.0	18.1	82.1	0.0	0.0	0.0	0.0	1.8	2.3	0.0	GREAT WEST LIFE ASR CO
96.6	1,020.3	0.1	11.0	77.1	1.1	1.4	9.0	0.0	0.3	0.1	0.6	• GREAT WESTERN INS CO
--	--	--	--	--	--	--	--	--	--	--	--	GREAT WESTERN LIFE INS CO
3,083.6	26,399.0	0.0	19.7	49.4	1.2	0.4	11.7	0.0	0.2	17.3	0.5	• GREAT-WEST LIFE & ANNUITY INS CO
130.7	1,072.5	0.8	16.4	69.9	0.3	0.0	9.8	0.0	0.0	2.8	0.0	• GREAT-WEST LIFE & ANNUITY INS OF NY
16.6	51.0 (*)	14.0	41.6	42.6	0.4	0.0	0.0	0.0	0.0	0.0	0.0	GREATER GEORGIA LIFE INS CO
1.4	7.5	16.6	38.6	44.8	0.0	0.0	0.0	0.0	0.0	0.0	0.0	GREENFIELDS LIFE INS CO
0.0	0.1	100.0	0.0	0.0	0.0	0.0	0.0	0.0	0.0	0.0	0.0	GRIFFIN LEGGETT BURIAL INS CO
101.9	467.7	1.1	31.3	53.5	2.5	1.3	8.4	0.0	0.2	1.7	1.4	• GUARANTEE TRUST LIFE INS CO
22.7	478.4	0.6	38.2	45.1	2.5	3.9	1.6	0.0	3.2	5.0	0.8	• GUARANTY INCOME LIFE INS CO
716.8	3,184.9	-0.4	5.3	80.0	2.8	0.0	7.1	0.0	0.0	5.2	1.0	• GUARDIAN INS & ANNUITY CO INC
3,863.9	43,179.8	0.0	6.1	64.6	4.7	3.8	7.9	0.0	1.0	12.1	3.8	• GUARDIAN LIFE INS CO OF AMERICA
371.9	8,975.5 (*)	0.1	27.8	40.1	3.2	4.5	4.0	0.0	0.0	18.3	14.6	• GUGGENHEIM LIFE & ANNUITY CO
3.2	15.6	18.1	0.0	26.0	0.0	41.1	4.6	0.0	9.8	1.3	24.2	GULF GUARANTY LIFE INS CO
0.0	2.6	15.3	0.0	43.0	0.0	29.1	0.0	0.0	3.1	9.5	0.0	GULF STATES LIFE INS CO INC
6.9	5.1	97.8	0.0	2.2	0.0	0.0	0.0	0.0	0.0	0.0	0.0	HALLMARK LIFE INS CO
122.2	2,479.8	0.0	3.5	92.5	3.2	0.0	0.7	0.0	0.0	0.1	0.1	• HANNOVER LIFE REASSUR CO OF AMERICA

• Bullets denote a more detailed analysis is available in Section II.
(*) Asset category percentages do not add up to 100%

INSURANCE COMPANY NAME	DOM. STATE	RATING	TOTAL ASSETS ($MIL)	CAPITAL & SURPLUS ($MIL)	RISK ADJUSTED CAPITAL RATIO 1	RISK ADJUSTED CAPITAL RATIO 2	CAPITAL-IZATION INDEX (PTS)	INVEST. SAFETY INDEX (PTS)	PROFIT-ABILITY INDEX (PTS)	LIQUIDITY INDEX (PTS)	STAB. INDEX (PTS)	STABILITY FACTORS
HARLEYSVILLE LIFE INS CO	PA	B	408.4	40.9	2.62	1.44	7.7	6.9	6.4	5.1	4.3	ADFT
HARTFORD INTL LIFE REASR CORP	CT	C+	10.9	10.9	5.23	4.71	4.0	9.3	4.0	7.0	3.4	DFT
HARTFORD LIFE & ACCIDENT INS CO	CT	C+	9024.5	1611.2	3.87	2.41	9.1	6.3	4.9	7.1	4.6	AIT
HARTFORD LIFE & ANNUITY INS CO	CT	B-	38138.2	2139.3	4.83	2.54	9.3	6.6	5.0	9.9	3.6	AT
HARTFORD LIFE INS CO	CT	C+	113812.0	4666.3	1.41	1.08	7.1	5.5	3.9	8.7	3.6	AT
HAWKEYE LIFE INS GROUP INC	IA	C	11.5	8.6	3.24	2.91	9.9	8.7	5.8	8.5	3.3	D
HAWTHORN LIFE INS CO	TX	D	10.4	2.1	0.18	0.17	0.0	3.0	6.4	6.6	0.0	ACDIT
HAYMARKET INS CO	NE	D-	435.1	19.5	1.01	0.91	6.3	3.2	1.4	7.0	1.2	DEGT
HCC LIFE INS CO	IN	B	1001.7	606.0	4.85	3.69	10.0	8.1	9.3	6.9	6.0	AD
HEALTH NET LIFE INS CO	CA	C	634.2	264.4	1.85	1.52	7.7	8.9	1.7	0.4	2.4	AFLT
HEALTHMARKETS INS CO	OK	C+	24.9	15.6	3.85	3.46	4.0	9.6	2.0	7.4	3.6	DFT
HEARTLAND NATIONAL LIFE INS CO	IN	B-	11.1	6.1	2.42	2.18	8.8	9.1	6.2	8.0	4.5	T
HERITAGE LIFE INS CO	AZ	C	4496.3	940.8	3.81	1.62	7.9	3.4	6.6	7.2	3.9	FGIT
HIGGINBOTHAM BURIAL INS CO	AR	F (5)	--	--	--	--	--	--	--	--	--	Z
HM LIFE INS CO	PA	B	646.6	356.5	3.72	2.73	9.6	5.3	8.8	7.2	5.5	ADI
HM LIFE INS CO OF NEW YORK	NY	B	69.9	38.3	3.12	2.46	9.2	8.7	6.5	7.2	5.5	ADFT
HOMESTEADERS LIFE CO	IA	B	2693.3	174.2	2.19	1.18	7.3	6.2	5.7	6.9	5.5	I
HORACE MANN LIFE INS CO	IL	B	8506.0	431.1	1.75	0.88	6.1	5.0	8.2	4.8	5.4	ACIL
HUMANA INS CO OF KENTUCKY	KY	C	195.7	145.1	3.91	2.88	9.8	8.0	2.3	7.0	3.4	FGT
HUMANA INS CO OF PUERTO RICO INC	PR	C+	69.6	47.4	2.58	2.06	8.6	8.4	2.8	6.8	4.6	FT
IA AMERICAN LIFE INS CO	TX	B-	225.3	131.2	0.96	0.93	6.4	4.8	5.8	7.1	5.2	AI
IBC LIFE INS CO	TX	U (2)	3.4	3.4	3.08	2.77	9.7	9.8	4.0	10.0	4.2	DFT
IDEALIFE INS CO	CT	C+	19.7	15.0	4.27	3.85	10.0	9.4	2.2	9.8	4.8	DF
ILLINOIS MUTUAL LIFE INS CO	IL	A-	1434.6	215.5	3.52	1.96	8.4	6.5	5.3	6.5	6.9	I
INDEPENDENCE INS INC	DE	U (2)	1.7	1.7	2.67	2.40	8.0	9.8	3.6	10.0	3.8	DF
▼ INDEPENDENCE LIFE & ANNUITY CO	DE	D-	2972.8	181.0	5.38	3.53	4.0	7.8	7.2	6.9	1.1	A
INDIVIDUAL ASR CO LIFE HEALTH & ACC	OK	D	21.5	8.7	2.44	1.73	8.1	5.6	2.8	7.5	1.4	GIT
INDUSTRIAL ALLIANCE INS & FIN SERV	TX	C-	213.3	39.4	3.17	1.88	8.3	4.6	1.5	6.1	2.0	DFIT
INTEGRITY LIFE INS CO	OH	B-	7432.8	717.4	1.38	0.99	6.9	5.0	6.5	7.8	4.9	GI
INTERNATIONAL AMERICAN LIFE INS CO	TX	D-	2.0	0.8	1.18	1.06	7.1	9.5	2.5	6.7	1.0	ADFT
INTRAMERICA LIFE INS CO	NY	B	32.3	10.0	2.08	1.87	8.3	9.0	7.7	10.0	5.8	AG
INVESTORS GROWTH LIFE INS CO	AZ	B-	14.7	11.9	3.45	3.11	10.0	6.0	8.0	8.2	4.4	DT
INVESTORS HERITAGE LIFE INS CO	KY	C	488.1	22.0	1.06	0.61	5.1	2.4	3.9	1.1	3.1	CILR
INVESTORS LIFE INS CO NORTH AMERICA	TX	B	643.0	54.2	2.71	1.42	4.0	5.2	8.5	5.7	6.1	AFI
INVESTORS PREFERRED LIFE INS CO	SD	E	162.9	1.2	0.13	0.11	0.0	9.8	1.6	10.0	0.0	CDEGT
JACKSON GRIFFIN INS CO	AR	E	11.7	0.6	0.29	0.26	0.1	0.6	0.8	1.4	0.1	CFIL
▼ JACKSON NATIONAL LIFE INS CO	MI	B	195328.0	3524.7	1.56	0.85	5.8	4.7	7.0	7.9	5.8	CI
JACKSON NATIONAL LIFE INS CO OF NY	NY	B	10960.4	436.5	4.40	2.22	8.8	5.4	7.5	10.0	5.4	I
JAMESTOWN LIFE INS CO	VA	B	124.6	66.9	7.15	5.53	10.0	7.3	3.7	6.8	4.7	ADT
JEFF DAVIS MORTUARY BENEFIT ASSOC	LA	D	5.4	1.3	0.85	0.77	5.2	6.3	1.8	8.2	2.1	DT
JEFFERSON LIFE INS CO	TX	D	2.4	1.5	1.86	1.67	8.0	9.7	1.5	9.1	1.7	DFT
JEFFERSON NATIONAL LIFE INS CO	TX	C-	4281.9	38.3	1.15	0.61	5.2	4.7	3.5	10.0	3.2	CF
JEFFERSON NATIONAL LIFE INS CO OF NY	NY	C-	37.5	7.2	1.86	1.68	8.0	8.5	2.1	10.0	3.2	ADEFG
JOHN ALDEN LIFE INS CO	WI	B-	253.8	23.7	3.39	2.22	8.8	7.3	3.4	6.6	3.8	AFT
JOHN HANCOCK LIFE & HEALTH INS CO	MA	B	11960.9	746.6	3.24	1.77	8.2	5.3	5.6	9.0	5.4	IT
JOHN HANCOCK LIFE INS CO (USA)	MI	B	238670.0	6087.5	0.95	0.64	4.6	3.2	3.5	7.4	4.9	CIT
JOHN HANCOCK LIFE INS CO OF NY	NY	B+	17005.3	1348.3	4.16	2.13	8.7	6.2	4.2	7.1	5.0	AGIT
JORDAN FUNERAL & INS CO INC	AL	F (5)	--	--	--	--	--	--	--	--	--	Z
JRD LIFE INS CO	AZ	U	--	--	--	--	--	--	--	--	--	Z
KANAWHA INS CO	SC	C+	1788.6	103.7	2.00	1.12	7.2	4.4	1.5	8.3	3.0	GIT
KANSAS CITY LIFE INS CO	MO	B	3337.0	299.4	1.86	1.09	7.1	5.0	5.6	5.7	6.3	I
KENTUCKY FUNERAL DIRECTORS LIFE INS	KY	B-	19.3	5.3	1.60	1.44	7.7	8.1	8.1	6.3	4.7	AD

See Page 27 for explanation of footnotes and Page 28 for explanation of stability factors.
Arrows denote recent upgrades ▲ or downgrades▼ (see Section VI for explanations)

42

www.weissratings.com

NET PREMIUM ($MIL)	IN-VESTED ASSETS ($MIL)	% OF INVESTED ASSETS IN:									INVEST. IN AFFIL	INSURANCE COMPANY NAME
		CASH	CMO & STRUCT. SECS.	OTH.INV. GRADE BONDS	NON-INV. GRADE BONDS	CMMON & PREF. STOCK	MORT IN GOOD STAND.	NON-PERF. MORT.	REAL ESTATE	OTHER INVEST-MENTS		
9.2	389.7	-0.8	13.8	85.5	0.0	0.0	0.0	0.0	0.0	1.5	0.0 ●	HARLEYSVILLE LIFE INS CO
0.0	10.2	0.1	0.0	100.0	0.0	0.0	0.0	0.0	0.0	0.0	0.0	HARTFORD INTL LIFE REASR CORP
1,141.4	8,446.7	0.1	17.4	64.9	3.7	1.5	9.3	0.1	0.0	2.8	0.7 ●	HARTFORD LIFE & ACCIDENT INS CO
152.8	7,071.0 (*)	4.0	19.6	50.1	3.3	5.2	7.8	0.0	0.0	4.0	1.0 ●	HARTFORD LIFE & ANNUITY INS CO
53.2	20,779.8 (*)	0.0	16.3	44.5	3.4	13.5	7.3	0.0	0.4	12.6	12.7 ●	HARTFORD LIFE INS CO
1.1	12.0	2.6	5.3	92.1	0.0	0.0	0.0	0.0	0.0	0.0	2.7	HAWKEYE LIFE INS GROUP INC
0.2	10.4	1.6	33.9	0.1	0.0	64.4	0.0	0.0	0.0	0.0	64.4	HAWTHORN LIFE INS CO
12.1	11.4	0.9	0.0	14.5	0.0	0.0	0.0	0.0	0.0	84.6	0.0	HAYMARKET INS CO
492.3	867.2	-1.2	47.9	52.7	0.4	0.2	0.0	0.0	0.0	0.2	0.0 ●	HCC LIFE INS CO
348.1	222.2	29.9	13.3	56.5	0.3	0.0	0.0	0.0	0.0	0.0	0.0 ●	HEALTH NET LIFE INS CO
0.0	4.7	37.8	0.0	62.2	0.0	0.0	0.0	0.0	0.0	0.0	0.0	HEALTHMARKETS INS CO
2.7	8.7	53.8	1.6	44.6	0.0	0.0	0.0	0.0	0.0	0.0	0.0	HEARTLAND NATIONAL LIFE INS CO
49.7	4,367.9	0.2	24.6	42.4	15.0	1.0	0.0	0.0	0.0	16.7	0.0 ●	HERITAGE LIFE INS CO
--	--	--	--	--	--	--	--	--	--	--	--	HIGGINBOTHAM BURIAL INS CO
340.4	566.6 (*)	6.3	11.1	61.8	10.7	4.0	0.0	0.0	0.0	0.0	0.0 ●	HM LIFE INS CO
36.6	62.1	4.3	22.7	73.0	0.0	0.0	0.0	0.0	0.0	0.0	0.0 ●	HM LIFE INS CO OF NEW YORK
226.8	2,561.0	0.9	20.4	74.8	0.9	0.0	2.3	0.1	0.4	0.2	0.0 ●	HOMESTEADERS LIFE CO
287.3	6,443.6	0.2	28.8	63.0	2.6	0.8	0.2	0.0	0.0	4.4	0.2 ●	HORACE MANN LIFE INS CO
29.3	152.4	0.3	51.9	42.1	0.5	0.0	0.0	0.0	0.0	5.2	0.0 ●	HUMANA INS CO OF KENTUCKY
54.2	62.4	27.2	47.8	24.1	1.0	0.0	0.0	0.0	0.0	0.0	0.0 ●	HUMANA INS CO OF PUERTO RICO INC
8.6	224.9	1.8	0.2	41.2	0.4	50.7	2.5	0.1	0.0	2.5	59.6 ●	IA AMERICAN LIFE INS CO
0.0	3.4	100.0	0.0	0.0	0.0	0.0	0.0	0.0	0.0	0.0	0.0	IBC LIFE INS CO
0.7	18.7	4.9	0.0	85.4	0.0	0.0	0.0	0.0	0.0	9.7	0.0	IDEALIFE INS CO
51.3	1,270.4	0.2	25.7	62.0	4.5	4.2	0.9	0.0	0.2	2.3	0.2 ●	ILLINOIS MUTUAL LIFE INS CO
0.0	1.7	91.3	0.0	8.7	0.0	0.0	0.0	0.0	0.0	0.0	0.0	INDEPENDENCE INS INC
-0.2	205.7	0.2	38.2	53.3	0.2	0.0	0.0	0.0	0.0	7.7	0.0 ●	INDEPENDENCE LIFE & ANNUITY CO
2.3	15.4 (*)	21.1	0.0	21.6	0.0	1.3	0.0	0.0	15.2	35.4	0.0	INDIVIDUAL ASR CO LIFE HEALTH & ACC
45.2	165.6	0.9	0.5	83.8	0.7	0.0	2.8	3.1	4.9	2.6	0.0 ●	INDUSTRIAL ALLIANCE INS & FIN SERV
666.1	4,284.5	0.4	22.6	48.0	5.6	12.7	1.4	0.0	0.0	5.8	9.1 ●	INTEGRITY LIFE INS CO
0.1	1.9	3.9	0.0	96.2	0.0	0.0	0.0	0.0	0.0	0.0	0.0	INTERNATIONAL AMERICAN LIFE INS CO
0.3	13.5	2.5	0.0	97.5	0.0	0.0	0.0	0.0	0.0	0.0	0.0	INTRAMERICA LIFE INS CO
0.4	19.1	10.6	0.0	65.1	2.9	20.9	0.0	0.0	0.0	0.5	0.0	INVESTORS GROWTH LIFE INS CO
22.8	459.6	0.2	16.3	70.6	2.3	1.9	7.2	0.0	0.1	1.5	1.0	INVESTORS HERITAGE LIFE INS CO
-0.2	419.0	-0.6	30.7	53.3	4.8	6.9	0.0	0.0	0.0	4.9	1.2 ●	INVESTORS LIFE INS CO NORTH AMERICA
24.0	8.1	7.8	0.0	0.0	0.0	0.0	0.0	0.0	0.0	92.2	0.0	INVESTORS PREFERRED LIFE INS CO
0.5	11.3	10.1	0.0	61.8	7.8	20.7	0.0	0.0	0.0	0.0	0.0	JACKSON GRIFFIN INS CO
9,126.8	60,713.8 (*)	-0.3	14.8	60.2	2.5	1.1	10.6	0.0	0.4	8.8	1.1 ●	JACKSON NATIONAL LIFE INS CO
637.9	1,902.0	0.3	24.9	71.8	3.1	0.0	0.0	0.0	0.0	0.0	0.0 ●	JACKSON NATIONAL LIFE INS CO OF NY
0.9	145.4	0.1	43.7	54.1	0.0	0.0	0.0	0.0	0.0	2.1	0.0 ●	JAMESTOWN LIFE INS CO
0.9	5.0	32.4	2.4	53.3	0.0	11.9	0.0	0.0	0.0	0.0	0.0	JEFF DAVIS MORTUARY BENEFIT ASSOC
0.2	2.4	71.4	0.0	18.8	0.0	0.0	0.0	0.0	0.0	9.8	0.0	JEFFERSON LIFE INS CO
320.8	506.6	0.7	47.8	37.9	4.4	4.1	4.1	0.0	0.1	1.1	1.5 ●	JEFFERSON NATIONAL LIFE INS CO
13.9	7.5	10.7	4.1	85.2	0.0	0.0	0.0	0.0	0.0	0.0	0.0	JEFFERSON NATIONAL LIFE INS CO OF NY
10.4	267.9	-0.3	7.5	83.1	1.4	1.4	0.0	0.0	0.0	7.0	0.0 ●	JOHN ALDEN LIFE INS CO
286.2	4,445.0 (*)	0.1	4.8	60.0	1.0	2.5	6.6	0.0	3.9	12.7	1.1 ●	JOHN HANCOCK LIFE & HEALTH INS CO
6,174.4	90,506.0 (*)	-0.3	6.9	45.4	2.5	4.3	11.6	0.0	7.5	10.4	4.9 ●	JOHN HANCOCK LIFE INS CO (USA)
523.0	7,159.2 (*)	0.0	7.0	57.1	1.7	1.8	11.3	0.0	2.5	8.1	0.8 ●	JOHN HANCOCK LIFE INS CO OF NY
--	--	--	--	--	--	--	--	--	--	--	--	JORDAN FUNERAL & INS CO INC
--	--	--	--	--	--	--	--	--	--	--	--	JRD LIFE INS CO
119.3	1,488.4	5.2	9.8	82.7	1.7	0.0	0.2	0.0	0.0	0.4	0.0 ●	KANAWHA INS CO
140.8	2,852.8	-0.1	6.6	63.4	1.4	3.1	17.6	0.0	4.5	3.7	1.9 ●	KANSAS CITY LIFE INS CO
1.3	18.3	1.1	0.1	96.6	1.7	0.6	0.0	0.0	0.0	0.0	0.0	KENTUCKY FUNERAL DIRECTORS LIFE INS

● Bullets denote a more detailed analysis is available in Section II.
(*) Asset category percentages do not add up to 100%

INSURANCE COMPANY NAME	DOM. STATE	RATING	TOTAL ASSETS ($MIL)	CAPITAL & SURPLUS ($MIL)	RISK ADJUSTED CAPITAL RATIO 1	RISK ADJUSTED CAPITAL RATIO 2	CAPITAL-IZATION INDEX (PTS)	INVEST. SAFETY INDEX (PTS)	PROFIT-ABILITY INDEX (PTS)	LIQUIDITY INDEX (PTS)	STAB. INDEX (PTS)	STABILITY FACTORS
KENTUCKY HOME LIFE INS CO	KY	D	5.8	3.6	3.01	2.71	9.6	7.8	6.2	7.4	1.9	A
KILPATRICK LIFE INS CO	LA	E+	188.8	7.4	0.62	0.36	2.0	0.4	2.5	1.2	0.8	CDIL
KNIGHTS OF COLUMBUS	CT	U	--	--	--	--	--	--	--	--	--	Z
KSKJ LIFE	IL	U	--	--	--	--	--	--	--	--	--	Z
LAFAYETTE LIFE INS CO	OH	B	4702.8	266.6	1.81	0.89	6.2	4.8	5.0	5.1	5.6	ACIL
LANDCAR LIFE INS CO	UT	C+	21.7	15.0	1.43	1.23	4.0	3.0	8.1	10.0	4.4	ADFIT
LANDMARK LIFE INS CO	TX	C	45.7	5.1	0.88	0.79	5.3	4.6	5.9	2.6	3.9	CDIL
LEADERS LIFE INS CO	OK	C	6.4	3.4	1.99	1.79	8.2	8.4	2.7	6.1	4.1	F
LEWER LIFE INS CO	MO	D+	30.0	8.8	2.03	1.49	7.7	6.3	2.6	6.5	2.5	D
LIBERTY BANKERS LIFE INS CO	OK	D+	1433.2	195.7	1.23	0.85	5.8	3.7	7.2	6.9	2.7	I
LIBERTY LIFE ASR CO OF BOSTON	NH	B	16655.8	987.6	1.78	1.02	7.0	6.0	6.4	6.4	6.2	AI
LIBERTY NATIONAL LIFE INS CO	NE	B	7686.0	560.4	2.00	1.04	7.1	4.8	5.1	2.6	4.6	AIL
LIFE ASR CO OF AMERICA	IL	C- (3)	6.2	2.7	1.37	1.23	7.3	6.3	4.0	7.3	2.0	DGT
LIFE ASSURANCE CO INC	OK	C-	4.7	2.3	1.53	1.38	7.6	9.6	2.6	9.1	3.0	FT
LIFE INS CO OF ALABAMA	AL	A-	118.6	39.6	3.32	1.98	8.5	5.6	9.0	6.5	6.3	I
LIFE INS CO OF BOSTON & NEW YORK	NY	A-	135.2	28.0	3.08	2.38	9.1	7.6	6.5	6.4	7.0	A
LIFE INS CO OF LOUISIANA	LA	D (2)	8.3	3.9	2.13	1.44	7.7	3.0	2.0	7.4	2.1	DFI
LIFE INS CO OF NORTH AMERICA	PA	B	8452.1	1479.5	2.26	1.45	7.7	5.4	7.2	6.6	5.8	AI
LIFE INS CO OF THE SOUTHWEST	TX	B	15767.3	914.8	1.75	0.86	6.1	4.2	8.4	3.3	5.3	ACIL
LIFE OF AMERICA INS CO	TX	C	12.6	2.0	0.63	0.48	2.8	6.7	2.1	0.0	2.1	CDGLT
LIFE OF THE SOUTH INS CO	GA	C	91.8	23.4	0.89	0.69	4.5	5.3	7.8	7.6	3.9	C
LIFE PROTECTION INS CO	TX	U (2)	7.7	7.1	3.68	3.31	10.0	4.9	3.1	10.0	3.3	DFIT
LIFECARE ASSURANCE CO	AZ	B-	2206.6	103.1	1.69	0.90	6.2	3.9	5.2	9.3	5.2	I
LIFEMAP ASR CO	OR	B-	80.3	36.6	1.43	1.06	7.1	4.9	2.0	6.4	5.2	FI
LIFESECURE INS CO	MI	D	292.9	28.6	1.93	1.25	7.4	7.1	1.3	8.6	2.0	
LIFESHIELD NATIONAL INS CO	OK	B-	69.2	24.5	2.15	1.25	7.4	3.8	8.4	7.7	5.0	I
LIFEWISE ASR CO	WA	A	143.3	100.2	6.44	4.63	10.0	7.8	9.3	6.9	7.0	AD
LILY LIFE INS CO	TX	E+	1.2	0.1	0.31	0.28	0.4	5.7	0.9	7.4	0.4	CDGT
LINCOLN BENEFIT LIFE CO	NE	C+	11496.8	527.5	1.48	0.74	5.7	3.8	4.6	6.2	4.4	CFGIT
LINCOLN HERITAGE LIFE INS CO	IL	B-	901.6	112.9	3.56	1.91	8.4	7.2	2.7	6.0	5.1	D
LINCOLN LIFE & ANNUITY CO OF NY	NY	B	13414.4	1114.3	4.00	2.04	8.6	5.9	3.9	5.1	5.5	AILT
LINCOLN NATIONAL LIFE INS CO	IN	B	219393.0	7403.2	1.56	1.01	7.0	6.0	6.8	6.7	5.8	AI
LOCOMOTIVE ENGRS&COND MUT PROT ASSN	MI	B+	63.0	54.3	7.76	5.50	10.0	5.8	7.5	9.0	5.8	DI
LOMBARD INTL LIFE ASR CO	PA	E	5610.7	25.7	0.47	0.27	0.6	8.1	2.0	9.6	0.2	CFGT
LOMBARD INTL LIFE ASR CO OF NY	NY	U (2)	4.7	4.4	3.04	2.74	9.6	8.7	6.0	10.0	6.2	DG
LONDON LIFE INS CO	MI	B-	23.4	15.6	4.02	3.62	10.0	8.3	6.1	9.2	4.5	ADFT
LONDON LIFE REINSURANCE CO	PA	C+	289.3	57.7	5.46	2.98	10.0	7.8	6.7	7.7	3.1	FT
LONE STAR LIFE INS CO	TX	F (5)	--	--	--	--	--	--	--	--	--	Z
▲ LONGEVITY INS CO	TX	B	7.8	7.6	3.74	3.37	8.0	9.7	1.9	10.0	5.7	AFT
LOYAL AMERICAN LIFE INS CO	OH	C+	270.0	86.5	1.00	0.86	5.9	6.1	5.2	6.7	4.6	D
LOYAL CHRISTIAN BENEFIT ASSN	PA	U	--	--	--	--	--	--	--	--	--	Z
M LIFE INS CO	CO	B-	302.0	94.6	5.80	3.80	10.0	7.8	4.2	7.1	5.1	DT
MADISON NATIONAL LIFE INS CO INC	WI	C+	329.6	180.1	2.38	1.86	8.3	4.7	6.9	0.3	3.2	FILT
MAGNOLIA GUARANTY LIFE INS CO	MS	C+	11.1	2.5	1.07	0.96	6.7	5.6	5.0	8.4	3.4	ADIT
MAJESTIC LIFE INS CO	LA	C (5)	--	--	--	--	--	--	--	--	--	Z
MANHATTAN LIFE INS CO	NY	B	487.7	50.9	1.26	0.96	6.7	6.8	3.6	6.8	5.4	ADGT
MANHATTAN NATIONAL LIFE INS CO	OH	B	168.8	11.9	1.38	1.24	7.4	4.3	3.2	9.4	5.4	AFGIT
MAPFRE LIFE INS CO	DE	C	30.2	20.6	5.30	4.77	10.0	9.1	2.8	9.0	2.1	FGT
▲ MAPFRE LIFE INS CO OF PR	PR	D	57.4	13.0	0.56	0.45	2.4	8.0	1.3	1.9	1.4	CFLT
MARQUETTE INDEMNITY & LIFE INS CO	AZ	D+	6.4	2.7	1.54	1.38	7.6	3.8	2.0	8.1	2.5	FIT
MASSACHUSETTS MUTUAL LIFE INS CO	MA	A-	226444.0	15964.8	1.79	1.26	7.4	6.0	6.9	6.8	7.0	I
MCS LIFE INS CO	PR	E	58.9	6.9	0.12	0.11	0.0	7.3	0.9	1.7	0.0	ACLT

NET PREMIUM ($MIL)	IN-VESTED ASSETS ($MIL)	% OF INVESTED ASSETS IN:										INSURANCE COMPANY NAME
		CASH	CMO & STRUCT. SECS.	OTH.INV. GRADE BONDS	NON-INV. GRADE BONDS	CMMON & PREF. STOCK	MORT IN GOOD STAND.	NON-PERF. MORT.	REAL ESTATE	OTHER INVEST-MENTS	INVEST. IN AFFIL	
1.0	5.5	4.7	0.0	91.6	0.0	3.7	0.0	0.0	0.0	0.0	0.0	KENTUCKY HOME LIFE INS CO
7.9	180.3	0.7	23.1	52.8	3.8	1.6	6.1	0.5	3.6	7.9	6.6	KILPATRICK LIFE INS CO
--	--	--	--	--	--	--	--	--	--	--	--	KNIGHTS OF COLUMBUS
--	--	--	--	--	--	--	--	--	--	--	--	KSKJ LIFE
292.2	4,409.7 (*)	0.1	16.8	54.2	5.3	1.7	7.2	0.0	0.0	13.6	0.6 ●	LAFAYETTE LIFE INS CO
0.0	21.1	1.3	0.0	18.5	0.0	79.0	1.3	0.0	0.0	0.0	43.1	LANDCAR LIFE INS CO
3.3	40.2	3.2	19.3	59.8	0.9	0.1	8.6	0.0	5.7	2.5	0.0	LANDMARK LIFE INS CO
2.1	4.0	28.7	0.0	61.1	0.0	10.2	0.0	0.0	0.0	0.1	0.0	LEADERS LIFE INS CO
5.1	29.8	1.3	9.1	77.2	1.3	9.9	0.0	0.0	0.0	1.2	0.0	LEWER LIFE INS CO
120.2	1,303.0	4.3	3.8	49.9	2.3	9.5	22.7	0.7	4.3	2.7	6.9 ●	LIBERTY BANKERS LIFE INS CO
1,371.0	15,592.4 (*)	0.1	9.4	76.3	2.5	0.1	5.8	0.0	0.0	2.7	0.1 ●	LIBERTY LIFE ASR CO OF BOSTON
376.6	6,340.2	0.0	4.1	72.5	6.6	4.9	0.0	0.0	0.0	11.6	8.5 ●	LIBERTY NATIONAL LIFE INS CO
0.3	6.1	4.3	26.2	38.5	0.4	27.0	0.0	0.0	0.0	3.6	0.0	LIFE ASR CO OF AMERICA
0.5	4.7	75.8	3.9	20.3	0.0	0.0	0.0	0.0	0.0	0.0	0.0	LIFE ASSURANCE CO INC
18.1	108.5	0.0	0.0	83.2	8.1	3.9	0.0	0.0	0.6	4.1	0.0 ●	LIFE INS CO OF ALABAMA
10.6	121.6	0.7	8.1	66.2	1.8	0.8	0.0	0.0	0.0	22.5	0.0 ●	LIFE INS CO OF BOSTON & NEW YORK
0.2	7.2	4.6	0.0	43.4	0.0	52.0	0.0	0.0	0.0	0.1	5.9	LIFE INS CO OF LOUISIANA
1,880.7	6,967.2	1.1	2.6	66.6	9.1	0.6	13.8	0.0	0.0	6.2	6.3 ●	LIFE INS CO OF NORTH AMERICA
891.2	14,428.7 (*)	0.0	20.8	52.2	5.7	0.5	14.7	0.1	0.0	4.0	0.0 ●	LIFE INS CO OF THE SOUTHWEST
4.7	3.3	27.8	0.0	51.1	6.4	0.8	13.7	0.0	0.0	0.2	0.0	LIFE OF AMERICA INS CO
31.1	79.6	1.2	9.3	67.4	0.0	17.3	0.0	0.0	0.0	5.6	11.0	LIFE OF THE SOUTH INS CO
0.0	7.7	15.2	1.1	54.2	0.0	29.5	0.0	0.0	0.0	0.0	0.0	LIFE PROTECTION INS CO
117.3	2,044.3	0.2	36.4	59.0	3.2	0.0	0.0	0.0	0.0	1.2	0.0 ●	LIFECARE ASSURANCE CO
39.9	78.5	2.3	33.1	41.6	1.7	21.3	0.0	0.0	0.0	0.0	2.2 ●	LIFEMAP ASR CO
29.4	254.6	0.3	16.1	83.7	0.0	0.0	0.0	0.0	0.0	0.0	0.0	LIFESECURE INS CO
11.6	64.4	3.0	46.5	17.4	13.1	18.1	0.0	0.0	0.0	2.1	1.7	LIFESHIELD NATIONAL INS CO
60.9	126.7	4.0	43.1	50.7	1.4	0.0	0.0	0.0	0.0	0.7	0.0 ●	LIFEWISE ASR CO
0.3	0.5 (*)	45.7	0.0	24.2	0.0	15.6	0.0	0.0	0.0	0.0	0.0	LILY LIFE INS CO
57.8	10,138.8	0.5	12.7	65.7	4.2	0.0	15.3	0.0	0.0	1.6	0.9 ●	LINCOLN BENEFIT LIFE CO
160.6	726.5	6.0	40.1	43.9	0.2	0.1	1.6	0.0	1.4	6.3	0.0 ●	LINCOLN HERITAGE LIFE INS CO
-1,181.3	8,068.5	0.0	7.4	76.7	4.7	0.0	7.2	0.0	0.0	4.2	0.0 ●	LINCOLN LIFE & ANNUITY CO OF NY
8,335.4	88,001.1 (*)	-0.1	6.2	72.3	3.4	2.9	8.8	0.0	0.1	4.8	3.5 ●	LINCOLN NATIONAL LIFE INS CO
9.7	59.7	0.7	0.7	77.8	0.3	20.4	0.0	0.0	0.0	0.0	0.0 ●	LOCOMOTIVE ENGRS&COND MUT PROT ASSN
334.8	113.4	4.5	0.0	11.7	0.0	4.1	0.0	0.0	0.0	79.7	4.1	LOMBARD INTL LIFE ASR CO
0.0	4.7	0.7	0.0	99.3	0.0	0.0	0.0	0.0	0.0	0.0	0.0	LOMBARD INTL LIFE ASR CO OF NY
0.5	22.6	1.2	5.4	93.4	0.0	0.0	0.0	0.0	0.0	0.0	0.0	LONDON LIFE INS CO
0.7	191.0	1.3	8.8	87.1	1.4	1.4	0.0	0.0	0.0	0.0	0.0 ●	LONDON LIFE REINSURANCE CO
--	--	--	--	--	--	--	--	--	--	--	--	LONE STAR LIFE INS CO
0.0	7.7	37.0	0.0	63.0	0.0	0.0	0.0	0.0	0.0	0.0	0.0	LONGEVITY INS CO
141.7	240.3	-0.4	1.2	78.5	1.0	19.7	0.0	0.0	0.0	0.0	19.7 ●	LOYAL AMERICAN LIFE INS CO
--	--	--	--	--	--	--	--	--	--	--	--	LOYAL CHRISTIAN BENEFIT ASSN
213.7	130.8	12.5	26.3	59.0	0.8	0.0	0.0	0.0	0.0	1.4	0.0 ●	M LIFE INS CO
43.9	234.0 (*)	1.3	0.2	70.0	0.0	22.1	0.0	0.0	0.0	2.4	22.8 ●	MADISON NATIONAL LIFE INS CO INC
1.3	9.7	2.2	2.9	68.8	4.1	21.7	0.0	0.0	0.0	0.4	0.0	MAGNOLIA GUARANTY LIFE INS CO
--	--	--	--	--	--	--	--	--	--	--	--	MAJESTIC LIFE INS CO
56.2	473.6	1.0	8.4	65.1	2.6	7.9	9.9	0.0	0.0	5.2	7.8 ●	MANHATTAN LIFE INS CO
1.0	161.0	-0.7	8.7	84.0	3.6	0.0	0.0	0.0	0.0	4.4	0.0	MANHATTAN NATIONAL LIFE INS CO
0.7	23.3	1.0	0.0	99.0	0.0	0.0	0.0	0.0	0.0	0.0	0.0	MAPFRE LIFE INS CO
60.2	47.9	37.6	0.4	59.5	0.5	1.5	0.0	0.0	0.0	0.5	0.0	MAPFRE LIFE INS CO OF PR
0.4	6.4 (*)	6.8	19.0	55.7	13.0	5.5	0.0	0.0	0.0	1.5	0.0	MARQUETTE INDEMNITY & LIFE INS CO
10,011.6	143,759.9 (*)	0.1	10.1	42.5	4.7	6.7	15.3	0.0	0.7	13.5	12.5 ●	MASSACHUSETTS MUTUAL LIFE INS CO
150.1	49.9	86.5	0.6	11.0	0.9	1.0	0.0	0.0	0.0	0.0	0.0	MCS LIFE INS CO

● Bullets denote a more detailed analysis is available in Section II.
(*) Asset category percentages do not add up to 100%

INSURANCE COMPANY NAME	DOM. STATE	RATING	TOTAL ASSETS ($MIL)	CAPITAL & SURPLUS ($MIL)	RISK ADJUSTED CAPITAL RATIO 1	RISK ADJUSTED CAPITAL RATIO 2	CAPITAL-IZATION INDEX (PTS)	INVEST. SAFETY INDEX (PTS)	PROFIT-ABILITY INDEX (PTS)	LIQUIDITY INDEX (PTS)	STAB. INDEX (PTS)	STABILITY FACTOR
▼ MEDAMERICA INS CO	PA	C+	914.3	31.7	1.17	0.63	5.3	0.8	2.2	9.0	4.6	CI
MEDAMERICA INS CO OF FL	FL	C+	33.7	3.2	0.68	0.61	3.9	4.0	2.0	9.7	3.9	CDI
MEDAMERICA INS CO OF NEW YORK	NY	E	697.8	6.1	0.56	0.34	1.5	1.9	0.7	9.0	0.0	C
MEDICAL BENEFITS MUTUAL LIFE INS CO	OH	D	16.2	11.4	2.45	1.78	8.2	3.8	1.3	6.9	1.7	DFIT
MEDICO CORP LIFE INS CO	NE	B+	45.2	22.6	4.33	3.90	8.0	8.4	6.3	7.0	6.5	FG
MEDICO INS CO	NE	B	77.2	33.8	4.36	3.92	10.0	6.4	2.4	6.9	5.8	FIT
MEDICO LIFE & HEALTH INS CO	IA	B	14.2	13.6	2.97	2.67	9.5	7.1	4.2	7.0	4.9	DT
MELLON LIFE INS CO	DE	U (2)	24.6	24.4	6.08	5.47	10.0	9.6	2.6	10.0	2.8	DFT
MEMBERS LIFE INS CO	IA	C	38.3	22.5	4.17	3.75	4.0	9.5	2.6	8.4	3.0	GT
MEMORIAL INS CO OF AMERICA	AR	D	1.2	1.1	2.22	1.87	8.3	7.3	4.0	0.0	1.9	AL
MEMORIAL LIFE INS CO	LA	C- (5)	--	--	--	--	--	--	--	--	--	Z
MERIT LIFE INS CO	IN	B	559.3	92.5	3.19	1.94	8.4	6.7	3.7	9.2	4.6	T
METLIFE INS CO USA	DE	B	184071.0	7552.5	4.04	1.97	8.5	6.7	6.1	8.0	4.4	AGT
METLIFE INS LTD GUAM BRANCH	GU	U (2)	3.1	2.2	2.16	1.94	8.4	9.8	7.0	10.0	6.8	DFT
METROPOLITAN LIFE INS CO	NY	B-	401502.0	14650.6	1.43	0.96	6.7	5.1	7.5	7.1	4.5	IT
METROPOLITAN TOWER LIFE INS CO	DE	B-	4588.5	722.4	3.27	1.48	7.7	3.2	6.9	6.4	5.1	FI
MID-WEST NATIONAL LIFE INS CO OF TN	TX	C+	167.2	73.0	8.01	7.21	10.0	8.5	6.0	8.2	3.3	FT
MIDLAND NATIONAL LIFE INS CO	IA	B+	47985.0	2899.9	1.93	1.01	7.0	4.7	9.1	6.1	6.5	AI
▲ MIDWESTERN UNITED LIFE INS CO	IN	A	235.0	129.4	13.03	11.73	10.0	8.0	7.4	6.9	7.6	ADF
MILILANI LIFE INS CO	HI	U (2)	1.9	1.8	2.55	2.30	9.0	9.8	2.7	10.0	2.9	D
MINNESOTA LIFE INS CO	MN	B+	38458.7	2825.3	2.36	1.48	7.7	5.6	7.1	6.7	6.5	I
MINNETONKA LIFE INS CO	AZ	U	--	--	--	--	--	--	--	--	--	Z
MISSOURI VALLEY LIFE AND HLTH INS CO	MO	C+	19.9	16.6	5.26	4.74	10.0	8.0	9.5	10.0	4.5	ADG
MML BAY STATE LIFE INS CO	CT	A	4737.2	242.5	5.06	3.60	10.0	7.3	8.2	7.5	7.7	A
MOLINA HEALTHCARE OF TEXAS INS CO	TX	C	6.5	5.2	3.19	1.28	7.4	9.5	9.6	7.0	3.3	AF
MONARCH LIFE INS CO	MA	F (2)	693.0	3.6	0.34	0.17	0.0	0.0	1.4	5.3	0.0	CFIT
MONITOR LIFE INS CO OF NEW YORK	NY	B	21.9	11.6	3.02	2.33	9.0	8.3	2.8	8.5	4.9	DT
MONY LIFE INS CO	NY	B-	7390.6	432.7	2.31	1.24	7.4	6.3	3.0	5.1	5.0	AFI
MONY LIFE INS CO OF AMERICA	AZ	B	2984.8	336.2	3.14	2.14	8.7	5.5	6.0	7.1	5.7	GIT
MOTHE LIFE INS CO	LA	F (5)	--	--	--	--	--	--	--	--	--	Z
MOTORISTS LIFE INS CO	OH	B	455.4	63.1	3.19	1.72	4.0	6.4	6.5	6.0	4.4	FIT
MOUNTAIN LIFE INS CO	TN	C-	10.8	5.2	1.99	1.80	8.2	8.4	2.6	9.4	2.9	T
MULHEARN PROTECTIVE INS CO	LA	D	11.9	2.1	0.78	0.47	3.2	1.3	2.9	7.6	2.2	CDI
MULTINATIONAL LIFE INS CO	PR	C-	113.3	16.1	1.58	0.88	6.0	3.6	3.2	7.2	3.3	FIT
MUNICH AMERICAN LIFE REINS CO	GA	C+ (5)	--	--	--	--	--	--	--	--	--	Z
MUNICH AMERICAN REASSURANCE CO	GA	C	7687.5	557.7	2.05	1.40	7.6	8.0	1.8	6.2	3.9	T
MUTUAL OF AMERICA LIFE INS CO	NY	A-	18135.8	1007.3	3.43	1.59	7.9	5.8	7.7	7.2	6.9	I
MUTUAL OF OMAHA INS CO	NE	B+	7112.9	2817.0	0.99	0.93	6.4	6.1	8.5	7.0	6.4	ACI
MUTUAL SAVINGS LIFE INS CO	AL	B	455.6	38.3	2.16	1.30	7.5	5.2	6.0	6.0	4.2	AIT
MUTUAL TRUST LIFE INS CO	IL	B	1933.2	140.8	2.27	1.17	7.3	6.0	5.5	4.8	5.9	IL
NATIONAL BENEFIT LIFE INS CO	NY	B	495.1	158.4	7.12	3.72	10.0	6.6	7.3	6.9	5.3	DT
NATIONAL FAMILY CARE LIFE INS CO	TX	C	16.4	9.5	3.06	2.75	9.6	9.6	6.3	8.7	4.2	D
NATIONAL FARM LIFE INS CO	TX	B	395.2	38.5	2.68	1.58	7.9	7.0	5.7	3.9	5.4	DL
NATIONAL FARMERS UNION LIFE INS CO	TX	B+	206.0	45.2	4.41	2.33	9.0	5.6	7.0	6.6	6.7	ADFI
NATIONAL FOUNDATION LIFE INS CO	TX	B-	32.4	18.1	2.18	1.69	8.0	6.7	9.0	7.1	5.3	A
NATIONAL GUARDIAN LIFE INS CO	WI	B-	3502.2	278.2	1.49	0.93	6.4	5.5	5.8	6.4	5.3	GT
NATIONAL HEALTH INS CO	TX	C	31.5	16.8	5.79	2.76	9.6	9.6	4.1	9.8	2.2	GT
NATIONAL INCOME LIFE INS CO	NY	B+	185.3	34.8	3.45	2.10	8.7	7.4	6.2	6.6	6.7	AD
NATIONAL INTEGRITY LIFE INS CO	NY	B-	4718.8	376.1	3.31	1.62	7.9	6.0	5.1	6.5	5.2	G
NATIONAL LIFE INS CO	VT	B	9158.4	1830.3	1.73	1.37	4.0	6.1	7.5	6.8	5.1	AFIT
NATIONAL SECURITY INS CO	AL	B	54.4	13.5	2.09	1.46	7.7	5.6	7.3	6.9	5.1	AI
NATIONAL SECURITY LIFE & ANNUITY CO	NY	B	442.8	32.4	2.73	2.46	9.2	7.2	5.5	10.0	5.2	ADFT

See Page 27 for explanation of footnotes and Page 28 for explanation of stability factors.
Arrows denote recent upgrades ▲ or downgrades▼ (see Section VI for explanations)

46

www.weissratings.com

NET PREMIUM ($MIL)	IN-VESTED ASSETS ($MIL)	CASH	CMO & STRUCT. SECS.	OTH.INV. GRADE BONDS	NON-INV. GRADE BONDS	CMMON & PREF. STOCK	MORT IN GOOD STAND.	NON-PERF. MORT.	REAL ESTATE	OTHER INVEST-MENTS	INVEST. IN AFFIL	INSURANCE COMPANY NAME
32.4	868.3 (*)	0.5	4.7	86.3	4.8	0.3	0.0	0.0	0.0	0.0	0.3 ●	MEDAMERICA INS CO
2.0	31.4	7.7	0.8	91.5	0.0	0.0	0.0	0.0	0.0	0.0	0.0	MEDAMERICA INS CO OF FL
23.0	613.8	0.9	1.4	97.2	0.2	0.0	0.0	0.0	0.3	0.0	0.0	MEDAMERICA INS CO OF NEW YORK
1.4	14.7	-0.1	10.8	36.5	0.0	39.9	0.0	0.0	12.8	0.0	15.7	MEDICAL BENEFITS MUTUAL LIFE INS CO
0.0	21.9	3.7	23.7	72.6	0.0	0.0	0.0	0.0	0.0	0.0	0.0	MEDICO CORP LIFE INS CO
0.3	45.7	2.5	22.7	68.9	0.0	0.2	0.0	0.0	5.3	0.5	0.0 ●	MEDICO INS CO
0.0	29.3	2.9	19.2	76.1	0.0	0.0	0.0	0.0	0.0	1.7	0.0	MEDICO LIFE & HEALTH INS CO
0.1	24.6	0.1	4.3	95.6	0.0	0.0	0.0	0.0	0.0	0.0	0.0	MELLON LIFE INS CO
0.0	29.8	3.4	7.9	88.7	0.0	0.0	0.0	0.0	0.0	0.0	0.0	MEMBERS LIFE INS CO
0.0	1.0	24.7	0.0	61.1	4.1	0.0	0.0	0.0	10.1	0.0	0.0	MEMORIAL INS CO OF AMERICA
--	--	--	--	--	--	--	--	--	--	--	--	MEMORIAL LIFE INS CO
62.6	555.6	0.3	23.7	61.6	2.6	0.8	11.0	0.0	0.0	0.3	0.0 ●	MERIT LIFE INS CO
6,895.6	64,129.4 (*)	0.2	22.6	49.5	4.2	0.7	10.9	0.0	0.1	6.3	1.2 ●	METLIFE INS CO USA
0.0	0.2	100.0	0.0	0.0	0.0	0.0	0.0	0.0	0.0	0.0	0.0	METLIFE INS LTD GUAM BRANCH
9,918.4	240,315.4 (*)	0.1	16.0	42.8	6.0	3.4	19.9	0.1	0.7	9.1	6.3 ●	METROPOLITAN LIFE INS CO
9.9	4,462.3	0.6	24.9	41.3	5.3	0.6	5.6	0.0	11.8	9.2	2.9 ●	METROPOLITAN TOWER LIFE INS CO
4.8	158.5	2.1	1.8	90.3	0.0	0.0	0.0	0.0	0.0	6.7	3.0 ●	MID-WEST NATIONAL LIFE INS CO OF TN
2,514.8	40,052.7	0.3	34.9	42.7	4.4	2.3	10.9	0.1	0.1	3.4	1.2 ●	MIDLAND NATIONAL LIFE INS CO
1.7	230.7	2.6	6.5	78.4	2.8	0.0	6.4	0.0	0.0	3.4	0.0 ●	MIDWESTERN UNITED LIFE INS CO
0.1	1.9	100.0	0.0	0.0	0.0	0.0	0.0	0.0	0.0	0.0	0.0	MILILANI LIFE INS CO
3,153.6	15,831.4 (*)	-0.5	22.0	48.0	3.9	4.4	13.4	0.0	0.0	7.5	3.9 ●	MINNESOTA LIFE INS CO
--	--	--	--	--	--	--	--	--	--	--	--	MINNETONKA LIFE INS CO
7.7	16.5	0.0	51.0	40.0	0.0	0.0	0.0	0.0	0.0	0.0	0.0	MISSOURI VALLEY LIFE AND HLTH INS CO
10.2	385.6	0.3	16.0	56.5	0.9	0.0	1.5	0.0	0.0	24.8	0.4 ●	MML BAY STATE LIFE INS CO
0.0	2.5	2.2	0.0	97.8	0.0	0.0	0.0	0.0	0.0	0.0	0.0	MOLINA HEALTHCARE OF TEXAS INS CO
4.6	478.9	0.8	12.1	70.9	1.6	0.0	0.0	0.0	0.0	14.7	0.0	MONARCH LIFE INS CO
8.7	20.6	12.3	0.1	75.7	0.0	9.1	0.0	0.0	0.0	2.9	2.4	MONITOR LIFE INS CO OF NEW YORK
113.6	7,066.0	1.1	8.8	72.3	0.9	1.5	4.3	0.0	0.0	11.0	0.0 ●	MONY LIFE INS CO
205.8	785.1 (*)	0.3	4.8	78.8	2.2	7.1	0.0	0.0	0.0	3.7	5.9 ●	MONY LIFE INS CO OF AMERICA
--	--	--	--	--	--	--	--	--	--	--	--	MOTHE LIFE INS CO
27.7	459.5	1.1	25.3	63.1	4.3	3.2	0.0	0.0	0.0	3.0	0.0 ●	MOTORISTS LIFE INS CO
1.5	10.0	31.3	0.0	63.5	0.0	0.0	0.0	0.0	5.2	0.0	0.0	MOUNTAIN LIFE INS CO
0.3	11.6	13.4	0.6	29.5	0.0	56.3	0.0	0.0	0.0	0.1	0.0	MULHEARN PROTECTIVE INS CO
16.8	104.9	10.5	29.1	45.1	3.3	0.1	0.7	0.0	9.1	2.2	0.0	MULTINATIONAL LIFE INS CO
--	--	--	--	--	--	--	--	--	--	--	--	MUNICH AMERICAN LIFE REINS CO
400.1	6,977.2	0.0	3.4	95.8	0.0	0.6	0.0	0.0	0.0	0.1	0.6 ●	MUNICH AMERICAN REASSURANCE CO
910.0	9,101.7	-0.1	39.0	50.9	5.3	0.4	0.0	0.0	2.9	1.5	0.2 ●	MUTUAL OF AMERICA LIFE INS CO
1,310.4	6,124.6	0.1	14.2	39.3	2.1	37.8	3.5	0.0	0.6	2.2	40.5 ●	MUTUAL OF OMAHA INS CO
20.1	431.7	1.0	2.7	87.9	2.7	1.0	0.0	0.0	0.0	4.0	0.9 ●	MUTUAL SAVINGS LIFE INS CO
75.8	1,849.1	0.2	12.9	62.7	2.4	0.5	5.0	0.0	0.4	15.8	0.0 ●	MUTUAL TRUST LIFE INS CO
36.5	472.4 (*)	-0.6	12.8	74.6	4.9	2.0	0.0	0.0	0.0	2.0	0.0 ●	NATIONAL BENEFIT LIFE INS CO
3.5	15.9	15.3	0.0	84.7	0.0	0.0	0.0	0.0	0.0	0.0	0.0	NATIONAL FAMILY CARE LIFE INS CO
12.3	375.9	0.2	4.2	83.4	1.7	2.3	2.1	0.0	0.1	6.0	0.5 ●	NATIONAL FARM LIFE INS CO
3.7	188.2	-0.3	29.7	43.5	4.0	12.0	4.0	0.0	0.0	7.2	2.7 ●	NATIONAL FARMERS UNION LIFE INS CO
19.1	22.9	-8.0	27.3	74.5	6.2	0.0	0.0	0.0	0.0	0.0	0.0	NATIONAL FOUNDATION LIFE INS CO
271.8	3,281.3	0.5	4.1	81.1	2.0	4.0	3.7	0.1	0.2	4.4	2.1 ●	NATIONAL GUARDIAN LIFE INS CO
3.8	20.6	92.2	0.0	7.8	0.0	0.0	0.0	0.0	0.0	0.0	0.0	NATIONAL HEALTH INS CO
36.0	147.2	3.0	2.2	88.9	1.0	0.0	0.0	0.0	0.0	4.9	0.0 ●	NATIONAL INCOME LIFE INS CO
180.8	2,889.7 (*)	-0.2	28.3	54.4	6.4	1.3	3.0	0.0	0.0	3.9	1.5 ●	NATIONAL INTEGRITY LIFE INS CO
143.3	7,795.1	0.2	17.2	47.1	4.6	10.8	7.1	0.0	1.0	11.7	10.8 ●	NATIONAL LIFE INS CO
3.1	51.6	1.0	19.8	61.8	3.5	5.4	0.4	0.0	4.5	3.7	0.0	NATIONAL SECURITY INS CO
12.4	49.7	0.6	18.2	79.3	1.9	0.0	0.0	0.0	0.0	0.0	0.0 ●	NATIONAL SECURITY LIFE & ANNUITY CO

INSURANCE COMPANY NAME	DOM. STATE	RATING	TOTAL ASSETS ($MIL)	CAPITAL & SURPLUS ($MIL)	RISK ADJUSTED CAPITAL RATIO 1	RISK ADJUSTED CAPITAL RATIO 2	CAPITAL-IZATION INDEX (PTS)	INVEST. SAFETY INDEX (PTS)	PROFIT-ABILITY INDEX (PTS)	LIQUIDITY INDEX (PTS)	STAB. INDEX (PTS)	STABILITY FACTORS
NATIONAL TEACHERS ASSOCIATES L I C	TX	B (3)	452.4	89.0	2.64	1.84	8.3	7.1	4.9	8.5	6.0	D
NATIONAL WESTERN LIFE INS CO	CO	A	10673.8	1203.1	3.80	2.01	8.5	6.8	7.6	6.0	7.5	I
NATIONWIDE LIFE & ANNUITY INS CO	OH	C	12581.2	729.0	2.47	1.20	7.3	5.0	1.9	6.6	4.3	AGT
NATIONWIDE LIFE INS CO	OH	B-	129443.0	4948.7	2.60	1.51	7.8	5.8	7.6	8.3	5.2	AT
NETCARE LIFE & HEALTH INS CO	GU	E+	26.9	6.2	1.34	1.05	7.1	8.5	6.7	5.8	0.7	CD
NEW ENGLAND LIFE INS CO	MA	B	10003.1	675.2	5.35	2.64	9.5	5.9	7.3	6.8	4.0	AIT
NEW ERA LIFE INS CO	TX	C	472.4	71.5	0.91	0.69	4.5	5.3	8.6	6.8	4.1	CDG
NEW ERA LIFE INS CO OF THE MIDWEST	TX	C	107.0	12.2	1.02	0.67	5.0	4.1	9.3	6.0	4.3	CDI
NEW FOUNDATION LIFE INS CO	AR	U (5)	--	--	--	--	--	--	--	--	--	Z
NEW YORK LIFE INS & ANNUITY CORP	DE	B+	137896.0	8383.1	3.78	1.83	8.2	6.1	8.2	6.6	6.7	I
NEW YORK LIFE INS CO	NY	A-	167828.0	19590.1	1.63	1.23	7.3	6.0	7.3	6.6	7.0	GI
NIAGARA LIFE & HEALTH INS CO	NY	B	16.9	8.6	3.32	2.99	10.0	8.9	3.1	9.1	6.3	G
NIPPON LIFE INS CO OF AMERICA	IA	A-	217.7	137.3	4.04	3.20	10.0	8.3	7.4	6.6	7.0	D
NORTH AMERICAN CO FOR LIFE & H INS	IA	B	20376.2	1096.9	1.86	0.86	6.3	3.8	7.6	5.9	5.8	CGI
NORTH AMERICAN INS CO	WI	C+	20.4	12.9	2.24	1.71	8.1	8.4	4.3	6.6	4.8	DF
NORTH AMERICAN NATIONAL RE INS CO	AZ	C	32.8	8.3	1.46	0.74	4.0	2.1	6.8	7.0	2.8	IT
NORTH CAROLINA MUTUAL LIFE INS CO	NC	E+	36.2	9.0	1.57	0.95	6.6	6.2	1.2	4.3	0.5	CDILT
NORTHWESTERN LONG TERM CARE INS CO	WI	B	166.0	80.9	6.54	2.63	9.4	9.6	3.6	6.1	6.0	FIT
NORTHWESTERN MUTUAL LIFE INS CO	WI	A-	244873.0	20053.9	3.47	1.74	8.1	5.8	7.0	5.7	7.3	I
NTA LIFE INS CO OF NEW YORK	NY	B	7.0	6.8	3.62	3.26	10.0	8.8	3.3	9.3	4.7	ADEG
NYLIFE INS CO OF ARIZONA	AZ	B	199.0	98.2	9.29	6.07	10.0	8.3	6.9	7.2	5.6	D
OCCIDENTAL LIFE INS CO OF NC	TX	C	254.7	32.9	3.27	2.01	8.5	7.4	3.0	5.4	4.2	AD
OHIO MOTORISTS LIFE INSURANCE CO	OH	B	10.5	10.4	4.21	3.79	10.0	8.9	7.3	10.0	6.2	A
OHIO NATIONAL LIFE ASR CORP	OH	B+	3833.0	275.9	2.21	1.14	7.2	5.6	5.8	5.5	6.4	AIL
OHIO NATIONAL LIFE INS CO	OH	B	28044.7	1061.4	1.47	0.98	6.8	5.7	7.7	7.9	5.8	AI
OHIO STATE LIFE INS CO	TX	B-	13.8	10.6	19.24	9.93	8.0	7.9	7.5	7.0	5.3	T
OLD AMERICAN INS CO	MO	B	253.5	21.1	2.26	1.13	7.2	3.8	3.0	4.0	5.6	DIL
OLD REPUBLIC LIFE INS CO	IL	B-	125.5	29.1	2.98	1.84	8.3	5.4	2.8	6.8	5.2	I
OLD SPARTAN LIFE INS CO INC	SC	C	21.8	15.5	2.15	1.35	7.5	2.7	6.7	9.3	3.8	I
OLD SURETY LIFE INS CO	OK	C	25.6	9.7	0.66	0.50	3.0	7.2	4.2	5.6	3.0	CD
OLD UNITED LIFE INS CO	AZ	B	81.3	43.4	5.71	5.14	10.0	7.3	5.8	10.0	4.8	ADT
OMAHA INS CO	NE	C+	83.9	52.0	2.98	1.59	7.9	8.2	1.9	5.3	3.2	FGT
OMAHA LIFE INS CO	NE	U (2)	10.8	10.8	4.29	3.86	8.0	8.9	4.1	10.0	5.8	D
OPTIMUM RE INS CO	TX	C+	153.8	34.4	2.70	1.69	8.0	7.3	2.4	8.8	4.6	
OPTUM INS OF OHIO INC	OH	B	113.1	37.6	4.06	3.65	8.0	9.8	7.7	7.0	5.5	AGT
ORDER UNITED COMM TRAVELERS OF AMER	OH	U	--	--	--	--	--	--	--	--	--	Z
OXFORD LIFE INS CO	AZ	B	1599.4	177.8	1.96	1.31	7.5	5.9	8.8	6.6	5.6	GI
OZARK NATIONAL LIFE INS CO	MO	B-	793.4	134.2	5.00	2.87	9.8	7.9	2.8	6.5	4.9	D
PACIFIC CENTURY LIFE INS CORP	AZ	B	354.6	351.6	31.33	22.17	10.0	7.4	6.5	10.0	4.9	T
PACIFIC GUARDIAN LIFE INS CO LTD	HI	A-	544.4	105.1	4.16	2.40	9.1	6.6	6.5	6.2	7.0	I
PACIFIC LIFE & ANNUITY CO	AZ	B+	6374.0	548.7	5.80	2.75	9.6	6.4	8.2	8.0	6.1	AI
PACIFIC LIFE INS CO	NE	A-	115113.0	8045.6	2.09	1.43	7.6	5.9	6.8	6.4	6.9	AI
PACIFICARE LIFE & HEALTH INS CO	IN	C+	207.0	179.9	18.15	16.33	10.0	8.2	5.4	9.6	3.4	ADT
PAN AMERICAN ASR CO	LA	B+	25.4	18.1	4.21	2.09	8.6	7.6	8.4	9.2	5.3	AT
PAN AMERICAN ASR CO INTL INC	FL	U (2)	5.0	4.9	3.25	2.93	8.0	9.0	9.0	7.0	8.0	DG
PAN AMERICAN LIFE INS CO OF PR	PR	B	8.4	5.5	1.94	1.50	7.8	3.8	2.0	4.1	5.9	ADFILT
PAN-AMERICAN LIFE INS CO	LA	B	1275.4	248.9	2.56	1.64	8.0	5.4	6.4	6.3	6.0	AFI
PARAGON LIFE INS CO OF INDIANA	IN	B-	1782.6	69.6	0.62	0.42	2.0	3.4	6.8	4.8	3.6	CILT
PARK AVENUE LIFE INS CO	DE	B	269.0	58.9	1.66	1.35	7.5	6.2	6.7	6.4	6.3	DFIT
PARKER CENTENNIAL ASR CO	WI	A	92.2	47.3	5.53	4.97	10.0	8.6	7.6	10.0	6.3	ADT
PATRIOT LIFE INS CO	MI	B	16.7	14.1	4.61	4.15	10.0	6.0	2.0	6.9	4.3	DFGIT
PAUL REVERE LIFE INS CO	MA	C+	3903.5	278.6	1.83	1.07	7.1	3.8	5.9	7.6	4.8	AFI

See Page 27 for explanation of footnotes and Page 28 for   48   www.weissratings.com
explanation of stability factors.
Arrows denote recent upgrades ▲ or downgrades▼ (see Section VI for explanations)

NET PREMIUM ($MIL)	IN-VESTED ASSETS ($MIL)	CASH	CMO & STRUCT. SECS.	OTH.INV. GRADE BONDS	NON-INV. GRADE BONDS	CMMON & PREF. STOCK	MORT IN GOOD STAND.	NON-PERF. MORT.	REAL ESTATE	OTHER INVEST-MENTS	INVEST. IN AFFIL	INSURANCE COMPANY NAME
					% OF INVESTED ASSETS IN:							
91.6	405.6	2.9	40.3	46.1	4.2	4.2	2.0	0.0	0.0	0.2	1.7 ●	NATIONAL TEACHERS ASSOCIATES L I C
495.6	10,377.9	-0.3	15.2	79.5	1.3	2.6	0.7	0.0	0.0	0.6	2.6 ●	NATIONAL WESTERN LIFE INS CO
1,923.8	9,128.8 (*)	0.2	5.7	68.5	4.9	0.0	15.4	0.0	0.0	4.0	0.9 ●	NATIONWIDE LIFE & ANNUITY INS CO
4,893.3	38,519.7 (*)	-0.2	16.9	53.2	4.4	2.1	17.9	0.0	0.0	4.0	2.7 ●	NATIONWIDE LIFE INS CO
9.6	23.7	-1.0	16.4	69.9	0.0	0.1	0.0	0.0	0.0	14.5	0.0	NETCARE LIFE & HEALTH INS CO
100.8	2,115.7	0.7	16.8	44.9	8.3	0.0	5.7	0.0	0.0	22.9	1.9 ●	NEW ENGLAND LIFE INS CO
93.2	435.6	4.4	11.2	47.1	7.6	11.7	16.8	0.0	0.9	0.2	10.9 ●	NEW ERA LIFE INS CO
33.4	93.0	2.3	7.8	64.8	6.6	0.0	18.5	0.0	0.0	0.1	0.0	NEW ERA LIFE INS CO OF THE MIDWEST
--	--	--	--	--	--	--	--	--	--	--	--	NEW FOUNDATION LIFE INS CO
7,262.2	89,201.0	-0.2	27.5	50.1	5.6	0.6	13.6	0.0	0.1	2.4	2.8 ●	NEW YORK LIFE INS & ANNUITY CORP
8,086.3	137,216.1	0.0	15.0	45.8	5.1	6.8	10.6	0.0	1.0	14.7	11.0 ●	NEW YORK LIFE INS CO
1.4	8.5	29.6	14.6	55.8	0.0	0.0	0.0	0.0	0.0	0.0	0.0	NIAGARA LIFE & HEALTH INS CO
141.8	204.8 (*)	2.3	12.2	74.6	0.0	1.4	0.0	0.0	0.0	0.0	0.0 ●	NIPPON LIFE INS CO OF AMERICA
1,506.5	18,584.6	0.1	34.3	44.5	5.0	1.0	11.2	0.0	0.0	2.9	0.2 ●	NORTH AMERICAN CO FOR LIFE & H INS
8.4	18.2	-3.9	10.3	93.0	0.6	0.0	0.0	0.0	0.0	0.0	0.0	NORTH AMERICAN INS CO
0.2	31.6 (*)	6.4	0.0	32.9	8.9	35.4	1.4	0.0	15.6	2.9	0.0	NORTH AMERICAN NATIONAL RE INS CO
6.9	28.6	7.1	0.0	38.5	0.0	3.7	24.5	0.1	0.3	25.9	13.7	NORTH CAROLINA MUTUAL LIFE INS CO
0.2	93.1	7.3	0.0	92.7	0.0	0.0	0.0	0.0	0.0	0.0	0.0 ●	NORTHWESTERN LONG TERM CARE INS CO
8,784.4	203,511.9	0.1	18.0	41.5	6.8	2.0	15.9	0.0	1.0	14.7	4.1 ●	NORTHWESTERN MUTUAL LIFE INS CO
0.4	7.0	2.0	70.0	28.0	0.0	0.0	0.0	0.0	0.0	0.0	0.0	NTA LIFE INS CO OF NEW YORK
9.6	166.0	-0.9	22.4	77.6	0.9	0.0	0.0	0.0	0.0	0.0	0.0 ●	NYLIFE INS CO OF ARIZONA
17.2	244.4 (*)	0.1	1.6	80.0	0.9	1.9	9.8	0.0	0.0	4.4	0.0 ●	OCCIDENTAL LIFE INS CO OF NC
0.0	10.3	0.2	0.0	99.8	0.0	0.0	0.0	0.0	0.0	0.0	0.0	OHIO MOTORISTS LIFE INSURANCE CO
117.0	3,129.3 (*)	0.0	15.8	62.6	3.8	0.5	12.3	0.0	0.0	3.3	0.0 ●	OHIO NATIONAL LIFE ASR CORP
1,137.7	7,348.7 (*)	3.3	17.5	50.9	2.9	5.8	10.8	0.0	0.4	6.5	4.8 ●	OHIO NATIONAL LIFE INS CO
0.0	11.6 (*)	0.0	48.2	52.5	0.0	9.0	0.0	0.0	0.0	0.0	0.0	OHIO STATE LIFE INS CO
39.3	229.9	-0.7	9.9	63.5	5.2	0.8	16.8	0.0	0.0	4.4	0.0	OLD AMERICAN INS CO
9.1	102.7	1.7	0.0	81.2	2.5	14.0	0.0	0.0	0.0	0.7	0.0 ●	OLD REPUBLIC LIFE INS CO
3.0	20.3	21.0	0.3	9.5	0.0	67.9	0.0	0.0	0.0	1.4	0.0	OLD SPARTAN LIFE INS CO INC
25.1	25.2	9.3	0.8	75.7	0.7	0.0	3.1	0.0	9.5	1.0	0.0	OLD SURETY LIFE INS CO
3.8	80.8	-0.1	15.1	78.1	4.6	2.2	0.0	0.0	0.0	0.1	0.0 ●	OLD UNITED LIFE INS CO
20.6	77.3	15.4	26.1	58.5	0.0	0.0	0.0	0.0	0.0	0.0	0.0 ●	OMAHA INS CO
0.0	10.8	14.9	52.0	33.2	0.0	0.0	0.0	0.0	0.0	0.0	0.0	OMAHA LIFE INS CO
19.1	140.4	1.8	0.0	89.9	2.5	1.4	0.0	0.0	2.3	2.3	0.0 ●	OPTIMUM RE INS CO
0.0	30.0	84.8	0.0	15.0	0.0	0.2	0.0	0.0	0.0	0.0	0.0 ●	OPTUM INS OF OHIO INC
--	--	--	--	--	--	--	--	--	--	--	--	ORDER UNITED COMM TRAVELERS OF AMER
167.4	1,462.7	-0.2	4.8	75.5	2.1	3.1	12.4	0.0	0.9	1.2	4.0 ●	OXFORD LIFE INS CO
43.1	732.0	0.3	17.5	78.4	0.0	0.0	0.0	0.0	0.7	3.1	0.0 ●	OZARK NATIONAL LIFE INS CO
0.2	350.1	9.0	0.0	1.5	0.0	0.0	89.4	0.0	0.0	0.0	0.0 ●	PACIFIC CENTURY LIFE INS CORP
41.0	501.7	0.7	20.7	36.8	0.1	0.0	36.1	0.0	0.0	5.7	0.0 ●	PACIFIC GUARDIAN LIFE INS CO LTD
157.3	3,646.4	1.2	7.0	76.6	2.0	0.2	12.4	0.0	0.0	0.5	0.0 ●	PACIFIC LIFE & ANNUITY CO
4,049.2	56,656.2	0.4	9.4	50.5	3.2	4.3	15.6	0.0	0.3	15.5	5.5 ●	PACIFIC LIFE INS CO
7.3	194.0	-1.3	23.9	77.3	0.0	0.0	0.0	0.0	0.0	0.0	0.0 ●	PACIFICARE LIFE & HEALTH INS CO
0.0	26.3	31.3	13.4	40.5	3.7	11.1	0.0	0.0	0.0	0.0	0.0	PAN AMERICAN ASR CO
0.0	4.9	0.0	0.0	100.0	0.0	0.0	0.0	0.0	0.0	0.0	0.0	PAN AMERICAN ASR CO INTL INC
7.7	7.0	21.0	14.4	50.4	14.0	0.0	0.0	0.0	0.0	0.2	0.0	PAN AMERICAN LIFE INS CO OF PR
115.2	1,182.2	1.5	11.0	61.8	7.3	6.6	0.9	0.0	0.6	9.8	2.0 ●	PAN-AMERICAN LIFE INS CO
35.5	1,154.1	0.8	52.4	20.5	0.2	7.3	9.0	0.0	0.0	9.9	9.9 ●	PARAGON LIFE INS CO OF INDIANA
1.1	262.4	0.3	0.4	85.7	2.1	10.5	0.0	0.0	0.0	1.1	10.5 ●	PARK AVENUE LIFE INS CO
0.8	89.8	0.0	0.0	99.4	0.6	0.0	0.0	0.0	0.0	0.0	0.0 ●	PARKER CENTENNIAL ASR CO
0.5	15.8	1.5	10.7	72.9	0.0	14.8	0.0	0.0	0.0	0.0	0.0	PATRIOT LIFE INS CO
49.6	3,777.7	0.0	4.1	80.2	7.8	3.6	3.0	0.0	0.1	1.3	1.9 ●	PAUL REVERE LIFE INS CO

● Bullets denote a more detailed analysis is available in Section II.
(*) Asset category percentages do not add up to 100%

INSURANCE COMPANY NAME	DOM. STATE	RATING	TOTAL ASSETS ($MIL)	CAPITAL & SURPLUS ($MIL)	RISK ADJUSTED CAPITAL RATIO 1	RISK ADJUSTED CAPITAL RATIO 2	CAPITAL-IZATION INDEX (PTS)	INVEST. SAFETY INDEX (PTS)	PROFIT-ABILITY INDEX (PTS)	LIQUIDITY INDEX (PTS)	STAB. INDEX (PTS)	STABILITY FACTORS
PAVONIA LIFE INS CO OF MICHIGAN	MI	C	1074.0	60.9	1.11	0.66	5.2	5.4	2.8	8.2	4.2	ACFGT
PAVONIA LIFE INS CO OF NEW YORK	NY	C	31.9	11.3	2.44	2.19	8.8	8.6	3.7	7.7	3.9	DT
PEKIN LIFE INS CO	IL	B	1426.6	118.7	1.91	1.14	7.2	6.6	4.0	5.7	6.2	
PELLERIN LIFE INS CO	LA	D	10.9	1.2	0.54	0.48	2.8	2.7	2.8	6.1	1.5	CDI
PENN INS & ANNUITY CO	DE	B-	4022.4	367.7	2.15	1.26	7.4	6.2	2.6	6.0	5.2	G
PENN MUTUAL LIFE INS CO	PA	B	18813.7	1773.1	2.12	1.38	7.6	6.0	7.1	6.7	4.4	GIT
PERFORMANCE LIFE OF AMERICA	LA	B-	31.6	19.5	4.12	3.71	10.0	8.6	9.5	9.2	5.1	AD
PHARMACISTS LIFE INS CO	IA	B	99.3	7.5	1.01	0.91	6.3	5.7	3.2	2.0	4.8	ACDGIL
PHILADELPHIA AMERICAN LIFE INS CO	TX	B	253.2	33.6	1.46	0.94	6.5	4.7	9.0	6.4	5.4	AI
PHL VARIABLE INS CO	CT	D-	6555.1	174.3	1.62	0.83	5.9	5.0	1.7	5.6	0.9	FGT
PHOENIX LIFE & ANNUITY CO	CT	D-	41.2	20.8	3.67	3.30	10.0	7.3	3.6	8.2	1.1	FT
PHOENIX LIFE INS CO	NY	E	12507.1	352.3	1.29	0.64	4.0	3.9	4.6	4.8	0.1	CFILT
PHYSICIANS BENEFITS TRUST LIFE INS	IL	C	8.5	5.7	2.54	2.29	8.9	8.9	1.1	7.3	3.4	DFT
PHYSICIANS LIFE INS CO	NE	A-	1549.0	139.0	2.92	1.48	7.7	6.3	6.3	5.6	6.9	I
PHYSICIANS MUTUAL INS CO	NE	A+	2153.3	895.4	3.52	2.65	9.5	6.4	7.4	7.6	7.9	I
PINE BELT LIFE INS CO	MS	D-	1.5	0.6	0.85	0.76	5.1	9.8	2.0	10.0	1.0	CDT
PIONEER AMERICAN INS CO	TX	C	61.0	20.1	2.78	2.50	9.3	8.5	2.7	6.8	4.0	DT
PIONEER MILITARY INS CO	NV	U (2)	1.6	1.6	2.61	2.35	8.0	9.8	3.7	10.0	3.9	DFT
PIONEER MUTUAL LIFE INS CO	ND	B	515.2	48.6	3.24	1.73	8.1	7.0	5.5	5.0	5.5	DL
PIONEER SECURITY LIFE INS CO	TX	C+	124.2	99.8	1.24	1.22	7.3	2.7	7.6	8.1	4.8	ADI
PLATEAU INS CO	TN	C+	25.8	11.4	2.47	1.94	8.4	8.6	2.9	7.7	4.6	ART
POPULAR LIFE RE	PR	C+	60.7	30.6	4.30	3.29	10.0	5.0	6.6	9.4	4.8	T
PORT-O-CALL LIFE INS CO	AR	U (2)	0.4	0.4	2.00	1.80	8.0	9.8	1.5	10.0	1.7	DFT
PREFERRED SECURITY LIFE INS CO	TX	U (2)	2.9	0.3	0.30	0.27	0.2	0.5	1.1	0.5	0.2	CDFILT
PRENEED REINS CO OF AMERICA	AZ	B	40.6	37.4	6.79	6.11	10.0	9.0	9.6	4.8	5.6	AL
PRESIDENTIAL LIFE INS CO	TX	C (1)	4.2	2.9	2.42	2.18	8.8	3.0	5.5	7.8	2.9	DFIT
PRIMERICA LIFE INS CO	MA	B	1315.9	535.1	1.25	1.07	7.1	4.3	8.1	6.9	5.7	GIT
PRINCIPAL LIFE INS CO	IA	B+	165432.0	4686.6	2.15	1.15	7.2	5.6	7.5	7.4	6.7	I
PRINCIPAL LIFE INS CO IOWA	IA	U (2)	331.4	331.3	1.25	1.11	7.2	9.7	6.6	10.0	7.0	DT
PRINCIPAL NATIONAL LIFE INS CO	IA	B	214.1	117.2	6.41	3.16	10.0	8.3	2.9	10.0	5.4	GT
▼ PROFESSIONAL INS CO	TX	D-	110.2	40.5	4.54	3.62	10.0	6.7	5.5	6.9	1.1	AD
PROFESSIONAL LIFE & CAS CO	IL	C	163.7	46.6	3.00	1.58	7.9	3.3	8.9	5.7	4.3	DI
PROTEC INS CO	IL	C	3.6	3.3	2.80	2.52	9.3	9.8	6.6	10.0	3.8	E
PROTECTIVE LIFE & ANNUITY INS CO	AL	B	1999.6	162.0	2.45	1.24	7.4	5.6	5.9	4.5	5.9	AFILT
PROTECTIVE LIFE INS CO	TN	B	43425.8	4265.6	1.64	1.21	7.3	5.7	5.6	6.0	5.8	AIT
PROVIDENT AMER LIFE & HEALTH INS CO	OH	B	18.6	17.0	2.86	2.49	9.2	8.5	8.5	7.9	5.7	ADT
PROVIDENT AMERICAN INS CO	TX	C-	20.5	11.5	0.71	0.63	4.0	7.9	8.7	5.0	3.2	CDT
PROVIDENT LIFE & ACCIDENT INS CO	TN	C+	8342.6	738.9	2.74	1.37	7.6	4.7	6.6	7.5	4.4	AI
PROVIDENT LIFE & CAS INS CO	TN	B-	767.5	152.4	4.54	2.43	9.1	4.6	7.4	7.1	5.3	ADI
PRUCO LIFE INS CO	AZ	C+	107972.0	1249.1	1.05	0.63	5.1	5.7	2.9	9.4	4.6	ACT
PRUCO LIFE INS CO OF NEW JERSEY	NJ	B-	13931.4	299.9	1.90	0.96	6.7	5.5	3.2	9.0	5.2	AT
▼ PRUDENTIAL ANNUITIES LIFE ASR CORP	AZ	C	75234.8	2233.9	4.00	1.88	4.0	6.4	1.2	7.0	4.1	GT
PRUDENTIAL INS CO OF AMERICA	NJ	B	253157.0	9430.1	1.34	1.00	4.0	6.0	7.2	8.0	4.1	AIT
PRUDENTIAL LEGACY INS CO OF NJ	NJ	C	(2) 61222.1	359.2	0.64	0.53	3.2	9.4	6.5	0.7	2.8	CFGLT
PRUDENTIAL RETIREMENT INS & ANNUITY	CT	B-	70736.0	941.9	1.66	0.77	6.0	3.1	6.2	7.3	5.1	ACI
▼ PURITAN LIFE INS CO	TX	D	14.4	12.3	2.48	1.57	7.9	3.0	7.6	10.0	2.0	ACDGT
PURITAN LIFE INS CO OF AMERICA	TX	D	37.2	6.6	2.07	1.86	8.3	7.6	2.4	7.4	2.0	DFT
PYRAMID LIFE INS CO	KS	C+	73.5	18.5	2.50	1.73	8.1	5.5	5.9	7.1	3.6	DFT
RABENHORST LIFE INS CO	LA	C- (1)	29.3	3.4	0.89	0.76	5.1	4.0	2.3	6.0	2.9	DFI
REGAL LIFE OF AMERICA INS CO	TX	D-	8.2	4.9	0.96	0.93	6.4	5.2	1.6	7.0	0.9	DFT
REGAL REINSURANCE COMPANY	MA	U (2)	6.1	5.8	0.80	0.79	5.3	4.4	4.0	9.9	4.2	CDIT
REINSURANCE CO OF MO INC	MO	C	1640.4	1603.4	1.01	0.94	6.5	1.4	7.3	8.6	2.8	GIT

See Page 27 for explanation of footnotes and Page 28 for explanation of stability factors.
Arrows denote recent upgrades ▲ or downgrades▼ (see Section VI for explanations)

50

www.weissratings.com

NET PREMIUM ($MIL)	IN-VESTED ASSETS ($MIL)	CASH	CMO & STRUCT. SECS.	OTH.INV. GRADE BONDS	NON-INV. GRADE BONDS	CMMON & PREF. STOCK	MORT IN GOOD STAND.	NON-PERF. MORT.	REAL ESTATE	OTHER INVEST-MENTS	INVEST. IN AFFIL	INSURANCE COMPANY NAME
30.8	1,045.4	3.1	16.1	70.4	2.5	1.0	0.0	0.0	0.0	6.9	1.0 ●	PAVONIA LIFE INS CO OF MICHIGAN
2.3	28.7	2.5	14.4	83.1	0.0	0.0	0.0	0.0	0.0	0.0	0.0	PAVONIA LIFE INS CO OF NEW YORK
113.0	1,347.8 (*)	0.3	28.9	63.5	0.2	1.1	1.2	0.0	0.0	1.2	0.0 ●	PEKIN LIFE INS CO
0.6	8.1	9.3	0.9	40.2	0.0	3.5	16.1	3.0	26.8	0.3	12.5	PELLERIN LIFE INS CO
174.5	2,902.6	0.4	21.5	51.5	4.3	1.2	0.0	0.0	0.0	21.1	3.2 ●	PENN INS & ANNUITY CO
632.9	10,186.8	1.0	28.6	49.7	3.0	5.3	0.0	0.0	0.3	11.6	5.5 ●	PENN MUTUAL LIFE INS CO
3.6	31.2 (*)	1.4	0.0	93.5	0.0	0.0	0.0	0.0	0.0	0.0	0.0	PERFORMANCE LIFE OF AMERICA
2.5	92.6	0.4	3.3	88.2	1.6	4.4	0.0	0.0	0.0	2.2	0.0	PHARMACISTS LIFE INS CO
76.3	227.5	1.6	16.0	68.8	9.4	0.2	4.0	0.0	0.0	0.2	0.0 ●	PHILADELPHIA AMERICAN LIFE INS CO
-1,266.1	1,949.2 (*)	4.1	18.7	65.2	4.0	1.4	0.0	0.0	0.0	5.2	0.0 ●	PHL VARIABLE INS CO
-0.1	32.8	21.3	20.1	51.0	4.3	0.0	0.0	0.0	0.0	3.3	0.0	PHOENIX LIFE & ANNUITY CO
149.2	11,229.8	3.9	15.6	46.9	5.7	1.8	0.0	0.0	0.0	0.3	26.1	0.1 ●	PHOENIX LIFE INS CO
2.3	8.4	4.7	0.0	95.3	0.0	0.0	0.0	0.0	0.0	0.0	0.0	PHYSICIANS BENEFITS TRUST LIFE INS
152.6	1,460.0	0.3	20.8	69.1	5.5	1.7	0.0	0.0	0.0	2.5	0.0 ●	PHYSICIANS LIFE INS CO
238.4	2,061.9	0.2	11.0	68.9	6.0	13.4	0.0	0.0	0.5	0.0	6.7 ●	PHYSICIANS MUTUAL INS CO
0.1	1.8	100.0	0.0	0.0	0.0	0.0	0.0	0.0	0.0	0.0	0.0	PINE BELT LIFE INS CO
5.3	56.4	0.0	0.0	84.8	0.0	0.4	5.5	0.0	0.0	9.3	0.0	PIONEER AMERICAN INS CO
0.0	1.6	100.0	0.0	0.0	0.0	0.0	0.0	0.0	0.0	0.0	0.0	PIONEER MILITARY INS CO
11.5	505.4	0.2	31.4	56.2	1.8	0.0	5.5	0.0	0.0	5.0	0.0 ●	PIONEER MUTUAL LIFE INS CO
3.2	115.1	0.0	0.0	28.4	0.0	68.1	0.3	0.0	0.0	3.2	68.1 ●	PIONEER SECURITY LIFE INS CO
9.2	22.9	32.9	0.0	62.6	0.0	2.9	0.0	0.0	0.8	0.8	1.3	PLATEAU INS CO
9.4	56.1	21.1	51.3	22.7	5.0	0.0	0.0	0.0	0.0	0.0	0.0 ●	POPULAR LIFE RE
0.0	0.4	99.9	0.2	0.0	0.0	0.0	0.0	0.0	0.0	0.0	0.0	PORT-O-CALL LIFE INS CO
0.0	2.8	1.9	0.0	59.5	5.0	20.1	-2.6	12.7	0.0	3.4	0.0	PREFERRED SECURITY LIFE INS CO
53.0	32.3	0.9	0.0	99.1	0.0	0.0	0.0	0.0	0.0	0.0	0.0 ●	PRENEED REINS CO OF AMERICA
0.0	4.0 (*)	13.1	3.6	3.4	1.7	29.7	0.0	0.0	0.0	1.2	0.0	PRESIDENTIAL LIFE INS CO
106.7	1,430.5 (*)	-1.4	9.9	52.0	4.3	31.6	0.0	0.0	0.0	0.1	28.9 ●	PRIMERICA LIFE INS CO
3,993.1	60,415.6	0.7	20.3	45.6	5.9	1.5	18.6	0.0	0.7	5.9	5.3 ●	PRINCIPAL LIFE INS CO
0.0	331.3	0.1	0.0	1.7	0.0	98.2	0.0	0.0	0.0	0.0	98.2	PRINCIPAL LIFE INS CO IOWA
0.0	94.9	0.9	10.1	89.0	0.0	0.0	0.0	0.0	0.0	0.0	0.0 ●	PRINCIPAL NATIONAL LIFE INS CO
12.4	100.9 (*)	0.1	11.2	74.8	6.4	0.0	0.0	0.0	0.0	5.1	0.0 ●	PROFESSIONAL INS CO
5.1	156.9	0.7	0.0	63.1	12.3	23.9	0.0	0.0	0.0	0.0	0.0 ●	PROFESSIONAL LIFE & CAS CO
0.1	3.1	52.2	0.0	47.8	0.0	0.0	0.0	0.0	0.0	0.0	0.0	PROTEC INS CO
30.8	1,763.1	0.0	13.9	72.6	4.3	1.7	5.7	0.0	0.0	1.9	0.0 ●	PROTECTIVE LIFE & ANNUITY INS CO
1,215.7	25,794.5	-0.1	13.1	57.6	3.8	7.8	13.0	0.0	0.2	3.7	9.1 ●	PROTECTIVE LIFE INS CO
4.4	16.6	1.5	0.0	80.6	0.0	17.9	0.0	0.0	0.0	0.0	17.9	PROVIDENT AMER LIFE & HEALTH INS CO
25.6	19.2	30.3	4.2	60.5	3.2	0.0	0.0	0.0	0.0	1.8	0.0	PROVIDENT AMERICAN INS CO
465.9	7,748.9	0.0	7.2	74.0	6.8	1.2	5.7	0.0	1.0	3.9	0.0 ●	PROVIDENT LIFE & ACCIDENT INS CO
46.3	734.7	0.0	7.1	79.2	9.4	0.0	3.6	0.0	0.0	0.9	0.0 ●	PROVIDENT LIFE & CAS INS CO
-1,256.0	8,947.8 (*)	0.0	15.5	44.6	4.0	5.0	15.4	0.0	0.0	13.4	7.4 ●	PRUCO LIFE INS CO
33.8	1,725.1	0.0	17.3	48.9	5.4	1.0	13.8	0.0	0.0	13.4	1.7 ●	PRUCO LIFE INS CO OF NEW JERSEY
12,157.7	2,048.1 (*)	-2.4	18.9	48.9	7.0	0.3	17.2	0.0	0.0	4.1	2.7 ●	PRUDENTIAL ANNUITIES LIFE ASR CORP
10,255.6	109,859.1 (*)	-0.5	16.7	47.0	4.0	6.9	16.3	0.0	0.5	7.0	10.6 ●	PRUDENTIAL INS CO OF AMERICA
55,309.0	290.6	0.0	0.0	100.0	0.0	0.0	0.0	0.0	0.0	0.0	0.0 ●	PRUDENTIAL LEGACY INS CO OF NJ
457.4	25,438.0 (*)	0.0	21.8	49.0	7.1	0.3	20.1	0.0	0.0	0.3	0.1 ●	PRUDENTIAL RETIREMENT INS & ANNUITY
0.1	6.8	4.2	0.0	95.8	0.0	0.0	0.0	0.0	0.0	0.0	0.0	PURITAN LIFE INS CO
1.3	35.6	2.0	35.8	55.2	2.9	1.3	0.0	0.0	0.0	3.0	0.0	PURITAN LIFE INS CO OF AMERICA
9.8	62.2	-1.3	3.7	85.3	0.0	12.1	0.0	0.0	0.0	0.2	0.0	PYRAMID LIFE INS CO
0.6	21.1	1.0	13.3	52.0	1.4	21.2	10.4	0.0	0.0	0.7	10.4	RABENHORST LIFE INS CO
1.0	8.4	11.5	0.0	30.4	0.0	55.1	0.0	0.0	0.0	3.0	55.1	REGAL LIFE OF AMERICA INS CO
0.0	6.0	0.7	0.0	40.0	0.0	59.3	0.0	0.0	0.0	0.0	59.3	REGAL REINSURANCE COMPANY
-22.5	1,646.5	0.1	2.3	6.2	0.1	91.3	0.0	0.0	0.0	0.0	91.3 ●	REINSURANCE CO OF MO INC

● Bullets denote a more detailed analysis is available in Section II.
(*) Asset category percentages do not add up to 100%

INSURANCE COMPANY NAME	DOM. STATE	RATING		TOTAL ASSETS ($MIL)	CAPITAL & SURPLUS ($MIL)	RISK ADJUSTED CAPITAL RATIO 1	RISK ADJUSTED CAPITAL RATIO 2	CAPITAL-IZATION INDEX (PTS)	INVEST. SAFETY INDEX (PTS)	PROFIT-ABILITY INDEX (PTS)	LIQUIDITY INDEX (PTS)	STAB. INDEX (PTS)	STABILITY FACTOR
RELIABLE LIFE INS CO	MO	B-		22.6	12.3	2.16	1.07	7.1	8.7	6.6	7.0	5.3	A
RELIABLE LIFE INS CO	LA	E+	(2)	7.1	1.7	1.08	0.66	5.1	1.8	1.6	8.0	0.5	FT
RELIABLE SERVICE INS CO	LA	U	(2)	0.1	0.1	1.36	1.23	7.3	3.0	6.9	7.0	5.0	DI
RELIANCE STANDARD LIFE INS CO	IL	B		10156.8	968.0	1.64	0.88	6.0	4.0	8.4	6.5	5.9	ACI
RELIANCE STANDARD LIFE INS CO OF TX	TX	U	(2)	876.4	819.4	1.17	1.04	7.1	6.5	7.7	10.0	7.0	IT
RELIASTAR LIFE INS CO	MN	C+		19884.7	1645.8	2.06	1.24	7.4	6.1	3.9	5.1	3.6	FT
RELIASTAR LIFE INS CO OF NEW YORK	NY	B		3067.1	304.7	3.41	1.83	8.2	6.5	4.6	5.9	5.8	A
RESERVE NATIONAL INS CO	OK	A-		123.3	40.1	2.01	1.53	7.8	8.0	4.1	6.1	6.2	A
RESOURCE LIFE INS CO	IL	U	(2)	7.0	6.5	3.46	3.11	4.0	9.0	6.4	9.7	5.6	DFT
RGA REINSURANCE CO	MO	B-		25223.7	1483.5	1.41	0.80	5.6	4.7	6.1	5.8	5.3	ACI
RHODES LIFE INS CO OF LA INC	LA	E	(2)	4.0	0.2	0.17	0.15	0.0	0.4	0.9	7.0	0.0	CIT
RIVERMONT LIFE INS CO I	SC	C		577.1	147.6	4.38	2.48	9.2	7.2	1.5	7.9	3.9	D
RIVERSOURCE LIFE INS CO	MN	C		102927.0	3504.4	2.03	1.25	7.4	5.9	5.0	7.8	4.1	T
RIVERSOURCE LIFE INS CO OF NY	NY	C		6638.3	330.6	3.59	1.79	8.2	6.0	3.0	7.5	4.3	A
ROYAL NEIGHBORS OF AMERICA	IL	U		--	--	--	--	--	--	--	--	--	Z
ROYAL STATE NATIONAL INS CO LTD	HI	C		45.7	28.8	4.70	3.13	10.0	5.9	3.8	6.9	4.2	DFT
S USA LIFE INS CO INC	AZ	B		13.3	7.7	2.73	2.46	9.2	8.4	2.7	7.8	5.0	AD
SAGICOR LIFE INS CO	TX	C-		1128.2	74.4	1.14	0.57	5.2	2.4	2.0	4.5	3.1	CILT
SAVINGS BANK LIFE INS CO OF MA	MA	B+		2957.5	218.7	1.66	1.07	7.1	6.2	6.5	6.0	6.4	I
SBLI USA MUT LIFE INS CO INC	NY	B		1533.2	118.5	1.98	1.11	7.2	6.0	7.8	3.6	5.6	CFIL
SCOR GLOBAL LIFE AMERICAS REIN CO	DE	C-		1286.8	193.4	1.19	0.84	5.7	6.6	2.4	7.9	3.3	ACFT
SCOR GLOBAL LIFE REINS CO OF DE	DE	C		381.4	83.3	2.88	1.77	8.2	8.7	2.0	7.7	3.7	AT
SCOR GLOBAL LIFE USA RE CO	DE	C		718.4	339.4	5.71	3.59	10.0	8.7	6.8	8.0	3.3	AFT
SCOTTISH RE US INC	DE	D+		1510.9	75.0	1.03	0.54	5.0	3.5	1.2	4.7	2.4	FGLT
SECU LIFE INS CO	NC	C		34.4	25.7	5.42	4.88	10.0	8.6	5.9	9.5	3.5	EGT
SECURIAN LIFE INS CO	MN	A-		478.9	204.4	5.84	3.80	10.0	7.5	6.9	6.9	7.2	AG
SECURICO LIFE INS CO	TX	U	(2)	2.7	2.6	2.93	2.64	8.0	5.9	2.8	10.0	3.0	DFT
SECURITAS FINANCIAL LIFE INS CO	NC	U	(2)	5.8	5.7	3.41	3.07	8.0	9.2	7.8	10.0	7.6	D
SECURITY BENEFIT LIFE INS CO	KS	B		28075.4	1227.3	1.73	0.80	6.1	3.8	7.5	7.6	5.8	ACIT
SECURITY LIFE INS CO OF AMERICA	MN	B		67.1	19.9	1.08	0.83	5.6	7.8	3.6	5.8	5.6	CDF
SECURITY LIFE OF DENVER INS CO	CO	C+		13328.9	770.6	0.69	0.47	2.6	5.5	3.2	5.5	3.3	CGT
SECURITY MUTUAL LIFE INS CO OF NY	NY	B		2679.1	127.7	1.49	0.80	5.7	6.0	6.2	1.9	4.0	CIL
SECURITY NATIONAL LIFE INS CO	UT	D-		551.0	33.5	0.83	0.49	3.6	1.9	7.4	7.7	1.3	CI
SECURITY PLAN LIFE INS CO	LA	C		325.2	46.3	1.85	1.26	7.4	6.1	4.3	6.7	3.4	AD
▼ SENIOR HEALTH INS CO OF PENNSYLVANIA	PA	E		2794.8	35.0	0.51	0.25	1.1	0.0	1.1	6.3	1.1	CFIT
SENIOR LIFE INS CO	GA	C-		48.8	8.0	1.48	0.75	5.7	3.0	2.0	6.7	2.9	DGIT
SENTINEL AMERICAN LIFE INS CO	TX	U	(2)	30.5	4.2	1.47	1.32	7.5	7.3	1.9	6.7	3.1	DF
▲ SENTINEL SECURITY LIFE INS CO	UT	D+		553.1	37.5	1.45	0.68	5.7	2.8	2.7	8.8	2.7	ACGIT
SENTRY LIFE INS CO	WI	A		5800.9	279.8	3.50	2.01	8.5	7.2	6.2	7.8	7.4	A
SENTRY LIFE INS CO OF NEW YORK	NY	B		78.6	10.5	1.35	1.22	7.3	7.9	6.1	7.8	5.7	DFGT
SERVCO LIFE INS CO	TX	U	(2)	5.0	3.6	2.51	2.26	4.0	4.7	6.1	10.0	4.3	DFIRT
SERVICE LIFE & CAS INS CO	TX	U	(2)	22.0	16.9	4.54	1.78	4.0	2.8	4.9	8.0	4.8	DFIRT
SETTLERS LIFE INS CO	WI	B		392.9	40.2	2.62	1.40	7.6	5.9	5.4	6.3	6.2	AI
SHELTER LIFE INS CO	MO	A-		1180.1	191.9	3.48	2.28	8.9	7.9	5.1	5.8	7.3	A
SHELTERPOINT INS CO	FL	U	(2)	8.6	7.7	4.00	3.60	8.0	8.7	3.7	7.0	3.9	FT
SHELTERPOINT LIFE INS CO	NY	A		105.4	56.0	2.36	1.99	8.5	7.5	7.9	7.0	6.7	D
SHENANDOAH LIFE INS CO	VA	B-		1128.1	87.1	2.09	1.10	7.2	5.8	6.0	3.9	5.2	FL
SHERIDAN LIFE INS CO	OK	U	(2)	2.2	2.0	2.64	2.37	9.1	9.8	6.8	10.0	5.0	DFT
▼ SMITH BURIAL & LIFE INS CO	AR	E		4.6	0.4	0.29	0.26	0.1	6.9	1.4	5.7	0.1	CD
SOUTHERN FARM BUREAU LIFE INS CO	MS	A		13583.7	2453.9	4.50	2.40	9.1	6.0	7.9	6.3	7.4	I
SOUTHERN FIDELITY LIFE INS CO	AR	U	(2)	0.1	0.1	1.89	1.70	8.1	7.7	2.9	10.0	3.1	D
SOUTHERN FINANCIAL LIFE INS CO	KY	C		4.9	4.0	2.64	2.38	9.1	8.8	8.2	8.4	4.2	AT

See Page 27 for explanation of footnotes and Page 28 for explanation of stability factors.
Arrows denote recent upgrades ▲ or downgrades▼ (see Section VI for explanations)

52

www.weissratings.com

NET PREMIUM ($MIL)	IN-VESTED ASSETS ($MIL)	CASH	CMO & STRUCT. SECS.	OTH.INV. GRADE BONDS	NON-INV. GRADE BONDS	CMMON & PREF. STOCK	MORT IN GOOD STAND.	NON-PERF. MORT.	REAL ESTATE	OTHER INVEST-MENTS	INVEST. IN AFFIL	INSURANCE COMPANY NAME
0.0	20.7 (*)	0.0	0.0	102.0	0.0	0.0	0.0	0.0	0.0	0.0	0.0	RELIABLE LIFE INS CO
0.6	6.8	22.5	0.0	22.5	0.0	51.4	0.0	0.0	3.5	0.0	1.0	RELIABLE LIFE INS CO
0.0	0.1	44.0	0.0	0.0	0.0	56.0	0.0	0.0	0.0	0.0	0.0	RELIABLE SERVICE INS CO
867.3	9,202.9	0.0	43.0	29.6	10.3	4.0	10.2	0.0	0.0	2.7	2.0 ●	RELIANCE STANDARD LIFE INS CO
0.1	875.0	0.1	0.0	6.6	0.0	93.4	0.0	0.0	0.0	0.0	97.9	RELIANCE STANDARD LIFE INS CO OF TX
394.9	17,009.2 (*)	1.1	10.8	62.4	3.7	2.2	12.7	0.0	0.0	6.0	3.4 ●	RELIASTAR LIFE INS CO
79.1	2,125.0 (*)	2.2	7.7	72.3	3.2	0.1	7.5	0.0	0.0	5.4	0.0 ●	RELIASTAR LIFE INS CO OF NEW YORK
70.4	101.3	3.7	3.0	90.1	0.0	0.0	0.0	0.0	0.0	3.3	0.2 ●	RESERVE NATIONAL INS CO
0.0	6.7 (*)	0.0	29.0	71.0	0.0	0.0	0.0	0.0	0.0	8.7	0.0	RESOURCE LIFE INS CO
1,190.6	17,599.0	1.8	16.4	43.6	8.8	2.0	15.8	0.0	0.0	11.0	4.1 ●	RGA REINSURANCE CO
0.6	4.0	7.7	0.9	63.9	0.0	0.2	19.3	0.0	8.1	0.0	0.0	RHODES LIFE INS CO OF LA INC
12.4	536.8	0.1	21.1	77.9	0.2	0.0	0.0	0.0	0.0	0.0	0.0 ●	RIVERMONT LIFE INS CO I
2,858.3	27,925.1 (*)	0.0	20.9	43.7	6.3	2.9	11.1	0.0	0.4	2.9	3.0 ●	RIVERSOURCE LIFE INS CO
176.9	2,056.0 (*)	0.0	21.6	60.3	3.9	0.0	6.7	0.0	0.0	2.4	0.0 ●	RIVERSOURCE LIFE INS CO OF NY
--	--	--	--	--	--	--	--	--	--	--	--	ROYAL NEIGHBORS OF AMERICA
2.7	43.9	0.6	14.2	66.6	0.6	17.0	0.0	0.0	0.0	0.6	3.2 ●	ROYAL STATE NATIONAL INS CO LTD
0.4	13.1	3.7	24.7	68.9	0.0	0.0	0.0	0.0	0.0	2.6	0.0	S USA LIFE INS CO INC
34.2	1,057.3 (*)	0.0	20.9	67.5	2.3	2.4	2.4	0.0	0.1	3.3	0.0 ●	SAGICOR LIFE INS CO
81.3	2,744.4	-0.3	19.6	67.2	4.1	5.2	0.0	0.0	0.2	3.5	2.8 ●	SAVINGS BANK LIFE INS CO OF MA
28.8	1,485.6	0.3	26.3	63.4	0.5	1.1	0.0	0.0	0.3	8.1	0.6 ●	SBLI USA MUT LIFE INS CO INC
52.5	1,032.7	1.0	17.5	65.1	7.0	7.6	0.0	0.0	0.0	1.6	7.6 ●	SCOR GLOBAL LIFE AMERICAS REIN CO
33.6	293.6	1.4	18.5	75.4	0.0	0.0	0.0	0.0	0.0	4.7	0.0 ●	SCOR GLOBAL LIFE REINS CO OF DE
87.0	468.9	1.2	10.1	86.3	0.0	0.0	0.0	0.0	0.0	2.4	0.0 ●	SCOR GLOBAL LIFE USA RE CO
68.8	1,347.2	0.1	50.5	46.6	2.8	0.0	0.0	0.0	0.0	0.1	0.0 ●	SCOTTISH RE US INC
3.6	31.2	23.2	0.0	40.3	0.0	0.0	36.5	0.0	0.0	0.0	0.0 ●	SECU LIFE INS CO
83.3	371.5	1.7	12.7	80.6	2.6	1.6	0.0	0.0	0.4	0.4	0.0 ●	SECURIAN LIFE INS CO
0.0	2.7	0.5	0.0	73.9	0.0	19.3	0.0	0.0	0.0	6.3	0.0	SECURICO LIFE INS CO
0.0	5.7	25.4	0.0	74.6	0.0	0.0	0.0	0.0	0.0	0.0	0.0	SECURITAS FINANCIAL LIFE INS CO
1,452.5	21,834.5 (*)	0.0	41.1	21.8	4.5	0.5	6.0	0.0	0.1	24.3	15.5 ●	SECURITY BENEFIT LIFE INS CO
43.7	61.2	2.2	7.6	79.9	0.3	1.7	6.6	0.0	0.0	1.8	0.0	SECURITY LIFE INS CO OF AMERICA
303.4	11,199.3 (*)	2.2	12.6	57.3	3.7	1.5	9.6	0.0	0.0	12.0	3.2 ●	SECURITY LIFE OF DENVER INS CO
93.7	2,506.0	0.1	4.2	74.6	0.3	0.1	6.7	0.0	0.4	13.7	0.1 ●	SECURITY MUTUAL LIFE INS CO OF NY
35.7	526.6	0.7	0.9	29.3	2.3	3.6	25.0	1.0	8.0	29.7	1.9 ●	SECURITY NATIONAL LIFE INS CO
22.8	307.9	3.9	2.4	77.3	3.9	8.6	0.0	0.0	1.4	2.5	3.7 ●	SECURITY PLAN LIFE INS CO
65.1	2,823.7	0.3	14.1	62.7	7.3	3.2	2.1	0.0	0.0	10.4	0.0 ●	SENIOR HEALTH INS CO OF PENNSYLVANIA
9.6	13.8	18.0	0.3	26.3	0.2	9.2	0.0	0.0	27.5	18.4	0.0	SENIOR LIFE INS CO
0.0	30.2	1.2	0.0	98.6	0.0	0.0	0.0	0.0	0.0	0.3	0.0	SENTINEL AMERICAN LIFE INS CO
23.5	489.2	0.9	48.8	36.7	4.8	2.1	5.2	0.0	1.2	0.3	0.0 ●	SENTINEL SECURITY LIFE INS CO
317.5	2,514.0	0.0	7.1	89.6	2.4	0.4	0.0	0.0	0.0	0.5	0.4 ●	SENTRY LIFE INS CO
5.0	33.2	0.8	2.7	91.4	3.2	0.0	0.0	0.0	0.0	2.0	0.0	SENTRY LIFE INS CO OF NEW YORK
0.0	5.0	11.3	0.0	57.1	0.0	31.6	0.0	0.0	0.0	0.0	0.0	SERVCO LIFE INS CO
-0.1	20.6	9.2	1.5	10.7	0.0	1.2	0.0	0.0	71.7	5.7	1.2	SERVICE LIFE & CAS INS CO
25.3	374.2	-0.1	5.7	84.4	3.3	3.0	0.0	0.0	1.0	2.7	0.0 ●	SETTLERS LIFE INS CO
64.1	1,091.7	0.2	19.0	71.7	0.6	1.1	0.9	0.0	0.0	6.6	2.3 ●	SHELTER LIFE INS CO
0.0	8.0	9.1	12.5	78.5	0.0	0.0	0.0	0.0	0.0	0.0	0.0	SHELTERPOINT INS CO
50.0	92.2	0.7	15.6	71.6	2.4	9.7	0.0	0.0	0.0	0.0	9.7 ●	SHELTERPOINT LIFE INS CO
21.1	1,092.6	0.1	23.0	64.1	1.6	0.7	6.7	0.0	0.0	3.9	0.0 ●	SHENANDOAH LIFE INS CO
0.0	2.2	100.0	0.0	0.0	0.0	0.0	0.0	0.0	0.0	0.0	0.0	SHERIDAN LIFE INS CO
0.2	4.6	15.2	0.0	81.3	0.0	3.5	0.0	0.0	0.0	0.0	0.0	SMITH BURIAL & LIFE INS CO
502.7	12,772.0	0.1	14.6	57.8	2.4	4.7	11.3	0.0	0.1	9.0	0.8 ●	SOUTHERN FARM BUREAU LIFE INS CO
0.0	0.1	90.9	0.0	0.0	0.0	9.1	0.0	0.0	0.0	0.0	0.0	SOUTHERN FIDELITY LIFE INS CO
0.8	4.5	0.3	6.9	86.1	0.0	6.7	0.0	0.0	0.0	0.0	0.0	SOUTHERN FINANCIAL LIFE INS CO

● Bullets denote a more detailed analysis is available in Section II.
(*) Asset category percentages do not add up to 100%

INSURANCE COMPANY NAME	DOM. STATE	RATING	TOTAL ASSETS ($MIL)	CAPITAL & SURPLUS ($MIL)	RISK ADJUSTED CAPITAL RATIO 1	RISK ADJUSTED CAPITAL RATIO 2	CAPITAL-IZATION INDEX (PTS)	INVEST. SAFETY INDEX (PTS)	PROFIT-ABILITY INDEX (PTS)	LIQUIDITY INDEX (PTS)	STAB. INDEX (PTS)	STABILITY FACTORS
SOUTHERN FINANCIAL LIFE INS CO	LA	D+	106.6	29.7	2.72	1.48	7.7	2.9	8.8	6.6	2.8	DI
SOUTHERN LIFE & HEALTH INS CO	WI	U (2)	85.5	33.4	1.86	1.73	8.1	6.4	7.1	7.6	6.4	DIT
SOUTHERN NATL LIFE INS CO INC	LA	B	15.0	11.5	1.97	1.58	7.9	6.0	1.9	7.0	5.2	FIT
▲ SOUTHERN PIONEER LIFE INS CO	AR	B+	16.8	12.4	4.07	3.67	10.0	8.5	6.7	9.1	6.6	ADFT
SOUTHERN SECURITY LIFE INS CO INC	MS	D+	1.6	1.6	2.58	2.32	8.0	7.8	4.2	10.0	2.2	A
SOUTHLAND NATIONAL INS CORP	NC	C-	301.0	36.0	2.56	1.23	4.0	1.7	4.6	9.1	3.3	FIT
SOUTHWEST CREDIT LIFE INC	NM	U (2)	0.7	0.6	2.15	1.94	4.0	9.2	2.4	10.0	2.6	DFT
SOUTHWEST SERVICE LIFE INS CO	TX	D-	10.8	4.4	0.84	0.75	5.0	8.4	1.4	6.7	1.2	ADFT
SPJST	TX	U	--	--	--	--	--	--	--	--	--	Z
SQUIRE REASSURANCE CO LLC	MI	U (2)	12.6	12.5	4.63	4.16	8.0	8.5	8.6	10.0	8.0	D
STANDARD INS CO	OR	B+	21220.5	1092.3	2.12	1.10	7.2	5.3	5.9	6.8	6.5	AI
STANDARD LIFE & ACCIDENT INS CO	TX	A-	511.2	275.1	5.87	3.61	10.0	4.9	8.6	6.9	6.9	AFI
STANDARD LIFE & CAS INS CO	UT	C-	30.7	4.4	0.97	0.49	4.8	2.8	3.5	4.9	3.0	CIL
STANDARD LIFE INS CO OF NY	NY	A-	283.1	83.2	4.21	2.74	9.6	7.4	7.6	7.3	7.2	A
STANDARD SECURITY LIFE INS CO OF NY	NY	A-	245.0	124.7	5.06	4.10	10.0	7.7	8.1	6.7	5.5	ADT
STARMOUNT LIFE INS CO	LA	B (3)	62.6	26.8	1.25	0.95	6.6	7.3	5.2	6.0	5.4	D
STARVED ROCK LIFE INS CO	AZ	U	--	--	--	--	--	--	--	--	--	Z
STATE FARM HEALTH INS CO	IL	U (2)	8.4	8.3	3.90	3.51	8.0	9.5	3.9	10.0	5.4	DF
STATE FARM LIFE & ACCIDENT ASR CO	IL	A+	2692.7	476.8	5.58	3.15	10.0	7.8	6.0	6.3	7.9	A
STATE FARM LIFE INS CO	IL	A+	68156.4	9873.7	4.45	2.50	9.3	6.6	6.5	6.1	7.9	AI
STATE LIFE INS CO	IN	B	6448.0	437.6	2.10	1.08	7.1	5.4	8.2	4.3	6.3	IL
STATE LIFE INS FUND	WI	B (5)	--	--	--	--	--	--	--	--	--	Z
STATE MUTUAL INS CO	GA	C-	281.2	30.1	1.96	1.02	7.0	4.4	4.2	6.4	3.0	DGT
▼ STERLING INVESTORS LIFE INS CO	IN	D+	20.3	7.3	1.53	0.96	6.7	6.7	2.2	7.0	2.4	FGT
STERLING LIFE INS CO	IL	C+ (5)	--	--	--	--	--	--	--	--	--	Z
STRUCTURED ANNUITY RE CO	IA	U (2)	1421.9	76.4	1.77	0.87	4.0	4.1	1.8	10.0	3.8	CEI
▼ SUN LIFE & HEALTH INS CO	MI	D-	494.0	199.2	4.10	2.70	9.6	7.2	2.0	7.1	1.1	AG
SUN LIFE ASR CO OF CANADA	MI	E	20273.9	1087.2	0.63	0.37	2.0	2.2	1.8	6.4	0.1	CGIT
SUNSET LIFE INS CO OF AMERICA	MO	B	333.0	30.4	2.70	1.38	7.6	6.0	6.1	4.9	4.7	DFILT
SUPERIOR FUNERAL & LIFE INS CO	AR	C+	173.0	22.7	2.49	1.31	7.5	3.9	6.5	5.3	4.4	DI
SURENCY LIFE & HEALTH INS CO	KS	C	9.4	7.1	3.20	2.69	9.5	7.4	2.0	7.7	3.4	DFG
SURETY LIFE & CASUALTY INS CO	ND	C-	11.1	4.3	1.76	1.58	7.9	4.0	8.4	7.7	2.8	D
SURETY LIFE INS CO	NE	D+	20.5	19.9	3.16	1.54	7.8	5.2	2.6	8.2	2.5	FGT
SWBC LIFE INS CO	TX	B	24.1	15.7	3.32	2.18	8.8	5.3	7.1	9.3	5.7	GI
SWISS RE LIFE & HEALTH AMER INC	MO	C	13844.0	1308.5	1.65	0.96	6.7	5.7	2.0	5.9	3.8	G
SYMETRA LIFE INS CO	IA	B+	33273.1	2064.9	2.08	1.13	7.2	5.3	8.2	6.6	6.7	GI
SYMETRA NATIONAL LIFE INS CO	IA	B	16.9	10.4	3.31	2.98	10.0	8.7	6.1	7.5	6.3	DF
T J M LIFE INS CO	TX	D+	16.1	1.7	0.64	0.58	3.6	5.2	3.7	5.1	2.7	CD
TEACHERS INS & ANNUITY ASN OF AM	NY	A+	276045.0	35070.3	5.10	2.69	9.5	6.6	8.6	6.9	7.9	I
TENNESSEE FARMERS LIFE INS CO	TN	A	2151.3	389.7	2.25	1.49	7.7	5.9	6.6	6.2	7.4	AI
TEXAS DIRECTORS LIFE INS CO	TX	B- (2)	5.8	1.1	0.68	0.61	3.9	5.5	8.5	6.5	3.9	CDF
TEXAS LIFE INS CO	TX	B	1078.6	82.2	1.82	1.01	7.0	5.8	5.2	6.5	5.4	AI
TEXAS SERVICE LIFE INS CO	TX	C-	62.8	10.1	1.45	1.31	7.5	8.1	2.8	8.0	3.1	D
THRIVENT FINANCIAL FOR LUTHERANS	WI	U	--	--	--	--	--	--	--	--	--	Z
THRIVENT LIFE INS CO	MN	B	3541.4	154.0	1.94	0.95	6.6	4.5	4.6	6.3	6.1	I
TIAA-CREF LIFE INS CO	NY	B	11505.5	400.8	2.14	1.12	7.2	5.9	2.0	5.6	6.3	I
TIME INS CO	WI	C+	613.4	355.9	2.15	1.74	5.9	6.6	2.8	0.1	3.0	AFLT
TIPPECANOE LIFE INS CO	AZ	U	--	--	--	--	--	--	--	--	--	Z
TOWN & COUNTRY LIFE INS CO	UT	C-	7.0	4.0	2.17	1.95	8.4	6.5	8.1	7.3	2.4	D
▲ TPM LIFE INS CO	PA	B	7.0	4.0	1.38	1.24	7.4	8.5	1.3	10.0	4.5	ACDFT
TRANS CITY LIFE INS CO	AZ	C-	19.5	9.5	3.36	3.02	10.0	6.9	2.5	9.9	2.9	D
TRANS OCEANIC LIFE INS CO	PR	A (2)	68.3	36.2	3.12	1.95	8.4	5.2	9.1	8.9	6.4	DI

See Page 27 for explanation of footnotes and Page 28 for explanation of stability factors.

Arrows denote recent upgrades ▲ or downgrades▼ (see Section VI for explanations)

54

www.weissratings.com

NET PREMIUM ($MIL)	IN-VESTED ASSETS ($MIL)	CASH	CMO & STRUCT. SECS.	OTH.INV. GRADE BONDS	NON-INV. GRADE BONDS	CMMON & PREF. STOCK	MORT IN GOOD STAND.	NON-PERF. MORT.	REAL ESTATE	OTHER INVEST-MENTS	INVEST. IN AFFIL	INSURANCE COMPANY NAME
8.3	98.0	0.7	0.0	46.9	17.2	30.0	0.0	0.0	0.0	5.2	0.0	● SOUTHERN FINANCIAL LIFE INS CO
0.0	84.7 (*)	0.2	0.1	59.6	0.0	29.3	0.0	0.0	0.0	1.7	24.5	SOUTHERN LIFE & HEALTH INS CO
3.7	13.3	-0.8	8.5	58.0	0.0	33.9	0.0	0.0	0.0	0.4	17.7	SOUTHERN NATL LIFE INS CO INC
0.4	15.3 (*)	2.6	22.6	74.1	0.0	0.7	0.0	0.0	0.0	2.7	0.0	SOUTHERN PIONEER LIFE INS CO
0.0	1.6	15.6	23.6	40.7	2.7	1.8	15.6	0.0	0.0	0.0	0.0	SOUTHERN SECURITY LIFE INS CO INC
2.6	296.1	27.6	0.3	20.4	39.0	9.4	0.2	0.0	0.0	3.1	59.9	● SOUTHLAND NATIONAL INS CORP
0.0	0.7	0.4	0.0	99.6	0.0	0.0	0.0	0.0	0.0	0.0	0.0	SOUTHWEST CREDIT LIFE INC
3.5	10.7	9.2	0.0	60.6	0.0	30.2	0.0	0.0	0.0	0.0	30.2	SOUTHWEST SERVICE LIFE INS CO
--	--	--	--	--	--	--	--	--	--	--	--	SPJST
0.0	12.5	0.0	9.4	90.4	0.0	0.2	0.0	0.0	0.0	0.0	0.0	SQUIRE REASSURANCE CO LLC
1,906.5	13,207.3 (*)	0.5	1.9	50.9	3.6	0.2	40.2	0.0	0.2	4.2	0.0	● STANDARD INS CO
46.6	493.5	-0.5	0.6	73.9	2.4	17.0	5.5	0.0	0.0	1.0	0.2	● STANDARD LIFE & ACCIDENT INS CO
5.8	27.3	4.3	0.2	60.7	5.1	0.0	24.7	0.0	0.7	4.3	0.0	STANDARD LIFE & CAS INS CO
42.5	264.2	4.8	0.0	50.6	1.0	0.0	43.6	0.0	0.0	0.0	0.0	● STANDARD LIFE INS CO OF NY
42.7	211.3 (*)	1.7	1.4	71.9	0.1	12.4	0.0	0.0	0.0	5.8	12.8	● STANDARD SECURITY LIFE INS CO OF NY
89.6	47.3	10.7	0.0	68.2	2.0	2.3	0.0	0.0	7.9	1.0	0.0	● STARMOUNT LIFE INS CO
--	--	--	--	--	--	--	--	--	--	--	--	STARVED ROCK LIFE INS CO
0.0	8.3 (*)	0.4	0.0	70.6	0.0	0.0	0.0	0.0	0.0	0.0	29.0	STATE FARM HEALTH INS CO
124.0	2,513.1	-0.1	21.7	70.5	0.6	0.0	0.0	0.0	0.0	6.5	0.7	● STATE FARM LIFE & ACCIDENT ASR CO
2,715.9	63,813.9	0.0	19.3	56.1	0.4	5.2	9.1	0.0	0.0	9.2	2.9	● STATE FARM LIFE INS CO
362.0	6,019.4	0.3	20.3	68.4	2.6	0.5	7.5	0.0	0.0	0.5	0.0	● STATE LIFE INS CO
--	--	--	--	--	--	--	--	--	--	--	--	STATE LIFE INS FUND
11.0	263.6	2.3	18.3	52.2	1.7	1.8	10.3	0.0	4.4	9.2	5.0	● STATE MUTUAL INS CO
6.8	14.7	14.0	13.6	61.9	0.0	10.4	0.0	0.0	0.0	0.1	0.0	STERLING INVESTORS LIFE INS CO
--	--	--	--	--	--	--	--	--	--	--	--	STERLING LIFE INS CO
0.0	1,370.4	0.1	0.0	84.5	3.4	0.7	6.4	0.0	0.0	5.1	4.2	STRUCTURED ANNUITY RE CO
167.6	403.0	0.0	38.5	46.5	1.1	0.3	11.8	0.0	0.0	2.0	0.0	● SUN LIFE & HEALTH INS CO
2,605.6	16,977.4 (*)	-0.2	7.5	56.6	1.9	5.0	15.9	0.1	6.6	3.7	1.5	● SUN LIFE ASR CO OF CANADA
3.6	332.2	-0.1	11.1	67.5	2.3	0.8	15.8	0.0	0.0	2.5	0.0	● SUNSET LIFE INS CO OF AMERICA
7.6	168.0	1.2	8.4	78.2	7.7	3.6	0.0	0.3	0.4	0.3	0.0	SUPERIOR FUNERAL & LIFE INS CO
6.2	8.7	43.4	4.3	44.4	0.0	8.0	0.0	0.0	0.0	0.0	0.0	SURENCY LIFE & HEALTH INS CO
0.7	10.4	11.4	0.0	57.2	10.6	15.8	0.0	0.0	0.9	4.1	0.0	SURETY LIFE & CASUALTY INS CO
0.0	19.3	-9.5	0.0	96.9	0.0	0.0	0.0	0.0	12.5	0.0	0.0	SURETY LIFE INS CO
7.0	22.7	20.2	0.0	50.6	8.4	20.8	0.0	0.0	0.0	0.0	5.6	SWBC LIFE INS CO
1,145.8	10,793.4	-0.2	15.4	68.7	4.3	0.1	6.8	0.0	0.0	4.9	5.8	● SWISS RE LIFE & HEALTH AMER INC
2,480.0	25,867.1	0.4	11.5	62.4	3.9	3.2	17.0	0.0	0.0	1.1	0.5	● SYMETRA LIFE INS CO
0.1	16.5	3.7	69.1	26.1	0.0	0.0	0.0	0.0	0.0	1.1	0.0	SYMETRA NATIONAL LIFE INS CO
0.6	15.0	3.1	52.8	25.8	0.0	0.0	0.0	0.0	14.2	4.1	0.0	T J M LIFE INS CO
7,304.9	234,718.0	0.2	28.7	42.7	5.9	1.4	8.1	0.0	0.8	11.8	9.4	● TEACHERS INS & ANNUITY ASN OF AM
104.4	1,997.3	0.3	0.0	61.1	8.5	27.5	0.2	0.0	0.8	1.7	23.4	● TENNESSEE FARMERS LIFE INS CO
0.2	5.6	1.9	0.9	90.6	5.9	0.5	0.0	0.0	0.0	0.2	0.0	TEXAS DIRECTORS LIFE INS CO
120.6	1,040.9	1.3	36.8	51.2	3.4	1.3	0.0	0.0	0.2	5.9	0.0	● TEXAS LIFE INS CO
10.6	50.9	29.3	44.8	22.9	0.0	0.1	0.0	0.0	1.6	1.3	0.0	TEXAS SERVICE LIFE INS CO
--	--	--	--	--	--	--	--	--	--	--	--	THRIVENT FINANCIAL FOR LUTHERANS
76.3	1,976.4	2.0	27.9	61.1	7.6	0.0	0.0	0.0	0.0	0.9	0.8	● THRIVENT LIFE INS CO
309.9	5,437.6	0.2	8.3	89.8	1.1	0.0	0.0	0.0	0.0	0.5	0.0	● TIAA-CREF LIFE INS CO
9.8	600.0	-16.4	12.8	95.2	1.5	5.0	0.0	0.0	1.8	0.1	0.0	● TIME INS CO
--	--	--	--	--	--	--	--	--	--	--	--	TIPPECANOE LIFE INS CO
2.2	6.9	16.6	2.2	37.2	0.0	20.1	23.9	0.0	0.0	0.0	0.0	TOWN & COUNTRY LIFE INS CO
1.8	7.0	83.6	0.0	16.4	0.0	0.0	0.0	0.0	0.0	0.0	0.0	TPM LIFE INS CO
0.9	18.8 (*)	27.8	0.0	40.6	0.0	24.4	0.0	0.0	2.9	0.0	23.5	TRANS CITY LIFE INS CO
30.4	62.8	32.6	23.5	27.3	4.3	1.6	0.0	0.0	10.4	0.3	0.0	● TRANS OCEANIC LIFE INS CO

● Bullets denote a more detailed analysis is available in Section II.
(*) Asset category percentages do not add up to 100%

INSURANCE COMPANY NAME	DOM. STATE	RATING	TOTAL ASSETS ($MIL)	CAPITAL & SURPLUS ($MIL)	RISK ADJUSTED CAPITAL RATIO 1	RISK ADJUSTED CAPITAL RATIO 2	CAPITAL-IZATION INDEX (PTS)	INVEST. SAFETY INDEX (PTS)	PROFIT-ABILITY INDEX (PTS)	LIQUIDITY INDEX (PTS)	STAB. INDEX (PTS)	STABILITY FACTORS
TRANS WORLD ASR CO	CA	B	350.2	82.6	2.36	1.80	8.2	5.9	8.3	6.5	6.1	DI
TRANS-WESTERN LIFE INS CO	TX	U (2)	0.5	0.5	2.19	1.81	8.0	9.8	4.0	10.0	4.2	F
TRANSAMERICA ADVISORS LIFE INS CO	AR	B-	8535.9	680.4	8.35	4.17	10.0	7.4	4.6	6.8	3.9	T
TRANSAMERICA FINANCIAL LIFE INS CO	NY	B	32355.4	1168.1	3.10	1.50	7.8	5.3	6.1	9.3	6.1	AI
TRANSAMERICA LIFE INS CO	IA	B	129413.0	5862.9	1.68	1.11	7.2	6.1	4.7	7.3	4.5	FIT
TRANSAMERICA PREMIER LIFE INS CO	IA	C+	43239.2	1436.1	1.28	0.74	5.4	4.4	6.6	6.4	3.3	CIT
TRINITY LIFE INS CO	OK	D-	166.9	10.8	0.61	0.43	2.2	2.0	7.1	0.7	0.9	CDIL
TRIPLE S VIDA INC	PR	B- (3)	572.3	64.9	1.12	0.74	5.2	4.7	7.8	3.9	5.2	CIL
TRIPLE-S BLUE II	PR	D- (5)	--	--	--	--	--	--	--	--	--	Z
TRUSTMARK INS CO	IL	B+	1430.6	290.6	2.82	1.58	7.9	4.9	5.8	7.2	6.8	I
TRUSTMARK LIFE INS CO	IL	B+	325.4	169.5	6.29	4.24	10.0	6.4	7.3	6.9	5.4	DFIT
TRUSTMARK LIFE INS CO OF NEW YORK	NY	B	8.5	7.5	3.48	3.13	10.0	9.2	2.0	9.0	5.3	DGT
UBS LIFE INS CO USA	CA	U (2)	41.3	39.8	6.85	6.17	10.0	9.1	7.2	7.0	6.3	DT
UNICARE LIFE & HEALTH INS CO	IN	B-	300.3	78.2	2.10	1.55	7.8	3.8	6.2	6.7	4.1	IT
UNIFIED LIFE INS CO	TX	B	184.2	24.1	1.91	1.19	7.3	4.8	6.4	5.4	6.3	FIL
UNIMERICA INS CO	WI	B	443.4	159.5	1.94	1.55	6.2	8.4	8.3	6.6	5.6	AD
UNIMERICA LIFE INS CO OF NY	NY	B	39.1	21.6	4.30	3.87	10.0	8.5	7.5	9.1	5.5	A
UNION FIDELITY LIFE INS CO	KS	D+	19529.4	495.1	0.98	0.50	4.8	2.7	1.7	8.3	2.7	CFI
UNION LABOR LIFE INS CO	MD	B-	3272.1	82.1	1.58	1.10	7.2	6.4	3.1	7.0	5.0	F
UNION NATIONAL LIFE INS CO	LA	B	19.6	15.3	4.90	2.45	8.0	8.9	8.8	10.0	5.6	A
UNION SECURITY INS CO	KS	B	3119.7	415.0	5.03	2.97	10.0	5.4	6.3	5.5	4.8	AFIT
UNION SECURITY LIFE INS CO OF NY	NY	B+	88.0	65.4	7.09	6.38	10.0	7.5	5.9	7.3	5.0	AFT
UNITED AMERICAN INS CO	NE	B-	1598.2	159.3	1.16	0.84	5.7	6.2	6.0	5.8	4.9	T
UNITED ASR LIFE INS CO	TX	D-	2.2	0.9	1.18	1.06	7.1	9.5	1.8	7.2	1.0	AD
UNITED BENEFIT LIFE INS CO	OH	U (2)	3.0	3.0	2.98	2.69	8.0	9.6	2.7	10.0	3.9	DFT
UNITED FARM FAMILY LIFE INS CO	IN	A	2234.9	310.9	3.25	1.93	8.4	6.9	6.0	5.8	7.4	I
UNITED FIDELITY LIFE INS CO	TX	C	741.5	441.0	0.73	0.71	4.7	3.4	6.9	6.8	4.4	CDI
UNITED FUNERAL BENEFIT LIFE INS CO	OK	D	46.9	6.4	0.88	0.73	4.8	7.1	5.8	6.8	1.4	AD
UNITED FUNERAL DIR BENEFIT LIC	TX	D-	116.9	5.8	0.47	0.37	1.4	1.7	7.2	5.6	1.2	CIT
UNITED HEALTHCARE INS CO	CT	C	15432.2	4212.0	0.81	0.68	4.4	6.6	8.7	1.8	3.8	CL
UNITED HERITAGE LIFE INS CO	ID	B	549.7	60.4	2.53	1.25	7.4	4.6	8.1	5.0	5.7	IL
UNITED HOME LIFE INS CO	IN	B	86.1	20.1	2.55	2.29	8.9	7.6	5.9	6.4	6.3	D
UNITED INS CO OF AMERICA	IL	B-	3704.1	423.4	1.64	0.96	6.7	4.4	6.2	5.6	5.3	AI
UNITED LIFE INS CO	IA	B	1532.7	138.7	2.71	1.43	7.6	6.2	4.7	5.6	4.9	AFIT
UNITED NATIONAL LIFE INS CO OF AM	IL	C	21.7	4.5	0.77	0.58	3.6	8.0	6.9	7.6	3.5	AC
UNITED OF OMAHA LIFE INS CO	NE	B	20032.6	1300.3	1.71	0.99	6.9	5.1	5.6	6.4	5.4	I
UNITED SECURITY ASR CO OF PA	PA	E (3)	154.9	4.9	0.60	0.41	1.9	0.6	1.0	6.8	1.7	CDI
UNITED STATES LIFE INS CO IN NYC	NY	B	29018.5	1988.5	2.59	1.27	7.4	5.1	7.9	6.0	5.8	AI
UNITED TEACHER ASSOCIATES INS CO	TX	C	1071.3	57.7	1.17	0.73	5.3	4.0	4.2	7.2	4.1	GIT
UNITED WORLD LIFE INS CO	NE	B+	122.6	50.0	4.84	2.05	8.6	7.6	5.3	7.0	6.7	A
UNITEDHEALTHCARE LIFE INS CO	WI	C	560.0	130.7	1.26	1.00	5.6	8.3	2.6	5.5	3.8	FGT
UNITY FINANCIAL LIFE INS CO	OH	C-	217.3	12.8	1.39	1.10	7.2	5.0	2.9	6.6	3.2	DI
UNIVANTAGE INS CO	UT	U (2)	1.9	1.9	2.74	2.47	8.0	9.6	4.1	10.0	4.3	D
UNIVERSAL FIDELITY LIFE INS CO	OK	D	10.9	4.3	1.57	1.28	7.4	6.4	2.9	5.1	1.7	T
UNIVERSAL GUARANTY LIFE INS CO	OH	C+	338.1	41.2	1.45	0.83	5.7	2.9	7.1	5.3	4.8	CDFI
UNIVERSAL LIFE INS CO	PR	B	1017.4	61.4	2.45	1.28	7.4	4.6	9.0	9.6	5.4	ACDI
UNIVERSAL UNDERWRITERS LIFE INS CO	KS	B-	156.6	27.7	2.95	2.65	9.5	7.8	3.0	6.1	5.1	AD
UNUM INS CO	ME	C	57.9	44.3	6.80	4.49	8.0	5.7	2.2	10.0	3.8	A
UNUM LIFE INS CO OF AMERICA	ME	C+	20748.9	1559.4	2.19	1.15	7.2	3.6	6.7	7.0	4.8	AI
US ALLIANCE LIFE & SECURITY CO	KS	D-	8.8	2.5	0.87	0.78	5.2	4.6	1.6	6.3	1.1	CEGIT
US FINANCIAL LIFE INS CO	OH	B	600.5	93.5	3.56	1.92	8.4	7.4	6.2	6.2	6.3	FT
USA INS CO	MS	C-	3.4	2.6	2.38	2.15	8.7	4.2	9.0	8.6	2.0	D

See Page 27 for explanation of footnotes and Page 28 for explanation of stability factors.
Arrows denote recent upgrades ▲ or downgrades▼ (see Section VI for explanations)

56

www.weissratings.com

NET PREMIUM ($MIL)	IN-VESTED ASSETS ($MIL)	% OF INVESTED ASSETS IN:									INVEST. IN AFFIL	INSURANCE COMPANY NAME
		CASH	CMO & STRUCT. SECS.	OTH.INV. GRADE BONDS	NON-INV. GRADE BONDS	CMMON & PREF. STOCK	MORT IN GOOD STAND.	NON-PERF. MORT.	REAL ESTATE	OTHER INVEST-MENTS		
5.7	345.4	3.1	0.0	73.9	2.3	8.4	7.2	0.0	4.1	1.1	15.2 ●	TRANS WORLD ASR CO
0.0	0.4	51.3	0.0	48.7	0.0	0.0	0.0	0.0	0.0	0.0	0.0	TRANS-WESTERN LIFE INS CO
3.4	2,667.7 (*)	-0.3	7.0	50.3	2.7	0.3	3.2	0.0	0.0	28.0	0.9 ●	TRANSAMERICA ADVISORS LIFE INS CO
2,975.5	8,951.5 (*)	-0.3	15.2	57.0	6.0	0.0	10.6	0.0	0.0	5.1	3.7 ●	TRANSAMERICA FINANCIAL LIFE INS CO
6,249.0	51,304.7 (*)	0.0	11.7	54.3	4.3	4.3	10.5	0.0	0.3	6.5	8.1 ●	TRANSAMERICA LIFE INS CO
1,587.1	19,359.2 (*)	-0.3	16.4	57.0	5.0	0.6	8.7	0.0	1.2	8.1	3.6 ●	TRANSAMERICA PREMIER LIFE INS CO
14.1	153.2	1.9	0.2	59.9	5.3	7.5	22.9	0.4	1.3	0.5	8.0	TRINITY LIFE INS CO
120.2	503.1	1.0	10.1	73.5	2.1	11.9	0.0	0.0	0.0	1.4	1.7 ●	TRIPLE S VIDA INC
--	--	--	--	--	--	--	--	--	--	--	--	TRIPLE-S BLUE II
159.3	1,377.2	0.3	29.2	44.1	7.6	9.9	1.9	0.0	1.7	5.4	0.0 ●	TRUSTMARK INS CO
80.2	300.0	-1.3	10.7	72.6	8.7	7.9	0.0	0.0	0.0	1.4	0.0 ●	TRUSTMARK LIFE INS CO
1.0	8.4	4.5	11.8	83.7	0.0	0.0	0.0	0.0	0.0	0.0	0.0	TRUSTMARK LIFE INS CO OF NEW YORK
0.0	39.6	6.8	0.0	93.2	0.0	0.0	0.0	0.0	0.0	0.0	0.0	UBS LIFE INS CO USA
131.7	258.5 (*)	1.1	0.9	80.3	14.0	0.4	0.0	0.0	0.0	0.0	0.0 ●	UNICARE LIFE & HEALTH INS CO
30.5	162.0	3.2	23.0	64.5	3.6	0.0	0.1	0.0	0.0	5.6	0.0	UNIFIED LIFE INS CO
367.0	374.1	-0.9	16.8	84.1	0.0	0.0	0.0	0.0	0.0	0.0	0.0 ●	UNIMERICA INS CO
3.3	36.5	9.4	27.8	62.8	0.0	0.0	0.0	0.0	0.0	0.0	0.0	UNIMERICA LIFE INS CO OF NY
132.7	18,972.1	0.3	12.7	76.7	3.5	0.4	4.3	0.0	0.0	2.1	1.1 ●	UNION FIDELITY LIFE INS CO
68.3	315.9	-0.1	24.0	61.2	0.0	6.8	6.1	0.0	0.0	1.9	6.8 ●	UNION LABOR LIFE INS CO
0.0	20.1	28.9	0.0	71.1	0.0	0.0	0.0	0.0	0.0	0.0	0.0	UNION NATIONAL LIFE INS CO
-1,470.5	2,924.7	-1.0	3.5	71.2	3.4	5.2	14.4	0.0	0.0	3.1	0.9 ●	UNION SECURITY INS CO
-72.5	110.2	-0.7	7.1	71.8	2.1	5.0	14.0	0.0	0.0	0.7	0.0 ●	UNION SECURITY LIFE INS CO OF NY
357.8	1,248.1	1.2	2.9	81.5	5.4	4.5	0.0	0.0	0.0	3.7	6.1 ●	UNITED AMERICAN INS CO
0.3	2.0	17.4	0.0	82.6	0.0	0.0	0.0	0.0	0.0	0.0	0.0	UNITED ASR LIFE INS CO
0.0	3.0	7.3	0.0	92.7	0.0	0.0	0.0	0.0	0.0	0.0	0.0	UNITED BENEFIT LIFE INS CO
68.5	2,133.9	0.5	9.7	64.2	0.0	2.9	16.6	0.1	0.2	5.8	1.5 ●	UNITED FARM FAMILY LIFE INS CO
3.6	748.5	-0.4	8.2	6.7	1.0	77.1	2.2	0.0	0.3	4.8	74.7 ●	UNITED FIDELITY LIFE INS CO
0.9	46.3	5.9	62.5	15.7	0.8	14.3	0.0	0.0	0.0	0.8	12.3	UNITED FUNERAL BENEFIT LIFE INS CO
3.7	110.4	4.9	63.6	22.1	2.7	5.7	0.7	0.0	0.0	0.3	3.7	UNITED FUNERAL DIR BENEFIT LIC
22,650.4	10,270.5	-0.7	16.4	53.9	5.5	23.0	0.0	0.0	0.0	1.9	19.5 ●	UNITED HEALTHCARE INS CO
36.0	527.7	0.4	7.6	76.3	8.0	2.4	2.1	0.0	2.0	1.4	0.0 ●	UNITED HERITAGE LIFE INS CO
10.3	67.3	2.8	11.7	78.4	0.0	3.2	0.0	0.0	0.0	3.9	0.0	UNITED HOME LIFE INS CO
183.8	3,427.8	1.1	3.8	61.5	9.1	5.5	0.0	0.0	4.4	14.8	3.5 ●	UNITED INS CO OF AMERICA
71.2	1,510.2	0.5	18.1	76.4	2.1	1.3	0.3	0.0	0.0	1.4	0.0 ●	UNITED LIFE INS CO
9.6	18.1	2.2	32.5	56.4	0.0	0.0	8.5	0.0	0.0	0.3	0.0	UNITED NATIONAL LIFE INS CO OF AM
1,930.9	15,804.9	2.6	22.4	54.1	3.9	1.2	11.6	0.0	0.3	3.0	1.1 ●	UNITED OF OMAHA LIFE INS CO
24.7	147.2	0.2	4.7	89.8	5.2	0.0	0.0	0.0	0.0	0.1	0.0	UNITED SECURITY ASR CO OF PA
1,107.1	23,035.8	-0.2	28.0	49.9	4.8	0.1	9.9	0.1	0.1	7.1	1.3 ●	UNITED STATES LIFE INS CO IN NYC
34.7	1,024.8	3.7	22.1	64.5	3.6	4.6	0.0	0.0	0.0	1.6	2.4 ●	UNITED TEACHER ASSOCIATES INS CO
0.6	125.2 (*)	7.0	24.4	62.9	0.8	0.0	0.0	0.0	0.0	0.5	0.0 ●	UNITED WORLD LIFE INS CO
486.6	389.6	6.7	7.8	85.5	0.0	0.0	0.0	0.0	0.0	0.0	0.0 ●	UNITEDHEALTHCARE LIFE INS CO
23.3	201.6	0.0	4.5	95.5	0.0	0.0	0.0	0.0	0.0	0.1	0.0	UNITY FINANCIAL LIFE INS CO
0.0	1.9	7.1	0.0	92.9	0.0	0.0	0.0	0.0	0.0	0.0	0.0	UNIVANTAGE INS CO
2.7	8.0	14.7	1.6	57.1	1.7	9.7	0.0	0.0	13.8	1.5	0.7	UNIVERSAL FIDELITY LIFE INS CO
3.6	328.3	2.9	0.0	52.7	4.8	14.1	3.6	0.9	7.3	13.8	6.4 ●	UNIVERSAL GUARANTY LIFE INS CO
52.0	371.3 (*)	2.8	12.3	70.9	4.5	4.1	0.0	0.0	0.0	1.4	0.0 ●	UNIVERSAL LIFE INS CO
3.1	152.3	0.2	40.5	54.0	0.2	0.0	0.0	0.0	0.0	5.1	0.0 ●	UNIVERSAL UNDERWRITERS LIFE INS CO
0.0	53.0	2.7	18.1	76.6	0.0	0.0	0.0	0.0	0.0	2.7	0.0 ●	UNUM INS CO
1,674.4	19,528.7	0.0	8.7	73.6	10.6	0.3	4.2	0.0	0.4	2.2	0.2 ●	UNUM LIFE INS CO OF AMERICA
4.2	7.1	11.8	21.2	47.6	11.7	7.7	0.0	0.0	0.0	0.0	0.0	US ALLIANCE LIFE & SECURITY CO
17.9	519.0	-1.2	0.2	93.6	1.9	0.8	0.0	0.0	0.0	4.7	0.0 ●	US FINANCIAL LIFE INS CO
0.2	2.8	14.5	0.0	0.0	0.0	0.0	54.2	0.0	29.1	2.2	5.0	USA INS CO

● Bullets denote a more detailed analysis is available in Section II.
(*) Asset category percentages do not add up to 100%

INSURANCE COMPANY NAME	DOM. STATE	RATING	TOTAL ASSETS ($MIL)	CAPITAL & SURPLUS ($MIL)	RISK ADJUSTED CAPITAL RATIO 1	RISK ADJUSTED CAPITAL RATIO 2	CAPITAL-IZATION INDEX (PTS)	INVEST. SAFETY INDEX (PTS)	PROFIT-ABILITY INDEX (PTS)	LIQUIDITY INDEX (PTS)	STAB. INDEX (PTS)	STABILITY FACTOR
USA LIFE ONE INS CO OF INDIANA	IN	D+	36.4	14.1	2.71	2.43	9.1	7.9	2.3	6.7	2.5	DF
USAA LIFE INS CO	TX	A	23536.5	2295.0	3.80	2.02	8.5	6.7	8.9	5.7	7.4	AI
USAA LIFE INS CO OF NEW YORK	NY	B+	720.8	73.3	2.48	1.28	7.4	5.2	8.5	4.8	6.6	IL
USABLE LIFE	AR	B+	482.3	224.6	2.13	1.57	7.9	6.3	8.6	6.5	6.4	I
USIC LIFE INS CO	PR	B	9.8	7.9	1.61	1.39	7.6	4.4	5.7	8.3	4.9	AGIT
UTIC INS CO	AL	B	79.1	20.3	2.66	2.04	8.6	7.2	7.2	8.2	4.6	AGT
VANTIS LIFE INS CO	CT	B-	252.8	83.5	5.10	3.07	4.0	4.9	5.5	6.6	4.6	FIT
VANTISLIFE INS CO OF NEW YORK	NY	B-	11.8	5.7	2.25	2.03	8.5	8.0	2.0	6.8	4.7	AD
VARIABLE ANNUITY LIFE INS CO	TX	B	75558.9	3043.9	2.46	1.21	7.3	5.2	6.1	5.8	5.8	AIT
VERSANT LIFE INS CO	MS	B-	6.0	4.6	2.73	2.45	9.2	8.7	6.6	9.6	4.3	AD
VOYA INS & ANNUITY CO	IA	B-	64700.6	1773.5	1.64	0.82	6.0	4.4	6.2	7.5	4.8	IT
VOYA RETIREMENT INS & ANNUITY CO	CT	B+	89930.9	1969.4	2.49	1.21	7.3	5.6	6.4	9.1	6.5	AI
WASHINGTON NATIONAL INS CO	IN	D+	4870.3	329.2	1.70	0.92	6.4	4.7	6.5	6.4	2.7	AIT
WEA INS CORP	WI	C	635.3	149.4	1.63	1.14	7.2	4.5	1.4	6.3	3.7	DF
WEST COAST LIFE INS CO	NE	C+	5058.3	376.2	2.38	1.16	7.2	4.9	2.6	5.8	4.6	AGI
WESTERN & SOUTHERN LIFE INS CO	OH	B	9959.3	4623.0	2.02	1.68	8.0	3.4	7.8	7.0	5.7	AI
▼ WESTERN AMERICAN LIFE INS CO	TX	D	29.0	2.6	0.58	0.53	3.2	5.4	5.1	5.1	2.2	ACD
WESTERN CATHOLIC UNION	IL	U	--	--	--	--	--	--	--	--	--	Z
WESTERN UNITED LIFE ASR CO	WA	B-	1142.3	71.8	1.64	0.78	6.0	3.2	8.5	4.3	4.8	CILT
WESTERN-SOUTHERN LIFE ASR CO	OH	B	12485.6	1038.4	2.22	1.17	7.3	5.2	6.6	5.5	5.1	AFIT
WICHITA NATIONAL LIFE INS CO	OK	C-	17.1	8.1	2.54	2.29	8.9	8.9	2.9	9.5	3.3	DF
WILCAC LIFE INS CO	IL	C	2331.2	146.2	3.11	1.69	8.0	6.2	5.2	10.0	2.6	FT
WILCO LIFE INS CO	IN	C	3299.2	139.5	1.30	0.68	5.5	3.7	4.7	4.6	3.6	CFILT
WILLIAM PENN LIFE INS CO OF NEW YORK	NY	C-	1167.3	154.6	3.24	1.52	7.8	3.8	1.7	6.4	3.1	GT
WILLIAMS PROGRESSIVE LIFE & ACC I C	LA	E	11.1	0.3	0.15	0.13	0.0	1.6	0.8	6.0	0.0	CFI
WILTON REASSURANCE CO	MN	C+	2860.6	676.5	0.75	0.66	4.3	4.3	7.9	6.7	4.2	ACIT
WILTON REASSURANCE LIFE CO OF NY	NY	B-	899.2	96.1	2.77	1.40	7.6	6.1	3.7	5.6	5.3	AFT
WINDSOR LIFE INS CO	TX	B-	3.2	2.9	2.72	2.44	9.2	7.8	4.2	10.0	3.7	ADF
XL LIFE INS & ANNUITY CO	IL	U (2)	16.7	16.5	10.67	9.60	8.0	9.6	4.1	10.0	6.1	A
ZALE LIFE INS CO	AZ	B-	12.0	9.6	3.73	3.36	10.0	6.7	7.6	10.0	4.9	AT
ZURICH AMERICAN LIFE INS CO	IL	C	12103.8	112.7	1.78	1.00	3.0	8.0	1.6	7.1	3.7	FGT
ZURICH AMERICAN LIFE INS CO OF NY	NY	C+	82.8	20.8	3.01	2.71	9.6	9.5	3.8	10.0	4.7	ADEG

See Page 27 for explanation of footnotes and Page 28 for explanation of stability factors.
Arrows denote recent upgrades ▲ or downgrades▼ (see Section VI for explanations)

58

www.weissratings.com

NET PREMIUM ($MIL)	IN-VESTED ASSETS ($MIL)	% OF INVESTED ASSETS IN:									INVEST. IN AFFIL	INSURANCE COMPANY NAME
		CASH	CMO & STRUCT. SECS.	OTH.INV. GRADE BONDS	NON-INV. GRADE BONDS	CMMON & PREF. STOCK	MORT IN GOOD STAND.	NON-PERF. MORT.	REAL ESTATE	OTHER INVEST-MENTS		
0.4	35.9	3.8	0.4	91.4	2.2	0.7	0.0	0.0	0.0	1.5	0.0	USA LIFE ONE INS CO OF INDIANA
864.3	22,249.8	0.0	20.7	71.9	3.2	1.2	1.7	0.0	0.0	1.2	0.4 ●	USAA LIFE INS CO
22.0	680.3	0.2	16.9	77.6	3.6	0.7	0.0	0.0	0.0	0.9	0.0 ●	USAA LIFE INS CO OF NEW YORK
301.2	409.7	1.0	11.8	69.3	1.4	9.9	2.7	0.0	1.6	2.2	0.7 ●	USABLE LIFE
2.1	6.2	36.2	0.0	45.1	9.7	9.0	0.0	0.0	0.0	0.0	0.0	USIC LIFE INS CO
11.5	67.0	6.1	4.6	85.8	0.0	3.6	0.0	0.0	0.0	0.0	0.0	UTIC INS CO
13.3	187.0	0.9	13.4	65.5	8.0	5.0	0.2	0.0	3.2	3.9	3.2 ●	VANTIS LIFE INS CO
2.0	10.2	1.8	9.1	87.5	0.0	1.2	0.0	0.0	0.0	0.4	0.0	VANTISLIFE INS CO OF NEW YORK
2,194.3	41,548.9	-0.1	39.4	36.1	4.6	0.3	10.0	0.2	0.1	8.7	9.8 ●	VARIABLE ANNUITY LIFE INS CO
0.5	5.7 (*)	7.3	0.0	88.2	0.0	0.0	0.0	0.0	0.0	0.0	0.0	VERSANT LIFE INS CO
1,149.4	28,736.5 (*)	2.2	11.8	67.1	3.2	0.4	11.2	0.0	0.1	1.1	0.3 ●	VOYA INS & ANNUITY CO
5,822.1	26,844.6 (*)	1.8	11.8	62.6	4.1	0.4	13.9	0.0	0.3	3.2	1.4 ●	VOYA RETIREMENT INS & ANNUITY CO
328.8	4,659.0	1.2	23.2	59.6	4.2	2.2	5.8	0.0	1.1	2.8	1.2 ●	WASHINGTON NATIONAL INS CO
248.4	634.4	0.8	23.7	55.4	0.0	20.1	0.0	0.0	0.0	0.0	0.0 ●	WEA INS CORP
7.3	4,522.7	0.9	5.0	75.5	4.0	2.6	11.3	0.0	0.0	0.8	0.0 ●	WEST COAST LIFE INS CO
121.6	8,516.9	-0.2	9.7	31.2	3.0	37.6	0.5	0.0	0.4	17.8	35.3 ●	WESTERN & SOUTHERN LIFE INS CO
1.2	28.6	0.1	62.9	35.9	0.3	0.1	0.0	0.0	0.0	0.8	0.0	WESTERN AMERICAN LIFE INS CO
--	--	--	--	--	--	--	--	--	--	--	--	WESTERN CATHOLIC UNION
88.5	1,081.1	0.6	27.3	67.0	2.9	0.7	0.0	0.0	1.4	0.1	0.0 ●	WESTERN UNITED LIFE ASR CO
330.5	11,734.7	0.4	32.3	48.1	7.3	2.4	6.7	0.0	0.0	2.4	1.8 ●	WESTERN-SOUTHERN LIFE ASR CO
1.7	17.0	78.4	3.0	0.2	0.0	11.9	0.0	0.0	1.3	5.3	11.9	WICHITA NATIONAL LIFE INS CO
0.0	1,962.3	0.8	20.4	72.4	3.2	2.9	0.0	0.0	0.0	0.3	0.0 ●	WILCAC LIFE INS CO
48.6	3,353.1	0.4	31.0	58.6	1.8	0.7	2.4	0.0	0.0	4.9	0.0 ●	WILCO LIFE INS CO
43.5	1,103.1	-1.0	9.1	55.6	12.9	0.0	20.6	0.0	0.0	2.9	0.0 ●	WILLIAM PENN LIFE INS CO OF NEW YORK
0.7	10.9	18.1	3.6	23.8	0.7	13.4	32.7	1.5	2.4	3.8	1.5	WILLIAMS PROGRESSIVE LIFE & ACC I C
87.7	2,589.9	0.5	25.3	40.3	2.1	24.4	0.0	0.0	0.0	7.3	23.0 ●	WILTON REASSURANCE CO
8.5	884.5 (*)	1.1	38.0	53.5	2.5	1.4	0.0	0.0	0.0	2.0	0.0 ●	WILTON REASSURANCE LIFE CO OF NY
0.0	3.0	3.2	0.0	93.5	3.3	0.0	0.0	0.0	0.0	0.0	0.0	WINDSOR LIFE INS CO
0.0	16.5	4.0	0.0	96.0	0.0	0.0	0.0	0.0	0.0	0.0	0.0	XL LIFE INS & ANNUITY CO
0.0	11.6	3.7	0.1	82.0	0.0	13.1	0.0	0.0	0.0	1.1	0.0	ZALE LIFE INS CO
12.5	512.2	1.4	28.8	55.4	0.4	4.1	0.0	0.0	0.0	9.9	4.1 ●	ZURICH AMERICAN LIFE INS CO
29.4	22.3	4.2	0.0	95.6	0.0	0.0	0.0	0.0	0.0	0.2	0.0	ZURICH AMERICAN LIFE INS CO OF NY

● Bullets denote a more detailed analysis is available in Section II.
(*) Asset category percentages do not add up to 100%

Section II

Analysis of Largest Companies

A summary analysis of those

U.S. Life and Annuity Insurers

with capital in excess of $25 million.

Companies are listed in alphabetical order.

Section II Contents

This section contains rating factors, historical data and general information on each of the largest life and health insurers. Companies with capital and surplus of less than $25 million, Blue Cross Blue Shield plans and companies lacking year-end data do not appear in this section. You can find information on these firms in Section I.

1. Safety Rating

The current rating appears to the right of the company name. Our ratings are designed to distinguish levels of insolvency risk and are measured on a scale from A (Excellent) to F (Failed). Highly rated companies are, in our opinion, less likely to experience financial difficulties than lower rated firms. See *About Weiss Safety Ratings* for more information.

2. Major Rating Factors

A synopsis of the key indexes and sub-factors that have most influenced the rating of a particular insurer. Items are presented in the approximate order of their importance to the rating. There may be additional factors which have influenced the rating but do not appear due to space limitations or confidentiality agreements with insurers.

3. Other Rating Factors

A summary of those Weiss Ratings indexes that were not included as Major Rating Factors, but nevertheless, may have had some impact on the final grade.

4. Principal Business

The major types of policies written by an insurer along with the percentages for each line in relation to the entire book of business, including direct premium and deposit funds (from Exhibit 1 Part 1 of the annual statutory statement). Lines of business written by life, health and annuity insurers are individual life, individual health, individual annuities, group life, group health, group retirement contracts, credit life, credit health and reinsurance. The data used to calculate these amounts are the latest available from the National Association of Insurance Commissioners.

Note: Percentages contained in this column may not agree with similar figures displayed in Section III which are based on net premium after reinsurance.

5. Principal Investments

The major investments in an insurer's portfolio. These include non CMO Bonds (debt obligations which are rated Class 1 through Class 6 based on risk of default), CMOs and other structured securities, which consist primarily of mortgage-backed bonds, real estate, mortgages in good standing, nonperforming mortgages, common and preferred stocks, policy loans (which are loans given to policyholders), miscellaneous investments and cash.

6. Investments in Affiliates
The percentage of bonds, common and preferred stocks and other financial instruments an insurer has invested with affiliated companies. This is not a subcategory of "Principal Investments."

7. Group Affiliation
The name of the group of companies to which a particular insurer belongs.

8. Licensed in
List of the states in which an insurer is licensed to conduct business.

9. Commenced Business
The date when the company first opened for business.

10. Address
The address of an insurer's corporate headquarters. This location may differ from the company's state of domicile.

11. Phone
The telephone number of an insurer's corporate headquarters.

12. Domicile State
The state that has primary regulatory responsibility for this company. You do not have to live in the domicile state to do business with this firm, provided it is registered to do business in your state.

13. NAIC Code
The identification number assigned to an insurer by the National Association of Insurance Commissioners (NAIC).

14. Historical Data
Five years of background data for Weiss Safety Rating, risk-adjusted capital ratios (moderate and severe loss scenarios), total assets, capital (including capital stock and retained earnings), net premium and net income. See the following page for more details on how to read the historical data table.

15. Customized Graph (or Table)
A graph or table depicting one of the company's major strengths or weaknesses. See the following page for more details.

How to Read the Historical Data Table

Data Date:
The quarterly or annual date of the financial statements that provide the source of the data.

RACR#1:
Ratio of the capital resources an insurer currently has to the resources that would be needed to deal with a modest loss scenario.

Total Assets:
Total admitted assets in millions of dollars, including investments and other business assets.

Net Premiums:
The total volume of premium dollars, in millions, retained by an insurer. This figure is equal to direct premiums written plus deposit funds, and reinsurance assumed, less reinsurance ceded.

Data Date	Safety Rating	RACR #1	RACR #2	Total Assets ($mil)	Capital ($mil)	Net Premium ($mil)	Net Income ($mil)
6-16	A	5.60	3.68	211.4	93.5	49.5	1.5
6-15	A	5.34	3.63	200.0	93.5	44.8	1.9
2015	A	5.63	3.67	200.0	93.1	86.9	5.5
2014	A	3.89	2.72	198.5	92.3	151.8	7.3
2013	A	3.92	2.79	186.9	89.9	148.4	6.4
2012	A-	3.43	2.51	187.2	84.4	170.1	6.2
2011	A-	3.49	2.61	174.6	79.7	171.5	6.9

Safety Rating:
Our opinion of the financial risk of an insurer based on data from that time period.

RACR #2:
Ratio of the capital resources an insurer currently has to the resources that would be needed to deal with a severe loss scenario.

Capital:
The equity or net worth of an insurer in millions of dollars.

Net Income:
Profit gained on operations and investments, after expenses and taxes.

Row Descriptions:

Row 1 contains the most recent quarterly data as filed with state regulators and is presented on a year-to-date basis. For example, the figure for third quarter premiums includes premiums received through the third quarter. Row 2 consists of data from the same quarter of the prior year. Compare current quarterly results to those of a year ago.

Row 3 contains data from the most recent annual statutory filing. **Rows 4-7** include data from year-end statements going back four years from the most recent annual filing. Compare current year-end results to those of the previous four years. With the exception of Total Assets and Capital, quarterly data are not comparable with annual data.

Customized Graphs

In the lower right-hand corner of each company section, a customized graph or text block highlights a key factor affecting that company's financial strength. One of fifteen types of information is found, identified by one of the following headings:

Adverse Trends in Operations lists changes in key balance sheet and income statement items which may be leading indicators of deteriorating business performance.

Exposure to Withdrawals Without Penalty answers the question: For each dollar of capital and surplus, how much does the company have in annuity and deposit funds that can be withdrawn by policyholders with minimal or no penalty? The figures do not include the effects of reinsurance or funds subject to withdrawals from cash value life insurance policies.

Group Ratings shows the group name, a composite Weiss Safety Rating for the group, and a list of the largest members with their ratings. The composite Safety Rating is made up of the weighted average, by assets, of the individual ratings of each company in the group (including life/health companies, property/casualty companies or HMOs) plus a factor for the financial strength of the holding company, where applicable.

High Risk Assets as a % of Capital answers the question: For each dollar of capital and surplus, how much does the company have in junk bonds, nonperforming mortgages and repossessed real estate? Accumulations in the Asset Valuation Reserve or AVR, which provide some protection against investment losses, have not been included in the figure for capital. These figures are based on year-end data.

Investment Income Compared to Needs of Reserves answers the question: Is the company earning enough investment income to meet the expectations of actuaries when they priced their policies and set reserve levels? According to state insurance regulators, it would be "unusual" if an insurer were to have less than $1.25 in actual investment income for each dollar of investment income that it projected in its actuarial forecasts. This provides an excess margin of at least 25 cents on the dollar to cover any unexpected decline in income or increase in claims. This graph shows whether or not the company is maintaining the appropriate 25% margin and is based on year-end data.

Junk Bonds as a % of Capital answers the question: For each dollar of capital and surplus, how much does the company have in junk bonds? In addition, it shows a breakdown of the junk bond portfolio by bond rating – BB, B, CCC or in default. Accumulations in the Asset Valuation Reserve or AVR, which provide some protection against investment losses, have not been included in the figure for capital. These figures are based on year-end data.

Net Income History plots operating gains and losses over the most recent five-year period.

Policy Leverage answers the question: To what degree is this insurer capable of handling an unexpected spike in claims? Low leverage indicates low exposure; high leverage is high exposure.

Premium Growth History depicts the change in the insurer's net premiums written. Such changes may be the result of issuing more policies or changes in reinsurance arrangements. In either case, growth rates above 20% per year are considered excessive. "Standard" growth is under 20%; "shrinkage" refers to net declines.

Rating Indexes illustrate the score and range – strong, good, fair or weak – on each of the five Weiss Ratings indexes. The indexes are **capitalization**, **stability**, **investment safety**, **profitability** and **liquidity**.

Risk-Adjusted Capital Ratio #1 answers the question: In each of the past five years, does the insurer have sufficient capital to cover potential losses in its investments and business operations in a *moderate* loss scenario?

Risk-Adjusted Capital Ratio #2 answers the question: In each of the past five years, does the insurer have sufficient capital to cover potential losses in its investments and business operations in a *severe* loss scenario?

Risk-Adjusted Capital Ratios answers these questions for both a moderate loss scenario (RACR #1 shown by the dark bar) and a severe loss scenario (RACR #2, light bar).

4 EVER LIFE INSURANCE COMPANY *

A   Excellent

Major Rating Factors: Good overall results on stability tests (6.1 on a scale of 0 to 10). Strengths that enhance stability include good operational trends and excellent risk diversification. Good quality investment portfolio (5.9) despite mixed results such as: no exposure to mortgages and substantial holdings of BBB bonds but small junk bond holdings. Good liquidity (6.9).

Other Rating Factors: Strong capitalization (10.0) based on excellent risk adjusted capital (severe loss scenario). Excellent profitability (7.4).

Principal Business: Group health insurance (80%), reinsurance (16%), and group life insurance (4%).

Principal Investments: NonCMO investment grade bonds (50%), CMOs and structured securities (27%), noninv. grade bonds (7%), common & preferred stock (6%), and cash (5%).

Investments in Affiliates: None
Group Affiliation: BCS Financial Corp
Licensed in: All states, the District of Columbia and Puerto Rico
Commenced Business: November 1949
Address: 2 Mid America Plaza Suite 200, Oakbrook Terrace, IL 60181
Phone: (312) 951-7700 **Domicile State:** IL **NAIC Code:** 80985

Data Date	Rating	RACR #1	RACR #2	Total Assets ($mil)	Capital ($mil)	Net Premium ($mil)	Net Income ($mil)
6-16	A	5.60	3.68	211.4	93.5	49.5	1.5
6-15	A	5.34	3.63	200.0	93.5	44.8	1.9
2015	A	5.63	3.67	200.0	93.1	86.9	5.5
2014	A	3.89	2.72	198.5	92.3	151.8	7.3
2013	A	3.92	2.79	186.9	89.9	148.4	6.4
2012	A-	3.43	2.51	187.2	84.4	170.1	6.2
2011	A-	3.49	2.61	174.6	79.7	171.5	6.9

Adverse Trends in Operations

Decrease in premium volume from 2014 to 2015 (43%)
Decrease in premium volume from 2012 to 2013 (13%)
Increase in policy surrenders from 2011 to 2012 (33%)

AAA LIFE INSURANCE COMPANY

B   Good

Major Rating Factors: Good quality investment portfolio (6.5 on a scale of 0 to 10) despite mixed results such as: large holdings of BBB rated bonds but moderate junk bond exposure. Good overall profitability (6.5). Excellent expense controls. Good liquidity (6.7) with sufficient resources to handle a spike in claims as well as a significant increase in policy surrenders.

Other Rating Factors: Good overall results on stability tests (6.1) excellent operational trends and excellent risk diversification. Strong capitalization (8.1) based on excellent risk adjusted capital (severe loss scenario).

Principal Business: Individual life insurance (46%), group life insurance (26%), individual annuities (18%), group health insurance (9%), and individual health insurance (1%).

Principal Investments: NonCMO investment grade bonds (69%), CMOs and structured securities (17%), noninv. grade bonds (8%), common & preferred stock (3%), and misc. investments (3%).

Investments in Affiliates: 1%
Group Affiliation: ACLI Acquisition Co
Licensed in: All states except NY, PR
Commenced Business: July 1969
Address: 17900 N Laurel Park Dr, Livonia, MI 48152
Phone: (734) 779-2600 **Domicile State:** MI **NAIC Code:** 71854

Data Date	Rating	RACR #1	RACR #2	Total Assets ($mil)	Capital ($mil)	Net Premium ($mil)	Net Income ($mil)
6-16	B	2.90	1.71	612.8	142.8	57.5	6.7
6-15	B	2.83	1.69	577.9	130.9	56.4	10.3
2015	B	2.91	1.73	614.9	137.0	114.8	17.1
2014	B	2.68	1.61	575.1	122.7	112.2	15.6
2013	B	2.27	1.39	539.2	104.1	119.4	7.2
2012	B	2.19	1.20	502.8	97.5	113.7	5.6
2011	B	2.61	1.49	468.4	87.8	113.6	4.2

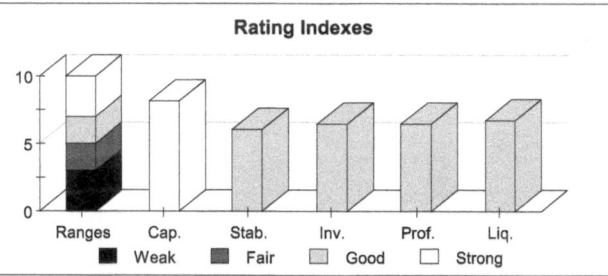

Rating Indexes

ACCORDIA LIFE & ANNUITY COMPANY

C   Fair

Major Rating Factors: Fair current capitalization (4.0 on a scale of 0 to 10) based on mixed results -- excessive policy leverage mitigated by good risk adjusted capital (severe loss scenario) reflecting significant improvement over results in 2013. Fair profitability (4.3) with operating losses during the first six months of 2016. Fair overall results on stability tests (3.7) including negative cash flow from operations for 2015, weak risk adjusted capital in prior years.

Other Rating Factors: Good quality investment portfolio (5.3). Good liquidity (5.8).

Principal Business: Reinsurance (61%) and individual life insurance (39%).

Principal Investments: NonCMO investment grade bonds (46%), CMOs and structured securities (28%), mortgages in good standing (9%), common & preferred stock (5%), and misc. investments (10%).

Investments in Affiliates: 6%
Group Affiliation: Global Atlantic Financial Group
Licensed in: All states except NY, PR
Commenced Business: September 1967
Address: 215 10th St Suite 1100, Des Moines, IA 50309
Phone: (800) 926-7599 **Domicile State:** IA **NAIC Code:** 62200

Data Date	Rating	RACR #1	RACR #2	Total Assets ($mil)	Capital ($mil)	Net Premium ($mil)	Net Income ($mil)
6-16	C	1.27	0.88	7,633.4	681.8	180.9	-41.5
6-15	C-	1.25	0.83	8,064.1	614.3	203.9	8.1
2015	C	1.16	0.80	7,674.9	612.0	-468.0	48.1
2014	C-	1.08	0.74	7,754.8	496.7	438.6	97.4
2013	D	0.64	0.48	7,059.0	382.2	4,725.1	-112.1
2012	U	3.36	3.02	5.7	5.6	0.0	0.7
2011	U	2.58	2.32	17.3	8.2	0.0	0.4

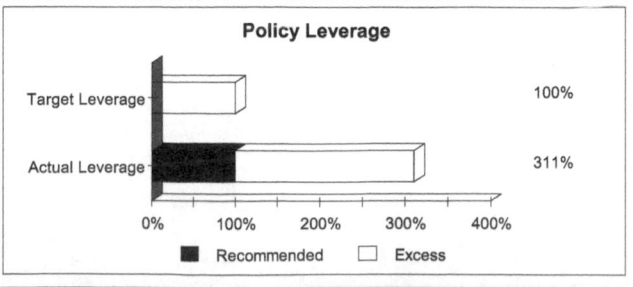

Policy Leverage

ADVANCE INSURANCE COMPANY OF KANSAS *   B+   Good

Major Rating Factors: Good overall results on stability tests (6.8 on a scale of 0 to 10). Stability strengths include excellent operational trends and excellent risk diversification. Fair quality investment portfolio (4.9). Strong capitalization (9.4) based on excellent risk adjusted capital (severe loss scenario). Moreover, capital levels have been consistently high over the last five years.

Other Rating Factors: Excellent profitability (8.4) with operating gains in each of the last five years. Excellent liquidity (7.2).

Principal Business: Group life insurance (55%), group health insurance (33%), and individual life insurance (12%).

Principal Investments: NonCMO investment grade bonds (46%), common & preferred stock (30%), CMOs and structured securities (23%), and cash (1%).

Investments in Affiliates: 2%

Group Affiliation: Blue Cross Blue Shield Kansas

Licensed in: KS

Commenced Business: July 2004

Address: 1133 SW Topeka Blvd, Topeka, KS 66629-0001

Phone: (785) 291-7052 **Domicile State:** KS **NAIC Code:** 12143

Data Date	Rating	RACR #1	RACR #2	Total Assets ($mil)	Capital ($mil)	Net Premium ($mil)	Net Income ($mil)
6-16	B+	3.93	2.61	54.9	46.0	5.4	0.6
6-15	B+	3.68	2.43	53.9	44.8	5.3	1.4
2015	B+	3.91	2.59	54.0	45.3	10.6	2.2
2014	B+	3.64	2.40	53.5	44.0	9.9	2.9
2013	B+	3.51	2.32	51.4	41.5	9.6	1.6
2012	B+	3.78	2.54	47.5	38.9	9.6	0.9
2011	B+	3.98	2.70	44.9	37.9	9.7	1.2

Rating Indexes

(Ranges, Cap., Stab., Inv., Prof., Liq. — Weak, Fair, Good, Strong)

AETNA HEALTH & LIFE INSURANCE COMPANY *   B+   Good

Major Rating Factors: Good overall results on stability tests (6.8 on a scale of 0 to 10) despite excessive premium growth. Other stability subfactors include excellent operational trends and excellent risk diversification. Good quality investment portfolio (6.0) despite substantial holdings of BBB bonds in addition to moderate junk bond exposure. Exposure to mortgages is significant, but the mortgage default rate has been low. Good overall profitability (6.1) although investment income, in comparison to reserve requirements, is below regulatory standards.

Other Rating Factors: Strong capitalization (7.6) based on excellent risk adjusted capital (severe loss scenario). Excellent liquidity (7.4).

Principal Business: Reinsurance (91%) and individual health insurance (9%).

Principal Investments: NonCMO investment grade bonds (62%), CMOs and structured securities (13%), mortgages in good standing (12%), and noninv. grade bonds (5%).

Investments in Affiliates: 4%

Group Affiliation: Aetna Inc

Licensed in: All states except PR

Commenced Business: October 1971

Address: 151 Farmington Avenue, Hartford, IL 06156-0417

Phone: (708) 245-4001 **Domicile State:** CT **NAIC Code:** 78700

Data Date	Rating	RACR #1	RACR #2	Total Assets ($mil)	Capital ($mil)	Net Premium ($mil)	Net Income ($mil)
6-16	B+	2.25	1.38	2,349.9	279.5	391.7	15.7
6-15	B+	3.00	1.80	2,293.3	326.2	313.2	48.9
2015	B+	2.59	1.58	2,290.6	299.9	655.8	76.8
2014	B+	3.11	1.86	2,254.6	319.7	568.8	85.2
2013	B+	3.04	1.80	2,148.2	280.6	501.0	71.2
2012	B+	3.11	1.77	1,988.1	256.3	420.1	53.4
2011	B+	3.21	1.77	1,913.0	248.8	369.5	56.3

Adverse Trends in Operations

Decrease in capital during 2015 (6%)

AETNA LIFE INSURANCE COMPANY   B   Good

Major Rating Factors: Good current capitalization (5.8 on a scale of 0 to 10) based on mixed results -- excessive policy leverage mitigated by good risk adjusted capital (severe loss scenario), although results have slipped from the excellent range during the last year. Good quality investment portfolio (6.2) despite large holdings of BBB rated bonds in addition to moderate junk bond exposure. Exposure to mortgages is significant, but the mortgage default rate has been low. Good liquidity (6.6).

Other Rating Factors: Good overall results on stability tests (6.0) good operational trends, excellent risk adjusted capital for prior years and excellent risk diversification. Excellent profitability (8.4).

Principal Business: Group health insurance (63%), individual health insurance (32%), group life insurance (4%), and reinsurance (1%).

Principal Investments: NonCMO investment grade bonds (61%), CMOs and structured securities (12%), mortgages in good standing (10%), noninv. grade bonds (6%), and real estate (2%).

Investments in Affiliates: 4%

Group Affiliation: Aetna Inc

Licensed in: All states, the District of Columbia and Puerto Rico

Commenced Business: December 1850

Address: 151 Farmington Ave, Hartford, CT 06156

Phone: (860) 273-0123 **Domicile State:** CT **NAIC Code:** 60054

Data Date	Rating	RACR #1	RACR #2	Total Assets ($mil)	Capital ($mil)	Net Premium ($mil)	Net Income ($mil)
6-16	B	1.34	0.99	22,194.2	3,130.1	9,212.2	572.7
6-15	B	1.57	1.15	22,067.0	3,545.3	8,464.5	579.6
2015	B	1.57	1.15	21,214.1	3,770.8	17,155.4	1,211.9
2014	B+	1.72	1.25	22,795.4	3,871.9	15,544.4	1,321.7
2013	B+	1.76	1.25	21,793.1	3,199.9	12,354.0	911.1
2012	B+	1.89	1.33	21,175.5	3,332.3	12,689.8	1,020.0
2011	B+	1.73	1.22	20,894.4	3,047.1	11,199.3	1,001.2

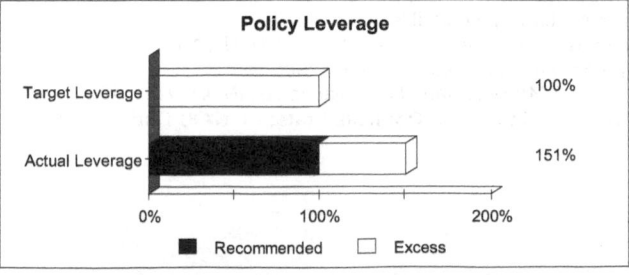

Policy Leverage

Target Leverage — 100%
Actual Leverage — 151%
(0%, 100%, 200% — Recommended, Excess)

AGC LIFE INSURANCE COMPANY   C   Fair

Major Rating Factors: Fair capitalization (4.3 on a scale of 0 to 10) based on fair risk adjusted capital (severe loss scenario). Fair overall results on stability tests (3.9) including fair risk adjusted capital in prior years. Good overall profitability (6.3). Excellent expense controls.
Other Rating Factors: Low quality investment portfolio (2.1). Excellent liquidity (7.5).
Principal Business: Reinsurance (100%).
Principal Investments: Common & preferred stock (94%), nonCMO investment grade bonds (3%), and CMOs and structured securities (3%).
Investments in Affiliates: 94%
Group Affiliation: American International Group
Licensed in: IL, MO, PA, SC, TN, TX
Commenced Business: September 1982
Address: 222 Monroe St, Jefferson City, MO 65101
Phone: (615) 749-1000   **Domicile State:** MO   **NAIC Code:** 97780

Data Date	Rating	RACR #1	RACR #2	Total Assets ($mil)	Capital ($mil)	Net Premium ($mil)	Net Income ($mil)
6-16	C	0.74	0.66	15,561.0	8,882.2	627.1	954.7
6-15	C	0.66	0.63	16,275.9	9,735.9	615.8	867.2
2015	C	0.70	0.62	15,059.5	8,376.3	1,260.0	2,590.1
2014	C	0.67	0.64	18,475.5	9,876.7	1,204.9	8,210.6
2013	U	0.90	0.80	20,893.3	15,038.3	1,123.4	3,668.0
2012	C	0.92	0.82	19,938.3	14,682.8	1,077.6	547.7
2011	U	0.78	0.69	15,966.8	11,173.6	1,055.4	1,199.8

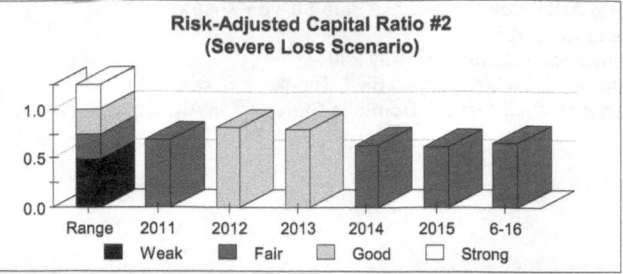

Risk-Adjusted Capital Ratio #2
(Severe Loss Scenario)

Range   2011   2012   2013   2014   2015   6-16
■ Weak   ■ Fair   ▨ Good   □ Strong

ALFA LIFE INSURANCE CORPORATION   B-   Good

Major Rating Factors: Good quality investment portfolio (5.3 on a scale of 0 to 10) despite mixed results such as: large holdings of BBB rated bonds but moderate junk bond exposure. Good liquidity (6.6) with sufficient resources to handle a spike in claims as well as a significant increase in policy surrenders. Good overall results on stability tests (5.2) excellent operational trends and excellent risk diversification.
Other Rating Factors: Weak profitability (2.9) with investment income below regulatory standards in relation to interest assumptions of reserves. Strong capitalization (7.8) based on excellent risk adjusted capital (severe loss scenario).
Principal Business: Individual life insurance (97%), individual annuities (2%), and group life insurance (1%).
Principal Investments: NonCMO investment grade bonds (68%), common & preferred stock (9%), policy loans (6%), noninv. grade bonds (6%), and misc. investments (11%).
Investments in Affiliates: None
Group Affiliation: Alfa Ins Group
Licensed in: AL, AR, FL, GA, LA, MS, MO, NC, SC, TN, VA
Commenced Business: March 1955
Address: 2108 East South Blvd, Montgomery, AL 36116-2015
Phone: (334) 288-3900   **Domicile State:** AL   **NAIC Code:** 79049

Data Date	Rating	RACR #1	RACR #2	Total Assets ($mil)	Capital ($mil)	Net Premium ($mil)	Net Income ($mil)
6-16	B-	2.70	1.52	1,412.5	236.6	77.9	0.3
6-15	B-	2.82	1.62	1,360.4	228.7	77.4	2.5
2015	B-	2.78	1.58	1,377.1	235.6	151.2	11.8
2014	B-	2.89	1.66	1,318.0	226.9	143.3	23.3
2013	B-	3.00	1.69	1,357.2	218.0	134.1	25.8
2012	B	2.72	1.56	1,295.4	202.4	148.0	11.5
2011	B+	2.93	1.70	1,218.6	188.0	136.9	21.8

Adverse Trends in Operations

Decrease in asset base during 2014 (3%)
Increase in policy surrenders from 2013 to 2014 (329%)
Decrease in premium volume from 2012 to 2013 (9%)

ALL SAVERS INSURANCE COMPANY   C   Fair

Major Rating Factors: Fair overall results on stability tests (3.7 on a scale of 0 to 10) including excessive premium growth and negative cash flow from operations for 2015. Weak profitability (1.9) with operating losses during the first six months of 2016. Strong capitalization (10.0) based on excellent risk adjusted capital (severe loss scenario).
Other Rating Factors: High quality investment portfolio (8.8). Excellent liquidity (7.3).
Principal Business: Individual health insurance (70%) and group health insurance (30%).
Principal Investments: NonCMO investment grade bonds (90%), cash (6%), and CMOs and structured securities (4%).
Investments in Affiliates: None
Group Affiliation: UnitedHealth Group Inc
Licensed in: All states except CA, MA, MN, NJ, NY, PR
Commenced Business: February 1986
Address: 7440 Woodland Dr, Indianapolis, IN 46278-1719
Phone: (317) 297-4123   **Domicile State:** IN   **NAIC Code:** 82406

Data Date	Rating	RACR #1	RACR #2	Total Assets ($mil)	Capital ($mil)	Net Premium ($mil)	Net Income ($mil)
6-16	C	5.43	4.23	1,437.0	821.5	800.3	-145.5
6-15	C	3.28	2.92	373.7	161.5	432.0	-89.0
2015	C	5.60	4.41	1,067.5	600.8	891.4	-339.5
2014	B-	1.51	1.25	61.6	31.1	111.9	5.0
2013	B-	1.19	0.99	29.6	16.4	76.3	1.5
2012	B-	1.31	1.09	18.9	11.1	46.8	2.0
2011	B-	2.05	1.70	15.4	9.1	24.6	3.6

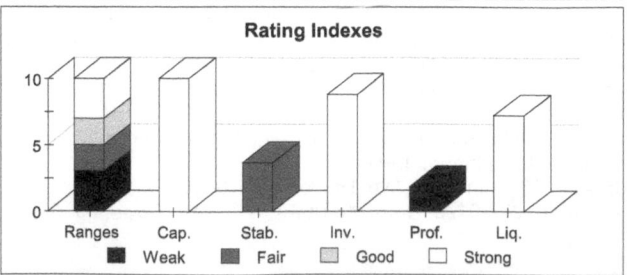

Rating Indexes

Ranges   Cap.   Stab.   Inv.   Prof.   Liq.
■ Weak   ■ Fair   ▨ Good   □ Strong

ALLIANZ LIFE INSURANCE COMPANY OF NEW YORK *   A-   Excellent

Major Rating Factors: Excellent overall results on stability tests (7.1 on a scale of 0 to 10). Strengths that enhance stability include excellent operational trends and excellent risk diversification. Strong capitalization (10.0) based on excellent risk adjusted capital (severe loss scenario). Furthermore, this high level of risk adjusted capital has been consistently maintained over the last five years. High quality investment portfolio (7.6).

Other Rating Factors: Excellent profitability (7.2) despite operating losses during the first six months of 2016. Excellent liquidity (9.5).

Principal Business: Individual annuities (98%) and individual health insurance (1%).

Principal Investments: NonCMO investment grade bonds (75%), CMOs and structured securities (21%), and noninv. grade bonds (1%).

Investments In Affiliates: None

Group Affiliation: Allianz Ins Group

Licensed in: CT, DC, IL, MN, MO, NY, ND

Commenced Business: April 1984

Address: One Chase Manhattan Plz 28 Fl, New York, NY 10005-1423

Phone: (212) 586-7733 **Domicile State:** NY **NAIC Code:** 64190

Data Date	Rating	RACR #1	RACR #2	Total Assets ($mil)	Capital ($mil)	Net Premium ($mil)	Net Income ($mil)
6-16	A-	7.33	4.84	3,131.2	248.6	136.0	-10.7
6-15	B	4.82	3.09	2,963.8	160.1	148.6	12.4
2015	B	5.88	4.15	2,943.5	198.8	280.8	34.3
2014	B	4.95	3.23	2,891.2	165.2	325.5	9.5
2013	B	3.07	1.60	2,668.0	97.8	317.4	7.4
2012	B-	4.79	2.58	2,294.7	135.4	346.7	30.4
2011	C	2.74	1.44	1,868.5	85.1	374.5	-7.8

Adverse Trends in Operations

Decrease in premium volume from 2014 to 2015 (14%)
Increase in policy surrenders from 2012 to 2013 (54%)
Decrease in capital during 2013 (28%)
Increase in policy surrenders from 2011 to 2012 (39%)
Decrease in premium volume from 2011 to 2012 (7%)

ALLIANZ LIFE INSURANCE COMPANY OF NORTH AMERICA   B   Good

Major Rating Factors: Good quality investment portfolio (5.2 on a scale of 0 to 10) despite mixed results such as: large holdings of BBB rated bonds but moderate junk bond exposure. Good overall profitability (6.0). Good liquidity (6.4) with sufficient resources to handle a spike in claims as well as a significant increase in policy surrenders.

Other Rating Factors: Good overall results on stability tests (5.4) despite excessive premium growth good operational trends, good risk adjusted capital for prior years and excellent risk diversification. Strong capitalization (7.9) based on excellent risk adjusted capital (severe loss scenario).

Principal Business: Individual annuities (93%), individual life insurance (5%), and individual health insurance (2%).

Principal Investments: NonCMO investment grade bonds (69%), CMOs and structured securities (14%), mortgages in good standing (10%), noninv. grade bonds (2%), and common & preferred stock (1%).

Investments in Affiliates: 1%

Group Affiliation: Allianz Ins Group

Licensed in: All states except NY

Commenced Business: December 1979

Address: 5701 Golden Hills Dr, Minneapolis, MN 55416-1297

Phone: (800) 328-5601 **Domicile State:** MN **NAIC Code:** 90611

Data Date	Rating	RACR #1	RACR #2	Total Assets ($mil)	Capital ($mil)	Net Premium ($mil)	Net Income ($mil)
6-16	B	2.84	1.60	125,342	6,059.1	7,080.3	525.8
6-15	C+	1.08	1.19	118,536	5,050.9	5,553.2	408.6
2015	B	2.91	1.67	120,594	5,822.1	10,965.7	1,473.2
2014	C+	2.08	1.27	116,906	5,955.2	14,964.5	701.4
2013	C+	1.63	0.98	104,723	4,426.2	8,775.2	269.3
2012	B	2.22	1.35	94,322.9	5,332.4	8,321.2	413.0
2011	C+	1.97	1.14	89,742.0	4,993.1	9,600.9	477.7

Rating Indexes

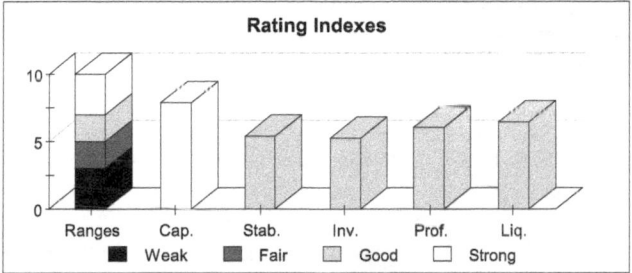

ALLSTATE ASSURANCE COMPANY   C+   Fair

Major Rating Factors: Fair overall results on stability tests (4.7 on a scale of 0 to 10) including negative cash flow from operations for 2015. Good quality investment portfolio (6.7) despite significant exposure to mortgages . Mortgage default rate has been low. large holdings of BBB rated bonds in addition to small junk bond holdings. Good liquidity (6.0).

Other Rating Factors: Weak profitability (1.8) with operating losses during the first six months of 2016. Strong capitalization (8.5) based on excellent risk adjusted capital (severe loss scenario).

Principal Business: Reinsurance (95%) and individual life insurance (5%).

Principal Investments: NonCMO investment grade bonds (70%), mortgages in good standing (16%), policy loans (7%), CMOs and structured securities (4%), and noninv. grade bonds (3%).

Investments in Affiliates: None

Group Affiliation: Allstate Group

Licensed in: All states except NY, PR

Commenced Business: July 1967

Address: 3100 Sanders Rd, Northbrook, IL 60062-7154

Phone: (847) 402-5000 **Domicile State:** IL **NAIC Code:** 70866

Data Date	Rating	RACR #1	RACR #2	Total Assets ($mil)	Capital ($mil)	Net Premium ($mil)	Net Income ($mil)
6-16	C+	3.63	2.00	654.6	123.1	58.4	-31.8
6-15	B-	7.74	6.88	606.7	74.6	509.6	-22.5
2015	B-	3.18	1.79	634.3	105.2	557.5	-45.8
2014	A-	4.03	3.63	12.2	10.7	0.0	0.3
2013	B	4.03	3.62	12.2	10.8	0.0	0.2
2012	U	4.03	3.63	12.1	10.7	0.0	0.4
2011	B	3.90	3.51	11.5	10.1	0.0	0.4

Rating Indexes

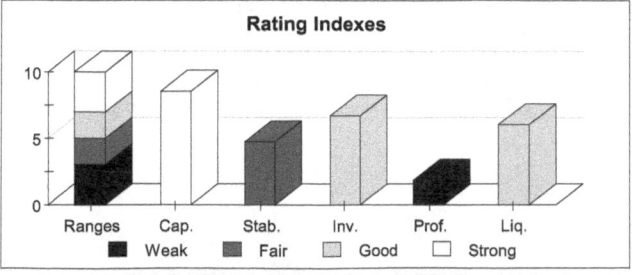

ALLSTATE LIFE INSURANCE COMPANY — B — Good

Major Rating Factors: Good overall capitalization (6.8 on a scale of 0 to 10) based on good risk adjusted capital (severe loss scenario). Nevertheless, capital levels have fluctuated during prior years. Good liquidity (6.6) with sufficient resources to cover a large increase in policy surrenders. Fair quality investment portfolio (4.5).

Other Rating Factors: Fair profitability (3.5) with investment income below regulatory standards in relation to interest assumptions of reserves. Fair overall results on stability tests (4.0) including negative cash flow from operations for 2015.

Principal Business: Reinsurance (70%), individual life insurance (24%), individual annuities (3%), group life insurance (2%), and group health insurance (1%).

Principal Investments: NonCMO investment grade bonds (47%), mortgages in good standing (11%), noninv. grade bonds (11%), CMOs and structured securities (11%), and misc. investments (20%).

Investments in Affiliates: 5%

Group Affiliation: Allstate Group

Licensed in: All states, the District of Columbia and Puerto Rico

Commenced Business: September 1957

Address: 3100 Sanders Rd, Northbrook, IL 60062-7127

Phone: (847) 402-5000 **Domicile State:** IL **NAIC Code:** 60186

Data Date	Rating	RACR #1	RACR #2	Total Assets ($mil)	Capital ($mil)	Net Premium ($mil)	Net Income ($mil)
6-16	B	1.68	0.97	32,095.1	2,902.1	602.6	104.6
6-15	B	1.75	1.02	33,113.4	2,881.3	143.7	153.0
2015	B	1.67	0.97	32,348.1	2,868.7	773.2	15.9
2014	B	1.70	1.00	34,120.9	2,712.3	-9,872.3	974.9
2013	B	1.31	0.80	47,858.5	2,875.1	2,377.5	425.1
2012	B	1.42	0.85	51,808.2	3,382.9	2,240.2	371.1
2011	B	1.33	0.78	53,978.8	3,455.7	1,976.7	-107.8

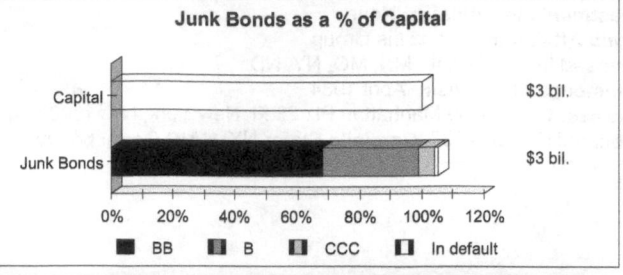

Junk Bonds as a % of Capital

ALLSTATE LIFE INSURANCE COMPANY OF NEW YORK — C+ — Fair

Major Rating Factors: Fair quality investment portfolio (4.9 on a scale of 0 to 10) with large holdings of BBB rated bonds in addition to junk bond exposure equal to 53% of capital. Exposure to mortgages is significant, but the mortgage default rate has been low. Fair overall results on stability tests (4.7) including negative cash flow from operations for 2015. Good liquidity (6.3).

Other Rating Factors: Weak profitability (2.5) with operating losses during the first six months of 2016. Strong capitalization (7.0) based on excellent risk adjusted capital (severe loss scenario).

Principal Business: Individual life insurance (85%), individual health insurance (8%), individual annuities (5%), and group retirement contracts (1%).

Principal Investments: NonCMO investment grade bonds (66%), mortgages in good standing (10%), CMOs and structured securities (9%), noninv. grade bonds (5%), and misc. investments (10%).

Investments in Affiliates: None

Group Affiliation: Allstate Group

Licensed in: CA, DC, DE, IL, MO, NE, NJ, NY, NC, PA, TX

Commenced Business: December 1967

Address: One Allstate Dr, Farmingville, NY 11738

Phone: (516) 451-5300 **Domicile State:** NY **NAIC Code:** 70874

Data Date	Rating	RACR #1	RACR #2	Total Assets ($mil)	Capital ($mil)	Net Premium ($mil)	Net Income ($mil)
6-16	C+	1.97	1.03	6,366.6	489.2	79.8	-39.2
6-15	B-	2.30	1.21	6,527.1	570.9	76.8	2.6
2015	B-	2.07	1.09	6,410.3	507.6	157.2	-63.9
2014	B-	2.29	1.21	6,600.9	562.1	153.2	31.3
2013	B-	2.21	1.17	6,741.9	553.9	153.2	25.9
2012	B-	2.15	1.11	6,918.8	540.0	118.3	18.8
2011	B-	2.14	1.09	7,244.9	524.0	123.8	46.0

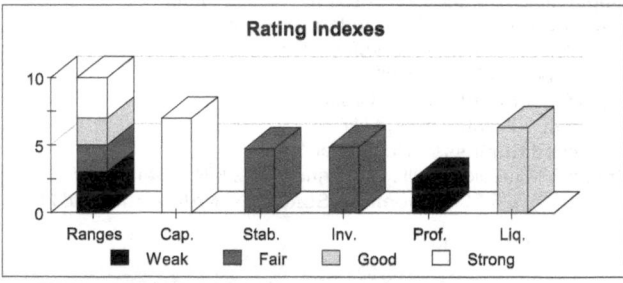

Rating Indexes

AMALGAMATED LIFE INSURANCE COMPANY * — A- — Excellent

Major Rating Factors: Good liquidity (6.4 on a scale of 0 to 10) with sufficient resources to handle a spike in claims. Strong capitalization (10.0) based on excellent risk adjusted capital (severe loss scenario). Furthermore, this high level of risk adjusted capital has been consistently maintained over the last five years. High quality investment portfolio (8.1).

Other Rating Factors: Excellent profitability (8.0). Excellent overall results on stability tests (7.0) excellent operational trends and excellent risk diversification.

Principal Business: Reinsurance (42%), group life insurance (33%), group health insurance (23%), and individual health insurance (1%).

Principal Investments: NonCMO investment grade bonds (68%) and CMOs and structured securities (32%).

Investments in Affiliates: None

Group Affiliation: National Retirement Fund

Licensed in: All states except PR

Commenced Business: February 1944

Address: 333 Westchester Ave, White Plains, NY 10604

Phone: (914) 367-5000 **Domicile State:** NY **NAIC Code:** 60216

Data Date	Rating	RACR #1	RACR #2	Total Assets ($mil)	Capital ($mil)	Net Premium ($mil)	Net Income ($mil)
6-16	A-	4.28	3.40	122.5	56.3	39.8	1.6
6-15	A-	3.99	3.16	113.4	53.4	37.9	1.7
2015	A-	4.12	3.27	119.9	55.6	75.6	3.0
2014	A-	3.82	3.03	111.8	51.0	72.4	3.5
2013	A-	3.45	2.72	99.9	47.2	64.3	3.5
2012	A-	3.31	2.64	88.6	42.2	56.3	3.7
2011	A-	2.99	2.36	78.9	38.3	55.7	1.9

Rating Indexes

AMERICAN BANKERS LIFE ASSURANCE COMPANY OF FLORID.   C+   Fair

Major Rating Factors: Fair overall results on stability tests (3.3 on a scale of 0 to 10) including weak results on operational trends and negative cash flow from operations for 2015. Good quality investment portfolio (6.6) despite mixed results such as: minimal exposure to mortgages and substantial holdings of BBB bonds but small junk bond holdings. Strong capitalization (10.0) based on excellent risk adjusted capital (severe loss scenario).

Other Rating Factors: Excellent profitability (7.4). Excellent liquidity (7.3).

Principal Business: Credit life insurance (44%), credit health insurance (34%), reinsurance (15%), group health insurance (3%), and other lines (4%).

Principal Investments: NonCMO investment grade bonds (59%), real estate (12%), CMOs and structured securities (10%), mortgages in good standing (8%), and misc. investments (12%).

Investments in Affiliates: None
Group Affiliation: Assurant Inc
Licensed in: All states except NY
Commenced Business: April 1952
Address: 11222 Quail Roost Dr, Miami, FL 33157
Phone: (305) 253-2244   **Domicile State:** FL   **NAIC Code:** 60275

Data Date	Rating	RACR #1	RACR #2	Total Assets ($mil)	Capital ($mil)	Net Premium ($mil)	Net Income ($mil)
6-16	C+	6.55	3.25	392.8	49.4	18.8	9.7
6-15	B	5.82	2.98	473.4	50.9	8.8	12.2
2015	C+	7.24	3.58	406.2	56.7	30.6	21.2
2014	B	5.37	2.87	489.6	55.9	67.9	18.6
2013	B	4.07	2.32	521.6	50.4	114.9	11.0
2012	B	3.76	2.25	553.8	67.3	127.7	13.4
2011	B	4.20	2.48	588.1	73.8	118.9	15.4

Adverse Trends in Operations

Decrease in premium volume from 2014 to 2015 (55%)
Decrease in asset base during 2015 (17%)
Decrease in premium volume from 2013 to 2014 (41%)
Decrease in premium volume from 2012 to 2013 (10%)
Decrease in capital during 2013 (25%)

AMERICAN CONTINENTAL INSURANCE COMPANY   B-   Good

Major Rating Factors: Good overall capitalization (5.6 on a scale of 0 to 10) based on mixed results -- excessive policy leverage mitigated by excellent risk adjusted capital (severe loss scenario). However, capital levels have fluctuated somewhat during past years. Good liquidity (5.3) with sufficient resources to handle a spike in claims. Fair overall results on stability tests (4.9).

Other Rating Factors: Weak profitability (1.8) with operating losses during the first six months of 2016. High quality investment portfolio (7.8).

Principal Business: Individual health insurance (89%) and individual life insurance (11%).

Principal Investments: NonCMO investment grade bonds (72%) and CMOs and structured securities (31%).

Investments in Affiliates: None
Group Affiliation: Aetna Inc
Licensed in: AL, AZ, AR, CO, FL, GA, IL, IN, IA, KS, KY, LA, MI, MN, MS, MO, MT, NE, NV, NM, NC, ND, OH, OK, PA, SC, SD, TN, TX, UT, VA, WV, WI, WY
Commenced Business: September 2005
Address: 800 Crescent Centre Dr, Franklin, TN 37067
Phone: (800) 264-4000   **Domicile State:** TN   **NAIC Code:** 12321

Data Date	Rating	RACR #1	RACR #2	Total Assets ($mil)	Capital ($mil)	Net Premium ($mil)	Net Income ($mil)
6-16	B-	1.34	1.02	208.7	75.0	234.5	-15.9
6-15	B-	1.39	1.06	174.7	70.4	212.7	-14.5
2015	B-	1.49	1.14	203.1	79.7	430.1	-15.3
2014	B	1.82	1.40	177.2	66.4	378.7	-12.7
2013	B	1.32	1.03	127.2	51.3	300.6	-13.5
2012	B	2.02	1.56	98.2	57.5	178.7	-6.0
2011	C	2.01	1.56	84.7	49.7	133.0	-12.0

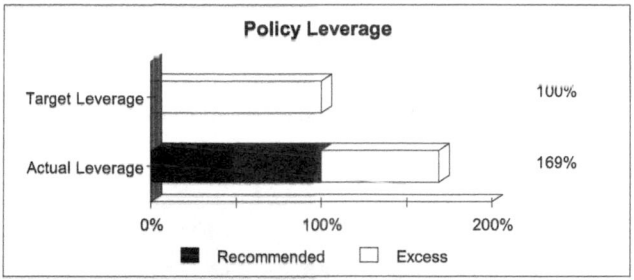

Policy Leverage

Target Leverage — 100%
Actual Leverage — 169%

0%   100%   200%
■ Recommended   □ Excess

AMERICAN EQUITY INVEST LIFE INSURANCE COMPANY   B   Good

Major Rating Factors: Good quality investment portfolio (6.0 on a scale of 0 to 10) despite mixed results such as: large holdings of BBB rated bonds but moderate junk bond exposure. Good overall profitability (6.2) although investment income, in comparison to reserve requirements, is below regulatory standards. Good liquidity (5.3).

Other Rating Factors: Good overall results on stability tests (6.3) excellent operational trends and excellent risk diversification. Strong capitalization (7.3) based on excellent risk adjusted capital (severe loss scenario).

Principal Business: Individual annuities (94%) and reinsurance (6%).

Principal Investments: NonCMO investment grade bonds (69%), CMOs and structured securities (19%), mortgages in good standing (7%), and noninv. grade bonds (3%).

Investments in Affiliates: None
Group Affiliation: American Equity Investment Group
Licensed in: All states except NY, PR
Commenced Business: January 1981
Address: 5000 Westown Parkway, West Des Moines, IA 50266
Phone: (888) 222-1234   **Domicile State:** IA   **NAIC Code:** 92738

Data Date	Rating	RACR #1	RACR #2	Total Assets ($mil)	Capital ($mil)	Net Premium ($mil)	Net Income ($mil)
6-16	B	2.26	1.18	44,851.9	2,431.5	3,013.1	11.3
6-15	B	2.68	1.38	38,746.1	2,251.1	2,846.3	97.0
2015	B	2.34	1.23	41,615.6	2,415.4	6,409.6	131.5
2014	B	2.77	1.43	36,129.7	2,172.5	3,866.6	340.0
2013	B	2.63	1.36	32,435.5	1,870.7	3,876.3	205.2
2012	B	2.64	1.36	28,079.0	1,658.9	3,484.8	82.0
2011	B	3.40	1.75	24,685.6	1,597.0	4,511.6	169.4

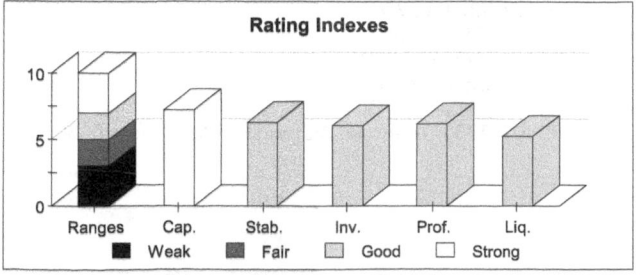

Rating Indexes

Ranges   Cap.   Stab.   Inv.   Prof.   Liq.
■ Weak   ■ Fair   □ Good   □ Strong

AMERICAN EQUITY INVESTMENT LIFE NEW YORK | B- | Good

Major Rating Factors: Good quality investment portfolio (6.3 on a scale of 0 to 10) despite mixed results such as: no exposure to mortgages and large holdings of BBB rated bonds but small junk bond holdings. Good overall profitability (5.6) although investment income, in comparison to reserve requirements, is below regulatory standards. Good liquidity (5.3).

Other Rating Factors: Fair overall results on stability tests (4.5) including negative cash flow from operations for 2015 and excessive premium growth. Strong capitalization (8.4) based on excellent risk adjusted capital (severe loss scenario).

Principal Business: Individual annuities (100%).

Principal Investments: NonCMO investment grade bonds (82%), CMOs and structured securities (15%), noninv. grade bonds (2%), and cash (1%).

Investments in Affiliates: None

Group Affiliation: American Equity Investment Group

Licensed in: NY

Commenced Business: July 2001

Address: 1979 Marcus Ave Suite 210, Lake Success, NY 11042

Phone: (866) 233-6660 **Domicile State:** NY **NAIC Code:** 11135

Data Date	Rating	RACR #1	RACR #2	Total Assets ($mil)	Capital ($mil)	Net Premium ($mil)	Net Income ($mil)
6-16	B-	3.16	1.90	215.2	31.1	0.2	1.0
6-15	B-	3.03	1.82	222.0	29.6	0.2	0.8
2015	B-	3.06	1.91	218.3	30.2	0.2	1.0
2014	B-	2.95	1.78	223.9	29.0	0.6	1.6
2013	B-	2.79	1.70	226.1	27.6	1.0	2.1
2012	B-	2.61	1.53	229.3	26.2	13.7	0.1
2011	B-	2.60	1.68	215.4	26.0	45.6	1.3

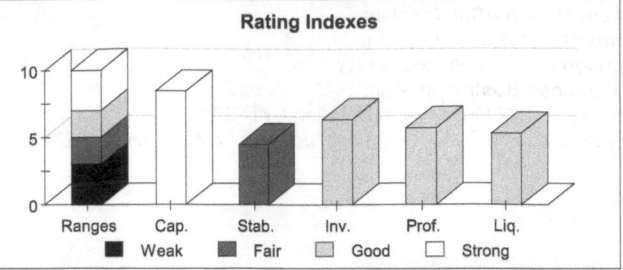

Rating Indexes

Ranges — Cap. — Stab. — Inv. — Prof. — Liq.

■ Weak ■ Fair ▨ Good ☐ Strong

AMERICAN FAMILY LIFE ASSUR COMPANY OF NEW YORK * | A- | Excellent

Major Rating Factors: Excellent overall results on stability tests (7.3 on a scale of 0 to 10). Strengths that enhance stability include excellent operational trends and excellent risk diversification. Strong capitalization (10.0) based on excellent risk adjusted capital (severe loss scenario). Furthermore, this high level of risk adjusted capital has been consistently maintained over the last five years. High quality investment portfolio (8.0).

Other Rating Factors: Excellent profitability (9.0). Excellent liquidity (7.7).

Principal Business: Individual health insurance (95%), individual life insurance (4%), and group health insurance (2%).

Principal Investments: NonCMO investment grade bonds (95%), cash (2%), CMOs and structured securities (1%), and noninv. grade bonds (1%).

Investments in Affiliates: None

Group Affiliation: AFLAC Inc

Licensed in: CT, MA, NJ, NY, ND, VT

Commenced Business: December 1964

Address: 22 Corporate Woods Blvd #2, Albany, NY 12211

Phone: (706) 660-7208 **Domicile State:** NY **NAIC Code:** 60526

Data Date	Rating	RACR #1	RACR #2	Total Assets ($mil)	Capital ($mil)	Net Premium ($mil)	Net Income ($mil)
6-16	A-	5.50	3.70	885.2	280.2	157.1	26.6
6-15	A-	5.70	3.92	798.1	274.5	151.9	22.1
2015	A-	6.11	4.20	817.9	298.5	304.2	47.4
2014	A-	5.39	3.76	735.9	250.1	293.5	26.8
2013	A-	4.96	3.49	645.3	221.8	285.5	45.4
2012	A-	4.18	2.99	555.9	176.2	271.1	40.0
2011	A-	3.17	2.29	454.0	123.4	251.8	26.5

Adverse Trends in Operations

Increase in policy surrenders from 2014 to 2015 (30%)
Increase in policy surrenders from 2013 to 2014 (49%)
Increase in policy surrenders from 2012 to 2013 (34%)
Increase in policy surrenders from 2011 to 2012 (92%)

AMERICAN FAMILY LIFE ASSURANCE COMPANY OF COLUMBU | B+ | Good

Major Rating Factors: Good quality investment portfolio (6.8 on a scale of 0 to 10) despite mixed results such as: large holdings of BBB rated bonds but moderate junk bond exposure. Good overall results on stability tests (6.7). Stability strengths include excellent operational trends and excellent risk diversification. Strong capitalization (8.2) based on excellent risk adjusted capital (severe loss scenario).

Other Rating Factors: Excellent profitability (7.2). Excellent liquidity (7.1).

Principal Business: Individual health insurance (72%), individual life insurance (24%), individual annuities (4%), and reinsurance (1%).

Principal Investments: NonCMO investment grade bonds (89%), noninv. grade bonds (4%), CMOs and structured securities (3%), common & preferred stock (2%), and cash (1%).

Investments in Affiliates: 2%

Group Affiliation: AFLAC Inc

Licensed in: All states except NY

Commenced Business: April 1956

Address: 1932 Wynnton Rd, Columbus, GA 31999

Phone: (706) 323-3431 **Domicile State:** NE **NAIC Code:** 60380

Data Date	Rating	RACR #1	RACR #2	Total Assets ($mil)	Capital ($mil)	Net Premium ($mil)	Net Income ($mil)
6-16	B+	2.54	1.78	117,278	11,448.6	9,356.4	1,406.9
6-15	B+	3.48	2.32	99,098.2	10,747.0	8,802.5	989.0
2015	B+	2.75	2.00	101,566	11,297.9	17,495.2	2,273.6
2014	B+	3.53	2.38	100,966	10,839.1	19,362.9	2,392.6
2013	B+	3.23	2.09	107,913	9,630.1	20,550.2	2,360.6
2012	B+	2.77	1.74	115,347	8,891.8	23,102.5	2,337.3
2011	B+	2.45	1.44	103,582	6,371.1	20,945.0	443.6

Adverse Trends in Operations

Decrease in premium volume from 2014 to 2015 (10%)
Decrease in premium volume from 2013 to 2014 (6%)
Decrease in asset base during 2014 (6%)
Decrease in asset base during 2013 (6%)
Decrease in premium volume from 2012 to 2013 (11%)

AMERICAN FAMILY LIFE INSURANCE COMPANY *　　　A+　　Excellent

Major Rating Factors: Good quality investment portfolio (6.4 on a scale of 0 to 10) despite significant exposure to mortgages . Mortgage default rate has been low. large holdings of BBB rated bonds in addition to small junk bond holdings. Good overall profitability (6.6). Good liquidity (6.4).

Other Rating Factors: Excellent overall results on stability tests (7.9) excellent operational trends and excellent risk diversification. Strong capitalization (9.2) based on excellent risk adjusted capital (severe loss scenario).

Principal Business: Individual life insurance (94%), individual annuities (4%), reinsurance (1%), and group life insurance (1%).

Principal Investments: NonCMO investment grade bonds (57%), CMOs and structured securities (20%), mortgages in good standing (11%), policy loans (4%), and misc. investments (8%).

Investments in Affiliates: None
Group Affiliation: American Family Ins Group
Licensed in: All states except NY, PR
Commenced Business: December 1957
Address: 6000 American Parkway, Madison, WI 53783-0001
Phone: (608) 242-4100 **Domicile State:** WI **NAIC Code:** 60399

Data Date	Rating	RACR #1	RACR #2	Total Assets ($mil)	Capital ($mil)	Net Premium ($mil)	Net Income ($mil)
6-16	A+	4.72	2.48	5,407.4	969.6	177.6	31.0
6-15	A+	4.65	2.45	5,303.7	918.1	170.7	35.2
2015	A+	4.69	2.48	5,331.7	945.1	338.0	51.7
2014	A+	4.57	2.42	5,230.5	888.6	341.1	80.7
2013	A+	4.66	2.47	5,074.0	822.8	347.9	66.2
2012	A+	4.63	2.48	4,839.9	736.4	372.2	69.3
2011	A+	4.76	2.74	4,598.7	691.5	371.9	69.5

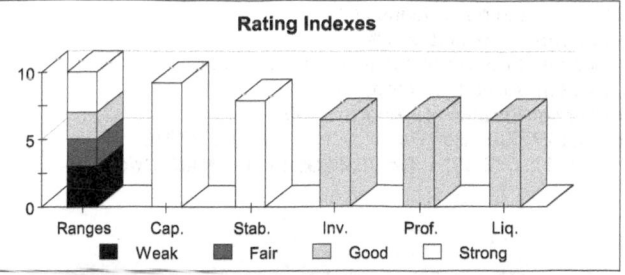

Rating Indexes

AMERICAN FIDELITY ASSURANCE COMPANY *　　　B+　　Good

Major Rating Factors: Good quality investment portfolio (6.0 on a scale of 0 to 10) despite mixed results such as: minimal exposure to mortgages and large holdings of BBB rated bonds but small junk bond holdings. Good liquidity (6.4) with sufficient resources to cover a large increase in policy surrenders. Good overall results on stability tests (6.8) excellent operational trends, good risk adjusted capital for prior years and excellent risk diversification.

Other Rating Factors: Strong capitalization (7.2) based on excellent risk adjusted capital (severe loss scenario). Excellent profitability (8.6).

Principal Business: Group health insurance (38%), individual health insurance (24%), individual annuities (20%), individual life insurance (12%), and other lines (5%).

Principal Investments: NonCMO investment grade bonds (65%), CMOs and structured securities (17%), mortgages in good standing (9%), cash (4%), and misc. investments (5%).

Investments in Affiliates: None
Group Affiliation: Cameron Associates Inc
Licensed in: All states except NY
Commenced Business: December 1960
Address: 2000 N Classen Blvd, Oklahoma City, OK 73106
Phone: (405) 523-2000 **Domicile State:** OK **NAIC Code:** 60410

Data Date	Rating	RACR #1	RACR #2	Total Assets ($mil)	Capital ($mil)	Net Premium ($mil)	Net Income ($mil)
6-16	B+	1.96	1.10	5,305.5	412.9	452.8	31.4
6-15	B+	1.84	1.07	5,091.4	389.0	529.3	33.8
2015	B+	1.97	1.13	5,181.1	408.5	957.9	75.4
2014	B+	1.93	1.11	4,959.0	380.4	822.5	69.3
2013	B+	1.82	1.05	4,709.9	342.7	780.9	71.7
2012	B+	1.60	0.95	4,358.1	308.9	765.7	58.5
2011	B+	1.74	1.01	3,994.1	295.0	712.8	55.6

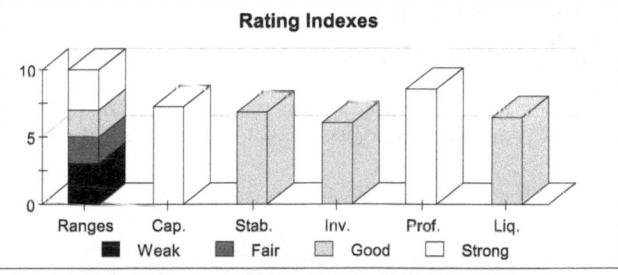

Rating Indexes

AMERICAN FIDELITY LIFE INSURANCE COMPANY　　　B-　　Good

Major Rating Factors: Good quality investment portfolio (6.0 on a scale of 0 to 10) despite mixed results such as: minimal exposure to mortgages and large holdings of BBB rated bonds but minimal holdings in junk bonds. Good overall profitability (5.7). Good liquidity (5.8).

Other Rating Factors: Good overall results on stability tests (5.3) excellent operational trends and good risk diversification. Strong capitalization (7.5) based on excellent risk adjusted capital (severe loss scenario).

Principal Business: Individual life insurance (61%), individual annuities (25%), and reinsurance (13%).

Principal Investments: NonCMO investment grade bonds (73%), mortgages in good standing (9%), real estate (7%), common & preferred stock (7%), and misc. investments (4%).

Investments in Affiliates: 12%
Group Affiliation: AMFI Corp
Licensed in: All states except NY, VT, PR
Commenced Business: September 1956
Address: 500 S Palafox Suite 200, Pensacola, FL 32502
Phone: (850) 456-7401 **Domicile State:** FL **NAIC Code:** 60429

Data Date	Rating	RACR #1	RACR #2	Total Assets ($mil)	Capital ($mil)	Net Premium ($mil)	Net Income ($mil)
6-16	B-	1.97	1.35	421.6	64.7	5.7	0.5
6-15	B-	2.19	1.50	427.5	66.8	5.9	1.6
2015	B-	2.03	1.40	426.4	67.7	10.3	2.4
2014	B-	2.23	1.54	433.1	68.1	10.6	-2.3
2013	B-	2.53	1.68	445.7	71.8	11.1	4.1
2012	B-	2.59	1.70	450.5	70.0	11.6	6.0
2011	B-	2.62	1.74	455.9	70.3	13.1	2.9

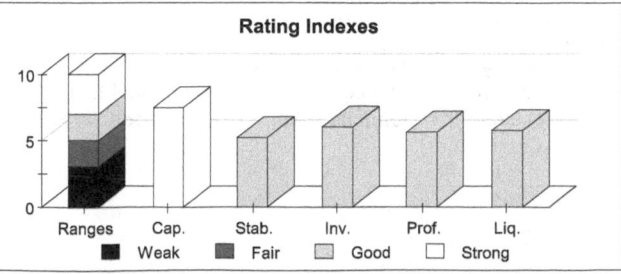

Rating Indexes

Winter 2016-17

AMERICAN GENERAL LIFE INSURANCE COMPANY — B — Good

Major Rating Factors: Good overall results on stability tests (5.8 on a scale of 0 to 10). Stability strengths include good operational trends and excellent risk diversification. Good overall profitability (6.1). Good liquidity (5.9) with sufficient resources to handle a spike in claims as well as a significant increase in policy surrenders.

Other Rating Factors: Fair quality investment portfolio (4.9). Strong capitalization (7.7) based on excellent risk adjusted capital (severe loss scenario).

Principal Business: Individual annuities (60%), group retirement contracts (21%), individual life insurance (17%), and individual health insurance (1%).

Principal Investments: NonCMO investment grade bonds (47%), CMOs and structured securities (30%), mortgages in good standing (8%), noninv. grade bonds (5%), and policy loans (1%).

Investments in Affiliates: 7%

Group Affiliation: American International Group

Licensed in: All states except NY

Commenced Business: August 1960

Address: 2727-A Allen Parkway, Houston, TX 77019

Phone: (713) 522-1111 **Domicile State:** TX **NAIC Code:** 60488

Data Date	Rating	RACR #1	RACR #2	Total Assets ($mil)	Capital ($mil)	Net Premium ($mil)	Net Income ($mil)
6-16	B	3.07	1.49	171,739	9,155.3	6,864.8	1,218.2
6-15	B	3.19	1.57	162,519	9,194.2	7,376.3	770.5
2015	B	3.07	1.51	166,711	8,893.8	15,632.0	1,412.9
2014	B	3.21	1.59	161,876	9,166.7	14,150.5	1,861.9
2013	B-	3.97	2.00	159,157	12,656.1	12,783.2	3,430.8
2012	C	3.50	1.84	149,628	11,514.5	7,937.0	3,641.2
2011	B	1.47	1.19	43,097.1	7,393.6	1,173.5	1,055.2

Adverse Trends in Operations

Decrease in capital during 2015 (3%)
Decrease in capital during 2014 (28%)
Change in premium mix from 2011 to 2012 (7.5%)
Increase in policy surrenders from 2011 to 2012 (562%)

AMERICAN HEALTH & LIFE INSURANCE COMPANY * — A- — Excellent

Major Rating Factors: Good overall results on stability tests (6.5 on a scale of 0 to 10). Strengths that enhance stability include good operational trends and excellent risk diversification. Good quality investment portfolio (6.3) despite mixed results such as: no exposure to mortgages and large holdings of BBB rated bonds but small junk bond holdings. Good overall profitability (6.9).

Other Rating Factors: Strong capitalization (9.0) based on excellent risk adjusted capital (severe loss scenario). Excellent liquidity (7.9).

Principal Business: Credit health insurance (33%), credit life insurance (31%), reinsurance (22%), group health insurance (7%), and other lines (7%).

Principal Investments: NonCMO investment grade bonds (75%), CMOs and structured securities (18%), noninv. grade bonds (5%), cash (2%), and common & preferred stock (1%).

Investments in Affiliates: None

Group Affiliation: Citigroup Inc

Licensed in: All states except NY, PR

Commenced Business: June 1954

Address: 307 West 7th Street, Ste 400, Fort Worth, TX 76102

Phone: (817) 348-7500 **Domicile State:** TX **NAIC Code:** 60518

Data Date	Rating	RACR #1	RACR #2	Total Assets ($mil)	Capital ($mil)	Net Premium ($mil)	Net Income ($mil)
6-16	A-	3.98	2.32	907.2	177.0	84.9	29.4
6-15	B	3.29	2.21	953.7	217.3	92.9	27.8
2015	A-	4.03	2.40	923.9	183.5	199.8	55.5
2014	B	2.88	1.96	912.8	188.6	209.9	70.0
2013	B-	3.08	2.11	941.1	208.6	221.8	84.1
2012	B-	3.52	2.39	972.0	234.7	213.5	110.0
2011	B-	2.52	2.05	1,153.2	371.7	214.8	123.8

Adverse Trends in Operations

Increase in policy surrenders from 2014 to 2015 (126%)
Increase in policy surrenders from 2013 to 2014 (249%)
Decrease in capital during 2013 (11%)
Decrease in asset base during 2012 (16%)
Decrease in capital during 2012 (37%)

AMERICAN HERITAGE LIFE INSURANCE COMPANY — B — Good

Major Rating Factors: Good overall results on stability tests (6.0 on a scale of 0 to 10). Stability strengths include excellent operational trends and excellent risk diversification. Good capitalization (6.0) based on good risk adjusted capital (severe loss scenario). Good quality investment portfolio (6.3).

Other Rating Factors: Good overall profitability (5.8). Good liquidity (6.5).

Principal Business: Group health insurance (56%), individual health insurance (27%), individual life insurance (10%), group life insurance (6%), and reinsurance (1%).

Principal Investments: NonCMO investment grade bonds (54%), policy loans (18%), common & preferred stock (13%), mortgages in good standing (10%), and misc. investments (6%).

Investments in Affiliates: 10%

Group Affiliation: Allstate Group

Licensed in: All states except NY

Commenced Business: December 1956

Address: 1776 American Heritage Life Dr, Jacksonville, FL 32224-6688

Phone: (904) 992-1776 **Domicile State:** FL **NAIC Code:** 60534

Data Date	Rating	RACR #1	RACR #2	Total Assets ($mil)	Capital ($mil)	Net Premium ($mil)	Net Income ($mil)
6-16	B	1.09	0.88	1,846.7	303.0	432.2	26.2
6-15	B	1.37	1.10	1,881.9	385.1	390.5	32.0
2015	B	1.19	0.96	1,830.9	329.7	785.9	56.3
2014	B	1.27	1.02	1,799.7	353.3	744.8	123.3
2013	B	1.18	0.97	1,770.2	337.7	707.7	57.0
2012	B	1.26	1.05	1,710.7	335.8	649.7	74.7
2011	B	1.24	1.02	1,650.1	293.7	639.9	41.5

Adverse Trends in Operations

Decrease in capital during 2015 (7%)

AMERICAN INCOME LIFE INSURANCE COMPANY B- Good

Major Rating Factors: Good capitalization (5.4 on a scale of 0 to 10) based on good risk adjusted capital (moderate loss scenario). Capital levels have been relatively consistent over the last five years. Good overall profitability (5.2) although investment income, in comparison to reserve requirements, is below regulatory standards. Fair quality investment portfolio (4.2).

Other Rating Factors: Fair overall results on stability tests (4.6). Weak liquidity (2.6).

Principal Business: Individual life insurance (91%), individual health insurance (7%), and group health insurance (1%).

Principal Investments: NonCMO investment grade bonds (79%), policy loans (6%), noninv. grade bonds (5%), common & preferred stock (3%), and misc. investments (7%).

Investments in Affiliates: 4%

Group Affiliation: Torchmark Corp

Licensed in: All states except NY, PR

Commenced Business: August 1954

Address: 8604 Allisonville Rd Suite 151, Indianapolis, IN 46250

Phone: (254) 761-6400 **Domicile State:** IN **NAIC Code:** 60577

Data Date	Rating	RACR #1	RACR #2	Total Assets ($mil)	Capital ($mil)	Net Premium ($mil)	Net Income ($mil)
6-16	B-	1.25	0.75	3,234.8	222.8	380.3	82.0
6-15	B-	1.20	0.74	3,014.9	199.9	363.5	72.4
2015	B-	1.38	0.84	3,078.1	242.5	730.4	141.5
2014	B-	1.39	0.86	2,898.6	228.9	713.7	151.6
2013	B-	1.36	0.86	2,694.7	232.3	747.9	132.6
2012	B-	1.28	0.78	2,518.3	219.7	723.1	122.2
2011	B-	1.34	0.80	2,291.1	195.4	669.6	107.7

Risk-Adjusted Capital Ratio #1
(Moderate Loss Scenario)

Range 2011 2012 2013 2014 2015 6-16
■ Weak ▨ Fair ☐ Good

AMERICAN LIFE & ACCIDENT INSURANCE COMPANY OF KENTL C Fair

Major Rating Factors: Fair overall results on stability tests (3.9 on a scale of 0 to 10) including negative cash flow from operations for 2015. Good overall profitability (6.8). Excellent expense controls. Good liquidity (6.0) with sufficient resources to handle a spike in claims.

Other Rating Factors: Low quality investment portfolio (2.3). Strong capitalization (8.3) based on excellent risk adjusted capital (severe loss scenario).

Principal Business: Reinsurance (100%).

Principal Investments: Common & preferred stock (61%), nonCMO investment grade bonds (22%), real estate (8%), CMOs and structured securities (2%), and cash (2%).

Investments in Affiliates: None

Group Affiliation: Hardscuffle Inc

Licensed in: AR, GA, IN, KY, MD, OH, PA, TN

Commenced Business: July 1906

Address: 3 Riverfront Plaza, Louisville, KY 40202-2975

Phone: (502) 585-5347 **Domicile State:** KY **NAIC Code:** 60666

Data Date	Rating	RACR #1	RACR #2	Total Assets ($mil)	Capital ($mil)	Net Premium ($mil)	Net Income ($mil)
6-16	C	3.29	1.89	207.9	112.1	101.9	0.2
6-15	C	2.89	1.67	237.1	120.4	99.8	17.0
2015	C	3.37	1.94	216.1	114.3	198.7	22.9
2014	C	2.94	1.70	248.8	119.8	78.1	59.3
2013	C	2.08	1.25	358.7	95.9	83.3	-4.6
2012	C-	2.26	1.35	319.6	86.0	82.1	16.1
2011	C-	2.16	1.29	307.5	76.1	96.5	-11.4

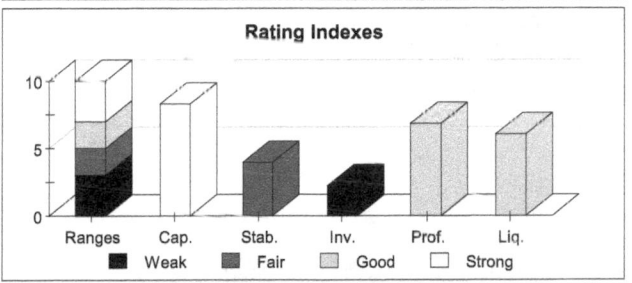

Rating Indexes

Ranges Cap. Stab. Inv. Prof. Liq.
■ Weak ▨ Fair ☐ Good ☐ Strong

AMERICAN LIFE INSURANCE COMPANY C Fair

Major Rating Factors: Fair quality investment portfolio (3.1 on a scale of 0 to 10). Fair overall results on stability tests (3.4) including fair risk adjusted capital in prior years. Good overall profitability (5.3).

Other Rating Factors: Strong capitalization (7.1) based on excellent risk adjusted capital (severe loss scenario). Excellent liquidity (7.5).

Principal Business: Individual life insurance (45%), group health insurance (21%), reinsurance (18%), individual health insurance (6%), and other lines (10%).

Principal Investments: Common & preferred stock (62%), nonCMO investment grade bonds (15%), noninv. grade bonds (13%), cash (7%), and misc. investments (4%).

Investments in Affiliates: 63%

Group Affiliation: MetLife Inc

Licensed in: (No states)

Commenced Business: August 1921

Address: One ALICO Plaza, Wilmington, DE 19801

Phone: (302) 594-2000 **Domicile State:** DE **NAIC Code:** 60690

Data Date	Rating	RACR #1	RACR #2	Total Assets ($mil)	Capital ($mil)	Net Premium ($mil)	Net Income ($mil)
6-16	C	1.13	1.07	11,974.0	6,284.6	652.6	311.2
6-15	C	1.43	1.26	11,065.3	6,144.9	650.6	374.8
2015	C	1.02	0.99	11,097.5	6,115.1	1,204.5	334.6
2014	C	0.93	0.89	8,215.9	3,358.5	1,409.1	-36.1
2013	C	0.92	0.88	7,296.4	2,711.2	1,140.4	630.5
2012	C	1.01	0.93	8,224.8	3,043.6	8,991.4	317.1
2011	C-	0.80	0.57	102,198	3,309.9	15,495.3	333.8

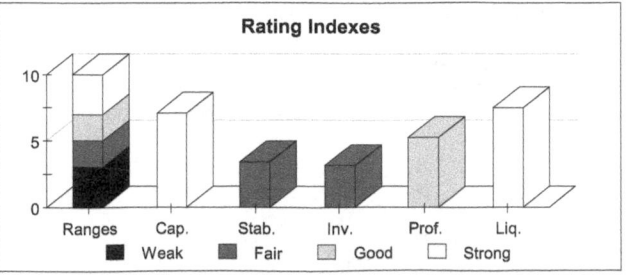

Rating Indexes

Ranges Cap. Stab. Inv. Prof. Liq.
■ Weak ▨ Fair ☐ Good ☐ Strong

AMERICAN MATURITY LIFE INSURANCE COMPANY — B — Good

Major Rating Factors: Good overall results on stability tests (5.8 on a scale of 0 to 10) despite fair financial strength of affiliated Hartford Financial Services Inc. Other stability subfactors include good operational trends and excellent risk diversification. Fair profitability (4.2). Strong capitalization (10.0) based on excellent risk adjusted capital (severe loss scenario).

Other Rating Factors: High quality investment portfolio (9.5). Excellent liquidity (7.0).

Principal Business: Group retirement contracts (72%) and individual annuities (28%).

Principal Investments: NonCMO investment grade bonds (100%).

Investments in Affiliates: None

Group Affiliation: Hartford Financial Services Inc

Licensed in: All states except PR

Commenced Business: March 1973

Address: 200 Hopmeadow St, Simsbury, CT 06070

Phone: (860) 843-5867 **Domicile State:** CT **NAIC Code:** 81213

Data Date	Rating	RACR #1	RACR #2	Total Assets ($mil)	Capital ($mil)	Net Premium ($mil)	Net Income ($mil)
6-16	B	6.66	6.00	60.5	47.9	0.0	0.3
6-15	B	6.56	5.90	61.5	47.4	0.0	0.2
2015	B	6.61	5.95	60.6	47.5	0.0	0.4
2014	B	6.54	5.88	61.7	47.3	0.0	0.0
2013	B	6.55	5.89	61.2	47.2	0.1	0.7
2012	B	6.55	5.89	60.0	46.8	0.0	0.6
2011	B	6.29	5.66	63.5	46.0	0.1	0.7

Hartford Financial Services Inc Composite Group Rating: C+ Largest Group Members	Assets ($mil)	Rating
HARTFORD LIFE INS CO	114421	C+
HARTFORD LIFE ANNUITY INS CO	40189	B-
HARTFORD FIRE INS CO	25426	B
HARTFORD ACCIDENT INDEMNITY CO	11522	B
HARTFORD LIFE ACCIDENT INS CO	8992	C+

AMERICAN MEMORIAL LIFE INS CO — B- — Good

Major Rating Factors: Good capitalization (5.7 on a scale of 0 to 10) based on good risk adjusted capital (moderate loss scenario). Good liquidity (5.6) with sufficient resources to handle a spike in claims as well as a significant increase in policy surrenders. Fair quality investment portfolio (3.3) with large holdings of BBB rated bonds in addition to significant exposure to junk bonds.

Other Rating Factors: Fair overall results on stability tests (4.9) including fair risk adjusted capital in prior years. Excellent profitability (7.1).

Principal Business: N/A

Principal Investments: NonCMO investment grade bonds (71%), CMOs and structured securities (9%), noninv. grade bonds (8%), mortgages in good standing (8%), and common & preferred stock (1%).

Investments in Affiliates: None

Group Affiliation: Assurant Inc

Licensed in: All states except NY, PR

Commenced Business: October 1959

Address: 440 Mount Rushmore Rd, Rapid City, SD 57701

Phone: (605) 348-1262 **Domicile State:** SD **NAIC Code:** 67989

Data Date	Rating	RACR #1	RACR #2	Total Assets ($mil)	Capital ($mil)	Net Premium ($mil)	Net Income ($mil)
6-16	B-	1.49	0.74	2,876.1	129.1	264.0	16.4
6-15	B-	1.48	0.75	2,736.8	116.9	245.5	10.9
2015	B-	1.41	0.71	2,761.6	115.7	495.6	26.5
2014	B-	1.45	0.73	2,655.5	112.4	489.9	26.7
2013	B-	1.48	0.75	2,493.7	103.5	483.2	20.4
2012	B-	1.50	0.76	2,345.8	102.9	431.3	25.9
2011	B-	1.51	0.76	2,202.9	100.3	389.9	14.6

Junk Bonds as a % of Capital

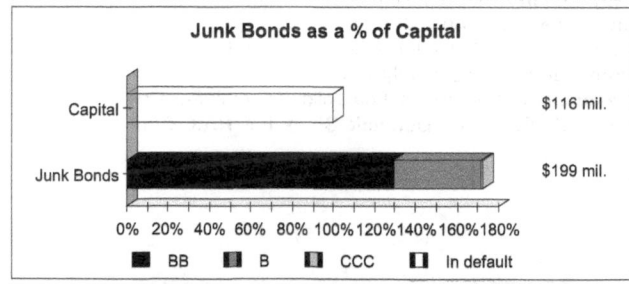

Capital — $116 mil.

Junk Bonds — $199 mil.

0% 20% 40% 60% 80% 100% 120% 140% 160% 180%

■ BB ▨ B ▥ CCC ▢ In default

AMERICAN MODERN LIFE INSURANCE COMPANY — B — Good

Major Rating Factors: Good overall results on stability tests (5.7 on a scale of 0 to 10) despite negative cash flow from operations for 2015. Other stability subfactors include good operational trends and excellent risk diversification. Strong capitalization (8.7) based on excellent risk adjusted capital (severe loss scenario). Moreover, capital levels have been consistently high over the last five years. High quality investment portfolio (8.0).

Other Rating Factors: Excellent profitability (7.5). Excellent liquidity (8.3).

Principal Business: Credit life insurance (57%), credit health insurance (42%), and reinsurance (1%).

Principal Investments: NonCMO investment grade bonds (62%), common & preferred stock (27%), CMOs and structured securities (8%), and cash (2%).

Investments in Affiliates: 27%

Group Affiliation: Securian Financial Group

Licensed in: All states except NH, NJ, PR

Commenced Business: January 1957

Address: 400 Robert St N, St Paul, MN 55101-2098

Phone: (800) 543-2644 **Domicile State:** OH **NAIC Code:** 65811

Data Date	Rating	RACR #1	RACR #2	Total Assets ($mil)	Capital ($mil)	Net Premium ($mil)	Net Income ($mil)
6-16	B	2.23	2.10	45.9	29.5	2.0	0.3
6-15	B	2.06	1.93	47.1	27.4	2.0	-0.1
2015	B	2.20	2.08	46.9	29.0	4.2	0.9
2014	B	2.09	1.96	47.8	27.9	5.1	2.1
2013	B	1.89	1.76	52.1	26.4	4.7	3.9
2012	B	1.55	1.43	58.8	23.1	8.1	1.9
2011	B	1.37	1.21	60.0	20.3	14.2	-3.6

Adverse Trends in Operations

Decrease in asset base during 2015 (2%)
Decrease in premium volume from 2014 to 2015 (17%)
Decrease in asset base during 2013 (11%)
Decrease in premium volume from 2012 to 2013 (42%)
Decrease in premium volume from 2011 to 2012 (43%)

AMERICAN NATIONAL INSURANCE COMPANY
B   **Good**

Major Rating Factors: Good current capitalization (6.9 on a scale of 0 to 10) based on good risk adjusted capital (severe loss scenario), although results have slipped from the excellent range during the last year. Good quality investment portfolio (5.3) despite significant exposure to mortgages . Mortgage default rate has been low. large holdings of BBB rated bonds in addition to small junk bond holdings. Good liquidity (6.5).

Other Rating Factors: Good overall results on stability tests (6.1) despite excessive premium growth excellent operational trends and excellent risk diversification. Excellent profitability (7.9).

Principal Business: Individual annuities (46%), individual life insurance (29%), group retirement contracts (13%), reinsurance (5%), and other lines (7%).

Principal Investments: NonCMO investment grade bonds (54%), mortgages in good standing (20%), common & preferred stock (13%), policy loans (2%), and misc. investments (11%).

Investments in Affiliates: 20%

Group Affiliation: American National Group Inc

Licensed in: All states except NY

Commenced Business: March 1905

Address: One Moody Plaza, Galveston, TX 77550-7999

Phone: (409) 763-4661 **Domicile State:** TX **NAIC Code:** 60739

Data Date	Rating	RACR #1	RACR #2	Total Assets ($mil)	Capital ($mil)	Net Premium ($mil)	Net Income ($mil)
6-16	B	1.20	0.99	18,521.1	2,920.3	946.6	10.4
6-15	B	1.31	1.07	17,944.6	2,960.1	592.4	61.8
2015	B	1.22	1.01	18,342.1	2,925.9	1,645.2	118.6
2014	B	1.29	1.06	18,113.0	2,879.2	1,318.6	134.6
2013	B	1.27	1.03	18,036.2	2,667.9	1,146.3	149.1
2012	B	1.23	0.99	17,787.3	2,260.3	1,340.5	193.7
2011	B	1.28	0.98	17,390.0	2,000.6	2,180.6	176.9

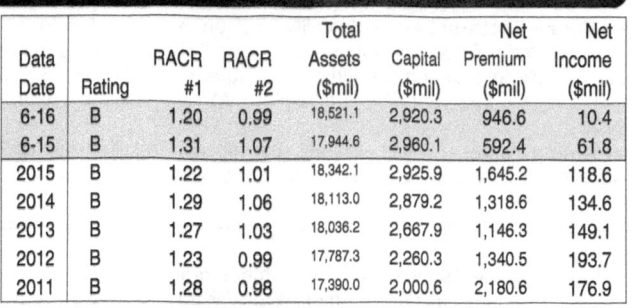

Risk-Adjusted Capital Ratio #2
(Severe Loss Scenario)

AMERICAN NATIONAL LIFE INSURANCE COMPANY OF NEW YO
B   **Good**

Major Rating Factors: Fair quality investment portfolio (4.9 on a scale of 0 to 10). Fair overall results on stability tests (4.4). Weak profitability (2.0). Excellent expense controls. Return on equity has been low, averaging -8.0%.

Other Rating Factors: Strong capitalization (7.5) based on excellent risk adjusted capital (severe loss scenario). Excellent liquidity (7.1).

Principal Business: Individual annuities (96%) and individual life insurance (4%).

Principal Investments: NonCMO investment grade bonds (94%), mortgages in good standing (4%), and noninv. grade bonds (2%).

Investments in Affiliates: None

Group Affiliation: American National Group Inc

Licensed in: NY

Commenced Business: March 2010

Address: 344 Route 9W, Glenmont, NY 12077

Phone: (409) 763-4661 **Domicile State:** NY **NAIC Code:** 13762

Data Date	Rating	RACR #1	RACR #2	Total Assets ($mil)	Capital ($mil)	Net Premium ($mil)	Net Income ($mil)
6-16	B	2.72	1.32	401.1	30.1	135.6	0.0
6-15	D	1.10	0.88	168.0	9.7	9.0	-0.8
2015	B	2.75	1.57	273.4	28.0	95.7	-2.0
2014	B	1.29	1.07	161.4	11.6	33.1	-2.1
2013	B	1.57	1.42	137.0	14.1	25.2	-1.5
2012	B	1.83	1.65	116.2	16.4	26.6	-0.4
2011	B	2.01	1.81	89.5	17.0	56.1	-1.3

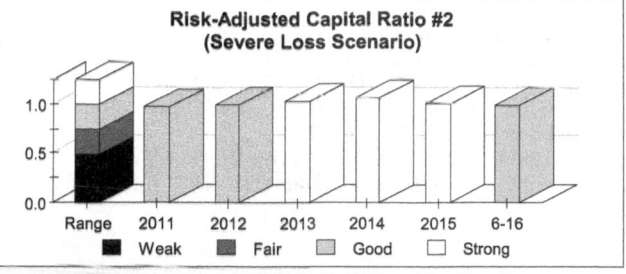

Rating Indexes

AMERICAN NATIONAL LIFE INSURANCE COMPANY OF TEXAS
B-   **Good**

Major Rating Factors: Good liquidity (5.9 on a scale of 0 to 10) with sufficient resources to handle a spike in claims. Good overall results on stability tests (5.0) despite negative cash flow from operations for 2015. Strengths include good financial support from affiliation with American National Group Inc, good operational trends and excellent risk diversification. Fair profitability (3.0) with operating losses during the first six months of 2016.

Other Rating Factors: Strong capitalization (10.0) based on excellent risk adjusted capital (severe loss scenario). High quality investment portfolio (7.1).

Principal Business: Group health insurance (49%), reinsurance (43%), individual life insurance (4%), and individual health insurance (4%).

Principal Investments: NonCMO investment grade bonds (94%), policy loans (4%), noninv. grade bonds (2%), and CMOs and structured securities (1%).

Investments in Affiliates: None

Group Affiliation: American National Group Inc

Licensed in: All states except ME, NJ, NY, VT, PR

Commenced Business: December 1954

Address: One Moody Plaza, Galveston, TX 77550

Phone: (409) 763-4661 **Domicile State:** TX **NAIC Code:** 71773

Data Date	Rating	RACR #1	RACR #2	Total Assets ($mil)	Capital ($mil)	Net Premium ($mil)	Net Income ($mil)
6-16	B-	3.80	3.11	123.5	34.0	14.0	-1.2
6-15	B-	4.16	3.19	136.2	37.6	18.7	-1.1
2015	B-	4.01	3.16	127.5	35.9	35.5	-5.3
2014	B-	4.06	3.10	136.3	36.8	38.4	0.6
2013	B-	4.55	3.17	135.1	41.4	45.1	2.1
2012	B-	4.01	2.80	133.5	39.2	52.8	-2.0
2011	B-	2.51	1.80	115.1	27.5	64.2	-0.8

American National Group Inc Composite Group Rating: B Largest Group Members	Assets ($mil)	Rating
AMERICAN NATIONAL INS CO	18342	B
FARM FAMILY LIFE INS CO	1309	B
AMERICAN NATIONAL PROPERTY CAS CO	1276	B
FARM FAMILY CASUALTY INS CO	1096	B+
STANDARD LIFE ACCIDENT INS CO	514	A-

AMERICAN PROGRESSIVE L&H INSURANCE COMPANY OF NY   C   Fair

Major Rating Factors: Fair profitability (3.2 on a scale of 0 to 10). Excellent expense controls. Good current capitalization (6.0) based on good risk adjusted capital (severe loss scenario), although results have slipped from the excellent range during the last year. Weak liquidity (0.6) as a spike in claims may stretch capacity.

Other Rating Factors: Weak overall results on stability tests (2.7) including negative cash flow from operations for 2015. High quality investment portfolio (7.4).

Principal Business: Individual health insurance (97%) and individual life insurance (3%).

Principal Investments: NonCMO investment grade bonds (73%), CMOs and structured securities (22%), common & preferred stock (2%), and , and misc. investments (3%).

Investments in Affiliates: None

Group Affiliation: Universal American Corp

Licensed in: AL, AR, CO, CT, DC, DE, GA, HI, IL, IN, LA, ME, MD, MA, MN, MO, NH, NJ, NY, NC, OH, OK, OR, PA, RI, SC, TX, VT, VA, WV

Commenced Business: March 1946

Address: 6 International Dr Suite 190, Rye Brook, NY 10573

Phone: (914) 934-8300 **Domicile State:** NY **NAIC Code:** 80624

Data Date	Rating	RACR #1	RACR #2	Total Assets ($mil)	Capital ($mil)	Net Premium ($mil)	Net Income ($mil)
6-16	C	1.21	0.97	222.7	102.5	258.4	2.1
6-15	B	1.35	1.07	211.8	102.8	204.6	-11.4
2015	C	1.29	1.03	211.5	101.3	420.8	-13.0
2014	B	1.49	1.18	227.7	116.4	412.9	2.7
2013	B	1.39	1.10	235.7	122.3	469.8	13.5
2012	B	1.84	1.46	263.8	145.4	419.3	14.8
2011	C+	1.39	1.11	252.1	132.0	507.7	4.8

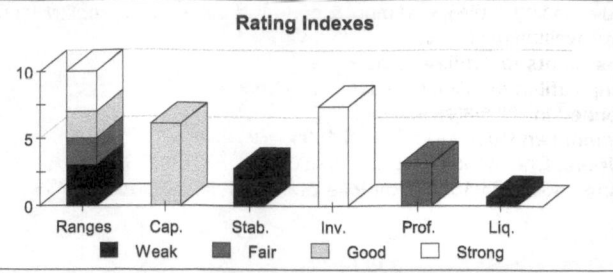

Rating Indexes

Ranges | Cap. | Stab. | Inv. | Prof. | Liq.

■ Weak   ■ Fair   □ Good   □ Strong

AMERICAN PUBLIC LIFE INSURANCE COMPANY   B   Good

Major Rating Factors: Good overall results on stability tests (5.6 on a scale of 0 to 10). Stability strengths include excellent operational trends and excellent risk diversification. Strong capitalization (7.7) based on excellent risk adjusted capital (severe loss scenario). Capital levels have been relatively consistent over the last five years. High quality investment portfolio (8.0).

Other Rating Factors: Excellent profitability (8.2). Excellent liquidity (7.1).

Principal Business: Group health insurance (72%), individual health insurance (23%), reinsurance (4%), and individual life insurance (2%).

Principal Investments: NonCMO investment grade bonds (58%), CMOs and structured securities (24%), mortgages in good standing (9%), cash (6%), and misc. investments (3%).

Investments in Affiliates: None

Group Affiliation: Cameron Associates Inc

Licensed in: All states except NY, PR

Commenced Business: March 1946

Address: 2305 Lakeland Drive, Jackson, MS 39208

Phone: (601) 936-6600 **Domicile State:** OK **NAIC Code:** 60801

Data Date	Rating	RACR #1	RACR #2	Total Assets ($mil)	Capital ($mil)	Net Premium ($mil)	Net Income ($mil)
6-16	B	2.00	1.48	91.4	25.9	36.2	2.4
6-15	B	2.03	1.48	85.2	24.3	29.7	2.7
2015	B	1.95	1.44	86.7	23.6	61.4	5.0
2014	B	1.92	1.41	83.2	21.6	52.8	4.4
2013	B	2.02	1.46	80.3	21.7	46.9	3.7
2012	B	1.77	1.27	75.1	18.7	42.5	1.7
2011	B	1.86	1.30	74.3	19.0	39.0	0.8

Adverse Trends in Operations

Increase in policy surrenders from 2014 to 2015 (36%)
Increase in policy surrenders from 2012 to 2013 (75%)
Decrease in capital during 2012 (2%)

AMERICAN REPUBLIC INSURANCE COMPANY *   A-   Excellent

Major Rating Factors: Good quality investment portfolio (6.9 on a scale of 0 to 10) despite mixed results such as: minimal exposure to mortgages and large holdings of BBB rated bonds but minimal holdings in junk bonds. Good liquidity (6.9) with sufficient resources to handle a spike in claims as well as a significant increase in policy surrenders. Good overall results on stability tests (6.9) excellent operational trends and excellent risk diversification.

Other Rating Factors: Strong capitalization (10.0) based on excellent risk adjusted capital (severe loss scenario). Excellent profitability (9.3).

Principal Business: Reinsurance (53%), individual health insurance (26%), group health insurance (16%), individual life insurance (4%), and credit health insurance (1%).

Principal Investments: NonCMO investment grade bonds (59%), CMOs and structured securities (22%), common & preferred stock (6%), real estate (5%), and misc. investments (8%).

Investments in Affiliates: 4%

Group Affiliation: American Enterprise Mutual Holding

Licensed in: All states except NY, PR

Commenced Business: May 1929

Address: 601 Sixth Ave, Des Moines, IA 50309

Phone: (515) 245-2000 **Domicile State:** IA **NAIC Code:** 60836

Data Date	Rating	RACR #1	RACR #2	Total Assets ($mil)	Capital ($mil)	Net Premium ($mil)	Net Income ($mil)
6-16	A-	5.00	3.51	909.7	488.4	191.6	8.9
6-15	A-	5.13	3.70	810.7	472.1	159.0	9.0
2015	A-	5.21	3.70	820.0	477.9	328.1	21.6
2014	A-	5.26	3.89	802.5	468.1	297.9	34.1
2013	A-	4.85	3.67	801.4	437.5	325.1	40.5
2012	A-	6.09	4.36	522.7	286.4	224.0	44.2
2011	A	4.60	3.35	538.6	259.3	294.5	17.1

Adverse Trends in Operations

Decrease in premium volume from 2013 to 2014 (8%)
Increase in policy surrenders from 2012 to 2013 (109%)
Decrease in asset base during 2012 (3%)
Decrease in premium volume from 2011 to 2012 (24%)

AMERICAN RETIREMENT LIFE INSURANCE COMPANY — C+ — Fair

Major Rating Factors: Fair overall results on stability tests (3.3 on a scale of 0 to 10) including weak results on operational trends, negative cash flow from operations for 2015 and excessive premium growth. Good current capitalization (5.7) based on good risk adjusted capital (severe loss scenario), although results have slipped from the excellent range during the last year. Weak profitability (1.6) with operating losses during the first six months of 2016.
Other Rating Factors: Weak liquidity (0.9). High quality investment portfolio (7.9).
Principal Business: Individual health insurance (100%).
Principal Investments: NonCMO investment grade bonds (106%).
Investments in Affiliates: None
Group Affiliation: CIGNA Corp
Licensed In: AL, AZ, AR, CA, CO, DE, FL, GA, IL, IN, IA, KS, KY, LA, MD, MN, MS, MO, MT, NE, NV, NH, NM, NC, ND, OH, OK, OR, PA, RI, SC, SD, TN, TX, UT, VA, WV, WI, WY
Commenced Business: November 1978
Address: 1300 E Ninth St, Cleveland, OH 44114
Phone: (512) 451-2224 **Domicile State:** OH **NAIC Code:** 88366

Data Date	Rating	RACR #1	RACR #2	Total Assets ($mil)	Capital ($mil)	Net Premium ($mil)	Net Income ($mil)
6-16	C+	1.09	0.84	77.1	42.6	122.1	-15.1
6-15	B-	1.35	1.04	72.9	47.7	90.8	-10.6
2015	C+	1.36	1.05	77.4	47.3	192.2	-22.1
2014	B-	1.11	0.86	55.7	31.0	120.4	-17.7
2013	B-	1.61	1.25	18.0	8.4	16.7	-4.3
2012	B-	3.32	2.99	5.7	5.4	-0.7	0.1
2011	U	3.13	2.82	6.4	5.5	0.0	0.0

Adverse Trends in Operations

Change in asset mix during 2015 (5%)
Increase in policy surrenders from 2014 to 2015 (8795%)
Change in asset mix during 2014 (18%)
Decrease in asset base during 2012 (11%)
Decrease in premium volume from 2011 to 2012 (29900%)

AMERICAN UNITED LIFE INSURANCE COMPANY * — B+ — Good

Major Rating Factors: Good quality investment portfolio (5.8 on a scale of 0 to 10) despite large holdings of BBB rated bonds in addition to moderate junk bond exposure. Exposure to mortgages is significant, but the mortgage default rate has been low. Good overall profitability (6.1). Good overall results on stability tests (6.6) excellent operational trends and excellent risk diversification.
Other Rating Factors: Strong capitalization (7.6) based on excellent risk adjusted capital (severe loss scenario). Excellent liquidity (7.4).
Principal Business: Group retirement contracts (79%), individual life insurance (6%), reinsurance (5%), individual annuities (4%), and other lines (5%).
Principal Investments: NonCMO investment grade bonds (62%), CMOs and structured securities (17%), mortgages in good standing (14%), policy loans (3%), and misc. investments (5%).
Investments in Affiliates: None
Group Affiliation: American United Life Group
Licensed in: All states except PR
Commenced Business: November 1877
Address: One American Square, Indianapolis, IN 46204
Phone: (317) 285-1877 **Domicile State:** IN **NAIC Code:** 60895

Data Date	Rating	RACR #1	RACR #2	Total Assets ($mil)	Capital ($mil)	Net Premium ($mil)	Net Income ($mil)
6-16	B+	2.75	1.38	23,906.8	927.2	1,652.5	13.3
6-15	B+	3.24	1.63	23,659.4	1,038.8	1,493.1	33.0
2015	B+	2.83	1.43	23,571.7	920.4	3,571.2	13.3
2014	B+	3.24	1.63	23,401.5	1,017.0	3,155.2	48.2
2013	B+	3.28	1.66	22,267.4	980.7	3,055.8	65.7
2012	B+	3.20	1.61	19,367.7	883.6	2,763.7	58.6
2011	B+	3.03	1.52	17,342.6	835.9	2,769.9	42.5

Adverse Trends in Operations

Decrease in capital during 2015 (10%)
Increase in policy surrenders from 2013 to 2014 (29%)

AMERICAN-AMICABLE LIFE INSURANCE COMPANY OF TEXAS — C — Fair

Major Rating Factors: Fair overall results on stability tests (4.3 on a scale of 0 to 10) including fair financial strength of affiliated Industrial Alliance Ins & Financial and excessive premium growth. Good quality investment portfolio (6.4) despite mixed results such as: minimal exposure to mortgages and substantial holdings of BBB bonds but minimal holdings in junk bonds. Good overall profitability (5.4) despite operating losses during the first six months of 2016.
Other Rating Factors: Good liquidity (6.4). Strong capitalization (7.1) based on excellent risk adjusted capital (severe loss scenario).
Principal Business: Individual life insurance (92%), individual annuities (4%), and group life insurance (4%).
Principal Investments: NonCMO investment grade bonds (66%), common & preferred stock (20%), policy loans (5%), mortgages in good standing (5%), and misc. investments (3%).
Investments in Affiliates: 20%
Group Affiliation: Industrial Alliance Ins & Financial
Licensed in: All states except IA, MA, MI, NH, NJ, NY, RI, VT, PR
Commenced Business: December 1981
Address: 425 Austin Ave, Waco, TX 76701
Phone: (254) 297-2777 **Domicile State:** TX **NAIC Code:** 68594

Data Date	Rating	RACR #1	RACR #2	Total Assets ($mil)	Capital ($mil)	Net Premium ($mil)	Net Income ($mil)
6-16	C	1.21	1.07	292.4	74.3	29.9	-5.1
6-15	C	1.23	1.10	285.1	79.8	22.6	10.2
2015	C	1.28	1.13	287.0	78.4	50.2	11.3
2014	C	1.44	1.29	285.9	93.4	42.0	8.7
2013	C	1.31	1.16	258.6	79.0	44.7	4.0
2012	C	1.54	1.29	235.8	64.9	52.4	7.6
2011	C+	1.23	0.91	446.4	57.4	48.9	12.0

Industrial Alliance Ins Financial
Composite Group Rating: C

Largest Group Members	Assets ($mil)	Rating
AMERICAN-AMICABLE LIFE INS CO OF TX	287	C
OCCIDENTAL LIFE INS CO OF NC	257	C
IA AMERICAN LIFE INS CO	229	B-
INDUSTRIAL ALLIANCE INS FIN SERV	202	C-
PIONEER SECURITY LIFE INS CO	125	C+

AMERICO FINANCIAL LIFE & ANNUITY INSURANCE | B- | Good

Major Rating Factors: Good current capitalization (6.8 on a scale of 0 to 10) based on good risk adjusted capital (severe loss scenario), although results have slipped from the excellent range during the last year. Good liquidity (6.1) with sufficient resources to cover a large increase in policy surrenders. Good overall results on stability tests (5.3) good operational trends, excellent risk adjusted capital for prior years and excellent risk diversification.

Other Rating Factors: Fair quality investment portfolio (4.6). Excellent profitability (7.1).

Principal Business: Individual annuities (56%), individual life insurance (25%), reinsurance (15%), and group life insurance (3%).

Principal Investments: NonCMO investment grade bonds (39%), CMOs and structured securities (35%), common & preferred stock (12%), mortgages in good standing (7%), and misc. investments (6%).

Investments in Affiliates: 3%

Group Affiliation: Americo Life Inc

Licensed in: All states except NY

Commenced Business: July 1946

Address: 500 North Akard, Dallas, TX 75201

Phone: (816) 391-2000 **Domicile State:** TX **NAIC Code:** 61999

Data Date	Rating	RACR #1	RACR #2	Total Assets ($mil)	Capital ($mil)	Net Premium ($mil)	Net Income ($mil)
6-16	B-	1.67	0.97	4,250.1	423.4	240.2	35.5
6-15	B-	1.71	1.01	4,053.4	427.9	271.4	33.6
2015	B-	1.77	1.05	4,117.9	432.4	543.2	55.6
2014	B-	1.85	1.10	3,921.9	458.7	436.4	84.4
2013	B-	1.92	1.15	3,804.4	442.3	233.4	54.7
2012	B-	1.86	1.11	3,777.8	402.3	295.5	63.3
2011	B-	1.75	1.04	3,747.5	371.1	349.7	89.2

Risk-Adjusted Capital Ratio #2
(Severe Loss Scenario)

AMERITAS LIFE INSURANCE CORP OF NEW YORK | B- | Good

Major Rating Factors: Good capitalization (6.8 on a scale of 0 to 10) based on good risk adjusted capital (severe loss scenario). Good quality investment portfolio (5.6) despite large holdings of BBB rated bonds in addition to moderate junk bond exposure. Exposure to mortgages is significant, but the mortgage default rate has been low. Fair liquidity (4.4).

Other Rating Factors: Fair overall results on stability tests (3.6). Weak profitability (1.8) with operating losses during the first six months of 2016.

Principal Business: N/A

Principal Investments: NonCMO investment grade bonds (65%), CMOs and structured securities (17%), mortgages in good standing (14%), policy loans (2%), and noninv. grade bonds (2%).

Investments in Affiliates: None

Group Affiliation: Ameritas Mutual Holding Co

Licensed in: NY

Commenced Business: May 1994

Address: 1350 Broadway Ste 2201, New York, NY 10018-7722

Phone: (845) 357-3816 **Domicile State:** NY **NAIC Code:** 60033

Data Date	Rating	RACR #1	RACR #2	Total Assets ($mil)	Capital ($mil)	Net Premium ($mil)	Net Income ($mil)
6-16	B-	1.81	0.98	1,188.8	77.3	65.7	-0.5
6-15	B-	1.99	1.09	1,140.0	80.8	55.7	-2.0
2015	B-	1.60	0.87	1,149.7	65.8	100.8	-17.1
2014	B-	2.15	1.18	1,128.8	86.9	95.3	-3.9
2013	B-	2.12	1.17	1,112.3	81.8	285.0	-45.8
2012	B-	3.72	3.07	122.3	33.5	71.4	-4.2
2011	B	4.09	3.50	104.6	36.6	71.6	-9.8

Risk-Adjusted Capital Ratio #2
(Severe Loss Scenario)

AMERITAS LIFE INSURANCE CORPORATION | B | Good

Major Rating Factors: Good overall profitability (6.0 on a scale of 0 to 10). Good liquidity (6.2) with sufficient resources to cover a large increase in policy surrenders. Fair quality investment portfolio (4.9) with significant exposure to mortgages . Mortgage default rate has been low.

Other Rating Factors: Fair overall results on stability tests (4.8). Strong capitalization (7.7) based on excellent risk adjusted capital (severe loss scenario).

Principal Business: Reinsurance (37%), group health insurance (17%), group retirement contracts (17%), individual life insurance (16%), and other lines (13%).

Principal Investments: NonCMO investment grade bonds (58%), CMOs and structured securities (15%), mortgages in good standing (13%), policy loans (5%), and misc. investments (10%).

Investments in Affiliates: 1%

Group Affiliation: Ameritas Mutual Holding Co

Licensed in: All states except NY, PR

Commenced Business: May 1887

Address: 5900 O Street, Lincoln, NE 68510

Phone: (402) 467-1122 **Domicile State:** NE **NAIC Code:** 61301

Data Date	Rating	RACR #1	RACR #2	Total Assets ($mil)	Capital ($mil)	Net Premium ($mil)	Net Income ($mil)
6-16	B	2.41	1.44	18,307.1	1,532.6	1,122.4	10.1
6-15	B	2.64	1.64	17,074.9	1,629.6	1,039.5	50.8
2015	B	2.40	1.45	18,148.8	1,511.5	3,359.6	-9.5
2014	B	2.67	1.67	16,822.0	1,623.5	2,119.7	129.8
2013	B	1.30	1.13	9,187.8	1,501.8	1,622.4	64.9
2012	B	1.31	1.13	7,997.9	1,298.4	1,494.5	0.0
2011	B	1.41	1.23	7,278.3	1,349.1	1,265.0	26.2

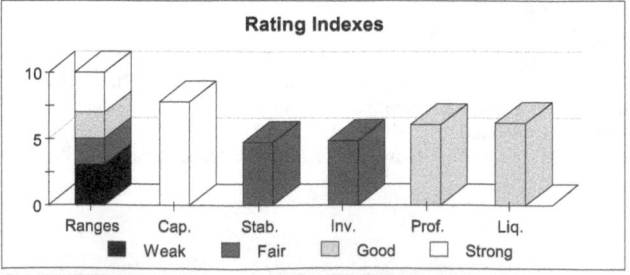

Rating Indexes

AMICA LIFE INSURANCE COMPANY　　　　　　　B　　　Good

Major Rating Factors: Good liquidity (6.5 on a scale of 0 to 10) with sufficient resources to cover a large increase in policy surrenders. Good overall results on stability tests (5.6). Stability strengths include excellent operational trends and excellent risk diversification. Fair profitability (4.9) with investment income below regulatory standards in relation to interest assumptions of reserves.

Other Rating Factors: Strong capitalization (9.9) based on excellent risk adjusted capital (severe loss scenario). High quality investment portfolio (7.2).

Principal Business: Individual life insurance (87%), individual annuities (9%), and group life insurance (4%).

Principal Investments: NonCMO investment grade bonds (58%), CMOs and structured securities (33%), common & preferred stock (4%), policy loans (1%), and noninv. grade bonds (1%).

Investments in Affiliates: None
Group Affiliation: Amica Mutual Group
Licensed in: All states except PR
Commenced Business: May 1970
Address: One Hundred Amica Way, Lincoln, RI 02867
Phone: (401) 334-6000　**Domicile State:** RI　**NAIC Code:** 72222

Data Date	Rating	RACR #1	RACR #2	Total Assets ($mil)	Capital ($mil)	Net Premium ($mil)	Net Income ($mil)
6-16	B	5.05	2.93	1,239.5	281.1	35.7	2.9
6-15	B	4.59	2.64	1,206.0	255.6	32.2	4.1
2015	B	5.18	3.00	1,224.7	287.5	63.6	5.0
2014	B	4.77	2.78	1,196.4	260.3	62.2	4.5
2013	B	4.16	2.43	1,133.1	217.5	61.8	5.6
2012	B	4.04	2.34	1,099.5	202.1	62.2	3.8
2011	A-	4.14	2.42	1,067.0	197.0	70.3	13.0

Exposure to Withdrawals Without Penalty (as a % of capital)

Capital — $288 mil.
Withdrawals w/o Penalty — $351 mil.

0%　　100%　　200%

ANNUITY INVESTORS LIFE INSURANCE COMPANY *　　A-　　Excellent

Major Rating Factors: Good overall results on stability tests (6.9 on a scale of 0 to 10). Strengths that enhance stability include excellent operational trends and excellent risk diversification. Good quality investment portfolio (6.4) despite mixed results such as: no exposure to mortgages and large holdings of BBB rated bonds but small junk bond holdings. Good liquidity (5.8).

Other Rating Factors: Strong capitalization (7.7) based on excellent risk adjusted capital (severe loss scenario). Excellent profitability (8.7).

Principal Business: Individual annuities (88%) and group retirement contracts (12%).

Principal Investments: NonCMO investment grade bonds (65%), CMOs and structured securities (30%), policy loans (2%), and noninv. grade bonds (2%).

Investments in Affiliates: None
Group Affiliation: American Financial Group Inc
Licensed in: All states except NY, VT, PR
Commenced Business: December 1981
Address: 250 E Fifth St, Cincinnati, OH 45202
Phone: (513) 357-3300　**Domicile State:** OH　**NAIC Code:** 93661

Data Date	Rating	RACR #1	RACR #2	Total Assets ($mil)	Capital ($mil)	Net Premium ($mil)	Net Income ($mil)
6-16	A-	2.93	1.48	3,041.6	256.8	101.8	9.0
6-15	B	2.84	1.43	3,037.1	235.3	113.0	11.5
2015	B	2.82	1.42	3,014.1	245.6	215.6	25.0
2014	B	2.77	1.40	2,994.8	227.1	229.2	27.6
2013	B	2.68	1.35	2,892.9	203.2	232.4	23.2
2012	B	2.52	1.25	2,693.8	178.5	267.7	29.5
2011	B	2.34	1.16	2,520.6	157.4	300.3	20.6

Adverse Trends in Operations

Decrease in premium volume from 2014 to 2015 (6%)
Decrease in premium volume from 2013 to 2014 (1%)
Decrease in premium volume from 2012 to 2013 (13%)
Decrease in premium volume from 2011 to 2012 (11%)

ANTHEM LIFE INSURANCE COMPANY *　　　A-　　Excellent

Major Rating Factors: Good overall profitability (6.7 on a scale of 0 to 10). Good liquidity (6.2) with sufficient resources to handle a spike in claims. Excellent overall results on stability tests (7.1). Strengths that enhance stability include excellent operational trends and excellent risk diversification.

Other Rating Factors: Strong capitalization (7.6) based on excellent risk adjusted capital (severe loss scenario). High quality investment portfolio (7.6).

Principal Business: Reinsurance (41%), group life insurance (32%), group health insurance (26%), and individual life insurance (1%).

Principal Investments: NonCMO investment grade bonds (62%), CMOs and structured securities (17%), cash (5%), and common & preferred stock (1%).

Investments in Affiliates: None
Group Affiliation: Anthem Inc
Licensed in: All states except NY, RI, VT, PR
Commenced Business: June 1956
Address: 6740 N High St Suite 200, Worthington, OH 43085
Phone: (614) 438-3959　**Domicile State:** IN　**NAIC Code:** 61069

Data Date	Rating	RACR #1	RACR #2	Total Assets ($mil)	Capital ($mil)	Net Premium ($mil)	Net Income ($mil)
6-16	A-	1.98	1.38	630.6	94.7	184.9	16.8
6-15	A-	1.92	1.34	600.5	90.3	186.3	14.9
2015	A-	1.64	1.16	633.7	95.9	368.9	18.2
2014	A-	1.92	1.34	582.4	109.1	357.8	34.4
2013	A-	2.17	1.51	575.3	120.4	345.1	47.1
2012	A-	1.60	1.12	565.4	87.4	336.1	13.8
2011	A-	1.46	1.03	542.7	77.8	206.6	6.4

Adverse Trends in Operations

Decrease in capital during 2015 (12%)
Decrease in capital during 2014 (9%)
Increase in policy surrenders from 2011 to 2012 (129%)

ASSURITY LIFE INSURANCE COMPANY * B+ Good

Major Rating Factors: Good quality investment portfolio (5.5 on a scale of 0 to 10) despite significant exposure to mortgages . Mortgage default rate has been low. large holdings of BBB rated bonds in addition to small junk bond holdings. Good overall profitability (6.5). Good liquidity (5.8).

Other Rating Factors: Good overall results on stability tests (6.6) excellent operational trends and excellent risk diversification. Strong capitalization (7.7) based on excellent risk adjusted capital (severe loss scenario).

Principal Business: Individual life insurance (50%), individual health insurance (27%), group health insurance (12%), individual annuities (4%), and other lines (6%).

Principal Investments: NonCMO investment grade bonds (57%), mortgages in good standing (14%), CMOs and structured securities (13%), policy loans (5%), and misc. investments (10%).

Investments in Affiliates: 1%

Group Affiliation: Assurity Security Group Inc

Licensed in: All states except NY, PR

Commenced Business: March 1964

Address: 2000 Q Street, Lincoln, NE 68503

Phone: (402) 476-6500 **Domicile State:** NE **NAIC Code:** 71439

Data Date	Rating	RACR #1	RACR #2	Total Assets ($mil)	Capital ($mil)	Net Premium ($mil)	Net Income ($mil)
6-16	B+	2.58	1.44	2,550.8	309.3	99.2	2.0
6-15	B+	3.08	1.63	2,474.1	309.7	94.6	10.5
2015	B+	2.71	1.51	2,472.0	318.1	189.5	20.8
2014	B+	3.03	1.61	2,463.6	300.5	189.7	19.2
2013	B+	3.17	1.69	2,449.3	306.4	191.2	14.6
2012	B+	3.00	1.57	2,419.2	262.7	225.0	21.9
2011	B+	2.77	1.45	2,403.2	257.8	240.6	23.0

Rating Indexes

ATHENE ANNUITY & LIFE ASSURANCE COMPANY C Fair

Major Rating Factors: Fair capitalization for the current period (4.6 on a scale of 0 to 10) based on fair risk adjusted capital (moderate loss scenario) reflecting some improvement over results in 2012. Fair quality investment portfolio (3.6) with substantial holdings of BBB bonds in addition to moderate junk bond exposure. Fair profitability (4.4). Excellent expense controls.

Other Rating Factors: Fair overall results on stability tests (3.7) including weak risk adjusted capital in prior years, negative cash flow from operations for 2015. Good liquidity (6.2).

Principal Business: Individual annuities (52%), individual life insurance (33%), reinsurance (7%), group health insurance (3%), and other lines (4%).

Principal Investments: CMOs and structured securities (33%), nonCMO investment grade bonds (18%), common & preferred stock (17%), mortgages in good standing (10%), and misc. investments (22%).

Investments in Affiliates: 31%

Group Affiliation: BRH Holdings GP Ltd

Licensed in: All states except NY, PR

Commenced Business: July 1909

Address: 2711 Centerville Rd Suite 400, Wilmington, DE 19808

Phone: (888) 266-8489 **Domicile State:** DE **NAIC Code:** 61492

Data Date	Rating	RACR #1	RACR #2	Total Assets ($mil)	Capital ($mil)	Net Premium ($mil)	Net Income ($mil)
6-16	C	0.88	0.70	10,581.5	1,252.7	12.9	11.3
6-15	C-	0.92	0.71	10,982.3	1,210.6	36.6	39.7
2015	C	0.88	0.70	10,847.8	1,250.8	40.4	67.8
2014	C-	0.89	0.70	11,159.9	1,154.1	113.7	116.2
2013	D+	0.87	0.66	11,775.6	1,050.1	200.1	49.5
2012	D+	0.54	0.34	10,481.2	276.9	3,166.8	11.5
2011	D+	0.46	0.25	7,482.7	142.6	2,154.6	-18.8

Risk-Adjusted Capital Ratio #1
(Moderate Loss Scenario)

ATHENE ANNUITY & LIFE ASSURANCE COMPANY OF NEW YOR C Fair

Major Rating Factors: Fair overall results on stability tests (3.7 on a scale of 0 to 10) including fair risk adjusted capital in prior years. Good capitalization (5.6) based on good risk adjusted capital (moderate loss scenario). Good overall profitability (6.8).

Other Rating Factors: Low quality investment portfolio (2.4). Excellent liquidity (9.1).

Principal Business: Individual annuities (55%), individual life insurance (44%), and individual health insurance (1%).

Principal Investments: CMOs and structured securities (58%), noninv. grade bonds (17%), nonCMO investment grade bonds (12%), mortgages in good standing (8%), and misc. investments (5%).

Investments in Affiliates: 1%

Group Affiliation: BRH Holdings GP Ltd

Licensed in: All states except PR

Commenced Business: October 1966

Address: 69 Lydecker St, Nyack, NY 10960

Phone: (800) 926-7599 **Domicile State:** NY **NAIC Code:** 68039

Data Date	Rating	RACR #1	RACR #2	Total Assets ($mil)	Capital ($mil)	Net Premium ($mil)	Net Income ($mil)
6-16	C	1.42	0.68	3,274.1	213.1	11.0	3.0
6-15	C	1.47	0.66	3,342.1	177.9	4.2	-0.8
2015	C	1.44	0.69	3,236.8	207.9	8.4	7.8
2014	C	1.42	0.64	3,382.9	168.1	11.5	7.1
2013	C	1.29	0.60	3,525.6	164.4	17.4	12.0
2012	C+	2.35	1.10	3,454.8	215.5	-2,478.7	125.5
2011	C+	2.39	1.19	3,561.2	345.4	62.4	51.3

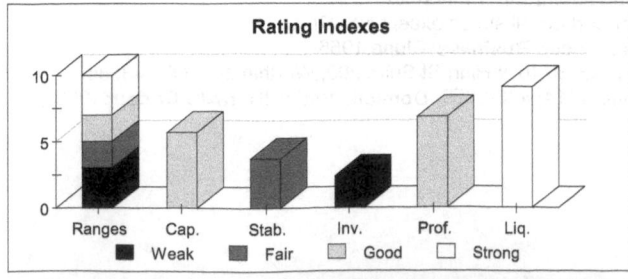

Rating Indexes

ATHENE ANNUITY & LIFE COMPANY C+ Fair

Major Rating Factors: Fair overall results on stability tests (4.5 on a scale of 0 to 10) including fair risk adjusted capital in prior years. Good capitalization (5.0) based on good risk adjusted capital (moderate loss scenario). Good overall profitability (5.1).
Other Rating Factors: Good liquidity (5.5). Low quality investment portfolio (2.3).
Principal Business: Individual annuities (69%), individual life insurance (18%), group retirement contracts (12%), and reinsurance (1%).
Principal Investments: NonCMO investment grade bonds (51%), CMOs and structured securities (29%), mortgages in good standing (10%), noninv. grade bonds (4%), and misc. investments (5%).
Investments in Affiliates: 3%
Group Affiliation: BRH Holdings GP Ltd
Licensed in: All states except NY, PR
Commenced Business: February 1896
Address: 7700 Mills Civic Parkway, West Des Moines, IA 50266
Phone: (888) 266-8489 **Domicile State:** IA **NAIC Code:** 61689

Data Date	Rating	RACR #1	RACR #2	Total Assets ($mil)	Capital ($mil)	Net Premium ($mil)	Net Income ($mil)
6-16	C+	1.01	0.53	45,056.3	1,104.4	549.6	56.3
6-15	C+	1.10	0.58	44,575.5	1,093.7	240.1	215.4
2015	C+	1.03	0.55	44,053.2	1,108.9	475.4	596.8
2014	C+	1.05	0.56	44,405.3	1,040.0	404.5	262.8
2013	C+	0.95	0.51	43,841.7	978.8	-25,903.0	43.1
2012	C+	1.44	0.84	51,044.2	2,868.5	5,610.1	-1.9
2011	C+	1.24	0.72	48,504.3	2,678.6	3,048.6	148.2

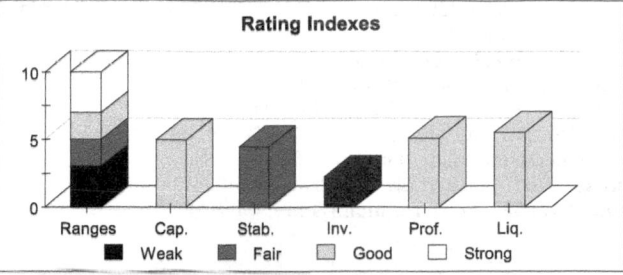

Rating Indexes

Ranges Cap. Stab. Inv. Prof. Liq.
■ Weak ■ Fair ☐ Good ☐ Strong

AURORA NATIONAL LIFE ASSURANCE COMPANY B Good

Major Rating Factors: Good overall results on stability tests (5.5 on a scale of 0 to 10) despite excessive premium growth and negative cash flow from operations for 2015. Other stability subfactors include good operational trends and excellent risk diversification. Good quality investment portfolio (6.7) despite significant exposure to mortgages . Mortgage default rate has been low. large holdings of BBB rated bonds in addition to small junk bond holdings. Good overall profitability (5.4) although investment income, in comparison to reserve requirements, is below regulatory standards.
Other Rating Factors: Good liquidity (6.9). Strong capitalization (8.4) based on excellent risk adjusted capital (severe loss scenario).
Principal Business: Individual life insurance (98%) and group life insurance (2%).
Principal Investments: NonCMO investment grade bonds (73%), mortgages in good standing (13%), policy loans (5%), CMOs and structured securities (5%), and misc. investments (3%).
Investments in Affiliates: None
Group Affiliation: Reinsurance Group of America Inc
Licensed in: All states except CT, ME, NH, NY, PR
Commenced Business: December 1961
Address: 2525 Colorado Ave, Bl C, Santa Monica, CA 90404-3540
Phone: (310) 264-3200 **Domicile State:** CA **NAIC Code:** 61182

Data Date	Rating	RACR #1	RACR #2	Total Assets ($mil)	Capital ($mil)	Net Premium ($mil)	Net Income ($mil)
6-16	B	3.83	1.91	2,899.3	310.7	0.4	8.7
6-15	B	3.23	1.65	3,070.8	329.1	0.2	10.9
2015	B	3.85	1.93	2,953.3	303.2	0.5	21.4
2014	B	4.27	2.22	3,061.6	321.1	0.6	18.0
2013	B-	4.39	2.27	3,143.7	341.5	0.6	17.8
2012	C+	5.06	2.63	3,007.1	368.7	0.7	34.9
2011	C+	5.13	2.67	2,818.7	355.9	0.8	18.1

Adverse Trends in Operations

Decrease in premium volume from 2014 to 2015 (11%)
Decrease in asset base during 2015 (4%)
Decrease in premium volume from 2012 to 2013 (11%)
Increase in policy surrenders from 2011 to 2012 (37%)
Decrease in premium volume from 2011 to 2012 (15%)

AUTO CLUB LIFE INSURANCE COMPANY C+ Fair

Major Rating Factors: Fair overall results on stability tests (4.4 on a scale of 0 to 10) including excessive premium growth. Good capitalization (5.6) based on good risk adjusted capital (severe loss scenario). Capital levels have been relatively consistent over the last five years. Good quality investment portfolio (6.0) despite mixed results such as: large holdings of BBB rated bonds but junk bond exposure equal to 61% of capital.
Other Rating Factors: Good liquidity (5.8). Weak profitability (2.0) with operating losses during the first six months of 2016.
Principal Business: Reinsurance (94%), individual life insurance (5%), and individual annuities (1%).
Principal Investments: NonCMO investment grade bonds (64%), CMOs and structured securities (18%), noninv. grade bonds (8%), common & preferred stock (6%), and policy loans (2%).
Investments in Affiliates: 6%
Group Affiliation: Automobile Club of Michigan Group
Licensed in: AZ, AR, CA, CO, IL, IN, IA, KS, KY, MD, MI, MN, MO, NE, NM, NC, ND, OH, OK, PA, SC, SD, TX, VA, WA, WI
Commenced Business: August 1974
Address: 1 Auto Club Dr, Dearborn, MI 48126
Phone: (734) 591-9442 **Domicile State:** MI **NAIC Code:** 84522

Data Date	Rating	RACR #1	RACR #2	Total Assets ($mil)	Capital ($mil)	Net Premium ($mil)	Net Income ($mil)
6-16	C+	1.16	0.83	681.0	78.2	89.6	-4.1
6-15	C+	1.22	0.87	587.5	74.4	62.9	-0.7
2015	C+	1.15	0.83	623.7	77.1	141.1	-3.2
2014	C+	1.22	0.87	562.5	73.6	117.6	-8.0
2013	C+	1.14	0.81	503.6	59.6	89.0	-6.7
2012	B-	1.32	0.92	475.8	63.7	74.4	-6.6
2011	B	1.58	1.10	453.0	68.3	63.9	1.2

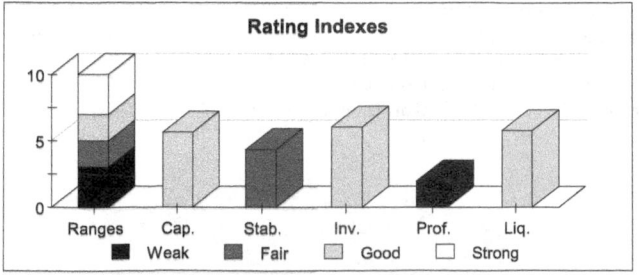

Rating Indexes

Ranges Cap. Stab. Inv. Prof. Liq.
■ Weak ■ Fair ☐ Good ☐ Strong

AUTO-OWNERS LIFE INSURANCE COMPANY * A- Excellent

Major Rating Factors: Good quality investment portfolio (5.9 on a scale of 0 to 10) despite mixed results such as: minimal exposure to mortgages and substantial holdings of BBB bonds but minimal holdings in junk bonds. Good overall profitability (5.4) although investment income, in comparison to reserve requirements, is below regulatory standards. Good liquidity (6.4).

Other Rating Factors: Good overall results on stability tests (6.9) excellent operational trends and excellent risk diversification. Strong capitalization (7.7) based on excellent risk adjusted capital (severe loss scenario).

Principal Business: Individual life insurance (41%), individual annuities (36%), group retirement contracts (16%), individual health insurance (6%), and group life insurance (1%).

Principal Investments: NonCMO investment grade bonds (63%), CMOs and structured securities (20%), mortgages in good standing (5%), real estate (4%), and misc. investments (8%).

Investments in Affiliates: None

Group Affiliation: Auto-Owners Group

Licensed in: AL, AZ, AR, CO, FL, GA, ID, IL, IN, IA, KS, KY, MI, MN, MS, MO, NE, NV, NM, NC, ND, OH, OR, PA, SC, SD, TN, UT, VA, WA, WI

Commenced Business: January 1966

Address: 6101 Anacapri Blvd, Lansing, MI 48917

Phone: (517) 323-1200 **Domicile State:** MI **NAIC Code:** 61190

Data Date	Rating	RACR #1	RACR #2	Total Assets ($mil)	Capital ($mil)	Net Premium ($mil)	Net Income ($mil)
6-16	A-	2.72	1.45	3,832.7	400.9	133.5	5.4
6-15	A-	2.46	1.31	3,699.4	355.5	123.2	12.2
2015	A-	2.59	1.39	3,739.3	391.9	259.5	23.7
2014	A	2.41	1.28	3,632.3	344.0	257.2	16.0
2013	A	2.24	1.20	3,509.2	323.5	248.4	22.7
2012	A	2.13	1.13	3,297.1	277.5	250.1	26.2
2011	A	1.97	1.05	3,106.7	257.4	406.5	14.3

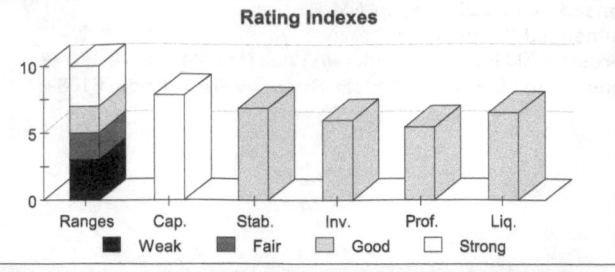

Rating Indexes

AUTOMOBILE CLUB OF SOUTHERN CALIFORNIA INSURANCE B- Good

Major Rating Factors: Good current capitalization (6.0 on a scale of 0 to 10) based on good risk adjusted capital (severe loss scenario) reflecting some improvement over results in 2012. Good liquidity (5.2) with sufficient resources to cover a large increase in policy surrenders. Good overall results on stability tests (5.1) despite excessive premium growth and fair risk adjusted capital in prior years excellent operational trends and excellent risk diversification.

Other Rating Factors: Fair quality investment portfolio (4.7). Weak profitability (1.9) with operating losses during the first six months of 2016.

Principal Business: Reinsurance (100%).

Principal Investments: NonCMO investment grade bonds (74%), CMOs and structured securities (18%), noninv. grade bonds (7%), and policy loans (1%).

Investments in Affiliates: None

Group Affiliation: Interins Exch Automobile Club

Licensed in: CA, MI

Commenced Business: December 1999

Address: 3333 Fairview Road, Costa Mesa, CA 92625

Phone: (714) 850-5111 **Domicile State:** CA **NAIC Code:** 60256

Data Date	Rating	RACR #1	RACR #2	Total Assets ($mil)	Capital ($mil)	Net Premium ($mil)	Net Income ($mil)
6-16	B-	1.54	0.87	1,031.3	77.3	148.9	-8.5
6-15	B-	1.64	0.92	890.7	72.3	103.5	-7.7
2015	B-	1.68	0.96	947.3	82.1	228.3	-14.9
2014	B	1.68	0.95	841.8	74.4	193.7	-9.4
2013	B	1.39	0.78	746.9	53.7	140.6	-15.2
2012	B	1.31	0.71	683.9	46.9	119.3	-12.0
2011	B	1.63	0.90	639.8	52.3	112.9	-3.3

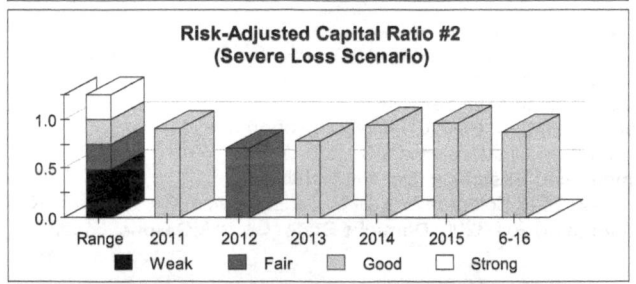

Risk-Adjusted Capital Ratio #2
(Severe Loss Scenario)

AVIVA LIFE & ANNUITY COMPANY OF NEW YORK C Fair

Major Rating Factors: Fair quality investment portfolio (4.9 on a scale of 0 to 10) with significant exposure to mortgages . Mortgage default rate has been low. Fair profitability (4.7). Excellent expense controls. Fair overall results on stability tests (3.3).

Other Rating Factors: Strong capitalization (7.4) based on excellent risk adjusted capital (severe loss scenario). Excellent liquidity (7.8).

Principal Business: Individual life insurance (92%), group life insurance (5%), reinsurance (1%), and individual health insurance (1%).

Principal Investments: NonCMO investment grade bonds (85%), mortgages in good standing (12%), CMOs and structured securities (2%), and noninv. grade bonds (1%).

Investments in Affiliates: None

Group Affiliation: BRH Holdings GP Ltd

Licensed in: CT, FL, IL, IN, IA, KS, KY, MA, MI, MS, NV, NJ, NY, NC, PA, RI, VT

Commenced Business: November 1958

Address: 324 S Service Rd Suite 200, Melville, NY 11747

Phone: (516) 364-5900 **Domicile State:** NY **NAIC Code:** 63932

Data Date	Rating	RACR #1	RACR #2	Total Assets ($mil)	Capital ($mil)	Net Premium ($mil)	Net Income ($mil)
6-16	C	2.68	1.25	944.2	75.2	0.4	4.6
6-15	C	1.59	0.74	1,803.2	57.1	0.8	3.1
2015	C	2.72	1.30	945.1	72.9	1.4	14.4
2014	C	1.56	0.72	1,861.2	54.8	2.2	88.1
2013	C	1.76	0.83	1,727.8	64.0	-661.7	-114.9
2012	C	1.46	0.76	1,679.7	76.1	52.1	-85.4
2011	C+	2.09	1.09	1,588.5	116.9	28.8	22.5

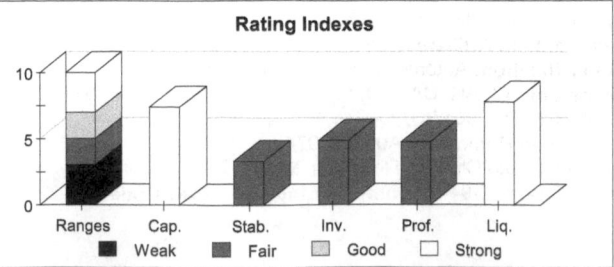

Rating Indexes

AXA CORPORATE SOLUTIONS LIFE REINSURANCE COMPANY   B   Good

Major Rating Factors: Fair quality investment portfolio (4.9 on a scale of 0 to 10). Fair profitability (3.6). Fair overall results on stability tests (4.4) including weak results on operational trends.

Other Rating Factors: Strong overall capitalization (8.2) based on excellent risk adjusted capital (severe loss scenario). Nevertheless, capital levels have fluctuated during prior years. Excellent liquidity (9.5).

Principal Business: Reinsurance (100%).

Principal Investments: NonCMO investment grade bonds (55%), common & preferred stock (30%), cash (10%), noninv. grade bonds (3%), and CMOs and structured securities (2%).

Investments in Affiliates: 30%

Group Affiliation: AXA Financial Inc

Licensed in: All states except FL, PR

Commenced Business: January 1983

Address: 2711 Centerville Rd Ste 400, Wilmington, DE 19808

Phone: (201) 743-7217 **Domicile State:** DE **NAIC Code:** 68365

Data Date	Rating	RACR #1	RACR #2	Total Assets ($mil)	Capital ($mil)	Net Premium ($mil)	Net Income ($mil)
6-16	B	2.06	1.79	258.3	173.1	2.6	1.5
6-15	B-	1.95	1.81	311.7	221.5	2.6	11.0
2015	B-	2.04	1.83	255.2	154.1	6.4	-6.0
2014	B-	2.43	2.22	490.9	419.5	-536.1	95.1
2013	B-	8.09	5.47	978.0	253.9	52.4	57.8
2012	B-	5.51	3.76	1,174.3	199.1	48.9	-43.3
2011	B-	6.94	4.51	1,387.0	279.8	72.3	-2.1

Adverse Trends in Operations

Decrease in asset base during 2015 (48%)
Decrease in capital during 2015 (63%)
Decrease in premium volume from 2013 to 2014 (1123%)
Decrease in asset base during 2012 (15%)
Decrease in premium volume from 2011 to 2012 (32%)

AXA EQUITABLE LIFE INSURANCE COMPANY *   B+   Good

Major Rating Factors: Good liquidity (6.8 on a scale of 0 to 10) with sufficient resources to cover a large increase in policy surrenders. Good overall results on stability tests (6.8). Stability strengths include excellent operational trends, good risk adjusted capital for prior years and excellent risk diversification. Strong capitalization (7.7) based on excellent risk adjusted capital (severe loss scenario).

Other Rating Factors: High quality investment portfolio (7.1). Excellent profitability (7.4).

Principal Business: Individual annuities (58%), group retirement contracts (22%), individual life insurance (19%), reinsurance (2%), and individual health insurance (1%).

Principal Investments: NonCMO investment grade bonds (65%), mortgages in good standing (16%), policy loans (7%), common & preferred stock (3%), and misc. investments (8%).

Investments in Affiliates: 6%

Group Affiliation: AXA Financial Inc

Licensed in: All states, the District of Columbia and Puerto Rico

Commenced Business: July 1859

Address: 1290 Avenue of the Americas, New York, NY 10104-0101

Phone: (212) 641-8231 **Domicile State:** NY **NAIC Code:** 62944

Data Date	Rating	RACR #1	RACR #2	Total Assets ($mil)	Capital ($mil)	Net Premium ($mil)	Net Income ($mil)
6-16	B+	2.41	1.45	171,038	5,853.1	6,294.0	447.8
6-15	B	2.00	1.25	168,264	5,350.3	6,069.8	942.4
2015	B	2.29	1.39	164,668	5,422.6	12,220.2	2,038.0
2014	B	1.96	1.23	165,942	5,170.0	12,108.2	1,663.8
2013	B	1.49	0.90	158,658	3,825.5	11,934.6	-28.5
2012	B	1.77	1.05	144,827	4,689.4	11,487.5	602.4
2011	C+	1.98	1.10	134,496	4,624.8	10,354.6	967.1

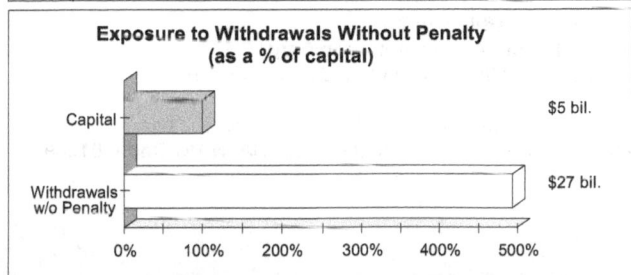

Exposure to Withdrawals Without Penalty
(as a % of capital)

Capital — $5 bil.
Withdrawals w/o Penalty — $27 bil.

0%   100%   200%   300%   400%   500%

BALTIMORE LIFE INSURANCE COMPANY   B   Good

Major Rating Factors: Good capitalization (6.3 on a scale of 0 to 10) based on good risk adjusted capital (severe loss scenario). Moreover, capital levels have been consistent over the last five years. Good overall profitability (5.9). Good overall results on stability tests (5.3) excellent operational trends and good risk diversification.

Other Rating Factors: Fair quality investment portfolio (4.3). Fair liquidity (3.3).

Principal Business: Individual life insurance (75%), individual annuities (13%), group life insurance (10%), and reinsurance (2%).

Principal Investments: NonCMO investment grade bonds (78%), noninv. grade bonds (5%), policy loans (4%), mortgages in good standing (3%), and misc. investments (8%).

Investments in Affiliates: None

Group Affiliation: Baltimore Life Holdings Inc

Licensed in: All states except NY, PR

Commenced Business: March 1882

Address: 10075 Red Run Blvd, Owings Mills, MD 21117-6050

Phone: (410) 581-6600 **Domicile State:** MD **NAIC Code:** 61212

Data Date	Rating	RACR #1	RACR #2	Total Assets ($mil)	Capital ($mil)	Net Premium ($mil)	Net Income ($mil)
6-16	B	1.77	0.91	1,216.4	80.1	67.6	1.5
6-15	B	1.92	1.01	1,163.2	78.3	65.1	2.5
2015	B	1.87	0.98	1,192.0	79.3	134.3	5.3
2014	B	1.87	0.98	1,140.4	74.7	139.1	4.5
2013	B	2.02	1.06	1,085.7	72.8	147.8	-2.6
2012	B	2.11	1.10	1,004.6	70.4	125.1	6.5
2011	B	1.93	1.02	944.3	65.4	106.2	4.8

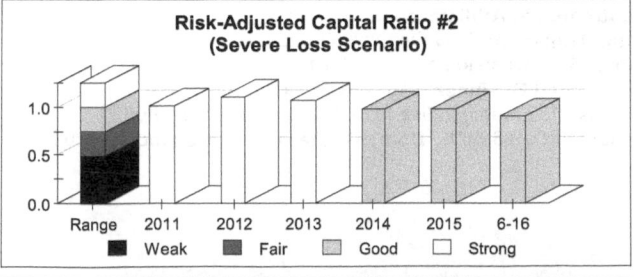

Risk-Adjusted Capital Ratio #2
(Severe Loss Scenario)

1.0
0.5
0.0

Range   2011   2012   2013   2014   2015   6-16

■ Weak   ■ Fair   ▨ Good   □ Strong

BANKERS CONSECO LIFE INSURANCE COMPANY | D | Weak

Major Rating Factors: Weak overall results on stability tests (1.8 on a scale of 0 to 10). Fair profitability (4.9). Excellent expense controls. Good liquidity (5.6) with sufficient resources to handle a spike in claims as well as a significant increase in policy surrenders.

Other Rating Factors: Strong capitalization (10.0) based on excellent risk adjusted capital (severe loss scenario). High quality investment portfolio (7.1).

Principal Business: Individual life insurance (68%), individual health insurance (26%), individual annuities (5%), and reinsurance (1%).

Principal Investments: NonCMO investment grade bonds (71%), CMOs and structured securities (22%), noninv. grade bonds (3%), policy loans (2%), and misc. investments (2%).

Investments in Affiliates: None

Group Affiliation: CNO Financial Group Inc

Licensed in: NY

Commenced Business: July 1987

Address: 11815 N Pennsylvania St, Carmel, IN 46032

Phone: (215) 244-1600 **Domicile State:** NY **NAIC Code:** 68560

Data Date	Rating	RACR #1	RACR #2	Total Assets ($mil)	Capital ($mil)	Net Premium ($mil)	Net Income ($mil)
6-16	D	5.24	3.18	226.5	51.6	27.8	4.1
6-15	D	3.55	2.33	214.0	34.2	26.4	2.5
2015	D	4.81	2.98	218.1	47.5	49.6	5.6
2014	D	3.25	2.36	207.6	31.2	46.9	-6.8
2013	D	4.11	2.30	383.2	45.5	49.2	21.7
2012	D	2.16	1.29	343.6	22.6	48.7	-2.0
2011	D	2.49	1.59	323.4	26.0	44.8	0.0

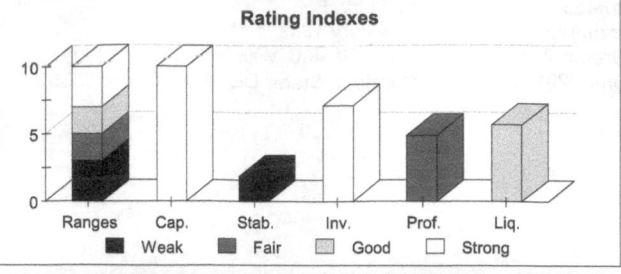

Rating Indexes

BANKERS FIDELITY LIFE INSURANCE COMPANY | B | Good

Major Rating Factors: Good overall capitalization (6.3 on a scale of 0 to 10) based on good risk adjusted capital (severe loss scenario). However, capital levels have fluctuated somewhat during past years. Good liquidity (5.7) with sufficient resources to handle a spike in claims. Good overall results on stability tests (5.7) excellent operational trends and good risk diversification.

Other Rating Factors: Fair quality investment portfolio (3.7). Excellent profitability (8.1).

Principal Business: Individual health insurance (87%), individual life insurance (11%), and reinsurance (1%).

Principal Investments: NonCMO investment grade bonds (66%), noninv. grade bonds (17%), common & preferred stock (11%), policy loans (2%), and cash (2%).

Investments in Affiliates: 7%

Group Affiliation: Atlantic American Corp

Licensed in: All states except CA, CT, NY, VT, PR

Commenced Business: November 1955

Address: 4370 Peachtree Rd NE, Atlanta, GA 30319

Phone: (800) 241-1439 **Domicile State:** GA **NAIC Code:** 61239

Data Date	Rating	RACR #1	RACR #2	Total Assets ($mil)	Capital ($mil)	Net Premium ($mil)	Net Income ($mil)
6-16	B	1.22	0.91	141.3	34.2	50.9	0.6
6-15	B	1.33	1.00	144.5	37.1	48.8	3.7
2015	B	1.28	0.96	143.9	35.3	96.1	4.0
2014	B	1.21	0.92	139.1	34.0	100.2	2.7
2013	B	1.58	1.14	138.8	34.5	99.6	3.0
2012	B	2.03	1.48	128.7	33.1	89.6	2.3
2011	B	2.32	1.67	122.1	32.1	70.7	3.6

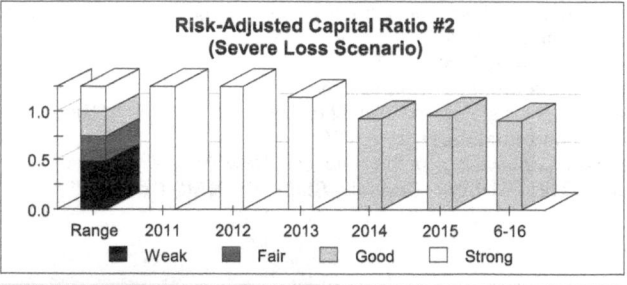

Risk-Adjusted Capital Ratio #2
(Severe Loss Scenario)

BANKERS LIFE & CASUALTY COMPANY | D+ | Weak

Major Rating Factors: Weak overall results on stability tests (2.7 on a scale of 0 to 10). Fair quality investment portfolio (4.7) with large holdings of BBB rated bonds in addition to junk bond exposure equal to 55% of capital. Good liquidity (5.5) with sufficient resources to cover a large increase in policy surrenders.

Other Rating Factors: Strong capitalization (7.2) based on excellent risk adjusted capital (severe loss scenario). Excellent profitability (9.0).

Principal Business: Individual health insurance (35%), individual annuities (32%), individual life insurance (19%), reinsurance (12%), and group health insurance (1%).

Principal Investments: NonCMO investment grade bonds (60%), CMOs and structured securities (24%), mortgages in good standing (7%), noninv. grade bonds (4%), and misc. investments (4%).

Investments in Affiliates: 1%

Group Affiliation: CNO Financial Group Inc

Licensed in: All states except NY, PR

Commenced Business: January 1879

Address: 222 Merchandise Mart Plaza, Chicago, IL 60654

Phone: (312) 396-6000 **Domicile State:** IL **NAIC Code:** 61263

Data Date	Rating	RACR #1	RACR #2	Total Assets ($mil)	Capital ($mil)	Net Premium ($mil)	Net Income ($mil)
6-16	D+	2.13	1.11	17,123.8	1,253.0	1,245.6	71.6
6-15	D+	2.16	1.12	16,755.8	1,236.8	1,158.1	108.7
2015	D+	2.23	1.16	16,905.4	1,238.6	2,385.0	188.7
2014	D+	2.12	1.10	16,590.7	1,193.1	2,387.1	211.6
2013	D+	2.04	1.06	15,839.5	1,057.0	2,323.5	161.9
2012	D+	1.83	0.96	14,941.3	914.6	2,282.5	231.3
2011	D+	1.60	0.86	14,515.9	816.8	2,518.6	212.0

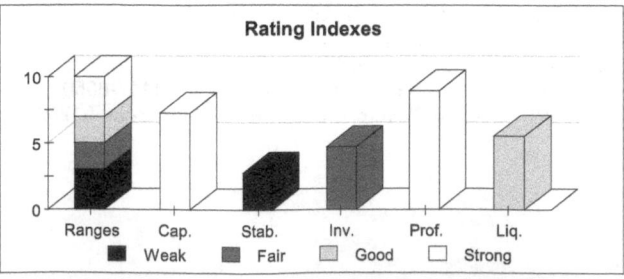

Rating Indexes

BANNER LIFE INSURANCE COMPANY — C+ — Fair

Major Rating Factors: Fair profitability (4.4 on a scale of 0 to 10). Excellent expense controls. Fair overall results on stability tests (4.6) including excessive premium growth. Good quality investment portfolio (5.9) despite significant exposure to mortgages . Mortgage default rate has been low. substantial holdings of BBB bonds in addition to small junk bond holdings.

Other Rating Factors: Strong capitalization (7.7) based on excellent risk adjusted capital (severe loss scenario). Excellent liquidity (7.1).

Principal Business: Individual life insurance (69%) and group retirement contracts (31%).

Principal Investments: NonCMO investment grade bonds (60%), mortgages in good standing (17%), common & preferred stock (10%), CMOs and structured securities (7%), and noninv. grade bonds (6%).

Investments in Affiliates: 10%

Group Affiliation: Legal & General America Inc

Licensed in: All states except NY, PR

Commenced Business: October 1981

Address: 3275 Bennett Creek Ave, Frederick, MD 21704

Phone: (301) 279-4800 **Domicile State:** MD **NAIC Code:** 94250

Data Date	Rating	RACR #1	RACR #2	Total Assets ($mil)	Capital ($mil)	Net Premium ($mil)	Net Income ($mil)
6-16	C+	2.05	1.49	2,469.4	413.8	201.5	104.2
6-15	D+	1.03	0.83	1,730.9	271.9	141.4	49.9
2015	C	1.85	1.37	2,213.7	337.2	291.2	126.4
2014	D	1.35	1.09	1,818.6	369.1	219.8	-73.9
2013	D	1.84	1.44	1,687.7	450.0	324.1	-44.0
2012	C	1.38	1.19	1,703.8	459.0	96.0	-17.9
2011	D	1.13	0.92	1,524.0	252.7	119.5	55.8

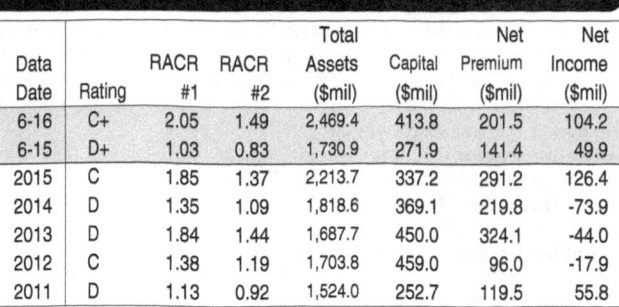

Rating Indexes

BENEFICIAL LIFE INSURANCE COMPANY — B — Good

Major Rating Factors: Good quality investment portfolio (5.3 on a scale of 0 to 10) despite mixed results such as: substantial holdings of BBB bonds but moderate junk bond exposure. Good overall profitability (6.8). Good liquidity (6.8) with sufficient resources to handle a spike in claims as well as a significant increase in policy surrenders.

Other Rating Factors: Good overall results on stability tests (5.3) despite negative cash flow from operations for 2015 good operational trends and excellent risk diversification. Strong capitalization (7.1) based on excellent risk adjusted capital (severe loss scenario).

Principal Business: Individual life insurance (88%), individual annuities (6%), and reinsurance (6%).

Principal Investments: NonCMO investment grade bonds (68%), CMOs and structured securities (21%), common & preferred stock (5%), policy loans (4%), and misc. investments (3%).

Investments in Affiliates: None

Group Affiliation: DMC Reserve Trust

Licensed in: All states except NY, PR

Commenced Business: May 1905

Address: 55 North 300 West Suite 375, Salt Lake City, UT 84101

Phone: (801) 933-1100 **Domicile State:** UT **NAIC Code:** 61395

Data Date	Rating	RACR #1	RACR #2	Total Assets ($mil)	Capital ($mil)	Net Premium ($mil)	Net Income ($mil)
6-16	B	1.92	1.06	2,339.7	187.5	18.2	51.3
6-15	B	4.95	2.71	2,869.2	581.6	20.6	23.4
2015	B	5.11	2.77	2,796.0	585.1	40.0	39.3
2014	B	5.09	2.75	2,010.0	558.6	39.0	60.1
2013	B	6.14	3.22	3,011.2	579.1	43.0	44.9
2012	B-	5.42	2.85	3,090.3	546.0	47.7	15.1
2011	C+	4.37	2.23	3,185.1	511.2	50.4	-0.6

Rating Indexes

BERKLEY LIFE & HEALTH INSURANCE COMPANY — B — Good

Major Rating Factors: Good overall results on stability tests (5.9 on a scale of 0 to 10) despite fair financial strength of affiliated W R Berkley Corp and excessive premium growth. Other stability subfactors include excellent operational trends and excellent risk diversification. Strong capitalization (10.0) based on excellent risk adjusted capital (severe loss scenario). Moreover, capital levels have been consistently high over the last five years. High quality investment portfolio (8.5).

Other Rating Factors: Excellent profitability (8.6) despite modest operating losses during 2011. Excellent liquidity (7.0).

Principal Business: Group health insurance (100%).

Principal Investments: NonCMO investment grade bonds (75%) and CMOs and structured securities (26%).

Investments in Affiliates: None

Group Affiliation: W R Berkley Corp

Licensed in: All states except PR

Commenced Business: July 1963

Address: 200 Clarendon St, Boston, MA 02117

Phone: (203) 851-1755 **Domicile State:** IA **NAIC Code:** 64890

Data Date	Rating	RACR #1	RACR #2	Total Assets ($mil)	Capital ($mil)	Net Premium ($mil)	Net Income ($mil)
6-16	B	5.21	4.03	243.3	137.5	112.3	8.7
6-15	B-	5.70	4.32	216.0	116.9	82.9	10.4
2015	B-	5.35	4.11	223.9	129.2	187.3	23.1
2014	B-	5.56	4.23	197.6	106.0	145.5	11.7
2013	B-	6.16	4.73	166.3	94.2	117.1	11.3
2012	B	5.25	4.11	148.7	83.3	123.9	7.7
2011	B	4.59	3.60	112.0	59.5	101.1	-0.6

W R Berkley Corp Composite Group Rating: C+ Largest Group Members	Assets ($mil)	Rating
BERKLEY INS CO	17109	B-
BERKLEY REGIONAL INS CO	712	C+
ADMIRAL INS CO	710	C
NAUTILUS INS CO	262	C
GREAT DIVIDE INS CO	225	C

BERKSHIRE HATHAWAY LIFE INSURANCE COMPANY OF NEBR — C+ — Fair

Major Rating Factors: Fair overall results on stability tests (3.0 on a scale of 0 to 10) including weak results on operational trends, fair risk adjusted capital in prior years. Good quality investment portfolio (6.4) with no exposure to mortgages and minimal holdings in junk bonds. Good overall profitability (6.6) despite operating losses during the first six months of 2016.

Other Rating Factors: Strong capitalization (7.5) based on excellent risk adjusted capital (severe loss scenario). Excellent liquidity (9.6).

Principal Business: Reinsurance (73%), group retirement contracts (25%), and individual annuities (2%).

Principal Investments: NonCMO investment grade bonds (44%), common & preferred stock (17%), cash (7%), CMOs and structured securities (4%), and noninv. grade bonds (2%).

Investments in Affiliates: 27%

Group Affiliation: Berkshire-Hathaway

Licensed in: All states except PR

Commenced Business: June 1993

Address: 3024 Harney St, Omaha, NE 68131

Phone: (402) 536-3000 **Domicile State:** NE **NAIC Code:** 62345

Data Date	Rating	RACR #1	RACR #2	Total Assets ($mil)	Capital ($mil)	Net Premium ($mil)	Net Income ($mil)
6-16	C+	1.55	1.30	16,826.7	3,587.5	1,210.8	-39.8
6-15	C+	1.37	1.13	15,874.5	3,437.3	1,685.6	217.6
2015	C+	1.56	1.31	16,287.3	3,684.5	2,943.9	406.4
2014	C+	1.42	1.21	14,786.4	3,283.3	1,693.6	361.1
2013	C+	1.35	1.19	13,768.3	2,701.4	4,073.2	1,527.4
2012	C+	0.95	0.85	10,938.2	2,238.4	3,452.0	-350.4
2011	C+	0.78	0.68	8,809.5	1,824.2	2,013.2	345.8

Adverse Trends in Operations

Change in premium mix from 2014 to 2015 (15.4%)
Change in asset mix during 2014 (4%)
Change in premium mix from 2013 to 2014 (20%)
Decrease in premium volume from 2013 to 2014 (58%)
Change in premium mix from 2012 to 2013 (13.3%)

BERKSHIRE LIFE INSURANCE COMPANY OF AMERICA — B — Good

Major Rating Factors: Good overall profitability (5.2 on a scale of 0 to 10). Good overall results on stability tests (6.2). Strengths include potential support from affiliation with Guardian Group, good operational trends and excellent risk diversification. Fair quality investment portfolio (3.9) with large holdings of BBB rated bonds in addition to junk bond exposure equal to 66% of capital.

Other Rating Factors: Strong capitalization (7.6) based on excellent risk adjusted capital (severe loss scenario). Excellent liquidity (7.2).

Principal Business: Individual health insurance (71%), reinsurance (28%), and individual life insurance (1%).

Principal Investments: NonCMO investment grade bonds (94%), noninv. grade bonds (4%), CMOs and structured securities (1%), and real estate (1%).

Investments in Affiliates: None

Group Affiliation: Guardian Group

Licensed in: All states except PR

Commenced Business: July 2001

Address: 700 South St, Pittsfield, MA 01201

Phone: (413) 499-4321 **Domicile State:** MA **NAIC Code:** 71714

Data Date	Rating	RACR #1	RACR #2	Total Assets ($mil)	Capital ($mil)	Net Premium ($mil)	Net Income ($mil)
6-16	B	3.02	1.39	3,436.0	217.1	61.7	11.1
6-15	B	3.24	1.55	3,445.6	214.8	58.3	11.9
2015	B	3.34	1.58	3,381.4	207.9	118.2	14.2
2014	A-	4.53	2.24	3,377.3	269.5	114.0	16.9
2013	A	8.68	4.24	3,461.4	583.0	115.9	60.0
2012	A	5.30	3.03	3,209.2	543.4	493.9	43.9
2011	A	5.44	3.14	3,034.7	530.9	477.9	29.3

Rating Indexes (Ranges, Cap., Stab., Inv., Prof., Liq. — Weak, Fair, Good, Strong)

BEST MERIDIAN INSURANCE COMPANY — B- — Good

Major Rating Factors: Good quality investment portfolio (6.0 on a scale of 0 to 10) despite significant exposure to mortgages . Mortgage default rate has been low. substantial holdings of BBB bonds in addition to minimal holdings in junk bonds. Good overall profitability (5.3) although investment income, in comparison to reserve requirements, is below regulatory standards. Good overall results on stability tests (5.3) despite excessive premium growth good operational trends, good risk adjusted capital for prior years and good risk diversification.

Other Rating Factors: Strong capitalization (7.3) based on excellent risk adjusted capital (severe loss scenario). Excellent liquidity (7.0).

Principal Business: Reinsurance (76%), individual life insurance (21%), and individual health insurance (3%).

Principal Investments: NonCMO investment grade bonds (42%), CMOs and structured securities (16%), mortgages in good standing (15%), cash (12%), and misc. investments (16%).

Investments in Affiliates: 1%

Group Affiliation: BMI Financial Group

Licensed in: (No states)

Commenced Business: August 1987

Address: 1320 S.Dixie Hwy, 6th Floor, Coral Gables, FL 33146

Phone: (305) 443-2898 **Domicile State:** FL **NAIC Code:** 63886

Data Date	Rating	RACR #1	RACR #2	Total Assets ($mil)	Capital ($mil)	Net Premium ($mil)	Net Income ($mil)
6-16	B-	1.84	1.18	309.9	59.0	74.6	0.3
6-15	B-	2.04	1.29	294.3	59.0	58.0	4.3
2015	B-	1.94	1.25	303.2	60.8	142.6	8.0
2014	B-	1.77	1.13	277.8	53.0	138.9	7.2
2013	B-	2.02	1.33	254.5	47.9	100.8	7.0
2012	B-	1.08	0.78	239.2	45.9	202.5	7.8
2011	B	2.00	1.25	216.8	41.3	69.5	3.6

Adverse Trends in Operations

Change in premium mix from 2013 to 2014 (9%)
Decrease in premium volume from 2012 to 2013 (50%)
Increase in policy surrenders from 2012 to 2013 (67%)
Change in asset mix during 2012 (4.2%)
Change in premium mix from 2011 to 2012 (4.5%)

BLUE CROSS BLUE SHIELD OF KANSAS INCORPORATED — B — Good

Major Rating Factors: Good liquidity (5.4 on a scale of 0 to 10) with sufficient resources to handle a spike in claims. Good overall results on stability tests (5.4) despite negative cash flow from operations for 2015. Other stability subfactors include good operational trends and excellent risk diversification. Fair quality investment portfolio (4.2).

Other Rating Factors: Fair profitability (3.1). Strong capitalization (7.6) based on excellent risk adjusted capital (severe loss scenario).

Principal Business: Group health insurance (74%) and individual health insurance (26%).

Principal Investments: NonCMO investment grade bonds (43%), common & preferred stock (30%), CMOs and structured securities (18%), real estate (3%), and noninv. grade bonds (2%).

Investments in Affiliates: 5%

Group Affiliation: Blue Cross Blue Shield Kansas

Licensed in: KS

Commenced Business: July 1942

Address: 1133 SW Topeka Blvd, Topeka, KS 66629-0001

Phone: (785) 291-7000 **Domicile State:** KS **NAIC Code:** 70729

Data Date	Rating	RACR #1	RACR #2	Total Assets ($mil)	Capital ($mil)	Net Premium ($mil)	Net Income ($mil)
6-16	B	1.92	1.43	1,497.5	741.3	939.3	8.0
6-15	B	2.05	1.50	1,626.0	763.3	923.9	-4.3
2015	B	1.84	1.39	1,408.9	686.6	1,854.4	-29.6
2014	B	2.05	1.50	1,555.1	753.6	1,797.7	-11.5
2013	B	2.26	1.62	1,541.9	800.8	1,689.2	78.6
2012	B	2.23	1.62	1,433.2	762.3	1,680.3	55.9
2011	B	2.09	1.55	1,285.8	666.9	1,683.1	77.5

Adverse Trends in Operations

Decrease in asset base during 2015 (9%)
Decrease in capital during 2015 (9%)
Decrease in capital during 2014 (6%)

BLUE SHIELD OF CALIFORNIA LIFE & HEALTH INS COMPANY — B — Good

Major Rating Factors: Good overall profitability (5.9 on a scale of 0 to 10). Excellent expense controls. Good liquidity (6.5) with sufficient resources to handle a spike in claims. Fair overall results on stability tests (4.9) including negative cash flow from operations for 2015.

Other Rating Factors: Strong capitalization (9.2) based on excellent risk adjusted capital (severe loss scenario). High quality investment portfolio (8.1).

Principal Business: Group health insurance (83%), individual health insurance (16%), and group life insurance (1%).

Principal Investments: NonCMO investment grade bonds (50%), CMOs and structured securities (48%), and cash (2%).

Investments in Affiliates: None

Group Affiliation: Blue Shield of California

Licensed in: CA

Commenced Business: July 1954

Address: 50 Beale St, San Francisco, CA 94105

Phone: (800) 642-5599 **Domicile State:** CA **NAIC Code:** 61557

Data Date	Rating	RACR #1	RACR #2	Total Assets ($mil)	Capital ($mil)	Net Premium ($mil)	Net Income ($mil)
6-16	B	3.10	2.44	483.6	318.5	157.9	17.8
6-15	A-	2.42	1.91	797.1	490.9	679.1	47.3
2015	B	2.98	2.37	665.2	481.1	1,249.2	39.5
2014	A-	1.93	1.53	743.7	444.3	1,794.5	78.5
2013	A-	1.22	0.97	890.7	367.1	2,381.3	12.3
2012	A-	1.20	0.95	802.7	297.3	1,937.3	-19.1
2011	A-	1.31	1.03	637.2	229.9	1,370.8	-41.4

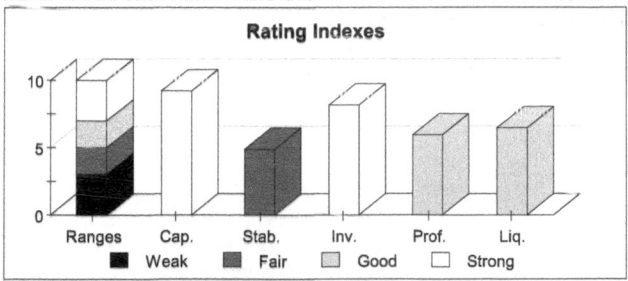

Rating Indexes

Ranges | Cap. | Stab. | Inv. | Prof. | Liq.

■ Weak ▦ Fair ▨ Good ☐ Strong

BLUEBONNET LIFE INSURANCE COMPANY * — B+ — Good

Major Rating Factors: Good overall results on stability tests (6.5 on a scale of 0 to 10). Stability strengths include excellent operational trends and good risk diversification. Strong capitalization (10.0) based on excellent risk adjusted capital (severe loss scenario). Moreover, capital levels have been consistently high over the last five years. High quality investment portfolio (8.1).

Other Rating Factors: Excellent profitability (9.2). Excellent liquidity (9.8).

Principal Business: Group life insurance (95%), individual life insurance (4%), reinsurance (1%), and group health insurance (1%).

Principal Investments: NonCMO investment grade bonds (58%), CMOs and structured securities (30%), noninv. grade bonds (1%), common & preferred stock (1%), and cash (1%).

Investments in Affiliates: None

Group Affiliation: Bl Cross & Bl Shield of Mississippi

Licensed in: AL, AR, LA, MS, TN

Commenced Business: June 1984

Address: 3545 Lakeland Drive, Flowood, MS 39232-8839

Phone: (601) 932-8269 **Domicile State:** MS **NAIC Code:** 68535

Data Date	Rating	RACR #1	RACR #2	Total Assets ($mil)	Capital ($mil)	Net Premium ($mil)	Net Income ($mil)
6-16	B+	7.72	6.95	58.9	54.3	2.4	1.3
6-15	B+	7.40	6.66	56.3	51.2	2.4	1.2
2015	B+	7.53	6.78	57.0	53.0	4.8	2.6
2014	B+	7.22	6.50	54.3	49.9	5.0	2.5
2013	B+	6.99	6.29	52.0	47.7	5.5	2.4
2012	B+	6.84	6.16	49.2	45.4	5.6	2.6
2011	B+	6.73	6.06	46.5	42.8	5.9	2.9

Adverse Trends in Operations

Decrease in premium volume from 2014 to 2015 (4%)
Decrease in premium volume from 2013 to 2014 (8%)
Decrease in premium volume from 2012 to 2013 (2%)
Decrease in premium volume from 2011 to 2012 (5%)

BOSTON MUTUAL LIFE INSURANCE COMPANY *   B+   Good

Major Rating Factors: Good quality investment portfolio (6.4 on a scale of 0 to 10) despite significant exposure to mortgages. Mortgage default rate has been low. substantial holdings of BBB bonds in addition to small junk bond holdings. Good overall profitability (6.1). Good overall results on stability tests (6.4) excellent operational trends and excellent risk diversification.

Other Rating Factors: Fair liquidity (4.7). Strong capitalization (7.5) based on excellent risk adjusted capital (severe loss scenario).

Principal Business: Individual life insurance (59%), group health insurance (20%), group life insurance (17%), and individual health insurance (5%).

Principal Investments: NonCMO investment grade bonds (62%), mortgages in good standing (14%), policy loans (13%), common & preferred stock (5%), and misc. investments (7%).

Investments in Affiliates: 2%

Group Affiliation: Boston Mutual Group

Licensed in: All states, the District of Columbia and Puerto Rico

Commenced Business: February 1892

Address: 120 Royall St, Canton, MA 02021-1098

Phone: (781) 828-7000 **Domicile State:** MA **NAIC Code:** 61476

Data Date	Rating	RACR #1	RACR #2	Total Assets ($mil)	Capital ($mil)	Net Premium ($mil)	Net Income ($mil)
6-16	B+	2.01	1.31	1,317.6	166.6	97.4	4.5
6-15	B+	1.97	1.29	1,267.9	151.0	96.5	4.7
2015	B+	1.98	1.31	1,297.1	159.1	185.7	12.8
2014	B+	1.95	1.29	1,245.2	145.3	185.3	9.9
2013	B+	2.07	1.36	1,188.8	142.5	182.6	16.0
2012	B+	1.97	1.27	1,138.4	126.0	180.4	12.8
2011	B+	1.95	1.29	1,102.7	126.3	180.1	12.1

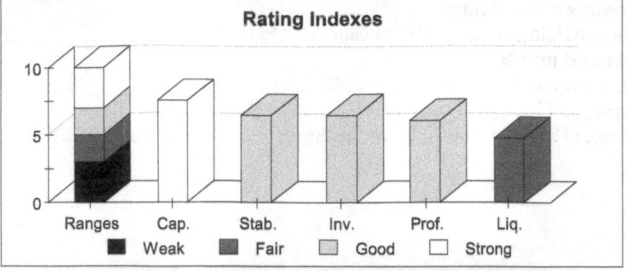

Rating Indexes

BROOKE LIFE INSURANCE COMPANY   C+   Fair

Major Rating Factors: Fair overall results on stability tests (4.8 on a scale of 0 to 10) including fair risk adjusted capital in prior years. Good current capitalization (5.2) based on good risk adjusted capital (severe loss scenario), although results have slipped from the excellent range during the last year. Low quality investment portfolio (1.2).

Other Rating Factors: Excellent profitability (8.6). Excellent liquidity (9.9).

Principal Business: Individual annuities (92%) and reinsurance (8%).

Principal Investments: Common & preferred stock (92%), nonCMO investment grade bonds (7%), and CMOs and structured securities (1%).

Investments in Affiliates: 92%

Group Affiliation: Prudential plc

Licensed in: MI

Commenced Business: August 1987

Address: 5901 Executive Dr, Lansing, MI 48911

Phone: (517) 394-3400 **Domicile State:** MI **NAIC Code:** 78620

Data Date	Rating	RACR #1	RACR #2	Total Assets ($mil)	Capital ($mil)	Net Premium ($mil)	Net Income ($mil)
6-16	C+	0.87	0.77	3,935.4	3,574.9	5.0	453.7
6-15	C+	1.13	1.01	4,831.7	4,454.1	4.6	612.8
2015	C+	1.16	1.03	5,131.1	4,765.0	10.6	716.0
2014	C+	1.15	1.02	4,914.3	4,526.6	9.1	655.7
2013	C+	1.06	0.94	4,783.6	4,042.2	14.8	408.4
2012	C	0.95	0.84	4,718.2	3,576.4	16.1	300.6
2011	C	0.81	0.72	4,056.6	2,628.5	15.7	476.9

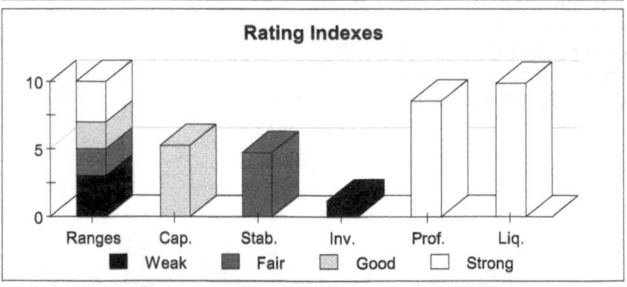

Rating Indexes

CANADA LIFE ASSURANCE COMPANY-US BRANCH   C   Fair

Major Rating Factors: Fair profitability (3.1 on a scale of 0 to 10) with investment income below regulatory standards in relation to interest assumptions of reserves. Fair overall results on stability tests (4.0) including negative cash flow from operations for 2015, fair risk adjusted capital in prior years. Good capitalization (5.3) based on good risk adjusted capital (moderate loss scenario).

Other Rating Factors: Good quality investment portfolio (5.7). Good liquidity (5.1).

Principal Business: Reinsurance (98%) and individual life insurance (2%).

Principal Investments: NonCMO investment grade bonds (66%), CMOs and structured securities (13%), mortgages in good standing (10%), policy loans (7%), and noninv. grade bonds (1%).

Investments in Affiliates: None

Group Affiliation: Great West Life Asr

Licensed in: All states except PR

Commenced Business: August 1847

Address: 330 University Ave, Toronto Ontario, CN M5G 1R8

Phone: (770) 953-1959 **Domicile State:** MI **NAIC Code:** 80659

Data Date	Rating	RACR #1	RACR #2	Total Assets ($mil)	Capital ($mil)	Net Premium ($mil)	Net Income ($mil)
6-16	C	1.17	0.61	4,463.0	151.5	69.1	5.8
6-15	C	1.07	0.56	4,409.3	125.1	64.4	6.6
2015	C	1.10	0.58	4,403.7	131.6	122.9	15.8
2014	C	1.14	0.60	4,425.1	136.2	132.2	5.7
2013	C	1.15	0.61	4,318.9	135.4	141.6	36.5
2012	C	1.36	0.71	4,766.7	165.2	52.3	-75.3
2011	B-	1.49	0.74	4,340.9	173.7	126.8	37.7

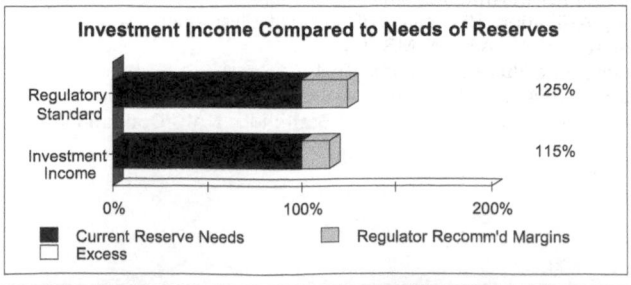

Investment Income Compared to Needs of Reserves

CENTRAL RESERVE LIFE INSURANCE COMPANY

C+ **Fair**

Major Rating Factors: Fair quality investment portfolio (4.3 on a scale of 0 to 10). Fair overall results on stability tests (4.6). Strong overall capitalization (7.7) based on excellent risk adjusted capital (severe loss scenario). However, capital levels have fluctuated somewhat during past years.

Other Rating Factors: Excellent profitability (8.1). Excellent liquidity (7.8).

Principal Business: Individual health insurance (90%), individual life insurance (8%), individual annuities (1%), and group health insurance (1%).

Principal Investments: Common & preferred stock (59%), nonCMO investment grade bonds (39%), and cash (1%).

Investments in Affiliates: 59%

Group Affiliation: CIGNA Corp

Licensed in: AL, AZ, AR, CO, DE, GA, IL, IN, IA, KS, KY, LA, MA, MS, MO, MT, NE, NV, NM, NC, ND, OH, OK, OR, PA, SC, SD, TN, TX, UT, VA, WV, WI, WY

Commenced Business: May 1965

Address: 1300 E Ninth St, Cleveland, OH 44114

Phone: (512) 451-2224 **Domicile State:** OH **NAIC Code:** 61727

Data Date	Rating	RACR #1	RACR #2	Total Assets ($mil)	Capital ($mil)	Net Premium ($mil)	Net Income ($mil)
6-16	C+	1.53	1.47	29.2	27.7	2.0	0.7
6-15	C+	1.50	1.43	26.7	24.8	2.4	0.5
2015	C+	1.48	1.44	28.3	26.4	4.7	1.1
2014	C+	1.45	1.40	25.8	23.7	5.5	1.0
2013	C+	1.41	1.35	23.0	20.9	6.5	1.1
2012	B-	1.21	1.17	30.1	27.4	2.0	3.0
2011	B-	1.10	1.05	29.8	20.6	9.6	1.2

Rating Indexes

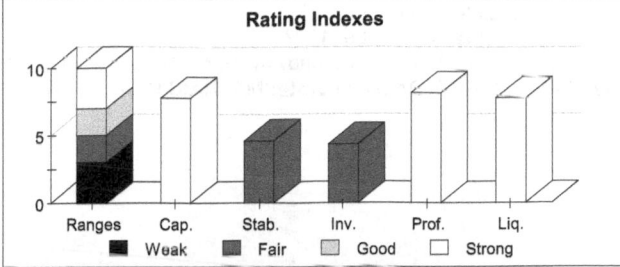

CENTRAL STATES HEALTH & LIFE COMPANY OF OMAHA *

A- **Excellent**

Major Rating Factors: Good quality investment portfolio (5.8 on a scale of 0 to 10) despite mixed results such as: minimal exposure to mortgages and substantial holdings of BBB bonds but minimal holdings in junk bonds. Good overall results on stability tests (6.9). Strengths that enhance stability include excellent operational trends and excellent risk diversification. Strong capitalization (9.9) based on excellent risk adjusted capital (severe loss scenario).

Other Rating Factors: Excellent profitability (7.5). Excellent liquidity (8.3).

Principal Business: Credit life insurance (55%), credit health insurance (31%), individual health insurance (10%), group health insurance (2%), and individual life insurance (2%).

Principal Investments: NonCMO investment grade bonds (43%), CMOs and structured securities (20%), common & preferred stock (11%), mortgages in good standing (5%), and misc. investments (16%).

Investments in Affiliates: 6%

Group Affiliation: Central States Group

Licensed in: All states except NY, PR

Commenced Business: June 1932

Address: 1212 N 96th St, Omaha, NE 68114

Phone: (402) 397-1111 **Domicile State:** NE **NAIC Code:** 61751

Data Date	Rating	RACR #1	RACR #2	Total Assets ($mil)	Capital ($mil)	Net Premium ($mil)	Net Income ($mil)
6-16	A-	4.09	2.92	421.1	127.1	27.4	5.0
6-15	A-	3.76	2.69	415.9	119.6	35.2	2.4
2015	A-	3.99	2.88	419.9	122.9	66.1	6.4
2014	A-	3.79	2.71	414.7	119.6	72.7	5.5
2013	A-	3.98	2.85	395.5	119.6	77.1	0.2
2012	A-	4.26	3.06	372.0	111.0	72.2	3.8
2011	A-	4.12	2.95	343.8	104.5	61.8	8.6

Adverse Trends In Operations

Decrease in premium volume from 2014 to 2015 (9%)
Decrease in premium volume from 2013 to 2014 (6%)

CENTRAL UNITED LIFE INSURANCE COMPANY

C **Fair**

Major Rating Factors: Fair capitalization (3.6 on a scale of 0 to 10) based on fair risk adjusted capital (severe loss scenario). Fair overall results on stability tests (3.6) including fair risk adjusted capital in prior years. Good quality investment portfolio (5.2) with large holdings in common stock of affiliates.

Other Rating Factors: Good liquidity (6.8). Weak profitability (2.4) with operating losses during the first six months of 2016.

Principal Business: Individual health insurance (65%), reinsurance (28%), group health insurance (4%), and individual life insurance (3%).

Principal Investments: Common & preferred stock (42%), nonCMO investment grade bonds (41%), real estate (8%), cash (5%), and misc. investments (4%).

Investments in Affiliates: 42%

Group Affiliation: Manhattan Life Group Inc

Licensed in: All states except CT, FL, NJ, NY, RI, VT, PR

Commenced Business: September 1963

Address: 2727 Allen Parkway,6th Floor, Houston, TX 77019-2115

Phone: (713) 529-0045 **Domicile State:** AR **NAIC Code:** 61883

Data Date	Rating	RACR #1	RACR #2	Total Assets ($mil)	Capital ($mil)	Net Premium ($mil)	Net Income ($mil)
6-16	C	0.62	0.57	381.6	92.6	50.7	-3.4
6-15	C	0.59	0.54	307.2	78.6	51.6	3.4
2015	C	0.64	0.59	327.0	92.9	100.0	2.6
2014	C	0.58	0.53	305.1	76.8	92.7	3.9
2013	C	0.59	0.54	307.2	76.6	88.8	3.8
2012	C	0.77	0.67	302.0	59.7	92.0	8.8
2011	D+	0.70	0.61	312.5	56.6	97.6	3.9

**Risk-Adjusted Capital Ratio #2
(Severe Loss Scenario)**

CENTRE LIFE INSURANCE COMPANY — B- Good

Major Rating Factors: Good quality investment portfolio (6.7 on a scale of 0 to 10) with no exposure to mortgages and no exposure to junk bonds. Fair overall results on stability tests (3.7) including fair financial strength of affiliated Zurich Financial Services Group and negative cash flow from operations for 2015. Weak profitability (2.4) with operating losses during the first six months of 2016.

Other Rating Factors: Strong capitalization (9.2) based on excellent risk adjusted capital (severe loss scenario). Excellent liquidity (9.3).

Principal Business: Reinsurance (61%) and individual health insurance (39%).

Principal Investments: NonCMO investment grade bonds (84%) and CMOs and structured securities (16%).

Investments in Affiliates: None

Group Affiliation: Zurich Financial Services Group

Licensed in: All states except PR

Commenced Business: October 1927

Address: One Liberty Plaza 165 Broadway, Springfield, MA 01103-1641

Phone: (847) 874-7400 **Domicile State:** MA **NAIC Code:** 80896

Data Date	Rating	RACR #1	RACR #2	Total Assets ($mil)	Capital ($mil)	Net Premium ($mil)	Net Income ($mil)
6-16	B-	3.81	2.47	1,850.7	90.8	0.7	-3.5
6-15	B-	3.96	2.46	1,901.9	95.9	0.8	-1.8
2015	B-	3.94	2.57	1,884.1	94.5	1.9	-3.7
2014	B-	4.03	2.54	1,926.1	98.0	0.0	-2.7
2013	B-	4.13	2.67	1,927.7	101.2	0.0	1.9
2012	C+	4.15	2.72	1,815.1	98.8	0.0	0.3
2011	C+	4.18	2.78	1,811.6	100.5	-1.5	0.3

Zurich Financial Services Group Composite Group Rating: C+ Largest Group Members	Assets ($mil)	Rating
ZURICH AMERICAN INS CO	30471	B-
ZURICH AMERICAN LIFE INS CO	12271	C
FARMERS NEW WORLD LIFE INS CO	7049	B-
RURAL COMMUNITY INS CO	3680	B
CENTRE LIFE INS CO	1884	B-

CENTURION LIFE INSURANCE COMPANY — D Weak

Major Rating Factors: Weak profitability (1.3 on a scale of 0 to 10) with investment income below regulatory standards in relation to interest assumptions of reserves. Weak overall results on stability tests (1.8). Good quality investment portfolio (6.8) despite mixed results such as: no exposure to mortgages and substantial holdings of BBB bonds but small junk bond holdings.

Other Rating Factors: Good liquidity (6.5). Strong capitalization (8.7) based on excellent risk adjusted capital (severe loss scenario).

Principal Business: Reinsurance (100%).

Principal Investments: CMOs and structured securities (48%), nonCMO investment grade bonds (46%), noninv. grade bonds (5%), and cash (1%).

Investments in Affiliates: None

Group Affiliation: Wells Fargo Group

Licensed in: All states except ME, NY, VT, PR

Commenced Business: July 1956

Address: 206 Eighth Street, Des Moines, IA 50309

Phone: (515) 243-2131 **Domicile State:** IA **NAIC Code:** 62383

Data Date	Rating	RACR #1	RACR #2	Total Assets ($mil)	Capital ($mil)	Net Premium ($mil)	Net Income ($mil)
6-16	D	3.52	2.10	1,275.3	306.5	83.3	10.2
6-15	D	2.75	1.64	1,253.9	264.7	90.3	14.4
2015	D	3.59	2.17	1,262.6	293.9	179.0	52.0
2014	D	2.64	1.59	1,259.3	251.2	314.0	-165.5
2013	D	4.92	2.88	1,209.0	397.3	204.6	-227.0
2012	C+	20.93	10.33	1,475.0	599.9	13.7	39.4
2011	C+	16.61	8.13	1,472.9	545.1	23.8	47.0

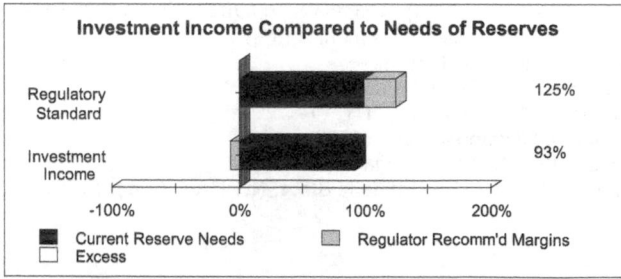

Investment Income Compared to Needs of Reserves

Regulatory Standard — 125%
Investment Income — 93%

-100% 0% 100% 200%

■ Current Reserve Needs ▨ Regulator Recomm'd Margins
□ Excess

CHESAPEAKE LIFE INSURANCE COMPANY — C+ Fair

Major Rating Factors: Fair overall results on stability tests (4.4 on a scale of 0 to 10) including fair risk adjusted capital in prior years. Weak profitability (2.9) with investment income below regulatory standards in relation to interest assumptions of reserves. Strong current capitalization (7.6) based on excellent risk adjusted capital (severe loss scenario) reflecting significant improvement over results in 2013.

Other Rating Factors: High quality investment portfolio (9.2). Excellent liquidity (8.2).

Principal Business: Individual health insurance (77%), individual life insurance (22%), and reinsurance (1%).

Principal Investments: NonCMO investment grade bonds (98%), CMOs and structured securities (1%), and cash (1%).

Investments in Affiliates: None

Group Affiliation: HealthMarkets

Licensed in: All states except NJ, NY, VT, PR

Commenced Business: October 1956

Address: 9151 Grapevine Highway, North Richland Hills, TX 76180

Phone: (817) 255-3100 **Domicile State:** OK **NAIC Code:** 61832

Data Date	Rating	RACR #1	RACR #2	Total Assets ($mil)	Capital ($mil)	Net Premium ($mil)	Net Income ($mil)
6-16	C+	1.78	1.42	118.2	64.5	92.3	5.8
6-15	C+	1.20	0.96	83.8	41.8	77.4	-2.3
2015	C+	1.38	1.11	99.8	46.8	159.6	-0.9
2014	C+	1.40	1.11	75.1	43.1	119.4	0.4
2013	C+	0.85	0.67	42.5	20.9	82.6	-3.2
2012	C+	1.60	1.22	36.2	23.3	47.1	-2.1
2011	C+	4.46	3.22	47.0	35.7	24.4	0.1

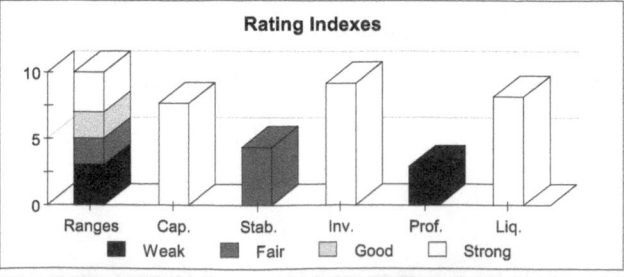

Rating Indexes

Ranges Cap. Stab. Inv. Prof. Liq.

■ Weak ▨ Fair ▤ Good □ Strong

CHESTERFIELD REINS CO   C   Fair

Major Rating Factors: Good quality investment portfolio (6.8 on a scale of 0 to 10) despite mixed results such as: no exposure to mortgages and large holdings of BBB rated bonds but no exposure to junk bonds. Weak profitability (1.4) with investment income below regulatory standards in relation to interest assumptions of reserves. Weak liquidity (0.0).
Other Rating Factors: Weak overall results on stability tests (2.8) including lack of operational experience. Strong capitalization (7.2) based on excellent risk adjusted capital (severe loss scenario).
Principal Business: Reinsurance (100%).
Principal Investments: NonCMO investment grade bonds (84%) and CMOs and structured securities (16%).
Investments in Affiliates: None
Group Affiliation: Reinsurance Group of America Inc
Licensed in: MO
Commenced Business: October 2014
Address: 16600 Swingley Ridge Rd, Chesterfield, MO 63017-1706
Phone: (636) 736-7000 **Domicile State:** MO **NAIC Code:** 15604

Data Date	Rating	RACR #1	RACR #2	Total Assets ($mil)	Capital ($mil)	Net Premium ($mil)	Net Income ($mil)
6-16	C	1.60	1.12	325.4	97.4	99.2	17.8
6-15	C+	1.53	1.07	314.5	93.0	97.1	15.2
2015	C	1.46	1.02	315.1	89.1	191.2	17.2
2014	C+	1.63	1.14	311.0	98.8	244.3	-247.6
2013	N/A	N/A	N/A	0.0	0.0	0.0	0.0
2012	N/A	N/A	N/A	0.0	0.0	0.0	0.0
2011	N/A	N/A	N/A	0.0	0.0	0.0	0.0

Rating Indexes

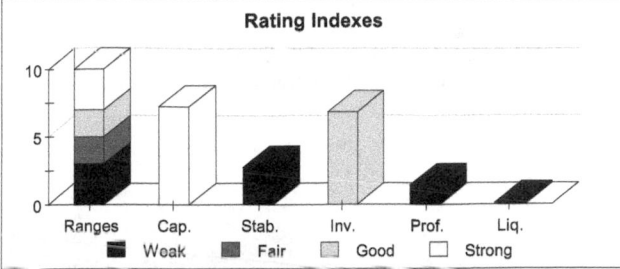

Ranges | Cap. | Stab. | Inv. | Prof. | Liq.
■ Weak   ■ Fair   ▨ Good   □ Strong

CHRISTIAN FIDELITY LIFE INSURANCE COMPANY   B   Good

Major Rating Factors: Good overall results on stability tests (5.9 on a scale of 0 to 10) despite fair financial strength of affiliated Amerco Corp. Other stability subfactors include excellent operational trends and good risk diversification. Strong capitalization (8.8) based on excellent risk adjusted capital (severe loss scenario). High quality investment portfolio (7.8).
Other Rating Factors: Excellent profitability (7.8). Excellent liquidity (7.0).
Principal Business: Individual health insurance (88%), group health insurance (8%), and individual life insurance (3%).
Principal Investments: NonCMO investment grade bonds (89%), mortgages in good standing (5%), CMOs and structured securities (4%), policy loans (1%), and misc. investments (2%).
Investments in Affiliates: None
Group Affiliation: Amerco Corp
Licensed in: AL, AZ, AR, CO, FL, GA, ID, IL, IN, KS, KY, LA, MS, MO, MT, NE, NV, NM, ND, OH, OK, OR, SC, SD, TN, TX, UT, VA, WA, WV, WY
Commenced Business: December 1935
Address: 2721 N Central Ave, Phoenix, AZ 85004-1172
Phone: (972) 937-4420 **Domicile State:** TX **NAIC Code:** 61859

Data Date	Rating	RACR #1	RACR #2	Total Assets ($mil)	Capital ($mil)	Net Premium ($mil)	Net Income ($mil)
6-16	B	3.04	2.21	70.6	32.4	17.6	3.5
6-15	B	2.79	2.06	74.0	32.6	19.8	4.1
2015	B	2.63	1.93	68.8	28.9	38.7	9.2
2014	B-	2.36	1.75	71.2	28.6	40.8	9.2
2013	B-	2.20	1.63	75.4	28.8	48.9	9.6
2012	B-	2.00	1.49	77.9	28.0	54.3	8.7
2011	B	1.64	1.34	85.3	36.2	49.1	8.5

Amerco Corp
Composite Group Rating: C+

Largest Group Members	Assets ($mil)	Rating
OXFORD LIFE INS CO	1490	B
REPWEST INS CO	303	D
CHRISTIAN FIDELITY LIFE INS CO	69	B
NORTH AMERICAN INS CO	21	C+
ARCOA RRG INC	14	E

CHURCH LIFE INSURANCE CORPORATION   B   Good

Major Rating Factors: Good quality investment portfolio (6.3 on a scale of 0 to 10) despite mixed results such as: no exposure to mortgages and large holdings of BBB rated bonds but small junk bond holdings. Good liquidity (6.1) with sufficient resources to handle a spike in claims as well as a significant increase in policy surrenders. Good overall results on stability tests (5.7) excellent operational trends and good risk diversification.
Other Rating Factors: Strong capitalization (8.7) based on excellent risk adjusted capital (severe loss scenario). Excellent profitability (7.4).
Principal Business: Group life insurance (52%), group retirement contracts (28%), individual annuities (18%), and individual life insurance (2%).
Principal Investments: NonCMO investment grade bonds (64%), CMOs and structured securities (27%), common & preferred stock (6%), and noninv. grade bonds (4%).
Investments in Affiliates: None
Group Affiliation: Church Pension Fund
Licensed in: All states except PR
Commenced Business: July 1922
Address: 445 Fifth Ave, New York, NY 10016
Phone: (212) 592-9473 **Domicile State:** NY **NAIC Code:** 61875

Data Date	Rating	RACR #1	RACR #2	Total Assets ($mil)	Capital ($mil)	Net Premium ($mil)	Net Income ($mil)
6-16	B	3.88	2.10	298.1	54.6	17.6	1.0
6-15	B	3.91	2.15	289.9	53.9	15.2	2.1
2015	B	3.91	2.14	291.7	53.3	35.4	2.0
2014	B	3.82	2.11	287.5	51.7	33.7	1.5
2013	B-	3.69	1.98	285.3	50.3	37.9	5.5
2012	B-	3.33	1.83	279.1	43.1	42.0	3.2
2011	B-	3.24	1.79	254.6	38.5	37.6	1.0

Adverse Trends in Operations

Decrease in premium volume from 2013 to 2014 (11%)
Decrease in premium volume from 2012 to 2013 (10%)
Increase in policy surrenders from 2011 to 2012 (46%)

CICA LIFE INSURANCE COMPANY OF AMERICA

D   **Weak**

Major Rating Factors: Poor capitalization (1.4 on a scale of 0 to 10) based on weak risk adjusted capital (moderate loss scenario). Weak profitability (2.4) with operating losses during the first six months of 2016. Weak overall results on stability tests (1.4) including weak risk adjusted capital in prior years.
Other Rating Factors: Fair quality investment portfolio (4.7). Good liquidity (6.0).
Principal Business: Individual life insurance (95%) and individual annuities (4%).
Principal Investments: NonCMO investment grade bonds (76%), common & preferred stock (7%), policy loans (7%), cash (6%), and misc. investments (4%).
Investments in Affiliates: 7%
Group Affiliation: Citizens Inc
Licensed in: AL, AZ, AR, CO, DC, GA, HI, ID, IN, KS, KY, LA, MN, MS, MO, MT, NE, NV, NM, ND, OK, OR, PA, SC, SD, TN, TX, UT, WA, WV, WY
Commenced Business: June 1968
Address: 1675 Broadway, Denver, CO 80202
Phone: (512) 837-7100 **Domicile State:** CO **NAIC Code:** 71463

Data Date	Rating	RACR #1	RACR #2	Total Assets ($mil)	Capital ($mil)	Net Premium ($mil)	Net Income ($mil)
6-16	D	0.48	0.37	878.2	33.7	70.8	-1.1
6-15	D	0.47	0.37	802.4	33.9	71.0	-1.8
2015	D	0.50	0.40	840.8	35.1	152.9	-5.0
2014	C-	0.65	0.51	773.3	42.0	146.8	-3.0
2013	C-	0.73	0.59	700.6	57.9	136.0	3.2
2012	C-	0.67	0.55	629.6	53.8	129.5	2.9
2011	C-	0.70	0.60	568.6	58.0	121.6	4.7

Risk-Adjusted Capital Ratio #1 (Moderate Loss Scenario)

Range | 2011 | 2012 | 2013 | 2014 | 2015 | 6-16

■ Weak   ▨ Fair   □ Good

CIGNA HEALTH & LIFE INSURANCE COMPANY

B   **Good**

Major Rating Factors: Strong capitalization (6.9 on a scale of 0 to 10) based on excellent risk adjusted capital (severe loss scenario). Moreover, capital levels have been consistently high over the last five years. Fair overall results on stability tests (4.2). Fair quality investment portfolio (3.7).
Other Rating Factors: Weak liquidity (1.8). Excellent profitability (9.8).
Principal Business: Group health insurance (79%), individual health insurance (20%), and reinsurance (1%).
Principal Investments: NonCMO investment grade bonds (41%), noninv. grade bonds (19%), common & preferred stock (12%), mortgages in good standing (11%), and CMOs and structured securities (2%).
Investments in Affiliates: 12%
Group Affiliation: CIGNA Corp
Licensed in: All states, the District of Columbia and Puerto Rico
Commenced Business: February 1964
Address: 900 Cottage Grove Rd, Hartford, CT 06152
Phone: (303) 729-7462 **Domicile State:** CT **NAIC Code:** 67369

Data Date	Rating	RACR #1	RACR #2	Total Assets ($mil)	Capital ($mil)	Net Premium ($mil)	Net Income ($mil)
6-16	B	1.74	1.38	6,742.1	3,124.0	5,796.5	654.0
6-15	B	1.86	1.45	6,688.7	2,835.4	5,755.9	537.4
2015	B	1.66	1.31	6,559.9	3,008.9	11,457.7	1,187.2
2014	B	1.89	1.48	6,204.5	2,799.7	9,789.3	1,047.0
2013	B	1.68	1.37	4,139.3	1,713.2	6,456.2	489.1
2012	B	1.92	1.66	1,681.4	1,017.9	1,883.9	300.7
2011	B	10.20	6.05	713.4	543.4	296.6	122.8

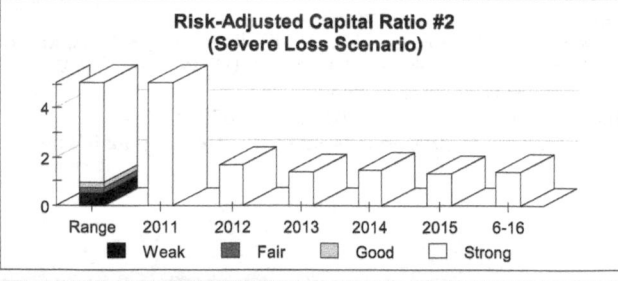

Risk-Adjusted Capital Ratio #2 (Severe Loss Scenario)

Range | 2011 | 2012 | 2013 | 2014 | 2015 | 6-16

■ Weak   ▨ Fair   ▨ Good   □ Strong

CIGNA LIFE INSURANCE COMPANY OF NEW YORK *

A-   **Excellent**

Major Rating Factors: Good quality investment portfolio (6.5 on a scale of 0 to 10) despite mixed results such as: large holdings of BBB rated bonds but moderate junk bond exposure. Good overall profitability (6.8) despite operating losses during the first six months of 2016. Excellent overall results on stability tests (7.0) excellent operational trends and excellent risk diversification.
Other Rating Factors: Strong capitalization (8.1) based on excellent risk adjusted capital (severe loss scenario). Excellent liquidity (7.3).
Principal Business: Group health insurance (67%) and group life insurance (33%).
Principal Investments: NonCMO investment grade bonds (88%), noninv. grade bonds (8%), and CMOs and structured securities (4%).
Investments in Affiliates: None
Group Affiliation: CIGNA Corp
Licensed in: AL, DC, MO, NY, PA, TN
Commenced Business: December 1965
Address: 140 E 45th St, New York, NY 10017
Phone: (212) 618-5757 **Domicile State:** NY **NAIC Code:** 64548

Data Date	Rating	RACR #1	RACR #2	Total Assets ($mil)	Capital ($mil)	Net Premium ($mil)	Net Income ($mil)
6-16	A-	2.65	1.74	380.3	96.0	82.4	-0.6
6-15	A-	3.61	2.33	381.3	114.5	74.2	11.8
2015	A-	2.69	1.78	364.4	97.4	150.3	18.9
2014	A-	3.25	2.08	368.1	102.8	128.0	24.7
2013	B+	3.21	2.03	375.9	93.5	119.9	16.9
2012	B+	3.54	2.38	376.0	93.8	115.6	15.8
2011	B	4.12	2.77	387.8	102.4	124.7	16.6

Adverse Trends in Operations

Decrease in capital during 2015 (5%)
Decrease in asset base during 2015 (1%)
Decrease in asset base during 2014 (2%)
Decrease in asset base during 2012 (3%)
Decrease in premium volume from 2011 to 2012 (7%)

CINCINNATI LIFE INSURANCE COMPANY   B   Good

Major Rating Factors: Good overall capitalization (5.6 on a scale of 0 to 10) based on good risk adjusted capital (moderate loss scenario). Nevertheless, capital levels have fluctuated during prior years. Good liquidity (5.0) with sufficient resources to cover a large increase in policy surrenders. Good overall results on stability tests (5.6) excellent operational trends and excellent risk diversification.

Other Rating Factors: Fair quality investment portfolio (3.4). Weak profitability (2.7).

Principal Business: Individual life insurance (86%), individual annuities (11%), individual health insurance (2%), and group life insurance (1%).

Principal Investments: NonCMO investment grade bonds (81%), noninv. grade bonds (8%), CMOs and structured securities (7%), policy loans (1%), and cash (1%).

Investments in Affiliates: None
Group Affiliation: Cincinnati Financial Corp
Licensed in: All states except NY, PR
Commenced Business: February 1988
Address: 6200 S Gilmore Rd, Fairfield, OH 45014-5141
Phone: (513) 870-2000   **Domicile State:** OH   **NAIC Code:** 76236

Data Date	Rating	RACR #1	RACR #2	Total Assets ($mil)	Capital ($mil)	Net Premium ($mil)	Net Income ($mil)
6-16	B	1.42	0.74	4,214.2	204.6	140.3	1.5
6-15	B	1.59	0.85	3,984.0	216.6	124.7	-3.7
2015	B	1.45	0.77	4,066.8	208.4	250.1	-11.5
2014	B	1.65	0.89	3,916.0	223.5	243.8	-18.6
2013	B	1.94	1.06	3,737.5	247.0	235.3	-19.7
2012	B	2.27	1.26	3,569.9	275.8	241.8	4.6
2011	B	2.50	1.41	3,357.3	281.2	299.7	-13.3

Junk Bonds as a % of Capital

Capital $208 mil.
Junk Bonds $253 mil.

0% 20% 40% 60% 80% 100% 120% 140%

■ BB   ▨ B   ▥ CCC   ▢ In default

CM LIFE INSURANCE COMPANY   B   Good

Major Rating Factors: Good quality investment portfolio (5.3 on a scale of 0 to 10) despite large holdings of BBB rated bonds in addition to moderate junk bond exposure. Exposure to mortgages is significant, but the mortgage default rate has been low. Good liquidity (6.4) with sufficient resources to cover a large increase in policy surrenders. Good overall results on stability tests (6.3) despite negative cash flow from operations for 2015 excellent operational trends and excellent risk diversification.

Other Rating Factors: Strong capitalization (8.4) based on excellent risk adjusted capital (severe loss scenario). Excellent profitability (9.0).

Principal Business: Individual annuities (51%) and individual life insurance (49%).

Principal Investments: NonCMO investment grade bonds (47%), mortgages in good standing (14%), CMOs and structured securities (11%), noninv. grade bonds (7%), and misc. investments (12%).

Investments in Affiliates: 10%
Group Affiliation: Massachusetts Mutual Group
Licensed in: All states except NY
Commenced Business: May 1981
Address: 100 Bright Meadow Blvd, Enfield, CT 06082
Phone: (413) 788-8411   **Domicile State:** CT   **NAIC Code:** 93432

Data Date	Rating	RACR #1	RACR #2	Total Assets ($mil)	Capital ($mil)	Net Premium ($mil)	Net Income ($mil)
6-16	B	3.09	1.90	9,489.1	1,522.2	154.2	25.3
6-15	B	2.89	1.78	8,751.4	1,322.3	153.8	68.3
2015	B	2.96	1.86	8,803.1	1,396.0	295.1	117.5
2014	B	2.85	1.75	8,792.5	1,304.8	316.1	160.4
2013	B	2.37	1.44	8,984.0	1,071.2	355.6	170.6
2012	B	2.16	1.32	8,594.3	960.8	383.6	94.4
2011	B	2.19	1.33	8,388.5	930.0	389.0	90.6

Adverse Trends in Operations

Decrease in premium volume from 2014 to 2015 (7%)
Decrease in asset base during 2014 (2%)
Decrease in premium volume from 2013 to 2014 (11%)
Decrease in premium volume from 2012 to 2013 (7%)
Decrease in premium volume from 2011 to 2012 (1%)

CMFG LIFE INSURANCE COMPANY   B-   Good

Major Rating Factors: Good liquidity (6.9 on a scale of 0 to 10) with sufficient resources to handle a spike in claims as well as a significant increase in policy surrenders. Good overall results on stability tests (5.0) despite excessive premium growth. Other stability subfactors include excellent operational trends, good risk adjusted capital for prior years and excellent risk diversification. Fair quality investment portfolio (4.8).

Other Rating Factors: Strong capitalization (7.3) based on excellent risk adjusted capital (severe loss scenario). Excellent profitability (8.2).

Principal Business: Group retirement contracts (30%), reinsurance (21%), individual life insurance (11%), credit health insurance (11%), and other lines (28%).

Principal Investments: NonCMO investment grade bonds (52%), mortgages in good standing (14%), CMOs and structured securities (12%), common & preferred stock (10%), and misc. investments (12%).

Investments in Affiliates: 10%
Group Affiliation: CUNA Mutual Ins Group
Licensed in: All states, the District of Columbia and Puerto Rico
Commenced Business: August 1935
Address: 2000 Heritage Way, Waverly, IA 50677
Phone: (608) 238-5851   **Domicile State:** IA   **NAIC Code:** 62626

Data Date	Rating	RACR #1	RACR #2	Total Assets ($mil)	Capital ($mil)	Net Premium ($mil)	Net Income ($mil)
6-16	B-	1.53	1.20	15,969.4	1,941.0	1,536.0	116.8
6-15	B-	1.42	1.11	15,510.3	1,761.8	1,211.0	116.6
2015	B-	1.47	1.16	15,475.9	1,858.4	3,110.2	256.2
2014	B-	1.33	1.04	15,490.1	1,632.9	2,479.9	106.9
2013	B-	1.26	0.98	15,659.8	1,553.5	1,923.4	101.9
2012	B-	1.19	0.91	14,664.2	1,458.0	1,874.0	97.0
2011	B-	1.18	0.89	13,762.3	1,401.0	2,166.0	80.6

Adverse Trends in Operations

Increase in policy surrenders from 2014 to 2015 (40%)
Increase in policy surrenders from 2013 to 2014 (49%)
Decrease in asset base during 2014 (1%)
Change in premium mix from 2011 to 2012 (4.6%)
Decrease in premium volume from 2011 to 2012 (13%)

COLONIAL LIFE & ACCIDENT INSURANCE COMPANY   C+   Fair

Major Rating Factors: Fair overall results on stability tests (4.7 on a scale of 0 to 10) including fair financial strength of affiliated Unum Group. Good quality investment portfolio (5.9) despite large holdings of BBB rated bonds in addition to moderate junk bond exposure. Exposure to mortgages is significant, but the mortgage default rate has been low. Good liquidity (6.9).
Other Rating Factors: Strong capitalization (7.9) based on excellent risk adjusted capital (severe loss scenario). Excellent profitability (8.3).
Principal Business: Individual health insurance (70%), individual life insurance (20%), group health insurance (8%), and group life insurance (1%).
Principal Investments: NonCMO investment grade bonds (73%), mortgages in good standing (12%), noninv. grade bonds (6%), CMOs and structured securities (4%), and misc. investments (6%).
Investments in Affiliates: None
Group Affiliation: Unum Group
Licensed in: All states except NY
Commenced Business: September 1939
Address: 6335 S. East Street, Suite A, Indianapolis, IN 46227
Phone: (803) 798-7000 **Domicile State:** SC **NAIC Code:** 62049

Data Date	Rating	RACR #1	RACR #2	Total Assets ($mil)	Capital ($mil)	Net Premium ($mil)	Net Income ($mil)
6-16	C+	2.59	1.60	3,091.7	567.4	709.4	65.5
6-15	C+	2.37	1.50	3,005.2	573.5	673.9	74.1
2015	C+	2.65	1.64	3,018.8	566.0	1,333.8	157.8
2014	C+	2.44	1.53	2,922.0	567.1	1,277.5	160.9
2013	C+	2.71	1.66	2,752.7	538.2	1,238.8	134.4
2012	C+	2.75	1.68	2,651.4	534.9	1,208.2	139.7
2011	C+	2.84	1.74	2,521.2	532.3	1,152.4	136.0

Unum Group
Composite Group Rating: C+
Largest Group Members

	Assets ($mil)	Rating
UNUM LIFE INS CO OF AMERICA	20552	C+
PROVIDENT LIFE ACCIDENT INS CO	8325	C+
PAUL REVERE LIFE INS CO	3977	C+
FIRST UNUM LIFE INS CO	3130	C+
COLONIAL LIFE ACCIDENT INS CO	3019	C+

COLONIAL PENN LIFE INSURANCE COMPANY   D+   Weak

Major Rating Factors: Weak overall results on stability tests (2.7 on a scale of 0 to 10) including weak financial strength of affiliated CNO Financial Group Inc and negative cash flow from operations for 2015. Weak profitability (1.9) with investment income below regulatory standards in relation to interest assumptions of reserves. Weak liquidity (0.7).
Other Rating Factors: Fair quality investment portfolio (4.7). Good capitalization (5.6) based on good risk adjusted capital (severe loss scenario).
Principal Business: Individual health insurance (61%), individual life insurance (22%), and group life insurance (17%).
Principal Investments: NonCMO investment grade bonds (69%), CMOs and structured securities (17%), policy loans (3%), noninv. grade bonds (3%), and misc. investments (9%).
Investments in Affiliates: None
Group Affiliation: CNO Financial Group Inc
Licensed in: All states except NY
Commenced Business: September 1959
Address: 399 Market St, Philadelphia, PA 19181
Phone: (215) 928-8000 **Domicile State:** PA **NAIC Code:** 62065

Data Date	Rating	RACR #1	RACR #2	Total Assets ($mil)	Capital ($mil)	Net Premium ($mil)	Net Income ($mil)
6-16	D+	1.42	0.82	845.9	108.1	188.1	8.5
6-15	D+	1.20	0.70	752.5	79.3	174.3	-6.3
2015	D+	1.13	0.66	816.0	79.3	330.3	-18.8
2014	D+	1.16	0.67	742.8	73.3	303.7	-17.1
2013	D+	1.05	0.60	740.3	62.0	277.8	-19.1
2012	D+	1.20	0.68	736.6	70.6	253.5	-3.9
2011	D+	1.41	0.78	743.9	76.7	222.8	9.2

CNO Financial Group Inc
Composite Group Rating: D+
Largest Group Members

	Assets ($mil)	Rating
BANKERS LIFE CAS CO	16905	D+
WASHINGTON NATIONAL INS CO	4808	D+
COLONIAL PENN LIFE INS CO	816	D+
BANKERS CONSECO LIFE INS CO	218	D

COLORADO BANKERS LIFE INSURANCE COMPANY   B   Good

Major Rating Factors: Fair current capitalization (4.0 on a scale of 0 to 10) based on mixed results -- excessive policy leverage mitigated by excellent risk adjusted capital (severe loss scenario) reflecting improvement over results in 2011. Fair overall results on stability tests (4.1) including negative cash flow from operations for 2015. Weak profitability (2.9) with investment income below regulatory standards in relation to interest assumptions of reserves.
Other Rating Factors: High quality investment portfolio (7.9). Excellent liquidity (9.1).
Principal Business: Individual life insurance (63%), individual annuities (33%), and individual health insurance (3%).
Principal Investments: NonCMO investment grade bonds (86%), cash (7%), CMOs and structured securities (5%), and policy loans (2%).
Investments in Affiliates: None
Group Affiliation: SNA Capital LLC
Licensed in: All states except NY
Commenced Business: November 1974
Address: 5990 Greenwood Plaza Blvd, Englewood, CO 80111
Phone: (303) 220-8500 **Domicile State:** NC **NAIC Code:** 84786

Data Date	Rating	RACR #1	RACR #2	Total Assets ($mil)	Capital ($mil)	Net Premium ($mil)	Net Income ($mil)
6-16	B	4.65	3.03	333.4	54.6	31.7	1.1
6-15	B+	2.83	1.62	295.7	35.7	44.8	2.1
2015	B	4.71	3.10	324.4	55.4	-72.2	9.6
2014	B+	2.72	1.57	284.2	33.9	90.2	3.9
2013	B+	2.49	1.46	256.9	28.9	89.4	3.2
2012	B+	2.46	1.42	232.5	27.5	87.8	-9.1
2011	B+	1.60	0.94	202.3	16.9	86.4	1.5

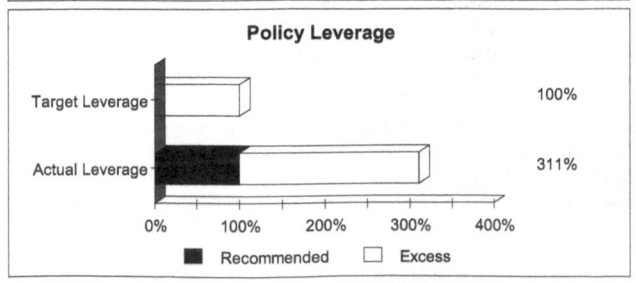

Policy Leverage

Target Leverage — 100%
Actual Leverage — 311%

0% 100% 200% 300% 400%

■ Recommended □ Excess

COLUMBIAN LIFE INSURANCE COMPANY C Fair

Major Rating Factors: Fair overall results on stability tests (4.3 on a scale of 0 to 10). Good liquidity (5.3) with sufficient resources to handle a spike in claims as well as a significant increase in policy surrenders. Weak profitability (2.2) with investment income below regulatory standards in relation to interest assumptions of reserves.

Other Rating Factors: Strong capitalization (7.2) based on excellent risk adjusted capital (severe loss scenario). High quality investment portfolio (7.3).

Principal Business: Individual life insurance (84%), group life insurance (12%), individual annuities (3%), and reinsurance (1%).

Principal Investments: NonCMO investment grade bonds (68%), CMOs and structured securities (17%), policy loans (6%), mortgages in good standing (6%), and misc. investments (3%).

Investments in Affiliates: 2%
Group Affiliation: Columbian Life Group
Licensed in: All states except AL, AK, ME, NY, ND, VT, PR
Commenced Business: June 1988
Address: Vestal Parkway East, Binghamton, NY 13902
Phone: (607) 724-2472 **Domicile State:** IL **NAIC Code:** 76023

Data Date	Rating	RACR #1	RACR #2	Total Assets ($mil)	Capital ($mil)	Net Premium ($mil)	Net Income ($mil)
6-16	C	1.72	1.13	318.3	31.2	28.6	0.7
6-15	C	1.99	1.31	309.9	35.0	28.8	-0.6
2015	C	1.71	1.12	306.8	30.8	53.4	-2.3
2014	C	2.15	1.43	314.5	37.9	58.0	-0.9
2013	C+	1.48	0.99	292.7	24.3	58.0	-2.1
2012	B-	1.24	0.83	274.8	20.2	58.6	-1.6
2011	B-	1.57	1.06	266.3	24.8	52.5	-1.6

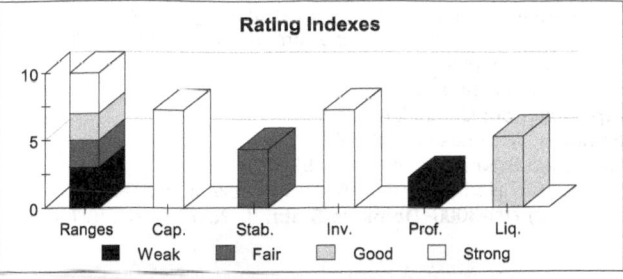

Rating Indexes

COLUMBIAN MUTUAL LIFE INSURANCE COMPANY B Good

Major Rating Factors: Good overall capitalization (6.1 on a scale of 0 to 10) based on good risk adjusted capital (severe loss scenario). Nevertheless, capital levels have fluctuated during prior years. Good quality investment portfolio (6.4) despite significant exposure to mortgages . Mortgage default rate has been low. large holdings of BBB rated bonds in addition to minimal holdings in junk bonds. Good overall profitability (5.4) although investment income, in comparison to reserve requirements, is below regulatory standards.

Other Rating Factors: Good liquidity (5.0). Good overall results on stability tests (5.4) good operational trends and good risk diversification.

Principal Business: Reinsurance (64%), individual life insurance (34%), individual health insurance (1%), and individual annuities (1%).

Principal Investments: NonCMO investment grade bonds (66%), mortgages in good standing (13%), CMOs and structured securities (12%), policy loans (5%), and common & preferred stock (3%).

Investments in Affiliates: 2%
Group Affiliation: Columbian Life Group
Licensed in: All states except PR
Commenced Business: February 1883
Address: Vestal Parkway East, Binghamton, NY 13902
Phone: (607) 724-2472 **Domicile State:** NY **NAIC Code:** 62103

Data Date	Rating	RACR #1	RACR #2	Total Assets ($mil)	Capital ($mil)	Net Premium ($mil)	Net Income ($mil)
6-16	B	1.36	0.89	1,377.6	85.1	91.8	2.5
6-15	B	1.04	0.71	1,336.0	67.5	88.2	2.7
2015	B	1.30	0.86	1,364.8	80.7	177.4	5.7
2014	B	1.19	0.82	1,326.3	79.2	175.3	5.6
2013	B	1.76	1.16	1,289.8	101.8	182.8	3.1
2012	B	1.71	1.10	1,251.1	89.5	-118.0	-0.9
2011	B+	1.55	1.01	1,230.4	88.5	184.3	-1.3

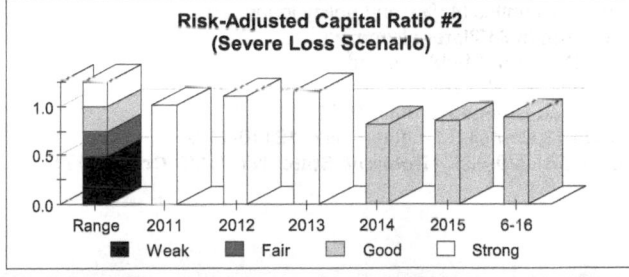

Risk-Adjusted Capital Ratio #2
(Severe Loss Scenario)

COLUMBUS LIFE INSURANCE COMPANY C+ Fair

Major Rating Factors: Fair quality investment portfolio (4.9 on a scale of 0 to 10) with large holdings of BBB rated bonds in addition to junk bond exposure equal to 72% of capital. Fair liquidity (4.8) due, in part, to cash value policies that are subject to withdrawals with minimal or no penalty. Fair overall results on stability tests (4.4).

Other Rating Factors: Weak profitability (2.0) with operating losses during the first six months of 2016. Strong capitalization (7.0) based on excellent risk adjusted capital (severe loss scenario).

Principal Business: Individual life insurance (71%) and individual annuities (29%).

Principal Investments: NonCMO investment grade bonds (62%), CMOs and structured securities (18%), noninv. grade bonds (6%), mortgages in good standing (5%), and misc. investments (10%).

Investments in Affiliates: 3%
Group Affiliation: Western & Southern Group
Licensed in: All states except NY, PR
Commenced Business: July 1988
Address: 400 E 4th St, Cincinnati, OH 45202
Phone: (513) 357-4000 **Domicile State:** OH **NAIC Code:** 99937

Data Date	Rating	RACR #1	RACR #2	Total Assets ($mil)	Capital ($mil)	Net Premium ($mil)	Net Income ($mil)
6-16	C+	1.96	1.02	3,642.9	263.7	144.4	-8.8
6-15	B-	1.77	0.93	3,393.9	215.7	115.7	2.0
2015	C+	2.04	1.07	3,474.7	272.7	229.9	-13.3
2014	B-	1.85	0.98	3,337.3	222.6	249.5	-23.7
2013	B	2.05	1.09	3,198.9	250.8	228.6	-24.8
2012	B+	2.02	1.04	3,011.2	214.8	191.8	1.1
2011	B+	1.91	0.98	2,958.7	206.2	238.6	7.8

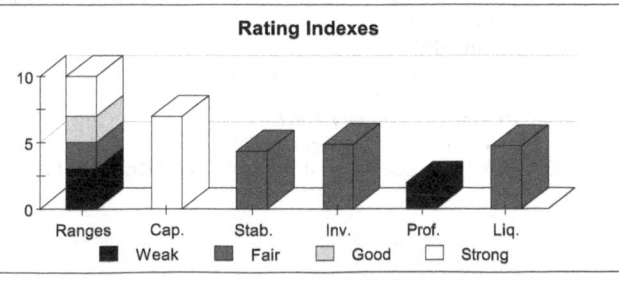

Rating Indexes

COMBINED INSURANCE COMPANY OF AMERICA C+ Fair

Major Rating Factors: Fair overall capitalization (4.0 on a scale of 0 to 10) based on mixed results -- excessive policy leverage mitigated by fair risk adjusted capital (moderate loss scenario). Fair quality investment portfolio (4.2) with large holdings of BBB rated bonds in addition to significant exposure to junk bonds. Fair overall results on stability tests (4.0) including negative cash flow from operations for 2015, fair risk adjusted capital in prior years.

Other Rating Factors: Good liquidity (6.5). Weak profitability (2.9) with investment income below regulatory standards in relation to interest assumptions of reserves.

Principal Business: Individual health insurance (64%), group health insurance (23%), individual life insurance (7%), reinsurance (3%), and group life insurance (2%).

Principal Investments: NonCMO investment grade bonds (63%), CMOs and structured securities (20%), noninv. grade bonds (10%), policy loans (3%), and misc. investments (4%).

Investments in Affiliates: 2%
Group Affiliation: Chubb Limited
Licensed in: All states except NY
Commenced Business: January 1922
Address: 1000 North Milwakee Ave, Glenview, IL 60025
Phone: (312) 701-3000 **Domicile State:** IL **NAIC Code:** 62146

Data Date	Rating	RACR #1	RACR #2	Total Assets ($mil)	Capital ($mil)	Net Premium ($mil)	Net Income ($mil)
6-16	C+	0.88	0.59	1,364.1	91.7	222.0	5.8
6-15	C+	0.99	0.69	1,392.3	121.7	220.7	13.0
2015	C	0.80	0.54	1,316.7	79.9	439.9	-14.1
2014	C+	1.10	0.78	1,378.3	134.4	434.5	60.1
2013	C+	1.99	1.54	1,588.9	324.6	428.1	71.8
2012	C+	2.06	1.61	1,543.6	320.7	151.5	195.8
2011	B-	1.96	1.68	1,995.5	496.6	597.2	121.4

Junk Bonds as a % of Capital

Capital — $80 mil.
Junk Bonds — $118 mil.

0% 20% 40% 60% 80% 100% 120% 140% 160%

■ BB ▨ B ▦ CCC □ In default

COMBINED LIFE INSURANCE COMPANY OF NEW YORK C+ Fair

Major Rating Factors: Fair capitalization for the current period (3.7 on a scale of 0 to 10) based on mixed results -- excessive policy leverage mitigated by fair risk adjusted capital (moderate loss scenario) reflecting some improvement over results in 2015. Fair overall results on stability tests (3.7) including weak risk adjusted capital in prior years. Good quality investment portfolio (6.8).

Other Rating Factors: Weak profitability (1.5) with investment income below regulatory standards in relation to interest assumptions of reserves. Excellent liquidity (7.1).

Principal Business: Individual health insurance (63%), reinsurance (17%), individual life insurance (11%), group health insurance (9%), and group life insurance (1%).

Principal Investments: NonCMO investment grade bonds (58%), CMOs and structured securities (41%), and policy loans (2%).

Investments in Affiliates: None
Group Affiliation: Chubb Limited
Licensed in: FL, IL, NY
Commenced Business: June 1971
Address: 13 Cornell Rd, Latham, NY 12110-1402
Phone: (518) 220-9333 **Domicile State:** NY **NAIC Code:** 78697

Data Date	Rating	RACR #1	RACR #2	Total Assets ($mil)	Capital ($mil)	Net Premium ($mil)	Net Income ($mil)
6-16	C+	0.83	0.59	407.6	29.2	77.5	4.7
6-15	C	0.81	0.57	413.7	26.9	82.5	-7.1
2015	C	0.63	0.45	397.3	21.9	156.2	-9.7
2014	B	1.32	0.92	391.9	39.9	127.5	6.1
2013	B	1.85	1.29	402.9	56.4	126.0	3.7
2012	B	2.23	1.55	398.9	67.7	126.0	7.2
2011	B	1.95	1.38	382.7	60.3	132.4	15.6

Policy Leverage

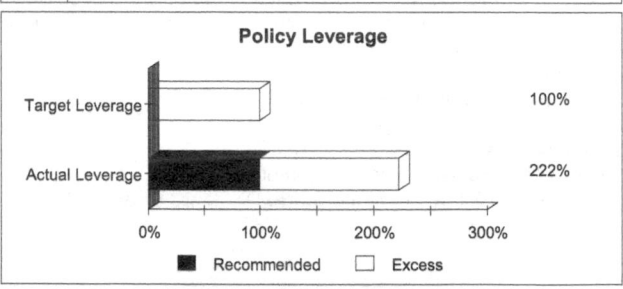

Target Leverage — 100%
Actual Leverage — 222%

0% 100% 200% 300%

■ Recommended □ Excess

COMMONWEALTH ANNUITY & LIFE INSURANCE COMPANY B- Good

Major Rating Factors: Good capitalization (5.7 on a scale of 0 to 10) based on good risk adjusted capital (severe loss scenario). Capital levels have been relatively consistent over the last five years. Good overall results on stability tests (5.0) despite negative cash flow from operations for 2015. Other stability subfactors include good operational trends and excellent risk diversification. Fair quality investment portfolio (4.7).

Other Rating Factors: Excellent profitability (7.1) despite modest operating losses during 2012 and 2013. Excellent liquidity (7.9).

Principal Business: Reinsurance (92%), individual life insurance (4%), and individual annuities (4%).

Principal Investments: CMOs and structured securities (38%), nonCMO investment grade bonds (26%), common & preferred stock (22%), policy loans (4%), and misc. investments (8%).

Investments in Affiliates: 22%
Group Affiliation: Global Atlantic Financial Group
Licensed in: All states except NY, PR
Commenced Business: January 1967
Address: 440 Lincoln St, Worcester, MA 01653
Phone: (508) 855-1000 **Domicile State:** MA **NAIC Code:** 84824

Data Date	Rating	RACR #1	RACR #2	Total Assets ($mil)	Capital ($mil)	Net Premium ($mil)	Net Income ($mil)
6-16	B-	0.95	0.84	12,253.5	2,259.8	127.3	-43.5
6-15	B-	0.99	0.85	11,754.6	1,899.6	155.9	-7.5
2015	B-	0.92	0.82	12,287.2	2,169.8	327.9	59.2
2014	C	0.91	0.82	10,497.0	1,646.0	552.4	215.5
2013	C	1.10	0.86	10,211.9	723.6	-637.5	-32.6
2012	C	1.25	0.76	9,089.8	327.4	-996.0	-7.4
2011	C	1.78	1.09	7,575.0	374.6	1,519.0	122.4

Risk-Adjusted Capital Ratio #2 (Severe Loss Scenario)

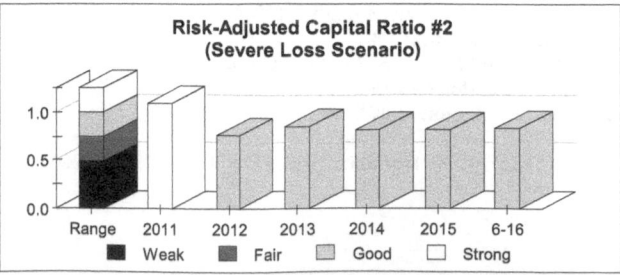

1.0

0.5

0.0

Range 2011 2012 2013 2014 2015 6-16

■ Weak ▨ Fair ▦ Good □ Strong

COMPANION LIFE INSURANCE COMPANY — C+ — Fair

Major Rating Factors: Fair quality investment portfolio (3.5 on a scale of 0 to 10) with large holdings of BBB rated bonds in addition to moderate junk bond exposure. Fair liquidity (4.0) due, in part, to cash value policies that are subject to withdrawals with minimal or no penalty. Fair overall results on stability tests (4.6).

Other Rating Factors: Good capitalization (5.6) based on good risk adjusted capital (moderate loss scenario). Weak profitability (2.0) with operating losses during the first six months of 2016.

Principal Business: Individual life insurance (73%), group life insurance (13%), group retirement contracts (9%), and individual annuities (5%).

Principal Investments: NonCMO investment grade bonds (62%), CMOs and structured securities (22%), mortgages in good standing (8%), policy loans (3%), and misc. investments (4%).

Investments in Affiliates: None

Group Affiliation: Mutual Of Omaha Group

Licensed in: CT, NJ, NY

Commenced Business: July 1949

Address: 888 Veterans Memorial Hwy #515, Hauppauge, NY 11788

Phone: (800) 877-5399 **Domicile State:** NY **NAIC Code:** 62243

Data Date	Rating	RACR #1	RACR #2	Total Assets ($mil)	Capital ($mil)	Net Premium ($mil)	Net Income ($mil)
6-16	C+	1.38	0.72	1,037.2	43.3	52.0	-3.8
6-15	C+	1.47	0.77	968.4	43.7	43.1	-11.1
2015	C+	1.59	0.84	1,013.4	50.9	98.8	-6.9
2014	B-	1.86	0.97	956.9	57.3	96.8	-5.5
2013	B-	1.61	0.84	883.2	47.0	84.5	0.3
2012	B	2.05	1.07	847.5	58.9	90.1	6.7
2011	B	2.37	1.24	809.3	65.7	78.4	-1.5

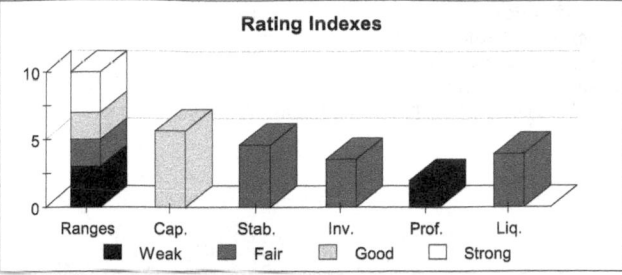

Rating Indexes

Ranges / Cap. / Stab. / Inv. / Prof. / Liq.
■ Weak ▦ Fair ▨ Good ☐ Strong

COMPANION LIFE INSURANCE COMPANY * — A- — Excellent

Major Rating Factors: Good quality investment portfolio (5.4 on a scale of 0 to 10) despite mixed results such as: no exposure to mortgages and large holdings of BBB rated bonds but minimal holdings in junk bonds. Good liquidity (6.9) with sufficient resources to handle a spike in claims. Excellent overall results on stability tests (7.2) excellent operational trends and excellent risk diversification.

Other Rating Factors: Strong capitalization (9.2) based on excellent risk adjusted capital (severe loss scenario). Excellent profitability (8.6).

Principal Business: Group health insurance (89%), reinsurance (7%), and group life insurance (4%).

Principal Investments: NonCMO investment grade bonds (50%), common & preferred stock (23%), CMOs and structured securities (19%), cash (7%), and noninv. grade bonds (1%).

Investments in Affiliates: 7%

Group Affiliation: Blue Cross Blue Shield of S Carolina

Licensed in: All states except CA, HI, NJ, NY, PR

Commenced Business: July 1970

Address: 2501 Faraway Dr, Columbia, SC 29219

Phone: (800) 753-0404 **Domicile State:** SC **NAIC Code:** 77828

Data Date	Rating	RACR #1	RACR #2	Total Assets ($mil)	Capital ($mil)	Net Premium ($mil)	Net Income ($mil)
6-16	A-	3.26	2.47	329.6	180.4	118.3	6.2
6-15	A-	3.03	2.35	303.4	154.1	110.7	8.6
2015	A-	3.15	2.44	300.4	160.4	221.6	13.7
2014	A-	2.95	2.30	284.9	149.0	220.5	15.6
2013	A-	2.92	2.31	251.7	138.0	202.8	14.5
2012	A-	2.75	2.19	203.8	120.7	181.8	12.5
2011	A-	2.53	2.02	186.8	110.0	177.8	8.7

Adverse Trends in Operations

Change in asset mix during 2015 (4%)

CONNECTICUT GENERAL LIFE INSURANCE COMPANY — B- — Good

Major Rating Factors: Fair quality investment portfolio (4.4 on a scale of 0 to 10). Fair overall results on stability tests (3.9). Strong capitalization (7.3) based on excellent risk adjusted capital (severe loss scenario). Moreover, capital levels have been consistently high over the last five years.

Other Rating Factors: Excellent profitability (8.6). Excellent liquidity (7.0).

Principal Business: Individual health insurance (32%), individual life insurance (28%), group life insurance (26%), group health insurance (6%), and other lines (8%).

Principal Investments: Common & preferred stock (33%), nonCMO investment grade bonds (33%), policy loans (15%), noninv. grade bonds (6%), and misc. investments (13%).

Investments in Affiliates: 35%

Group Affiliation: CIGNA Corp

Licensed in: All states, the District of Columbia and Puerto Rico

Commenced Business: October 1865

Address: 900 Cottage Grove Rd, S-330, Bloomfield, CT 06002

Phone: (860) 726-7234 **Domicile State:** CT **NAIC Code:** 62308

Data Date	Rating	RACR #1	RACR #2	Total Assets ($mil)	Capital ($mil)	Net Premium ($mil)	Net Income ($mil)
6-16	B-	1.35	1.21	17,491.2	3,846.5	202.1	644.2
6-15	B-	1.31	1.16	17,766.6	3,476.8	367.6	449.4
2015	B-	1.33	1.19	17,374.4	3,631.0	485.0	916.2
2014	B-	1.34	1.19	17,768.9	3,473.3	1,115.7	212.6
2013	B-	1.63	1.33	18,573.6	3,246.4	3,380.1	601.8
2012	B-	1.78	1.35	20,921.6	3,040.9	7,272.6	588.9
2011	B-	2.04	1.48	20,751.9	2,918.2	6,803.9	590.3

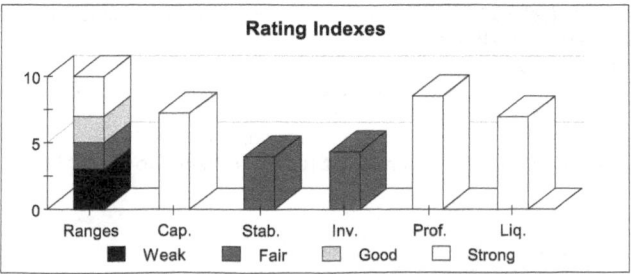

Rating Indexes

Ranges / Cap. / Stab. / Inv. / Prof. / Liq.
■ Weak ▦ Fair ▨ Good ☐ Strong

CONSTITUTION LIFE INSURANCE COMPANY   C+   Fair

Major Rating Factors: Fair overall results on stability tests (4.5 on a scale of 0 to 10) including negative cash flow from operations for 2015. Weak profitability (2.8) with investment income below regulatory standards in relation to interest assumptions of reserves. Strong capitalization (8.6) based on excellent risk adjusted capital (severe loss scenario).

Other Rating Factors: High quality investment portfolio (7.4). Excellent liquidity (7.3).

Principal Business: Individual health insurance (55%), reinsurance (26%), group health insurance (9%), and individual life insurance (9%).

Principal Investments: NonCMO investment grade bonds (65%) and CMOs and structured securities (35%).

Investments in Affiliates: None

Group Affiliation: Universal American Corp

Licensed in: All states except NJ, NY, PR

Commenced Business: June 1929

Address: 4211 Norbourne Blvd, Louisville, KY 40207-4048

Phone: (214) 954-7111 **Domicile State:** TX **NAIC Code:** 62359

Data Date	Rating	RACR #1	RACR #2	Total Assets ($mil)	Capital ($mil)	Net Premium ($mil)	Net Income ($mil)
6-16	C+	3.07	2.05	393.9	72.0	56.8	6.1
6-15	C+	N/A	N/A	404.9	52.3	63.9	5.9
2015	C+	2.75	1.84	394.8	66.6	123.3	34.9
2014	C+	1.88	1.23	316.5	37.0	94.4	11.1
2013	C+	1.56	1.05	317.3	33.5	109.5	9.2
2012	B-	1.52	1.16	57.4	28.4	69.2	4.5
2011	C	1.66	1.26	56.7	27.1	56.0	4.9

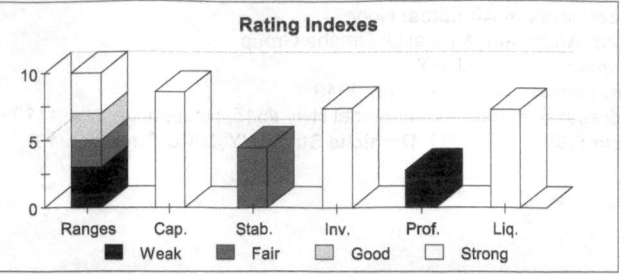

Rating Indexes

CONTINENTAL AMERICAN INSURANCE COMPANY   B   Good

Major Rating Factors: Fair profitability (4.3 on a scale of 0 to 10). Fair overall results on stability tests (4.5) including excessive premium growth. Strong overall capitalization (7.6) based on excellent risk adjusted capital (severe loss scenario). However, capital levels have fluctuated somewhat during past years.

Other Rating Factors: High quality investment portfolio (8.2). Excellent liquidity (7.1).

Principal Business: Group health insurance (65%), reinsurance (32%), and group life insurance (2%).

Principal Investments: NonCMO investment grade bonds (94%), cash (5%), and policy loans (1%).

Investments in Affiliates: None

Group Affiliation: AFLAC Inc

Licensed in: All states except NY, PR

Commenced Business: January 1969

Address: 2801 Devine St, Columbia, SC 29205

Phone: (803) 256-6265 **Domicile State:** SC **NAIC Code:** 71730

Data Date	Rating	RACR #1	RACR #2	Total Assets ($mil)	Capital ($mil)	Net Premium ($mil)	Net Income ($mil)
6-16	B	1.94	1.43	582.5	158.8	267.1	23.7
6-15	B	2.38	1.73	435.3	126.0	195.0	10.0
2015	B	1.84	1.37	512.3	138.0	436.8	26.2
2014	B	2.49	1.78	397.0	109.7	240.6	-17.3
2013	B	3.47	2.49	382.4	138.0	233.4	18.8
2012	B	4.36	3.13	344.0	137.4	183.7	-21.2
2011	B	1.68	1.32	167.4	36.0	162.6	-32.4

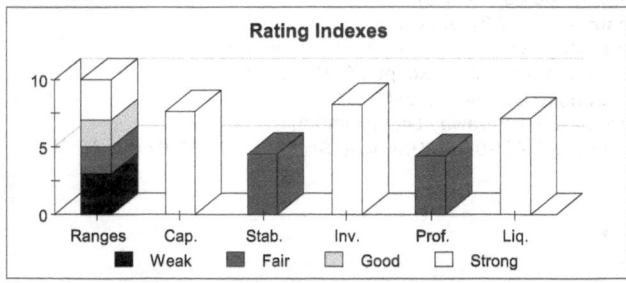

Rating Indexes

CONTINENTAL LIFE INSURANCE COMPANY OF BRENTWOOD   B   Good

Major Rating Factors: Good current capitalization (6.8 on a scale of 0 to 10) based on good risk adjusted capital (severe loss scenario) reflecting some improvement over results in 2011. Good quality investment portfolio (5.5) despite mixed results such as: no exposure to mortgages and substantial holdings of BBB bonds but minimal holdings in junk bonds. Good liquidity (6.5).

Other Rating Factors: Good overall results on stability tests (5.5) despite fair risk adjusted capital in prior years good operational trends and excellent risk diversification. Fair profitability (4.1) with operating losses during the first six months of 2016.

Principal Business: Individual health insurance (97%), group health insurance (1%), and individual life insurance (1%).

Principal Investments: NonCMO investment grade bonds (43%), common & preferred stock (32%), and CMOs and structured securities (27%).

Investments in Affiliates: 32%

Group Affiliation: Aetna Inc

Licensed in: All states except AK, CT, DC, HI, ME, MA, NY, WA, PR

Commenced Business: December 1983

Address: 800 Crescent Centre Dr, Franklin, TN 37067

Phone: (800) 264-4000 **Domicile State:** TN **NAIC Code:** 68500

Data Date	Rating	RACR #1	RACR #2	Total Assets ($mil)	Capital ($mil)	Net Premium ($mil)	Net Income ($mil)
6-16	B	1.10	0.98	283.3	147.0	209.6	-9.5
6-15	B	1.02	0.92	259.9	136.6	187.4	-5.6
2015	B	1.11	0.99	274.0	144.3	380.6	-1.2
2014	B	1.19	1.08	277.8	156.4	330.6	3.0
2013	B	1.12	1.01	205.6	97.0	256.6	3.2
2012	B	0.97	0.89	175.6	80.2	166.4	9.7
2011	C	0.71	0.65	144.3	54.2	139.0	5.7

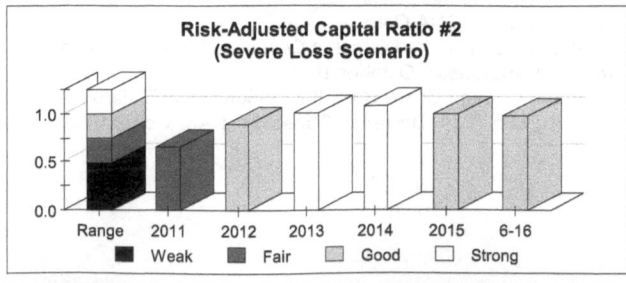

Risk-Adjusted Capital Ratio #2
(Severe Loss Scenario)

COTTON STATES LIFE INSURANCE COMPANY *   A-   Excellent

Major Rating Factors: Good quality investment portfolio (6.8 on a scale of 0 to 10) despite mixed results such as: minimal exposure to mortgages and large holdings of BBB rated bonds but minimal holdings in junk bonds. Good liquidity (6.2) with sufficient resources to handle a spike in claims as well as a significant increase in policy surrenders. Strong capitalization (9.2) based on excellent risk adjusted capital (severe loss scenario).

Other Rating Factors: Excellent profitability (8.2). Excellent overall results on stability tests (7.3) excellent operational trends and excellent risk diversification.

Principal Business: Individual life insurance (100%).

Principal Investments: NonCMO investment grade bonds (71%), CMOs and structured securities (18%), policy loans (5%), common & preferred stock (4%), and noninv. grade bonds (2%).

Investments in Affiliates: None

Group Affiliation: COUNTRY Financial

Licensed in: AL, FL, GA, KY, LA, MS, NC, SC, TN, VA

Commenced Business: December 1955

Address: 13560 Morris Rd Suite 4000, Alpharetta, GA 30004

Phone: (309) 821-3000 **Domicile State:** GA **NAIC Code:** 62537

Data Date	Rating	RACR #1	RACR #2	Total Assets ($mil)	Capital ($mil)	Net Premium ($mil)	Net Income ($mil)
6-16	A-	4.49	2.49	334.6	68.1	12.0	2.4
6-15	A-	4.06	2.24	334.0	64.2	12.8	2.3
2015	A-	4.46	2.51	333.9	66.1	25.3	4.0
2014	A-	4.11	2.32	332.3	62.8	27.6	6.4
2013	A-	3.82	2.15	329.6	58.2	29.7	5.2
2012	A-	3.67	2.05	322.3	53.1	32.4	5.2
2011	B+	3.27	1.80	315.0	48.4	35.3	4.5

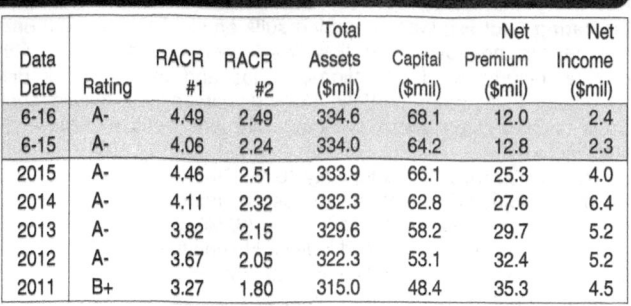

Rating Indexes

COUNTRY INVESTORS LIFE ASSURANCE COMPANY *   A-   Excellent

Major Rating Factors: Strong capitalization (8.0 on a scale of 0 to 10) based on excellent risk adjusted capital (severe loss scenario). Furthermore, this high level of risk adjusted capital has been consistently maintained over the last five years. High quality investment portfolio (8.2) with no exposure to mortgages and minimal holdings in junk bonds. Excellent profitability (7.9).

Other Rating Factors: Excellent liquidity (8.5). Excellent overall results on stability tests (7.1) excellent operational trends and excellent risk diversification.

Principal Business: Individual annuities (78%) and individual life insurance (22%).

Principal Investments: NonCMO investment grade bonds (81%), CMOs and structured securities (18%), and noninv. grade bonds (1%).

Investments in Affiliates: None

Group Affiliation: COUNTRY Financial

Licensed in: All states except CA, DC, HI, NH, NJ, NY, UT, VT, PR

Commenced Business: November 1981

Address: 1701 N Towanda Ave, Bloomington, IL 61701

Phone: (309) 821-3000 **Domicile State:** IL **NAIC Code:** 94218

Data Date	Rating	RACR #1	RACR #2	Total Assets ($mil)	Capital ($mil)	Net Premium ($mil)	Net Income ($mil)
6-16	A-	12.42	6.06	297.1	186.5	0.0	2.2
6-15	A-	13.63	6.68	296.9	180.8	0.0	2.6
2015	A-	14.70	7.21	292.9	184.2	0.0	5.6
2014	A-	15.10	7.48	286.5	178.3	0.0	4.7
2013	A-	14.95	7.35	286.9	173.4	0.0	4.8
2012	A-	15.53	7.66	260.8	169.2	0.0	4.9
2011	A-	16.08	7.96	248.3	164.7	0.0	4.7

Risk-Adjusted Capital Ratios (Since 2011)

COUNTRY LIFE INSURANCE COMPANY *   A+   Excellent

Major Rating Factors: Good quality investment portfolio (5.8 on a scale of 0 to 10) despite mixed results such as: large holdings of BBB rated bonds but moderate junk bond exposure. Good liquidity (5.8) with sufficient resources to handle a spike in claims as well as a significant increase in policy surrenders. Strong capitalization (7.5) based on excellent risk adjusted capital (severe loss scenario).

Other Rating Factors: Excellent profitability (7.5). Excellent overall results on stability tests (7.5) excellent operational trends and excellent risk diversification.

Principal Business: Individual life insurance (57%), reinsurance (26%), individual health insurance (15%), and group life insurance (1%).

Principal Investments: NonCMO investment grade bonds (59%), CMOs and structured securities (20%), common & preferred stock (7%), policy loans (4%), and misc. investments (8%).

Investments in Affiliates: 4%

Group Affiliation: COUNTRY Financial

Licensed in: All states except CA, DC, HI, NH, NJ, NY, VT, PR

Commenced Business: December 1928

Address: 1701 N Towanda Ave, Bloomington, IL 61701-2090

Phone: (309) 821-3000 **Domicile State:** IL **NAIC Code:** 62553

Data Date	Rating	RACR #1	RACR #2	Total Assets ($mil)	Capital ($mil)	Net Premium ($mil)	Net Income ($mil)
6-16	A+	2.07	1.35	10,264.7	1,133.6	360.3	21.2
6-15	A+	2.10	1.37	10,929.6	1,124.8	337.5	22.1
2015	A+	2.11	1.40	10,093.0	1,135.9	641.9	32.9
2014	A+	2.13	1.41	10,697.2	1,124.0	612.1	51.5
2013	A+	2.15	1.42	10,262.6	1,096.3	612.7	55.6
2012	A+	2.04	1.35	9,553.0	1,027.4	638.4	43.2
2011	A+	2.06	1.37	8,947.4	1,000.9	588.7	34.1

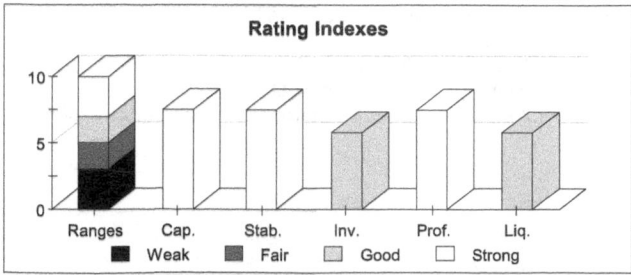

Rating Indexes

DEARBORN NATIONAL LIFE INSURANCE COMPANY *   B+   Good

Major Rating Factors: Good overall results on stability tests (6.0 on a scale of 0 to 10) despite negative cash flow from operations for 2015. Other stability subfactors include good operational trends and excellent risk diversification. Good quality investment portfolio (6.4) despite mixed results such as: large holdings of BBB rated bonds but moderate junk bond exposure. Good overall profitability (6.8).

Other Rating Factors: Good liquidity (6.5). Strong capitalization (9.0) based on excellent risk adjusted capital (severe loss scenario).

Principal Business: Group life insurance (63%), group health insurance (34%), individual life insurance (2%), and individual annuities (1%).

Principal Investments: NonCMO investment grade bonds (64%), CMOs and structured securities (24%), noninv. grade bonds (8%), common & preferred stock (1%), and mortgages in good standing (1%).

Investments in Affiliates: 1%

Group Affiliation: HCSC Group

Licensed in: All states except NY

Commenced Business: April 1969

Address: 300 East Randolph Street, Chicago, IL 60601-5099

Phone: (800) 633-3696 **Domicile State:** IL **NAIC Code:** 71129

Data Date	Rating	RACR #1	RACR #2	Total Assets ($mil)	Capital ($mil)	Net Premium ($mil)	Net Income ($mil)
6-16	B+	3.70	2.30	1,969.6	535.0	202.2	13.4
6-15	B+	2.91	1.94	2,076.7	530.7	191.0	18.1
2015	B+	3.63	2.25	1,990.5	522.1	382.5	59.1
2014	A-	2.86	1.91	2,145.5	514.7	379.9	54.8
2013	A-	2.27	1.52	2,324.1	439.7	495.5	42.3
2012	A-	1.85	1.21	2,621.0	402.8	563.1	-6.1
2011	A-	1.75	1.10	2,895.8	399.7	694.6	-10.8

Adverse Trends in Operations

Decrease in asset base during 2015 (7%)
Decrease in premium volume from 2013 to 2014 (23%)
Decrease in premium volume from 2012 to 2013 (12%)
Decrease in asset base during 2013 (11%)
Decrease in premium volume from 2011 to 2012 (19%)

DELAWARE AMERICAN LIFE INSURANCE COMPANY *   A-   Excellent

Major Rating Factors: Good overall profitability (6.8 on a scale of 0 to 10). Good liquidity (6.8) with sufficient resources to handle a spike in claims. Excellent overall results on stability tests (7.2). Strengths that enhance stability include excellent operational trends and excellent risk diversification.

Other Rating Factors: Strong capitalization (9.4) based on excellent risk adjusted capital (severe loss scenario). High quality investment portfolio (7.6).

Principal Business: Group health insurance (61%), reinsurance (26%), group life insurance (12%), and individual life insurance (1%).

Principal Investments: NonCMO investment grade bonds (52%), CMOs and structured securities (38%), and cash (6%).

Investments in Affiliates: 3%

Group Affiliation: MetLife Inc

Licensed in: All states except PR

Commenced Business: August 1966

Address: 600 King St, Wilmington, DE 19801

Phone: (302) 594-2000 **Domicile State:** DE **NAIC Code:** 62634

Data Date	Rating	RACR #1	RACR #2	Total Assets ($mil)	Capital ($mil)	Net Premium ($mil)	Net Income ($mil)
6-16	A-	3.55	2.61	145.9	65.2	57.6	2.9
6-15	A-	3.86	2.83	143.7	69.5	55.6	-1.3
2015	A-	3.53	2.60	136.6	63.5	108.7	1.8
2014	A-	3.88	2.81	136.7	69.3	102.1	10.0
2013	B	4.89	3.54	137.1	74.3	91.1	17.1
2012	B	3.60	2.62	128.7	54.6	76.1	7.7
2011	B	3.08	2.23	135.8	51.4	72.4	12.6

Adverse Trends in Operations

Decrease in capital during 2015 (8%)
Decrease in capital during 2014 (7%)
Decrease in asset base during 2012 (5%)

DELAWARE LIFE INSURANCE COMPANY   C   Fair

Major Rating Factors: Fair quality investment portfolio (4.7 on a scale of 0 to 10) with large holdings of BBB rated bonds in addition to moderate junk bond exposure. Fair overall results on stability tests (3.9) including excessive premium growth and fair risk adjusted capital in prior years. Good capitalization (6.0) based on good risk adjusted capital (severe loss scenario).

Other Rating Factors: Good overall profitability (5.8). Excellent liquidity (8.5).

Principal Business: Individual annuities (86%), group retirement contracts (9%), and individual life insurance (5%).

Principal Investments: NonCMO investment grade bonds (33%), CMOs and structured securities (27%), policy loans (6%), common & preferred stock (6%), and misc. investments (14%).

Investments in Affiliates: 9%

Group Affiliation: Delaware Life Partners LLC

Licensed in: All states except NY

Commenced Business: January 1973

Address: 1209 Orange St, Wilmington, DE 19801

Phone: (781) 237-6030 **Domicile State:** DE **NAIC Code:** 79065

Data Date	Rating	RACR #1	RACR #2	Total Assets ($mil)	Capital ($mil)	Net Premium ($mil)	Net Income ($mil)
6-16	C	1.40	0.88	40,645.8	1,485.7	936.9	114.7
6-15	C	1.47	0.94	39,920.3	1,576.5	580.1	128.3
2015	C	1.67	1.07	36,876.9	1,635.9	1,321.2	348.8
2014	C	1.52	0.98	40,699.8	1,591.5	1,783.1	315.8
2013	D+	1.43	0.93	39,279.2	1,410.4	1,559.4	682.9
2012	D	1.08	0.67	42,526.4	1,235.9	415.9	-400.8
2011	D	1.38	0.83	43,017.2	1,315.3	3,230.2	-517.1

Rating Indexes

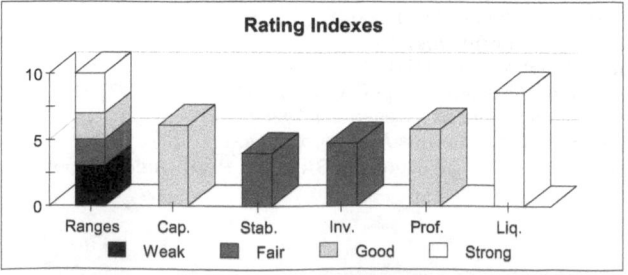

DELAWARE LIFE INSURANCE COMPANY OF NEW YORK   C+   Fair

Major Rating Factors: Fair overall results on stability tests (3.6 on a scale of 0 to 10) including fair financial strength of affiliated Delaware Life Partners LLC and negative cash flow from operations for 2015. Good quality investment portfolio (6.4) despite mixed results such as: minimal exposure to mortgages and large holdings of BBB rated bonds but minimal holdings in junk bonds. Strong capitalization (10.0) based on excellent risk adjusted capital (severe loss scenario).

Other Rating Factors: Excellent profitability (7.0). Excellent liquidity (7.1).

Principal Business: Individual annuities (61%) and individual life insurance (39%).

Principal Investments: NonCMO investment grade bonds (62%), CMOs and structured securities (33%), noninv. grade bonds (2%), common & preferred stock (2%), and mortgages in good standing (2%).

Investments in Affiliates: None

Group Affiliation: Delaware Life Partners LLC

Licensed in: CT, NY, RI

Commenced Business: August 1985

Address: 1115 Broadway 12th Floor, New York, NY 10010

Phone: (781) 237-6030 **Domicile State:** NY **NAIC Code:** 72664

Data Date	Rating	RACR #1	RACR #2	Total Assets ($mil)	Capital ($mil)	Net Premium ($mil)	Net Income ($mil)
6-16	C+	7.39	3.58	2,815.6	411.4	10.0	21.3
6-15	C+	8.10	4.03	2,889.4	435.4	17.0	9.8
2015	C+	7.91	3.83	2,731.0	401.8	27.2	15.8
2014	C+	7.61	3.80	2,952.2	417.6	-16.3	37.5
2013	C	7.96	3.91	3,194.6	399.9	-8.7	16.9
2012	C	4.96	2.73	3,509.7	348.6	145.0	37.6
2011	C	4.65	2.48	3,503.0	304.9	387.8	5.3

Delaware Life Partners LLC Composite Group Rating: C Largest Group Members	Assets ($mil)	Rating
DELAWARE LIFE INS CO	36877	C
DELAWARE LIFE INS CO OF NEW YORK	2731	C+

EAGLE LIFE INSURANCE COMPANY   B   Good

Major Rating Factors: Good quality investment portfolio (6.8 on a scale of 0 to 10) despite mixed results such as: minimal exposure to mortgages and large holdings of BBB rated bonds but minimal holdings in junk bonds. Good liquidity (6.9) with sufficient resources to handle a spike in claims as well as a significant increase in policy surrenders. Good overall results on stability tests (5.8) excellent operational trends, good risk adjusted capital for prior years and excellent risk diversification.

Other Rating Factors: Fair profitability (3.0) with investment income below regulatory standards in relation to interest assumptions of reserves. Strong capitalization (8.6) based on excellent risk adjusted capital (severe loss scenario).

Principal Business: Individual annuities (100%).

Principal Investments: NonCMO investment grade bonds (72%), CMOs and structured securities (20%), mortgages in good standing (4%), cash (2%), and noninv. grade bonds (1%).

Investments in Affiliates: None

Group Affiliation: American Equity Investment Group

Licensed in: All states except ID, NY, PR

Commenced Business: August 2008

Address: 5000 Westown Pkwy, West Des Moines, IA 50266-5921

Phone: (515) 221-0002 **Domicile State:** IA **NAIC Code:** 13183

Data Date	Rating	RACR #1	RACR #2	Total Assets ($mil)	Capital ($mil)	Net Premium ($mil)	Net Income ($mil)
6-16	B	4.24	2.09	393.4	64.7	75.6	2.0
6-15	B	4.31	2.51	242.5	42.4	25.9	0.0
2015	B	4.75	2.41	313.9	62.9	74.8	0.3
2014	B	4.29	2.68	216.4	42.3	24.0	3.0
2013	B	4.10	2.87	188.7	39.5	22.9	-2.2
2012	B	1.32	1.13	139.0	12.0	31.4	-2.5
2011	B	1.09	0.99	106.1	9.7	56.9	-2.7

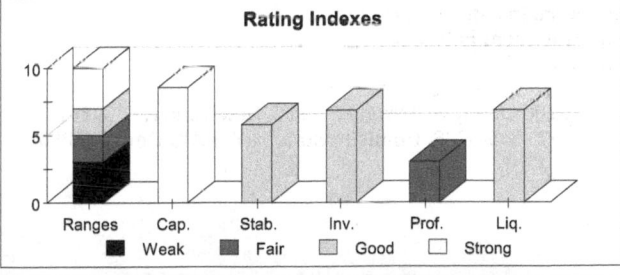

Rating Indexes — Ranges, Cap., Stab., Inv., Prof., Liq. (Weak, Fair, Good, Strong)

ELCO MUTUAL LIFE & ANNUITY   C-   Fair

Major Rating Factors: Fair quality investment portfolio (3.6 on a scale of 0 to 10) with large holdings of BBB rated bonds in addition to moderate junk bond exposure. Fair overall results on stability tests (3.0). Weak profitability (2.8) with investment income below regulatory standards in relation to interest assumptions of reserves.

Other Rating Factors: Good capitalization (5.7) based on good risk adjusted capital (moderate loss scenario). Excellent liquidity (7.7).

Principal Business: Individual annuities (96%) and individual life insurance (3%).

Principal Investments: NonCMO investment grade bonds (92%), cash (4%), noninv. grade bonds (2%), mortgages in good standing (1%), and real estate (1%).

Investments in Affiliates: None

Group Affiliation: None

Licensed in: All states except AK, CT, DC, HI, MA, NH, NJ, NY, RI, VT, PR

Commenced Business: May 1946

Address: 916 Sherwood Dr, Lake Bluff, IL 60044-2285

Phone: (847) 295-6000 **Domicile State:** IL **NAIC Code:** 84174

Data Date	Rating	RACR #1	RACR #2	Total Assets ($mil)	Capital ($mil)	Net Premium ($mil)	Net Income ($mil)
6-16	C-	1.46	0.70	680.2	47.5	99.2	4.0
6-15	C-	1.57	0.79	582.0	44.6	158.2	0.2
2015	C-	1.53	0.75	642.3	45.0	305.8	0.1
2014	C-	1.54	0.79	526.7	44.5	130.4	1.5
2013	B-	1.72	0.88	362.8	40.8	17.3	4.3
2012	B-	1.47	0.75	553.5	35.1	20.0	6.9
2011	B-	1.73	0.91	460.1	29.1	23.4	4.7

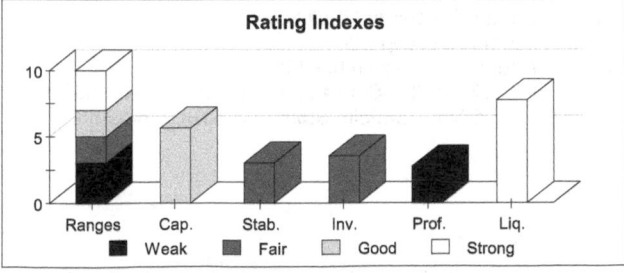

Rating Indexes — Ranges, Cap., Stab., Inv., Prof., Liq. (Weak, Fair, Good, Strong)

EMC NATIONAL LIFE COMPANY   B   Good

Major Rating Factors: Good quality investment portfolio (6.5 on a scale of 0 to 10) despite mixed results such as: minimal exposure to mortgages and large holdings of BBB rated bonds but minimal holdings in junk bonds. Good liquidity (5.2) with sufficient resources to cover a large increase in policy surrenders. Good overall results on stability tests (5.7) despite negative cash flow from operations for 2015 good operational trends and excellent risk diversification.

Other Rating Factors: Strong capitalization (7.6) based on excellent risk adjusted capital (severe loss scenario). Excellent profitability (7.5).

Principal Business: Individual life insurance (58%), individual annuities (31%), group life insurance (6%), reinsurance (3%), and individual health insurance (1%).

Principal Investments: NonCMO investment grade bonds (82%), CMOs and structured securities (7%), common & preferred stock (4%), mortgages in good standing (4%), and misc. investments (3%).

Investments in Affiliates: None

Group Affiliation: Employers Mutual Group

Licensed in: All states except NJ, NY, PR

Commenced Business: April 1963

Address: 4095 NW Urbandale Dr, Urbandale, IA 50322

Phone: (515) 280-2511 **Domicile State:** IA **NAIC Code:** 62928

Data Date	Rating	RACR #1	RACR #2	Total Assets ($mil)	Capital ($mil)	Net Premium ($mil)	Net Income ($mil)
6-16	B	2.52	1.43	965.4	104.5	34.0	5.2
6-15	B	2.44	1.42	995.2	99.5	30.0	2.8
2015	B	2.47	1.41	978.9	99.5	60.9	4.5
2014	B	2.43	1.42	1,009.8	98.8	57.8	10.5
2013	B-	2.14	1.24	1,030.2	87.9	60.6	5.6
2012	C	1.99	1.16	1,053.1	82.2	64.9	7.7
2011	C	2.16	1.25	1,043.3	79.9	98.2	9.1

Adverse Trends in Operations
Decrease in premium volume from 2013 to 2014 (5%)
Decrease in asset base during 2014 (2%)
Increase in policy surrenders from 2012 to 2013 (58%)
Change in premium mix from 2011 to 2012 (4.4%)
Decrease in premium volume from 2011 to 2012 (34%)

EMPIRE FIDELITY INVESTMENTS LIFE INSURANCE COMPANY *   B+   Good

Major Rating Factors: Good overall results on stability tests (6.7 on a scale of 0 to 10). Strengths include potential support from affiliation with FMR LLC, excellent operational trends and excellent risk diversification. Fair profitability (3.3) with investment income below regulatory standards in relation to interest assumptions of reserves. Strong capitalization (8.9) based on excellent risk adjusted capital (severe loss scenario).

Other Rating Factors: High quality investment portfolio (8.1). Excellent liquidity (7.0).

Principal Business: Individual annuities (99%) and individual life insurance (1%).

Principal Investments: NonCMO investment grade bonds (95%), CMOs and structured securities (4%), and noninv. grade bonds (1%).

Investments in Affiliates: None

Group Affiliation: FMR LLC

Licensed in: NY

Commenced Business: June 1992

Address: 200 Liberty St 1 World Financl, New York, NY 10281

Phone: (212) 335-5706 **Domicile State:** NY **NAIC Code:** 71228

Data Date	Rating	RACR #1	RACR #2	Total Assets ($mil)	Capital ($mil)	Net Premium ($mil)	Net Income ($mil)
6-16	B+	2.67	2.29	2,497.9	78.7	92.2	0.7
6-15	B+	2.53	2.25	2,503.0	74.7	94.3	2.4
2015	B+	2.60	2.34	2,441.3	76.9	155.8	4.4
2014	B+	2.45	2.21	2,443.7	72.5	159.7	5.0
2013	B+	2.40	2.16	2,270.4	67.4	202.1	2.3
2012	B+	2.59	2.33	1,926.4	64.9	179.8	2.5
2011	B+	2.67	2.41	1,663.5	60.7	155.9	2.9

FMR LLC Composite Group Rating: A- Largest Group Members	Assets ($mil)	Rating
FIDELITY INVESTMENTS LIFE INS CO	24854	A-
EMPIRE FIDELITY INVESTMENTS L I C	2441	B+

EMPLOYERS REASSURANCE CORPORATION   C   Fair

Major Rating Factors: Fair overall results on stability tests (4.2 on a scale of 0 to 10) including fair financial strength of affiliated GE Insurance Solutions and negative cash flow from operations for 2015, fair risk adjusted capital in prior years. Fair profitability (3.3). Excellent expense controls. Good capitalization (5.2) based on good risk adjusted capital (severe loss scenario).

Other Rating Factors: Good quality investment portfolio (5.8). Good liquidity (6.9).

Principal Business: Reinsurance (100%).

Principal Investments: NonCMO investment grade bonds (70%), CMOs and structured securities (18%), mortgages in good standing (5%), common & preferred stock (4%), and noninv. grade bonds (1%).

Investments in Affiliates: 5%

Group Affiliation: GE Insurance Solutions

Licensed in: All states except NY

Commenced Business: November 1907

Address: 7101 College Blvd Ste 1400, Overland Park, KS 66210

Phone: (913) 676-5724 **Domicile State:** KS **NAIC Code:** 68276

Data Date	Rating	RACR #1	RACR #2	Total Assets ($mil)	Capital ($mil)	Net Premium ($mil)	Net Income ($mil)
6-16	C	1.03	0.77	10,616.1	643.4	152.7	7.4
6-15	C	1.22	0.97	10,755.4	851.0	169.8	56.7
2015	C	1.28	0.99	10,708.7	775.8	366.1	63.9
2014	C	1.19	0.94	10,776.3	830.4	410.8	-44.5
2013	C	1.53	1.21	11,002.6	1,224.8	441.3	453.8
2012	C-	0.93	0.71	10,766.2	763.3	488.8	-418.0
2011	C-	0.91	0.69	10,960.8	653.9	504.1	-115.5

GE Insurance Solutions Composite Group Rating: C- Largest Group Members	Assets ($mil)	Rating
UNION FIDELITY LIFE INS CO	19365	D+
EMPLOYERS REASSURANCE CORP	10709	C

EQUITABLE LIFE & CASUALTY INSURANCE COMPANY   B   Good

Major Rating Factors: Good overall profitability (5.9 on a scale of 0 to 10). Good overall results on stability tests (5.7). Stability strengths include excellent operational trends and good risk diversification. Strong capitalization (8.7) based on excellent risk adjusted capital (severe loss scenario). Capital levels have been relatively consistent over the last five years.

Other Rating Factors: High quality investment portfolio (7.6). Excellent liquidity (7.0).

Principal Business: Individual health insurance (92%), individual life insurance (7%), and reinsurance (1%).

Principal Investments: NonCMO investment grade bonds (76%), CMOs and structured securities (18%), mortgages in good standing (5%), and cash (1%).

Investments in Affiliates: None

Group Affiliation: Insurance Investment Co

Licensed in: All states except CA, FL, MN, NJ, NY, PR

Commenced Business: June 1935

Address: 3 Triad Center Suite 200, Salt Lake City, UT 84180

Phone: (801) 579-3400 **Domicile State:** UT **NAIC Code:** 62952

Data Date	Rating	RACR #1	RACR #2	Total Assets ($mil)	Capital ($mil)	Net Premium ($mil)	Net Income ($mil)
6-16	B	3.29	2.16	317.1	51.3	32.7	4.5
6-15	B	2.93	1.97	302.9	46.1	36.4	4.7
2015	B	2.94	1.96	306.4	46.2	69.7	9.5
2014	B	2.72	1.84	295.9	41.8	70.4	10.3
2013	D+	2.15	1.51	275.8	39.1	91.1	-0.3
2012	C-	1.51	1.08	243.0	30.3	111.1	1.8
2011	C-	1.61	1.15	230.6	30.9	110.1	1.4

Adverse Trends in Operations

Increase in policy surrenders from 2014 to 2015 (33%)
Decrease in premium volume from 2013 to 2014 (23%)
Increase in policy surrenders from 2012 to 2013 (75%)
Decrease in premium volume from 2012 to 2013 (18%)
Decrease in capital during 2012 (2%)

EQUITRUST LIFE INSURANCE COMPANY   B-   Good

Major Rating Factors: Good capitalization (5.3 on a scale of 0 to 10) based on good risk adjusted capital (moderate loss scenario). Good overall profitability (6.7). Excellent expense controls. Good overall results on stability tests (5.0) despite fair risk adjusted capital in prior years. Other stability subfactors include excellent operational trends and excellent risk diversification.

Other Rating Factors: Fair quality investment portfolio (4.1). Excellent liquidity (8.3).

Principal Business: Individual annuities (68%), individual life insurance (17%), and group retirement contracts (14%).

Principal Investments: NonCMO investment grade bonds (41%), CMOs and structured securities (31%), mortgages in good standing (10%), noninv. grade bonds (3%), and misc. investments (14%).

Investments in Affiliates: None

Group Affiliation: Magic Johnson Enterprises Inc

Licensed in: All states except NY, PR

Commenced Business: July 1967

Address: 228 W Monroe St Suite 4900, Chicago, IL 60606

Phone: (515) 225-5400 **Domicile State:** IL **NAIC Code:** 62510

Data Date	Rating	RACR #1	RACR #2	Total Assets ($mil)	Capital ($mil)	Net Premium ($mil)	Net Income ($mil)
6-16	B-	1.17	0.58	16,791.6	748.5	942.5	76.2
6-15	B-	1.16	0.61	15,129.1	743.7	1,035.6	23.1
2015	B-	1.32	0.66	15,881.3	819.0	2,099.1	164.7
2014	B-	1.63	0.87	14,454.7	897.0	2,205.2	179.6
2013	B-	2.33	1.07	12,615.5	846.2	2,131.9	203.6
2012	B-	1.82	0.85	11,418.6	710.0	1,391.4	185.4
2011	B-	2.31	1.04	7,238.9	437.1	647.3	19.7

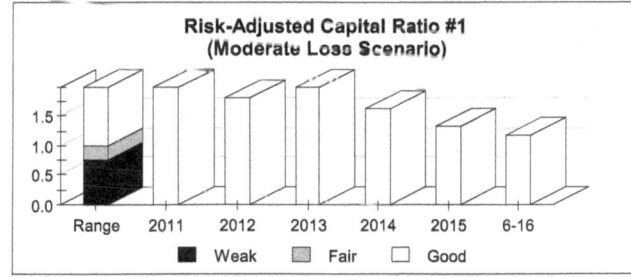

**Risk-Adjusted Capital Ratio #1
(Moderate Loss Scenario)**

Range 2011 2012 2013 2014 2015 6-16
■ Weak ▨ Fair □ Good

ERIE FAMILY LIFE INSURANCE COMPANY *   A-   Excellent

Major Rating Factors: Good quality investment portfolio (5.9 on a scale of 0 to 10) despite mixed results such as: minimal exposure to mortgages and large holdings of BBB rated bonds but small junk bond holdings. Excellent overall results on stability tests (7.1). Strengths that enhance stability include excellent operational trends and excellent risk diversification. Strong capitalization (8.2) based on excellent risk adjusted capital (severe loss scenario).

Other Rating Factors: Excellent profitability (8.0). Excellent liquidity (7.9).

Principal Business: Individual life insurance (81%) and individual annuities (18%).

Principal Investments: NonCMO investment grade bonds (92%), common & preferred stock (3%), noninv. grade bonds (2%), CMOs and structured securities (2%), and policy loans (1%).

Investments in Affiliates: None

Group Affiliation: Erie Ins Group

Licensed in: DC, IL, IN, KY, MD, MN, NC, OH, PA, TN, VA, WV, WI

Commenced Business: September 1967

Address: 100 Erie Insurance Pl, Erie, PA 16530

Phone: (800) 458-0811 **Domicile State:** PA **NAIC Code:** 70769

Data Date	Rating	RACR #1	RACR #2	Total Assets ($mil)	Capital ($mil)	Net Premium ($mil)	Net Income ($mil)
6-16	A-	3.30	1.79	2,217.2	311.9	82.2	2.2
6-15	A-	3.44	1.89	2,133.4	308.2	75.6	4.0
2015	A-	3.29	1.81	2,169.0	310.8	151.1	8.7
2014	A-	3.43	1.90	2,096.9	303.5	150.3	10.1
2013	A-	3.36	1.86	2,021.4	290.7	137.2	14.9
2012	A-	3.44	1.90	1,933.1	281.5	130.7	25.5
2011	B+	3.19	1.74	1,838.9	244.9	133.9	33.8

Adverse Trends in Operations

Decrease in premium volume from 2011 to 2012 (2%)

FAMILY HERITAGE LIFE INSURANCE COMPANY OF AMERICA *   A-   Excellent

Major Rating Factors: Good quality investment portfolio (6.6 on a scale of 0 to 10) despite mixed results such as: no exposure to mortgages and large holdings of BBB rated bonds but small junk bond holdings. Excellent overall results on stability tests (7.3). Strengths that enhance stability include excellent operational trends and excellent risk diversification. Strong capitalization (7.3) based on excellent risk adjusted capital (severe loss scenario).

Other Rating Factors: Excellent profitability (9.5). Excellent liquidity (7.9).

Principal Business: Individual health insurance (62%), reinsurance (34%), group health insurance (2%), and individual life insurance (1%).

Principal Investments: NonCMO investment grade bonds (97%) and noninv. grade bonds (1%).

Investments in Affiliates: None

Group Affiliation: Torchmark Corp

Licensed in: All states except NY

Commenced Business: November 1989

Address: 6001 E Royalton Rd Suite 200, Cleveland, OH 44147-3529

Phone: (440) 922-5200 **Domicile State:** OH **NAIC Code:** 77968

Data Date	Rating	RACR #1	RACR #2	Total Assets ($mil)	Capital ($mil)	Net Premium ($mil)	Net Income ($mil)
6-16	A-	1.81	1.18	1,004.9	77.5	136.6	9.9
6-15	A-	1.78	1.20	841.0	68.9	131.1	8.4
2015	A-	1.92	1.27	921.0	78.3	254.1	19.1
2014	A-	1.87	1.27	775.2	67.4	237.0	18.1
2013	A-	2.09	1.48	641.5	66.9	192.7	17.0
2012	B+	2.15	1.57	571.1	62.1	177.0	16.5
2011	B+	2.22	1.71	488.5	55.3	161.0	15.6

Adverse Trends in Operations

Increase in policy surrenders from 2014 to 2015 (118%)
Increase in policy surrenders from 2012 to 2013 (77%)

FAMILY LIFE INSURANCE COMPANY   C   Fair

Major Rating Factors: Fair overall results on stability tests (4.2 on a scale of 0 to 10). Good liquidity (6.8) with sufficient resources to handle a spike in claims as well as a significant increase in policy surrenders. Weak profitability (2.9) with investment income below regulatory standards in relation to interest assumptions of reserves.

Other Rating Factors: Strong capitalization (10.0) based on excellent risk adjusted capital (severe loss scenario). High quality investment portfolio (8.5).

Principal Business: Individual health insurance (66%) and individual life insurance (34%).

Principal Investments: NonCMO investment grade bonds (83%), policy loans (10%), CMOs and structured securities (4%), and mortgages in good standing (2%).

Investments in Affiliates: None

Group Affiliation: Manhattan Life Group Inc

Licensed in: All states except NY, PR

Commenced Business: June 1949

Address: 1200 6th Ave Park Place Bldg, Seattle, WA 98101

Phone: (512) 404-5284 **Domicile State:** TX **NAIC Code:** 63053

Data Date	Rating	RACR #1	RACR #2	Total Assets ($mil)	Capital ($mil)	Net Premium ($mil)	Net Income ($mil)
6-16	C	3.66	2.98	158.6	34.6	13.2	1.9
6-15	C	3.77	3.14	160.2	35.2	13.4	1.3
2015	C	3.79	3.13	158.7	35.8	26.5	2.7
2014	C	3.87	3.33	146.5	36.2	25.2	1.7
2013	C	3.41	2.69	147.6	31.9	26.0	3.5
2012	C	3.39	2.63	147.4	31.7	27.9	5.8
2011	C	3.23	2.77	126.4	29.5	23.2	3.7

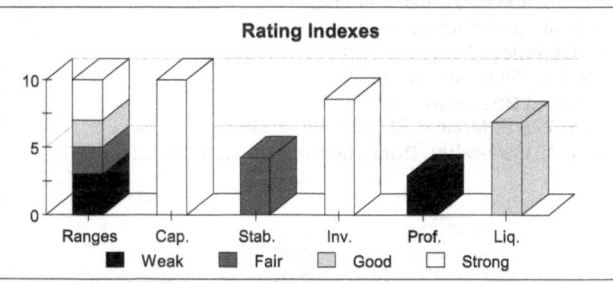

Rating Indexes

Ranges Cap. Stab. Inv. Prof. Liq.
■ Weak ■ Fair ▨ Good □ Strong

FARM BUREAU LIFE INSURANCE COMPANY *   B+   Good

Major Rating Factors: Good quality investment portfolio (5.4 on a scale of 0 to 10) despite mixed results such as: large holdings of BBB rated bonds but moderate junk bond exposure. Good overall results on stability tests (6.0). Stability strengths include excellent operational trends and excellent risk diversification. Fair liquidity (4.0).

Other Rating Factors: Strong capitalization (7.1) based on excellent risk adjusted capital (severe loss scenario). Excellent profitability (7.9).

Principal Business: Individual annuities (48%), individual life insurance (48%), reinsurance (2%), group retirement contracts (1%), and individual health insurance (1%).

Principal Investments: NonCMO investment grade bonds (57%), CMOs and structured securities (23%), mortgages in good standing (9%), noninv. grade bonds (3%), and misc. investments (7%).

Investments in Affiliates: None

Group Affiliation: Iowa Farm Bureau

Licensed in: AZ, CO, ID, IA, KS, MN, MT, NE, NV, NM, ND, OK, OR, SD, UT, WA, WI, WY

Commenced Business: January 1945

Address: 5400 University Ave, West Des Moines, IA 50266-5997

Phone: (515) 225-5400 **Domicile State:** IA **NAIC Code:** 63088

Data Date	Rating	RACR #1	RACR #2	Total Assets ($mil)	Capital ($mil)	Net Premium ($mil)	Net Income ($mil)
6-16	B+	2.10	1.08	8,582.6	592.6	356.7	48.7
6-15	B+	2.12	1.10	8,295.2	573.0	323.9	49.1
2015	B+	2.17	1.13	8,402.0	603.1	684.0	106.0
2014	B+	2.09	1.09	8,088.8	552.0	647.4	97.4
2013	B+	2.01	1.03	7,723.0	492.5	636.8	94.6
2012	B+	2.20	1.11	7,415.2	547.4	648.2	86.6
2011	B+	2.16	1.08	6,956.3	509.2	690.0	72.7

Adverse Trends in Operations

Decrease in capital during 2013 (10%)
Decrease in premium volume from 2012 to 2013 (2%)
Decrease in premium volume from 2011 to 2012 (6%)

FARM BUREAU LIFE INSURANCE COMPANY OF MICHIGAN *   A-   Excellent

Major Rating Factors: Good quality investment portfolio (6.0 on a scale of 0 to 10) despite significant exposure to mortgages . Mortgage default rate has been low. large holdings of BBB rated bonds in addition to small junk bond holdings. Good liquidity (5.6) with sufficient resources to cover a large increase in policy surrenders. Good overall results on stability tests (6.9) excellent operational trends and excellent risk diversification.

Other Rating Factors: Strong capitalization (8.3) based on excellent risk adjusted capital (severe loss scenario). Excellent profitability (7.3).

Principal Business: Individual life insurance (66%), individual annuities (31%), group retirement contracts (2%), and group life insurance (1%).

Principal Investments: NonCMO investment grade bonds (67%), mortgages in good standing (19%), common & preferred stock (7%), noninv. grade bonds (3%), and misc. investments (4%).

Investments in Affiliates: 1%

Group Affiliation: Michigan Farm Bureau

Licensed in: MI

Commenced Business: September 1951

Address: 7373 West Saginaw Hwy, Lansing, MI 48909

Phone: (517) 323-7000 **Domicile State:** MI **NAIC Code:** 63096

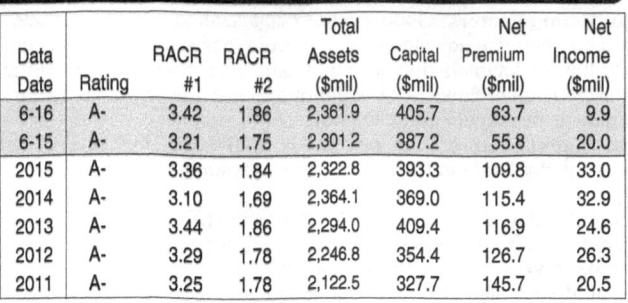

Data Date	Rating	RACR #1	RACR #2	Total Assets ($mil)	Capital ($mil)	Net Premium ($mil)	Net Income ($mil)
6-16	A-	3.42	1.86	2,361.9	405.7	63.7	9.9
6-15	A-	3.21	1.75	2,301.2	387.2	55.8	20.0
2015	A-	3.36	1.84	2,322.8	393.3	109.8	33.0
2014	A-	3.10	1.69	2,364.1	369.0	115.4	32.9
2013	A-	3.44	1.86	2,294.0	409.4	116.9	24.6
2012	A-	3.29	1.78	2,246.8	354.4	126.7	26.3
2011	A-	3.25	1.78	2,122.5	327.7	145.7	20.5

Rating Indexes: Ranges, Cap., Stab., Inv., Prof., Liq. — Weak, Fair, Good, Strong

FARM BUREAU LIFE INSURANCE COMPANY OF MISSOURI *   A-   Excellent

Major Rating Factors: Good quality investment portfolio (5.2 on a scale of 0 to 10) despite mixed results such as: no exposure to mortgages and large holdings of BBB rated bonds but minimal holdings in junk bonds. Good overall profitability (5.6) although investment income, in comparison to reserve requirements, is below regulatory standards. Good liquidity (5.5).

Other Rating Factors: Good overall results on stability tests (6.9) excellent operational trends and excellent risk diversification. Strong capitalization (7.2) based on excellent risk adjusted capital (severe loss scenario).

Principal Business: Individual life insurance (79%), individual annuities (19%), group life insurance (1%), and group health insurance (1%).

Principal Investments: NonCMO investment grade bonds (64%), CMOs and structured securities (17%), common & preferred stock (12%), and policy loans (4%).

Investments in Affiliates: 2%

Group Affiliation: Missouri Farm Bureau

Licensed in: MO

Commenced Business: July 1950

Address: 701 S Country Club Dr, Jefferson City, MO 65109

Phone: (573) 893-1400 **Domicile State:** MO **NAIC Code:** 63118

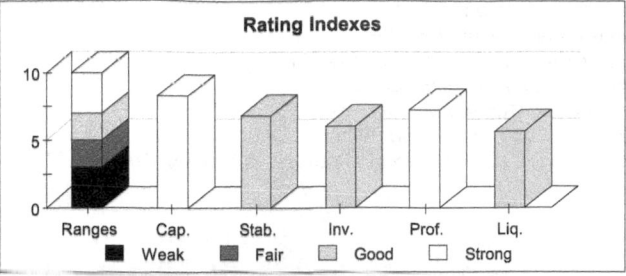

Data Date	Rating	RACR #1	RACR #2	Total Assets ($mil)	Capital ($mil)	Net Premium ($mil)	Net Income ($mil)
6-16	A-	1.77	1.15	558.9	61.4	23.3	0.3
6-15	A-	1.84	1.19	537.5	58.4	22.5	0.6
2015	A-	1.74	1.13	542.7	59.7	39.4	3.8
2014	A-	1.91	1.24	528.3	60.0	38.6	4.0
2013	A-	1.98	1.25	506.1	54.2	42.3	4.6
2012	A-	1.94	1.22	472.7	52.8	38.0	2.1
2011	A-	2.61	1.59	446.8	49.2	36.8	1.8

Rating Indexes: Ranges, Cap., Stab., Inv., Prof., Liq. — Weak, Fair, Good, Strong

FARM FAMILY LIFE INSURANCE COMPANY   B   Good

Major Rating Factors: Good quality investment portfolio (5.0 on a scale of 0 to 10) despite mixed results such as: minimal exposure to mortgages and large holdings of BBB rated bonds but small junk bond holdings. Good overall profitability (5.5) although investment income, in comparison to reserve requirements, is below regulatory standards. Good liquidity (5.3).

Other Rating Factors: Good overall results on stability tests (6.0) excellent operational trends and excellent risk diversification. Strong capitalization (7.5) based on excellent risk adjusted capital (severe loss scenario).

Principal Business: Individual life insurance (69%), individual annuities (24%), and individual health insurance (6%).

Principal Investments: NonCMO investment grade bonds (75%), common & preferred stock (9%), mortgages in good standing (6%), policy loans (3%), and misc. investments (7%).

Investments in Affiliates: None

Group Affiliation: American National Group Inc

Licensed in: CT, DE, ME, MD, MA, NH, NJ, NY, PA, RI, VT, VA, WV

Commenced Business: January 1954

Address: 344 Route 9W, Glenmont, NY 12077

Phone: (518) 431-5000 **Domicile State:** NY **NAIC Code:** 63126

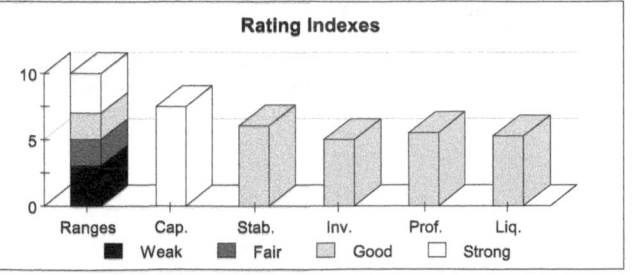

Data Date	Rating	RACR #1	RACR #2	Total Assets ($mil)	Capital ($mil)	Net Premium ($mil)	Net Income ($mil)
6-16	B	2.38	1.33	1,327.5	171.2	37.7	4.1
6-15	B	2.49	1.38	1,299.9	165.5	37.7	6.2
2015	B	2.42	1.36	1,308.9	166.5	75.5	9.4
2014	B	2.43	1.35	1,284.6	160.5	70.8	10.2
2013	B	2.15	1.22	1,248.4	151.9	72.2	18.6
2012	B	2.26	1.25	1,196.4	134.2	76.6	10.7
2011	B	2.22	1.22	1,149.3	124.5	82.3	15.1

Rating Indexes: Ranges, Cap., Stab., Inv., Prof., Liq. — Weak, Fair, Good, Strong

FARMERS NEW WORLD LIFE INSURANCE COMPANY   B-   Good

Major Rating Factors: Good overall capitalization (5.7 on a scale of 0 to 10) based on good risk adjusted capital (severe loss scenario). Nevertheless, capital levels have fluctuated during prior years. Fair overall results on stability tests (4.9) including fair financial strength of affiliated Zurich Financial Services Group. Fair quality investment portfolio (4.6).

Other Rating Factors: Fair profitability (3.0) with investment income below regulatory standards in relation to interest assumptions of reserves. Fair liquidity (4.7).

Principal Business: Individual life insurance (92%), individual annuities (5%), reinsurance (2%), and individual health insurance (2%).

Principal Investments: NonCMO investment grade bonds (62%), CMOs and structured securities (18%), mortgages in good standing (9%), policy loans (5%), and misc. investments (6%).

Investments in Affiliates: 2%

Group Affiliation: Zurich Financial Services Group

Licensed in: All states except NY, PR

Commenced Business: May 1911

Address: 3003 77th Ave SE, Mercer Island, WA 98040-2890

Phone: (206) 232-8400 **Domicile State:** WA **NAIC Code:** 63177

Data Date	Rating	RACR #1	RACR #2	Total Assets ($mil)	Capital ($mil)	Net Premium ($mil)	Net Income ($mil)
6-16	B-	1.41	0.84	7,148.3	512.7	304.1	72.2
6-15	B-	1.50	0.89	7,057.0	490.3	300.2	51.9
2015	B-	1.38	0.82	7,048.9	481.5	600.0	101.4
2014	B-	1.66	0.98	7,063.7	497.6	588.9	117.0
2013	B-	2.39	1.33	7,141.0	566.6	469.3	79.8
2012	B-	2.40	1.33	6,995.4	578.6	609.1	209.6
2011	B-	2.46	1.38	6,859.6	601.0	630.2	137.2

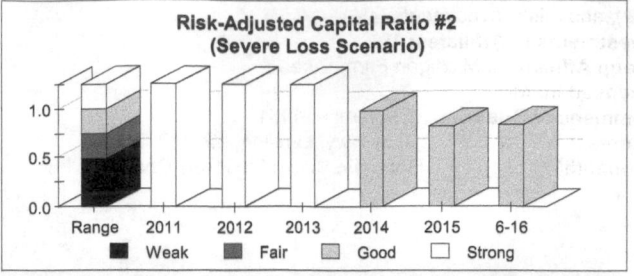

Risk-Adjusted Capital Ratio #2
(Severe Loss Scenario)

Range · 2011 · 2012 · 2013 · 2014 · 2015 · 6-16
■ Weak ■ Fair ▨ Good □ Strong

FEDERATED LIFE INSURANCE COMPANY *   A   Excellent

Major Rating Factors: Good quality investment portfolio (6.7 on a scale of 0 to 10) despite mixed results such as: no exposure to mortgages and large holdings of BBB rated bonds but small junk bond holdings. Good liquidity (6.6) with sufficient resources to handle a spike in claims as well as a significant increase in policy surrenders. Excellent overall results on stability tests (7.4) excellent operational trends and excellent risk diversification.

Other Rating Factors: Strong capitalization (9.2) based on excellent risk adjusted capital (severe loss scenario). Excellent profitability (8.7).

Principal Business: Individual life insurance (70%), individual annuities (14%), individual health insurance (13%), and group life insurance (3%).

Principal Investments: NonCMO investment grade bonds (84%), CMOs and structured securities (10%), noninv. grade bonds (3%), common & preferred stock (2%), and policy loans (1%).

Investments in Affiliates: None

Group Affiliation: Federated Mutual Ins Group

Licensed in: All states except AK, DC, HI, PR

Commenced Business: January 1959

Address: 121 E Park Square, Owatonna, MN 55060

Phone: (507) 455-5200 **Domicile State:** MN **NAIC Code:** 63258

Data Date	Rating	RACR #1	RACR #2	Total Assets ($mil)	Capital ($mil)	Net Premium ($mil)	Net Income ($mil)
6-16	A	4.53	2.45	1,710.7	348.0	97.3	14.4
6-15	A	4.62	2.56	1,580.6	321.1	85.6	12.4
2015	A	4.56	2.53	1,648.9	335.5	180.9	22.7
2014	A	4.47	2.49	1,526.3	308.1	168.9	19.3
2013	A	4.42	2.46	1,435.5	293.5	179.5	13.9
2012	A	4.29	2.35	1,309.3	275.9	177.0	13.8
2011	A	4.37	2.41	1,187.5	261.5	153.5	17.8

Adverse Trends in Operations

Decrease in premium volume from 2013 to 2014 (6%)

FIDELITY & GUARANTY LIFE INSURANCE COMPANY   C+   Fair

Major Rating Factors: Fair quality investment portfolio (3.4 on a scale of 0 to 10) with large holdings of BBB rated bonds in addition to junk bond exposure equal to 98% of capital. Fair overall results on stability tests (4.6) including fair risk adjusted capital in prior years. Good capitalization (5.5) based on good risk adjusted capital (moderate loss scenario).

Other Rating Factors: Good liquidity (5.6). Excellent profitability (8.2).

Principal Business: N/A

Principal Investments: NonCMO investment grade bonds (57%), CMOs and structured securities (23%), noninv. grade bonds (6%), common & preferred stock (5%), and misc. investments (7%).

Investments in Affiliates: 4%

Group Affiliation: HRG Group Inc

Licensed in: All states except NY

Commenced Business: November 1960

Address: 1001 Fleet St, Baltimore, MD 21202

Phone: (410) 895-0100 **Domicile State:** IA **NAIC Code:** 63274

Data Date	Rating	RACR #1	RACR #2	Total Assets ($mil)	Capital ($mil)	Net Premium ($mil)	Net Income ($mil)
6-16	C+	1.30	0.71	20,647.2	1,251.5	1,368.4	18.9
6-15	C+	1.32	0.73	19,688.2	1,235.1	1,186.6	-22.5
2015	C+	1.31	0.73	19,810.1	1,239.0	2,185.6	-52.9
2014	C+	1.31	0.73	18,973.2	1,211.6	2,526.1	104.6
2013	C+	1.36	0.77	17,422.5	1,108.3	1,363.8	118.2
2012	C+	1.35	0.79	16,698.7	900.5	324.8	102.2
2011	C+	1.61	0.86	15,784.8	846.4	-631.8	110.3

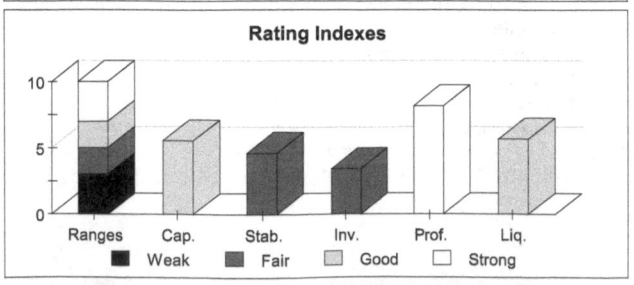

Rating Indexes

Ranges · Cap. · Stab. · Inv. · Prof. · Liq.
■ Weak ■ Fair ▨ Good □ Strong

FIDELITY & GUARANTY LIFE INSURANCE COMPANY OF NEW YO   B-   Good

Major Rating Factors: Good overall results on stability tests (5.1 on a scale of 0 to 10) despite fair financial strength of affiliated HRG Group Inc and negative cash flow from operations for 2015. Other stability subfactors include good operational trends and excellent risk diversification. Good quality investment portfolio (5.2) despite mixed results such as: large holdings of BBB rated bonds but moderate junk bond exposure. Good overall profitability (6.4).

Other Rating Factors: Good liquidity (6.4). Strong capitalization (8.0) based on excellent risk adjusted capital (severe loss scenario).

Principal Business: Individual annuities (92%) and individual life insurance (8%).

Principal Investments: NonCMO investment grade bonds (71%), CMOs and structured securities (17%), noninv. grade bonds (4%), and common & preferred stock (4%).

Investments in Affiliates: None

Group Affiliation: HRG Group Inc

Licensed in: NY

Commenced Business: November 1962

Address: 445 Park Ave 10th Floor, New York, NY 10022

Phone: (888) 697-5433 **Domicile State:** NY **NAIC Code:** 69434

Data Date	Rating	RACR #1	RACR #2	Total Assets ($mil)	Capital ($mil)	Net Premium ($mil)	Net Income ($mil)
6-16	B-	3.37	1.64	526.8	61.9	5.7	3.1
6-15	B-	3.19	1.63	529.2	62.7	14.2	3.0
2015	B-	3.29	1.63	526.0	59.5	27.0	-1.2
2014	B-	3.18	1.63	522.1	61.2	31.5	1.9
2013	B-	3.55	1.82	504.3	61.9	33.5	1.3
2012	B-	2.49	1.27	472.7	41.1	18.9	1.0
2011	B-	2.91	1.45	471.8	44.7	9.7	4.5

HRG Group Inc
Composite Group Rating: C+
Largest Group Members

	Assets ($mil)	Rating
FIDELITY GUARANTY LIFE INS CO	19810	C+
FIDELITY GUARANTY LIFE INS CO NY	526	B-

FIDELITY INVESTMENTS LIFE INSURANCE COMPANY *   A-   Excellent

Major Rating Factors: Good quality investment portfolio (6.6 on a scale of 0 to 10) despite mixed results such as: no exposure to mortgages and large holdings of BBB rated bonds but minimal holdings in junk bonds. Good overall results on stability tests (6.9). Strengths that enhance stability include good operational trends and excellent risk diversification. Strong capitalization (8.6) based on excellent risk adjusted capital (severe loss scenario).

Other Rating Factors: Excellent profitability (8.9). Excellent liquidity (7.0).

Principal Business: Individual annuities (99%) and individual life insurance (1%).

Principal Investments: NonCMO investment grade bonds (82%), common & preferred stock (8%), noninv. grade bonds (7%), and CMOs and structured securities (3%).

Investments in Affiliates: 8%

Group Affiliation: FMR LLC

Licensed in: All states except NY, PR

Commenced Business: December 1981

Address: 175 E 400 S 8th Floor, Salt Lake City, UT 84111

Phone: (617) 563-9106 **Domicile State:** UT **NAIC Code:** 93696

Data Date	Rating	RACR #1	RACR #2	Total Assets ($mil)	Capital ($mil)	Net Premium ($mil)	Net Income ($mil)
6-16	A-	3.39	2.06	25,080.7	792.6	640.5	39.5
6-15	A-	3.07	1.85	25,459.9	710.7	1,100.9	20.4
2015	A-	3.23	1.96	24,854.3	750.9	1,836.4	62.3
2014	A-	3.03	1.83	24,504.3	685.8	1,874.6	66.0
2013	A-	2.90	1.75	22,477.4	614.7	1,871.3	56.1
2012	A-	2.97	1.83	18,981.4	554.4	1,704.8	64.4
2011	A-	4.44	2.74	16,892.5	766.9	1,606.0	21.6

Adverse Trends in Operations

Decrease in premium volume from 2014 to 2015 (2%)
Change in asset mix during 2012 (4.8%)
Decrease in capital during 2012 (28%)

FIDELITY LIFE ASSOCIATION   C   Fair

Major Rating Factors: Fair profitability (3.0 on a scale of 0 to 10) with operating losses during the first six months of 2016. Fair overall results on stability tests (4.0). Good quality investment portfolio (6.3) despite mixed results such as: minimal exposure to mortgages and large holdings of BBB rated bonds but small junk bond holdings.

Other Rating Factors: Good liquidity (6.9). Strong capitalization (10.0) based on excellent risk adjusted capital (severe loss scenario).

Principal Business: Individual life insurance (75%), group life insurance (17%), reinsurance (6%), and group health insurance (1%).

Principal Investments: NonCMO investment grade bonds (52%), CMOs and structured securities (29%), mortgages in good standing (7%), noninv. grade bonds (5%), and misc. investments (7%).

Investments in Affiliates: None

Group Affiliation: Vericity Inc

Licensed in: All states except NY, WY, PR

Commenced Business: February 1896

Address: 8700 W Bryn Mawr Ave Ste 900S, Chicago, IL 60631

Phone: (312) 379-2397 **Domicile State:** IL **NAIC Code:** 63290

Data Date	Rating	RACR #1	RACR #2	Total Assets ($mil)	Capital ($mil)	Net Premium ($mil)	Net Income ($mil)
6-16	C	6.18	3.31	405.4	126.6	32.4	-3.8
6-15	C	6.99	3.79	414.8	139.2	33.3	4.1
2015	C	6.62	3.54	421.2	134.6	70.0	13.1
2014	C	7.19	3.87	411.9	134.7	59.9	30.2
2013	C	5.12	2.88	414.6	124.1	44.3	-22.8
2012	C	5.20	2.94	441.7	135.8	71.5	-30.3
2011	C+	6.56	3.71	463.7	175.3	72.0	-14.3

Rating Indexes

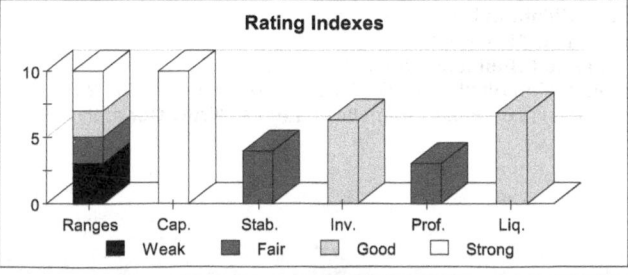

FIDELITY SECURITY LIFE INSURANCE COMPANY · B · Good

Major Rating Factors: Good liquidity (5.6 on a scale of 0 to 10) with sufficient resources to cover a large increase in policy surrenders. Fair overall results on stability tests (4.9). Strong capitalization (8.2) based on excellent risk adjusted capital (severe loss scenario). Moreover, capital levels have been consistently high over the last five years.

Other Rating Factors: High quality investment portfolio (7.0). Excellent profitability (7.8).

Principal Business: Group health insurance (90%), reinsurance (4%), individual health insurance (2%), group life insurance (1%), and other lines (2%).

Principal Investments: NonCMO investment grade bonds (47%), CMOs and structured securities (40%), cash (4%), common & preferred stock (3%), and misc. investments (6%).

Investments in Affiliates: 2%

Group Affiliation: Fidelity Security Group

Licensed in: All states except PR

Commenced Business: July 1969

Address: 3130 Broadway, Kansas City, MO 64111

Phone: (816) 750-1060 **Domicile State:** MO **NAIC Code:** 71870

Data Date	Rating	RACR #1	RACR #2	Total Assets ($mil)	Capital ($mil)	Net Premium ($mil)	Net Income ($mil)
6-16	B	2.64	1.81	864.4	178.2	62.5	9.5
6-15	B-	2.36	1.59	862.0	159.4	201.3	7.8
2015	B	2.02	1.44	864.2	169.0	420.4	18.1
2014	B-	2.65	1.73	831.7	151.9	204.6	18.4
2013	B-	2.99	1.83	819.5	135.3	109.2	13.9
2012	B	2.79	1.67	789.7	123.2	202.7	2.3
2011	B+	3.01	1.85	702.7	122.8	117.3	14.9

Exposure to Withdrawals Without Penalty (as a % of capital)

Capital — $169 mil.
Withdrawals w/o Penalty — $377 mil.

FIRST ALLMERICA FINANCIAL LIFE INSURANCE · C · Fair

Major Rating Factors: Fair overall capitalization (4.0 on a scale of 0 to 10) based on mixed results -- excessive policy leverage mitigated by excellent risk adjusted capital (severe loss scenario). However, capital levels have fluctuated somewhat during past years. Fair profitability (4.3) with investment income below regulatory standards in relation to interest assumptions of reserves. Good quality investment portfolio (6.6).

Other Rating Factors: Good liquidity (6.0). Weak overall results on stability tests (2.8) including weak results on operational trends, negative cash flow from operations for 2015.

Principal Business: Reinsurance (83%), individual life insurance (16%), and group retirement contracts (1%).

Principal Investments: NonCMO investment grade bonds (67%), CMOs and structured securities (29%), policy loans (1%), noninv. grade bonds (1%), and misc. investments (2%).

Investments in Affiliates: None

Group Affiliation: Global Atlantic Financial Group

Licensed in: All states except PR

Commenced Business: June 1845

Address: 440 Lincoln St, Worcester, MA 01653

Phone: (508) 855-1000 **Domicile State:** MA **NAIC Code:** 69140

Data Date	Rating	RACR #1	RACR #2	Total Assets ($mil)	Capital ($mil)	Net Premium ($mil)	Net Income ($mil)
6-16	C	4.02	1.86	3,403.1	181.9	13.5	17.0
6-15	C	4.37	2.08	4,153.9	235.4	36.9	18.7
2015	C	4.56	2.11	3,559.5	237.6	-535.1	22.3
2014	C	4.40	2.09	4,240.5	216.4	78.8	73.8
2013	D	3.47	1.65	4,206.0	154.7	-313.6	-38.7
2012	C	2.93	1.46	2,898.3	125.4	1,632.8	19.6
2011	C	8.28	3.93	1,276.4	85.9	27.2	19.5

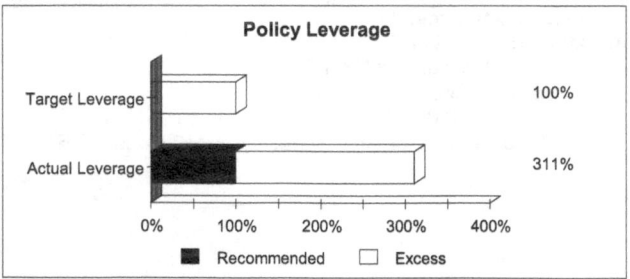

Policy Leverage

Target Leverage — 100%
Actual Leverage — 311%

■ Recommended   □ Excess

FIRST ASSURANCE LIFE OF AMERICA · B · Good

Major Rating Factors: Good overall results on stability tests (5.7 on a scale of 0 to 10) despite fair financial strength of affiliated LDS Group. Other stability subfactors include excellent operational trends and good risk diversification. Strong capitalization (10.0) based on excellent risk adjusted capital (severe loss scenario). Capital levels have been relatively consistent over the last five years. High quality investment portfolio (8.8).

Other Rating Factors: Excellent profitability (8.2). Excellent liquidity (8.2).

Principal Business: Credit life insurance (79%) and credit health insurance (21%).

Principal Investments: NonCMO investment grade bonds (70%), common & preferred stock (25%), and cash (2%).

Investments in Affiliates: 25%

Group Affiliation: LDS Group

Licensed in: AL, LA, MS, TN

Commenced Business: September 1981

Address: 9016 Bluebonnet Blvd, Baton Rouge, LA 70884-2810

Phone: (504) 769-9923 **Domicile State:** LA **NAIC Code:** 94579

Data Date	Rating	RACR #1	RACR #2	Total Assets ($mil)	Capital ($mil)	Net Premium ($mil)	Net Income ($mil)
6-16	B	3.25	3.06	39.4	33.7	1.4	0.4
6-15	B	3.21	3.04	38.5	32.8	1.4	0.4
2015	B	3.21	3.02	39.0	33.3	3.1	0.8
2014	B	3.17	3.01	37.8	32.4	3.5	0.6
2013	B	3.14	2.98	36.8	31.7	3.0	0.7
2012	B	3.10	2.95	35.8	31.1	3.2	0.9
2011	B	4.02	3.78	31.3	27.0	2.7	1.0

LDS Group
Composite Group Rating: C+

Largest Group Members	Assets ($mil)	Rating
FIRST ASR LIFE OF AMERICA	39	B
VERSANT CASUALTY INS CO	36	C
PERFORMANCE LIFE OF AMERICA	32	B-
VERSANT LIFE INS CO	6	B-

FIRST BERKSHIRE HATHAWAY LIFE INSURANCE COMPANY   C   Fair

Major Rating Factors: Fair quality investment portfolio (3.6 on a scale of 0 to 10) with substantial holdings of BBB bonds in addition to moderate junk bond exposure. Weak profitability (1.7) with investment income below regulatory standards in relation to interest assumptions of reserves. Weak overall results on stability tests (2.9) including weak results on operational trends.

Other Rating Factors: Strong capitalization (10.0) based on excellent risk adjusted capital (severe loss scenario). Excellent liquidity (10.0).

Principal Business: Group retirement contracts (100%).

Principal Investments: NonCMO investment grade bonds (34%), CMOs and structured securities (26%), noninv. grade bonds (26%), cash (19%), and common & preferred stock (7%).

Investments in Affiliates: 10%

Group Affiliation: Berkshire-Hathaway

Licensed in: MO, NE, NY

Commenced Business: March 2003

Address: Marine Air Terminal LaGuardia, Flushing, NY 11371

Phone: (402) 536-3000 **Domicile State:** NY **NAIC Code:** 11591

Data Date	Rating	RACR #1	RACR #2	Total Assets ($mil)	Capital ($mil)	Net Premium ($mil)	Net Income ($mil)
6-16	C	10.49	5.55	162.7	97.5	1.0	1.0
6-15	C	9.19	6.59	164.5	103.7	1.9	1.5
2015	C	10.67	6.03	159.9	99.6	2.0	2.4
2014	C+	10.08	6.34	386.4	114.6	-79.4	80.3
2013	C	2.48	2.23	286.6	25.5	80.1	-87.3
2012	B-	1.74	1.57	63.4	12.5	30.0	2.3
2011	C+	3.03	2.73	18.4	10.1	1.6	-1.4

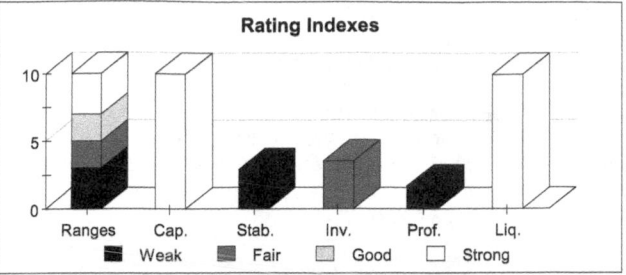

Rating Indexes

FIRST HEALTH LIFE & HEALTH INSURANCE COMPANY   B-   Good

Major Rating Factors: Good liquidity (5.3 on a scale of 0 to 10) with sufficient resources to handle a spike in claims. Fair overall results on stability tests (3.5). Weak profitability (1.9) with operating losses during the first six months of 2016.

Other Rating Factors: Strong capitalization (7.4) based on excellent risk adjusted capital (severe loss scenario). High quality investment portfolio (8.7).

Principal Business: Individual health insurance (97%) and group health insurance (3%).

Principal Investments: NonCMO investment grade bonds (71%), cash (23%), CMOs and structured securities (5%), and noninv. grade bonds (1%).

Investments in Affiliates: None

Group Affiliation: Aetna Inc

Licensed in: All states except PR

Commenced Business: June 1979

Address: 300 W 11th St, Kansas City, MO 64199-3487

Phone: (816) 391-2231 **Domicile State:** TX **NAIC Code:** 90328

Data Date	Rating	RACR #1	RACR #2	Total Assets ($mil)	Capital ($mil)	Net Premium ($mil)	Net Income ($mil)
6-16	B-	1.56	1.28	650.1	209.8	400.9	-55.0
6-15	B-	1.12	0.93	516.5	198.7	372.5	-19.0
2015	B-	2.24	1.85	582.9	291.3	714.5	23.4
2014	B	1.15	0.96	475.0	226.0	925.3	-6.6
2013	B	1.02	0.85	505.6	233.3	1,420.5	-175.3
2012	C+	1.46	1.22	600.2	412.2	1,494.9	48.3
2011	C+	1.19	0.99	577.0	363.5	1,156.5	28.4

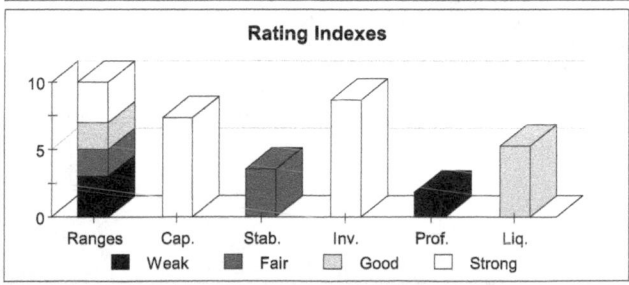

Rating Indexes

FIRST METLIFE INVESTORS INSURANCE COMPANY   C+   Fair

Major Rating Factors: Fair profitability (3.0 on a scale of 0 to 10). Fair overall results on stability tests (3.7). Good quality investment portfolio (6.3) despite significant exposure to mortgages . Mortgage default rate has been low. large holdings of BBB rated bonds in addition to small junk bond holdings.

Other Rating Factors: Strong capitalization (8.7) based on excellent risk adjusted capital (severe loss scenario). Excellent liquidity (7.3).

Principal Business: Individual annuities (59%) and individual life insurance (41%).

Principal Investments: NonCMO investment grade bonds (60%), CMOs and structured securities (23%), mortgages in good standing (11%), and noninv. grade bonds (5%).

Investments in Affiliates: None

Group Affiliation: MetLife Inc

Licensed in: NY

Commenced Business: March 1993

Address: 200 Park Avenue, New York, NY 10166-0188

Phone: (212) 578-2211 **Domicile State:** NY **NAIC Code:** 60992

Data Date	Rating	RACR #1	RACR #2	Total Assets ($mil)	Capital ($mil)	Net Premium ($mil)	Net Income ($mil)
6-16	C+	4.23	2.10	6,131.2	322.9	24.2	4.0
6-15	C	3.96	1.97	6,407.5	308.1	22.2	6.0
2015	C+	4.29	2.14	6,115.2	320.7	53.9	17.2
2014	C	3.81	1.89	6,504.7	297.4	-4,181.7	10.6
2013	C	2.12	1.07	6,244.5	124.4	295.6	-23.8
2012	C	2.63	1.31	5,530.6	176.5	595.9	-22.7
2011	C	3.24	1.63	4,688.3	196.0	1,049.9	-21.1

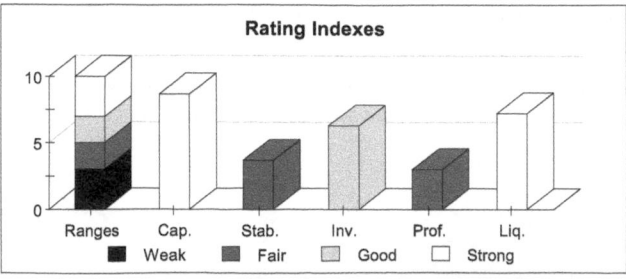

Rating Indexes

FIRST PENN-PACIFIC LIFE INSURANCE COMPANY | B | Good

Major Rating Factors: Good overall results on stability tests (5.0 on a scale of 0 to 10) despite negative cash flow from operations for 2015 and excessive premium growth. Other stability subfactors include good operational trends and excellent risk diversification. Good quality investment portfolio (5.7) despite mixed results such as: large holdings of BBB rated bonds but moderate junk bond exposure. Good overall profitability (5.8) despite operating losses during the first six months of 2016.

Other Rating Factors: Good liquidity (5.2). Strong capitalization (7.5) based on excellent risk adjusted capital (severe loss scenario).

Principal Business: Individual life insurance (61%) and reinsurance (38%).

Principal Investments: NonCMO investment grade bonds (72%), CMOs and structured securities (11%), mortgages in good standing (10%), noninv. grade bonds (5%), and policy loans (2%).

Investments in Affiliates: None

Group Affiliation: Lincoln National Corp

Licensed in: All states except NY, PR

Commenced Business: June 1964

Address: 1300 S Clinton St, Fort Wayne, IN 46802-3518

Phone: (260) 455-2000 **Domicile State:** IN **NAIC Code:** 67652

Data Date	Rating	RACR #1	RACR #2	Total Assets ($mil)	Capital ($mil)	Net Premium ($mil)	Net Income ($mil)
6-16	B	2.54	1.36	1,568.0	183.3	62.5	-16.8
6-15	B	2.94	1.59	1,650.6	223.2	44.9	18.3
2015	B	2.77	1.48	1,609.3	201.3	112.8	51.6
2014	B	2.75	1.50	1,741.8	208.4	145.7	54.2
2013	B	2.95	1.60	1,817.4	235.6	129.8	64.1
2012	B	2.98	1.59	1,897.3	257.5	127.0	80.4
2011	B	2.33	1.24	1,880.4	209.7	132.4	31.0

Adverse Trends in Operations

Decrease in asset base during 2015 (8%)
Decrease in capital during 2015 (3%)
Decrease in premium volume from 2014 to 2015 (23%)
Decrease in capital during 2014 (12%)
Decrease in premium volume from 2011 to 2012 (4%)

FIRST RELIANCE STANDARD LIFE INSURANCE COMPANY * | A | Excellent

Major Rating Factors: Good overall results on stability tests (6.0 on a scale of 0 to 10). Strengths that enhance stability include excellent operational trends and excellent risk diversification. Good quality investment portfolio (6.5) despite mixed results such as: no exposure to mortgages and substantial holdings of BBB bonds but small junk bond holdings. Good liquidity (6.9).

Other Rating Factors: Strong capitalization (10.0) based on excellent risk adjusted capital (severe loss scenario). Excellent profitability (7.1).

Principal Business: Group health insurance (57%) and group life insurance (43%).

Principal Investments: NonCMO investment grade bonds (69%), CMOs and structured securities (22%), and noninv. grade bonds (8%).

Investments in Affiliates: None

Group Affiliation: Tokio Marine Holdings Inc

Licensed in: DC, DE, NY

Commenced Business: October 1984

Address: 590 Madison Ave 29th Floor, New York, NY 10022

Phone: (215) 787-4000 **Domicile State:** NY **NAIC Code:** 71005

Data Date	Rating	RACR #1	RACR #2	Total Assets ($mil)	Capital ($mil)	Net Premium ($mil)	Net Income ($mil)
6-16	A	6.38	4.25	190.3	70.8	30.9	5.2
6-15	A	5.57	3.41	188.7	66.8	28.0	2.5
2015	A	5.72	3.61	184.0	65.5	57.9	6.5
2014	A	5.62	3.53	184.1	66.4	57.0	7.8
2013	A	5.71	3.72	182.7	64.2	56.8	5.9
2012	A	6.69	4.70	176.2	63.6	53.5	6.7
2011	B	6.47	4.93	166.3	60.5	48.3	4.1

Adverse Trends in Operations

Decrease in capital during 2015 (1%)

FIRST SECURITY BENEFIT LIFE & ANNUITY | B | Good

Major Rating Factors: Good capitalization (5.1 on a scale of 0 to 10) based on good risk adjusted capital (moderate loss scenario). Good liquidity (5.3) with sufficient resources to cover a large increase in policy surrenders. Fair overall results on stability tests (4.5) including negative cash flow from operations for 2015, fair risk adjusted capital in prior years.

Other Rating Factors: Low quality investment portfolio (0.8). Weak profitability (2.4).

Principal Business: Individual annuities (54%) and group retirement contracts (45%).

Principal Investments: CMOs and structured securities (46%), nonCMO investment grade bonds (42%), noninv. grade bonds (10%), and cash (2%).

Investments in Affiliates: None

Group Affiliation: Sammons Enterprises Inc

Licensed in: KS, NY

Commenced Business: July 1995

Address: 800 Westchester Ave Ste 641 N, Rye Brook, NY 10573

Phone: (785) 431-3000 **Domicile State:** NY **NAIC Code:** 60084

Data Date	Rating	RACR #1	RACR #2	Total Assets ($mil)	Capital ($mil)	Net Premium ($mil)	Net Income ($mil)
6-16	B	1.12	0.51	683.1	26.4	6.3	0.7
6-15	B	1.13	0.52	700.0	26.1	13.3	1.2
2015	B	1.13	0.51	684.2	27.1	23.5	2.5
2014	B	1.22	0.58	691.3	25.6	97.3	-3.8
2013	B	1.92	0.96	617.1	30.6	216.9	-3.8
2012	B	0.88	0.69	380.6	9.8	77.1	-2.9
2011	B	1.25	1.13	158.4	11.9	4.2	0.3

Junk Bonds as a % of Capital

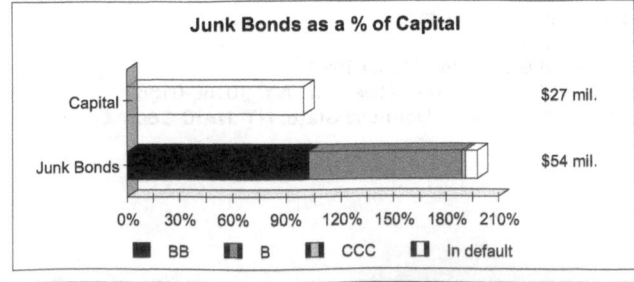

Capital — $27 mil.

Junk Bonds — $54 mil.

0% 30% 60% 90% 120% 150% 180% 210%

■ BB ▨ B ▥ CCC ▯ In default

FIRST SYMETRA NATIONAL LIFE INSURANCE COMPANY OF NE   A   Excellent

Major Rating Factors: Good quality investment portfolio (6.1 on a scale of 0 to 10) despite significant exposure to mortgages . Mortgage default rate has been low. large holdings of BBB rated bonds in addition to minimal holdings in junk bonds. Good liquidity (6.5) with sufficient resources to handle a spike in claims as well as a significant increase in policy surrenders. Excellent overall results on stability tests (7.5) excellent operational trends and excellent risk diversification.

Other Rating Factors: Strong capitalization (7.7) based on excellent risk adjusted capital (severe loss scenario). Excellent profitability (9.1).

Principal Business: Individual annuities (95%), group health insurance (4%), and individual life insurance (1%).

Principal Investments: NonCMO investment grade bonds (75%), CMOs and structured securities (13%), mortgages in good standing (11%), noninv. grade bonds (1%), and cash (1%).

Investments in Affiliates: None

Group Affiliation: Sumitomo Life Ins Company

Licensed in: NY

Commenced Business: January 1990

Address: 260 Madison Ave 8th Floor, New York, NY 10016

Phone: (425) 256-8000 **Domicile State:** NY **NAIC Code:** 78417

Data Date	Rating	RACR #1	RACR #2	Total Assets ($mil)	Capital ($mil)	Net Premium ($mil)	Net Income ($mil)
6-16	A	2.98	1.45	1,467.2	115.9	236.3	2.8
6-15	A	3.78	1.84	1,080.4	110.6	157.6	3.8
2015	A	3.20	1.57	1,261.0	113.7	386.5	8.2
2014	A-	3.96	1.97	962.4	106.1	218.0	9.1
2013	A-	4.03	2.02	813.2	96.7	154.6	11.9
2012	B+	3.68	1.91	727.3	85.9	110.8	12.5
2011	B	3.08	1.62	705.6	74.6	121.9	5.2

Adverse Trends in Operations

Increase in policy surrenders from 2011 to 2012 (40%)
Decrease in premium volume from 2011 to 2012 (9%)

FIRST UNITED AMERICAN LIFE INSURANCE COMPANY *   B+   Good

Major Rating Factors: Good overall results on stability tests (6.7 on a scale of 0 to 10). Stability strengths include excellent operational trends and excellent risk diversification. Good quality investment portfolio (5.0) despite mixed results such as: large holdings of BBB rated bonds but moderate junk bond exposure. Good liquidity (5.0) with sufficient resources to handle a spike in claims.

Other Rating Factors: Strong capitalization (7.6) based on excellent risk adjusted capital (severe loss scenario). Excellent profitability (7.5).

Principal Business: Individual health insurance (56%), individual life insurance (35%), individual annuities (7%), and group health insurance (3%).

Principal Investments: NonCMO investment grade bonds (83%), noninv. grade bonds (6%), CMOs and structured securities (4%), policy loans (4%), and cash (1%).

Investments in Affiliates: None

Group Affiliation: Torchmark Corp

Licensed in: NY

Commenced Business: December 1984

Address: 1020 7th North St, Liverpool, NY 13088

Phone: (315) 451-2544 **Domicile State:** NY **NAIC Code:** 74101

Data Date	Rating	RACR #1	RACR #2	Total Assets ($mil)	Capital ($mil)	Net Premium ($mil)	Net Income ($mil)
6-16	B+	2.26	1.42	219.9	37.0	40.2	4.5
6-15	B+	2.28	1.47	201.8	34.8	38.9	2.0
2015	B+	2.26	1.43	209.7	35.6	72.9	3.0
2014	B+	2.40	1.54	194.7	35.9	72.7	4.9
2013	B+	2.18	1.42	178.0	34.2	78.7	3.1
2012	B+	2.31	1.49	165.4	34.3	88.7	9.9
2011	B+	2.46	1.60	140.4	33.5	66.2	4.4

Adverse Trends in Operations

Decrease in premium volume from 2013 to 2014 (8%)
Decrease in premium volume from 2012 to 2013 (11%)
Change in premium mix from 2011 to 2012 (4.6%)

FIRST UNUM LIFE INSURANCE COMPANY   C+   Fair

Major Rating Factors: Fair overall results on stability tests (4.8 on a scale of 0 to 10) including fair financial strength of affiliated Unum Group. Fair quality investment portfolio (3.7) with large holdings of BBB rated bonds in addition to significant exposure to junk bonds. Good overall profitability (5.9).

Other Rating Factors: Strong capitalization (7.3) based on excellent risk adjusted capital (severe loss scenario). Excellent liquidity (7.1).

Principal Business: Group health insurance (55%), individual health insurance (24%), group life insurance (18%), and individual life insurance (2%).

Principal Investments: NonCMO investment grade bonds (75%), noninv. grade bonds (12%), CMOs and structured securities (7%), and mortgages in good standing (5%).

Investments in Affiliates: None

Group Affiliation: Unum Group

Licensed in: NY

Commenced Business: January 1960

Address: Christiana Bldg Suite 100, Tarrytown, NY 10591

Phone: (914) 524-4056 **Domicile State:** NY **NAIC Code:** 64297

Data Date	Rating	RACR #1	RACR #2	Total Assets ($mil)	Capital ($mil)	Net Premium ($mil)	Net Income ($mil)
6-16	C+	2.44	1.21	3,181.3	258.1	186.2	38.9
6-15	C+	2.63	1.33	3,049.9	275.2	182.6	6.6
2015	C+	2.54	1.27	3,130.4	263.5	363.2	26.5
2014	C+	2.63	1.33	2,976.2	272.1	360.0	-5.4
2013	C+	2.75	1.42	2,704.1	266.3	348.7	20.4
2012	C+	2.65	1.41	2,682.6	251.8	360.2	11.3
2011	C+	3.16	1.82	2,398.7	269.3	381.1	30.7

Unum Group
Composite Group Rating: C+
Largest Group Members

Largest Group Members	Assets ($mil)	Rating
UNUM LIFE INS CO OF AMERICA	20552	C+
PROVIDENT LIFE ACCIDENT INS CO	8325	C+
PAUL REVERE LIFE INS CO	3977	C+
FIRST UNUM LIFE INS CO	3130	C+
COLONIAL LIFE ACCIDENT INS CO	3019	C+

FIVE STAR LIFE INSURANCE COMPANY   C+   Fair

Major Rating Factors: Fair overall results on stability tests (4.4 on a scale of 0 to 10). Good quality investment portfolio (6.6) despite mixed results such as: large holdings of BBB rated bonds but moderate junk bond exposure. Good liquidity (5.9) with sufficient resources to handle a spike in claims as well as a significant increase in policy surrenders.

Other Rating Factors: Weak profitability (1.8) with operating losses during the first six months of 2016. Strong capitalization (7.6) based on excellent risk adjusted capital (severe loss scenario).

Principal Business: Group life insurance (73%) and individual life insurance (26%).

Principal Investments: NonCMO investment grade bonds (68%), CMOs and structured securities (18%), noninv. grade bonds (6%), cash (5%), and policy loans (3%).

Investments in Affiliates: None
Group Affiliation: 5 Star Financial LLC
Licensed in: All states except NY
Commenced Business: May 1943
Address: 8440 Jefferson Hwy Ste 301, Baton Rouge, LA 70809-7652
Phone: (800) 776-2322 **Domicile State:** LA **NAIC Code:** 77879

Data Date	Rating	RACR #1	RACR #2	Total Assets ($mil)	Capital ($mil)	Net Premium ($mil)	Net Income ($mil)
6-16	C+	2.23	1.37	270.7	31.6	65.7	-4.9
6-15	C+	2.84	1.75	277.5	39.8	63.6	-3.0
2015	C+	2.69	1.64	273.6	38.5	124.2	-5.8
2014	C+	2.93	1.82	268.6	40.8	124.2	-9.6
2013	B-	2.98	1.87	248.7	40.5	116.0	-6.2
2012	B	3.95	2.51	243.2	52.4	111.6	2.0
2011	B	2.00	1.40	218.4	54.3	107.6	1.5

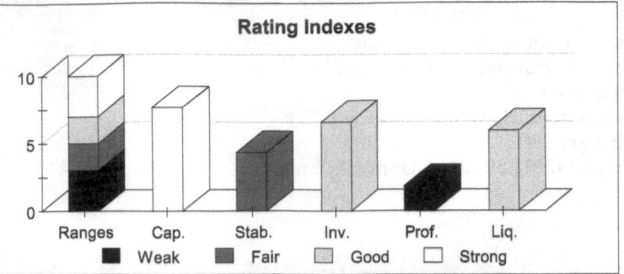

Rating Indexes

FLORIDA COMBINED LIFE INSURANCE COMPANY INCORPORA⊤   C   Fair

Major Rating Factors: Fair quality investment portfolio (4.8 on a scale of 0 to 10). Fair profitability (4.1) with operating losses during the first six months of 2016. Fair overall results on stability tests (4.3).

Other Rating Factors: Strong capitalization (8.0) based on excellent risk adjusted capital (severe loss scenario). Excellent liquidity (7.3).

Principal Business: Group health insurance (42%), individual health insurance (34%), group life insurance (22%), individual life insurance (2%), and reinsurance (1%).

Principal Investments: NonCMO investment grade bonds (19%), cash (8%), and CMOs and structured securities (3%).

Investments in Affiliates: 70%
Group Affiliation: Blue Cross Blue Shield of Florida
Licensed in: AL, FL, GA, NC, SC
Commenced Business: May 1988
Address: 4800 Deerwood Campus Pkwy, Jacksonville, FL 32246
Phone: (800) 333-3256 **Domicile State:** FL **NAIC Code:** 76031

Data Date	Rating	RACR #1	RACR #2	Total Assets ($mil)	Capital ($mil)	Net Premium ($mil)	Net Income ($mil)
6-16	C	4.80	3.14	51.7	28.4	0.0	-0.3
6-15	C+	4.63	3.42	49.7	26.2	0.0	-0.4
2015	C	4.60	3.45	50.2	27.1	0.0	0.3
2014	B	4.59	3.64	46.9	25.8	0.0	0.1
2013	B+	4.40	3.96	42.8	23.4	0.0	0.2
2012	B+	4.87	4.24	35.3	22.4	0.0	0.1
2011	B+	4.85	4.36	34.5	22.0	0.0	0.2

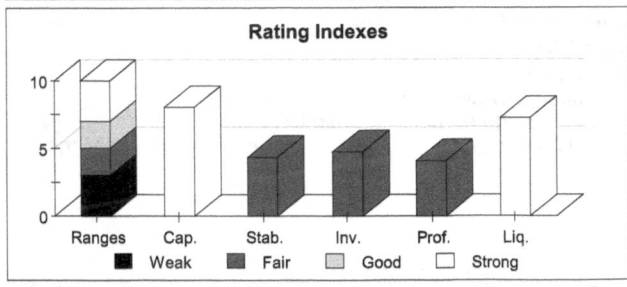

Rating Indexes

FORESTERS LIFE INSURANCE & ANNUITY COMPANY   C+   Fair

Major Rating Factors: Fair quality investment portfolio (4.7 on a scale of 0 to 10) with large holdings of BBB rated bonds in addition to junk bond exposure equal to 52% of capital. Fair profitability (3.5) with investment income below regulatory standards in relation to interest assumptions of reserves. Fair overall results on stability tests (4.5).

Other Rating Factors: Good capitalization (6.7) based on good risk adjusted capital (severe loss scenario). Good liquidity (6.0).

Principal Business: Individual annuities (66%) and individual life insurance (34%).

Principal Investments: NonCMO investment grade bonds (78%), policy loans (14%), and noninv. grade bonds (5%).

Investments in Affiliates: None
Group Affiliation: Independent Order of Foresters
Licensed in: All states except SD, PR
Commenced Business: December 1962
Address: 110 Wall Street, New York, NY 10005
Phone: (800) 832-7783 **Domicile State:** NY **NAIC Code:** 63495

Data Date	Rating	RACR #1	RACR #2	Total Assets ($mil)	Capital ($mil)	Net Premium ($mil)	Net Income ($mil)
6-16	C+	1.86	0.96	2,002.0	61.5	102.2	1.9
6-15	B-	2.06	1.08	1,927.6	60.7	90.4	2.7
2015	C+	1.91	1.01	1,932.9	60.3	203.7	8.3
2014	B-	2.08	1.10	1,852.8	58.7	240.4	8.0
2013	B	2.23	1.19	1,641.4	51.8	182.1	9.9
2012	B+	2.36	1.27	1,341.1	46.5	126.6	10.3
2011	B+	2.16	1.18	1,192.2	36.5	111.6	10.2

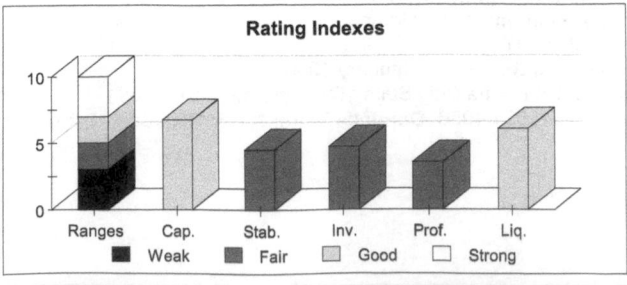

Rating Indexes

FORETHOUGHT LIFE INSURANCE COMPANY   B   Good

Major Rating Factors: Good quality investment portfolio (5.6 on a scale of 0 to 10) despite significant exposure to mortgages . Mortgage default rate has been low. substantial holdings of BBB bonds in addition to small junk bond holdings. Good overall results on stability tests (6.2). Stability strengths include excellent operational trends and excellent risk diversification. Strong capitalization (7.4) based on excellent risk adjusted capital (severe loss scenario).

Other Rating Factors: Excellent profitability (8.1). Excellent liquidity (7.4).

Principal Business: Individual annuities (90%), group retirement contracts (5%), group life insurance (3%), individual health insurance (1%), and individual life insurance (1%).

Principal Investments: CMOs and structured securities (51%), nonCMO investment grade bonds (35%), mortgages in good standing (10%), noninv. grade bonds (2%), and cash (1%).

Investments in Affiliates: None

Group Affiliation: Global Atlantic Financial Group

Licensed in: All states except NY

Commenced Business: September 1980

Address: Forethought Center, Batesville, IN 47006

Phone: (812) 933-6600   **Domicile State:** IN   **NAIC Code:** 91642

Data Date	Rating	RACR #1	RACR #2	Total Assets ($mil)	Capital ($mil)	Net Premium ($mil)	Net Income ($mil)
6-16	B	2.64	1.27	22,257.6	1,319.6	3,385.5	43.2
6-15	B-	2.74	1.32	15,683.8	999.5	3,199.1	42.4
2015	B	2.70	1.32	18,822.8	1,194.1	6,772.9	83.7
2014	B-	2.64	1.31	12,583.9	805.0	4,907.9	170.3
2013	B	2.73	1.38	7,957.2	522.5	2,331.0	23.0
2012	B	2.93	1.49	6,256.1	461.4	1,413.8	69.0
2011	B	2.94	1.47	5,465.8	416.4	877.3	50.7

Adverse Trends in Operations

Increase in policy surrenders from 2013 to 2014 (44%)
Increase in policy surrenders from 2012 to 2013 (32%)
Increase in policy surrenders from 2011 to 2012 (26%)

FRANDISCO LIFE INSURANCE COMPANY *   A   Excellent

Major Rating Factors: Good overall results on stability tests (6.7 on a scale of 0 to 10). Strengths that enhance stability include excellent operational trends and good risk diversification. Strong capitalization (10.0) based on excellent risk adjusted capital (severe loss scenario). Furthermore, this high level of risk adjusted capital has been consistently maintained over the last five years. High quality investment portfolio (8.9).

Other Rating Factors: Excellent profitability (9.8). Excellent liquidity (9.5).

Principal Business: Reinsurance (100%).

Principal Investments: NonCMO investment grade bonds (100%).

Investments in Affiliates: None

Group Affiliation: 1st Franklin Financial Corp

Licensed in: GA

Commenced Business: November 1977

Address: 135 E Tugalo St, Toccoa, GA 30577

Phone: (706) 886-7571   **Domicile State:** GA   **NAIC Code:** 89079

Data Date	Rating	RACR #1	RACR #2	Total Assets ($mil)	Capital ($mil)	Net Premium ($mil)	Net Income ($mil)
6-16	A	8.84	7.96	78.5	69.9	5.6	2.4
6-15	A-	8.65	7.79	71.4	64.7	9.8	2.6
2015	A-	8.51	7.66	76.2	67.3	18.9	5.4
2014	A-	8.33	7.50	66.4	62.3	14.6	5.6
2013	A-	7.86	7.07	60.5	56.7	14.5	5.0
2012	A-	7.40	6.66	54.6	51.6	13.0	4.7
2011	A-	7.00	6.30	49.3	46.7	12.0	4.3

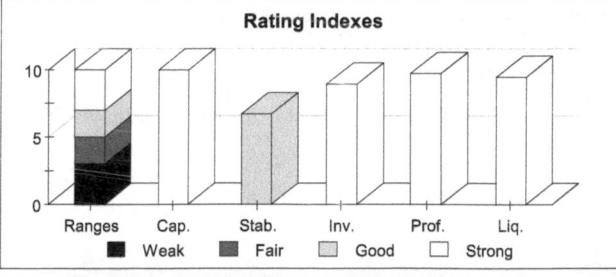

Rating Indexes

FREEDOM LIFE INSURANCE COMPANY OF AMERICA   C+   Fair

Major Rating Factors: Fair capitalization (4.4 on a scale of 0 to 10) based on fair risk adjusted capital (moderate loss scenario). Fair overall results on stability tests (4.4) including excessive premium growth and fair risk adjusted capital in prior years. Good quality investment portfolio (6.7) despite mixed results such as: no exposure to mortgages and substantial holdings of BBB bonds but minimal holdings in junk bonds.

Other Rating Factors: Excellent profitability (8.4). Excellent liquidity (7.2).

Principal Business: Group health insurance (69%), individual health insurance (22%), and individual life insurance (9%).

Principal Investments: NonCMO investment grade bonds (76%), common & preferred stock (32%), CMOs and structured securities (6%), and noninv. grade bonds (1%).

Investments in Affiliates: 32%

Group Affiliation: Credit Suisse Group

Licensed in: AL, AZ, AR, CO, DE, FL, GA, IL, IN, IA, KS, KY, LA, MD, MI, MN, MS, MO, NE, NV, NM, NC, OH, OK, OR, PA, SC, SD, TN, TX, UT, VA, WA, WV, WY

Commenced Business: June 1956

Address: 110 W 7th St Suite 300, Fort Worth, TX 76102

Phone: (817) 878-3300   **Domicile State:** TX   **NAIC Code:** 62324

Data Date	Rating	RACR #1	RACR #2	Total Assets ($mil)	Capital ($mil)	Net Premium ($mil)	Net Income ($mil)
6-16	C+	0.79	0.68	83.9	42.7	90.4	4.7
6-15	C	0.85	0.74	64.3	33.7	64.9	8.0
2015	C+	0.75	0.65	77.3	37.0	140.1	14.9
2014	C	0.69	0.60	59.9	25.7	109.7	10.1
2013	C	0.67	0.59	56.2	22.6	98.1	12.3
2012	C	0.73	0.65	41.5	19.6	68.8	5.9
2011	C-	0.74	0.65	34.4	13.9	44.9	0.6

Risk-Adjusted Capital Ratio #1
(Moderate Loss Scenario)

FRINGE BENEFIT LIFE INSURANCE COMPANY   C-   Fair

Major Rating Factors: Fair quality investment portfolio (4.3 on a scale of 0 to 10) with large exposure to mortgages . Mortgage default rate has been low. Fair overall results on stability tests (3.3) including negative cash flow from operations for 2015. Good liquidity (6.9) with sufficient resources to handle a spike in claims.
Other Rating Factors: Strong capitalization (9.7) based on excellent risk adjusted capital (severe loss scenario). Excellent profitability (7.1).
Principal Business: Reinsurance (96%) and individual life insurance (4%).
Principal Investments: Mortgages in good standing (45%), common & preferred stock (19%), nonCMO investment grade bonds (16%), noninv. grade bonds (7%), and misc. investments (14%).
Investments in Affiliates: None
Group Affiliation: FBH Inc
Licensed in: MN, OK, TX
Commenced Business: March 1982
Address: 2901 Morton St, Fort Worth, TX 76107
Phone: (817) 885-8223 **Domicile State:** TX **NAIC Code:** 99457

Data Date	Rating	RACR #1	RACR #2	Total Assets ($mil)	Capital ($mil)	Net Premium ($mil)	Net Income ($mil)
6-16	C-	5.13	2.78	42.0	28.1	0.0	0.1
6-15	D+	4.87	3.03	43.8	28.5	0.0	0.3
2015	D+	4.93	2.75	41.6	27.6	0.1	-0.1
2014	D+	4.92	2.82	45.1	28.8	0.1	2.6
2013	D+	4.39	2.30	44.3	26.9	0.2	1.6
2012	D+	4.48	2.55	42.7	24.9	0.3	1.9
2011	D+	4.23	2.71	41.5	23.1	0.3	1.7

Rating Indexes

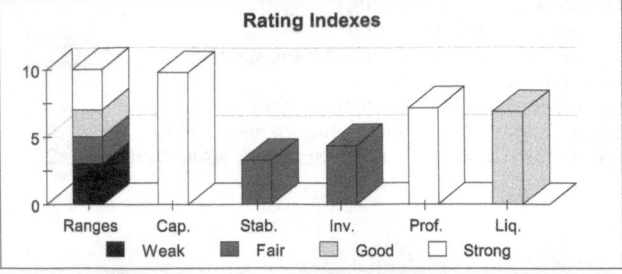

FUNERAL DIRECTORS LIFE INSURANCE COMPANY   B-   Good

Major Rating Factors: Good quality investment portfolio (6.2 on a scale of 0 to 10) despite mixed results such as: minimal exposure to mortgages and large holdings of BBB rated bonds but small junk bond holdings. Fair overall results on stability tests (4.6). Weak liquidity (2.6) as a spike in claims may stretch capacity.
Other Rating Factors: Strong capitalization (7.3) based on excellent risk adjusted capital (severe loss scenario). Excellent profitability (8.0).
Principal Business: Individual annuities (66%), group life insurance (21%), and individual life insurance (13%).
Principal Investments: NonCMO investment grade bonds (87%), mortgages in good standing (8%), real estate (2%), noninv. grade bonds (1%), and CMOs and structured securities (1%).
Investments in Affiliates: 1%
Group Affiliation: Directors Investment Group
Licensed in: All states except DC, ME, MA, NH, NY, WY, PR
Commenced Business: April 1981
Address: 6550 Directors Pkwy, Abilene, TX 79606
Phone: (915) 695-3412 **Domicile State:** TX **NAIC Code:** 99775

Data Date	Rating	RACR #1	RACR #2	Total Assets ($mil)	Capital ($mil)	Net Premium ($mil)	Net Income ($mil)
6-16	B-	2.25	1.21	1,199.9	103.5	110.2	5.2
6-15	B-	2.24	1.22	1,109.2	94.5	109.6	3.4
2015	B-	2.20	1.20	1,159.1	99.1	218.1	8.0
2014	B-	2.23	1.23	1,068.9	91.9	209.0	7.1
2013	B-	2.26	1.26	978.5	85.6	205.5	6.0
2012	B-	2.27	1.25	884.2	80.5	180.2	7.7
2011	B-	2.12	1.16	799.0	72.9	178.7	8.4

Rating Indexes

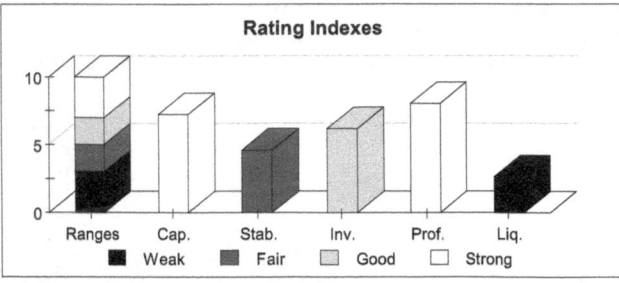

GARDEN STATE LIFE INSURANCE COMPANY *   A-   Excellent

Major Rating Factors: Good quality investment portfolio (6.7 on a scale of 0 to 10) despite mixed results such as: no exposure to mortgages and large holdings of BBB rated bonds but no exposure to junk bonds. Good liquidity (6.9) with sufficient resources to handle a spike in claims. Excellent overall results on stability tests (7.2) excellent operational trends and excellent risk diversification.
Other Rating Factors: Strong capitalization (10.0) based on excellent risk adjusted capital (severe loss scenario). Excellent profitability (8.6).
Principal Business: Individual life insurance (100%).
Principal Investments: NonCMO investment grade bonds (97%), policy loans (3%), and CMOs and structured securities (1%).
Investments in Affiliates: None
Group Affiliation: American National Group Inc
Licensed in: All states except PR
Commenced Business: November 1956
Address: 2450 S Shore Blvd Suite 301, League City, TX 77573
Phone: (409) 763-4661 **Domicile State:** TX **NAIC Code:** 63657

Data Date	Rating	RACR #1	RACR #2	Total Assets ($mil)	Capital ($mil)	Net Premium ($mil)	Net Income ($mil)
6-16	A-	7.22	6.50	126.5	65.6	11.0	3.6
6-15	A-	6.46	5.82	122.7	58.4	11.7	3.2
2015	A-	6.83	6.15	127.2	62.1	22.6	6.9
2014	A-	6.13	5.52	121.5	55.3	24.2	5.8
2013	A-	5.42	4.88	117.1	48.5	26.2	5.6
2012	A-	5.04	4.54	116.5	44.9	28.5	9.1
2011	B+	4.76	3.42	115.2	41.5	30.9	8.5

Adverse Trends in Operations

Decrease in premium volume from 2014 to 2015 (7%)
Decrease in premium volume from 2013 to 2014 (8%)
Decrease in premium volume from 2012 to 2013 (8%)
Decrease in premium volume from 2011 to 2012 (8%)

GENERAL AMERICAN LIFE INSURANCE COMPANY   B   Good

Major Rating Factors: Good overall results on stability tests (6.2 on a scale of 0 to 10). Stability strengths include excellent operational trends and excellent risk diversification. Good quality investment portfolio (6.0) despite mixed results such as: substantial holdings of BBB bonds but junk bond exposure equal to 55% of capital. Good liquidity (5.6).
Other Rating Factors: Strong capitalization (7.8) based on excellent risk adjusted capital (severe loss scenario). Excellent profitability (8.4).
Principal Business: Reinsurance (60%), individual life insurance (38%), individual annuities (1%), and individual health insurance (1%).
Principal Investments: NonCMO investment grade bonds (50%), policy loans (16%), CMOs and structured securities (15%), mortgages in good standing (8%), and misc. investments (10%).
Investments in Affiliates: 3%
Group Affiliation: MetLife Inc
Licensed in: All states except NY
Commenced Business: September 1933
Address: 700 Market St, St Louis, MO 63101
Phone: (314) 843-8700 **Domicile State:** MO **NAIC Code:** 63665

Data Date	Rating	RACR #1	RACR #2	Total Assets ($mil)	Capital ($mil)	Net Premium ($mil)	Net Income ($mil)
6-16	B	3.41	1.54	12,497.0	1,000.6	410.0	0.4
6-15	B	2.90	1.32	12,111.8	867.9	384.9	61.8
2015	B	3.37	1.53	12,305.3	983.5	757.0	204.4
2014	B	2.92	1.32	12,213.4	866.5	663.3	129.1
2013	B	2.84	1.29	12,025.7	818.1	587.0	60.2
2012	B	2.91	1.31	11,865.7	872.9	519.7	19.1
2011	B	2.99	1.34	11,395.8	825.1	350.9	127.8

Adverse Trends in Operations

Decrease in capital during 2013 (6%)
Increase in policy surrenders from 2012 to 2013 (37%)

GENERAL RE LIFE CORPORATION   B   Good

Major Rating Factors: Good overall results on stability tests (5.4 on a scale of 0 to 10). Stability strengths include excellent operational trends and excellent risk diversification. Good quality investment portfolio (5.1) despite mixed results such as: substantial holdings of BBB bonds but moderate junk bond exposure. Fair profitability (3.0) with investment income below regulatory standards in relation to interest assumptions of reserves.
Other Rating Factors: Strong capitalization (7.5) based on excellent risk adjusted capital (severe loss scenario). Excellent liquidity (8.5).
Principal Business: Reinsurance (100%).
Principal Investments: NonCMO investment grade bonds (68%), common & preferred stock (10%), and noninv. grade bonds (7%).
Investments in Affiliates: 16%
Group Affiliation: Berkshire-Hathaway
Licensed in: All states except PR
Commenced Business: August 1967
Address: 120 Long Ridge Rd, Stamford, CT 06902-1843
Phone: (203) 352-3000 **Domicile State:** CT **NAIC Code:** 86258

Data Date	Rating	RACR #1	RACR #2	Total Assets ($mil)	Capital ($mil)	Net Premium ($mil)	Net Income ($mil)
6-16	B	2.15	1.34	3,389.4	615.1	491.0	15.6
6-15	B+	2.46	1.53	3,430.0	718.5	513.1	16.1
2015	B	2.08	1.30	3,351.9	594.5	1,040.3	49.9
2014	B+	2.39	1.49	3,422.2	702.5	1,055.6	140.0
2013	B	2.31	1.44	3,337.4	667.2	1,047.7	121.2
2012	B	2.18	1.32	3,100.6	587.3	1,043.6	14.7
2011	B	2.31	1.36	2,917.2	638.2	1,020.5	87.4

Adverse Trends in Operations

Decrease in asset base during 2015 (2%)
Decrease in capital during 2015 (15%)
Increase in policy surrenders from 2014 to 2015 (259%)
Increase in policy surrenders from 2013 to 2014 (95%)
Decrease in capital during 2012 (8%)

GENERATION LIFE INSURANCE COMPANY   B   Good

Major Rating Factors: Good overall results on stability tests (5.8 on a scale of 0 to 10). Strengths include good financial support from affiliation with Tennessee Farmers Ins Companies, excellent operational trends and excellent risk diversification. Weak profitability (2.0) with operating losses during the first six months of 2016. Strong capitalization (10.0) based on excellent risk adjusted capital (severe loss scenario).
Other Rating Factors: High quality investment portfolio (7.8). Excellent liquidity (10.0).
Principal Business: Individual life insurance (100%).
Principal Investments: Cash (61%), nonCMO investment grade bonds (35%), and common & preferred stock (4%).
Investments in Affiliates: None
Group Affiliation: Tennessee Farmers Ins Companies
Licensed in: All states except CA, CT, ME, MA, NH, NJ, NY, PR
Commenced Business: May 1966
Address: 5025 N Central Ave #546, Phoenix, AZ 85012
Phone: (855) 436-4533 **Domicile State:** AZ **NAIC Code:** 73504

Data Date	Rating	RACR #1	RACR #2	Total Assets ($mil)	Capital ($mil)	Net Premium ($mil)	Net Income ($mil)
6-16	B	6.18	5.56	32.9	29.6	2.0	-0.3
6-15	B	6.03	5.43	31.1	29.2	2.3	-1.4
2015	B	6.23	5.60	32.2	30.0	4.4	-0.5
2014	B	6.36	5.73	32.3	30.6	3.2	-3.6
2013	B	6.40	5.76	32.6	31.1	1.1	-4.2
2012	U	6.09	5.48	26.1	25.3	0.0	-1.5
2011	U	4.47	4.02	12.8	12.2	0.0	-0.4

Tennessee Farmers Ins Companies
Composite Group Rating: B+
Largest Group Members

	Assets ($mil)	Rating
TENNESSEE FARMERS MUTUAL INS CO	2659	B+
TENNESSEE FARMERS LIFE INS CO	2091	A
TENNESSEE FARMERS ASR CO	1303	B+
GENERATION LIFE INS CO	32	B

GENWORTH LIFE & ANNUITY INSURANCE COMPANY | B- | Good

Major Rating Factors: Good quality investment portfolio (5.6 on a scale of 0 to 10) despite large holdings of BBB rated bonds in addition to moderate junk bond exposure. Exposure to mortgages is significant, but the mortgage default rate has been low. Good liquidity (6.3) with sufficient resources to handle a spike in claims as well as a significant increase in policy surrenders. Fair overall results on stability tests (3.5) including fair financial strength of affiliated Genworth Financial and weak results on operational trends.

Other Rating Factors: Weak profitability (2.7) with operating losses during the first six months of 2016. Strong capitalization (7.0) based on excellent risk adjusted capital (severe loss scenario).

Principal Business: Individual life insurance (54%), individual annuities (26%), reinsurance (17%), and individual health insurance (2%).

Principal Investments: NonCMO investment grade bonds (53%), CMOs and structured securities (23%), mortgages in good standing (11%), noninv. grade bonds (4%), and misc. investments (7%).

Investments in Affiliates: 3%

Group Affiliation: Genworth Financial

Licensed in: All states except NY, PR

Commenced Business: April 1871

Address: 6610 W Broad St, Richmond, VA 23230

Phone: (804) 662-2400 **Domicile State:** VA **NAIC Code:** 65536

Data Date	Rating	RACR #1	RACR #2	Total Assets ($mil)	Capital ($mil)	Net Premium ($mil)	Net Income ($mil)
6-16	B-	1.60	1.00	23,144.6	1,585.9	-2,349.4	-273.1
6-15	B-	1.42	1.01	23,886.3	2,036.5	-254.9	92.4
2015	B-	1.71	1.08	23,410.5	1,668.8	328.8	-283.1
2014	B-	1.51	1.09	24,242.0	2,148.2	1,638.6	199.8
2013	B-	1.51	1.11	24,161.7	2,235.0	1,893.8	343.9
2012	B-	1.35	1.00	24,030.7	2,255.3	-266.4	353.8
2011	B-	1.15	0.84	23,484.5	1,842.9	1,129.5	-91.1

Genworth Financial
Composite Group Rating: C+
Largest Group Members

	Assets ($mil)	Rating
GENWORTH LIFE INS CO	38504	B-
GENWORTH LIFE ANNUITY INS CO	23411	B-
GENWORTH LIFE INS CO OF NEW YORK	8372	C+
GENWORTH MORTGAGE INS CORP	2627	C
RIVERMONT LIFE INS CO I	544	C

GENWORTH LIFE INSURANCE COMPANY | B- | Good

Major Rating Factors: Fair current capitalization (4.8 on a scale of 0 to 10) based on fair risk adjusted capital (severe loss scenario), although results have slipped from the good range during the last year. Fair profitability (4.2). Excellent expense controls. Fair overall results on stability tests (4.8).

Other Rating Factors: Good quality investment portfolio (5.5). Excellent liquidity (7.2).

Principal Business: Individual health insurance (59%), individual life insurance (11%), reinsurance (11%), individual annuities (11%), and group health insurance (8%).

Principal Investments: NonCMO investment grade bonds (61%), CMOs and structured securities (14%), mortgages in good standing (10%), common & preferred stock (6%), and misc. investments (8%).

Investments in Affiliates: 6%

Group Affiliation: Genworth Financial

Licensed in: All states except NY

Commenced Business: October 1956

Address: 6604 West Broad St, Richmond, VA 23230

Phone: (800) 255-7836 **Domicile State:** DE **NAIC Code:** 70025

Data Date	Rating	RACR #1	RACR #2	Total Assets ($mil)	Capital ($mil)	Net Premium ($mil)	Net Income ($mil)
6-16	B-	0.97	0.73	39,497.6	2,629.6	659.2	97.3
6-15	B-	1.01	0.79	38,375.2	3,165.8	754.3	22.5
2015	B-	1.02	0.78	38,504.3	2,740.7	1,587.2	35.2
2014	B-	1.02	0.81	38,163.2	3,224.4	1,713.3	-179.7
2013	C+	1.06	0.85	36,445.4	3,487.2	2,569.0	329.8
2012	C+	1.01	0.80	36,783.8	3,410.5	1,659.0	201.0
2011	C+	1.04	0.80	35,784.2	3,097.3	1,607.6	22.9

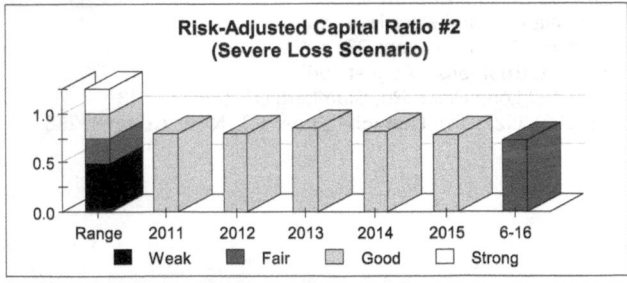

Risk-Adjusted Capital Ratio #2 (Severe Loss Scenario)

GENWORTH LIFE INSURANCE COMPANY OF NEW YORK | C+ | Fair

Major Rating Factors: Fair overall results on stability tests (4.4 on a scale of 0 to 10). Good quality investment portfolio (5.5) despite large holdings of BBB rated bonds in addition to junk bond exposure equal to 53% of capital. Exposure to mortgages is significant, but the mortgage default rate has been low. Good liquidity (6.7) with sufficient resources to handle a spike in claims as well as a significant increase in policy surrenders.

Other Rating Factors: Weak profitability (2.7) with investment income below regulatory standards in relation to interest assumptions of reserves. Strong capitalization (7.3) based on excellent risk adjusted capital (severe loss scenario).

Principal Business: Individual health insurance (44%), individual annuities (23%), individual life insurance (17%), reinsurance (13%), and group health insurance (3%).

Principal Investments: NonCMO investment grade bonds (60%), CMOs and structured securities (22%), mortgages in good standing (11%), noninv. grade bonds (4%), and common & preferred stock (1%).

Investments in Affiliates: None

Group Affiliation: Genworth Financial

Licensed in: CT, DC, DE, FL, IL, NJ, NY, RI, VA

Commenced Business: October 1988

Address: 125 Park Ave 6th Floor, New York, NY 10017-5529

Phone: (800) 357-1066 **Domicile State:** NY **NAIC Code:** 72990

Data Date	Rating	RACR #1	RACR #2	Total Assets ($mil)	Capital ($mil)	Net Premium ($mil)	Net Income ($mil)
6-16	C+	2.36	1.18	8,470.8	530.6	145.6	25.9
6-15	B-	2.40	1.20	8,492.9	544.1	181.6	10.3
2015	C+	2.22	1.12	8,372.2	494.8	356.1	-39.8
2014	B-	2.14	1.08	8,474.6	481.1	521.7	-93.3
2013	B	2.29	1.15	8,139.0	527.3	610.9	13.1
2012	B	2.36	1.18	7,815.8	540.1	542.6	19.1
2011	B-	2.45	1.23	7,691.7	559.5	576.6	6.5

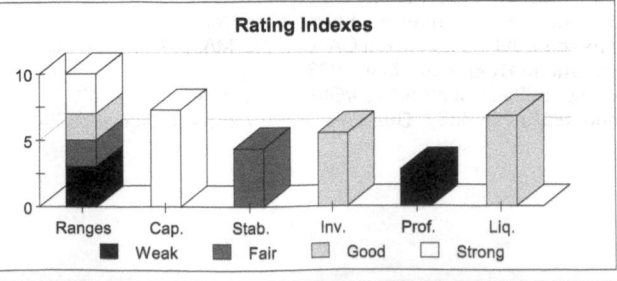

Rating Indexes

GERBER LIFE INSURANCE COMPANY *   B+   Good

Major Rating Factors: Good quality investment portfolio (6.1 on a scale of 0 to 10) despite mixed results such as: no exposure to mortgages and large holdings of BBB rated bonds but small junk bond holdings. Good overall profitability (6.4). Excellent expense controls. Good liquidity (5.6).

Other Rating Factors: Good overall results on stability tests (6.8) excellent operational trends and excellent risk diversification. Strong capitalization (7.2) based on excellent risk adjusted capital (severe loss scenario).

Principal Business: Individual life insurance (43%), group health insurance (37%), individual health insurance (14%), and reinsurance (6%).

Principal Investments: NonCMO investment grade bonds (73%), CMOs and structured securities (18%), policy loans (5%), common & preferred stock (3%), and noninv. grade bonds (2%).

Investments in Affiliates: None

Group Affiliation: Nestle SA

Licensed in: All states, the District of Columbia and Puerto Rico

Commenced Business: September 1968

Address: 1311 Mamaroneck Ave, White Plains, NY 10605

Phone: (877) 778-0839   **Domicile State:** NY   **NAIC Code:** 70939

Data Date	Rating	RACR #1	RACR #2	Total Assets ($mil)	Capital ($mil)	Net Premium ($mil)	Net Income ($mil)
6-16	B+	1.88	1.13	3,240.4	299.7	354.1	4.0
6-15	A-	1.96	1.18	2,958.4	291.1	310.8	9.0
2015	B+	1.90	1.14	3,088.3	295.8	604.2	18.5
2014	A-	1.97	1.20	2,812.2	285.3	565.3	24.2
2013	A-	2.00	1.21	2,548.1	263.5	506.8	22.7
2012	A-	1.96	1.17	2,306.7	237.9	464.1	20.2
2011	A-	1.91	1.15	2,110.0	215.5	432.2	4.9

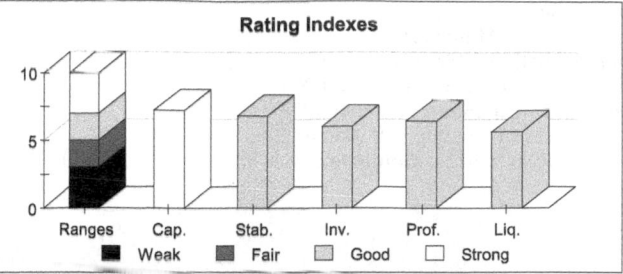

Rating Indexes

GLOBE LIFE & ACCIDENT INSURANCE COMPANY   B-   Good

Major Rating Factors: Good overall capitalization (6.3 on a scale of 0 to 10) based on good risk adjusted capital (severe loss scenario). Nevertheless, capital levels have fluctuated during prior years. Good overall profitability (5.2) although investment income, in comparison to reserve requirements, is below regulatory standards. Good overall results on stability tests (5.3) excellent operational trends and excellent risk diversification.

Other Rating Factors: Fair quality investment portfolio (4.2). Fair liquidity (3.7).

Principal Business: Group life insurance (54%), individual life insurance (42%), and individual health insurance (4%).

Principal Investments: NonCMO investment grade bonds (86%), noninv. grade bonds (6%), CMOs and structured securities (3%), and policy loans (2%).

Investments in Affiliates: 2%

Group Affiliation: Torchmark Corp

Licensed in: All states except NY, PR

Commenced Business: September 1980

Address: 10306 Regency Parkway Bldg, Omaha, NE 68114-3743

Phone: (405) 270-1400   **Domicile State:** NE   **NAIC Code:** 91472

Data Date	Rating	RACR #1	RACR #2	Total Assets ($mil)	Capital ($mil)	Net Premium ($mil)	Net Income ($mil)
6-16	B-	1.71	0.91	3,889.2	272.7	364.8	46.0
6-15	B	1.82	0.99	3,685.9	268.1	353.8	41.5
2015	B-	1.57	0.86	3,733.3	243.7	657.2	84.0
2014	B	1.60	0.89	3,519.4	239.4	630.4	82.3
2013	B	1.74	0.95	3,363.5	258.3	618.0	314.8
2012	B	1.31	0.97	3,454.4	477.6	577.1	203.3
2011	B	1.28	0.93	3,208.3	436.8	570.7	178.8

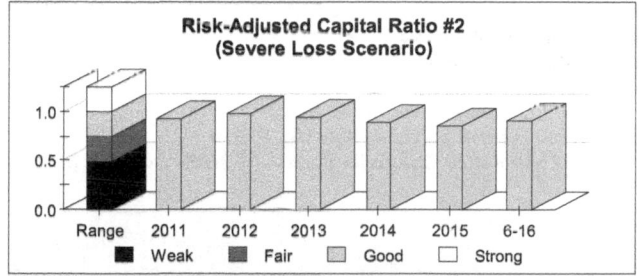

Risk-Adjusted Capital Ratio #2 (Severe Loss Scenario)

GOLDEN RULE INSURANCE COMPANY   B   Good

Major Rating Factors: Good current capitalization (5.5 on a scale of 0 to 10) based on mixed results -- excessive policy leverage mitigated by excellent risk adjusted capital (severe loss scenario) reflecting improvement over results in 2013. Good liquidity (6.2) with sufficient resources to cover a large increase in policy surrenders. Fair overall results on stability tests (4.7) including fair financial strength of affiliated UnitedHealth Group Inc.

Other Rating Factors: High quality investment portfolio (8.0). Excellent profitability (7.0).

Principal Business: Group health insurance (83%), individual health insurance (14%), and individual life insurance (2%).

Principal Investments: NonCMO investment grade bonds (75%), CMOs and structured securities (22%), real estate (1%), and , and misc. investments (2%).

Investments in Affiliates: None

Group Affiliation: UnitedHealth Group Inc

Licensed in: All states except NY, PR

Commenced Business: June 1961

Address: 712 Eleventh St, Lawrenceville, IL 62439-2395

Phone: (317) 290-8100   **Domicile State:** IN   **NAIC Code:** 62286

Data Date	Rating	RACR #1	RACR #2	Total Assets ($mil)	Capital ($mil)	Net Premium ($mil)	Net Income ($mil)
6-16	B	1.45	1.13	618.1	262.5	669.9	53.8
6-15	B	1.36	1.07	674.6	278.3	751.1	67.4
2015	B	1.37	1.07	635.6	268.0	1,501.3	106.8
2014	B	1.30	1.03	718.2	313.2	1,850.6	76.7
2013	B	1.12	0.89	759.8	293.5	2,020.6	129.4
2012	B	1.19	0.94	782.5	292.3	1,879.5	127.6
2011	B	1.43	1.13	814.9	312.1	1,673.4	104.6

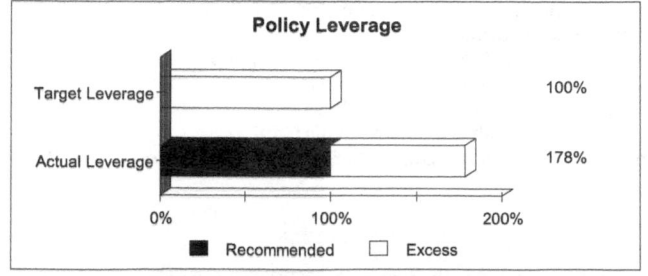

Policy Leverage

GOVERNMENT PERSONNEL MUTUAL LIFE INSURANCE CO *   B+   Good

Major Rating Factors: Good liquidity (5.4 on a scale of 0 to 10) with sufficient resources to handle a spike in claims as well as a significant increase in policy surrenders. Good overall results on stability tests (6.4). Stability strengths include excellent operational trends and excellent risk diversification. Strong capitalization (8.1) based on excellent risk adjusted capital (severe loss scenario).

Other Rating Factors: High quality investment portfolio (7.0). Excellent profitability (7.2).

Principal Business: Individual life insurance (58%), individual health insurance (41%), individual annuities (1%), and reinsurance (1%).

Principal Investments: NonCMO investment grade bonds (69%), mortgages in good standing (15%), policy loans (9%), common & preferred stock (3%), and misc. investments (4%).

Investments in Affiliates: 2%

Group Affiliation: GPM Life Group

Licensed in: All states except NJ, NY, PR

Commenced Business: October 1934

Address: 2211 NW Loop 410, San Antonio, TX 78217

Phone: (800) 938-9765   **Domicile State:** TX   **NAIC Code:** 63967

Data Date	Rating	RACR #1	RACR #2	Total Assets ($mil)	Capital ($mil)	Net Premium ($mil)	Net Income ($mil)
6-16	B+	2.79	1.74	834.7	116.6	23.0	0.6
6-15	B+	2.73	1.72	836.7	114.5	23.2	1.9
2015	B+	2.81	1.76	836.1	116.2	46.3	2.6
2014	B+	2.72	1.73	837.5	112.4	46.2	3.3
2013	B+	2.69	1.72	830.9	109.2	46.9	4.1
2012	B+	2.64	1.69	833.7	104.8	51.1	4.9
2011	B+	3.51	1.92	834.1	97.0	54.6	6.8

Adverse Trends in Operations

Decrease in premium volume from 2013 to 2014 (2%)
Decrease in premium volume from 2012 to 2013 (8%)
Decrease in premium volume from 2011 to 2012 (6%)

GRANGE LIFE INSURANCE COMPANY   C+   Fair

Major Rating Factors: Fair overall results on stability tests (4.6 on a scale of 0 to 10). Good quality investment portfolio (6.4) despite mixed results such as: substantial holdings of BBB bonds but moderate junk bond exposure. Good liquidity (6.6) with sufficient resources to handle a spike in claims as well as a significant increase in policy surrenders.

Other Rating Factors: Weak profitability (2.3) with operating losses during the first six months of 2016. Strong capitalization (7.0) based on excellent risk adjusted capital (severe loss scenario).

Principal Business: Individual life insurance (93%), reinsurance (3%), group life insurance (2%), and individual annuities (1%).

Principal Investments: NonCMO investment grade bonds (45%), CMOs and structured securities (36%), cash (7%), noninv. grade bonds (4%), and misc. investments (6%).

Investments in Affiliates: 3%

Group Affiliation: Grange Mutual Casualty Group

Licensed in: GA, IL, IN, IA, KS, KY, MI, MN, MO, OH, PA, SC, TN, VA, WI

Commenced Business: July 1968

Address: 650 S Front St, Columbus, OH 43216

Phone: (614) 445-2820   **Domicile State:** OH   **NAIC Code:** 71218

Data Date	Rating	RACR #1	RACR #2	Total Assets ($mil)	Capital ($mil)	Net Premium ($mil)	Net Income ($mil)
6-16	C+	1.50	1.00	401.8	36.6	29.6	-6.4
6-15	B-	2.46	1.57	380.0	53.1	28.0	0.1
2015	B-	1.75	1.17	393.2	42.5	56.6	-1.6
2014	B-	2.61	1.67	370.7	56.1	49.9	2.0
2013	B-	2.51	1.63	353.4	51.0	46.4	3.0
2012	B-	2.61	1.70	347.6	49.1	44.8	1.3
2011	B	3.06	1.80	316.6	42.4	47.7	2.2

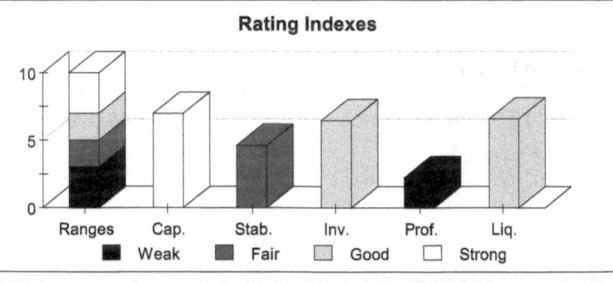

Rating Indexes

Ranges   Cap.   Stab.   Inv.   Prof.   Liq.
■ Weak   ■ Fair   □ Good   □ Strong

GREAT AMERICAN LIFE INSURANCE COMPANY   B-   Good

Major Rating Factors: Good capitalization (6.7 on a scale of 0 to 10) based on good risk adjusted capital (severe loss scenario). Moreover, capital levels have been consistent over the last five years. Good quality investment portfolio (5.2) despite mixed results such as: large holdings of BBB rated bonds but moderate junk bond exposure. Good liquidity (5.4).

Other Rating Factors: Good overall results on stability tests (5.3) despite excessive premium growth excellent operational trends and excellent risk diversification. Excellent profitability (9.0).

Principal Business: Individual annuities (97%), reinsurance (1%), and individual life insurance (1%).

Principal Investments: NonCMO investment grade bonds (58%), CMOs and structured securities (30%), noninv. grade bonds (3%), common & preferred stock (3%), and mortgages in good standing (3%).

Investments in Affiliates: 1%

Group Affiliation: American Financial Group Inc

Licensed in: All states except NY, PR

Commenced Business: August 1963

Address: 250 E Fifth St, Cincinnati, OH 45202

Phone: (800) 854-3649   **Domicile State:** OH   **NAIC Code:** 63312

Data Date	Rating	RACR #1	RACR #2	Total Assets ($mil)	Capital ($mil)	Net Premium ($mil)	Net Income ($mil)
6-16	B-	1.71	0.96	27,716.3	1,893.8	2,283.4	32.7
6-15	B-	1.76	0.99	24,303.5	1,701.7	1,599.9	203.7
2015	B-	1.61	0.91	25,936.0	1,721.3	3,963.1	375.3
2014	B-	1.74	0.99	22,772.6	1,636.0	3,469.4	356.0
2013	B-	1.82	1.04	20,182.2	1,511.8	3,801.6	262.2
2012	B-	1.82	1.05	16,508.6	1,274.7	2,955.4	155.6
2011	B-	1.67	0.95	13,950.5	1,070.5	2,802.9	152.2

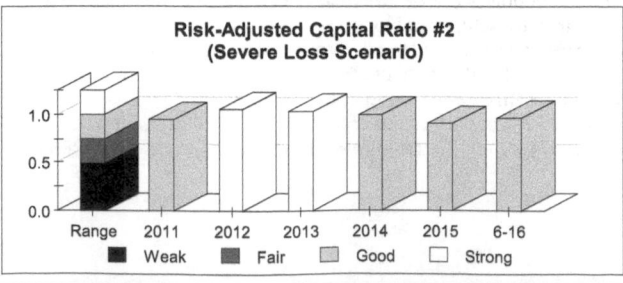

Risk-Adjusted Capital Ratio #2
(Severe Loss Scenario)

Range   2011   2012   2013   2014   2015   6-16
■ Weak   ■ Fair   □ Good   □ Strong

GREAT SOUTHERN LIFE INSURANCE COMPANY *   B+   Good

Major Rating Factors: Good overall results on stability tests (6.0 on a scale of 0 to 10). Stability strengths include good operational trends and excellent risk diversification. Good quality investment portfolio (6.5) despite mixed results such as: minimal exposure to mortgages and large holdings of BBB rated bonds but minimal holdings in junk bonds. Strong capitalization (9.6) based on excellent risk adjusted capital (severe loss scenario).

Other Rating Factors: Excellent profitability (9.2). Excellent liquidity (7.5).
Principal Business: Individual life insurance (87%), group life insurance (7%), group health insurance (3%), individual annuities (1%), and reinsurance (1%).
Principal Investments: NonCMO investment grade bonds (60%), CMOs and structured securities (28%), common & preferred stock (10%), and noninv. grade bonds (2%).

Investments in Affiliates: None
Group Affiliation: Americo Life Inc
Licensed in: All states except NH, NY, RI, VT, PR
Commenced Business: November 1909
Address: 500 N Akard, Dallas, TX 75201
Phone: (214) 954-8100 **Domicile State:** TX **NAIC Code:** 90212

Data Date	Rating	RACR #1	RACR #2	Total Assets ($mil)	Capital ($mil)	Net Premium ($mil)	Net Income ($mil)
6-16	B+	5.11	2.72	218.2	46.8	0.1	1.4
6-15	B	4.82	2.51	224.4	44.0	0.1	1.4
2015	B+	4.96	2.63	220.1	45.3	0.3	3.1
2014	B	4.72	2.42	224.8	42.9	0.2	2.9
2013	B	4.43	2.29	231.9	40.3	0.8	2.3
2012	B	4.23	1.95	233.1	38.8	0.2	1.5
2011	B	4.02	1.99	242.9	37.1	0.2	2.5

Adverse Trends in Operations

Increase in policy surrenders from 2014 to 2015 (79%)
Decrease in asset base during 2015 (2%)
Decrease in asset base during 2014 (3%)
Decrease in premium volume from 2013 to 2014 (72%)
Decrease in asset base during 2012 (4%)

GREAT WESTERN INSURANCE COMPANY   B   Good

Major Rating Factors: Good overall profitability (6.2 on a scale of 0 to 10). Good overall results on stability tests (5.5). Stability strengths include good operational trends and good risk diversification. Fair quality investment portfolio (4.9).
Other Rating Factors: Strong capitalization (7.0) based on excellent risk adjusted capital (severe loss scenario). Excellent liquidity (7.2).
Principal Business: Group life insurance (75%), individual life insurance (22%), individual annuities (2%), and reinsurance (1%).
Principal Investments: NonCMO investment grade bonds (77%), CMOs and structured securities (11%), mortgages in good standing (9%), noninv. grade bonds (1%), and common & preferred stock (1%).

Investments in Affiliates: 1%
Group Affiliation: JAMEL Ltd
Licensed in: All states except AK, CT, HI, NY, PR
Commenced Business: May 1983
Address: 3434 Washington Blvd, Ogden, UT 84401
Phone: (801) 621-5688 **Domicile State:** UT **NAIC Code:** 71480

Data Date	Rating	RACR #1	RACR #2	Total Assets ($mil)	Capital ($mil)	Net Premium ($mil)	Net Income ($mil)
6-16	B	1.94	1.00	1,149.2	73.6	96.6	2.8
6-15	B	2.06	1.06	1,001.2	69.2	87.5	4.1
2015	B	2.06	1.08	1,051.5	71.7	181.4	8.0
2014	B	2.09	1.10	900.0	66.3	415.9	5.7
2013	B-	2.78	1.54	496.5	60.6	39.0	14.2
2012	B-	2.51	1.40	503.8	52.0	54.1	13.6
2011	B-	1.86	1.01	492.2	40.2	64.0	0.8

Adverse Trends in Operations

Decrease in premium volume from 2014 to 2015 (56%)
Change in premium mix from 2012 to 2013 (4.5%)
Decrease in premium volume from 2012 to 2013 (28%)
Decrease in premium volume from 2011 to 2012 (15%)
Change in premium mix from 2011 to 2012 (5.5%)

GREAT-WEST LIFE & ANNUITY INSURANCE COMPANY   B-   Good

Major Rating Factors: Good capitalization (5.2 on a scale of 0 to 10) based on good risk adjusted capital (moderate loss scenario). Good quality investment portfolio (5.3) despite large holdings of BBB rated bonds in addition to moderate junk bond exposure. Exposure to mortgages is significant, but the mortgage default rate has been low. Good overall profitability (6.1).
Other Rating Factors: Good liquidity (6.4). Good overall results on stability tests (5.0) despite excessive premium growth and fair risk adjusted capital in prior years excellent operational trends and excellent risk diversification.
Principal Business: Group retirement contracts (78%), individual life insurance (15%), individual annuities (4%), group life insurance (2%), and group health insurance (1%).
Principal Investments: NonCMO investment grade bonds (49%), CMOs and structured securities (20%), policy loans (15%), mortgages in good standing (12%), and noninv. grade bonds (1%).

Investments in Affiliates: 1%
Group Affiliation: Great West Life Asr
Licensed in: All states, the District of Columbia and Puerto Rico
Commenced Business: April 1907
Address: 8515 E Orchard Rd, Englewood, CO 80111
Phone: (800) 537-2033 **Domicile State:** CO **NAIC Code:** 68322

Data Date	Rating	RACR #1	RACR #2	Total Assets ($mil)	Capital ($mil)	Net Premium ($mil)	Net Income ($mil)
6-16	B-	1.15	0.62	58,321.7	1,028.1	3,083.6	23.3
6-15	B-	1.10	0.59	57,333.9	954.9	2,462.6	82.1
2015	B-	1.29	0.71	54,460.5	1,114.8	5,729.5	187.2
2014	B-	1.19	0.64	54,523.5	1,000.9	5,634.0	134.1
2013	B-	1.33	0.75	52,282.0	1,200.6	5,610.4	175.3
2012	B-	1.30	0.72	49,029.5	1,109.5	5,498.0	147.7
2011	B-	1.27	0.71	45,163.1	1,069.5	-823.2	146.9

Risk-Adjusted Capital Ratio #1
(Moderate Loss Scenario)

GREAT-WEST LIFE & ANNUITY INSURANCE COMPANY OF NEW   B   Good

Major Rating Factors: Good overall results on stability tests (5.9 on a scale of 0 to 10) despite fair financial strength of affiliated Great West Life Asr. Other stability subfactors include excellent operational trends and excellent risk diversification. Good quality investment portfolio (6.5) despite mixed results such as: minimal exposure to mortgages and large holdings of BBB rated bonds but minimal holdings in junk bonds. Good overall profitability (5.6).

Other Rating Factors: Good liquidity (6.0). Strong capitalization (7.7) based on excellent risk adjusted capital (severe loss scenario).

Principal Business: Group retirement contracts (73%), individual life insurance (23%), and individual annuities (5%).

Principal Investments: NonCMO investment grade bonds (70%), CMOs and structured securities (16%), mortgages in good standing (10%), policy loans (2%), and cash (1%).

Investments in Affiliates: None

Group Affiliation: Great West Life Asr

Licensed in: NY

Commenced Business: January 1972

Address: 50 Main St 9th Floor, White Plains, NY 10606

Phone: (914) 682-3611 **Domicile State:** NY **NAIC Code:** 79359

Data Date	Rating	RACR #1	RACR #2	Total Assets ($mil)	Capital ($mil)	Net Premium ($mil)	Net Income ($mil)
6-16	B	2.74	1.46	1,801.4	89.8	130.7	1.1
6-15	B	2.79	1.47	1,685.8	84.7	120.4	2.2
2015	B	2.83	1.53	1,718.6	89.7	301.6	6.3
2014	B	2.79	1.48	1,594.6	82.9	272.8	1.5
2013	B	2.91	1.52	1,456.3	79.5	248.1	-4.5
2012	B	3.34	1.75	1,213.9	83.0	237.3	4.5
2011	B	3.43	1.77	1,010.6	77.4	203.4	6.9

Great West Life Asr
Composite Group Rating: C+
Largest Group Members

	Assets ($mil)	Rating
GREAT-WEST LIFE ANNUITY INS CO	54461	B-
CANADA LIFE ASSURANCE CO-US BRANCH	4404	C
GREAT-WEST LIFE ANNUITY INS OF NY	1719	B
LONDON LIFE REINSURANCE CO	301	C+
GREAT WEST LIFE ASR CO	77	C+

GUARANTEE TRUST LIFE INSURANCE COMPANY   B   Good

Major Rating Factors: Good quality investment portfolio (6.6 on a scale of 0 to 10) despite mixed results such as: minimal exposure to mortgages and substantial holdings of BBB bonds but small junk bond holdings. Good overall results on stability tests (6.0). Stability strengths include excellent operational trends, good risk adjusted capital for prior years and excellent risk diversification. Strong capitalization (7.3) based on excellent risk adjusted capital (severe loss scenario).

Other Rating Factors: Excellent profitability (8.2). Excellent liquidity (7.6).

Principal Business: Individual health insurance (75%), group health insurance (16%), individual life insurance (7%), reinsurance (1%), and credit life insurance (1%).

Principal Investments: NonCMO investment grade bonds (54%), CMOs and structured securities (31%), mortgages in good standing (8%), noninv. grade bonds (2%), and misc. investments (3%).

Investments in Affiliates: 1%

Group Affiliation: Guarantee Trust

Licensed in: All states except NY

Commenced Business: June 1936

Address: 1275 Milwaukee Ave, Glenview, IL 60025

Phone: (847) 699-0600 **Domicile State:** IL **NAIC Code:** 64211

Data Date	Rating	RACR #1	RACR #2	Total Assets ($mil)	Capital ($mil)	Net Premium ($mil)	Net Income ($mil)
6-16	B	1.84	1.23	515.0	73.6	101.9	4.5
6-15	B	1.68	1.14	455.0	64.3	102.2	3.5
2015	B	1.75	1.18	495.8	70.0	221.4	8.7
2014	B	1.67	1.15	433.3	62.3	210.7	9.7
2013	B	1.49	1.03	366.1	54.3	196.4	7.1
2012	B	1.36	0.97	325.0	44.2	182.9	3.3
2011	B	1.38	0.98	283.7	42.1	165.2	4.9

Adverse Trends in Operations

Increase in policy surrenders from 2012 to 2013 (127%)
Increase in policy surrenders from 2011 to 2012 (33%)

GUARANTY INCOME LIFE INSURANCE COMPANY   C   Fair

Major Rating Factors: Fair quality investment portfolio (3.9 on a scale of 0 to 10) with substantial holdings of BBB bonds in addition to moderate junk bond exposure. Fair overall results on stability tests (4.4) including excessive premium growth. Good liquidity (5.1) with sufficient resources to handle a spike in claims as well as a significant increase in policy surrenders.

Other Rating Factors: Strong capitalization (7.4) based on excellent risk adjusted capital (severe loss scenario). Excellent profitability (8.2).

Principal Business: Individual annuities (84%), individual health insurance (9%), and individual life insurance (7%).

Principal Investments: NonCMO investment grade bonds (45%), CMOs and structured securities (38%), common & preferred stock (4%), noninv. grade bonds (3%), and misc. investments (6%).

Investments in Affiliates: 1%

Group Affiliation: Guaranty Corp

Licensed in: AL, AZ, AR, CA, CO, FL, GA, IL, IN, IA, KS, KY, LA, MI, MS, MO, MT, NE, NV, NM, NC, ND, OH, OK, OR, SC, TN, TX, UT, WA, WY

Commenced Business: February 1926

Address: 929 Government St, Baton Rouge, LA 70802

Phone: (225) 383-0355 **Domicile State:** LA **NAIC Code:** 64238

Data Date	Rating	RACR #1	RACR #2	Total Assets ($mil)	Capital ($mil)	Net Premium ($mil)	Net Income ($mil)
6-16	C	2.57	1.26	491.3	41.3	22.7	2.5
6-15	C	2.45	1.18	481.6	36.0	17.8	2.8
2015	C	2.45	1.21	483.4	39.7	37.1	4.8
2014	C	2.45	1.18	479.5	34.0	32.8	5.4
2013	C-	2.35	1.13	477.9	31.0	26.7	5.2
2012	C-	1.85	0.86	476.7	23.2	22.6	2.7
2011	C-	1.90	1.22	488.9	21.9	30.3	0.0

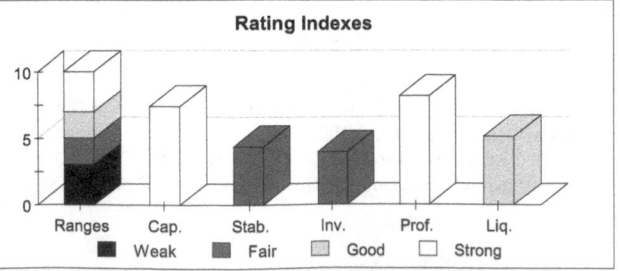

Rating Indexes

Ranges · Cap. · Stab. · Inv. · Prof. · Liq.
■ Weak ■ Fair ▨ Good □ Strong

GUARDIAN INSURANCE & ANNUITY COMPANY INCORPORATED   B   Good

Major Rating Factors: Good overall capitalization (5.4 on a scale of 0 to 10) based on good risk adjusted capital (moderate loss scenario). However, capital levels have fluctuated somewhat during past years. Good quality investment portfolio (5.5) despite mixed results such as: large holdings of BBB rated bonds but moderate junk bond exposure. Good overall results on stability tests (5.4) excellent operational trends and excellent risk diversification.

Other Rating Factors: Fair profitability (3.6) with operating losses during the first six months of 2016. Excellent liquidity (9.2).

Principal Business: Individual annuities (76%), group retirement contracts (22%), and individual life insurance (2%).

Principal Investments: NonCMO investment grade bonds (80%), mortgages in good standing (7%), CMOs and structured securities (5%), policy loans (4%), and noninv. grade bonds (3%).

Investments in Affiliates: 1%

Group Affiliation: Guardian Group

Licensed in: All states except PR

Commenced Business: December 1971

Address: 1209 Orange St, Wilmington, DE 19801

Phone: (212) 598-8000 **Domicile State:** DE **NAIC Code:** 78778

Data Date	Rating	RACR #1	RACR #2	Total Assets ($mil)	Capital ($mil)	Net Premium ($mil)	Net Income ($mil)
6-16	B	1.25	0.63	16,278.3	190.4	716.8	-68.4
6-15	B	1.55	0.79	15,957.5	217.6	748.0	-27.2
2015	B	1.65	0.84	15,883.4	259.8	1,678.6	-23.6
2014	B	1.61	0.82	15,656.2	227.2	1,504.4	-0.4
2013	B	1.62	0.85	14,529.6	180.9	1,420.3	-82.5
2012	B	2.21	1.18	12,073.3	215.1	1,932.6	-28.9
2011	B	2.99	1.52	10,135.1	253.8	1,531.1	0.2

Risk-Adjusted Capital Ratio #1
(Moderate Loss Scenario)

GUARDIAN LIFE INSURANCE COMPANY OF AMERICA *   A   Excellent

Major Rating Factors: Good quality investment portfolio (6.0 on a scale of 0 to 10) despite mixed results such as: large holdings of BBB rated bonds but moderate junk bond exposure. Good liquidity (5.9) with sufficient resources to handle a spike in claims as well as a significant increase in policy surrenders. Strong capitalization (7.9) based on excellent risk adjusted capital (severe loss scenario).

Other Rating Factors: Excellent profitability (7.6). Excellent overall results on stability tests (7.5) excellent operational trends and excellent risk diversification.

Principal Business: Individual life insurance (49%), group health insurance (35%), group life insurance (6%), roinsurance (6%), and individual health insurance (3%).

Principal Investments: NonCMO investment grade bonds (65%), mortgages in good standing (8%), policy loans (8%), CMOs and structured securities (6%), and misc. investments (14%).

Investments in Affiliates: 4%

Group Affiliation: Guardian Group

Licensed in: All states except PR

Commenced Business: July 1860

Address: 7 Hanover Square, New York, NY 10004-4025

Phone: (212) 598-8000 **Domicile State:** NY **NAIC Code:** 64246

Data Date	Rating	RACR #1	RACR #2	Total Assets ($mil)	Capital ($mil)	Net Premium ($mil)	Net Income ($mil)
6-16	A	2.45	1.58	50,389.3	6,144.3	3,863.9	124.3
6-15	A	2.83	1.82	47,260.8	6,070.2	3,634.7	298.8
2015	A	2.55	1.66	48,120.9	6,089.7	7,337.7	433.1
2014	A	2.76	1.80	45,297.4	5,691.6	6,994.0	711.8
2013	A	2.64	1.73	42,066.0	5,011.9	6,701.0	285.5
2012	A	2.59	1.70	37,530.7	4,752.0	6,011.2	253.3
2011	A	2.63	1.70	35,130.0	4,572.6	5,874.6	195.9

Rating Indexes

GUGGENHEIM LIFE & ANNUITY COMPANY   B-   Good

Major Rating Factors: Good capitalization (5.1 on a scale of 0 to 10) based on good risk adjusted capital (moderate loss scenario). Good overall profitability (5.7) although investment income, in comparison to reserve requirements, is below regulatory standards. Fair quality investment portfolio (4.3) with large holdings of BBB rated bonds in addition to moderate junk bond exposure.

Other Rating Factors: Fair overall results on stability tests (4.9) including fair risk adjusted capital in prior years. Excellent liquidity (7.2).

Principal Business: Reinsurance (53%) and individual annuities (47%).

Principal Investments: NonCMO investment grade bonds (40%), CMOs and structured securities (28%), policy loans (6%), common & preferred stock (5%), and misc. investments (16%).

Investments in Affiliates: 15%

Group Affiliation: Sammons Enterprises Inc

Licensed in: All states except NY, PR

Commenced Business: October 1985

Address: 2711 Centerville Rd Suite 400, Wilmington, DE 19808-1645

Phone: (317) 396-9950 **Domicile State:** DE **NAIC Code:** 83607

Data Date	Rating	RACR #1	RACR #2	Total Assets ($mil)	Capital ($mil)	Net Premium ($mil)	Net Income ($mil)
6-16	B-	1.07	0.63	13,900.3	589.2	371.9	94.9
6-15	B-	1.16	0.65	13,143.4	580.3	665.7	45.1
2015	B-	1.19	0.71	13,397.7	662.7	1,162.6	128.6
2014	B-	1.32	0.74	12,812.4	646.0	1,674.3	146.7
2013	B-	1.34	0.75	11,101.8	550.8	1,726.0	107.8
2012	B-	1.38	0.77	9,134.0	490.3	676.8	122.0
2011	C-	1.39	0.69	5,908.2	312.8	608.2	118.4

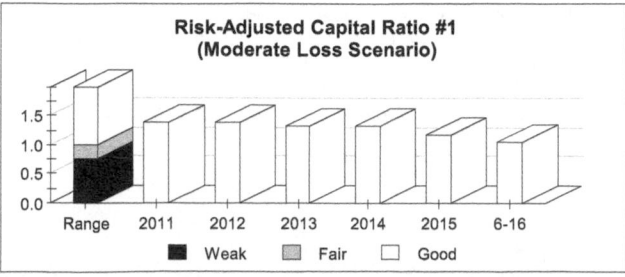

Risk-Adjusted Capital Ratio #1
(Moderate Loss Scenario)

HANNOVER LIFE REASSURANCE COMPANY OF AMERICA   B-   Good

Major Rating Factors: Good current capitalization (5.8 on a scale of 0 to 10) based on good risk adjusted capital (moderate loss scenario) reflecting some improvement over results in 2012. Good quality investment portfolio (6.6) despite mixed results such as: large holdings of BBB rated bonds but moderate junk bond exposure. Fair overall results on stability tests (4.4) including fair risk adjusted capital in prior years.

Other Rating Factors: Excellent profitability (7.9). Excellent liquidity (7.2).

Principal Business: N/A

Principal Investments: NonCMO investment grade bonds (92%), CMOs and structured securities (4%), noninv. grade bonds (3%), and mortgages in good standing (1%).

Investments in Affiliates: None

Group Affiliation: Talanx AG

Licensed in: All states, the District of Columbia and Puerto Rico

Commenced Business: October 1988

Address: 200 S Orange Ave Suite 1900, Orlando, FL 32801

Phone: (407) 649-8411 **Domicile State:** FL **NAIC Code:** 88340

Data Date	Rating	RACR #1	RACR #2	Total Assets ($mil)	Capital ($mil)	Net Premium ($mil)	Net Income ($mil)
6-16	B-	1.50	0.83	4,177.5	239.6	122.2	23.3
6-15	C	1.24	0.72	4,387.1	221.8	140.4	9.8
2015	B-	1.46	0.81	4,251.0	229.5	281.0	16.7
2014	C	1.21	0.71	4,346.7	212.1	287.6	26.9
2013	C	1.03	0.60	4,528.0	196.9	412.4	23.2
2012	C	0.87	0.50	4,617.8	181.0	399.0	9.4
2011	C	0.89	0.50	4,296.2	175.3	359.9	4.1

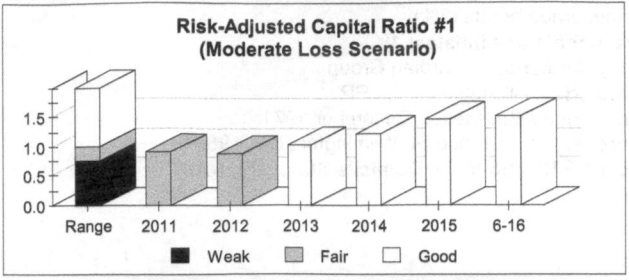

Risk-Adjusted Capital Ratio #1 (Moderate Loss Scenario)

HARLEYSVILLE LIFE INSURANCE COMPANY   B   Good

Major Rating Factors: Good quality investment portfolio (6.9 on a scale of 0 to 10) despite mixed results such as: no exposure to mortgages and large holdings of BBB rated bonds but no exposure to junk bonds. Good overall profitability (6.4). Excellent expense controls. Good liquidity (5.1).

Other Rating Factors: Fair overall results on stability tests (4.3) including negative cash flow from operations for 2015, fair risk adjusted capital in prior years. Strong capitalization (7.7) based on excellent risk adjusted capital (severe loss scenario).

Principal Business: Individual life insurance (83%), individual annuities (9%), group health insurance (4%), and group life insurance (4%).

Principal Investments: NonCMO investment grade bonds (85%), CMOs and structured securities (14%), and policy loans (1%).

Investments in Affiliates: None

Group Affiliation: Nationwide Corp

Licensed in: AL, AZ, AR, CT, DC, DE, FL, GA, IL, IN, IA, KY, MD, MA, MI, MN, NE, NH, NJ, NM, NC, ND, OH, PA, RI, SC, SD, TN, TX, UT, VA, WV, WI

Commenced Business: June 1961

Address: 355 Maple Ave, Harleysville, PA 19438-2285

Phone: (215) 256-5000 **Domicile State:** PA **NAIC Code:** 64327

Data Date	Rating	RACR #1	RACR #2	Total Assets ($mil)	Capital ($mil)	Net Premium ($mil)	Net Income ($mil)
6-16	B	2.62	1.44	408.4	40.9	9.2	1.2
6-15	B	2.03	1.17	412.1	36.8	11.1	2.7
2015	B	2.60	1.43	410.4	40.7	19.4	6.8
2014	B	1.86	1.08	415.1	34.1	34.8	7.9
2013	B	1.39	0.80	415.0	26.0	37.6	3.2
2012	B	1.17	0.69	405.5	21.6	40.6	-2.5
2011	C+	1.20	0.75	392.4	20.4	51.0	-2.2

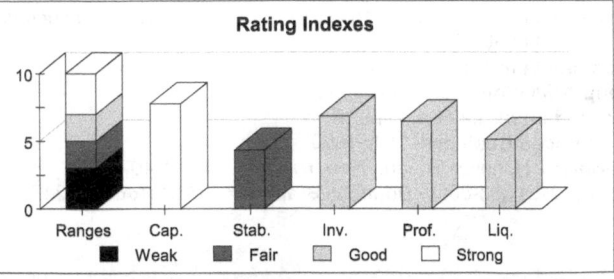

Rating Indexes

HARTFORD LIFE & ACCIDENT INSURANCE COMPANY   C+   Fair

Major Rating Factors: Fair profitability (4.9 on a scale of 0 to 10). Fair overall results on stability tests (4.6). Good quality investment portfolio (6.3) despite mixed results such as: minimal exposure to mortgages and large holdings of BBB rated bonds but small junk bond holdings.

Other Rating Factors: Strong capitalization (9.1) based on excellent risk adjusted capital (severe loss scenario). Excellent liquidity (7.1).

Principal Business: Group health insurance (52%), group life insurance (38%), reinsurance (9%), and individual life insurance (1%).

Principal Investments: NonCMO investment grade bonds (65%), CMOs and structured securities (17%), mortgages in good standing (9%), noninv. grade bonds (4%), and common & preferred stock (2%).

Investments in Affiliates: 1%

Group Affiliation: Hartford Financial Services Inc

Licensed in: All states, the District of Columbia and Puerto Rico

Commenced Business: February 1967

Address: 200 Hopmeadow St, Simsbury, CT 06070

Phone: (860) 547-5000 **Domicile State:** CT **NAIC Code:** 70815

Data Date	Rating	RACR #1	RACR #2	Total Assets ($mil)	Capital ($mil)	Net Premium ($mil)	Net Income ($mil)
6-16	C+	3.87	2.41	9,024.5	1,611.2	1,141.4	105.4
6-15	C	3.31	2.07	9,020.7	1,499.9	1,141.0	125.2
2015	C	3.96	2.47	8,992.2	1,651.4	2,296.5	168.1
2014	C	3.43	2.15	9,086.9	1,592.3	2,486.3	-331.3
2013	B-	1.05	1.00	13,890.8	5,595.2	1,974.0	-174.0
2012	B-	1.07	1.01	14,404.8	5,767.3	2,878.5	-397.8
2011	B-	1.06	1.01	15,388.3	6,737.2	3,178.7	-23.0

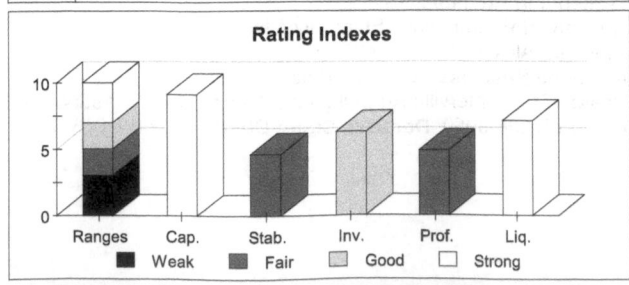

Rating Indexes

HARTFORD LIFE & ANNUITY INSURANCE COMPANY   B-   Good

Major Rating Factors: Good quality investment portfolio (6.6 on a scale of 0 to 10) despite mixed results such as: minimal exposure to mortgages and substantial holdings of BBB bonds but small junk bond holdings. Good profitability (5.0). Fair overall results on stability tests (3.6) including fair financial strength of affiliated Hartford Financial Services Inc and weak results on operational trends.

Other Rating Factors: Strong capitalization (9.3) based on excellent risk adjusted capital (severe loss scenario). Excellent liquidity (9.9).

Principal Business: Individual life insurance (69%), individual annuities (24%), and reinsurance (7%).

Principal Investments: NonCMO investment grade bonds (50%), CMOs and structured securities (20%), mortgages in good standing (8%), common & preferred stock (5%), and misc. investments (11%).

Investments in Affiliates: 1%

Group Affiliation: Hartford Financial Services Inc

Licensed in: All states except NY

Commenced Business: July 1965

Address: 200 Hopmeadow St, Simsbury, CT 06070

Phone: (860) 547-5000 **Domicile State:** CT **NAIC Code:** 71153

Data Date	Rating	RACR #1	RACR #2	Total Assets ($mil)	Capital ($mil)	Net Premium ($mil)	Net Income ($mil)
6-16	B-	4.83	2.54	38,138.2	2,139.3	152.8	112.4
6-15	B-	5.79	3.04	44,406.2	2,887.6	163.4	-40.8
2015	B-	5.83	3.06	40,189.1	2,625.3	313.1	80.9
2014	B-	6.70	3.51	47,246.3	3,408.9	41,392.8	95.2
2013	B-	6.35	3.36	54,556.9	3,080.6	-2,982.6	721.8
2012	B-	2.42	1.68	65,710.7	3,026.2	1,288.8	711.4
2011	C	2.76	1.98	67,758.0	3,931.4	1,401.1	-857.9

Hartford Financial Services Inc Composite Group Rating: C+ Largest Group Members	Assets ($mil)	Rating
HARTFORD LIFE INS CO	114421	C+
HARTFORD LIFE ANNUITY INS CO	40189	B-
HARTFORD FIRE INS CO	25426	B
HARTFORD ACCIDENT INDEMNITY CO	11522	B
HARTFORD LIFE ACCIDENT INS CO	8992	C+

HARTFORD LIFE INSURANCE COMPANY   C+   Fair

Major Rating Factors: Fair profitability (3.9 on a scale of 0 to 10) with investment income below regulatory standards in relation to interest assumptions of reserves. Fair overall results on stability tests (3.6). Good quality investment portfolio (5.5) despite mixed results such as: minimal exposure to mortgages and substantial holdings of BBB bonds but small junk bond holdings.

Other Rating Factors: Strong capitalization (7.1) based on excellent risk adjusted capital (severe loss scenario). Excellent liquidity (8.7).

Principal Business: Group retirement contracts (71%), individual annuities (10%), individual life insurance (7%), group life insurance (6%), and group health insurance (6%).

Principal Investments: NonCMO investment grade bonds (45%), CMOs and structured securities (16%), common & preferred stock (14%), mortgages in good standing (7%), and misc. investments (15%).

Investments in Affiliates: 13%

Group Affiliation: Hartford Financial Services Inc

Licensed in: All states except PR

Commenced Business: January 1979

Address: 200 Hopmeadow St, Simsbury, CT 06070

Phone: (860) 547-5000 **Domicile State:** CT **NAIC Code:** 88072

Data Date	Rating	RACR #1	RACR #2	Total Assets ($mil)	Capital ($mil)	Net Premium ($mil)	Net Income ($mil)
6-16	C+	1.41	1.08	113,812	4,666.3	53.2	609.3
6-15	C+	1.24	0.99	122,612	5,049.7	1,167.7	86.0
2015	C+	1.47	1.12	114,421	4,939.5	1,406.9	295.2
2014	C+	1.32	1.06	123,445	5,564.4	-1,087.6	35.4
2013	C+	1.28	0.99	128,074	5,005.0	-7,168.0	549.9
2012	C+	1.22	0.92	140,501	5,015.5	3,115.8	224.3
2011	C	1.15	0.90	144,044	5,920.1	3,614.0	184.2

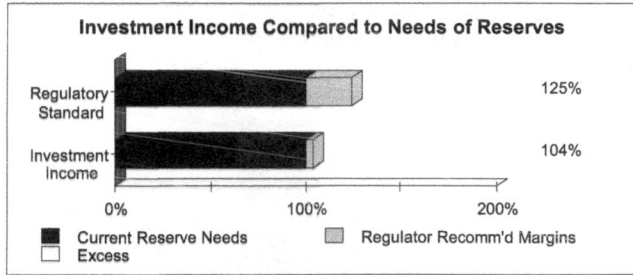

Investment Income Compared to Needs of Reserves

Regulatory Standard — 125%
Investment Income — 104%

0%   100%   200%

■ Current Reserve Needs   ▨ Regulator Recomm'd Margins
□ Excess

HCC LIFE INSURANCE COMPANY   B   Good

Major Rating Factors: Good overall results on stability tests (6.0 on a scale of 0 to 10). Stability strengths include excellent operational trends and excellent risk diversification. Good liquidity (6.9) with sufficient resources to handle a spike in claims. Strong capitalization (10.0) based on excellent risk adjusted capital (severe loss scenario).

Other Rating Factors: High quality investment portfolio (8.1). Excellent profitability (9.3).

Principal Business: Group health insurance (90%) and individual health insurance (10%).

Principal Investments: NonCMO investment grade bonds (53%) and CMOs and structured securities (48%).

Investments in Affiliates: None

Group Affiliation: HCC Ins Holdings Inc

Licensed in: All states except PR

Commenced Business: March 1981

Address: 150 W Market St Suite 800, Indianapolis, IN 46204

Phone: (713) 996-1200 **Domicile State:** IN **NAIC Code:** 92711

Data Date	Rating	RACR #1	RACR #2	Total Assets ($mil)	Capital ($mil)	Net Premium ($mil)	Net Income ($mil)
6-16	B	4.85	3.69	1,001.7	606.0	492.3	52.4
6-15	B	5.01	3.89	966.6	608.3	490.5	55.0
2015	B	4.44	3.40	921.5	552.7	973.3	112.1
2014	B	4.61	3.60	923.5	554.3	956.4	116.1
2013	B	3.61	2.96	750.2	436.9	854.6	142.1
2012	B	2.72	2.34	731.2	413.7	821.0	100.2
2011	B	2.97	2.57	655.7	400.2	686.0	89.0

Rating Indexes

10

5

0

Ranges   Cap.   Stab.   Inv.   Prof.   Liq.

■ Weak   ▨ Fair   ▤ Good   □ Strong

HEALTH NET LIFE INSURANCE COMPANY   C   Fair

Major Rating Factors: Weak overall results on stability tests (2.4 on a scale of 0 to 10) including fair financial strength of affiliated Centene Corporation and negative cash flow from operations for 2015. Weak profitability (1.7) with operating losses during the first six months of 2016. Weak liquidity (0.4) as a spike in claims may stretch capacity.

Other Rating Factors: Strong capitalization (7.7) based on excellent risk adjusted capital (severe loss scenario). High quality investment portfolio (8.9).

Principal Business: Group health insurance (50%) and individual health insurance (50%).

Principal Investments: NonCMO investment grade bonds (57%), cash (30%), and CMOs and structured securities (13%).

Investments in Affiliates: None

Group Affiliation: Centene Corporation

Licensed in: All states except NY, PR

Commenced Business: January 1987

Address: 225 N Main St, Pueblo, CO 81003

Phone: (719) 585-8017 **Domicile State:** CA **NAIC Code:** 66141

Data Date	Rating	RACR #1	RACR #2	Total Assets ($mil)	Capital ($mil)	Net Premium ($mil)	Net Income ($mil)
6-16	C	1.85	1.52	634.2	264.4	348.1	-220.5
6-15	C	1.91	1.57	612.2	319.6	572.5	-47.9
2015	C	1.84	1.52	618.5	331.3	1,181.3	-93.2
2014	C	2.26	1.84	624.0	363.9	1,040.9	-9.3
2013	B	1.88	1.52	485.1	257.2	916.1	22.9
2012	C+	2.25	1.82	632.0	365.6	1,079.4	107.7
2011	C+	1.99	1.63	548.6	352.9	1,178.4	22.6

Centene Corporation Composite Group Rating: C- Largest Group Members	Assets ($mil)	Rating
SUNSHINE HEALTH	693	E
SUPERIOR HEALTHPLAN INC	620	C+
HEALTH NET LIFE INS CO	619	C
BUCKEYE COMMUNITY HEALTH PLAN INC	455	C+
HEALTH NET OF ARIZONA INC	451	C

HERITAGE LIFE INSURANCE COMPANY   C   Fair

Major Rating Factors: Fair quality investment portfolio (3.4 on a scale of 0 to 10) with large holdings of BBB rated bonds in addition to junk bond exposure equal to 70% of capital. Fair overall results on stability tests (3.9) including negative cash flow from operations for 2015. Good overall profitability (6.6).

Other Rating Factors: Strong capitalization (7.9) based on excellent risk adjusted capital (severe loss scenario). Excellent liquidity (7.2).

Principal Business: Reinsurance (100%).

Principal Investments: NonCMO investment grade bonds (42%), CMOs and structured securities (25%), noninv. grade bonds (15%), and common & preferred stock (1%).

Investments in Affiliates: None

Group Affiliation: Calton Holdings LLC

Licensed in: All states except NY, PR

Commenced Business: August 1957

Address: 8601 N Scottsdale Rd Ste 300, Scottsdale, AZ 85253

Phone: (312) 977-0904 **Domicile State:** AZ **NAIC Code:** 64394

Data Date	Rating	RACR #1	RACR #2	Total Assets ($mil)	Capital ($mil)	Net Premium ($mil)	Net Income ($mil)
6-16	C	3.81	1.62	4,496.3	940.8	49.7	41.9
6-15	C	3.80	1.55	4,518.9	976.9	19.1	18.1
2015	C	3.95	1.68	4,508.2	992.4	46.1	65.0
2014	C	3.97	1.62	4,685.9	1,027.6	36.8	57.6
2013	C-	4.49	1.94	4,872.4	1,018.0	85.8	34.0
2012	U	14.27	8.59	3,893.5	1,000.1	0.0	-0.2
2011	U	9.83	8.84	8.7	8.2	0.0	-0.9

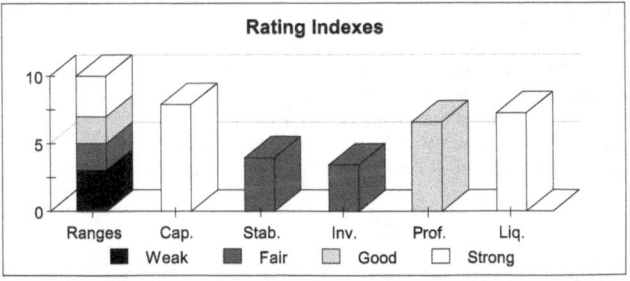

Rating Indexes

Ranges | Cap. | Stab. | Inv. | Prof. | Liq.
■ Weak ■ Fair ▨ Good □ Strong

HM LIFE INSURANCE COMPANY   B   Good

Major Rating Factors: Good overall results on stability tests (5.5 on a scale of 0 to 10) despite fair financial strength of affiliated Highmark Inc. Other stability subfactors include excellent operational trends and excellent risk diversification. Good quality investment portfolio (5.3) with no exposure to mortgages and small junk bond holdings. Strong capitalization (9.6) based on excellent risk adjusted capital (severe loss scenario).

Other Rating Factors: Excellent profitability (8.8). Excellent liquidity (7.2).

Principal Business: Group health insurance (86%) and reinsurance (14%).

Principal Investments: NonCMO investment grade bonds (62%), CMOs and structured securities (11%), noninv. grade bonds (11%), cash (6%), and common & preferred stock (4%).

Investments in Affiliates: None

Group Affiliation: Highmark Inc

Licensed in: All states except NY, PR

Commenced Business: May 1981

Address: 120 Fifth Avenue, Pittsburgh, PA 15222

Phone: (800) 328-5433 **Domicile State:** PA **NAIC Code:** 93440

Data Date	Rating	RACR #1	RACR #2	Total Assets ($mil)	Capital ($mil)	Net Premium ($mil)	Net Income ($mil)
6-16	B	3.72	2.73	646.6	356.5	340.4	8.5
6-15	B	3.41	2.58	582.7	316.4	313.3	7.3
2015	B	3.73	2.73	620.8	348.6	640.3	37.3
2014	B	3.28	2.49	574.5	309.2	647.9	24.1
2013	B	3.07	2.35	557.9	284.6	634.0	35.5
2012	B	2.87	2.20	491.3	250.0	588.8	25.4
2011	B-	2.64	2.03	471.6	219.5	568.8	27.7

Highmark Inc Composite Group Rating: C+ Largest Group Members	Assets ($mil)	Rating
HIGHMARK INC	7565	C
HIGHMARK WEST VIRGINIA INC	629	B
HM LIFE INS CO	621	B
GATEWAY HEALTH PLAN INC	582	B-
HIGHMARK CASUALTY INS CO	457	C

HM LIFE INSURANCE COMPANY OF NEW YORK | B | Good

Major Rating Factors: Good overall results on stability tests (5.5 on a scale of 0 to 10) despite fair financial strength of affiliated Highmark Inc and negative cash flow from operations for 2015. Other stability subfactors include good operational trends and good risk diversification. Good overall profitability (6.5) despite operating losses during the first six months of 2016. Strong capitalization (9.2) based on excellent risk adjusted capital (severe loss scenario).

Other Rating Factors: High quality investment portfolio (8.7). Excellent liquidity (7.2).

Principal Business: Group health insurance (96%) and reinsurance (4%).

Principal Investments: NonCMO investment grade bonds (73%), CMOs and structured securities (23%), and cash (4%).

Investments in Affiliates: None

Group Affiliation: Highmark Inc

Licensed in: DC, NY, RI

Commenced Business: March 1997

Address: 420 Fifth Ave 3rd Floor, New York, NY 10018

Phone: (800) 328-5433 **Domicile State:** NY **NAIC Code:** 60213

Data Date	Rating	RACR #1	RACR #2	Total Assets ($mil)	Capital ($mil)	Net Premium ($mil)	Net Income ($mil)
6-16	B	3.12	2.46	69.9	38.3	36.6	-0.4
6-15	B+	3.37	2.62	66.0	40.4	32.3	1.1
2015	B	3.33	2.64	65.7	38.9	66.2	-1.1
2014	B+	3.12	2.47	71.4	39.2	75.4	8.0
2013	B+	2.28	1.81	76.1	31.9	85.4	-0.4
2012	B+	2.00	1.59	66.5	31.8	88.4	9.0
2011	B-	1.90	1.50	44.9	22.9	63.1	2.5

Highmark Inc
Composite Group Rating: C+

Largest Group Members	Assets ($mil)	Rating
HIGHMARK INC	7565	C
HIGHMARK WEST VIRGINIA INC	629	B
HM LIFE INS CO	621	B
GATEWAY HEALTH PLAN INC	582	B-
HIGHMARK CASUALTY INS CO	457	C

HOMESTEADERS LIFE COMPANY | B | Good

Major Rating Factors: Good quality investment portfolio (6.2 on a scale of 0 to 10) despite mixed results such as: minimal exposure to mortgages and substantial holdings of BBB bonds but small junk bond holdings. Good overall profitability (5.7) although investment income, in comparison to reserve requirements, is below regulatory standards. Good liquidity (6.9).

Other Rating Factors: Good overall results on stability tests (5.5) excellent operational trends and excellent risk diversification. Strong capitalization (7.3) based on excellent risk adjusted capital (severe loss scenario).

Principal Business: Group life insurance (94%), individual life insurance (3%), and individual annuities (3%).

Principal Investments: NonCMO investment grade bonds (75%), CMOs and structured securities (20%), mortgages in good standing (2%), noninv. grade bonds (1%), and cash (1%).

Investments in Affiliates: None

Group Affiliation: None

Licensed in: All states except NY, PR

Commenced Business: February 1906

Address: 5700 Westown Parkway, West Des Moines, IA 50266-8221

Phone: (515) 440-7777 **Domicile State:** IA **NAIC Code:** 64505

Data Date	Rating	RACR #1	RACR #2	Total Assets ($mil)	Capital ($mil)	Net Premium ($mil)	Net Income ($mil)
6-16	B	2.19	1.18	2,693.3	174.2	226.8	6.2
6-15	B	2.21	1.25	2,550.8	165.7	207.7	4.4
2015	B	2.22	1.24	2,623.9	168.7	422.3	10.5
2014	B	2.19	1.24	2,500.8	161.1	399.8	12.4
2013	B	2.02	1.16	2,378.1	149.6	396.7	12.6
2012	B	1.97	1.13	2,249.0	132.5	413.8	15.3
2011	B-	2.06	1.14	2,093.3	119.7	397.4	15.9

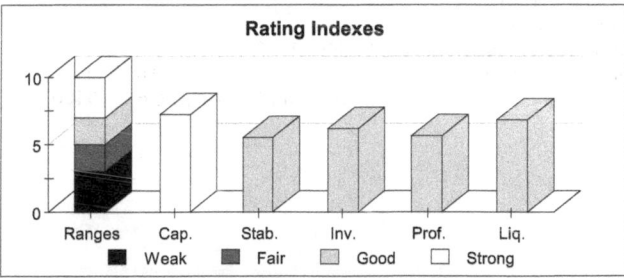

Rating Indexes

HORACE MANN LIFE INSURANCE COMPANY | B | Good

Major Rating Factors: Good capitalization (6.1 on a scale of 0 to 10) based on good risk adjusted capital (moderate loss scenario). Moreover, capital levels have been consistent over the last five years. Good quality investment portfolio (5.0) despite mixed results such as: large holdings of BBB rated bonds but moderate junk bond exposure. Good overall results on stability tests (5.4) excellent operational trends and excellent risk diversification.

Other Rating Factors: Fair liquidity (4.8). Excellent profitability (8.2).

Principal Business: Individual annuities (71%), individual life insurance (16%), and group retirement contracts (12%).

Principal Investments: NonCMO investment grade bonds (63%), CMOs and structured securities (29%), noninv. grade bonds (3%), policy loans (2%), and common & preferred stock (1%).

Investments in Affiliates: None

Group Affiliation: Horace Mann Educators Corp

Licensed in: All states except NJ, NY, PR

Commenced Business: September 1949

Address: 1 Horace Mann Plaza, Springfield, IL 62715

Phone: (800) 999-1030 **Domicile State:** IL **NAIC Code:** 64513

Data Date	Rating	RACR #1	RACR #2	Total Assets ($mil)	Capital ($mil)	Net Premium ($mil)	Net Income ($mil)
6-16	B	1.75	0.88	8,506.0	431.1	287.3	28.3
6-15	B	1.77	0.89	8,178.8	403.7	330.9	16.7
2015	B	1.74	0.88	8,358.8	421.9	648.8	43.2
2014	B	1.80	0.90	7,894.0	398.7	580.3	46.8
2013	B	1.90	0.96	7,281.4	372.4	520.1	54.1
2012	B	1.92	0.95	6,302.5	347.7	514.1	44.8
2011	B	2.11	1.05	5,817.2	339.7	530.7	53.7

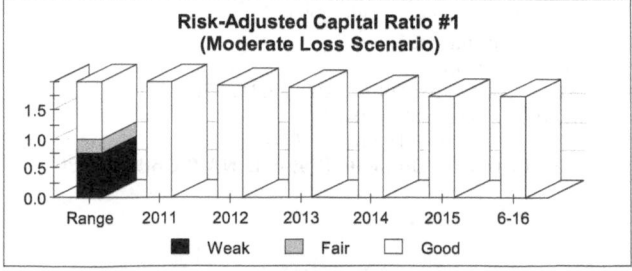

Risk-Adjusted Capital Ratio #1
(Moderate Loss Scenario)

HUMANA INSURANCE COMPANY OF KENTUCKY | C | Fair

Major Rating Factors: Fair overall results on stability tests (3.4 on a scale of 0 to 10) including negative cash flow from operations for 2015. Weak profitability (2.3) with investment income below regulatory standards in relation to interest assumptions of reserves. Strong capitalization (9.8) based on excellent risk adjusted capital (severe loss scenario).

Other Rating Factors: High quality investment portfolio (8.0). Excellent liquidity (7.0).

Principal Business: Reinsurance (82%), individual health insurance (10%), group life insurance (7%), and group health insurance (1%).

Principal Investments: CMOs and structured securities (52%), nonCMO investment grade bonds (42%), and policy loans (5%).

Investments in Affiliates: None

Group Affiliation: Humana Inc

Licensed in: KY

Commenced Business: January 2001

Address: 500 W Main St, Louisville, KY 40202

Phone: (502) 580-1000 **Domicile State:** KY **NAIC Code:** 60219

Data Date	Rating	RACR #1	RACR #2	Total Assets ($mil)	Capital ($mil)	Net Premium ($mil)	Net Income ($mil)
6-16	C	3.91	2.88	195.7	145.1	29.3	22.9
6-15	B-	2.26	1.77	412.0	98.7	133.6	-8.4
2015	C	2.61	1.95	432.9	122.2	269.9	-2.8
2014	B-	2.71	2.11	418.0	107.6	157.8	-5.8
2013	B-	2.03	1.57	108.6	61.1	111.5	15.7
2012	B-	1.73	1.35	42.3	24.8	40.8	6.4
2011	B-	1.40	1.10	35.9	18.5	36.6	-1.9

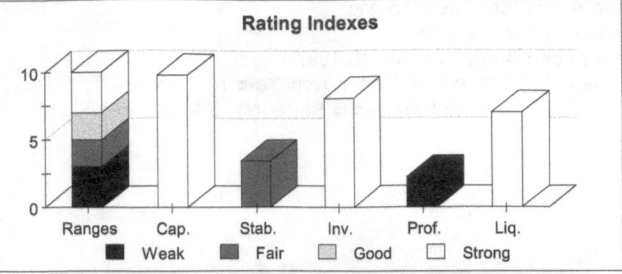

Rating Indexes

HUMANA INSURANCE COMPANY OF PUERTO RICO INCORPORA | C+ | Fair

Major Rating Factors: Fair overall results on stability tests (4.6 on a scale of 0 to 10) including negative cash flow from operations for 2015. Good liquidity (6.8) with sufficient resources to handle a spike in claims. Weak profitability (2.8) with operating losses during the first six months of 2016.

Other Rating Factors: Strong capitalization (8.6) based on excellent risk adjusted capital (severe loss scenario). High quality investment portfolio (8.4).

Principal Business: Group health insurance (85%) and individual health insurance (15%).

Principal Investments: CMOs and structured securities (48%), cash (27%), nonCMO investment grade bonds (24%), and noninv. grade bonds (1%).

Investments in Affiliates: None

Group Affiliation: Humana Inc

Licensed in: PR

Commenced Business: September 1971

Address: 383 F D Roosevelt Ave, San Juan, PR 00918-2131

Phone: (787) 282-7900 **Domicile State:** PR **NAIC Code:** 84603

Data Date	Rating	RACR #1	RACR #2	Total Assets ($mil)	Capital ($mil)	Net Premium ($mil)	Net Income ($mil)
6-16	C+	2.58	2.06	69.6	47.4	54.2	-3.6
6-15	B-	2.80	2.23	75.2	49.5	48.7	-0.3
2015	B-	2.85	2.28	69.3	51.2	96.9	1.5
2014	B-	2.80	2.22	70.2	49.8	93.3	-6.6
2013	B-	3.20	2.52	73.3	57.0	93.2	4.7
2012	C+	2.86	2.27	70.2	52.1	98.6	4.6
2011	C	3.28	2.60	73.6	48.8	88.1	7.9

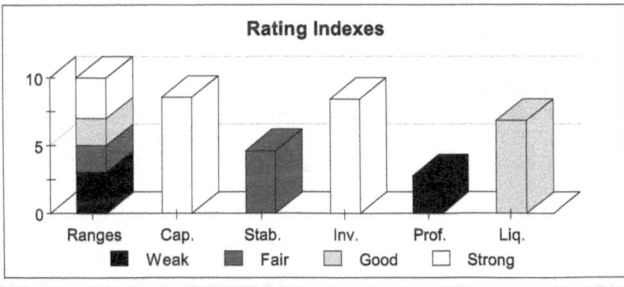

Rating Indexes

ILLINOIS MUTUAL LIFE INSURANCE COMPANY * | A- | Excellent

Major Rating Factors: Good quality investment portfolio (6.5 on a scale of 0 to 10) despite mixed results such as: substantial holdings of BBB bonds but moderate junk bond exposure. Good overall profitability (5.3) although investment income, in comparison to reserve requirements, is below regulatory standards. Good liquidity (6.5).

Other Rating Factors: Good overall results on stability tests (6.9) excellent operational trends and excellent risk diversification. Strong capitalization (8.4) based on excellent risk adjusted capital (severe loss scenario).

Principal Business: Individual health insurance (51%), individual life insurance (46%), group health insurance (2%), and individual annuities (1%).

Principal Investments: NonCMO investment grade bonds (62%), CMOs and structured securities (26%), noninv. grade bonds (5%), common & preferred stock (4%), and misc. investments (3%).

Investments in Affiliates: None

Group Affiliation: None

Licensed in: All states except AK, DC, HI, NY, PR

Commenced Business: July 1912

Address: 300 SW Adams, Peoria, IL 61634

Phone: (309) 674-8255 **Domicile State:** IL **NAIC Code:** 64580

Data Date	Rating	RACR #1	RACR #2	Total Assets ($mil)	Capital ($mil)	Net Premium ($mil)	Net Income ($mil)
6-16	A-	3.52	1.96	1,434.6	215.5	51.3	2.8
6-15	A-	3.37	1.91	1,380.5	201.8	49.7	6.1
2015	A-	3.53	1.99	1,388.9	211.7	100.3	14.8
2014	A-	3.27	1.84	1,367.7	196.3	100.5	28.2
2013	A-	3.57	2.05	1,329.4	173.7	104.2	26.7
2012	B	3.07	1.76	1,289.1	144.2	102.0	27.0
2011	B	2.58	1.46	1,227.9	115.6	104.3	22.3

Rating Indexes

INDEPENDENCE LIFE & ANNUITY COMPANY — D- — Weak

Major Rating Factors: Weak overall results on stability tests (1.1 on a scale of 0 to 10) including potential financial drain due to affiliation with Sun Life Assurance Group. Fair overall capitalization (4.0) based on mixed results -- excessive policy leverage mitigated by excellent risk adjusted capital (severe loss scenario). Capital levels have been relatively consistent over the last five years. Good liquidity (6.9).

Other Rating Factors: High quality investment portfolio (7.8). Excellent profitability (7.2).

Principal Business: Reinsurance (100%).

Principal Investments: NonCMO investment grade bonds (54%), CMOs and structured securities (38%), and policy loans (8%).

Investments in Affiliates: None

Group Affiliation: Sun Life Assurance Group

Licensed in: All states except NY, PR

Commenced Business: November 1945

Address: 1209 Orange St, Wilmington, DE 19801

Phone: (781) 237-6030 **Domicile State:** DE **NAIC Code:** 64602

Data Date	Rating	RACR #1	RACR #2	Total Assets ($mil)	Capital ($mil)	Net Premium ($mil)	Net Income ($mil)
6-16	D-	5.38	3.53	2,972.8	181.0	-0.2	1.8
6-15	C	4.05	2.15	2,630.1	127.7	-0.2	1.3
2015	C	5.33	3.55	2,862.7	179.3	-0.4	3.0
2014	C	4.01	2.60	2,639.5	126.5	-0.4	-1.3
2013	C	4.48	2.72	2,284.3	127.3	-0.4	1.2
2012	C-	7.04	6.33	128.5	64.2	-0.4	2.4
2011	B-	6.80	6.12	126.0	61.8	-0.4	4.1

Sun Life Assurance Group Composite Group Rating: E Largest Group Members	Assets ($mil)	Rating
SUN LIFE ASR CO OF CANADA	18222	E
INDEPENDENCE LIFE ANNUITY CO	2863	D-
SUN LIFE HEALTH INS CO	448	D-
PROFESSIONAL INS CO	109	D-

INDUSTRIAL ALLIANCE INS & FIN SERV — C- — Fair

Major Rating Factors: Fair quality investment portfolio (4.6 on a scale of 0 to 10). Weak profitability (1.5) with operating losses during the first six months of 2016. Weak overall results on stability tests (2.0) including weak results on operational trends, negative cash flow from operations for 2015.

Other Rating Factors: Good liquidity (6.1). Strong capitalization (8.3) based on excellent risk adjusted capital (severe loss scenario).

Principal Business: Reinsurance (84%), individual life insurance (9%), and individual annuities (7%).

Principal Investments: NonCMO investment grade bonds (83%), real estate (5%), mortgages in good standing (3%), policy loans (3%), and misc. investments (6%).

Investments in Affiliates: None

Group Affiliation: Industrial Alliance Ins & Financial

Licensed in: All states except AL, CT, FL, MN, NY, NC, PR

Commenced Business: June 1967

Address: 425 Austin Ave, Waco, TX 76701

Phone: (480) 473-5540 **Domicile State:** TX **NAIC Code:** 14406

Data Date	Rating	RACR #1	RACR #2	Total Assets ($mil)	Capital ($mil)	Net Premium ($mil)	Net Income ($mil)
6-16	C-	3.17	1.88	213.3	39.4	45.2	-5.9
6-15	C	4.23	2.52	202.3	54.7	37.1	-3.9
2015	C-	3.67	2.18	202.4	44.8	71.4	-10.0
2014	C	4.59	2.73	193.7	59.6	54.4	-0.7
2013	C	5.59	3.22	200.7	73.2	31.7	-18.5
2012	C+	8.43	4.19	221.3	83.4	60.0	12.2
2011	N/A	N/A	N/A	0.0	0.0	0.0	0.0

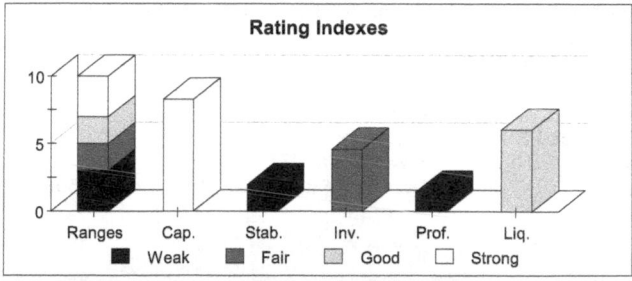

Rating Indexes

(Ranges, Cap., Stab., Inv., Prof., Liq.) — ■ Weak ■ Fair ▨ Good □ Strong

INTEGRITY LIFE INSURANCE COMPANY — B- — Good

Major Rating Factors: Good current capitalization (6.9 on a scale of 0 to 10) based on good risk adjusted capital (severe loss scenario), although results have slipped from the excellent range during the last year. Good quality investment portfolio (5.0) despite mixed results such as: large holdings of BBB rated bonds but moderate junk bond exposure. Good overall profitability (6.5).

Other Rating Factors: Fair overall results on stability tests (4.9) including excessive premium growth. Excellent liquidity (7.8).

Principal Business: Individual annuities (100%).

Principal Investments: NonCMO investment grade bonds (48%), CMOs and structured securities (23%), common & preferred stock (13%), noninv. grade bonds (6%), and misc. investments (10%).

Investments in Affiliates: 9%

Group Affiliation: Western & Southern Group

Licensed in: All states except NH, NY, PR

Commenced Business: May 1966

Address: 400 Broadway St, Cincinnati, OH 45202-3341

Phone: (513) 629-1800 **Domicile State:** OH **NAIC Code:** 74780

Data Date	Rating	RACR #1	RACR #2	Total Assets ($mil)	Capital ($mil)	Net Premium ($mil)	Net Income ($mil)
6-16	B-	1.38	0.99	7,432.8	717.4	666.1	23.4
6-15	B-	1.41	1.06	6,553.7	711.0	481.3	22.7
2015	B-	1.36	1.00	6,844.3	678.6	1,101.2	67.2
2014	B-	1.35	1.03	6,107.1	663.8	407.5	57.0
2013	B-	1.52	1.12	6,056.7	668.0	249.8	42.2
2012	B-	1.43	1.04	5,988.3	599.7	302.2	33.7
2011	B-	1.37	0.98	5,916.1	547.2	352.2	25.3

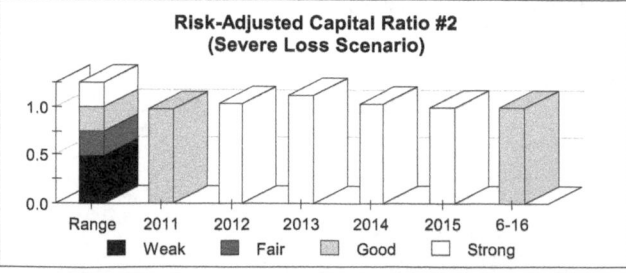

Risk-Adjusted Capital Ratio #2
(Severe Loss Scenario)

(Range, 2011, 2012, 2013, 2014, 2015, 6-16) — ■ Weak ■ Fair ▨ Good □ Strong

INVESTORS LIFE INSURANCE COMPANY NORTH AMERICA — B — Good

Major Rating Factors: Good overall results on stability tests (6.1 on a scale of 0 to 10) despite negative cash flow from operations for 2015. Other stability subfactors include excellent operational trends, good risk adjusted capital for prior years and excellent risk diversification. Good quality investment portfolio (5.2) despite mixed results such as: large holdings of BBB rated bonds but moderate junk bond exposure. Good liquidity (5.7).

Other Rating Factors: Fair overall capitalization (4.0) based on mixed results -- excessive policy leverage mitigated by excellent risk adjusted capital (severe loss scenario). Excellent profitability (8.5) despite operating losses during the first six months of 2016.

Principal Business: Individual life insurance (98%), individual annuities (1%), and reinsurance (1%).

Principal Investments: NonCMO investment grade bonds (53%), CMOs and structured securities (31%), common & preferred stock (7%), noninv. grade bonds (5%), and misc. investments (4%).

Investments in Affiliates: 1%

Group Affiliation: Americo Life Inc

Licensed in: All states except NY, PR

Commenced Business: December 1963

Address: 6500 River Place Blvd Bldg One, Austin, TX 78730

Phone: (512) 404-5000 **Domicile State:** TX **NAIC Code:** 63487

Data Date	Rating	RACR #1	RACR #2	Total Assets ($mil)	Capital ($mil)	Net Premium ($mil)	Net Income ($mil)
6-16	B	2.71	1.42	643.0	54.2	-0.2	-0.1
6-15	B	2.78	1.51	673.7	54.0	-0.2	0.6
2015	B	2.88	1.54	648.2	54.2	-0.1	1.7
2014	B	2.84	1.54	680.7	53.3	-0.1	2.8
2013	B-	2.45	1.25	691.3	49.2	-0.1	1.9
2012	C+	2.41	1.21	691.7	45.7	-0.3	2.1
2011	C	2.06	0.98	705.8	44.0	-0.1	3.2

Adverse Trends in Operations

Decrease in asset base during 2015 (5%)
Decrease in asset base during 2014 (2%)
Decrease in asset base during 2012 (2%)
Decrease in premium volume from 2011 to 2012 (177%)

IOWA AMERICAN LIFE INSURANCE COMPANY — B- — Good

Major Rating Factors: Good overall results on stability tests (5.2 on a scale of 0 to 10) despite fair financial strength of affiliated Industrial Alliance Ins & Financial and fair risk adjusted capital in prior years. Other stability subfactors include good operational trends and excellent risk diversification. Good current capitalization (6.4) based on good risk adjusted capital (severe loss scenario) reflecting some improvement over results in 2011. Good overall profitability (5.8) despite operating losses during the first six months of 2016.

Other Rating Factors: Fair quality investment portfolio (4.8). Excellent liquidity (7.1).

Principal Business: Individual life insurance (77%), reinsurance (18%), individual health insurance (3%), and individual annuities (2%).

Principal Investments: Common & preferred stock (51%), nonCMO investment grade bonds (41%), policy loans (3%), mortgages in good standing (3%), and cash (2%).

Investments in Affiliates: 60%

Group Affiliation: Industrial Alliance Ins & Financial

Licensed in: All states except NY, PR

Commenced Business: May 1980

Address: 425 Austin Ave, Waco, TX 76701

Phone: (480) 473-5540 **Domicile State:** TX **NAIC Code:** 91693

Data Date	Rating	RACR #1	RACR #2	Total Assets ($mil)	Capital ($mil)	Net Premium ($mil)	Net Income ($mil)
6-16	B-	0.96	0.93	225.3	131.2	8.6	-0.8
6-15	C	0.98	0.92	229.8	131.3	7.0	13.7
2015	C	0.86	0.86	229.2	133.2	15.0	9.4
2014	C	0.85	0.86	241.4	141.1	11.4	-4.3
2013	C-	0.75	0.78	218.1	124.6	10.6	0.6
2012	C-	1.10	1.03	205.5	106.3	11.5	7.2
2011	D	0.60	0.67	182.5	81.7	12.4	-2.8

Industrial Alliance Ins Financial
Composite Group Rating: C

Largest Group Members	Assets ($mil)	Rating
AMERICAN-AMICABLE LIFE INS CO OF TX	287	C
OCCIDENTAL LIFE INS CO OF NC	257	C
IA AMERICAN LIFE INS CO	229	B-
INDUSTRIAL ALLIANCE INS FIN SERV	202	C-
PIONEER SECURITY LIFE INS CO	125	C+

JACKSON NATIONAL LIFE INSURANCE CO OF NEW YORK — B — Good

Major Rating Factors: Good quality investment portfolio (5.4 on a scale of 0 to 10) despite mixed results such as: no exposure to mortgages and large holdings of BBB rated bonds but small junk bond holdings. Good overall results on stability tests (5.4). Stability strengths include excellent operational trends and excellent risk diversification. Strong capitalization (8.8) based on excellent risk adjusted capital (severe loss scenario).

Other Rating Factors: Excellent profitability (7.5) despite operating losses during the first six months of 2016. Excellent liquidity (10.0).

Principal Business: Individual annuities (100%).

Principal Investments: NonCMO investment grade bonds (72%), CMOs and structured securities (25%), and noninv. grade bonds (3%).

Investments in Affiliates: None

Group Affiliation: Prudential plc

Licensed in: DE, MI, NY

Commenced Business: August 1996

Address: 5901 Executive Dr, Lansing, MI 48911

Phone: (517) 394-3400 **Domicile State:** NY **NAIC Code:** 60140

Data Date	Rating	RACR #1	RACR #2	Total Assets ($mil)	Capital ($mil)	Net Premium ($mil)	Net Income ($mil)
6-16	B	4.40	2.22	10,960.4	436.5	637.9	-15.3
6-15	B	4.66	2.57	10,261.3	428.5	833.9	17.6
2015	B	4.47	2.55	10,434.7	443.5	1,658.1	30.7
2014	B	4.46	2.55	9,608.5	409.8	1,766.8	32.7
2013	B	4.75	2.33	8,079.2	370.9	1,317.3	57.6
2012	B-	4.74	2.20	6,335.7	317.0	1,079.4	46.2
2011	B-	4.22	1.98	5,137.0	268.5	1,103.8	15.9

Adverse Trends in Operations

Decrease in premium volume from 2014 to 2015 (6%)
Increase in policy surrenders from 2012 to 2013 (31%)
Decrease in premium volume from 2011 to 2012 (2%)

JACKSON NATIONAL LIFE INSURANCE COMPANY | B | Good

Major Rating Factors: Good current capitalization (5.8 on a scale of 0 to 10) based on good risk adjusted capital (severe loss scenario), although results have slipped from the excellent range during the last year. Good overall results on stability tests (5.8). Strengths include good financial support from affiliation with Prudential plc, excellent operational trends, excellent risk adjusted capital for prior years and excellent risk diversification. Fair quality investment portfolio (4.7).

Other Rating Factors: Excellent profitability (7.0) despite modest operating losses during 2011. Excellent liquidity (7.9).

Principal Business: Individual annuities (83%), group retirement contracts (11%), individual life insurance (4%), and reinsurance (1%).

Principal Investments: NonCMO investment grade bonds (60%), CMOs and structured securities (15%), mortgages in good standing (11%), policy loans (7%), and misc. investments (5%).

Investments in Affiliates: 1%

Group Affiliation: Prudential plc

Licensed in: All states except NY, PR

Commenced Business: August 1961

Address: 5901 Executive Dr, Lansing, MI 48911

Phone: (517) 394-3400 **Domicile State:** MI **NAIC Code:** 65056

Data Date	Rating	RACR #1	RACR #2	Total Assets ($mil)	Capital ($mil)	Net Premium ($mil)	Net Income ($mil)
6-16	B	1.56	0.85	195,328	3,524.7	9,126.8	-1,595.7
6-15	B+	1.93	1.04	188,370	4,410.8	11,998.0	368.0
2015	B+	2.07	1.13	189,097	4,718.5	23,650.6	627.0
2014	B+	2.00	1.08	180,834	4,486.1	23,578.6	878.3
2013	B+	2.00	1.06	163,834	4,353.8	22,736.2	741.3
2012	B+	2.28	1.16	136,820	4,296.2	18,356.3	847.2
2011	B+	2.21	1.15	102,932	3,645.8	19,052.6	-591.1

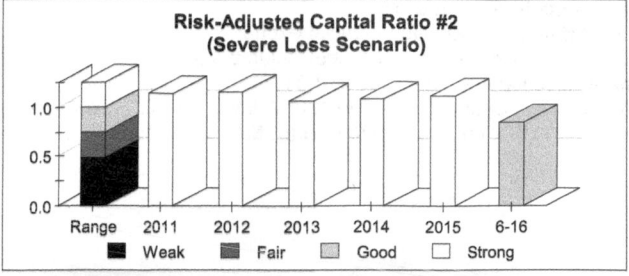

Risk-Adjusted Capital Ratio #2 (Severe Loss Scenario)

Range | 2011 | 2012 | 2013 | 2014 | 2015 | 6-16
■ Weak ■ Fair ▨ Good ▢ Strong

JAMESTOWN LIFE INSURANCE COMPANY | B | Good

Major Rating Factors: Good liquidity (6.8 on a scale of 0 to 10) with sufficient resources to handle a spike in claims. Fair overall results on stability tests (4.7) including fair financial strength of affiliated Genworth Financial. Fair profitability (3.7) with investment income below regulatory standards in relation to interest assumptions of reserves.

Other Rating Factors: Strong capitalization (10.0) based on excellent risk adjusted capital (severe loss scenario). High quality investment portfolio (7.3).

Principal Business: Reinsurance (100%).

Principal Investments: NonCMO investment grade bonds (54%) and CMOs and structured securities (44%).

Investments in Affiliates: None

Group Affiliation: Genworth Financial

Licensed in: VA

Commenced Business: December 1982

Address: 700 Main St, Lynchburg, VA 24504

Phone: (804) 845-0911 **Domicile State:** VA **NAIC Code:** 97144

Data Date	Rating	RACR #1	RACR #2	Total Assets ($mil)	Capital ($mil)	Net Premium ($mil)	Net Income ($mil)
6-16	B	7.15	5.53	124.6	66.9	0.9	31.7
6-15	B	3.78	2.65	146.3	35.0	2.4	-1.8
2015	B	3.87	2.81	148.3	36.0	4.9	-1.3
2014	B	3.97	2.89	145.0	36.7	5.1	3.1
2013	B	3.59	2.68	141.1	33.0	5.5	2.2
2012	B	3.69	3.07	141.2	34.0	5.6	3.2
2011	B	3.87	3.08	143.3	35.6	6.7	4.6

Genworth Financial Composite Group Rating: C+ Largest Group Members	Assets ($mil)	Rating
GENWORTH LIFE INS CO	38504	B-
GENWORTH LIFE ANNUITY INS CO	23411	B-
GENWORTH LIFE INS CO OF NEW YORK	8372	C+
GENWORTH MORTGAGE INS CORP	2627	C
RIVERMONT LIFE INS CO I	544	C

JEFFERSON NATIONAL LIFE INSURANCE COMPANY | C- | Fair

Major Rating Factors: Fair quality investment portfolio (4.7 on a scale of 0 to 10) with large holdings of BBB rated bonds in addition to junk bond exposure equal to 58% of capital. Fair profitability (3.5) with operating losses during the first six months of 2016. Fair overall results on stability tests (3.2) including negative cash flow from operations for 2015, fair risk adjusted capital in prior years.

Other Rating Factors: Good overall capitalization (5.2) based on mixed results -- excessive policy leverage mitigated by good risk adjusted capital (moderate loss scenario). Excellent liquidity (10.0).

Principal Business: Individual annuities (97%) and individual life insurance (2%).

Principal Investments: CMOs and structured securities (48%), nonCMO investment grade bonds (38%), noninv. grade bonds (4%), common & preferred stock (4%), and misc. investments (6%).

Investments in Affiliates: 1%

Group Affiliation: Jefferson National Financial Corp

Licensed in: All states except NY, PR

Commenced Business: February 1937

Address: 350 N St Paul St, Dallas, TX 75201

Phone: (502) 587-7626 **Domicile State:** TX **NAIC Code:** 64017

Data Date	Rating	RACR #1	RACR #2	Total Assets ($mil)	Capital ($mil)	Net Premium ($mil)	Net Income ($mil)
6-16	C-	1.15	0.61	4,281.9	38.3	320.8	0.0
6-15	C-	1.28	0.64	4,067.5	39.3	439.2	-0.4
2015	C-	1.18	0.63	4,058.0	38.3	789.0	-0.8
2014	C-	1.33	0.71	3,714.0	39.8	795.2	-2.9
2013	C-	1.55	0.78	3,053.5	39.4	740.9	-1.1
2012	D	1.69	0.85	2,259.0	41.5	420.3	-2.9
2011	D	2.08	1.05	1,862.0	47.2	275.6	-4.8

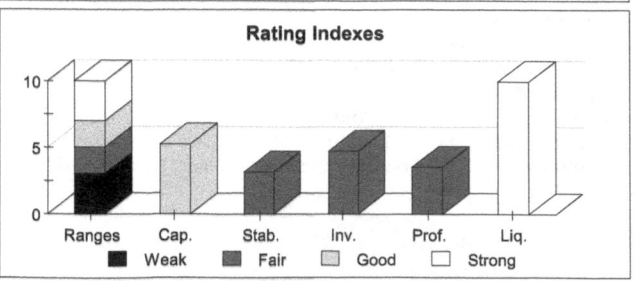

Rating Indexes

Ranges | Cap. | Stab. | Inv. | Prof. | Liq.
■ Weak ■ Fair ▨ Good ▢ Strong

JOHN HANCOCK LIFE & HEALTH INSURANCE COMPANY   B   Good

Major Rating Factors: Good quality investment portfolio (5.3 on a scale of 0 to 10) with minimal exposure to mortgages and minimal holdings in junk bonds. Good overall profitability (5.6) despite operating losses during the first six months of 2016. Good overall results on stability tests (5.4) good operational trends and excellent risk diversification.

Other Rating Factors: Strong capitalization (8.2) based on excellent risk adjusted capital (severe loss scenario). Excellent liquidity (9.0).

Principal Business: Group health insurance (70%), individual health insurance (26%), and reinsurance (4%).

Principal Investments: NonCMO investment grade bonds (60%), mortgages in good standing (7%), CMOs and structured securities (5%), real estate (4%), and misc. investments (17%).

Investments in Affiliates: 1%

Group Affiliation: Manulife Financial Group

Licensed in: All states, the District of Columbia and Puerto Rico

Commenced Business: October 1981

Address: 2711 Centerville Rd Ste 400, Wilmington, DE 19808

Phone: (617) 572-6000 **Domicile State:** MA **NAIC Code:** 93610

Data Date	Rating	RACR #1	RACR #2	Total Assets ($mil)	Capital ($mil)	Net Premium ($mil)	Net Income ($mil)
6-16	B	3.24	1.77	11,960.9	746.6	286.2	-32.8
6-15	B	3.59	1.99	10,811.8	762.1	282.7	21.6
2015	B	3.22	1.76	11,150.5	704.6	575.4	40.3
2014	B	3.85	2.14	10,700.1	745.8	576.0	2.8
2013	B	3.05	1.81	9,737.6	682.7	565.5	82.4
2012	B	3.50	1.94	10,039.5	664.9	562.3	12.0
2011	B	3.09	1.78	8,947.4	597.9	491.2	93.1

Adverse Trends in Operations

Decrease in capital during 2015 (6%)
Increase in policy surrenders from 2013 to 2014 (364%)
Increase in policy surrenders from 2012 to 2013 (30%)
Decrease in asset base during 2013 (3%)

JOHN HANCOCK LIFE INSURANCE COMPANY (USA)   B   Good

Major Rating Factors: Fair capitalization (4.6 on a scale of 0 to 10) based on fair risk adjusted capital (moderate loss scenario). Fair quality investment portfolio (3.2) with substantial holdings of BBB bonds in addition to moderate junk bond exposure. Exposure to mortgages is significant, but the mortgage default rate has been low. Fair profitability (3.5) with operating losses during the first six months of 2016.

Other Rating Factors: Fair overall results on stability tests (4.9) including fair risk adjusted capital in prior years. Excellent liquidity (7.4).

Principal Business: Group retirement contracts (62%), individual life insurance (22%), reinsurance (8%), individual health insurance (5%), and group health insurance (2%).

Principal Investments: NonCMO investment grade bonds (45%), mortgages in good standing (12%), real estate (8%), CMOs and structured securities (7%), and misc. investments (16%).

Investments in Affiliates: 5%

Group Affiliation: Manulife Financial Group

Licensed in: All states except NY

Commenced Business: January 1956

Address: 38500 Woodward Ave, Bloomfield Hills, MI 48304

Phone: (416) 926-0100 **Domicile State:** MI **NAIC Code:** 65838

Data Date	Rating	RACR #1	RACR #2	Total Assets ($mil)	Capital ($mil)	Net Premium ($mil)	Net Income ($mil)
6-16	B	0.95	0.64	238,670	6,087.5	6,174.4	-1,961.2
6-15	B	1.06	0.66	239,959	5,592.1	6,622.3	951.1
2015	B	0.87	0.58	227,843	5,443.8	16,323.5	694.1
2014	B	1.11	0.71	245,892	5,328.3	12,738.4	-2,464.4
2013	B	0.97	0.62	239,096	5,809.2	12,881.7	3,015.4
2012	B	1.04	0.65	227,142	5,794.1	7,546.5	221.1
2011	B	1.08	0.67	218,287	4,971.2	11,040.3	-2,887.5

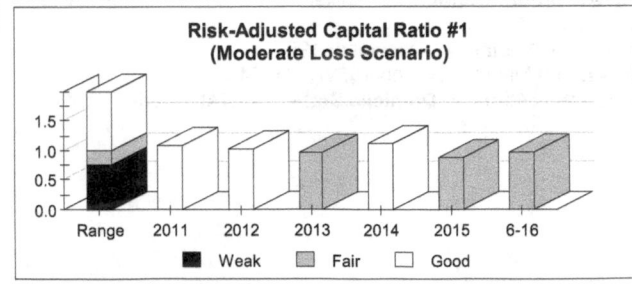

Risk-Adjusted Capital Ratio #1 (Moderate Loss Scenario)

JOHN HANCOCK LIFE INSURANCE COMPANY OF NEW YORK *   B+   Good

Major Rating Factors: Good overall results on stability tests (5.0 on a scale of 0 to 10). Stability strengths include excellent risk diversification. Good quality investment portfolio (6.2) despite significant exposure to mortgages . Mortgage default rate has been low. substantial holdings of BBB bonds in addition to minimal holdings in junk bonds. Fair profitability (4.2) with operating losses during the first six months of 2016.

Other Rating Factors: Strong capitalization (8.7) based on excellent risk adjusted capital (severe loss scenario). Excellent liquidity (7.1).

Principal Business: Reinsurance (51%), group retirement contracts (32%), individual life insurance (16%), and individual annuities (1%).

Principal Investments: NonCMO investment grade bonds (57%), mortgages in good standing (11%), CMOs and structured securities (7%), real estate (3%), and misc. investments (12%).

Investments in Affiliates: 1%

Group Affiliation: Manulife Financial Group

Licensed in: MI, NY

Commenced Business: July 1992

Address: 100 Summit Lake Dr 2nd Floor, Valhalla, NY 10595

Phone: (800) 344-1029 **Domicile State:** NY **NAIC Code:** 86375

Data Date	Rating	RACR #1	RACR #2	Total Assets ($mil)	Capital ($mil)	Net Premium ($mil)	Net Income ($mil)
6-16	B+	4.16	2.13	17,005.3	1,348.3	523.0	-182.0
6-15	A-	4.12	2.04	17,350.1	1,319.9	467.7	83.1
2015	B+	4.21	2.16	16,390.2	1,310.3	1,751.4	-18.2
2014	A-	4.27	2.08	17,475.5	1,215.7	1,041.4	-232.1
2013	A-	2.77	1.62	17,315.6	1,284.3	1,043.3	465.8
2012	A-	4.06	1.98	16,677.6	1,005.1	-504.9	69.1
2011	A-	3.19	1.54	17,559.8	890.4	1,177.9	-282.5

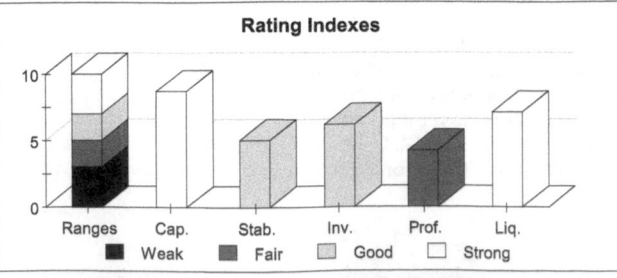

Rating Indexes

KANAWHA INSURANCE COMPANY — C+ Fair

Major Rating Factors: Fair quality investment portfolio (4.4 on a scale of 0 to 10). Fair overall results on stability tests (3.0) including weak results on operational trends. Weak profitability (1.5) with operating losses during the first six months of 2016.

Other Rating Factors: Strong capitalization (7.2) based on excellent risk adjusted capital (severe loss scenario). Excellent liquidity (8.3).

Principal Business: Individual health insurance (39%), group health insurance (38%), individual life insurance (16%), group life insurance (6%), and reinsurance (2%).

Principal Investments: NonCMO investment grade bonds (83%), CMOs and structured securities (10%), cash (5%), and noninv. grade bonds (2%).

Investments in Affiliates: None

Group Affiliation: Humana Inc

Licensed in: All states except PR

Commenced Business: December 1958

Address: 210 S White St, Lancaster, SC 29721

Phone: (803) 283-5300 **Domicile State:** SC **NAIC Code:** 65110

Data Date	Rating	RACR #1	RACR #2	Total Assets ($mil)	Capital ($mil)	Net Premium ($mil)	Net Income ($mil)
6-16	C+	2.00	1.12	1,788.6	103.7	119.3	-27.1
6-15	C	4.51	2.21	1,484.8	123.4	19.3	-1.7
2015	C	4.41	2.12	1,518.9	133.2	38.5	0.7
2014	C	3.63	1.94	1,458.8	122.1	169.5	-38.5
2013	C	2.68	1.67	1,623.0	155.1	228.1	-174.9
2012	C	4.02	2.54	1,456.8	255.5	252.2	-112.4
2011	C	3.22	2.03	1,288.9	190.5	206.5	-77.4

Adverse Trends in Operations

Decrease in premium volume from 2014 to 2015 (77%)
Decrease in capital during 2014 (21%)
Decrease in premium volume from 2013 to 2014 (26%)
Decrease in capital during 2013 (39%)
Increase in policy surrenders from 2011 to 2012 (728%)

KANSAS CITY LIFE INSURANCE COMPANY — B Good

Major Rating Factors: Good quality investment portfolio (5.0 on a scale of 0 to 10) despite significant exposure to mortgages . Mortgage default rate has been low. large holdings of BBB rated bonds in addition to small junk bond holdings. Good overall profitability (5.6). Good liquidity (5.7).

Other Rating Factors: Good overall results on stability tests (6.3) excellent operational trends and excellent risk diversification. Strong capitalization (7.1) based on excellent risk adjusted capital (severe loss scenario).

Principal Business: Individual life insurance (39%), individual annuities (30%), group health insurance (16%), reinsurance (10%), and group life insurance (4%).

Principal Investments: NonCMO investment grade bonds (63%), mortgages in good standing (18%), CMOs and structured securities (7%), real estate (5%), and misc. investments (7%).

Investments in Affiliates: 2%

Group Affiliation: Kansas City Life Group

Licensed in: All states except NY, VT, PR

Commenced Business: May 1895

Address: 3520 Broadway, Kansas City, MO 64111-2565

Phone: (816) 753-7000 **Domicile State:** MO **NAIC Code:** 65129

Data Date	Rating	RACR #1	RACR #2	Total Assets ($mil)	Capital ($mil)	Net Premium ($mil)	Net Income ($mil)
6-16	B	1.86	1.09	3,337.0	299.4	140.8	8.3
6-15	B	1.46	0.92	3,401.2	338.3	146.8	12.6
2015	B	1.86	1.09	3,324.3	297.6	282.8	29.1
2014	B	1.51	0.94	3,402.1	338.4	303.4	26.7
2013	B	1.74	1.08	3,386.4	330.6	329.4	0.3
2012	B	2.05	1.26	3,317.6	327.4	277.0	46.5
2011	B	2.00	1.18	3,224.4	307.2	265.7	22.6

Rating Indexes

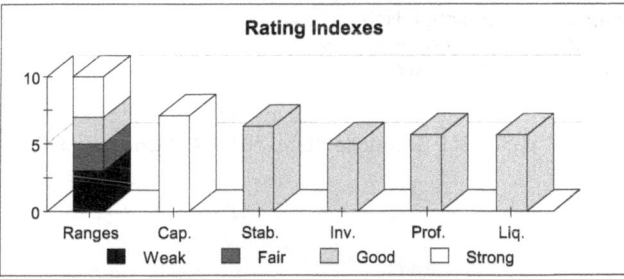

Ranges | Cap. | Stab. | Inv. | Prof. | Liq.
■ Weak ▨ Fair ▨ Good ☐ Strong

LAFAYETTE LIFE INSURANCE COMPANY — B Good

Major Rating Factors: Good overall results on stability tests (5.6 on a scale of 0 to 10). Stability strengths include excellent operational trends and excellent risk diversification. Good capitalization (6.2) based on good risk adjusted capital (moderate loss scenario). Moreover, capital levels have been consistent over the last five years. Good profitability (5.0).

Other Rating Factors: Good liquidity (5.1). Fair quality investment portfolio (4.8).

Principal Business: Individual life insurance (75%), individual annuities (22%), and group retirement contracts (3%).

Principal Investments: NonCMO investment grade bonds (54%), CMOs and structured securities (17%), policy loans (10%), mortgages in good standing (7%), and misc. investments (10%).

Investments in Affiliates: 1%

Group Affiliation: Western & Southern Group

Licensed in: All states except AK, NY, PR

Commenced Business: December 1905

Address: 400 Broadway, Cincinnati, OH 45202

Phone: (513) 362-4900 **Domicile State:** OH **NAIC Code:** 65242

Data Date	Rating	RACR #1	RACR #2	Total Assets ($mil)	Capital ($mil)	Net Premium ($mil)	Net Income ($mil)
6-16	B	1.81	0.89	4,702.8	266.6	292.2	5.0
6-15	B	1.66	0.84	4,250.5	210.1	262.1	10.8
2015	B	1.85	0.93	4,548.1	261.4	532.9	32.9
2014	B	1.67	0.85	4,067.8	204.4	536.8	8.9
2013	B	1.70	0.88	3,836.5	193.7	593.3	-7.8
2012	B	1.76	0.91	3,322.1	160.7	561.3	16.3
2011	B	1.77	0.90	2,996.1	152.3	612.9	5.7

Adverse Trends in Operations

Decrease in premium volume from 2013 to 2014 (10%)
Increase in policy surrenders from 2013 to 2014 (26%)
Decrease in premium volume from 2011 to 2012 (8%)

LIBERTY BANKERS LIFE INSURANCE COMPANY   D+   Weak

Major Rating Factors: Weak overall results on stability tests (2.7 on a scale of 0 to 10). Fair quality investment portfolio (3.7) with significant exposure to mortgages . Mortgage default rate has been low. Good current capitalization (5.8) based on good risk adjusted capital (severe loss scenario) reflecting some improvement over results in 2011.

Other Rating Factors: Good liquidity (6.9). Excellent profitability (7.2) despite operating losses during the first six months of 2016.

Principal Business: Individual annuities (93%) and individual life insurance (7%).

Principal Investments: NonCMO investment grade bonds (50%), mortgages in good standing (22%), common & preferred stock (9%), cash (4%), and misc. investments (13%).

Investments in Affiliates: 7%

Group Affiliation: Liberty Life Group Trust

Licensed in: All states except AL, AK, CT, ME, MN, NH, NJ, NY, PR

Commenced Business: February 1958

Address: 1800 Valley View Lane Ste 300, Dallas, TX 75234

Phone: (800) 745-4927 **Domicile State:** OK **NAIC Code:** 68543

Data Date	Rating	RACR #1	RACR #2	Total Assets ($mil)	Capital ($mil)	Net Premium ($mil)	Net Income ($mil)
6-16	D+	1.23	0.85	1,433.2	195.7	120.2	-1.4
6-15	D+	1.36	0.92	1,264.3	197.5	173.8	4.5
2015	D+	1.30	0.91	1,356.1	197.9	326.4	9.0
2014	D+	1.47	1.01	1,141.4	195.5	234.5	11.5
2013	D+	1.23	0.84	1,035.3	168.0	205.5	10.3
2012	D+	1.11	0.79	952.0	160.5	-259.6	15.2
2011	D+	0.77	0.54	1,302.0	130.5	242.8	2.6

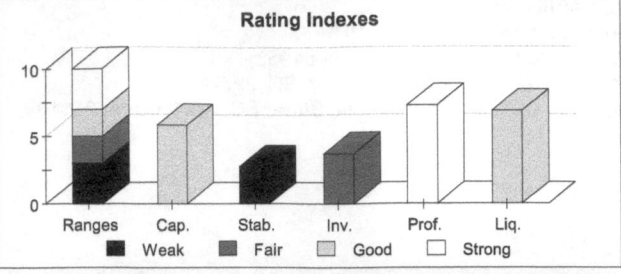

Rating Indexes

LIBERTY LIFE ASSURANCE COMPANY OF BOSTON   B   Good

Major Rating Factors: Good overall results on stability tests (6.2 on a scale of 0 to 10). Stability strengths include excellent operational trends and excellent risk diversification. Good quality investment portfolio (6.0) despite mixed results such as: large holdings of BBB rated bonds but moderate junk bond exposure. Good overall profitability (6.4).

Other Rating Factors: Good liquidity (6.4). Strong capitalization (7.0) based on excellent risk adjusted capital (severe loss scenario).

Principal Business: Group health insurance (33%), individual annuities (26%), individual life insurance (26%), and group life insurance (15%).

Principal Investments: NonCMO investment grade bonds (77%), CMOs and structured securities (9%), mortgages in good standing (6%), noninv. grade bonds (3%), and policy loans (1%).

Investments in Affiliates: None

Group Affiliation: Liberty Mutual Group

Licensed in: All states except PR

Commenced Business: January 1964

Address: 175 Berkeley St, Boston, MA 02117

Phone: (617) 357-9500 **Domicile State:** NH **NAIC Code:** 65315

Data Date	Rating	RACR #1	RACR #2	Total Assets ($mil)	Capital ($mil)	Net Premium ($mil)	Net Income ($mil)
6-16	B	1.78	1.02	16,655.8	987.6	1,371.0	25.1
6-15	B	1.89	1.08	15,369.6	930.9	1,261.6	30.6
2015	B	1.77	1.04	16,054.1	966.4	2,501.1	69.9
2014	B	1.88	1.09	14,628.8	902.4	2,410.6	37.0
2013	B	1.83	1.07	13,115.1	716.9	2,095.9	39.2
2012	B	1.63	1.03	12,403.2	688.6	1,807.1	31.3
2011	B	1.65	1.04	15,165.1	660.6	1,641.5	53.4

Adverse Trends in Operations

Increase in policy surrenders from 2012 to 2013 (38%)
Decrease in asset base during 2012 (18%)

LIBERTY NATIONAL LIFE INSURANCE COMPANY   B   Good

Major Rating Factors: Good overall profitability (5.1 on a scale of 0 to 10) although investment income, in comparison to reserve requirements, is below regulatory standards. Fair overall results on stability tests (4.6) including excessive premium growth. Fair quality investment portfolio (4.8).

Other Rating Factors: Weak liquidity (2.6). Strong capitalization (7.1) based on excellent risk adjusted capital (severe loss scenario).

Principal Business: Individual life insurance (51%), reinsurance (21%), individual health insurance (18%), group life insurance (7%), and individual annuities (2%).

Principal Investments: NonCMO investment grade bonds (73%), noninv. grade bonds (7%), common & preferred stock (5%), CMOs and structured securities (4%), and policy loans (4%).

Investments in Affiliates: 9%

Group Affiliation: Torchmark Corp

Licensed in: All states except NY, PR

Commenced Business: July 1929

Address: 10306 Regency Parkway Dr, Omaha, NE 68114

Phone: (205) 325-4918 **Domicile State:** NE **NAIC Code:** 65331

Data Date	Rating	RACR #1	RACR #2	Total Assets ($mil)	Capital ($mil)	Net Premium ($mil)	Net Income ($mil)
6-16	B	2.00	1.04	7,686.0	560.4	376.6	62.2
6-15	B	2.16	1.14	7,514.8	571.7	299.5	68.3
2015	B	1.90	1.00	7,559.6	525.8	626.5	73.9
2014	B	2.13	1.13	7,419.6	578.5	575.3	164.7
2013	B	2.16	1.13	7,257.9	589.7	565.9	151.1
2012	B	2.16	1.12	7,102.6	592.2	584.2	174.3
2011	B	2.26	1.17	6,802.8	622.4	538.0	175.9

Investment Income Compared to Needs of Reserves

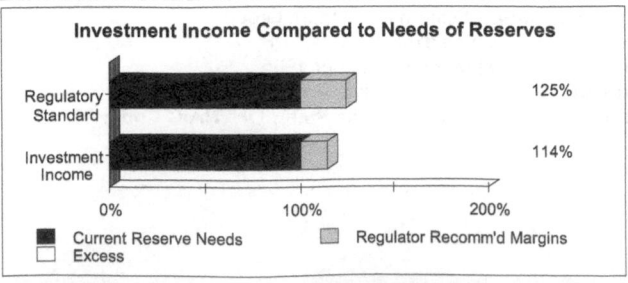

LIFE INSURANCE COMPANY OF ALABAMA *   A-   Excellent

Major Rating Factors: Good quality investment portfolio (5.6 on a scale of 0 to 10) despite mixed results such as: no exposure to mortgages and large holdings of BBB rated bonds but small junk bond holdings. Good liquidity (6.5) with sufficient resources to handle a spike in claims. Good overall results on stability tests (6.3) excellent operational trends and good risk diversification.

Other Rating Factors: Strong capitalization (8.5) based on excellent risk adjusted capital (severe loss scenario). Excellent profitability (9.0).

Principal Business: Individual health insurance (74%), individual life insurance (19%), and group health insurance (7%).

Principal Investments: NonCMO investment grade bonds (83%), noninv. grade bonds (8%), common & preferred stock (4%), policy loans (3%), and real estate (1%).

Investments in Affiliates: None

Group Affiliation: None

Licensed in: AL, AR, FL, GA, KY, LA, MS, NC, OK, SC, TN

Commenced Business: August 1952

Address: 302 Broad St, Gadsden, AL 35901

Phone: (205) 543-2022 **Domicile State:** AL **NAIC Code:** 65412

Data Date	Rating	RACR #1	RACR #2	Total Assets ($mil)	Capital ($mil)	Net Premium ($mil)	Net Income ($mil)
6-16	A-	3.32	1.98	118.6	39.6	18.1	1.4
6-15	A-	3.25	2.10	114.2	37.4	18.4	1.5
2015	A-	3.37	2.10	116.6	38.7	36.3	2.8
2014	A-	3.33	2.22	113.5	37.3	37.4	7.0
2013	A-	2.88	1.95	108.0	33.0	37.2	2.7
2012	A-	2.52	1.74	102.6	29.4	38.0	3.0
2011	A-	2.03	1.43	94.9	25.0	39.2	3.1

Adverse Trends in Operations

Decrease in premium volume from 2014 to 2015 (3%)
Decrease in premium volume from 2012 to 2013 (2%)
Decrease in premium volume from 2011 to 2012 (3%)

LIFE INSURANCE COMPANY OF BOSTON & NEW YORK *   A-   Excellent

Major Rating Factors: Good overall profitability (6.5 on a scale of 0 to 10). Excellent expense controls. Good liquidity (6.4) with sufficient resources to handle a spike in claims as well as a significant increase in policy surrenders. Excellent overall results on stability tests (7.0). Strengths that enhance stability include excellent operational trends and good risk diversification.

Other Rating Factors: Strong capitalization (9.1) based on excellent risk adjusted capital (severe loss scenario). High quality investment portfolio (7.6).

Principal Business: Individual life insurance (54%), group health insurance (24%), and individual health insurance (22%).

Principal Investments: NonCMO investment grade bonds (66%), policy loans (22%), CMOs and structured securities (8%), noninv. grade bonds (2%), and misc. investments (2%).

Investments in Affiliates: None

Group Affiliation: Boston Mutual Group

Licensed in: NY

Commenced Business: March 1990

Address: 277 North Ave Suite 200, New Rochelle, NY 10801

Phone: (212) 684-2000 **Domicile State:** NY **NAIC Code:** 78140

Data Date	Rating	RACR #1	RACR #2	Total Assets ($mil)	Capital ($mil)	Net Premium ($mil)	Net Income ($mil)
6-16	A-	3.08	2.38	135.2	28.0	10.6	0.9
6-15	A-	2.76	2.15	127.7	25.0	10.7	1.3
2015	A-	2.91	2.40	130.4	26.6	21.5	3.3
2014	A-	2.64	2.07	124.1	23.9	24.8	1.8
2013	A-	2.42	2.00	117.3	21.8	23.9	-1.4
2012	A-	2.06	1.85	103.0	18.3	18.8	1.4
2011	A-	1.99	1.79	93.7	17.2	16.7	1.8

Adverse Trends in Operations

Decrease in premium volume from 2014 to 2015 (13%)
Increase in policy surrenders from 2013 to 2014 (41%)

LIFE INSURANCE COMPANY OF NORTH AMERICA   B   Good

Major Rating Factors: Good overall results on stability tests (5.8 on a scale of 0 to 10). Stability strengths include good operational trends and excellent risk diversification. Good quality investment portfolio (5.4) despite large holdings of BBB rated bonds in addition to moderate junk bond exposure. Exposure to mortgages is significant, but the mortgage default rate has been low. Good liquidity (6.6).

Other Rating Factors: Strong capitalization (7.7) based on excellent risk adjusted capital (severe loss scenario). Excellent profitability (7.2) despite operating losses during the first six months of 2016.

Principal Business: Group health insurance (53%), group life insurance (41%), and reinsurance (6%).

Principal Investments: NonCMO investment grade bonds (66%), mortgages in good standing (14%), noninv. grade bonds (9%), CMOs and structured securities (3%), and misc. investments (8%).

Investments in Affiliates: 6%

Group Affiliation: CIGNA Corp

Licensed in: All states, the District of Columbia and Puerto Rico

Commenced Business: September 1957

Address: 1601 Chestnut ST,2 Liberty Pl, Philadelphia, PA 19192-2235

Phone: (860) 726-7234 **Domicile State:** PA **NAIC Code:** 65498

Data Date	Rating	RACR #1	RACR #2	Total Assets ($mil)	Capital ($mil)	Net Premium ($mil)	Net Income ($mil)
6-16	B	2.26	1.45	8,452.1	1,479.5	1,880.7	-23.7
6-15	B	2.47	1.57	7,878.5	1,397.0	1,723.1	91.7
2015	B	2.34	1.51	8,141.6	1,495.3	3,674.5	236.6
2014	B	2.42	1.54	7,562.6	1,346.0	3,192.3	287.8
2013	B	2.20	1.39	6,711.9	1,103.5	3,232.7	173.3
2012	B	2.10	1.34	6,089.4	884.4	2,705.9	198.7
2011	B-	2.28	1.47	5,628.9	872.4	2,474.3	202.0

Adverse Trends in Operations

Change in premium mix from 2014 to 2015 (5.6%)
Increase in policy surrenders from 2014 to 2015 (994%)
Decrease in premium volume from 2013 to 2014 (1%)
Change in premium mix from 2013 to 2014 (6%)
Increase in policy surrenders from 2011 to 2012 (72%)

LIFE INSURANCE COMPANY OF THE SOUTHWEST — B — Good

Major Rating Factors: Good capitalization (6.1 on a scale of 0 to 10) based on good risk adjusted capital (moderate loss scenario). Moreover, capital levels have been consistent over the last five years. Good overall results on stability tests (5.3). Stability strengths include excellent operational trends and excellent risk diversification. Fair quality investment portfolio (4.2).

Other Rating Factors: Fair liquidity (3.3). Excellent profitability (8.4).

Principal Business: Individual annuities (58%), individual life insurance (37%), and group retirement contracts (5%).

Principal Investments: NonCMO investment grade bonds (52%), CMOs and structured securities (21%), mortgages in good standing (15%), noninv. grade bonds (6%), and policy loans (2%).

Investments in Affiliates: None

Group Affiliation: National Life Group

Licensed in: All states except NY, PR

Commenced Business: January 1956

Address: 1300 W Mockingbird Lane, Dallas, TX 75247

Phone: (800) 579-2878 **Domicile State:** TX **NAIC Code:** 65528

Data Date	Rating	RACR #1	RACR #2	Total Assets ($mil)	Capital ($mil)	Net Premium ($mil)	Net Income ($mil)
6-16	B	1.75	0.86	15,767.3	914.8	891.2	87.7
6-15	B	1.83	0.90	13,874.6	793.8	768.2	36.5
2015	B	1.70	0.85	14,681.0	840.9	1,583.6	35.9
2014	B	1.87	0.93	13,382.0	779.0	1,577.7	105.6
2013	B	2.10	1.03	12,354.9	720.2	1,329.9	142.5
2012	B	1.67	0.83	10,952.0	625.2	1,360.6	98.7
2011	B	1.52	0.76	9,913.2	567.0	1,200.8	89.3

Risk-Adjusted Capital Ratio #1
(Moderate Loss Scenario)

■ Weak　▧ Fair　□ Good

LIFECARE ASSURANCE COMPANY — B- — Good

Major Rating Factors: Good capitalization (6.2 on a scale of 0 to 10) based on good risk adjusted capital (severe loss scenario). Capital levels have been relatively consistent over the last five years. Good overall profitability (5.2) despite operating losses during the first six months of 2016. Good overall results on stability tests (5.2) excellent operational trends and excellent risk diversification.

Other Rating Factors: Fair quality investment portfolio (3.9). Excellent liquidity (9.3).

Principal Business: Reinsurance (100%).

Principal Investments: NonCMO investment grade bonds (59%), CMOs and structured securities (36%), and noninv. grade bonds (3%).

Investments in Affiliates: None

Group Affiliation: 21st Century Life & Health Co Inc

Licensed in: All states except CT, FL, MA, MN, NH, NY, RI, SC, WY, PR

Commenced Business: July 1980

Address: 8601 N Scottsdale Rd Ste 300, Scottsdale, AZ 85253

Phone: (818) 887-4436 **Domicile State:** AZ **NAIC Code:** 91898

Data Date	Rating	RACR #1	RACR #2	Total Assets ($mil)	Capital ($mil)	Net Premium ($mil)	Net Income ($mil)
6-16	B-	1.69	0.90	2,206.6	103.1	117.3	-0.3
6-15	B-	1.68	0.90	2,030.4	98.3	116.5	1.2
2015	B-	1.79	0.96	2,113.1	107.2	231.6	10.0
2014	B-	1.83	0.99	1,945.6	107.1	230.3	21.0
2013	B-	1.71	0.94	1,780.0	95.7	233.9	17.7
2012	B-	1.51	0.86	1,596.7	80.8	239.7	15.4
2011	B-	1.43	0.83	1,400.7	73.2	237.5	11.7

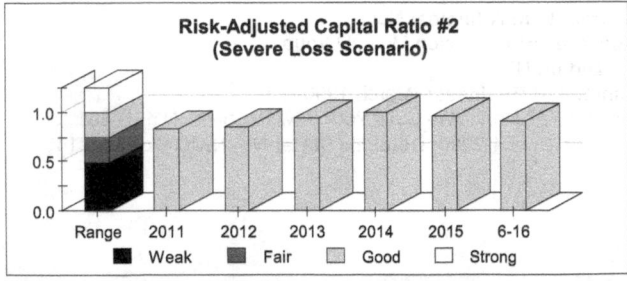

Risk-Adjusted Capital Ratio #2
(Severe Loss Scenario)

■ Weak　▨ Fair　▥ Good　□ Strong

LIFEMAP ASSURANCE COMPANY — B- — Good

Major Rating Factors: Good liquidity (6.4 on a scale of 0 to 10) with sufficient resources to handle a spike in claims. Good overall results on stability tests (5.2) despite negative cash flow from operations for 2015. Strengths include good financial support from affiliation with Regence Group, good operational trends and good risk diversification. Fair quality investment portfolio (4.9).

Other Rating Factors: Weak profitability (2.0) with operating losses during the first six months of 2016. Strong capitalization (7.1) based on excellent risk adjusted capital (severe loss scenario).

Principal Business: Group health insurance (66%), group life insurance (26%), and individual health insurance (7%).

Principal Investments: NonCMO investment grade bonds (42%), CMOs and structured securities (33%), common & preferred stock (21%), noninv. grade bonds (2%), and cash (2%).

Investments in Affiliates: 2%

Group Affiliation: Regence Group

Licensed in: AK, AZ, CA, ID, MT, OR, RI, UT, WA, WY

Commenced Business: July 1966

Address: 100 SW Market St, Portland, OR 97201

Phone: (503) 225-6048 **Domicile State:** OR **NAIC Code:** 97985

Data Date	Rating	RACR #1	RACR #2	Total Assets ($mil)	Capital ($mil)	Net Premium ($mil)	Net Income ($mil)
6-16	B-	1.43	1.06	80.3	36.6	39.9	-2.3
6-15	B	1.67	1.21	82.7	40.3	36.4	-0.9
2015	B-	1.55	1.14	83.1	39.4	76.4	-1.4
2014	B	1.80	1.32	85.1	43.1	68.9	-0.1
2013	B	1.96	1.41	89.6	45.3	64.1	-0.5
2012	B+	2.17	1.56	86.1	44.9	55.0	-1.8
2011	B+	2.38	1.71	89.5	46.8	49.5	-0.1

Regence Group Composite Group Rating: B Largest Group Members	Assets ($mil)	Rating
REGENCE BLUESHIELD	1612	B
REGENCE BL CROSS BL SHIELD OREGON	1046	B+
REGENCE BLUE CROSS BLUE SHIELD OF UT	530	B-
REGENCE BLUESHIELD OF IDAHO INC	238	C+
ASURIS NORTHWEST HEALTH	92	C+

LIFESECURE INSURANCE COMPANY

D   Weak

Major Rating Factors: Weak profitability (1.3 on a scale of 0 to 10) with operating losses during the first six months of 2016. Weak overall results on stability tests (2.0). Strong current capitalization (7.4) based on excellent risk adjusted capital (severe loss scenario) reflecting improvement over results in 2015.

Other Rating Factors: High quality investment portfolio (7.1). Excellent liquidity (8.6).

Principal Business: Individual health insurance (50%), reinsurance (38%), individual life insurance (11%), and individual annuities (1%).

Principal Investments: NonCMO investment grade bonds (84%) and CMOs and structured securities (16%).

Investments in Affiliates: None

Group Affiliation: Blue Cross Blue Shield of Michigan

Licensed in: All states except ME, MA, NH, NY, PR

Commenced Business: July 1954

Address: 1005 Congress Ave, Ste 825, Austin, TX 78701

Phone: (847) 402-5000   **Domicile State:** MI   **NAIC Code:** 77720

Data Date	Rating	RACR #1	RACR #2	Total Assets ($mil)	Capital ($mil)	Net Premium ($mil)	Net Income ($mil)
6-16	D	1.93	1.25	292.9	28.6	29.4	-5.2
6-15	D	1.43	0.94	238.2	17.4	24.5	-2.7
2015	D	1.32	0.85	262.3	18.0	50.4	-10.3
2014	D-	1.76	1.16	226.9	20.4	42.5	-13.0
2013	D-	2.10	1.34	189.7	20.2	33.4	-3.9
2012	E+	2.50	1.79	174.9	23.8	28.2	-6.2
2011	E+	2.78	2.11	148.3	26.0	25.2	-3.1

Investment Income Compared to Needs of Reserves

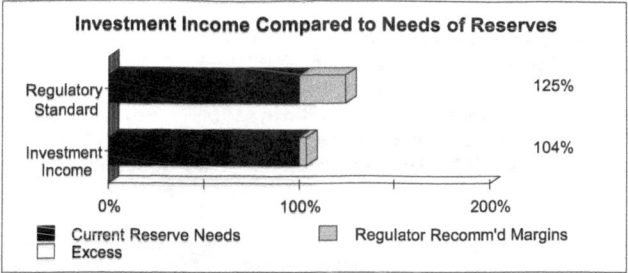

Regulatory Standard — 125%
Investment Income — 104%

■ Current Reserve Needs   ▨ Regulator Recomm'd Margins
□ Excess

LIFEWISE ASSURANCE COMPANY *

A   Excellent

Major Rating Factors: Good liquidity (6.9 on a scale of 0 to 10) with sufficient resources to handle a spike in claims. Excellent overall results on stability tests (7.0). Strengths that enhance stability include excellent operational trends and excellent risk diversification. Strong capitalization (10.0) based on excellent risk adjusted capital (severe loss scenario). Furthermore, this high level of risk adjusted capital has been consistently maintained over the last five years.

Other Rating Factors: High quality investment portfolio (7.8). Excellent profitability (9.3).

Principal Business: Group health insurance (100%).

Principal Investments: NonCMO investment grade bonds (51%), CMOs and structured securities (43%), cash (4%), and noninv. grade bonds (1%).

Investments in Affiliates: None

Group Affiliation: PREMERA

Licensed in: AK, AZ, CA, CO, ID, KS, MD, MT, NV, NM, ND, OK, OR, TX, UT, WA, WY

Commenced Business: November 1981

Address: 7007 220th SW, Mountlake Terrace, WA 98043

Phone: (206) 670-4584   **Domicile State:** WA   **NAIC Code:** 94188

Data Date	Rating	RACR #1	RACR #2	Total Assets ($mil)	Capital ($mil)	Net Premium ($mil)	Net Income ($mil)
6-16	A	6.44	4.63	143.3	100.2	60.9	3.7
6-15	A	7.40	5.55	134.7	94.1	51.9	4.2
2015	A	6.80	5.11	133.5	96.5	105.7	6.7
2014	A	7.38	5.56	127.0	89.9	90.9	9.3
2013	A	6.19	4.70	119.4	81.1	85.4	9.5
2012	A	5.90	4.42	118.4	71.6	84.3	12.8
2011	A	2.94	2.22	94.5	57.8	89.7	4.3

Adverse Trends in Operations

Decrease in premium volume from 2011 to 2012 (6%)

LINCOLN BENEFIT LIFE COMPANY

C+   Fair

Major Rating Factors: Fair quality investment portfolio (3.8 on a scale of 0 to 10) with large holdings of BBB rated bonds in addition to junk bond exposure equal to 80% of capital. Exposure to mortgages is significant, but the mortgage default rate has been low. Fair profitability (4.6) with investment income below regulatory standards in relation to interest assumptions of reserves. Fair overall results on stability tests (4.4) including negative cash flow from operations for 2015, fair risk adjusted capital in prior years.

Other Rating Factors: Good capitalization (5.7) based on good risk adjusted capital (moderate loss scenario). Good liquidity (6.2).

Principal Business: Individual life insurance (89%), individual annuities (5%), individual health insurance (4%), and group life insurance (2%).

Principal Investments: NonCMO investment grade bonds (65%), mortgages in good standing (15%), CMOs and structured securities (13%), noninv. grade bonds (4%), and policy loans (1%).

Investments in Affiliates: 1%

Group Affiliation: Resolution Life Holdings Inc

Licensed in: All states except NY, PR

Commenced Business: October 1938

Address: 206 S 13th St, Suite 200, Lincoln, NE 68508

Phone: (800) 525-9287   **Domicile State:** NE   **NAIC Code:** 65595

Data Date	Rating	RACR #1	RACR #2	Total Assets ($mil)	Capital ($mil)	Net Premium ($mil)	Net Income ($mil)
6-16	C+	1.48	0.74	11,496.8	527.5	57.6	21.8
6-15	B	1.71	0.85	12,228.1	670.6	49.2	72.4
2015	C+	1.34	0.72	11,701.1	555.2	82.2	74.1
2014	B	1.53	0.84	12,651.3	719.0	7,038.0	226.0
2013	B+	3.75	1.87	2,070.9	332.5	0.0	7.7
2012	B+	3.57	1.78	2,008.9	323.9	0.0	8.5
2011	B+	3.47	1.73	2,052.4	319.5	0.0	8.6

Rating Indexes

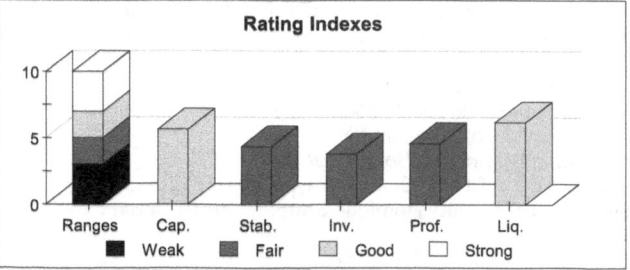

Ranges   Cap.   Stab.   Inv.   Prof.   Liq.

■ Weak   ▨ Fair   ▨ Good   □ Strong

LINCOLN HERITAGE LIFE INSURANCE COMPANY | B- | Good

Major Rating Factors: Good liquidity (6.0 on a scale of 0 to 10) with sufficient resources to handle a spike in claims as well as a significant increase in policy surrenders. Good overall results on stability tests (5.1). Stability strengths include excellent operational trends and excellent risk diversification. Weak profitability (2.7) with investment income below regulatory standards in relation to interest assumptions of reserves.

Other Rating Factors: Strong capitalization (8.4) based on excellent risk adjusted capital (severe loss scenario). High quality investment portfolio (7.2).

Principal Business: Individual life insurance (93%), reinsurance (3%), group life insurance (2%), and individual health insurance (1%).

Principal Investments: NonCMO investment grade bonds (44%), CMOs and structured securities (40%), policy loans (6%), cash (6%), and misc. investments (3%).

Investments in Affiliates: None

Group Affiliation: Londen Ins Group

Licensed in: All states except NY, PR

Commenced Business: October 1963

Address: Government Ctr 200 Pleasant St, Malden, MA 02148

Phone: (602) 957-1650 **Domicile State:** IL **NAIC Code:** 65927

Data Date	Rating	RACR #1	RACR #2	Total Assets ($mil)	Capital ($mil)	Net Premium ($mil)	Net Income ($mil)
6-16	B-	3.56	1.91	901.6	112.9	160.6	2.0
6-15	B-	3.92	2.14	840.1	112.2	154.3	3.3
2015	B-	3.52	1.91	873.4	110.0	311.4	3.1
2014	B-	3.78	2.06	805.2	109.0	314.9	4.7
2013	B-	3.71	1.96	740.8	101.2	259.8	3.9
2012	B	4.15	2.26	692.8	106.0	204.3	4.2
2011	B	4.01	2.15	664.8	108.3	189.0	9.6

Adverse Trends in Operations

Decrease in premium volume from 2014 to 2015 (1%)
Decrease in capital during 2013 (5%)
Decrease in capital during 2012 (2%)

LINCOLN LIFE & ANNUITY COMPANY OF NEW YORK | B | Good

Major Rating Factors: Good quality investment portfolio (5.9 on a scale of 0 to 10) despite mixed results such as: large holdings of BBB rated bonds but moderate junk bond exposure. Good liquidity (5.1) with sufficient resources to cover a large increase in policy surrenders. Good overall results on stability tests (5.5) good operational trends and excellent risk diversification.

Other Rating Factors: Fair profitability (3.9). Strong capitalization (8.6) based on excellent risk adjusted capital (severe loss scenario).

Principal Business: Individual annuities (47%), individual life insurance (22%), group retirement contracts (14%), reinsurance (11%), and other lines (6%).

Principal Investments: NonCMO investment grade bonds (77%), mortgages in good standing (7%), CMOs and structured securities (7%), noninv. grade bonds (5%), and policy loans (4%).

Investments in Affiliates: None

Group Affiliation: Lincoln National Corp

Licensed in: All states except PR

Commenced Business: December 1897

Address: 100 Madison St Suite 1860, Syracuse, NY 13202-2802

Phone: (336) 691-3000 **Domicile State:** NY **NAIC Code:** 62057

Data Date	Rating	RACR #1	RACR #2	Total Assets ($mil)	Capital ($mil)	Net Premium ($mil)	Net Income ($mil)
6-16	B	4.00	2.04	13,414.4	1,114.3	-1,181.3	181.4
6-15	B	2.61	1.35	13,124.7	695.4	607.0	41.3
2015	B	1.97	1.02	13,176.6	512.2	1,263.5	-55.2
2014	B	2.49	1.29	12,840.2	652.5	1,291.4	39.4
2013	B-	2.76	1.43	12,046.4	713.0	1,229.4	161.2
2012	C	2.54	1.29	10,925.5	648.4	1,034.0	73.5
2011	C	2.34	1.18	10,160.0	586.1	959.3	-121.0

Adverse Trends in Operations

Decrease in capital during 2015 (22%)
Decrease in premium volume from 2014 to 2015 (2%)
Decrease in capital during 2014 (8%)

LINCOLN NATIONAL LIFE INSURANCE COMPANY | B | Good

Major Rating Factors: Good quality investment portfolio (6.0 on a scale of 0 to 10) despite mixed results such as: large holdings of BBB rated bonds but moderate junk bond exposure. Good overall profitability (6.8). Good liquidity (6.7) with sufficient resources to handle a spike in claims as well as a significant increase in policy surrenders.

Other Rating Factors: Good overall results on stability tests (5.8) excellent operational trends, good risk adjusted capital for prior years and excellent risk diversification. Strong capitalization (7.0) based on excellent risk adjusted capital (severe loss scenario).

Principal Business: Individual annuities (51%), individual life insurance (23%), group retirement contracts (12%), group health insurance (6%), and other lines (8%).

Principal Investments: NonCMO investment grade bonds (73%), mortgages in good standing (9%), CMOs and structured securities (6%), noninv. grade bonds (3%), and misc. investments (8%).

Investments in Affiliates: 4%

Group Affiliation: Lincoln National Corp

Licensed in: All states except NY

Commenced Business: September 1905

Address: 1300 S Clinton St, Fort Wayne, IN 46802

Phone: (260) 455-2000 **Domicile State:** IN **NAIC Code:** 65676

Data Date	Rating	RACR #1	RACR #2	Total Assets ($mil)	Capital ($mil)	Net Premium ($mil)	Net Income ($mil)
6-16	B	1.56	1.01	219,393	7,403.2	8,335.4	448.8
6-15	B	1.48	0.99	215,889	7,104.8	9,590.9	453.9
2015	B	1.55	1.01	213,891	7,117.1	19,605.3	1,056.9
2014	B	1.57	1.05	213,625	7,526.3	22,068.4	1,520.3
2013	B-	1.40	0.93	200,018	6,836.1	21,752.4	577.6
2012	B-	1.40	0.93	180,025	6,399.6	18,518.2	602.8
2011	B-	1.43	0.97	165,222	6,754.8	18,326.9	207.0

Rating Indexes

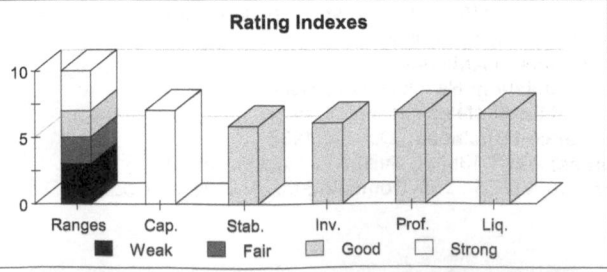

LOCOMOTIVE ENGINEERS & CONDUCTORS MUTUAL PROTECT   B+   Good

Major Rating Factors: Good quality investment portfolio (5.8 on a scale of 0 to 10) with no exposure to mortgages and minimal holdings in junk bonds. Good overall results on stability tests (5.8). Stability strengths include excellent operational trends and good risk diversification. Strong capitalization (10.0) based on excellent risk adjusted capital (severe loss scenario).
Other Rating Factors: Excellent profitability (7.5). Excellent liquidity (9.0).
Principal Business: Individual life insurance (100%).
Principal Investments: NonCMO investment grade bonds (78%), common & preferred stock (20%), cash (1%), and CMOs and structured securities (1%).
Investments in Affiliates: None
Group Affiliation: None
Licensed in: MI, NE, NM, TX
Commenced Business: July 1910
Address: 4000 Town Center Suite 1250, Southfield, MI 48075-1407
Phone: (800) 514-0010   **Domicile State:** MI   **NAIC Code:** 87920

Data Date	Rating	RACR #1	RACR #2	Total Assets ($mil)	Capital ($mil)	Net Premium ($mil)	Net Income ($mil)
6-16	B+	7.76	5.50	63.0	54.3	9.7	2.7
6-15	B+	7.38	6.10	58.6	50.5	9.9	3.4
2015	B+	7.27	5.93	59.9	50.8	20.0	4.1
2014	B+	6.89	5.92	56.2	47.0	19.9	3.3
2013	B+	6.50	5.85	52.1	43.2	19.9	5.5
2012	B	6.06	5.45	45.2	36.9	19.5	4.5
2011	B	5.84	5.26	39.5	32.4	18.7	5.8

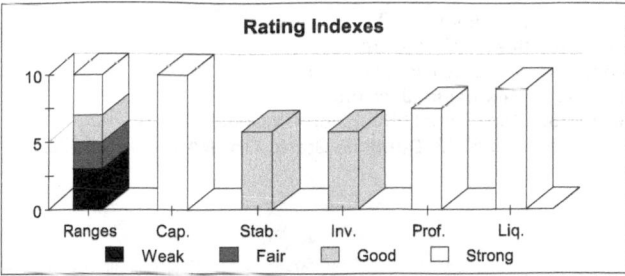

Rating Indexes

LOMBARD INTERNATIONAL LIFE ASSURANCE CO   E   Very Weak

Major Rating Factors: Poor overall capitalization (0.6 on a scale of 0 to 10) based on excessive policy leverage and weak risk adjusted capital (moderate loss scenario). Weak profitability (2.0) with operating losses during the first six months of 2016. Weak overall results on stability tests (0.2) including weak risk adjusted capital in prior years, negative cash flow from operations for 2015.
Other Rating Factors: High quality investment portfolio (8.1), Excellent liquidity (9.6).
Principal Business: Group retirement contracts (72%), individual annuities (15%), individual life insurance (12%), and group life insurance (1%).
Principal Investments: Policy loans (80%), nonCMO investment grade bonds (12%), common & preferred stock (4%), and cash (4%).
Investments in Affiliates: 4%
Group Affiliation: Blackstone Group Mgmt LLC
Licensed in: All states except NH, NY, PR
Commenced Business: September 1960
Address: 1650 Market St 54th Floor, Philadelphia, PA 19103
Phone: (800) 492-3057   **Domicile State:** PA   **NAIC Code:** 60232

Data Date	Rating	RACR #1	RACR #2	Total Assets ($mil)	Capital ($mil)	Net Premium ($mil)	Net Income ($mil)
6-16	E	0.47	0.27	5,610.7	25.7	334.8	-3.2
6-15	E	0.38	0.22	5,095.3	19.0	326.9	17.2
2015	F	0.40	0.24	5,336.4	21.7	723.3	15.1
2014	E	0.40	0.23	4,010.4	20.1	441.5	2.1
2013	E	0.41	0.24	4,746.5	20.1	394.3	0.4
2012	E	0.42	0.24	4,156.1	18.4	331.7	-0.9
2011	D+	0.69	0.41	3,660.3	25.2	62.0	-2.3

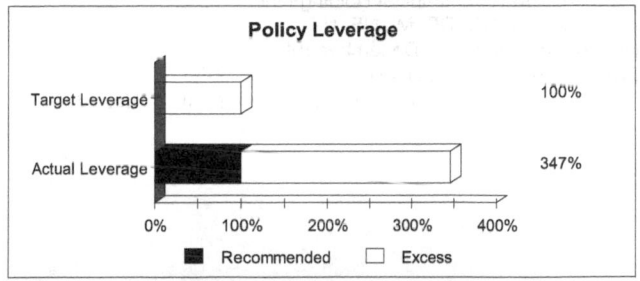

Policy Leverage

Target Leverage   100%
Actual Leverage   347%

■ Recommended   □ Excess

LONDON LIFE REINSURANCE COMPANY   C+   Fair

Major Rating Factors: Fair overall results on stability tests (3.1 on a scale of 0 to 10) including negative cash flow from operations for 2015. Good overall profitability (6.7). Excellent expense controls. Strong capitalization (10.0) based on excellent risk adjusted capital (severe loss scenario).
Other Rating Factors: High quality investment portfolio (7.8). Excellent liquidity (7.7).
Principal Business: Reinsurance (100%).
Principal Investments: NonCMO investment grade bonds (87%), CMOs and structured securities (9%), noninv. grade bonds (1%), common & preferred stock (1%), and cash (1%).
Investments in Affiliates: None
Group Affiliation: Great West Life Asr
Licensed in: All states, the District of Columbia and Puerto Rico
Commenced Business: December 1969
Address: 1787 Sentry Parkway, Ste 420, Blue Bell, PA 1942-22
Phone: (215) 542-7200   **Domicile State:** PA   **NAIC Code:** 76694

Data Date	Rating	RACR #1	RACR #2	Total Assets ($mil)	Capital ($mil)	Net Premium ($mil)	Net Income ($mil)
6-16	C+	5.46	2.98	289.3	57.7	0.7	0.3
6-15	C+	5.02	2.51	304.2	56.3	0.9	1.0
2015	C+	5.43	2.91	301.3	57.4	1.9	2.1
2014	C+	5.29	2.81	316.2	56.6	2.2	4.2
2013	C+	4.74	2.39	344.1	52.9	-8.1	2.3
2012	C+	4.67	2.38	424.6	67.2	29.9	1.6
2011	B-	3.85	2.06	464.4	69.9	39.2	2.0

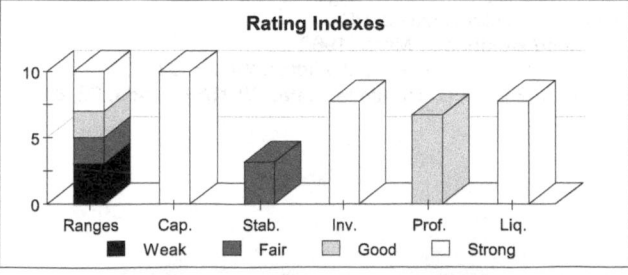

Rating Indexes

LOYAL AMERICAN LIFE INSURANCE COMPANY

C+　　**Fair**

Major Rating Factors: Fair overall results on stability tests (4.6 on a scale of 0 to 10) including fair risk adjusted capital in prior years. Good current capitalization (5.9) based on good risk adjusted capital (severe loss scenario) reflecting some improvement over results in 2011. Good quality investment portfolio (6.1).
Other Rating Factors: Good overall profitability (5.2) although investment income, in comparison to reserve requirements, is below regulatory standards. Good liquidity (6.7).
Principal Business: Individual health insurance (53%), reinsurance (43%), group health insurance (2%), and individual life insurance (2%).
Principal Investments: NonCMO investment grade bonds (79%), common & preferred stock (20%), noninv. grade bonds (1%), and CMOs and structured securities (1%).
Investments in Affiliates: 20%
Group Affiliation: CIGNA Corp
Licensed in: All states except NY, PR
Commenced Business: July 1955
Address: 525 Vine Street,20th Floor, Cincinnati, OH 45202
Phone: (800) 633-6752 **Domicile State:** OH **NAIC Code:** 65722

Data Date	Rating	RACR #1	RACR #2	Total Assets ($mil)	Capital ($mil)	Net Premium ($mil)	Net Income ($mil)
6-16	C+	1.00	0.86	270.0	86.5	141.7	7.1
6-15	C	1.01	0.82	254.8	73.8	140.9	6.8
2015	C+	1.00	0.86	266.7	85.6	278.5	16.5
2014	C	1.11	0.93	249.3	73.5	243.7	20.2
2013	C	1.53	1.18	244.0	71.5	260.0	14.3
2012	C	1.71	1.32	282.3	78.2	-80.2	-22.2
2011	C	0.97	0.67	438.9	40.8	103.3	2.8

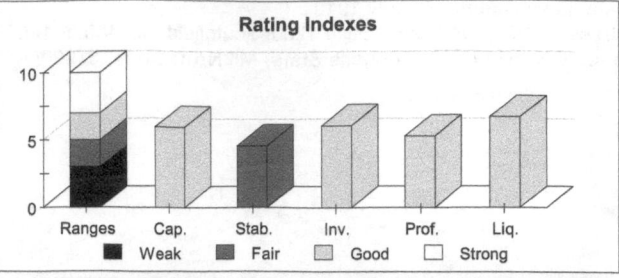

Rating Indexes

M LIFE INSURANCE COMPANY

B-　　**Good**

Major Rating Factors: Good overall results on stability tests (5.1 on a scale of 0 to 10). Stability strengths include good operational trends and good risk diversification. Fair profitability (4.2) with investment income below regulatory standards in relation to interest assumptions of reserves. Strong capitalization (10.0) based on excellent risk adjusted capital (severe loss scenario).
Other Rating Factors: High quality investment portfolio (7.8). Excellent liquidity (7.1).
Principal Business: Reinsurance (100%).
Principal Investments: NonCMO investment grade bonds (59%), CMOs and structured securities (26%), cash (13%), and noninv. grade bonds (1%).
Investments in Affiliates: None
Group Affiliation: M Financial Holdings Inc
Licensed in: AZ, CO, DE, MI, NE, NJ
Commenced Business: December 1981
Address: 1290 Broaday, Denver, CO 80203-5699
Phone: (503) 232-6960 **Domicile State:** CO **NAIC Code:** 93580

Data Date	Rating	RACR #1	RACR #2	Total Assets ($mil)	Capital ($mil)	Net Premium ($mil)	Net Income ($mil)
6-16	B-	5.80	3.80	302.0	94.6	213.7	9.8
6-15	C	5.09	3.35	274.2	78.6	202.9	6.5
2015	C	4.60	3.03	252.6	74.4	420.6	11.3
2014	C	4.84	3.19	285.4	74.2	403.2	10.0
2013	C	6.05	4.02	257.0	87.0	347.6	39.5
2012	C	5.56	3.68	284.4	74.0	322.1	27.6
2011	B-	5.14	3.62	285.1	59.8	225.4	58.0

Adverse Trends in Operations

Decrease in asset base during 2015 (11%)
Decrease in capital during 2014 (15%)
Decrease in asset base during 2013 (10%)
Change in asset mix during 2012 (10.7%)
Increase in policy surrenders from 2011 to 2012 (47%)

MADISON NATIONAL LIFE INSURANCE COMPANY INCORPORAT

C+　　**Fair**

Major Rating Factors: Fair quality investment portfolio (4.7 on a scale of 0 to 10). Fair overall results on stability tests (3.2) including negative cash flow from operations for 2015. Good overall profitability (6.9).
Other Rating Factors: Weak liquidity (0.3) as a spike in claims may stretch capacity. Strong capitalization (8.3) based on excellent risk adjusted capital (severe loss scenario).
Principal Business: Group health insurance (59%), group life insurance (14%), reinsurance (10%), individual life insurance (9%), and individual annuities (7%).
Principal Investments: NonCMO investment grade bonds (70%), common & preferred stock (22%), and cash (1%).
Investments in Affiliates: 23%
Group Affiliation: Geneve Holdings Inc
Licensed in: All states except PR
Commenced Business: March 1962
Address: 6120 University Ave, Middleton, WI 53562
Phone: (608) 238-2691 **Domicile State:** WI **NAIC Code:** 65781

Data Date	Rating	RACR #1	RACR #2	Total Assets ($mil)	Capital ($mil)	Net Premium ($mil)	Net Income ($mil)
6-16	C+	2.38	1.86	329.6	180.1	43.9	6.5
6-15	B	1.25	1.06	492.6	84.8	72.7	4.4
2015	B-	1.95	1.71	256.9	116.7	126.4	20.3
2014	C+	1.26	1.06	496.7	81.5	147.5	9.9
2013	C+	1.20	1.00	488.6	78.0	168.8	11.7
2012	B	1.12	0.89	689.7	72.3	136.4	11.9
2011	B	1.09	0.84	686.7	70.3	140.2	15.1

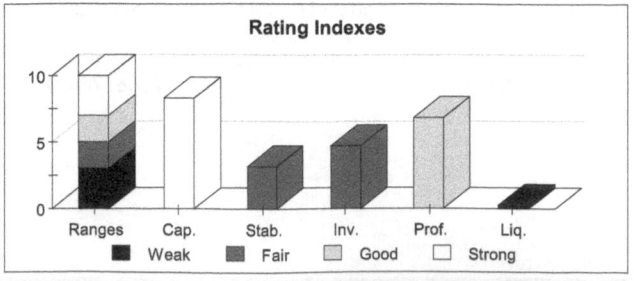

Rating Indexes

MANHATTAN LIFE INSURANCE COMPANY   B   Good

Major Rating Factors: Good overall results on stability tests (5.4 on a scale of 0 to 10) despite fair financial strength of affiliated Manhattan Life Group Inc. Other stability subfactors include good operational trends and good risk diversification. Good capitalization (6.7) based on good risk adjusted capital (severe loss scenario). Capital levels have been relatively consistent over the last five years. Good quality investment portfolio (6.8).

Other Rating Factors: Good liquidity (6.8). Fair profitability (3.6) with investment income below regulatory standards in relation to interest assumptions of reserves.

Principal Business: Individual annuities (66%), individual health insurance (25%), individual life insurance (7%), group health insurance (1%), and reinsurance (1%).

Principal Investments: NonCMO investment grade bonds (65%), mortgages in good standing (10%), common & preferred stock (8%), CMOs and structured securities (8%), and misc. investments (9%).

Investments in Affiliates: 8%

Group Affiliation: Manhattan Life Group Inc

Licensed in: All states, the District of Columbia and Puerto Rico

Commenced Business: August 1850

Address: 111 W 57th St, New York, NY 10019

Phone: (212) 484-9300 **Domicile State:** NY **NAIC Code:** 65870

Data Date	Rating	RACR #1	RACR #2	Total Assets ($mil)	Capital ($mil)	Net Premium ($mil)	Net Income ($mil)
6-16	B	1.26	0.96	487.7	50.9	56.2	12.0
6-15	B	1.13	0.91	434.5	40.5	85.2	3.6
2015	B	1.18	0.91	484.6	47.1	152.1	11.2
2014	B	1.17	0.96	362.4	41.0	71.1	2.8
2013	B	1.23	1.03	310.4	36.9	12.1	3.7
2012	C+	1.32	1.15	320.8	39.4	12.4	2.4
2011	C+	1.40	1.20	330.9	40.3	12.7	4.0

Manhattan Life Group Inc Composite Group Rating: C+ Largest Group Members	Assets ($mil)	Rating
WESTERN UNITED LIFE ASR CO	1096	B-
MANHATTAN LIFE INS CO	485	B
CENTRAL UNITED LIFE INS CO	327	C
FAMILY LIFE INS CO	159	C

MASSACHUSETTS MUTUAL LIFE INSURANCE COMPANY *   A-   Excellent

Major Rating Factors: Good quality investment portfolio (6.0 on a scale of 0 to 10) despite large holdings of BBB rated bonds in addition to moderate junk bond exposure. Exposure to mortgages is significant, but the mortgage default rate has been low. Good overall profitability (6.9) despite operating losses during the first six months of 2016. Good liquidity (6.8).

Other Rating Factors: Strong capitalization (7.4) based on excellent risk adjusted capital (severe loss scenario). Excellent overall results on stability tests (7.0) excellent operational trends and excellent risk diversification.

Principal Business: Group retirement contracts (47%), individual life insurance (26%), individual annuities (10%), reinsurance (7%), and other lines (9%).

Principal Investments: NonCMO investment grade bonds (43%), mortgages in good standing (15%), CMOs and structured securities (10%), policy loans (8%), and misc. investments (18%).

Investments in Affiliates: 12%

Group Affiliation: Massachusetts Mutual Group

Licensed in: All states, the District of Columbia and Puerto Rico

Commenced Business: August 1851

Address: 1295 State St, Springfield, MA 01111

Phone: (413) 788-8411 **Domicile State:** MA **NAIC Code:** 65935

Data Date	Rating	RACR #1	RACR #2	Total Assets ($mil)	Capital ($mil)	Net Premium ($mil)	Net Income ($mil)
6-16	A-	1.79	1.26	226,444	15,964.8	10,011.6	-154.9
6-15	A-	1.78	1.28	202,230	14,659.6	10,191.4	326.8
2015	A-	1.76	1.26	210,359	14,982.5	21,530.4	412.2
2014	A-	1.77	1.27	197,189	14,231.3	18,377.0	623.1
2013	A-	1.80	1.28	182,776	12,524.4	20,418.8	-285.6
2012	A	1.92	1.38	155,649	12,686.9	20,309.5	755.5
2011	A	1.92	1.37	136,968	11,417.4	13,478.5	344.6

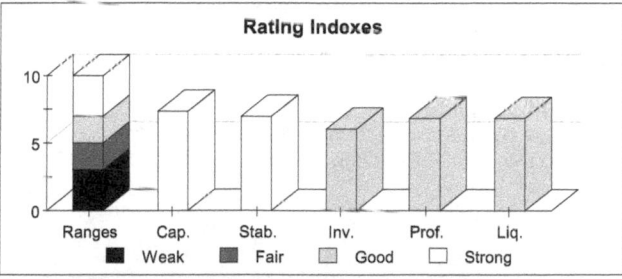

Rating Indexes

(Ranges, Cap., Stab., Inv., Prof., Liq. — ■ Weak ▨ Fair ▢ Good □ Strong)

MEDAMERICA INSURANCE COMPANY   C+   Fair

Major Rating Factors: Fair overall results on stability tests (4.6 on a scale of 0 to 10) including fair risk adjusted capital in prior years. Good capitalization (5.3) based on good risk adjusted capital (moderate loss scenario). Low quality investment portfolio (0.8) containing large holdings of BBB rated bonds in addition to significant exposure to junk bonds.

Other Rating Factors: Weak profitability (2.2) with operating losses during the first six months of 2016. Excellent liquidity (9.0).

Principal Business: Individual health insurance (64%), reinsurance (28%), and group health insurance (8%).

Principal Investments: NonCMO investment grade bonds (86%), CMOs and structured securities (5%), and noninv. grade bonds (5%).

Investments in Affiliates: None

Group Affiliation: Lifetime Healthcare Inc

Licensed in: All states except FL, NY, PR

Commenced Business: August 1966

Address: Foster Plaza VIII 730 Holiday, Pittsburgh, PA 15220

Phone: (410) 684-3200 **Domicile State:** PA **NAIC Code:** 69515

Data Date	Rating	RACR #1	RACR #2	Total Assets ($mil)	Capital ($mil)	Net Premium ($mil)	Net Income ($mil)
6-16	C+	1.17	0.63	914.3	31.7	32.4	-1.1
6-15	B	1.54	0.84	924.3	40.8	31.5	-1.1
2015	B	1.23	0.67	890.9	34.4	63.2	-45.8
2014	B	1.66	0.91	859.4	43.2	60.9	-1.9
2013	B	1.85	1.00	866.2	43.6	54.6	1.7
2012	B	1.44	0.78	733.7	28.7	49.0	-7.7
2011	B	1.71	0.99	678.0	33.8	50.0	-8.1

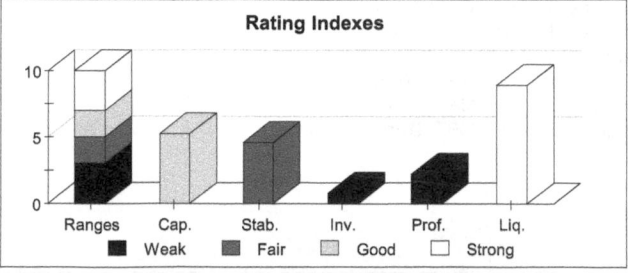

Rating Indexes

(Ranges, Cap., Stab., Inv., Prof., Liq. — ■ Weak ▨ Fair ▢ Good □ Strong)

MEDICO INSURANCE COMPANY   B   Good

Major Rating Factors: Good quality investment portfolio (6.4 on a scale of 0 to 10) despite mixed results such as: no exposure to mortgages and large holdings of BBB rated bonds but no exposure to junk bonds. Good liquidity (6.9) with sufficient resources to handle a spike in claims. Good overall results on stability tests (5.8) despite negative cash flow from operations for 2015 good operational trends and good risk diversification.
Other Rating Factors: Weak profitability (2.4). Strong capitalization (10.0) based on excellent risk adjusted capital (severe loss scenario).
Principal Business: Individual health insurance (76%), group health insurance (22%), individual life insurance (1%), and reinsurance (1%).
Principal Investments: NonCMO investment grade bonds (69%), CMOs and structured securities (23%), real estate (5%), and cash (3%).
Investments in Affiliates: None
Group Affiliation: American Enterprise Mutual Holding
Licensed in: All states except CT, NJ, NY, PR
Commenced Business: April 1930
Address: 1515 S 75th St, Omaha, NE 68124
Phone: (402) 391-6900 **Domicile State:** NE **NAIC Code:** 31119

Data Date	Rating	RACR #1	RACR #2	Total Assets ($mil)	Capital ($mil)	Net Premium ($mil)	Net Income ($mil)
6-16	B	4.36	3.92	77.2	33.8	0.3	1.0
6-15	B	4.34	3.91	71.4	32.6	0.4	1.8
2015	B	4.12	3.71	74.3	31.9	0.7	2.1
2014	B	4.14	3.73	69.1	30.9	0.9	-0.2
2013	B	4.06	3.66	65.7	29.7	0.9	0.8
2012	B	4.07	2.82	55.1	31.5	25.4	-12.4
2011	D+	2.06	1.28	91.0	21.0	39.9	-13.7

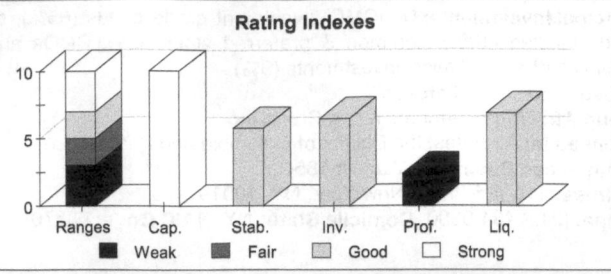

Rating Indexes

MERIT LIFE INSURANCE COMPANY   B   Good

Major Rating Factors: Good quality investment portfolio (6.7 on a scale of 0 to 10) despite significant exposure to mortgages . Mortgage default rate has been low. large holdings of BBB rated bonds in addition to small junk bond holdings. Fair profitability (3.7) with investment income below regulatory standards in relation to interest assumptions of reserves. Fair overall results on stability tests (4.6).
Other Rating Factors: Strong capitalization (8.4) based on excellent risk adjusted capital (severe loss scenario). Excellent liquidity (9.2).
Principal Business: Credit health insurance (36%), credit life insurance (36%), individual life insurance (16%), and individual health insurance (12%).
Principal Investments: NonCMO investment grade bonds (61%), CMOs and structured securities (24%), mortgages in good standing (11%), noninv. grade bonds (3%), and common & preferred stock (1%).
Investments in Affiliates: None
Group Affiliation: Fortress Investment Group LLC
Licensed in: All states except AK, MA, VT, PR
Commenced Business: October 1957
Address: 601 NW Second St, Evansville, IN 47708-1013
Phone: (812) 424-8031 **Domicile State:** IN **NAIC Code:** 65951

Data Date	Rating	RACR #1	RACR #2	Total Assets ($mil)	Capital ($mil)	Net Premium ($mil)	Net Income ($mil)
6-16	B	3.19	1.94	559.3	92.5	62.6	9.0
6-15	B	3.88	2.40	560.6	115.6	69.9	-0.9
2015	B	4.11	2.56	588.8	122.8	150.1	-0.9
2014	B+	5.53	3.47	588.2	171.4	157.1	-2.4
2013	B+	6.34	4.09	532.0	184.5	128.1	3.3
2012	B+	10.53	5.92	549.0	245.4	85.9	10.1
2011	B+	13.33	7.16	630.4	334.8	79.3	8.5

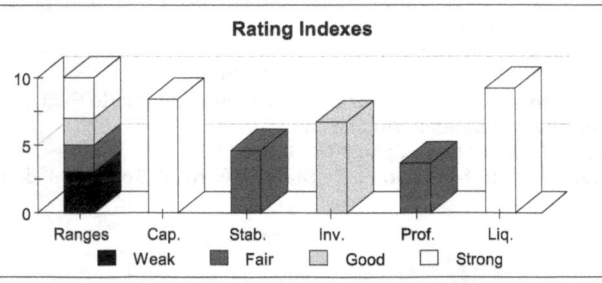

Rating Indexes

METLIFE INSURANCE COMPANY USA   B   Good

Major Rating Factors: Good quality investment portfolio (6.7 on a scale of 0 to 10) despite substantial holdings of BBB bonds in addition to moderate junk bond exposure. Exposure to mortgages is significant, but the mortgage default rate has been low. Good overall profitability (6.1) despite operating losses during the first six months of 2016. Fair overall results on stability tests (4.4).
Other Rating Factors: Strong capitalization (8.5) based on excellent risk adjusted capital (severe loss scenario). Excellent liquidity (8.0).
Principal Business: Individual annuities (57%), individual life insurance (26%), group life insurance (10%), reinsurance (4%), and other lines (3%).
Principal Investments: NonCMO investment grade bonds (49%), CMOs and structured securities (23%), mortgages in good standing (11%), noninv. grade bonds (4%), and misc. investments (7%).
Investments in Affiliates: 1%
Group Affiliation: MetLife Inc
Licensed in: All states except NY
Commenced Business: April 1864
Address: One Cityplace, Hartford, CT 06103-3415
Phone: (860) 308-7397 **Domicile State:** DE **NAIC Code:** 87726

Data Date	Rating	RACR #1	RACR #2	Total Assets ($mil)	Capital ($mil)	Net Premium ($mil)	Net Income ($mil)
6-16	B	4.04	1.97	184,071	7,552.5	6,895.6	-280.2
6-15	B	2.79	1.39	177,455	5,516.8	3,104.6	432.0
2015	B	3.37	1.66	173,762	5,942.0	7,568.0	-1,022.5
2014	B	3.15	1.57	174,606	6,041.5	-1,076.6	1,543.5
2013	B	1.52	1.09	60,275.2	4,794.6	1,361.1	789.5
2012	B	1.71	1.18	63,750.3	5,331.0	1,306.9	848.0
2011	B	1.66	1.15	64,781.2	5,133.3	1,436.6	46.2

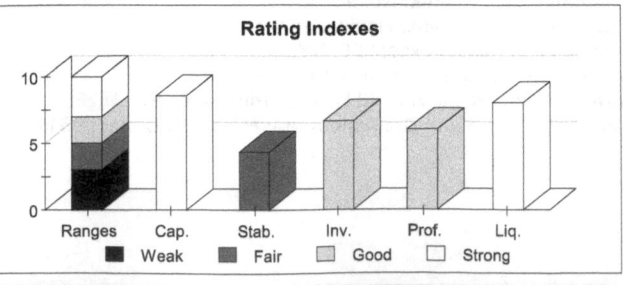

Rating Indexes

METROPOLITAN LIFE INSURANCE COMPANY | B- | Good

Major Rating Factors: Good capitalization (6.7 on a scale of 0 to 10) based on good risk adjusted capital (severe loss scenario). Capital levels have been relatively consistent over the last five years. Good quality investment portfolio (5.1) despite substantial holdings of BBB bonds in addition to significant exposure to junk bonds. Exposure to mortgages is significant, but the mortgage default rate has been low. Fair overall results on stability tests (4.5).

Other Rating Factors: Excellent profitability (7.5). Excellent liquidity (7.1).

Principal Business: Group retirement contracts (31%), group life insurance (25%), group health insurance (19%), individual life insurance (11%), and other lines (15%).

Principal Investments: NonCMO investment grade bonds (43%), mortgages in good standing (20%), CMOs and structured securities (16%), noninv. grade bonds (6%), and misc. investments (13%).

Investments in Affiliates: 6%

Group Affiliation: MetLife Inc

Licensed in: All states, the District of Columbia and Puerto Rico

Commenced Business: May 1867

Address: 200 Park Avenue, New York, NY 10166-0188

Phone: (212) 578-2211 **Domicile State:** NY **NAIC Code:** 65978

Data Date	Rating	RACR #1	RACR #2	Total Assets ($mil)	Capital ($mil)	Net Premium ($mil)	Net Income ($mil)
6-16	B-	1.43	0.96	401,502	14,650.6	9,918.4	706.5
6-15	B-	1.27	0.83	396,543	12,265.9	13,092.4	1,551.2
2015	B-	1.43	0.96	390,843	14,485.0	28,388.6	3,703.3
2014	B-	1.24	0.82	391,925	12,007.9	41,932.0	1,487.1
2013	B-	1.24	0.82	373,393	12,428.1	30,808.0	369.0
2012	B-	1.40	0.92	360,501	14,294.8	35,781.3	1,320.0
2011	B-	1.09	0.78	333,261	13,506.8	36,579.6	1,970.5

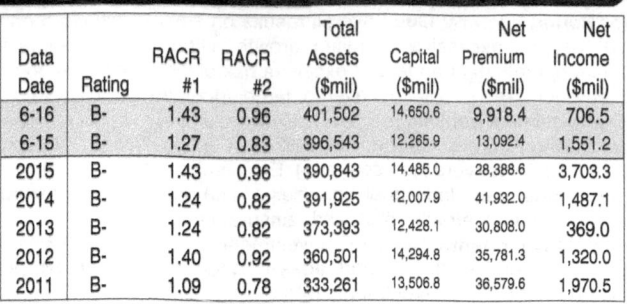

Junk Bonds as a % of Capital

Capital — $14 bil.
Junk Bonds — $15 bil.

0% 20% 40% 60% 80% 100% 120%

BB B CCC In default

METROPOLITAN TOWER LIFE INSURANCE COMPANY | B- | Good

Major Rating Factors: Good overall profitability (6.9 on a scale of 0 to 10) despite operating losses during the first six months of 2016. Good liquidity (6.4) with sufficient resources to handle a spike in claims as well as a significant increase in policy surrenders. Good overall results on stability tests (5.1) despite negative cash flow from operations for 2015 good operational trends and excellent risk diversification.

Other Rating Factors: Fair quality investment portfolio (3.2). Strong capitalization (7.7) based on excellent risk adjusted capital (severe loss scenario).

Principal Business: Individual life insurance (98%) and individual annuities (2%).

Principal Investments: NonCMO investment grade bonds (41%), CMOs and structured securities (25%), real estate (12%), policy loans (6%), and misc. investments (16%).

Investments in Affiliates: 3%

Group Affiliation: MetLife Inc

Licensed in: All states except PR

Commenced Business: February 1983

Address: 200 Park Avenue, New York, NY 10166-0188

Phone: (212) 578-2211 **Domicile State:** DE **NAIC Code:** 97136

Data Date	Rating	RACR #1	RACR #2	Total Assets ($mil)	Capital ($mil)	Net Premium ($mil)	Net Income ($mil)
6-16	B-	3.27	1.48	4,588.5	722.4	9.9	-14.5
6-15	B-	3.18	1.41	4,849.2	787.8	11.6	-28.3
2015	B-	3.22	1.45	4,665.6	709.8	20.5	-41.5
2014	B-	3.10	1.37	4,999.2	767.2	23.8	51.1
2013	B-	2.55	1.08	4,942.8	735.5	27.6	51.5
2012	B-	2.17	1.00	5,055.6	781.3	30.7	60.9
2011	B-	2.32	1.05	5,041.7	828.5	35.9	63.0

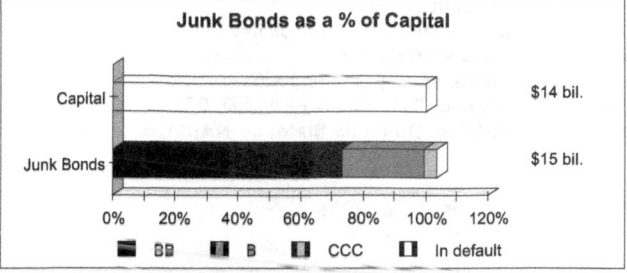

Adverse Trends in Operations

Decrease in asset base during 2015 (7%)
Decrease in premium volume from 2014 to 2015 (14%)
Decrease in premium volume from 2013 to 2014 (14%)
Decrease in premium volume from 2012 to 2013 (10%)
Decrease in premium volume from 2011 to 2012 (14%)

MID-WEST NATIONAL LIFE INSURANCE COMPANY OF TENNESS | C+ | Fair

Major Rating Factors: Fair overall results on stability tests (3.3 on a scale of 0 to 10) including negative cash flow from operations for 2015. Good overall profitability (6.0). Strong overall capitalization (10.0) based on excellent risk adjusted capital (severe loss scenario). Nevertheless, capital levels have fluctuated during prior years.

Other Rating Factors: High quality investment portfolio (8.5). Excellent liquidity (8.2).

Principal Business: Group health insurance (50%), individual life insurance (23%), individual health insurance (22%), group life insurance (2%), and individual annuities (2%).

Principal Investments: NonCMO investment grade bonds (90%), CMOs and structured securities (2%), and cash (2%).

Investments in Affiliates: 3%

Group Affiliation: HealthMarkets

Licensed in: All states except NY, VT, PR

Commenced Business: May 1965

Address: 9151 Grapevine Highway, North Richland Hills, TX 76180

Phone: (817) 255-3100 **Domicile State:** TX **NAIC Code:** 66087

Data Date	Rating	RACR #1	RACR #2	Total Assets ($mil)	Capital ($mil)	Net Premium ($mil)	Net Income ($mil)
6-16	C+	8.01	7.21	167.2	73.0	4.8	7.0
6-15	B-	4.75	3.23	214.5	81.0	25.3	12.4
2015	C+	7.62	6.21	166.2	71.5	32.2	17.8
2014	B-	2.91	2.07	291.8	90.6	194.1	19.0
2013	B-	4.24	3.34	92.0	51.7	80.4	6.4
2012	B-	3.78	2.95	103.9	56.6	108.9	13.3
2011	B-	3.78	2.92	137.8	73.7	141.5	12.8

Rating Indexes

Ranges Cap. Stab. Inv. Prof. Liq.

Weak Fair Good Strong

MIDLAND NATIONAL LIFE INSURANCE COMPANY * B+ Good

Major Rating Factors: Good overall results on stability tests (6.5 on a scale of 0 to 10) despite excessive premium growth. Other stability subfactors include excellent operational trends and excellent risk diversification. Good liquidity (6.1) with sufficient resources to cover a large increase in policy surrenders. Fair quality investment portfolio (4.7).

Other Rating Factors: Strong capitalization (7.0) based on excellent risk adjusted capital (severe loss scenario). Excellent profitability (9.1).

Principal Business: Individual annuities (61%), individual life insurance (26%), group retirement contracts (8%), and reinsurance (5%).

Principal Investments: NonCMO investment grade bonds (43%), CMOs and structured securities (35%), mortgages in good standing (11%), noninv. grade bonds (4%), and misc. investments (6%).

Investments in Affiliates: 1%

Group Affiliation: Sammons Enterprises Inc

Licensed in: All states except NY

Commenced Business: September 1906

Address: One Midland Plaza, Sioux Falls, SD 57193

Phone: (605) 335-5700 **Domicile State:** IA **NAIC Code:** 66044

Data Date	Rating	RACR #1	RACR #2	Total Assets ($mil)	Capital ($mil)	Net Premium ($mil)	Net Income ($mil)
6-16	B+	1.93	1.01	47,985.0	2,899.9	2,514.8	129.0
6-15	B+	1.95	1.02	42,955.4	2,919.3	1,965.4	192.2
2015	B+	1.92	1.00	44,729.3	2,857.0	4,264.1	271.3
2014	B+	1.94	1.03	41,138.7	2,794.0	3,276.2	203.4
2013	B+	2.16	1.11	37,441.0	2,563.1	3,631.9	455.7
2012	B+	2.18	1.10	32,851.3	2,124.3	2,941.7	343.8
2011	B+	2.06	1.00	30,132.9	1,854.2	2,544.4	318.2

Adverse Trends in Operations

Decrease in premium volume from 2013 to 2014 (10%)

MIDWESTERN UNITED LIFE INSURANCE COMPANY * A Excellent

Major Rating Factors: Good liquidity (6.9 on a scale of 0 to 10) with sufficient resources to handle a spike in claims as well as a significant increase in policy surrenders. Excellent overall results on stability tests (7.6). Strengths that enhance stability include excellent operational trends and excellent risk diversification. Strong capitalization (10.0) based on excellent risk adjusted capital (severe loss scenario).

Other Rating Factors: High quality investment portfolio (8.0). Excellent profitability (7.4).

Principal Business: Individual life insurance (99%).

Principal Investments: NonCMO investment grade bonds (78%), CMOs and structured securities (7%), mortgages in good standing (6%), policy loans (3%), and misc. investments (6%).

Investments in Affiliates: None

Group Affiliation: Voya Financial Inc

Licensed in: All states except NY, PR

Commenced Business: August 1948

Address: 8605 Kings Mill Pl, Fort Wayne, IN 46804

Phone: (303) 860-1290 **Domicile State:** IN **NAIC Code:** 66109

Data Date	Rating	RACR #1	RACR #2	Total Assets ($mil)	Capital ($mil)	Net Premium ($mil)	Net Income ($mil)
6-16	A	13.03	11.73	235.0	129.4	1.7	1.5
6-15	A-	12.65	11.39	236.9	126.0	1.7	1.2
2015	A-	12.85	11.56	234.9	127.7	3.2	3.5
2014	A-	12.53	11.27	236.5	124.8	3.6	2.7
2013	B	12.23	11.01	238.7	122.0	3.7	1.9
2012	B	12.01	10.81	242.1	120.1	3.7	3.5
2011	B	11.61	10.45	242.7	115.5	3.9	4.0

Adverse Trends in Operations

Decrease in premium volume from 2014 to 2015 (10%)
Decrease in premium volume from 2013 to 2014 (2%)
Decrease in asset base during 2013 (1%)
Decrease in premium volume from 2011 to 2012 (4%)

MINNESOTA LIFE INSURANCE COMPANY * B+ Good

Major Rating Factors: Good quality investment portfolio (5.6 on a scale of 0 to 10) despite significant exposure to mortgages . Mortgage default rate has been low. large holdings of BBB rated bonds in addition to small junk bond holdings. Good liquidity (6.7) with sufficient resources to handle a spike in claims as well as a significant increase in policy surrenders. Good overall results on stability tests (6.5) excellent operational trends and excellent risk diversification.

Other Rating Factors: Strong capitalization (7.7) based on excellent risk adjusted capital (severe loss scenario). Excellent profitability (7.1) despite operating losses during the first six months of 2016.

Principal Business: Group life insurance (30%), group retirement contracts (28%), individual life insurance (22%), individual annuities (11%), and other lines (8%).

Principal Investments: NonCMO investment grade bonds (48%), CMOs and structured securities (22%), mortgages in good standing (13%), noninv. grade bonds (4%), and misc. investments (12%).

Investments in Affiliates: 4%

Group Affiliation: Securian Financial Group

Licensed in: All states except NY

Commenced Business: August 1880

Address: 400 N Robert St, St Paul, MN 55101

Phone: (612) 665-3500 **Domicile State:** MN **NAIC Code:** 66168

Data Date	Rating	RACR #1	RACR #2	Total Assets ($mil)	Capital ($mil)	Net Premium ($mil)	Net Income ($mil)
6-16	B+	2.36	1.48	38,458.7	2,825.3	3,153.6	-23.7
6-15	B+	2.38	1.49	36,845.3	2,684.2	3,039.6	121.8
2015	B+	2.36	1.49	36,910.4	2,766.4	6,040.7	212.8
2014	B+	2.38	1.50	35,716.0	2,600.4	5,597.8	204.0
2013	B+	2.29	1.44	33,154.4	2,329.7	5,261.5	118.9
2012	B+	2.39	1.50	28,415.0	2,181.8	4,574.7	129.5
2011	B	2.47	1.54	25,661.6	2,037.1	4,124.9	123.3

Rating Indexes

	Ranges	Cap.	Stab.	Inv.	Prof.	Liq.
	■ Weak	■ Fair	□ Good	□ Strong		

MML BAY STATE LIFE INSURANCE COMPANY *   A   Excellent

Major Rating Factors: Excellent overall results on stability tests (7.7 on a scale of 0 to 10). Strengths that enhance stability include excellent operational trends and excellent risk diversification. Strong capitalization (10.0) based on excellent risk adjusted capital (severe loss scenario). Furthermore, this high level of risk adjusted capital has been consistently maintained over the last five years. High quality investment portfolio (7.3).

Other Rating Factors: Excellent profitability (8.2). Excellent liquidity (7.5).

Principal Business: Individual life insurance (94%) and group life insurance (6%).

Principal Investments: NonCMO investment grade bonds (56%), policy loans (25%), CMOs and structured securities (16%), mortgages in good standing (2%), and noninv. grade bonds (1%).

Investments in Affiliates: None

Group Affiliation: Massachusetts Mutual Group

Licensed in: All states except NY, PR

Commenced Business: July 1894

Address: 100 Bright Meadow Blvd, Enfield, CT 06082

Phone: (413) 788-8411 **Domicile State:** CT **NAIC Code:** 70416

Data Date	Rating	RACR #1	RACR #2	Total Assets ($mil)	Capital ($mil)	Net Premium ($mil)	Net Income ($mil)
6-16	A	5.06	3.60	4,737.2	242.5	10.2	10.9
6-15	A	4.64	3.17	4,706.0	221.7	15.1	10.2
2015	A	4.68	3.37	4,700.1	231.3	24.5	20.7
2014	A-	4.31	2.99	4,671.0	211.7	24.1	15.8
2013	A-	4.06	2.80	4,587.9	196.0	28.5	22.3
2012	B	4.13	2.83	4,489.2	196.2	29.8	22.2
2011	A	3.76	2.66	4,411.4	176.5	29.0	29.2

Adverse Trends in Operations

Decrease in premium volume from 2013 to 2014 (15%)
Decrease in premium volume from 2012 to 2013 (4%)
Change in asset mix during 2012 (5.0%)
Increase in policy surrenders from 2011 to 2012 (156%)

MONY LIFE INSURANCE COMPANY   B-   Good

Major Rating Factors: Good quality investment portfolio (6.3 on a scale of 0 to 10) despite mixed results such as: minimal exposure to mortgages and large holdings of BBB rated bonds but small junk bond holdings. Good liquidity (5.1) with sufficient resources to cover a large increase in policy surrenders. Good overall results on stability tests (5.0) despite negative cash flow from operations for 2015, fair risk adjusted capital in prior years good operational trends and excellent risk diversification.

Other Rating Factors: Fair profitability (3.0) with investment income below regulatory standards in relation to interest assumptions of reserves. Strong capitalization (7.4) based on excellent risk adjusted capital (severe loss scenario).

Principal Business: Individual life insurance (84%), individual health insurance (14%), and individual annuities (2%).

Principal Investments: NonCMO investment grade bonds (72%), policy loans (11%), CMOs and structured securities (9%), mortgages in good standing (4%), and misc. investments (4%).

Investments in Affiliates: None

Group Affiliation: Protective Life Group

Licensed in: All states, the District of Columbia and Puerto Rico

Commenced Business: February 1843

Address: 5788 Widewaters Pkwy 2 Floor, Syracuse, NY 13214

Phone: (800) 487-6669 **Domicile State:** NY **NAIC Code:** 66370

Data Date	Rating	RACR #1	RACR #2	Total Assets ($mil)	Capital ($mil)	Net Premium ($mil)	Net Income ($mil)
6-16	B-	2.31	1.24	7,390.6	432.7	113.6	24.2
6-15	B-	2.72	1.46	7,611.0	530.4	135.0	37.0
2015	B-	2.41	1.30	7,482.7	455.9	269.2	59.1
2014	B-	2.52	1.34	7,674.5	490.6	281.8	137.8
2013	B-	1.60	0.84	7,683.1	309.2	305.0	-567.1
2012	C+	1.03	0.75	8,441.1	619.6	325.5	174.4
2011	C	0.84	0.59	8,505.7	440.2	363.4	112.5

Adverse Trends in Operations

Decrease in asset base during 2015 (2%)
Decrease in capital during 2015 (7%)
Decrease in asset base during 2013 (9%)
Decrease in capital during 2013 (50%)
Decrease in premium volume from 2011 to 2012 (10%)

MONY LIFE INSURANCE COMPANY OF AMERICA   B   Good

Major Rating Factors: Good quality investment portfolio (5.5 on a scale of 0 to 10) despite mixed results such as: no exposure to mortgages and large holdings of BBB rated bonds but minimal holdings in junk bonds. Good overall profitability (6.0) despite operating losses during the first six months of 2016. Good overall results on stability tests (5.7) good operational trends and excellent risk diversification.

Other Rating Factors: Strong capitalization (8.7) based on excellent risk adjusted capital (severe loss scenario). Excellent liquidity (7.1).

Principal Business: Individual life insurance (95%), individual annuities (4%), and group life insurance (1%).

Principal Investments: NonCMO investment grade bonds (79%), common & preferred stock (7%), CMOs and structured securities (5%), policy loans (4%), and noninv. grade bonds (2%).

Investments in Affiliates: 6%

Group Affiliation: AXA Financial Inc

Licensed in: All states except NY

Commenced Business: June 1969

Address: 2025 N Third St Suite 260, Phoenix, AZ 85004

Phone: (212) 554-1234 **Domicile State:** AZ **NAIC Code:** 78077

Data Date	Rating	RACR #1	RACR #2	Total Assets ($mil)	Capital ($mil)	Net Premium ($mil)	Net Income ($mil)
6-16	B	3.14	2.14	2,984.8	336.2	205.8	-12.5
6-15	B-	3.63	2.49	2,912.5	378.8	197.2	5.6
2015	B	3.39	2.34	2,912.8	352.8	446.2	-3.6
2014	B-	3.80	2.63	2,830.6	384.9	298.0	11.7
2013	B-	4.02	2.70	2,794.3	356.7	-1,140.4	33.6
2012	B-	2.16	1.30	3,936.0	281.9	267.0	33.3
2011	B-	1.77	1.03	3,830.9	224.5	252.4	35.2

Adverse Trends in Operations

Increase in policy surrenders from 2014 to 2015 (53%)
Change in premium mix from 2013 to 2014 (11%)
Change in asset mix during 2013 (4.1%)
Decrease in asset base during 2013 (29%)
Decrease in premium volume from 2012 to 2013 (527%)

MOTORISTS LIFE INSURANCE COMPANY   B   Good

Major Rating Factors: Good quality investment portfolio (6.4 on a scale of 0 to 10) with no exposure to mortgages and moderate junk bond exposure. Good overall profitability (6.5). Good liquidity (6.0) with sufficient resources to handle a spike in claims as well as a significant increase in policy surrenders.

Other Rating Factors: Fair overall capitalization (4.0) based on mixed results -- excessive policy leverage mitigated by excellent risk adjusted capital (severe loss scenario). Fair overall results on stability tests (4.4) including negative cash flow from operations for 2015.

Principal Business: Individual life insurance (80%), individual annuities (19%), and group life insurance (1%).

Principal Investments: NonCMO investment grade bonds (63%), CMOs and structured securities (25%), noninv. grade bonds (4%), common & preferred stock (3%), and misc. investments (4%).

Investments in Affiliates: None

Group Affiliation: The Motorists Group

Licensed in: FL, GA, IL, IN, IA, KY, MI, MN, NE, OH, PA, SC, TN, VA, WV, WI

Commenced Business: January 1967

Address: 471 E Broad St, Columbus, OH 43215

Phone: (888) 876-6542 **Domicile State:** OH **NAIC Code:** 66311

Data Date	Rating	RACR #1	RACR #2	Total Assets ($mil)	Capital ($mil)	Net Premium ($mil)	Net Income ($mil)
6-16	B	3.19	1.72	455.4	63.1	27.7	1.7
6-15	B	2.48	1.36	533.6	58.6	27.7	1.0
2015	B	3.08	1.65	490.0	61.8	-53.8	4.0
2014	B	2.47	1.37	523.6	56.4	64.8	2.4
2013	B	2.54	1.42	495.3	54.7	70.7	3.6
2012	B	2.73	1.54	458.5	56.1	68.1	3.0
2011	B	3.08	1.77	418.1	53.5	59.3	1.9

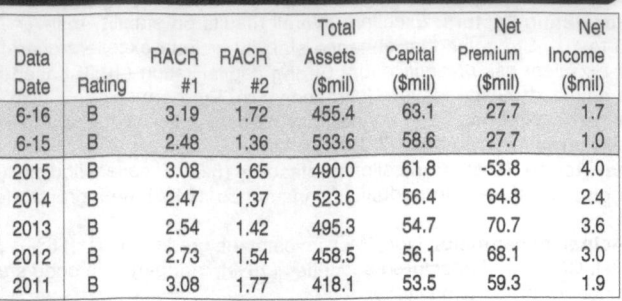

Rating Indexes

MUNICH AMERICAN REASSURANCE COMPANY   C   Fair

Major Rating Factors: Fair overall results on stability tests (3.9 on a scale of 0 to 10). Good liquidity (6.2) with sufficient resources to handle a spike in claims as well as a significant increase in policy surrenders. Weak profitability (1.8) with operating losses during the first six months of 2016.

Other Rating Factors: Strong capitalization (7.6) based on excellent risk adjusted capital (severe loss scenario). High quality investment portfolio (8.0).

Principal Business: Reinsurance (100%).

Principal Investments: NonCMO investment grade bonds (96%), CMOs and structured securities (3%), and common & preferred stock (1%).

Investments in Affiliates: 1%

Group Affiliation: Munchener R-G AG

Licensed in: All states, the District of Columbia and Puerto Rico

Commenced Business: November 1959

Address: 56 Perimeter Ctr E NE Ste 200, Atlanta, GA 30346-2290

Phone: (770) 394-5665 **Domicile State:** GA **NAIC Code:** 66346

Data Date	Rating	RACR #1	RACR #2	Total Assets ($mil)	Capital ($mil)	Net Premium ($mil)	Net Income ($mil)
6-16	C	2.05	1.40	7,687.5	557.7	400.1	-20.9
6-15	C	2.25	1.55	7,386.5	674.9	489.8	-78.6
2015	C	2.27	1.56	7,626.7	625.7	991.6	-86.3
2014	C+	2.41	1.68	7,289.5	737.9	1,451.5	-59.2
2013	B-	2.05	1.43	6,981.2	789.9	261.1	-29.0
2012	B-	2.35	1.63	6,363.8	810.8	224.2	21.4
2011	B-	2.41	1.67	5,865.7	818.0	167.7	-20.6

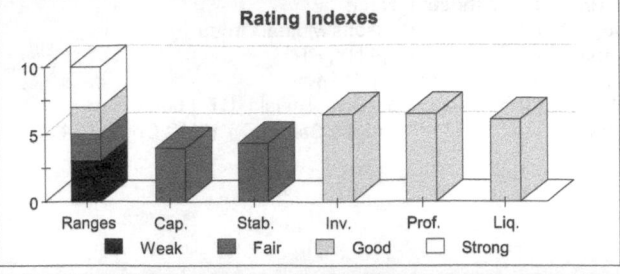

Rating Indexes

MUTUAL OF AMERICA LIFE INSURANCE COMPANY *   A-   Excellent

Major Rating Factors: Good quality investment portfolio (5.8 on a scale of 0 to 10) despite mixed results such as: large holdings of BBB rated bonds but moderate junk bond exposure. Good overall results on stability tests (6.9). Strengths that enhance stability include excellent operational trends and excellent risk diversification. Strong capitalization (7.9) based on excellent risk adjusted capital (severe loss scenario).

Other Rating Factors: Excellent profitability (7.7). Excellent liquidity (7.2).

Principal Business: Group retirement contracts (75%) and individual annuities (25%).

Principal Investments: NonCMO investment grade bonds (51%), CMOs and structured securities (39%), noninv. grade bonds (5%), real estate (3%), and policy loans (1%).

Investments in Affiliates: None

Group Affiliation: None

Licensed in: All states except PR

Commenced Business: October 1945

Address: 320 Park Ave, New York, NY 10022

Phone: (212) 224-1879 **Domicile State:** NY **NAIC Code:** 88668

Data Date	Rating	RACR #1	RACR #2	Total Assets ($mil)	Capital ($mil)	Net Premium ($mil)	Net Income ($mil)
6-16	A-	3.43	1.59	18,135.8	1,007.3	918.0	3.3
6-15	A-	3.62	1.71	18,016.4	1,014.6	897.9	29.4
2015	A-	3.70	1.75	17,865.4	1,032.2	2,043.3	64.5
2014	A-	3.57	1.68	17,790.9	997.7	1,963.7	59.2
2013	A-	3.41	1.62	16,666.7	951.2	1,771.8	49.4
2012	B	3.22	1.55	14,643.8	907.9	1,684.6	45.1
2011	B	3.09	1.49	13,502.3	846.2	1,552.7	40.9

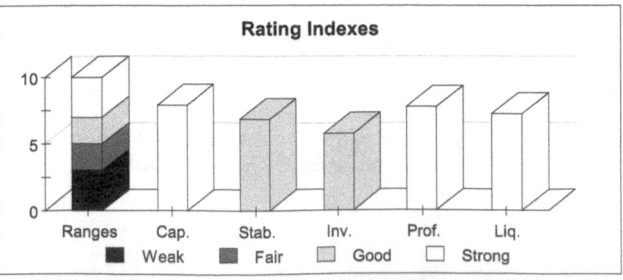

Rating Indexes

MUTUAL OF OMAHA INSURANCE COMPANY *   B+   Good

Major Rating Factors: Good overall results on stability tests (6.4 on a scale of 0 to 10). Stability strengths include excellent operational trends and excellent risk diversification. Good capitalization (6.4) based on good risk adjusted capital (severe loss scenario). Capital levels have been relatively consistent over the last five years. Good quality investment portfolio (6.1).
Other Rating Factors: Excellent profitability (8.5). Excellent liquidity (7.0).
Principal Business: Reinsurance (53%), individual health insurance (37%), and group health insurance (10%).
Principal Investments: NonCMO investment grade bonds (39%), common & preferred stock (38%), CMOs and structured securities (14%), mortgages in good standing (3%), and misc. investments (5%).
Investments in Affiliates: 41%
Group Affiliation: Mutual Of Omaha Group
Licensed in: All states, the District of Columbia and Puerto Rico
Commenced Business: January 1910
Address: 3300 Mutual Of Omaha Plaza, Omaha, NE 68175
Phone: (402) 342-7600 **Domicile State:** NE **NAIC Code:** 71412

Data Date	Rating	RACR #1	RACR #2	Total Assets ($mil)	Capital ($mil)	Net Premium ($mil)	Net Income ($mil)
6-16	B+	0.99	0.93	7,112.9	2,817.0	1,310.4	95.4
6-15	B+	1.05	0.98	6,760.1	2,881.2	1,173.4	28.5
2015	B+	1.02	0.95	6,945.1	2,862.8	2,411.8	11.2
2014	B+	1.02	0.96	6,426.8	2,795.7	2,186.3	30.4
2013	B+	1.11	1.04	5,795.4	2,674.5	2,071.2	105.8
2012	B+	1.09	1.02	5,549.8	2,406.0	1,946.8	56.8
2011	B+	1.05	0.97	5,247.4	2,314.9	1,909.5	33.0

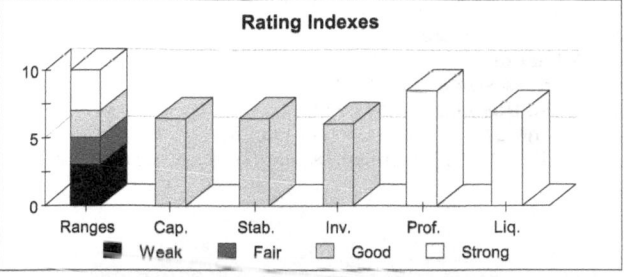

Rating Indexes

MUTUAL SAVINGS LIFE INSURANCE COMPANY   B   Good

Major Rating Factors: Good quality investment portfolio (5.2 on a scale of 0 to 10) despite mixed results such as: large holdings of BBB rated bonds but moderate junk bond exposure. Good overall profitability (6.0). Excellent expense controls. Good liquidity (6.0) with sufficient resources to handle a spike in claims as well as a significant increase in policy surrenders.
Other Rating Factors: Fair overall results on stability tests (4.2). Strong capitalization (7.5) based on excellent risk adjusted capital (severe loss scenario).
Principal Business: Individual life insurance (84%), individual health insurance (13%), and reinsurance (4%).
Principal Investments: NonCMO investment grade bonds (88%), policy loans (5%), CMOs and structured securities (3%), noninv. grade bonds (3%), and misc. investments (2%).
Investments in Affiliates: 1%
Group Affiliation: Kemper Corporation
Licensed in: AL, FL, GA, IN, LA, MS, TN
Commenced Business: January 1927
Address: 12115 Lackland Rd, St Louis, MO 63146-4003
Phone: (205) 552-7347 **Domicile State:** AL **NAIC Code:** 66397

Data Date	Rating	RACR #1	RACR #2	Total Assets ($mil)	Capital ($mil)	Net Premium ($mil)	Net Income ($mil)
6-16	B	2.16	1.30	455.6	38.3	20.1	3.0
6-15	B	2.04	1.25	447.0	34.7	20.4	3.2
2015	B	2.06	1.26	450.3	35.4	38.9	6.4
2014	B	1.88	1.15	445.1	31.6	39.9	10.2
2013	B+	2.80	1.76	464.3	57.3	41.6	6.7
2012	B+	2.52	1.58	454.5	50.6	43.3	8.1
2011	B	2.20	1.39	446.8	42.7	44.3	10.2

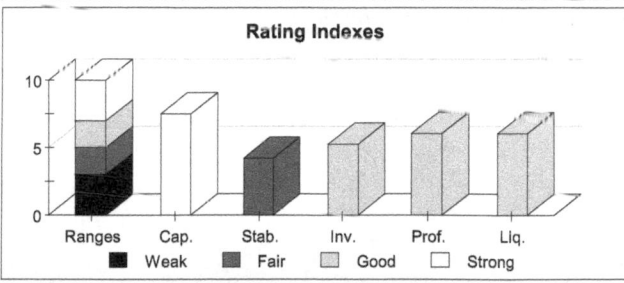

Rating Indexes

MUTUAL TRUST LIFE INSURANCE COMPANY   B   Good

Major Rating Factors: Good quality investment portfolio (6.0 on a scale of 0 to 10) despite mixed results such as: large holdings of BBB rated bonds but moderate junk bond exposure. Good overall profitability (5.5) although investment income, in comparison to reserve requirements, is below regulatory standards. Good overall results on stability tests (5.9) excellent operational trends and excellent risk diversification.
Other Rating Factors: Fair liquidity (4.8). Strong capitalization (7.3) based on excellent risk adjusted capital (severe loss scenario).
Principal Business: Individual life insurance (98%) and individual annuities (2%).
Principal Investments: NonCMO investment grade bonds (63%), policy loans (15%), CMOs and structured securities (13%), mortgages in good standing (5%), and noninv. grade bonds (3%).
Investments in Affiliates: None
Group Affiliation: Pan-American Life
Licensed in: All states except NY, PR
Commenced Business: April 1905
Address: 1200 Jorie Blvd, Oak Brook, IL 60523
Phone: (800) 323-7320 **Domicile State:** IL **NAIC Code:** 66427

Data Date	Rating	RACR #1	RACR #2	Total Assets ($mil)	Capital ($mil)	Net Premium ($mil)	Net Income ($mil)
6-16	B	2.27	1.17	1,933.2	140.8	75.8	3.1
6-15	B	2.18	1.15	1,931.4	135.7	76.5	5.0
2015	B	2.27	1.18	1,931.1	138.0	156.2	3.8
2014	B	2.13	1.12	1,928.0	132.0	174.4	7.5
2013	B	2.04	1.09	1,894.9	127.8	201.2	2.0
2012	B	1.90	1.04	1,780.8	89.6	219.4	1.6
2011	B	2.31	1.21	1,652.2	96.4	228.6	0.1

Adverse Trends in Operations

Decrease in premium volume from 2014 to 2015 (10%)
Decrease in premium volume from 2013 to 2014 (13%)
Increase in policy surrenders from 2012 to 2013 (26%)
Decrease in capital during 2012 (7%)
Decrease in premium volume from 2011 to 2012 (4%)

NATIONAL BENEFIT LIFE INSURANCE COMPANY · B · Good

Major Rating Factors: Good quality investment portfolio (6.6 on a scale of 0 to 10) despite mixed results such as: no exposure to mortgages and large holdings of BBB rated bonds but small junk bond holdings. Good liquidity (6.9) with sufficient resources to handle a spike in claims as well as a significant increase in policy surrenders. Good overall results on stability tests (5.3) good operational trends and excellent risk diversification.

Other Rating Factors: Strong capitalization (10.0) based on excellent risk adjusted capital (severe loss scenario). Excellent profitability (7.3).

Principal Business: Individual life insurance (99%), group life insurance (1%), and group health insurance (1%).

Principal Investments: NonCMO investment grade bonds (74%), CMOs and structured securities (13%), noninv. grade bonds (5%), common & preferred stock (2%), and misc. investments (1%).

Investments in Affiliates: None
Group Affiliation: Primerica Inc
Licensed in: All states except PR
Commenced Business: May 1963
Address: One Court Square, Long Island City, NY 11120-0001
Phone: (718) 248-8000 **Domicile State:** NY **NAIC Code:** 61409

Data Date	Rating	RACR #1	RACR #2	Total Assets ($mil)	Capital ($mil)	Net Premium ($mil)	Net Income ($mil)
6-16	B	7.12	3.72	495.1	158.4	36.5	7.2
6-15	B	7.29	3.85	497.7	160.3	31.9	5.6
2015	B	7.68	4.07	493.8	169.7	65.9	14.1
2014	B	8.00	4.28	481.6	171.9	60.9	20.3
2013	B+	7.13	4.02	484.0	174.5	88.8	22.3
2012	B+	7.55	4.30	489.1	175.9	85.7	24.9
2011	B+	7.60	4.36	498.6	173.7	84.5	15.8

Adverse Trends in Operations

Decrease in capital during 2015 (1%)
Decrease in premium volume from 2013 to 2014 (31%)
Decrease in capital during 2014 (1%)
Change in premium mix from 2013 to 2014 (9%)
Decrease in asset base during 2012 (2%)

NATIONAL FARM LIFE INSURANCE COMPANY · B · Good

Major Rating Factors: Good overall profitability (5.7 on a scale of 0 to 10). Good overall results on stability tests (5.4). Stability strengths include excellent operational trends and good risk diversification. Fair liquidity (3.9) due, in part, to cash value policies that are subject to withdrawals with minimal or no penalty.

Other Rating Factors: Strong capitalization (7.9) based on excellent risk adjusted capital (severe loss scenario). High quality investment portfolio (7.0).

Principal Business: Individual life insurance (93%) and individual annuities (7%).

Principal Investments: NonCMO investment grade bonds (84%), policy loans (6%), CMOs and structured securities (4%), common & preferred stock (2%), and misc. investments (4%).

Investments in Affiliates: None
Group Affiliation: National Farm Group
Licensed in: TX
Commenced Business: May 1946
Address: 6001 Bridge St, Fort Worth, TX 76112-2619
Phone: (817) 496-2637 **Domicile State:** TX **NAIC Code:** 66532

Data Date	Rating	RACR #1	RACR #2	Total Assets ($mil)	Capital ($mil)	Net Premium ($mil)	Net Income ($mil)
6-16	B	2.68	1.58	395.2	38.5	12.3	1.9
6-15	B	2.57	1.53	385.3	34.9	13.3	1.2
2015	B	2.60	1.55	390.2	36.6	26.8	2.6
2014	B-	2.57	1.53	378.0	33.9	26.6	2.8
2013	B-	2.48	1.47	366.3	32.6	26.1	2.9
2012	B-	2.35	1.38	352.6	30.0	24.6	3.8
2011	B-	2.34	1.36	301.6	27.1	25.7	1.9

Adverse Trends in Operations

Decrease in premium volume from 2011 to 2012 (4%)

NATIONAL FARMERS UNION LIFE INSURANCE COMPANY * · B+ · Good

Major Rating Factors: Good overall results on stability tests (6.7 on a scale of 0 to 10) despite negative cash flow from operations for 2015 and excessive premium growth. Other stability subfactors include excellent operational trends and excellent risk diversification. Good quality investment portfolio (5.6) despite mixed results such as: minimal exposure to mortgages and large holdings of BBB rated bonds but small junk bond holdings. Good liquidity (6.6).

Other Rating Factors: Strong capitalization (9.0) based on excellent risk adjusted capital (severe loss scenario). Excellent profitability (7.0).

Principal Business: Individual life insurance (72%), reinsurance (26%), group life insurance (1%), and individual annuities (1%).

Principal Investments: NonCMO investment grade bonds (43%), CMOs and structured securities (30%), common & preferred stock (12%), policy loans (5%), and misc. investments (10%).

Investments in Affiliates: 3%
Group Affiliation: Americo Life Inc
Licensed in: AK, AZ, AR, CA, CO, DC, ID, IL, IN, IA, KS, KY, MI, MN, MS, MO, MT, NE, NV, NM, ND, OH, OK, OR, PA, SD, TX, UT, VA, WA, WI, WY
Commenced Business: April 1938
Address: 500 North Akard, Dallas, TX 75201
Phone: (816) 391-2000 **Domicile State:** TX **NAIC Code:** 66540

Data Date	Rating	RACR #1	RACR #2	Total Assets ($mil)	Capital ($mil)	Net Premium ($mil)	Net Income ($mil)
6-16	B+	4.41	2.33	206.0	45.2	3.7	1.8
6-15	B+	4.30	2.25	211.2	46.4	2.9	2.7
2015	B+	4.28	2.24	206.7	43.4	6.1	4.5
2014	B+	4.13	2.17	216.6	43.7	4.9	4.7
2013	B	4.09	2.17	221.6	43.2	4.8	3.8
2012	B	4.10	2.16	225.9	42.4	5.5	4.2
2011	B	4.03	2.03	236.8	44.2	5.9	5.2

Adverse Trends in Operations

Decrease in asset base during 2015 (5%)
Decrease in asset base during 2014 (2%)
Decrease in premium volume from 2012 to 2013 (11%)
Decrease in capital during 2012 (4%)
Decrease in premium volume from 2011 to 2012 (7%)

NATIONAL GUARDIAN LIFE INSURANCE COMPANY

B- **Good**

Major Rating Factors: Good capitalization (6.4 on a scale of 0 to 10) based on good risk adjusted capital (severe loss scenario). Moreover, capital levels have been consistent over the last five years. Good quality investment portfolio (5.5) despite mixed results such as: minimal exposure to mortgages and large holdings of BBB rated bonds but small junk bond holdings. Good overall profitability (5.8).

Other Rating Factors: Good liquidity (6.4). Good overall results on stability tests (5.3) good operational trends and excellent risk diversification.

Principal Business: Group health insurance (29%), reinsurance (27%), group life insurance (24%), individual life insurance (16%), and other lines (3%).

Principal Investments: NonCMO investment grade bonds (81%), common & preferred stock (4%), mortgages in good standing (4%), CMOs and structured securities (4%), and misc. investments (7%).

Investments in Affiliates: 2%

Group Affiliation: NGL Ins Group

Licensed in: All states except NY, PR

Commenced Business: October 1910

Address: 2 E Gilman St, Madison, WI 53703

Phone: (608) 257-5611 **Domicile State:** WI **NAIC Code:** 66583

Data Date	Rating	RACR #1	RACR #2	Total Assets ($mil)	Capital ($mil)	Net Premium ($mil)	Net Income ($mil)
6-16	B-	1.49	0.93	3,502.2	278.2	271.8	9.2
6-15	B	1.46	0.95	3,026.6	251.4	246.4	1.1
2015	B-	1.45	0.91	3,422.2	271.1	790.0	-4.5
2014	B	1.47	0.96	2,948.3	250.1	476.1	24.4
2013	B	1.51	0.99	2,730.8	241.3	416.1	28.8
2012	B	1.43	0.93	2,532.8	196.4	395.8	18.9
2011	B	1.29	0.84	2,331.4	182.4	494.2	8.7

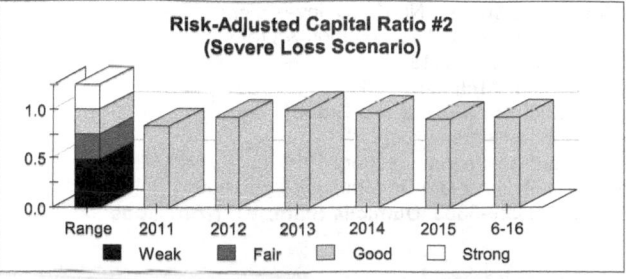

Risk-Adjusted Capital Ratio #2
(Severe Loss Scenario)

NATIONAL INCOME LIFE INSURANCE COMPANY *

B+ **Good**

Major Rating Factors: Good overall results on stability tests (6.7 on a scale of 0 to 10). Stability strengths include excellent operational trends and excellent risk diversification. Good overall profitability (6.2). Return on equity has been excellent over the last five years averaging 20.5%. Good liquidity (6.6).

Other Rating Factors: Strong capitalization (8.7) based on excellent risk adjusted capital (severe loss scenario). High quality investment portfolio (7.4).

Principal Business: Individual life insurance (90%) and individual health insurance (10%).

Principal Investments: NonCMO investment grade bonds (89%), policy loans (4%), cash (3%), CMOs and structured securities (2%), and noninv. grade bonds (1%).

Investments in Affiliates: None

Group Affiliation: Torchmark Corp

Licensed in: NY

Commenced Business: November 2000

Address: 1020 Seventh N St Suite 130, Liverpool, NY 13088

Phone: (315) 451-2544 **Domicile State:** NY **NAIC Code:** 10093

Data Date	Rating	RACR #1	RACR #2	Total Assets ($mil)	Capital ($mil)	Net Premium ($mil)	Net Income ($mil)
6-16	B+	3.45	2.10	185.3	34.8	36.0	5.2
6-15	B+	3.49	2.26	157.5	32.1	31.8	4.4
2015	B+	3.47	2.14	171.7	34.1	64.9	8.1
2014	B+	3.27	2.21	146.6	30.1	58.4	5.8
2013	B+	3.90	2.76	132.5	35.7	53.9	5.0
2012	B+	3.36	2.36	110.9	30.2	49.9	4.5
2011	B	2.19	1.41	81.4	17.5	42.7	5.0

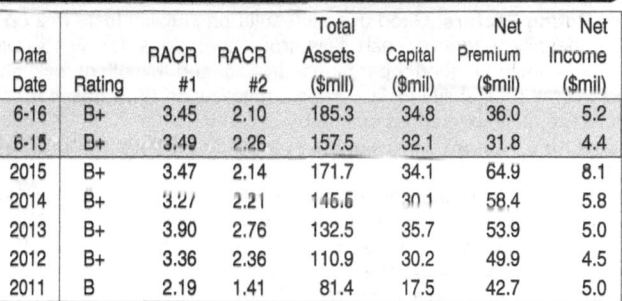

Rating Indexes

NATIONAL INTEGRITY LIFE INSURANCE COMPANY

B- **Good**

Major Rating Factors: Good quality investment portfolio (6.0 on a scale of 0 to 10) despite mixed results such as: large holdings of BBB rated bonds but moderate junk bond exposure. Good overall profitability (5.1) although investment income, in comparison to reserve requirements, is below regulatory standards. Good liquidity (6.5).

Other Rating Factors: Good overall results on stability tests (5.2) despite excessive premium growth excellent operational trends and excellent risk diversification. Strong capitalization (7.9) based on excellent risk adjusted capital (severe loss scenario).

Principal Business: Individual annuities (89%) and individual life insurance (11%).

Principal Investments: NonCMO investment grade bonds (55%), CMOs and structured securities (28%), noninv. grade bonds (6%), mortgages in good standing (3%), and misc. investments (5%).

Investments in Affiliates: 1%

Group Affiliation: Western & Southern Group

Licensed in: CT, DC, FL, ME, NH, NY, OH, RI, VT

Commenced Business: December 1968

Address: 15 Matthews St Suite 200, Goshen, NY 10924

Phone: (513) 629-1402 **Domicile State:** NY **NAIC Code:** 75264

Data Date	Rating	RACR #1	RACR #2	Total Assets ($mil)	Capital ($mil)	Net Premium ($mil)	Net Income ($mil)
6-16	B-	3.31	1.62	4,718.8	376.1	180.8	16.6
6-15	B-	3.73	1.84	4,789.6	399.0	122.0	20.2
2015	B-	3.24	1.60	4,739.0	356.6	255.1	34.3
2014	B-	3.46	1.71	4,777.0	377.5	247.1	48.3
2013	B-	3.07	1.50	4,767.1	321.0	215.3	34.4
2012	B-	3.09	1.51	4,758.8	301.7	204.1	41.3
2011	B-	2.87	1.39	4,723.3	272.5	302.0	30.6

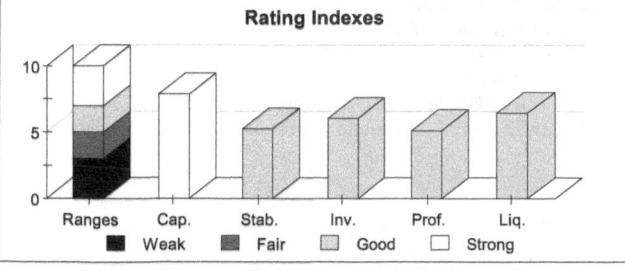

Rating Indexes

NATIONAL LIFE INSURANCE COMPANY | B | Good

Major Rating Factors: Good overall results on stability tests (5.1 on a scale of 0 to 10) despite negative cash flow from operations for 2015. Other stability subfactors include good operational trends, excellent risk adjusted capital for prior years and excellent risk diversification. Good quality investment portfolio (6.1) despite mixed results such as: minimal exposure to mortgages and large holdings of BBB rated bonds but small junk bond holdings. Good liquidity (6.8).

Other Rating Factors: Fair overall capitalization (4.0) based on mixed results -- excessive policy leverage mitigated by excellent risk adjusted capital (severe loss scenario). Excellent profitability (7.5) despite operating losses during the first six months of 2016.

Principal Business: Individual life insurance (86%), individual annuities (5%), individual health insurance (5%), and group retirement contracts (3%).

Principal Investments: NonCMO investment grade bonds (47%), CMOs and structured securities (17%), common & preferred stock (11%), policy loans (7%), and misc. investments (18%).

Investments in Affiliates: 11%

Group Affiliation: National Life Group

Licensed in: All states except PR

Commenced Business: January 1850

Address: 1 National Life Dr, Montpelier, VT 05604

Phone: (802) 229-3333 **Domicile State:** VT **NAIC Code:** 66680

Data Date	Rating	RACR #1	RACR #2	Total Assets ($mil)	Capital ($mil)	Net Premium ($mil)	Net Income ($mil)
6-16	B	1.73	1.37	9,158.4	1,830.3	143.3	-3.2
6-15	B	1.50	1.17	9,254.5	1,560.8	177.2	6.3
2015	B	1.72	1.37	9,148.7	1,778.0	-2,919.0	12.0
2014	B	1.50	1.18	9,209.9	1,541.2	411.8	19.1
2013	B	1.52	1.19	9,091.3	1,413.1	418.3	88.5
2012	B	1.54	1.17	8,855.8	1,287.1	421.1	64.6
2011	B	1.47	1.10	8,774.6	1,142.7	445.1	25.9

Adverse Trends in Operations

Decrease in premium volume from 2014 to 2015 (809%)
Decrease in premium volume from 2013 to 2014 (2%)
Decrease in premium volume from 2011 to 2012 (5%)

NATIONAL SECURITY LIFE & ANNUITY COMPANY | B | Good

Major Rating Factors: Good overall results on stability tests (5.2 on a scale of 0 to 10) despite negative cash flow from operations for 2015. Other stability subfactors include good operational trends and excellent risk diversification. Good overall profitability (5.5). Strong capitalization (9.2) based on excellent risk adjusted capital (severe loss scenario).

Other Rating Factors: High quality investment portfolio (7.2). Excellent liquidity (10.0).

Principal Business: Individual annuities (97%) and reinsurance (3%).

Principal Investments: NonCMO investment grade bonds (79%), CMOs and structured securities (18%), noninv. grade bonds (2%), and cash (1%).

Investments in Affiliates: None

Group Affiliation: Ohio Natonal Mutual Inc

Licensed in: AZ, AR, DC, IL, IN, IA, KS, LA, NE, NH, NJ, NY, OH, OK, OR, PA, SC, SD, TX, UT

Commenced Business: July 1975

Address: Court House Square, Binghamton, NY 13901

Phone: (303) 860-1290 **Domicile State:** NY **NAIC Code:** 85472

Data Date	Rating	RACR #1	RACR #2	Total Assets ($mil)	Capital ($mil)	Net Premium ($mil)	Net Income ($mil)
6-16	B	2.73	2.46	442.8	32.4	12.4	0.2
6-15	B	2.67	2.40	443.8	31.3	25.7	0.6
2015	B	2.71	2.44	435.5	32.2	44.7	1.4
2014	B	2.61	2.35	419.4	30.6	74.5	1.5
2013	B	2.56	2.31	354.8	28.6	71.9	6.2
2012	B-	2.43	2.18	257.7	25.0	31.6	1.1
2011	B-	2.01	1.81	209.7	19.8	10.2	-6.1

Adverse Trends in Operations

Decrease in premium volume from 2014 to 2015 (40%)
Increase in policy surrenders from 2013 to 2014 (68%)
Increase in policy surrenders from 2011 to 2012 (104%)

NATIONAL TEACHERS ASSOCIATES LIFE INSURANCE COMPAN | B | Good

Major Rating Factors: Good overall results on stability tests (6.0 on a scale of 0 to 10). Stability strengths include excellent operational trends and good risk diversification. Fair profitability (4.9) with investment income below regulatory standards in relation to interest assumptions of reserves. Strong capitalization (8.3) based on excellent risk adjusted capital (severe loss scenario).

Other Rating Factors: High quality investment portfolio (7.1). Excellent liquidity (8.5).

Principal Business: Individual health insurance (98%) and individual life insurance (2%).

Principal Investments: NonCMO investment grade bonds (46%), CMOs and structured securities (40%), noninv. grade bonds (4%), common & preferred stock (4%), and misc. investments (5%).

Investments in Affiliates: 2%

Group Affiliation: Ellard Family Holdings Inc

Licensed in: All states except NY, PR

Commenced Business: July 1938

Address: 4949 Keller Springs Rd, Addison, TX 75001-5910

Phone: (972) 532-2100 **Domicile State:** TX **NAIC Code:** 87963

Data Date	Rating	RACR #1	RACR #2	Total Assets ($mil)	Capital ($mil)	Net Premium ($mil)	Net Income ($mil)
9-15	B	2.64	1.84	452.4	89.0	91.6	9.0
9-14	B	2.46	1.74	418.4	78.4	87.5	5.3
2014	B	2.47	1.73	422.9	80.9	117.5	7.8
2013	B	2.55	1.84	381.8	73.1	108.1	7.0
2012	B+	3.40	2.34	347.2	67.1	99.0	9.2
2011	B+	2.95	2.01	325.6	56.3	92.8	12.0
2010	B	2.43	1.65	309.4	44.5	88.1	8.8

Adverse Trends in Operations

Increase in policy surrenders from 2012 to 2013 (29%)

NATIONAL WESTERN LIFE INSURANCE COMPANY *   A   Excellent

Major Rating Factors: Good quality investment portfolio (6.8 on a scale of 0 to 10) despite mixed results such as: minimal exposure to mortgages and large holdings of BBB rated bonds but small junk bond holdings. Good liquidity (6.0) with sufficient resources to handle a spike in claims as well as a significant increase in policy surrenders. Strong capitalization (8.5) based on excellent risk adjusted capital (severe loss scenario).

Other Rating Factors: Excellent profitability (7.6). Excellent overall results on stability tests (7.5) excellent operational trends and excellent risk diversification.

Principal Business: Individual annuities (72%) and individual life insurance (28%).

Principal Investments: NonCMO investment grade bonds (80%), CMOs and structured securities (15%), common & preferred stock (3%), policy loans (1%), and misc. investments (2%).

Investments in Affiliates: 3%

Group Affiliation: None

Licensed in: All states except NY

Commenced Business: June 1957

Address: 850 East Anderson Lane, Austin, TX 78752

Phone: (512) 836-1010 **Domicile State:** CO **NAIC Code:** 66850

Data Date	Rating	RACR #1	RACR #2	Total Assets ($mil)	Capital ($mil)	Net Premium ($mil)	Net Income ($mil)
6-16	A	3.80	2.01	10,673.8	1,203.1	495.6	36.6
6-15	A	4.58	2.36	10,446.9	1,204.8	518.7	11.2
2015	A	3.81	2.05	10,544.6	1,171.2	1,051.5	7.1
2014	A	4.60	2.37	10,262.7	1,185.6	1,109.9	77.2
2013	B+	4.35	2.38	9,771.2	1,126.2	1,105.4	106.2
2012	B+	4.09	2.15	9,164.8	1,004.8	1,088.0	84.5
2011	B+	3.71	1.99	8,669.7	922.5	1,564.0	53.9

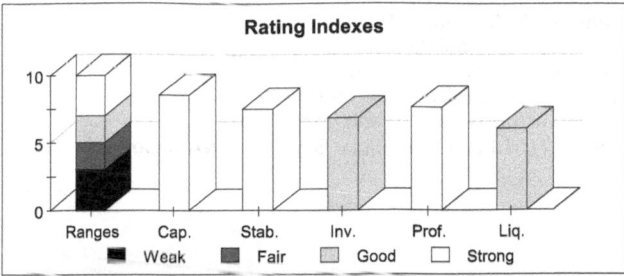

Rating Indexes

NATIONWIDE LIFE & ANNUITY INSURANCE COMPANY   C   Fair

Major Rating Factors: Fair overall results on stability tests (4.3 on a scale of 0 to 10). Good quality investment portfolio (5.0) despite large holdings of BBB rated bonds in addition to junk bond exposure equal to 62% of capital. Exposure to mortgages is significant, but the mortgage default rate has been low. Good liquidity (6.6) with sufficient resources to handle a spike in claims as well as a significant increase in policy surrenders.

Other Rating Factors: Weak profitability (1.9) with operating losses during the first six months of 2016. Strong capitalization (7.3) based on excellent risk adjusted capital (severe loss scenario).

Principal Business: Individual annuities (69%) and individual life insurance (31%).

Principal Investments: NonCMO investment grade bonds (68%), mortgages in good standing (15%), CMOs and structured securities (6%), noninv. grade bonds (5%), and policy loans (1%).

Investments in Affiliates: 1%

Group Affiliation: Nationwide Corp

Licensed in: All states except NY, PR

Commenced Business: May 1981

Address: One West Nationwide Blvd, Columbus, OH 43216

Phone: (614) 249-5227 **Domicile State:** OH **NAIC Code:** 92657

Data Date	Rating	RACR #1	RACR #2	Total Assets ($mil)	Capital ($mil)	Net Premium ($mil)	Net Income ($mil)
6-16	C	2.47	1.20	12,581.2	729.0	1,923.8	-98.0
6-15	C	2.74	1.38	8,470.6	573.0	819.9	-92.3
2015	C	2.74	1.37	10,757.6	735.0	3,314.9	-99.5
2014	C	3.37	1.73	7,896.7	690.6	1,086.7	-122.4
2013	B-	3.13	1.60	6,901.6	534.1	84.3	-103.3
2012	B-	2.03	1.04	6,243.3	311.0	404.6	-54.1
2011	B-	2.30	1.17	5,357.4	302.5	337.9	-61.2

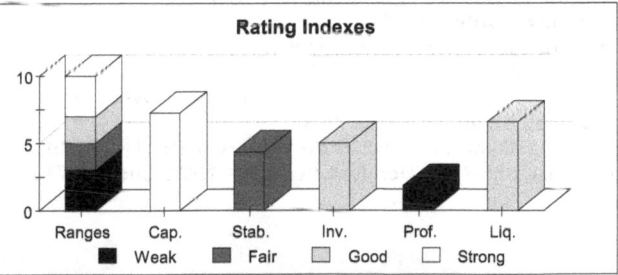

Rating Indexes

NATIONWIDE LIFE INSURANCE COMPANY   B-   Good

Major Rating Factors: Good quality investment portfolio (5.8 on a scale of 0 to 10) despite large holdings of BBB rated bonds in addition to moderate junk bond exposure. Exposure to mortgages is significant, but the mortgage default rate has been low. Good overall results on stability tests (5.2). Stability strengths include excellent operational trends and excellent risk diversification. Strong capitalization (7.8) based on excellent risk adjusted capital (severe loss scenario).

Other Rating Factors: Excellent profitability (7.6). Excellent liquidity (8.3).

Principal Business: Individual annuities (52%), group retirement contracts (27%), group life insurance (12%), individual life insurance (6%), and group health insurance (2%).

Principal Investments: NonCMO investment grade bonds (53%), mortgages in good standing (18%), CMOs and structured securities (17%), noninv. grade bonds (4%), and misc. investments (5%).

Investments in Affiliates: 3%

Group Affiliation: Nationwide Corp

Licensed in: All states, the District of Columbia and Puerto Rico

Commenced Business: January 1931

Address: One Nationwide Plaza, Columbus, OH 43215-2220

Phone: (614) 249-5227 **Domicile State:** OH **NAIC Code:** 66869

Data Date	Rating	RACR #1	RACR #2	Total Assets ($mil)	Capital ($mil)	Net Premium ($mil)	Net Income ($mil)
6-16	B-	2.60	1.51	129,443	4,948.7	4,893.3	261.4
6-15	B-	2.48	1.46	128,198	4,442.1	5,345.1	298.7
2015	B-	2.48	1.47	126,861	4,566.5	11,305.1	166.8
2014	B-	2.50	1.48	128,585	4,408.0	11,645.4	341.5
2013	B	2.30	1.34	120,676	3,550.0	11,604.5	262.2
2012	B	2.91	1.60	106,578	3,836.6	10,383.7	764.4
2011	B	2.80	1.52	99,940.8	3,590.9	12,670.9	18.4

Adverse Trends in Operations

Decrease in premium volume from 2014 to 2015 (3%)
Decrease in asset base during 2015 (1%)
Increase in policy surrenders from 2013 to 2014 (1434%)
Decrease in capital during 2013 (7%)
Decrease in premium volume from 2011 to 2012 (18%)

NEW ENGLAND LIFE INSURANCE COMPANY　　　　B　　　Good

Major Rating Factors: Good quality investment portfolio (5.9 on a scale of 0 to 10) despite mixed results such as: large holdings of BBB rated bonds but moderate junk bond exposure. Good liquidity (6.8) with sufficient resources to handle a spike in claims as well as a significant increase in policy surrenders. Fair overall results on stability tests (4.0).

Other Rating Factors: Strong capitalization (9.5) based on excellent risk adjusted capital (severe loss scenario). Excellent profitability (7.3).

Principal Business: Individual life insurance (78%), individual annuities (20%), and individual health insurance (3%).

Principal Investments: NonCMO investment grade bonds (45%), policy loans (20%), CMOs and structured securities (17%), noninv. grade bonds (8%), and misc. investments (10%).

Investments in Affiliates: 2%

Group Affiliation: MetLife Inc

Licensed in: All states except PR

Commenced Business: December 1980

Address: 501 Boylston St, Boston, MA 02117

Phone: (617) 578-2000 **Domicile State:** MA **NAIC Code:** 91626

Data Date	Rating	RACR #1	RACR #2	Total Assets ($mil)	Capital ($mil)	Net Premium ($mil)	Net Income ($mil)
6-16	B	5.35	2.64	10,003.1	675.2	100.8	40.2
6-15	B	5.82	2.88	10,956.9	753.0	105.1	76.3
2015	B	5.02	2.48	10,172.8	631.9	204.0	156.8
2014	B	5.04	2.48	11,179.5	675.2	-3,295.8	303.2
2013	B	3.73	2.01	11,640.2	571.1	260.1	102.7
2012	B	3.65	1.93	10,601.4	538.6	348.1	78.7
2011	B-	3.70	2.06	10,142.1	529.4	354.1	63.0

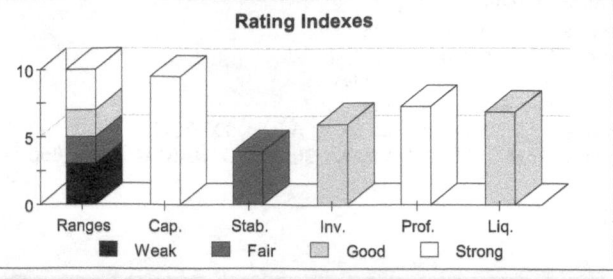

Rating Indexes

(Ranges, Cap., Stab., Inv., Prof., Liq. — Weak, Fair, Good, Strong)

NEW ERA LIFE INSURANCE COMPANY　　　　C　　　Fair

Major Rating Factors: Fair capitalization (4.5 on a scale of 0 to 10) based on fair risk adjusted capital (moderate loss scenario). Fair overall results on stability tests (4.1) including excessive premium growth and fair risk adjusted capital in prior years. Good quality investment portfolio (5.3) despite large holdings of BBB rated bonds in addition to moderate junk bond exposure. Exposure to mortgages is significant, but the mortgage default rate has been low.

Other Rating Factors: Good liquidity (6.8). Excellent profitability (8.6).

Principal Business: Individual health insurance (53%), individual annuities (45%), and individual life insurance (1%).

Principal Investments: NonCMO investment grade bonds (47%), mortgages in good standing (17%), common & preferred stock (12%), CMOs and structured securities (11%), and misc. investments (13%).

Investments in Affiliates: 11%

Group Affiliation: New Era Life Group

Licensed in: AL, AZ, AR, CA, CO, DE, FL, GA, IN, KS, KY, LA, MI, MS, MO, MT, NE, NM, NC, ND, OH, OK, PA, SC, SD, TN, TX, UT, WA, WV

Commenced Business: June 1924

Address: 11720 Katy Freeway Suite 1700, Houston, TX 77079

Phone: (281) 368-7200 **Domicile State:** TX **NAIC Code:** 78743

Data Date	Rating	RACR #1	RACR #2	Total Assets ($mil)	Capital ($mil)	Net Premium ($mil)	Net Income ($mil)
6-16	C	0.91	0.69	472.4	71.5	93.2	1.3
6-15	C	0.97	0.75	437.1	68.5	54.5	2.4
2015	C	0.95	0.73	463.5	70.7	111.2	5.1
2014	C	0.95	0.73	402.5	66.2	99.3	4.3
2013	C	0.90	0.69	371.3	58.0	77.3	4.6
2012	C	0.86	0.65	352.2	52.0	68.3	2.1
2011	C	0.81	0.62	353.6	47.1	67.0	-4.2

Risk-Adjusted Capital Ratio #1
(Moderate Loss Scenario)

(Range, 2011, 2012, 2013, 2014, 2015, 6-16 — Weak, Fair, Good)

NEW YORK LIFE INSURANCE & ANNUITY CORPORATION *　　B+　　Good

Major Rating Factors: Good quality investment portfolio (6.1 on a scale of 0 to 10) despite large holdings of BBB rated bonds in addition to junk bond exposure equal to 60% of capital. Exposure to mortgages is significant, but the mortgage default rate has been low. Good liquidity (6.6) with sufficient resources to cover a large increase in policy surrenders. Good overall results on stability tests (6.7) excellent operational trends and excellent risk diversification.

Other Rating Factors: Strong capitalization (8.2) based on excellent risk adjusted capital (severe loss scenario). Excellent profitability (8.2).

Principal Business: Individual annuities (81%), individual life insurance (17%), group retirement contracts (1%), and group life insurance (1%).

Principal Investments: NonCMO investment grade bonds (51%), CMOs and structured securities (27%), mortgages in good standing (14%), noninv. grade bonds (6%), and misc. investments (3%).

Investments in Affiliates: 3%

Group Affiliation: New York Life Group

Licensed in: All states except PR

Commenced Business: December 1980

Address: 200 Continental Dr, Newark, DE 19713

Phone: (212) 576-7000 **Domicile State:** DE **NAIC Code:** 91596

Data Date	Rating	RACR #1	RACR #2	Total Assets ($mil)	Capital ($mil)	Net Premium ($mil)	Net Income ($mil)
6-16	B+	3.78	1.83	137,896	8,383.1	7,262.2	230.4
6-15	B+	3.42	1.67	130,332	7,831.4	6,294.4	361.0
2015	B+	3.80	1.85	132,239	8,145.8	12,674.2	396.8
2014	B+	3.46	1.70	126,837	7,668.5	12,028.2	742.7
2013	B+	3.15	1.53	119,947	6,748.1	10,411.6	798.0
2012	B+	3.16	1.53	109,510	6,398.6	8,330.2	638.9
2011	B+	2.95	1.42	103,287	5,794.2	9,219.5	293.9

Adverse Trends in Operations

Increase in policy surrenders from 2013 to 2014 (45%)
Decrease in premium volume from 2011 to 2012 (10%)

NEW YORK LIFE INSURANCE COMPANY *　　　　A-　　Excellent

Major Rating Factors: Good quality investment portfolio (6.0 on a scale of 0 to 10) despite substantial holdings of BBB bonds in addition to moderate junk bond exposure. Exposure to mortgages is significant, but the mortgage default rate has been low. Good liquidity (6.6) with sufficient resources to handle a spike in claims as well as a significant increase in policy surrenders. Strong capitalization (7.3) based on excellent risk adjusted capital (severe loss scenario).

Other Rating Factors: Excellent profitability (7.3). Excellent overall results on stability tests (7.0) excellent operational trends and excellent risk diversification.

Principal Business: Reinsurance (44%), individual life insurance (27%), group retirement contracts (19%), group life insurance (7%), and individual health insurance (1%).

Principal Investments: NonCMO investment grade bonds (46%), CMOs and structured securities (15%), mortgages in good standing (11%), policy loans (8%), and misc. investments (20%).

Investments in Affiliates: 11%
Group Affiliation: New York Life Group
Licensed in: All states, the District of Columbia and Puerto Rico
Commenced Business: April 1845
Address: 51 Madison Ave, New York, NY 10010
Phone: (212) 576-7000 **Domicile State:** NY **NAIC Code:** 66915

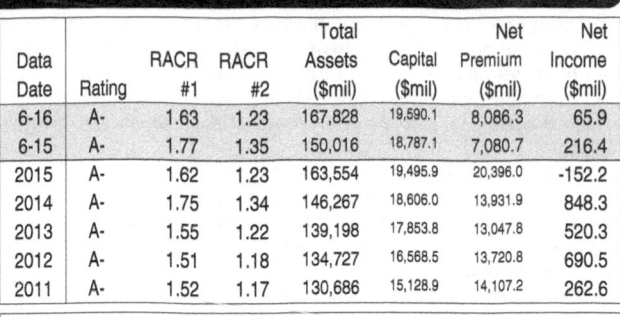

Data Date	Rating	RACR #1	RACR #2	Total Assets ($mil)	Capital ($mil)	Net Premium ($mil)	Net Income ($mil)
6-16	A-	1.63	1.23	167,828	19,590.1	8,086.3	65.9
6-15	A-	1.77	1.35	150,016	18,787.1	7,080.7	216.4
2015	A-	1.62	1.23	163,554	19,495.9	20,396.0	-152.2
2014	A-	1.75	1.34	146,267	18,606.0	13,931.9	848.3
2013	A-	1.55	1.22	139,198	17,853.8	13,047.8	520.3
2012	A-	1.51	1.18	134,727	16,568.5	13,720.8	690.5
2011	A-	1.52	1.17	130,686	15,128.9	14,107.2	262.6

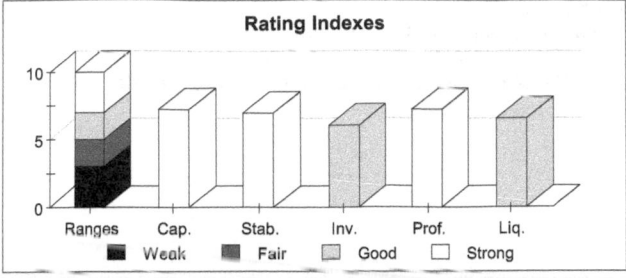

Rating Indexes (Ranges, Cap., Stab., Inv., Prof., Liq. — Weak, Fair, Good, Strong)

NIPPON LIFE INSURANCE COMPANY OF AMERICA *　　　A-　　Excellent

Major Rating Factors: Good liquidity (6.6 on a scale of 0 to 10) with sufficient resources to handle a spike in claims. Strong capitalization (10.0) based on excellent risk adjusted capital (severe loss scenario). Furthermore, this high level of risk adjusted capital has been consistently maintained over the last five years. High quality investment portfolio (8.3).

Other Rating Factors: Excellent profitability (7.4) despite operating losses during the first six months of 2016. Excellent overall results on stability tests (7.0) excellent operational trends and excellent risk diversification.

Principal Business: Group health insurance (99%) and group life insurance (1%).

Principal Investments: NonCMO investment grade bonds (75%), CMOs and structured securities (12%), cash (2%), and common & preferred stock (1%).

Investments in Affiliates: None
Group Affiliation: Nippon Life Ins Co Japan
Licensed in: All states except ME, NH, WY, PR
Commenced Business: July 1973
Address: 650 8th St, Des Moines, IA 50309
Phone: (212) 682-3992 **Domicile State:** IA **NAIC Code:** 81264

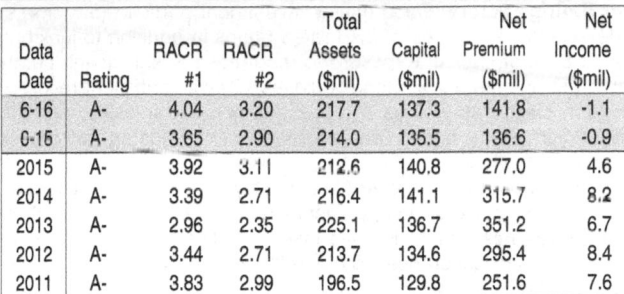

Data Date	Rating	RACR #1	RACR #2	Total Assets ($mil)	Capital ($mil)	Net Premium ($mil)	Net Income ($mil)
6-16	A-	4.04	3.20	217.7	137.3	141.8	-1.1
6-15	A-	3.65	2.90	214.0	135.5	136.6	-0.9
2015	A-	3.92	3.11	212.6	140.8	277.0	4.6
2014	A-	3.39	2.71	216.4	141.1	315.7	8.2
2013	A-	2.96	2.35	225.1	136.7	351.2	6.7
2012	A-	3.44	2.71	213.7	134.6	295.4	8.4
2011	A-	3.83	2.99	196.5	129.8	251.6	7.6

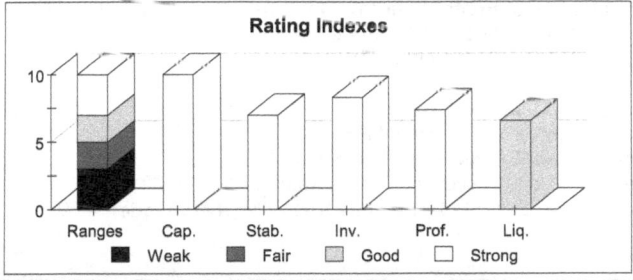

Rating Indexes (Ranges, Cap., Stab., Inv., Prof., Liq. — Weak, Fair, Good, Strong)

NORTH AMERICAN COMPANY FOR LIFE & HEALTH INSURANCE　　B　　Good

Major Rating Factors: Good capitalization (6.3 on a scale of 0 to 10) based on good risk adjusted capital (moderate loss scenario). Capital levels have been relatively consistent over the last five years. Good liquidity (5.9) with sufficient resources to cover a large increase in policy surrenders. Good overall results on stability tests (5.8) despite excessive premium growth excellent operational trends and excellent risk diversification.

Other Rating Factors: Fair quality investment portfolio (3.8). Excellent profitability (7.6) despite modest operating losses during 2015.

Principal Business: Individual annuities (60%), individual life insurance (29%), group retirement contracts (9%), group life insurance (1%), and reinsurance (1%).

Principal Investments: NonCMO investment grade bonds (45%), CMOs and structured securities (34%), mortgages in good standing (11%), noninv. grade bonds (5%), and common & preferred stock (1%).

Investments in Affiliates: None
Group Affiliation: Sammons Enterprises Inc
Licensed in: All states except NY
Commenced Business: June 1886
Address: 525 W VanBuren, Chicago, IL 60607
Phone: (312) 648-7600 **Domicile State:** IA **NAIC Code:** 66974

Data Date	Rating	RACR #1	RACR #2	Total Assets ($mil)	Capital ($mil)	Net Premium ($mil)	Net Income ($mil)
6-16	B	1.86	0.86	20,376.2	1,096.9	1,506.5	-28.1
6-15	B	2.10	0.96	17,888.6	1,142.6	994.0	2.0
2015	B	1.92	0.88	18,900.2	1,129.3	2,317.2	-44.8
2014	B	2.29	1.06	16,970.0	1,176.7	1,653.4	85.4
2013	B	2.38	1.09	15,021.7	1,065.1	1,713.6	121.9
2012	B	2.55	1.18	13,018.7	977.4	1,576.0	130.2
2011	B	2.22	1.02	11,728.9	842.9	2,064.4	135.5

Risk-Adjusted Capital Ratio #1 (Moderate Loss Scenario) — Range, 2011, 2012, 2013, 2014, 2015, 6-16 — Weak, Fair, Good

NORTHWESTERN LONG TERM CARE INSURANCE COMPANY   B   Good

Major Rating Factors: Good liquidity (6.1 on a scale of 0 to 10) with sufficient resources to handle a spike in claims. Good overall results on stability tests (6.0) despite negative cash flow from operations for 2015. Strengths include potential support from affiliation with Northwestern Mutual Group, good operational trends, good risk adjusted capital for prior years and excellent risk diversification. Fair profitability (3.6).

Other Rating Factors: Strong capitalization (9.4) based on excellent risk adjusted capital (severe loss scenario). High quality investment portfolio (9.6).

Principal Business: Individual health insurance (100%).

Principal Investments: NonCMO investment grade bonds (93%) and cash (7%).

Investments in Affiliates: None

Group Affiliation: Northwestern Mutual Group

Licensed in: All states except PR

Commenced Business: October 1953

Address: 720 E Wisconsin Ave, Milwaukee, WI 53202

Phone: (414) 299-3136   **Domicile State:** WI   **NAIC Code:** 69000

Data Date	Rating	RACR #1	RACR #2	Total Assets ($mil)	Capital ($mil)	Net Premium ($mil)	Net Income ($mil)
6-16	B	6.54	2.63	166.0	80.9	0.2	1.4
6-15	B	8.18	7.36	158.4	78.2	0.2	1.2
2015	B	6.57	2.65	166.0	79.5	0.3	2.5
2014	B	8.08	7.27	161.4	77.2	-1,548.3	403.6
2013	B	1.76	0.99	2,220.1	213.8	457.3	-84.2
2012	B	2.45	1.40	1,861.6	274.7	387.1	-192.9
2011	B	2.14	1.29	1,193.9	210.1	300.6	10.5

Northwestern Mutual Group Composite Group Rating: A- Largest Group Members	Assets ($mil)	Rating
NORTHWESTERN MUTUAL LIFE INS CO	238544	A-
NORTHWESTERN LONG TERM CARE INS CO	166	B

NORTHWESTERN MUTUAL LIFE INSURANCE COMPANY *   A-   Excellent

Major Rating Factors: Good quality investment portfolio (5.8 on a scale of 0 to 10) despite large holdings of BBB rated bonds in addition to junk bond exposure equal to 68% of capital. Exposure to mortgages is significant, but the mortgage default rate has been low. Good liquidity (5.7) with sufficient resources to handle a spike in claims as well as a significant increase in policy surrenders. Strong capitalization (8.1) based on excellent risk adjusted capital (severe loss scenario).

Other Rating Factors: Excellent profitability (7.0). Excellent overall results on stability tests (7.3) excellent operational trends and excellent risk diversification.

Principal Business: Individual life insurance (77%), individual annuities (13%), individual health insurance (6%), reinsurance (3%), and group retirement contracts (1%).

Principal Investments: NonCMO investment grade bonds (42%), CMOs and structured securities (18%), mortgages in good standing (16%), policy loans (8%), and misc. investments (16%).

Investments in Affiliates: 4%

Group Affiliation: Northwestern Mutual Group

Licensed in: All states except PR

Commenced Business: November 1858

Address: 720 E Wisconsin Ave, Milwaukee, WI 53202

Phone: (414) 271-1444   **Domicile State:** WI   **NAIC Code:** 67091

Data Date	Rating	RACR #1	RACR #2	Total Assets ($mil)	Capital ($mil)	Net Premium ($mil)	Net Income ($mil)
6-16	A-	3.47	1.74	244,873	20,053.9	8,784.4	410.6
6-15	A-	3.56	1.81	236,021	19,447.2	8,749.0	495.9
2015	A-	3.57	1.81	238,544	19,659.6	17,581.3	801.2
2014	A-	3.59	1.83	230,004	19,055.1	18,362.1	330.9
2013	A-	3.60	1.84	215,165	17,198.8	15,995.2	886.4
2012	A-	3.15	1.71	200,945	16,175.8	14,924.6	976.7
2011	A-	2.87	1.56	188,692	14,813.4	14,255.1	634.6

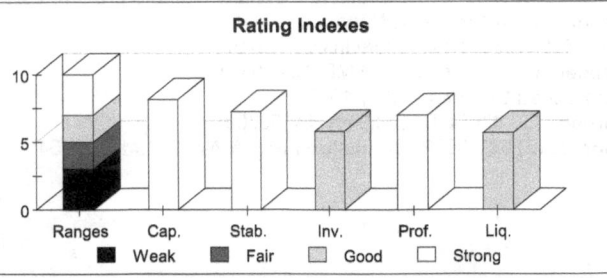

Rating Indexes

NYLIFE INSURANCE COMPANY OF ARIZONA   B   Good

Major Rating Factors: Good overall profitability (6.9 on a scale of 0 to 10). Excellent expense controls. Good overall results on stability tests (5.6). Stability strengths include good operational trends and excellent risk diversification. Strong capitalization (10.0) based on excellent risk adjusted capital (severe loss scenario). Moreover, capital levels have been consistently high over the last five years.

Other Rating Factors: High quality investment portfolio (8.3). Excellent liquidity (7.2).

Principal Business: Individual life insurance (99%) and reinsurance (1%).

Principal Investments: NonCMO investment grade bonds (78%), CMOs and structured securities (22%), and noninv. grade bonds (1%).

Investments in Affiliates: None

Group Affiliation: New York Life Group

Licensed in: All states except ME, NY, PR

Commenced Business: December 1987

Address: 14850 N Scottsdale Rd Ste 400, Scottsdale, AZ 85254

Phone: (212) 576-7000   **Domicile State:** AZ   **NAIC Code:** 81353

Data Date	Rating	RACR #1	RACR #2	Total Assets ($mil)	Capital ($mil)	Net Premium ($mil)	Net Income ($mil)
6-16	B	9.29	6.07	199.0	98.2	9.6	6.4
6-15	B	6.98	4.62	197.6	85.3	12.4	5.2
2015	B	8.61	5.63	200.5	91.2	23.3	12.0
2014	B	6.39	4.20	199.8	79.6	33.0	11.0
2013	B	6.08	3.94	194.9	68.2	24.9	8.1
2012	B	4.84	3.14	197.1	59.0	29.4	3.8
2011	B	4.48	2.93	199.7	59.5	35.2	0.8

Adverse Trends in Operations
Decrease in premium volume from 2014 to 2015 (29%)
Decrease in premium volume from 2012 to 2013 (15%)
Decrease in asset base during 2013 (1%)
Decrease in asset base during 2012 (1%)
Decrease in premium volume from 2011 to 2012 (16%)

OCCIDENTAL LIFE INSURANCE COMPANY OF NORTH CAROLIN — C — Fair

Major Rating Factors: Fair overall results on stability tests (4.2 on a scale of 0 to 10) including fair financial strength of affiliated Industrial Alliance Ins & Financial. Fair profitability (3.0) with investment income below regulatory standards in relation to interest assumptions of reserves. Good liquidity (5.4).
Other Rating Factors: Strong capitalization (8.5) based on excellent risk adjusted capital (severe loss scenario). High quality investment portfolio (7.4).
Principal Business: N/A
Principal Investments: NonCMO investment grade bonds (80%), mortgages in good standing (10%), policy loans (4%), common & preferred stock (2%), and misc. Investments (3%).
Investments in Affiliates: None
Group Affiliation: Industrial Alliance Ins & Financial
Licensed in: All states except NY
Commenced Business: November 1906
Address: 425 Austin Avenue, Waco, TX 76701
Phone: (254) 297-2775 **Domicile State:** TX **NAIC Code:** 67148

Data Date	Rating	RACR #1	RACR #2	Total Assets ($mil)	Capital ($mil)	Net Premium ($mil)	Net Income ($mil)
6-16	C	3.27	2.01	254.7	32.9	17.2	1.5
6-15	C	2.90	1.75	251.0	29.0	17.1	3.2
2015	C	3.17	1.93	256.7	31.7	34.6	7.6
2014	C	3.66	2.19	261.4	36.9	34.0	3.7
2013	C	3.30	2.01	249.9	33.0	37.1	5.3
2012	C	2.79	1.71	246.9	28.0	41.1	1.8
2011	C	1.64	0.95	259.6	22.0	39.1	3.4

Industrial Alliance Ins Financial
Composite Group Rating: C

Largest Group Members	Assets ($mil)	Rating
AMERICAN-AMICABLE LIFE INS CO OF TX	287	C
OCCIDENTAL LIFE INS CO OF NC	257	C
IA AMERICAN LIFE INS CO	229	B-
INDUSTRIAL ALLIANCE INS FIN SERV	202	C-
PIONEER SECURITY LIFE INS CO	125	C+

OHIO NATIONAL LIFE ASSURANCE CORPORATION * — B+ — Good

Major Rating Factors: Good overall results on stability tests (6.4 on a scale of 0 to 10). Stability strengths include excellent operational trends and excellent risk diversification. Good quality investment portfolio (5.6) despite large holdings of BBB rated bonds in addition to moderate junk bond exposure. Exposure to mortgages is significant, but the mortgage default rate has been low. Good overall profitability (5.8).
Other Rating Factors: Good liquidity (5.5). Strong capitalization (7.2) based on excellent risk adjusted capital (severe loss scenario).
Principal Business: Individual life insurance (96%) and individual health insurance (3%).
Principal Investments: NonCMO investment grade bonds (62%), CMOs and structured securities (16%), mortgages in good standing (12%), noninv. grade bonds (4%), and misc. investments (4%).
Investments in Affiliates: None
Group Affiliation: Ohio Natonal Mutual Inc
Licensed in: All states except NY
Commenced Business: August 1979
Address: One Financial Way, Cincinnati, OH 45242
Phone: (513) 794-6100 **Domicile State:** OH **NAIC Code:** 89206

Data Date	Rating	RACR #1	RACR #2	Total Assets ($mil)	Capital ($mil)	Net Premium ($mil)	Net Income ($mil)
6-16	B+	2.21	1.14	3,833.0	275.9	117.0	4.6
6-15	B+	2.21	1.18	3,674.2	284.3	134.4	2.1
2015	B+	2.33	1.22	3,688.5	281.5	238.1	20.8
2014	B+	2.30	1.23	3,605.8	296.0	281.2	18.1
2013	B+	2.82	1.45	3,408.1	316.8	278.6	13.6
2012	B+	2.76	1.42	3,315.3	317.4	213.1	30.1
2011	B+	2.96	1.53	3,172.5	332.4	205.9	34.6

Adverse Trends in Operations

Decrease in capital during 2015 (5%)
Decrease in premium volume from 2014 to 2015 (15%)
Change in premium mix from 2013 to 2014 (5%)
Decrease in capital during 2014 (7%)
Decrease in capital during 2013 (3%)

OHIO NATIONAL LIFE INSURANCE COMPANY — B — Good

Major Rating Factors: Good current capitalization (6.8 on a scale of 0 to 10) based on good risk adjusted capital (severe loss scenario), although results have slipped from the excellent range during the last year. Good quality investment portfolio (5.7) despite significant exposure to mortgages . Mortgage default rate has been low. large holdings of BBB rated bonds in addition to small junk bond holdings. Good overall results on stability tests (5.8) excellent operational trends and excellent risk diversification.
Other Rating Factors: Excellent profitability (7.7). Excellent liquidity (7.9).
Principal Business: Individual annuities (68%), individual life insurance (17%), group retirement contracts (9%), and reinsurance (6%).
Principal Investments: NonCMO investment grade bonds (50%), CMOs and structured securities (18%), mortgages in good standing (11%), common & preferred stock (6%), and misc. investments (12%).
Investments in Affiliates: 5%
Group Affiliation: Ohio Natonal Mutual Inc
Licensed in: All states except NY
Commenced Business: October 1910
Address: One Financial Way, Cincinnati, OH 45242
Phone: (513) 794-6100 **Domicile State:** OH **NAIC Code:** 67172

Data Date	Rating	RACR #1	RACR #2	Total Assets ($mil)	Capital ($mil)	Net Premium ($mil)	Net Income ($mil)
6-16	B	1.47	0.98	28,044.7	1,061.4	1,137.7	6.1
6-15	B	1.49	1.00	28,147.8	1,042.7	1,309.4	15.1
2015	B	1.52	1.03	27,589.8	1,087.2	2,538.3	62.7
2014	B	1.59	1.07	27,449.3	1,097.1	2,758.9	90.4
2013	B	1.38	0.97	25,381.8	1,002.7	2,830.6	61.6
2012	B	1.33	0.96	21,631.2	1,048.3	3,259.8	107.6
2011	B	1.27	0.94	18,129.0	902.5	1,948.4	73.4

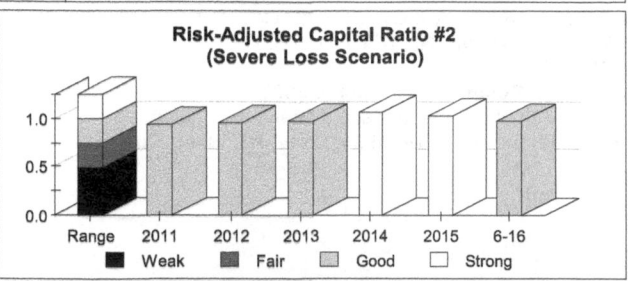

Risk-Adjusted Capital Ratio #2
(Severe Loss Scenario)

OLD REPUBLIC LIFE INSURANCE COMPANY

B-   **Good**

Major Rating Factors: Good quality investment portfolio (5.4 on a scale of 0 to 10) despite mixed results such as: no exposure to mortgages and substantial holdings of BBB bonds but minimal holdings in junk bonds. Good liquidity (6.8) with sufficient resources to handle a spike in claims. Good overall results on stability tests (5.2) good operational trends and excellent risk diversification.

Other Rating Factors: Weak profitability (2.8) with operating losses during the first six months of 2016. Strong capitalization (8.3) based on excellent risk adjusted capital (severe loss scenario).

Principal Business: Group health insurance (55%), individual life insurance (32%), and reinsurance (13%).

Principal Investments: NonCMO investment grade bonds (81%), common & preferred stock (14%), noninv. grade bonds (2%), cash (2%), and policy loans (1%).

Investments in Affiliates: None

Group Affiliation: Old Republic Group

Licensed in: All states except NY

Commenced Business: April 1923

Address: 307 N Michigan Ave, Chicago, IL 60601

Phone: (312) 346-8100 **Domicile State:** IL **NAIC Code:** 67261

Data Date	Rating	RACR #1	RACR #2	Total Assets ($mil)	Capital ($mil)	Net Premium ($mil)	Net Income ($mil)
6-16	B-	2.98	1.84	125.5	29.1	9.1	-0.4
6-15	B-	3.10	1.94	124.5	29.9	8.6	0.5
2015	B-	2.84	1.77	126.9	27.0	18.1	-0.3
2014	B-	3.22	2.02	125.1	30.6	20.1	0.8
2013	B-	4.30	2.81	131.7	36.4	21.2	2.2
2012	B	4.68	3.13	138.4	40.6	21.0	1.6
2011	B+	4.69	3.12	142.3	41.0	22.4	4.8

Adverse Trends in Operations

Decrease in capital during 2015 (12%)
Decrease in capital during 2014 (16%)
Decrease in capital during 2013 (10%)
Decrease in premium volume from 2011 to 2012 (6%)
Increase in policy surrenders from 2011 to 2012 (75%)

OLD UNITED LIFE INSURANCE COMPANY

B   **Good**

Major Rating Factors: Good overall profitability (5.8 on a scale of 0 to 10). Fair overall results on stability tests (4.8) including excessive premium growth. Strong overall capitalization (10.0) based on excellent risk adjusted capital (severe loss scenario). Nevertheless, capital levels have fluctuated during prior years.

Other Rating Factors: High quality investment portfolio (7.3). Excellent liquidity (10.0).

Principal Business: Credit health insurance (51%) and credit life insurance (49%).

Principal Investments: NonCMO investment grade bonds (78%), CMOs and structured securities (15%), noninv. grade bonds (5%), and common & preferred stock (2%).

Investments in Affiliates: None

Group Affiliation: Berkshire Hathaway Inc

Licensed in: All states except ME, NH, NY, PR

Commenced Business: January 1964

Address: 8500 W Shawnee Mission Pky 200, Merriam, KS 66202

Phone: (913) 432-6400 **Domicile State:** AZ **NAIC Code:** 76007

Data Date	Rating	RACR #1	RACR #2	Total Assets ($mil)	Capital ($mil)	Net Premium ($mil)	Net Income ($mil)
6-16	B	5.71	5.14	81.3	43.4	3.8	1.3
6-15	B	6.31	3.80	92.3	50.6	2.9	3.0
2015	B	5.56	5.01	82.5	42.0	6.2	4.2
2014	B	6.13	3.70	91.4	46.3	8.2	2.4
2013	B	6.08	3.55	87.4	44.9	8.5	0.4
2012	B	5.95	3.86	82.3	43.9	9.8	1.0
2011	B	6.03	5.15	76.2	43.6	4.9	2.2

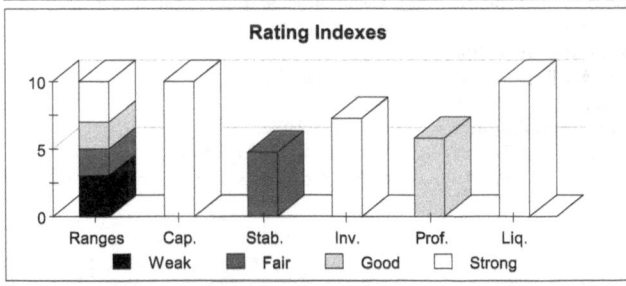

Rating Indexes

OMAHA INS CO

C+   **Fair**

Major Rating Factors: Fair overall results on stability tests (3.2 on a scale of 0 to 10) including excessive premium growth, weak results on operational trends and negative cash flow from operations for 2015. Good liquidity (5.3) with sufficient resources to handle a spike in claims. Weak profitability (1.9) with operating losses during the first six months of 2016.

Other Rating Factors: Strong capitalization (7.9) based on excellent risk adjusted capital (severe loss scenario). High quality investment portfolio (8.2).

Principal Business: Individual health insurance (100%).

Principal Investments: NonCMO investment grade bonds (59%), CMOs and structured securities (26%), and cash (15%).

Investments in Affiliates: None

Group Affiliation: Mutual Of Omaha Group

Licensed in: AK, AZ, AR, CT, DC, DE, GA, HI, IN, IA, KS, KY, ME, MD, MA, MI, MN, MS, MO, MT, NE, NJ, NM, ND, OH, OK, OR, PA, SC, SD, TN, TX, UT, VA, WA, WV, WY

Commenced Business: November 2006

Address: Mutual of Omaha Plaza, Omaha, NE 68175

Phone: (402) 342-7600 **Domicile State:** NE **NAIC Code:** 13100

Data Date	Rating	RACR #1	RACR #2	Total Assets ($mil)	Capital ($mil)	Net Premium ($mil)	Net Income ($mil)
6-16	C+	2.98	1.59	83.9	52.0	20.6	-2.4
6-15	B-	1.69	0.91	45.8	20.0	13.1	-1.1
2015	C+	3.70	1.97	88.2	54.1	29.3	-5.4
2014	B-	2.47	1.33	43.8	21.1	14.3	-3.9
2013	B-	4.16	2.72	22.9	15.9	5.1	-2.0
2012	B-	4.64	4.18	19.9	16.3	0.6	-2.2
2011	U	4.23	3.81	10.5	10.5	0.0	0.0

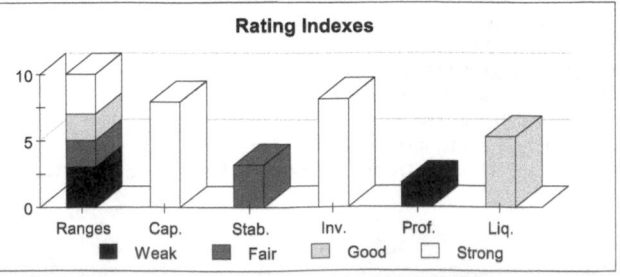

Rating Indexes

OPTIMUM RE INSURANCE COMPANY

C+   **Fair**

Major Rating Factors: Fair overall results on stability tests (4.6 on a scale of 0 to 10). Weak profitability (2.4) with investment income below regulatory standards in relation to interest assumptions of reserves. Strong capitalization (8.0) based on excellent risk adjusted capital (severe loss scenario). Moreover, capital levels have been consistently high over the last five years.

Other Rating Factors: High quality investment portfolio (7.3). Excellent liquidity (8.8).

Principal Business: Reinsurance (100%).

Principal Investments: NonCMO investment grade bonds (90%), noninv. grade bonds (2%), cash (2%), real estate (2%), and common & preferred stock (1%).

Investments in Affiliates: None

Group Affiliation: Optimum Group Inc

Licensed in: All states except NY

Commenced Business: June 1978

Address: 2505 Turtle Creek Blvd, Dallas, TX 75219-4713

Phone: (214) 528-2020 **Domicile State:** TX **NAIC Code:** 88099

Data Date	Rating	RACR #1	RACR #2	Total Assets ($mil)	Capital ($mil)	Net Premium ($mil)	Net Income ($mil)
6-16	C+	2.70	1.69	153.8	34.4	19.1	2.9
6-15	C+	2.44	1.54	134.9	31.3	19.2	2.5
2015	C+	2.46	1.52	145.9	31.5	38.1	4.4
2014	C+	2.25	1.42	132.7	29.2	44.2	2.2
2013	B-	2.36	1.51	114.9	27.9	44.3	2.0
2012	B-	2.12	1.38	103.7	26.7	45.6	2.1
2011	B-	1.81	1.18	92.5	26.2	45.0	2.6

Rating Indexes

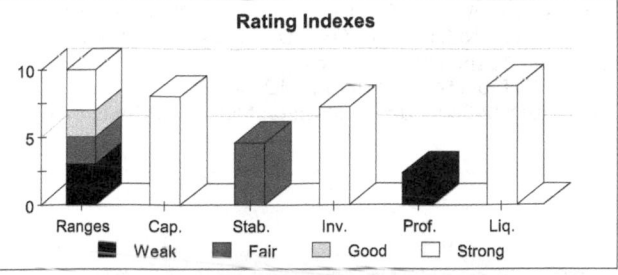

Ranges | Cap. | Stab. | Inv. | Prof. | Liq.

■ Weak ▧ Fair ▨ Good ☐ Strong

OPTUM INSURANCE OF OHIO INC

B   **Good**

Major Rating Factors: Good overall results on stability tests (5.5 on a scale of 0 to 10) despite fair financial strength of affiliated UnitedHealth Group Inc. Other stability subfactors include good operational trends and excellent risk diversification. Strong capitalization (8.0) based on excellent risk adjusted capital (severe loss scenario). Moreover, capital levels have been consistently high over the last five years. High quality investment portfolio (9.8).

Other Rating Factors: Excellent profitability (7.7) despite modest operating losses during 2011. Excellent liquidity (7.0).

Principal Business: Individual life insurance (85%) and individual annuities (14%).

Principal Investments: Cash (85%) and nonCMO investment grade bonds (15%).

Investments in Affiliates: None

Group Affiliation: UnitedHealth Group Inc

Licensed in: All states except ME, NY, PR

Commenced Business: December 1978

Address: 50 W Broad St Suite 1800, Columbus, OH 43215

Phone: (630) 577-3100 **Domicile State:** OH **NAIC Code:** 69647

Data Date	Rating	RACR #1	RACR #2	Total Assets ($mil)	Capital ($mil)	Net Premium ($mil)	Net Income ($mil)
6-16	B	4.06	3.65	113.1	37.6	0.0	4.5
6-15	B	4.19	3.77	40.5	26.1	0.0	5.2
2015	B+	3.11	3.07	147.0	31.5	0.0	10.6
2014	C+	2.00	1.80	52.3	20.3	0.0	12.0
2013	C+	4.16	3.75	9.2	8.9	0.0	0.3
2012	C+	4.15	3.73	8.9	8.6	0.0	0.0
2011	C+	4.16	3.74	8.9	8.6	0.0	0.0

UnitedHealth Group Inc
Composite Group Rating: C+
Largest Group Members

	Assets ($mil)	Rating
UNITED HEALTHCARE INS CO	15791	C
OXFORD HEALTH INS INC	2195	B
SIERRA HEALTH AND LIFE INS CO INC	1677	B
UNITED HEALTHCARE INS CO OF NY	1223	B-
UNITEDHEALTHCARE PLAN RIVER VALLEY	1131	B-

OXFORD LIFE INSURANCE COMPANY

B   **Good**

Major Rating Factors: Good quality investment portfolio (5.9 on a scale of 0 to 10) despite significant exposure to mortgages . Mortgage default rate has been low. large holdings of BBB rated bonds in addition to small junk bond holdings. Good liquidity (6.6) with sufficient resources to handle a spike in claims as well as a significant increase in policy surrenders. Good overall results on stability tests (5.6) good operational trends and excellent risk diversification.

Other Rating Factors: Strong capitalization (7.5) based on excellent risk adjusted capital (severe loss scenario). Excellent profitability (8.8).

Principal Business: Individual annuities (72%), individual life insurance (13%), individual health insurance (11%), and reinsurance (4%).

Principal Investments: NonCMO investment grade bonds (75%), mortgages in good standing (12%), CMOs and structured securities (5%), common & preferred stock (3%), and misc. investments (4%).

Investments in Affiliates: 4%

Group Affiliation: Amerco Corp

Licensed in: All states except NY, VT, PR

Commenced Business: June 1968

Address: 2721 N Central Ave, Phoenix, AZ 85004-1120

Phone: (602) 263-6666 **Domicile State:** AZ **NAIC Code:** 76112

Data Date	Rating	RACR #1	RACR #2	Total Assets ($mil)	Capital ($mil)	Net Premium ($mil)	Net Income ($mil)
6-16	B	1.96	1.31	1,599.4	177.8	167.4	2.0
6-15	B-	1.43	1.04	1,341.4	164.5	161.3	1.7
2015	B	2.00	1.39	1,490.4	172.3	372.2	12.2
2014	B-	1.64	1.19	1,197.5	158.5	191.4	12.1
2013	B-	2.05	1.42	1,097.7	148.5	197.1	11.1
2012	B-	2.04	1.45	968.6	137.7	350.9	19.7
2011	B-	1.73	1.35	693.5	129.4	188.5	4.0

Adverse Trends in Operations

Increase in policy surrenders from 2013 to 2014 (52%)
Decrease in premium volume from 2013 to 2014 (3%)
Increase in policy surrenders from 2012 to 2013 (26%)
Decrease in premium volume from 2012 to 2013 (44%)
Change in premium mix from 2011 to 2012 (15.6%)

OZARK NATIONAL LIFE INSURANCE COMPANY · B- · Good

Major Rating Factors: Good liquidity (6.5 on a scale of 0 to 10) with sufficient resources to handle a spike in claims as well as a significant increase in policy surrenders. Fair overall results on stability tests (4.9). Weak profitability (2.8) with investment income below regulatory standards in relation to interest assumptions of reserves.

Other Rating Factors: Strong capitalization (9.8) based on excellent risk adjusted capital (severe loss scenario). High quality investment portfolio (7.9).

Principal Business: Individual life insurance (99%).

Principal Investments: NonCMO investment grade bonds (79%), CMOs and structured securities (17%), policy loans (3%), and real estate (1%).

Investments in Affiliates: None

Group Affiliation: CNS Corp

Licensed in: AL, AZ, AR, CA, CO, FL, GA, IL, IN, IA, KS, KY, LA, MI, MN, MS, MO, MT, NE, NV, NM, ND, OH, OK, SD, TN, TX, UT, WI, WY

Commenced Business: June 1964

Address: 500 E 9th St, Kansas City, MO 64106

Phone: (816) 842-6300 **Domicile State:** MO **NAIC Code:** 67393

Data Date	Rating	RACR #1	RACR #2	Total Assets ($mil)	Capital ($mil)	Net Premium ($mil)	Net Income ($mil)
6-16	B-	5.00	2.87	793.4	134.2	43.1	8.0
6-15	B-	4.86	2.83	760.2	124.9	43.0	6.3
2015	B-	4.92	2.83	775.2	130.6	82.8	15.7
2014	B-	4.91	2.88	750.2	124.5	82.8	13.2
2013	B-	5.07	3.02	730.6	123.4	82.3	14.9
2012	B-	5.05	3.00	711.4	122.1	82.0	15.4
2011	B-	5.45	3.30	690.6	118.7	82.9	16.9

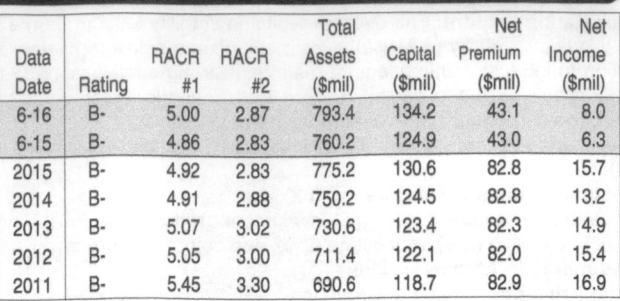

Rating Indexes

PACIFIC CENTURY LIFE INSURANCE CORPORATION · B · Good

Major Rating Factors: Good overall profitability (6.5 on a scale of 0 to 10). Fair overall results on stability tests (4.9). Strong overall capitalization (10.0) based on excellent risk adjusted capital (severe loss scenario). However, capital levels have fluctuated somewhat during past years.

Other Rating Factors: High quality investment portfolio (7.4). Excellent liquidity (10.0).

Principal Business: N/A

Principal Investments: Mortgages in good standing (89%), cash (9%), and nonCMO investment grade bonds (2%).

Investments in Affiliates: None

Group Affiliation: Bank of Hawaii Corp

Licensed in: AZ, HI

Commenced Business: February 1982

Address: 2700 N Third St Ste 2000, Phoenix, AZ 85004

Phone: (602) 200-6900 **Domicile State:** AZ **NAIC Code:** 93815

Data Date	Rating	RACR #1	RACR #2	Total Assets ($mil)	Capital ($mil)	Net Premium ($mil)	Net Income ($mil)
6-16	B	31.33	22.17	354.6	351.6	0.2	3.6
6-15	B	30.83	20.84	347.7	344.1	0.2	3.8
2015	B	31.00	21.87	351.3	347.9	0.4	7.7
2014	B	30.50	21.00	344.3	340.2	0.8	7.5
2013	B	30.00	22.50	336.8	332.8	1.1	7.4
2012	B-	30.00	25.79	336.7	332.8	1.1	7.3
2011	C+	29.82	22.97	333.4	329.8	0.7	7.7

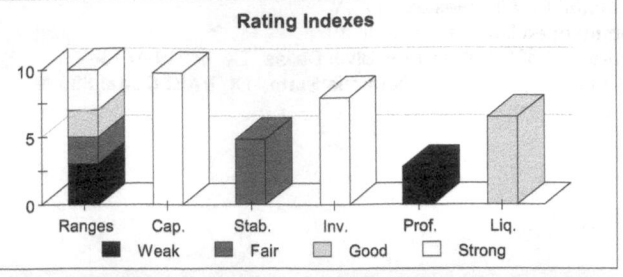

Rating Indexes

PACIFIC GUARDIAN LIFE INSURANCE COMPANY LIMITED * · A- · Excellent

Major Rating Factors: Good quality investment portfolio (6.6 on a scale of 0 to 10) despite large exposure to mortgages . Mortgage default rate has been low. substantial holdings of BBB bonds in addition to minimal holdings in junk bonds. Good overall profitability (6.5). Good liquidity (6.2).

Other Rating Factors: Strong capitalization (9.1) based on excellent risk adjusted capital (severe loss scenario). Excellent overall results on stability tests (7.0) excellent operational trends and excellent risk diversification.

Principal Business: N/A

Principal Investments: NonCMO investment grade bonds (37%), mortgages in good standing (36%), CMOs and structured securities (21%), policy loans (6%), and cash (1%).

Investments in Affiliates: None

Group Affiliation: Meiji Yasuda Life Ins Co

Licensed in: AK, AZ, CA, CO, HI, ID, IA, LA, MO, MT, NE, NV, NM, OK, OR, SD, TX, UT, WA, WY

Commenced Business: June 1962

Address: 1440 Kapiolani Blvd Ste 1700, Honolulu, HI 96814

Phone: (808) 955-2236 **Domicile State:** HI **NAIC Code:** 64343

Data Date	Rating	RACR #1	RACR #2	Total Assets ($mil)	Capital ($mil)	Net Premium ($mil)	Net Income ($mil)
6-16	A-	4.16	2.40	544.4	105.1	41.0	3.3
6-15	A-	4.38	2.52	529.0	104.3	39.4	3.6
2015	A-	4.52	2.62	528.4	108.5	70.2	6.7
2014	A-	4.72	2.73	515.6	108.8	68.4	8.1
2013	A-	5.09	2.93	504.7	108.0	69.8	6.9
2012	A-	4.98	2.91	486.8	99.8	70.5	6.2
2011	A-	4.90	2.87	464.2	99.6	66.3	7.0

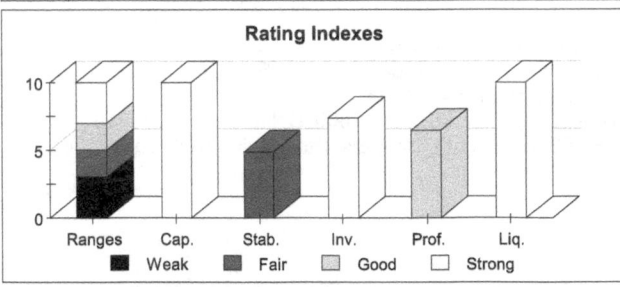

Rating Indexes

PACIFIC LIFE & ANNUITY COMPANY *   B+   Good

Major Rating Factors: Good quality investment portfolio (6.4 on a scale of 0 to 10) despite significant exposure to mortgages . Mortgage default rate has been low. large holdings of BBB rated bonds in addition to small junk bond holdings. Good overall results on stability tests (6.1). Stability strengths include good operational trends and excellent risk diversification. Strong capitalization (9.6) based on excellent risk adjusted capital (severe loss scenario).

Other Rating Factors: Excellent profitability (8.2). Excellent liquidity (8.0).

Principal Business: Individual annuities (92%), individual life insurance (6%), and reinsurance (2%).

Principal Investments: NonCMO investment grade bonds (77%), mortgages in good standing (12%), CMOs and structured securities (7%), noninv. grade bonds (2%), and cash (1%).

Investments in Affiliates: None
Group Affiliation: Pacific LifeCorp
Licensed in: All states except PR
Commenced Business: July 1983
Address: 3800 N Central Ave Suite 460, Phoenix, AZ 85012
Phone: (714) 640-3011 **Domicile State:** AZ **NAIC Code:** 97268

Data Date	Rating	RACR #1	RACR #2	Total Assets ($mil)	Capital ($mil)	Net Premium ($mil)	Net Income ($mil)
6-16	B+	5.80	2.75	6,374.0	548.7	157.3	15.4
6-15	B+	5.57	2.70	6,277.8	542.3	182.6	25.5
2015	B+	6.09	2.91	6,217.1	531.5	341.6	53.7
2014	B+	5.58	2.71	6,151.1	512.6	469.0	53.1
2013	B+	5.06	2.49	5,819.5	495.4	455.5	45.8
2012	B+	4.86	2.33	5,329.8	488.6	384.9	84.0
2011	B+	5.53	2.56	4,927.2	447.7	747.5	17.0

Adverse Trends in Operations

Decrease in premium volume from 2014 to 2015 (27%)
Decrease in premium volume from 2011 to 2012 (49%)

PACIFIC LIFE INSURANCE COMPANY *   A-   Excellent

Major Rating Factors: Good quality investment portfolio (5.9 on a scale of 0 to 10) despite significant exposure to mortgages . Mortgage default rate has been low. large holdings of BBB rated bonds in addition to small junk bond holdings. Good overall profitability (6.8). Excellent expense controls. Good liquidity (6.4).

Other Rating Factors: Good overall results on stability tests (6.9) excellent operational trends and excellent risk diversification. Strong capitalization (7.6) based on excellent risk adjusted capital (severe loss scenario).

Principal Business: Individual annuities (55%), individual life insurance (29%), reinsurance (12%), and group retirement contracts (4%).

Principal Investments: NonCMO investment grade bonds (51%), mortgages in good standing (16%), policy loans (13%), CMOs and structured securities (9%), and misc. investments (10%).

Investments in Affiliates: 6%
Group Affiliation: Pacific LifeCorp
Licensed in: All states except NY, PR
Commenced Business: May 1868
Address: 1299 Farnam St, Omaha, NE 68102
Phone: (714) 630-3011 **Domicile State:** NE **NAIC Code:** 67466

Data Date	Rating	RACR #1	RACR #2	Total Assets ($mil)	Capital ($mil)	Net Premium ($mil)	Net Income ($mil)
6-16	A-	2.09	1.43	115,113	8,045.6	4,049.2	377.4
6-15	A-	2.13	1.46	113,494	7,667.6	4,138.3	425.5
2015	A-	2.06	1.43	113,242	7,762.5	9,039.7	519.8
2014	A-	2.00	1.39	112,503	7,171.6	8,573.9	634.8
2013	A-	2.01	1.36	109,065	6,502.9	8,702.0	521.4
2012	A-	2.02	1.33	101,001	6,175.1	7,606.7	961.8
2011	A-	2.03	1.35	95,724.4	5,577.0	5,911.2	-735.5

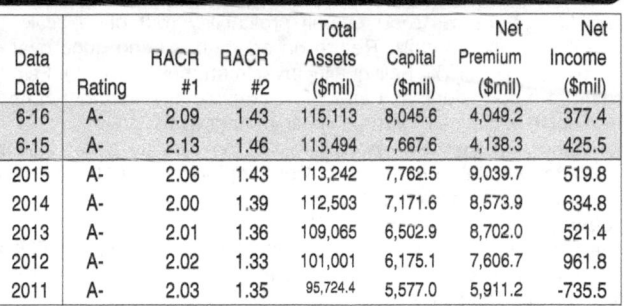

Rating Indexes

Ranges | Cap. | Stab. | Inv. | Prof. | Liq.
■ Weak ■ Fair ▨ Good ☐ Strong

PACIFICARE LIFE & HEALTH INSURANCE COMPANY   C+   Fair

Major Rating Factors: Fair overall results on stability tests (3.4 on a scale of 0 to 10) including fair financial strength of affiliated UnitedHealth Group Inc. Good overall profitability (5.4). Excellent expense controls. Strong overall capitalization (10.0) based on excellent risk adjusted capital (severe loss scenario). Nevertheless, capital levels have fluctuated during prior years.

Other Rating Factors: High quality investment portfolio (8.2). Excellent liquidity (9.6).

Principal Business: Individual health insurance (73%) and group health insurance (27%).

Principal Investments: NonCMO investment grade bonds (77%) and CMOs and structured securities (24%).

Investments in Affiliates: None
Group Affiliation: UnitedHealth Group Inc
Licensed in: All states except NY, PR
Commenced Business: September 1967
Address: 23046 Avenida Dela Carlota 700, Laguna Hills, CA 92653-1519
Phone: (714) 226-3321 **Domicile State:** IN **NAIC Code:** 70785

Data Date	Rating	RACR #1	RACR #2	Total Assets ($mil)	Capital ($mil)	Net Premium ($mil)	Net Income ($mil)
6-16	C+	18.15	16.33	207.0	179.9	7.3	2.3
6-15	C+	19.67	17.70	204.6	195.1	8.1	1.7
2015	C+	19.90	17.91	205.7	197.4	15.8	4.1
2014	C+	19.49	17.54	204.8	193.3	36.3	7.9
2013	C+	29.46	19.62	616.2	592.6	104.7	13.2
2012	C+	23.08	15.56	622.2	582.0	139.3	18.7
2011	C+	19.76	14.03	695.3	650.6	205.8	87.4

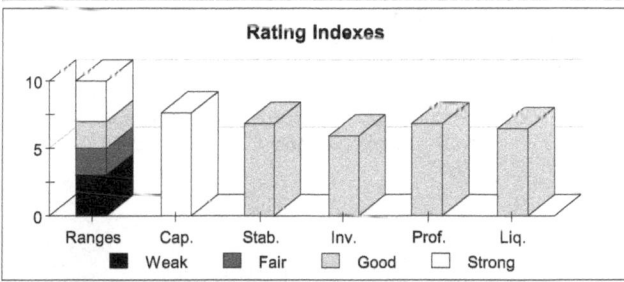

UnitedHealth Group Inc
Composite Group Rating: C+
Largest Group Members

	Assets ($mil)	Rating
UNITED HEALTHCARE INS CO	15791	C
OXFORD HEALTH INS INC	2195	B
SIERRA HEALTH AND LIFE INS CO INC	1677	B
UNITED HEALTHCARE INS CO OF NY	1223	B-
UNITEDHEALTHCARE PLAN RIVER VALLEY	1131	B-

PAN-AMERICAN LIFE INSURANCE COMPANY | B | Good

Major Rating Factors: Good overall results on stability tests (6.0 on a scale of 0 to 10) despite negative cash flow from operations for 2015. Other stability subfactors include good operational trends and excellent risk diversification. Good quality investment portfolio (5.4) despite mixed results such as: large holdings of BBB rated bonds but moderate junk bond exposure. Good overall profitability (6.4).

Other Rating Factors: Good liquidity (6.3). Strong capitalization (8.0) based on excellent risk adjusted capital (severe loss scenario).

Principal Business: Group health insurance (69%), reinsurance (11%), individual life insurance (11%), individual health insurance (6%), and group life insurance (4%).

Principal Investments: NonCMO investment grade bonds (62%), CMOs and structured securities (11%), noninv. grade bonds (7%), common & preferred stock (7%), and misc. investments (12%).

Investments in Affiliates: 2%

Group Affiliation: Pan-American Life

Licensed in: All states except ME, NY, VT

Commenced Business: March 1912

Address: Pan American Life Center, New Orleans, LA 70130

Phone: (504) 566-1300 **Domicile State:** LA **NAIC Code:** 67539

Data Date	Rating	RACR #1	RACR #2	Total Assets ($mil)	Capital ($mil)	Net Premium ($mil)	Net Income ($mil)
6-16	B	2.56	1.64	1,275.4	248.9	115.2	8.7
6-15	B	2.13	1.36	1,330.0	240.4	131.7	10.4
2015	B	2.52	1.62	1,293.7	244.9	237.9	22.0
2014	B	2.20	1.40	1,345.4	237.5	238.9	23.8
2013	B	2.29	1.43	1,425.5	244.6	270.3	27.3
2012	B	2.12	1.31	1,444.4	226.6	255.0	15.3
2011	B	2.36	1.45	1,478.2	248.4	239.3	23.0

Adverse Trends in Operations

Decrease in asset base during 2015 (4%)
Decrease in capital during 2014 (3%)
Decrease in premium volume from 2013 to 2014 (12%)
Decrease in asset base during 2013 (1%)
Decrease in asset base during 2012 (2%)

PARAGON LIFE INSURANCE COMPANY OF INDIANA | B- | Good

Major Rating Factors: Good overall profitability (6.8 on a scale of 0 to 10). Excellent expense controls. Return on equity has been good over the last five years, averaging 12.9%. Fair quality investment portfolio (3.4). Fair liquidity (4.8) as cash from operations and sale of marketable assets may not be adequate to cover a spike in claims or a run on policy withdrawals.

Other Rating Factors: Fair overall results on stability tests (3.6) including fair risk adjusted capital in prior years. Poor capitalization (2.0) based on weak risk adjusted capital (moderate loss scenario).

Principal Business: Reinsurance (100%).

Principal Investments: CMOs and structured securities (52%), nonCMO investment grade bonds (21%), mortgages in good standing (9%), common & preferred stock (7%), and cash (1%).

Investments in Affiliates: 10%

Group Affiliation: Sammons Enterprises Inc

Licensed in: DE, IN

Commenced Business: February 2011

Address: 8425 Woodfield Crossing #305 E, Indianapolis, IN 46240

Phone: (317) 396-9953 **Domicile State:** IN **NAIC Code:** 14029

Data Date	Rating	RACR #1	RACR #2	Total Assets ($mil)	Capital ($mil)	Net Premium ($mil)	Net Income ($mil)
6-16	B-	0.62	0.42	1,782.6	69.6	35.5	7.4
6-15	B-	1.07	0.64	1,830.5	78.6	30.6	6.4
2015	B-	1.06	0.73	1,874.4	117.4	57.5	31.1
2014	B-	1.04	0.62	1,837.6	78.1	108.3	18.1
2013	B-	1.02	0.62	1,792.7	71.2	189.2	20.9
2012	B-	0.88	0.57	1,697.7	66.6	292.9	6.0
2011	B-	1.83	1.07	1,490.5	56.7	355.0	-1.5

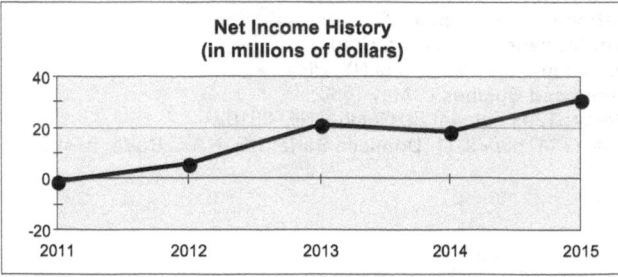

Net Income History (in millions of dollars)

PARK AVENUE LIFE INSURANCE COMPANY | B | Good

Major Rating Factors: Good quality investment portfolio (6.2 on a scale of 0 to 10) despite mixed results such as: no exposure to mortgages and large holdings of BBB rated bonds but minimal holdings in junk bonds. Good overall profitability (6.7). Excellent expense controls. Good liquidity (6.4) with sufficient resources to handle a spike in claims.

Other Rating Factors: Good overall results on stability tests (6.3) despite negative cash flow from operations for 2015 good operational trends and excellent risk diversification. Strong capitalization (7.5) based on excellent risk adjusted capital (severe loss scenario).

Principal Business: Reinsurance (76%) and individual life insurance (24%).

Principal Investments: NonCMO investment grade bonds (86%), common & preferred stock (10%), noninv. grade bonds (2%), and policy loans (1%).

Investments in Affiliates: 10%

Group Affiliation: Guardian Group

Licensed in: All states except HI, NY, PR

Commenced Business: April 1965

Address: 2711 Centerville Rd Ste 400, Wilmington, DE 19808

Phone: (800) 538-6203 **Domicile State:** DE **NAIC Code:** 60003

Data Date	Rating	RACR #1	RACR #2	Total Assets ($mil)	Capital ($mil)	Net Premium ($mil)	Net Income ($mil)
6-16	B	1.66	1.35	269.0	58.9	1.1	3.1
6-15	B+	1.97	1.63	304.4	79.8	1.3	2.1
2015	B	1.49	1.22	268.8	50.7	2.3	4.9
2014	B+	1.89	1.56	305.3	75.7	2.7	2.2
2013	B	1.94	1.54	305.8	67.8	3.0	6.7
2012	B	1.79	1.38	309.9	57.7	3.4	5.3
2011	B	1.56	1.25	307.0	55.4	3.9	0.7

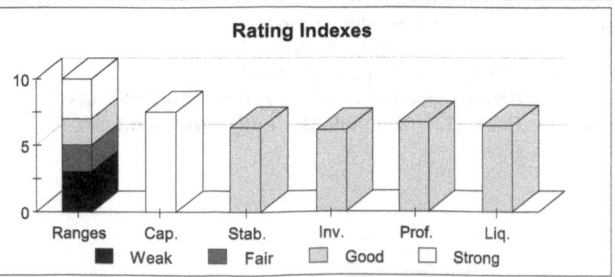

Rating Indexes

PARKER CENTENNIAL ASSURANCE COMPANY *   A   Excellent

Major Rating Factors: Good overall results on stability tests (6.3 on a scale of 0 to 10). Strengths that enhance stability include good operational trends and excellent risk diversification. Strong capitalization (10.0) based on excellent risk adjusted capital (severe loss scenario). Furthermore, this high level of risk adjusted capital has been consistently maintained over the last five years. High quality investment portfolio (8.6).

Other Rating Factors: Excellent profitability (7.6). Excellent liquidity (10.0).
Principal Business: Group retirement contracts (100%).
Principal Investments: NonCMO investment grade bonds (99%) and noninv. grade bonds (1%).
Investments in Affiliates: None
Group Affiliation: Sentry Ins Group
Licensed in: All states except NY, PR
Commenced Business: August 1973
Address: 2345 Waukegan Rd #5210, Bannockburn, IL 60015-1553
Phone: (614) 764-7000 **Domicile State:** WI **NAIC Code:** 71099

Data Date	Rating	RACR #1	RACR #2	Total Assets ($mil)	Capital ($mil)	Net Premium ($mil)	Net Income ($mil)
6-16	A	5.53	4.97	92.2	47.3	0.8	1.1
6-15	A	5.55	5.00	92.1	47.0	1.6	1.0
2015	A	5.40	4.86	91.3	46.2	4.2	1.6
2014	A	5.44	4.89	89.4	46.0	5.1	1.8
2013	A	5.55	5.00	84.4	45.8	5.0	1.6
2012	B+	5.64	5.07	81.2	45.7	5.1	1.6
2011	B	5.58	5.02	76.6	44.2	2.8	1.8

Adverse Trends in Operations

Decrease in premium volume from 2014 to 2015 (18%)
Decrease in premium volume from 2012 to 2013 (2%)

PAUL REVERE LIFE INSURANCE COMPANY   C+   Fair

Major Rating Factors: Fair overall results on stability tests (4.8 on a scale of 0 to 10) including fair financial strength of affiliated Unum Group and negative cash flow from operations for 2015. Fair quality investment portfolio (3.8) with large holdings of BBB rated bonds in addition to significant exposure to junk bonds. Good overall profitability (5.9).

Other Rating Factors: Strong capitalization (7.1) based on excellent risk adjusted capital (severe loss scenario). Excellent liquidity (7.6).
Principal Business: Individual health insurance (67%), reinsurance (25%), group health insurance (4%), individual life insurance (3%), and group life insurance (1%).
Principal Investments: NonCMO investment grade bonds (80%), noninv. grade bonds (8%), common & preferred stock (4%), CMOs and structured securities (4%), and mortgages in good standing (3%).
Investments in Affiliates: 2%
Group Affiliation: Unum Group
Licensed in: All states except PR
Commenced Business: July 1930
Address: 18 Chestnut St, Worcester, MA 01608
Phone: (508) 792-6377 **Domicile State:** MA **NAIC Code:** 67598

Data Date	Rating	RACR #1	RACR #2	Total Assets ($mil)	Capital ($mil)	Net Premium ($mil)	Net Income ($mil)
6-16	C+	1.83	1.07	3,903.5	278.6	49.6	28.0
6-15	C+	1.99	1.17	4,103.5	303.5	49.6	31.3
2015	C+	1.72	1.02	3,977.0	257.7	96.8	63.1
2014	C+	1.85	1.09	4,145.1	278.0	91.0	76.5
2013	C+	1.78	1.13	4,301.8	336.1	90.4	66.5
2012	C+	1.99	1.23	4,458.2	368.3	91.9	81.7
2011	C+	2.21	1.36	4,602.4	408.0	93.4	89.8

Unum Group
Composite Group Rating: C+

Largest Group Members	Assets ($mil)	Rating
UNUM LIFE INS CO OF AMERICA	20552	C+
PROVIDENT LIFE ACCIDENT INS CO	8325	C+
PAUL REVERE LIFE INS CO	3977	C+
FIRST UNUM LIFE INS CO	3130	C+
COLONIAL LIFE ACCIDENT INS CO	3019	C+

PAVONIA LIFE INSURANCE COMPANY OF MICHIGAN   C   Fair

Major Rating Factors: Fair overall results on stability tests (4.2 on a scale of 0 to 10) including fair financial strength of affiliated Enstar Group Limited and negative cash flow from operations for 2015. Good overall capitalization (5.2) based on good risk adjusted capital (moderate loss scenario). Nevertheless, capital levels have fluctuated during prior years. Good quality investment portfolio (5.4).

Other Rating Factors: Weak profitability (2.8) with investment income below regulatory standards in relation to interest assumptions of reserves. Excellent liquidity (8.2).
Principal Business: Individual life insurance (29%), reinsurance (26%), credit life insurance (24%), credit health insurance (10%), and other lines (11%).
Principal Investments: NonCMO investment grade bonds (71%), CMOs and structured securities (16%), cash (3%), noninv. grade bonds (2%), and misc. investments (8%).
Investments in Affiliates: 1%
Group Affiliation: Enstar Group Limited
Licensed in: All states except NY, PR
Commenced Business: January 1981
Address: 500 Woodward Ave., Ste 4000, Detroit, MI 48226
Phone: (810) 848-7811 **Domicile State:** MI **NAIC Code:** 93777

Data Date	Rating	RACR #1	RACR #2	Total Assets ($mil)	Capital ($mil)	Net Premium ($mil)	Net Income ($mil)
6-16	C	1.11	0.66	1,074.0	60.9	30.8	3.2
6-15	C	1.64	1.17	387.1	58.5	42.6	-4.8
2015	C	1.53	0.90	1,106.8	91.4	79.5	-3.5
2014	C	2.38	1.72	405.9	82.3	96.4	11.3
2013	C	2.39	1.77	445.9	99.8	112.0	25.1
2012	C	1.51	1.17	432.1	65.5	144.7	-45.5
2011	B	6.69	5.17	707.1	356.8	171.2	7.1

Enstar Group Limited
Composite Group Rating: C

Largest Group Members	Assets ($mil)	Rating
PAVONIA LIFE INS CO OF MICHIGAN	1107	C
CLARENDON NATIONAL INS CO	933	C
SUSSEX INS CO	843	C
STARSTONE NATIONAL INS CO	249	C
STARSTONE SPECIALTY INS CO	173	C-

PEKIN LIFE INSURANCE COMPANY — B — Good

Major Rating Factors: Good quality investment portfolio (6.6 on a scale of 0 to 10) despite mixed results such as: minimal exposure to mortgages and substantial holdings of BBB bonds but minimal holdings in junk bonds. Good liquidity (5.7) with sufficient resources to cover a large increase in policy surrenders. Good overall results on stability tests (6.2) excellent operational trends and excellent risk diversification.

Other Rating Factors: Fair profitability (4.0) with operating losses during the first six months of 2016. Strong capitalization (7.2) based on excellent risk adjusted capital (severe loss scenario).

Principal Business: Individual life insurance (32%), group health insurance (20%), group life insurance (19%), individual health insurance (11%), and other lines (18%).

Principal Investments: NonCMO investment grade bonds (63%), CMOs and structured securities (29%), policy loans (1%), common & preferred stock (1%), and mortgages in good standing (1%).

Investments in Affiliates: None

Group Affiliation: Farmers Automobile Ins Assn

Licensed in: AL, AZ, AR, GA, IL, IN, IA, KS, KY, LA, MI, MN, MS, MO, NE, OH, PA, TN, TX, VA, WI

Commenced Business: September 1965

Address: 2505 Court St, Pekin, IL 61558

Phone: (309) 346-1161 **Domicile State:** IL **NAIC Code:** 67628

Data Date	Rating	RACR #1	RACR #2	Total Assets ($mil)	Capital ($mil)	Net Premium ($mil)	Net Income ($mil)
6-16	B	1.91	1.14	1,426.6	118.7	113.0	-3.8
6-15	B	2.06	1.25	1,374.4	119.5	108.4	-0.5
2015	B	1.98	1.19	1,393.6	120.2	215.7	-1.3
2014	B	2.11	1.28	1,324.1	120.3	206.2	5.9
2013	B	2.24	1.37	1,301.6	122.7	227.0	2.4
2012	B	2.24	1.39	1,209.2	119.2	221.1	7.6
2011	B+	2.31	1.44	1,124.2	117.9	224.4	3.1

Adverse Trends in Operations

Decrease in capital during 2014 (2%)
Decrease in premium volume from 2013 to 2014 (9%)
Decrease in premium volume from 2011 to 2012 (1%)

PENN INSURANCE & ANNUITY COMPANY — B- — Good

Major Rating Factors: Good quality investment portfolio (6.2 on a scale of 0 to 10) despite mixed results such as: large holdings of BBB rated bonds but moderate junk bond exposure. Good liquidity (6.0) with sufficient resources to handle a spike in claims as well as a significant increase in policy surrenders. Good overall results on stability tests (5.2) despite excessive premium growth good operational trends and excellent risk diversification.

Other Rating Factors: Weak profitability (2.6) with investment income below regulatory standards in relation to interest assumptions of reserves. Strong capitalization (7.4) based on excellent risk adjusted capital (severe loss scenario).

Principal Business: Reinsurance (61%) and individual life insurance (39%).

Principal Investments: NonCMO investment grade bonds (52%), CMOs and structured securities (21%), policy loans (16%), noninv. grade bonds (4%), and common & preferred stock (1%).

Investments in Affiliates: 3%

Group Affiliation: Penn Mutual Group

Licensed in: All states except NH, NY, PR

Commenced Business: April 1981

Address: 1209 Orange St, Wilmington, DE 19801

Phone: (215) 956-8000 **Domicile State:** DE **NAIC Code:** 93262

Data Date	Rating	RACR #1	RACR #2	Total Assets ($mil)	Capital ($mil)	Net Premium ($mil)	Net Income ($mil)
6-16	B-	2.15	1.26	4,022.4	367.7	174.5	5.9
6-15	B	3.27	1.83	3,410.7	395.8	97.1	12.5
2015	B-	2.03	1.29	3,780.5	363.1	488.3	-32.9
2014	B	2.81	1.84	3,254.7	417.2	211.1	25.4
2013	B	2.73	1.73	2,307.3	310.7	-108.0	-2.4
2012	B	2.57	1.38	2,027.0	190.4	411.7	-24.1
2011	B	2.21	1.18	1,592.9	131.2	345.7	-15.9

Adverse Trends in Operations

Decrease in capital during 2015 (13%)
Increase in policy surrenders from 2012 to 2013 (48%)
Decrease in premium volume from 2012 to 2013 (126%)
Increase in policy surrenders from 2011 to 2012 (27%)

PENN MUTUAL LIFE INSURANCE COMPANY — B — Good

Major Rating Factors: Good quality investment portfolio (6.0 on a scale of 0 to 10) despite mixed results such as: no exposure to mortgages and large holdings of BBB rated bonds but small junk bond holdings. Good liquidity (6.7) with sufficient resources to handle a spike in claims as well as a significant increase in policy surrenders. Fair overall results on stability tests (4.4).

Other Rating Factors: Strong capitalization (7.6) based on excellent risk adjusted capital (severe loss scenario). Excellent profitability (7.1) despite modest operating losses during 2012 and 2013.

Principal Business: Individual life insurance (59%), individual annuities (36%), reinsurance (4%), group retirement contracts (1%), and individual health insurance (1%).

Principal Investments: NonCMO investment grade bonds (49%), CMOs and structured securities (29%), common & preferred stock (5%), policy loans (3%), and misc. investments (13%).

Investments in Affiliates: 6%

Group Affiliation: Penn Mutual Group

Licensed in: All states except PR

Commenced Business: May 1847

Address: 600 Dresher Rd, Horsham, PA 19044

Phone: (215) 956-8000 **Domicile State:** PA **NAIC Code:** 67644

Data Date	Rating	RACR #1	RACR #2	Total Assets ($mil)	Capital ($mil)	Net Premium ($mil)	Net Income ($mil)
6-16	B	2.12	1.38	18,813.7	1,773.1	632.9	54.4
6-15	B	2.14	1.46	18,125.9	1,766.4	784.3	33.6
2015	B	2.22	1.46	18,235.0	1,787.7	1,192.2	101.3
2014	B	2.21	1.52	17,270.8	1,799.8	657.2	9.3
2013	B	2.19	1.48	15,945.2	1,490.7	1,483.0	-34.4
2012	A-	2.67	1.70	14,330.7	1,495.4	1,616.8	-38.9
2011	A-	3.25	2.00	13,059.8	1,542.7	1,484.9	12.4

Rating Indexes

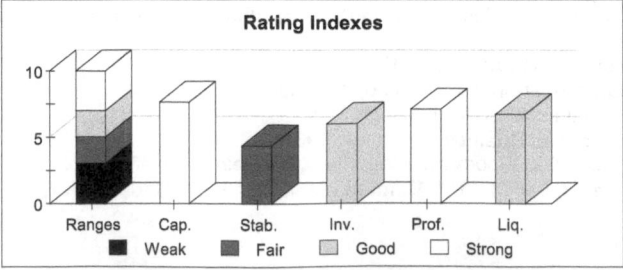

PHILADELPHIA AMERICAN LIFE INSURANCE COMPANY   B   Good

Major Rating Factors: Good overall results on stability tests (5.4 on a scale of 0 to 10) despite fair financial strength of affiliated New Era Life Group. Other stability subfactors include excellent operational trends and good risk diversification. Good capitalization (6.5) based on good risk adjusted capital (severe loss scenario). Capital levels have been relatively consistent over the last five years. Good liquidity (6.4).

Other Rating Factors: Fair quality investment portfolio (4.7). Excellent profitability (9.0).

Principal Business: Individual health insurance (82%), individual annuities (14%), individual life insurance (2%), and group health insurance (2%).

Principal Investments: NonCMO investment grade bonds (69%), CMOs and structured securities (16%), noninv. grade bonds (9%), mortgages in good standing (4%), and cash (2%).

Investments in Affiliates: None

Group Affiliation: New Era Life Group

Licensed in: All states except NY, RI, PR

Commenced Business: March 1978

Address: 11720 Katy Freeway Ste 1700, Houston, TX 77079

Phone: (281) 368-7200 **Domicile State:** TX **NAIC Code:** 67784

Data Date	Rating	RACR #1	RACR #2	Total Assets ($mil)	Capital ($mil)	Net Premium ($mil)	Net Income ($mil)
6-16	B	1.46	0.94	253.2	33.6	76.3	0.0
6-15	B-	1.47	0.94	224.5	33.5	77.8	1.1
2015	B	1.46	0.95	235.2	33.9	160.1	1.1
2014	B-	1.50	0.96	220.2	33.2	144.1	5.9
2013	B-	1.38	0.88	205.7	29.0	120.4	3.1
2012	B-	1.68	0.99	197.6	26.1	69.5	4.3
2011	C+	1.70	0.95	194.8	24.5	62.9	3.4

New Era Life Group
Composite Group Rating: C+

Largest Group Members	Assets ($mil)	Rating
NEW ERA LIFE INS CO	463	C
PHILADELPHIA AMERICAN LIFE INS CO	235	B
NEW ERA LIFE INS CO OF THE MIDWEST	98	C
LIFE OF AMERICA INS CO	13	C

PHL VARIABLE INSURANCE COMPANY   D-   Weak

Major Rating Factors: Weak profitability (1.7 on a scale of 0 to 10) with operating losses during the first six months of 2016. Weak overall results on stability tests (0.9) Including negative cash flow from operations for 2015. Good overall capitalization (5.9) based on good risk adjusted capital (moderate loss scenario). Nevertheless, capital levels have fluctuated during prior years.

Other Rating Factors: Good quality investment portfolio (5.0). Good liquidity (5.6).

Principal Business: Reinsurance (44%), individual annuities (36%), and individual life insurance (20%).

Principal Investments: NonCMO investment grade bonds (65%), CMOs and structured securities (19%), policy loans (4%), noninv. grade bonds (4%), and misc. investments (7%).

Investments in Affiliates: None

Group Affiliation: Nassau Reinsurance Group Holdings LP

Licensed in: All states except ME, NY

Commenced Business: July 1981

Address: 200 Park Ave 7th Floor, New York, NY 10166

Phone: (860) 403-1179 **Domicile State:** CT **NAIC Code:** 93548

Data Date	Rating	RACR #1	RACR #2	Total Assets ($mil)	Capital ($mil)	Net Premium ($mil)	Net Income ($mil)
6-16	D-	1.62	0.83	6,555.1	174.3	-1,266.1	-45.2
6-15	E	1.80	0.92	6,684.9	190.7	1,328.0	15.7
2015	E+	1.02	0.99	6,397.8	194.5	1,749.4	-14.0
2014	C-	1.91	0.99	6,533.9	198.6	927.0	41.1
2013	C	2.29	1.18	6,163.6	222.9	854.8	-86.1
2012	C	3.51	1.76	5,657.1	313.5	1,011.0	49.7
2011	C	2.84	1.46	5,438.3	312.8	1,168.2	61.4

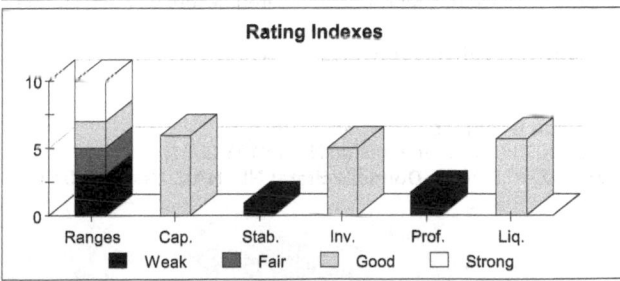

Rating Indexes

PHOENIX LIFE INSURANCE COMPANY   E   Very Weak

Major Rating Factors: Weak overall results on stability tests (0.1 on a scale of 0 to 10) including negative cash flow from operations for 2015. Fair overall capitalization (4.0) based on mixed results -- excessive policy leverage mitigated by good risk adjusted capital (moderate loss scenario). Fair quality investment portfolio (3.9).

Other Rating Factors: Fair profitability (4.6) with investment income below regulatory standards in relation to interest assumptions of reserves. Fair liquidity (4.8).

Principal Business: Individual life insurance (92%), reinsurance (7%), and individual annuities (1%).

Principal Investments: NonCMO investment grade bonds (46%), policy loans (21%), CMOs and structured securities (16%), noninv. grade bonds (6%), and misc. investments (11%).

Investments in Affiliates: None

Group Affiliation: Nassau Reinsurance Group Holdings LP

Licensed in: All states, the District of Columbia and Puerto Rico

Commenced Business: May 1851

Address: 100 Bright Meadow Blvd, Enfield, CT 06083-1900

Phone: (860) 403-1000 **Domicile State:** NY **NAIC Code:** 67814

Data Date	Rating	RACR #1	RACR #2	Total Assets ($mil)	Capital ($mil)	Net Premium ($mil)	Net Income ($mil)
6-16	E	1.29	0.64	12,507.1	352.3	149.2	28.5
6-15	C	1.33	0.79	13,298.0	675.0	-676.5	12.4
2015	E	1.40	0.70	12,716.8	382.0	-516.8	-660.7
2014	C	1.23	0.74	13,249.3	609.2	314.5	132.5
2013	C	1.12	0.68	13,564.2	597.0	330.1	-21.0
2012	C	1.20	0.74	13,837.2	793.6	366.5	156.2
2011	C	1.09	0.67	14,057.8	728.8	-2,429.2	95.0

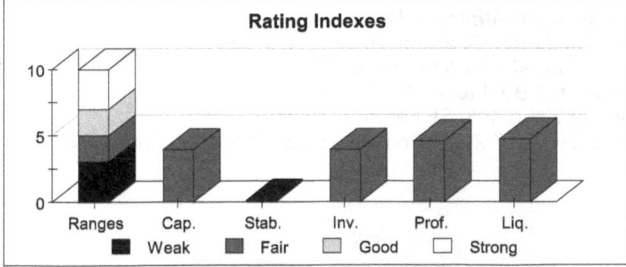

Rating Indexes

PHYSICIANS LIFE INSURANCE COMPANY *

A-   **Excellent**

Major Rating Factors: Good quality investment portfolio (6.3 on a scale of 0 to 10) despite mixed results such as: substantial holdings of BBB bonds but junk bond exposure equal to 58% of capital. Good overall profitability (6.3). Good liquidity (5.6) with sufficient resources to handle a spike in claims as well as a significant increase in policy surrenders.

Other Rating Factors: Good overall results on stability tests (6.9) excellent operational trends and excellent risk diversification. Strong capitalization (7.7) based on excellent risk adjusted capital (severe loss scenario).

Principal Business: Individual life insurance (45%), individual health insurance (21%), individual annuities (18%), group life insurance (15%), and reinsurance (1%).

Principal Investments: NonCMO investment grade bonds (69%), CMOs and structured securities (21%), noninv. grade bonds (6%), common & preferred stock (2%), and policy loans (2%).

Investments in Affiliates: None

Group Affiliation: Physicians Mutual Group

Licensed in: All states except NY, PR

Commenced Business: January 1970

Address: 2600 Dodge St, Omaha, NE 68131-2671

Phone: (402) 633-1000 **Domicile State:** NE **NAIC Code:** 72125

Data Date	Rating	RACR #1	RACR #2	Total Assets ($mil)	Capital ($mil)	Net Premium ($mil)	Net Income ($mil)
6-16	A-	2.92	1.48	1,549.0	139.0	152.6	4.3
6-15	A-	2.74	1.35	1,452.9	130.1	133.1	2.0
2015	A-	2.93	1.50	1,490.7	137.9	275.0	6.4
2014	A-	2.77	1.36	1,430.5	130.1	262.4	7.0
2013	A-	2.94	1.45	1,378.7	122.7	248.6	8.3
2012	A-	3.02	1.50	1,285.0	115.8	211.2	8.7
2011	A-	2.78	1.40	1,268.9	108.7	200.9	4.4

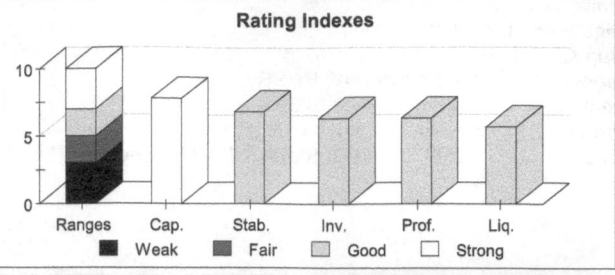

Rating Indexes

(Ranges, Cap., Stab., Inv., Prof., Liq. — ■ Weak ■ Fair ▨ Good ☐ Strong)

PHYSICIANS MUTUAL INSURANCE COMPANY *

A+   **Excellent**

Major Rating Factors: Good quality investment portfolio (6.4 on a scale of 0 to 10) despite mixed results such as: no exposure to mortgages and large holdings of BBB rated bonds but small junk bond holdings. Strong capitalization (9.5) based on excellent risk adjusted capital (severe loss scenario). Furthermore, this high level of risk adjusted capital has been consistently maintained over the last five years. Excellent profitability (7.4).

Other Rating Factors: Excellent liquidity (7.6). Excellent overall results on stability tests (7.9) excellent operational trends and excellent risk diversification.

Principal Business: Individual health insurance (62%), reinsurance (30%), and group health insurance (8%).

Principal Investments: NonCMO investment grade bonds (69%), common & preferred stock (13%), CMOs and structured securities (11%), and noninv. grade bonds (6%).

Investments in Affiliates: 7%

Group Affiliation: Physicians Mutual Group

Licensed in: All states except PR

Commenced Business: February 1902

Address: 2600 Dodge St, Omaha, NE 68131-2671

Phone: (402) 633-1000 **Domicile State:** NE **NAIC Code:** 80578

Data Date	Rating	RACR #1	RACR #2	Total Assets ($mil)	Capital ($mil)	Net Premium ($mil)	Net Income ($mil)
6-16	A+	3.52	2.65	2,153.3	895.4	238.4	14.1
6-15	A+	3.59	2.71	2,090.9	859.9	229.9	18.9
2015	A+	3.51	2.65	2,106.2	885.5	454.2	39.6
2014	A+	3.67	2.78	2,026.2	845.5	424.5	42.8
2013	A+	4.23	3.22	1,920.5	931.1	453.9	33.6
2012	A+	4.02	3.04	1,829.7	866.1	447.6	30.2
2011	A+	4.19	3.19	1,732.5	843.4	434.3	35.8

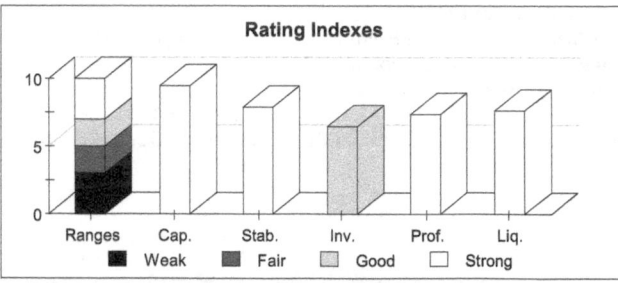

Rating Indexes

(Ranges, Cap., Stab., Inv., Prof., Liq. — ■ Weak ■ Fair ▨ Good ☐ Strong)

PIONEER MUTUAL LIFE INSURANCE COMPANY

B   **Good**

Major Rating Factors: Good overall profitability (5.5 on a scale of 0 to 10). Excellent expense controls. Good liquidity (5.0) with sufficient resources to cover a large increase in policy surrenders. Good overall results on stability tests (5.5). Strengths include good financial support from affiliation with American United Life Group, excellent operational trends and excellent risk diversification.

Other Rating Factors: Strong capitalization (8.1) based on excellent risk adjusted capital (severe loss scenario). High quality investment portfolio (7.0).

Principal Business: Individual life insurance (94%) and individual annuities (6%).

Principal Investments: NonCMO investment grade bonds (57%), CMOs and structured securities (31%), policy loans (5%), mortgages in good standing (5%), and noninv. grade bonds (2%).

Investments in Affiliates: None

Group Affiliation: American United Life Group

Licensed in: All states except AK, NY, PR

Commenced Business: November 1947

Address: 203 N 10th St, Fargo, ND 58102

Phone: (701) 277-2300 **Domicile State:** ND **NAIC Code:** 67911

Data Date	Rating	RACR #1	RACR #2	Total Assets ($mil)	Capital ($mil)	Net Premium ($mil)	Net Income ($mil)
6-16	B	3.24	1.73	515.2	48.6	11.5	1.5
6-15	B	2.79	1.49	518.3	40.9	13.1	2.7
2015	B	3.18	1.70	516.9	47.5	24.1	9.8
2014	B	2.66	1.42	511.4	38.3	26.4	-2.5
2013	B+	2.76	1.46	500.1	39.9	24.7	-1.4
2012	B+	2.81	1.47	492.2	41.1	26.1	1.6
2011	B	2.66	1.38	486.8	39.2	25.4	3.5

American United Life Group Composite Group Rating: B+ Largest Group Members	Assets ($mil)	Rating
AMERICAN UNITED LIFE INS CO	23572	B+
STATE LIFE INS CO	6119	B
PIONEER MUTUAL LIFE INS CO	517	B

PIONEER SECURITY LIFE INSURANCE COMPANY — C+ — Fair

Major Rating Factors: Fair overall results on stability tests (4.8 on a scale of 0 to 10) including fair financial strength of affiliated Industrial Alliance Ins & Financial. Low quality investment portfolio (2.7). Strong overall capitalization (7.3) based on excellent risk adjusted capital (severe loss scenario). However, capital levels have fluctuated somewhat during past years.

Other Rating Factors: Excellent profitability (7.6). Excellent liquidity (8.1).

Principal Business: Individual life insurance (100%).

Principal Investments: Common & preferred stock (68%), nonCMO investment grade bonds (28%), and policy loans (1%).

Investments in Affiliates: 68%

Group Affiliation: Industrial Alliance Ins & Financial

Licensed in: AL, AR, CA, CO, DC, DE, FL, GA, HI, ID, IL, IN, KS, KY, LA, MD, MN, MS, MO, MT, NE, NM, NC, ND, OK, OR, PA, SC, SD, TN, TX, UT, VA, WA, WV, WI

Commenced Business: November 1956

Address: 425 Austin Ave, Waco, TX 76701

Phone: (254) 297-2778 **Domicile State:** TX **NAIC Code:** 67946

Data Date	Rating	RACR #1	RACR #2	Total Assets ($mil)	Capital ($mil)	Net Premium ($mil)	Net Income ($mil)
6-16	C+	1.24	1.22	124.2	99.8	3.2	2.4
6-15	C+	1.06	1.05	126.5	101.3	3.1	20.4
2015	C+	1.26	1.24	125.5	101.4	7.7	23.6
2014	C+	1.16	1.14	132.2	109.7	8.0	4.5
2013	C+	1.11	1.10	109.7	89.3	10.1	2.0
2012	C+	1.10	1.09	89.6	73.1	9.9	6.8
2011	B-	1.06	1.04	84.3	62.6	6.8	4.0

Industrial Alliance Ins Financial
Composite Group Rating: C

Largest Group Members	Assets ($mil)	Rating
AMERICAN-AMICABLE LIFE INS CO OF TX	287	C
OCCIDENTAL LIFE INS CO OF NC	257	C
IA AMERICAN LIFE INS CO	229	B-
INDUSTRIAL ALLIANCE INS FIN SERV	202	C-
PIONEER SECURITY LIFE INS CO	125	C+

POPULAR LIFE RE — C+ — Fair

Major Rating Factors: Fair overall results on stability tests (4.8 on a scale of 0 to 10). Good quality investment portfolio (5.0) with no exposure to mortgages and minimal holdings in junk bonds. Good overall profitability (6.6). Excellent expense controls. Return on equity has been good over the last five years, averaging 11.4%.

Other Rating Factors: Strong capitalization (10.0) based on excellent risk adjusted capital (severe loss scenario). Excellent liquidity (9.4).

Principal Business: Reinsurance (100%).

Principal Investments: CMOs and structured securities (51%), nonCMO investment grade bonds (23%), cash (21%), and noninv. grade bonds (5%).

Investments in Affiliates: None

Group Affiliation: Popular Inc

Licensed in: (No states)

Commenced Business: December 2003

Address: Solar A Marginal Martinez Nada, Guaynabo, PR 00966

Phone: (787) 759-0080 **Domicile State:** PR **NAIC Code:** 11876

Data Date	Rating	RACR #1	RACR #2	Total Assets ($mil)	Capital ($mil)	Net Premium ($mil)	Net Income ($mil)
6-16	C+	4.30	3.29	60.7	30.6	9.4	2.3
6-15	C+	3.95	2.22	56.6	27.8	9.4	-0.3
2015	C+	4.03	3.31	58.2	28.7	19.3	2.4
2014	C+	4.14	3.72	56.8	29.2	19.2	2.0
2013	C+	3.96	3.26	52.6	27.2	18.0	3.4
2012	C+	5.85	5.27	66.2	43.7	17.1	4.1
2011	C+	5.45	4.91	61.7	39.6	15.5	3.6

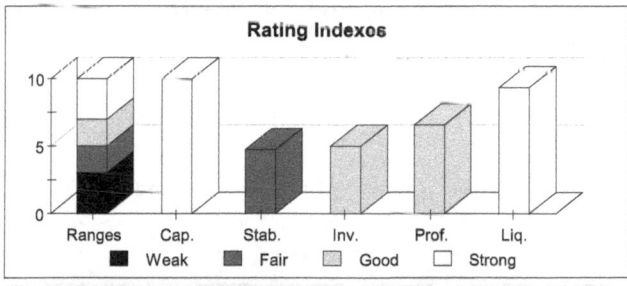

Rating Indexes

Ranges — Cap. — Stab. — Inv. — Prof. — Liq.
■ Weak ▨ Fair ▢ Good ☐ Strong

PRENEED REINSURANCE COMPANY OF AMERICA — B — Good

Major Rating Factors: Good overall results on stability tests (5.6 on a scale of 0 to 10). Stability strengths include excellent operational trends and good risk diversification. Fair liquidity (4.8) as cash from operations and sale of marketable assets may not be adequate to cover a spike in claims. Strong capitalization (10.0) based on excellent risk adjusted capital (severe loss scenario).

Other Rating Factors: High quality investment portfolio (9.0). Excellent profitability (9.6) with operating gains in each of the last five years.

Principal Business: Reinsurance (100%).

Principal Investments: NonCMO investment grade bonds (99%) and cash (1%).

Investments in Affiliates: None

Group Affiliation: NGL Ins Group

Licensed in: AZ

Commenced Business: October 2001

Address: 2999 N 44th St Suite 250, Phoenix, AZ 82018

Phone: (608) 257-5611 **Domicile State:** AZ **NAIC Code:** 11155

Data Date	Rating	RACR #1	RACR #2	Total Assets ($mil)	Capital ($mil)	Net Premium ($mil)	Net Income ($mil)
6-16	B	6.79	6.11	40.6	37.4	53.0	2.1
6-15	B	6.61	5.95	36.8	33.5	52.3	2.7
2015	B	6.61	5.94	38.6	36.4	105.2	5.5
2014	B	6.36	5.72	34.5	32.2	101.2	5.1
2013	B	6.03	5.43	29.3	27.2	99.6	5.2
2012	B	5.58	5.02	25.1	23.1	101.4	5.8
2011	B	4.96	4.47	20.7	18.8	100.5	5.2

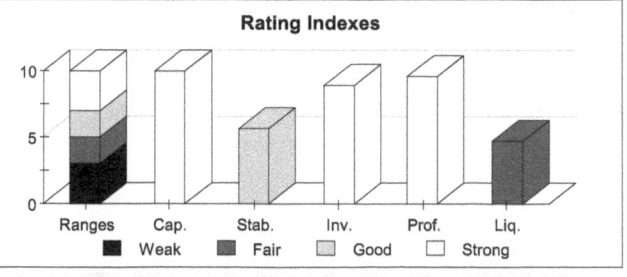

Rating Indexes

Ranges — Cap. — Stab. — Inv. — Prof. — Liq.
■ Weak ▨ Fair ▢ Good ☐ Strong

PRIMERICA LIFE INSURANCE COMPANY

B **Good**

Major Rating Factors: Good liquidity (6.9 on a scale of 0 to 10) with sufficient resources to handle a spike in claims as well as a significant increase in policy surrenders. Good overall results on stability tests (5.7). Stability strengths include good operational trends and excellent risk diversification. Fair quality investment portfolio (4.3).

Other Rating Factors: Strong capitalization (7.1) based on excellent risk adjusted capital (severe loss scenario). Excellent profitability (8.1).

Principal Business: Individual life insurance (100%).

Principal Investments: NonCMO investment grade bonds (52%), common & preferred stock (32%), CMOs and structured securities (10%), and noninv. grade bonds (4%).

Investments in Affiliates: 29%

Group Affiliation: Primerica Inc

Licensed in: All states except NY

Commenced Business: January 1903

Address: One Federal Street, Boston, MA 02110

Phone: (770) 381-1000 **Domicile State:** MA **NAIC Code:** 65919

Data Date	Rating	RACR #1	RACR #2	Total Assets ($mil)	Capital ($mil)	Net Premium ($mil)	Net Income ($mil)
6-16	B	1.25	1.07	1,315.9	535.1	106.7	204.3
6-15	B	1.39	1.15	1,277.8	543.8	38.8	206.5
2015	B	1.29	1.11	1,320.9	560.9	116.3	435.4
2014	B	1.35	1.13	1,279.4	499.0	277.1	268.3
2013	B	1.54	1.27	1,479.8	563.3	255.7	307.1
2012	B	1.80	1.49	1,569.7	670.4	230.5	257.3
2011	B	1.87	1.37	1,575.8	443.1	297.6	182.4

Adverse Trends in Operations

Decrease in premium volume from 2014 to 2015 (58%)
Decrease in asset base during 2014 (14%)
Decrease in capital during 2013 (16%)
Decrease in premium volume from 2011 to 2012 (23%)
Increase in policy surrenders from 2011 to 2012 (240%)

PRINCIPAL LIFE INSURANCE COMPANY *

B+ **Good**

Major Rating Factors: Good quality investment portfolio (5.6 on a scale of 0 to 10) despite substantial holdings of BBB bonds in addition to junk bond exposure equal to 76% of capital. Exposure to mortgages is significant, but the mortgage default rate has been low. Good overall results on stability tests (6.7). Stability strengths include excellent operational trends and excellent risk diversification. Strong capitalization (7.2) based on excellent risk adjusted capital (severe loss scenario).

Other Rating Factors: Excellent profitability (7.5). Excellent liquidity (7.4).

Principal Business: Individual annuities (37%), group retirement contracts (22%), group health insurance (13%), individual life insurance (13%), and other lines (15%).

Principal Investments: NonCMO investment grade bonds (46%), CMOs and structured securities (20%), mortgages in good standing (19%), noninv. grade bonds (6%), and misc. investments (9%).

Investments in Affiliates: 5%

Group Affiliation: Principal Financial Group

Licensed in: All states, the District of Columbia and Puerto Rico

Commenced Business: September 1879

Address: 711 High St, Des Moines, IA 50392-0420

Phone: (800) 986-3343 **Domicile State:** IA **NAIC Code:** 61271

Data Date	Rating	RACR #1	RACR #2	Total Assets ($mil)	Capital ($mil)	Net Premium ($mil)	Net Income ($mil)
6-16	B+	2.15	1.15	165,432	4,686.6	3,993.1	421.7
6-15	B+	1.95	1.06	158,383	4,156.3	3,572.1	300.6
2015	B+	2.13	1.14	157,775	4,496.7	7,693.4	948.6
2014	B+	1.99	1.08	154,074	4,202.1	5,533.2	535.5
2013	B+	2.05	1.09	143,742	4,142.2	5,267.0	607.9
2012	B+	2.11	1.09	130,020	3,944.3	5,388.6	576.1
2011	B+	2.27	1.16	121,390	4,218.2	4,800.3	326.8

Adverse Trends in Operations

Decrease in premium volume from 2012 to 2013 (2%)
Decrease in capital during 2012 (6%)

PRINCIPAL NATIONAL LIFE INSURANCE CO

B **Good**

Major Rating Factors: Good overall results on stability tests (5.4 on a scale of 0 to 10). Strengths include good financial support from affiliation with Principal Financial Group, good operational trends and excellent risk diversification. Weak profitability (2.9) with operating losses during the first six months of 2016. Strong capitalization (10.0) based on excellent risk adjusted capital (severe loss scenario).

Other Rating Factors: High quality investment portfolio (8.3). Excellent liquidity (10.0).

Principal Business: Individual life insurance (100%).

Principal Investments: NonCMO investment grade bonds (89%), CMOs and structured securities (10%), and cash (1%).

Investments in Affiliates: None

Group Affiliation: Principal Financial Group

Licensed in: All states except NY, PR

Commenced Business: March 1968

Address: 711 High St, Des Moines, IA 50392-0001

Phone: (515) 247-5111 **Domicile State:** IA **NAIC Code:** 71161

Data Date	Rating	RACR #1	RACR #2	Total Assets ($mil)	Capital ($mil)	Net Premium ($mil)	Net Income ($mil)
6-16	B	6.41	3.16	214.1	117.2	0.0	-1.4
6-15	B	5.57	2.75	168.5	98.4	0.0	-1.9
2015	B	5.85	2.89	185.1	103.7	0.0	-4.5
2014	B	4.88	2.42	141.2	84.8	0.0	-4.5
2013	B	6.16	3.04	110.4	84.2	0.0	-6.4
2012	B	7.09	3.54	84.9	70.8	0.0	-6.0
2011	B	7.82	4.72	65.1	58.1	0.0	-7.0

Principal Financial Group
Composite Group Rating: B+
Largest Group Members

	Assets ($mil)	Rating
PRINCIPAL LIFE INS CO	157775	B+
PRINCIPAL NATIONAL LIFE INS CO	185	B

PROFESSIONAL INSURANCE COMPANY   D-   Weak

Major Rating Factors: Weak overall results on stability tests (1.1 on a scale of 0 to 10) including potential financial drain due to affiliation with Sun Life Assurance Group. Good quality investment portfolio (6.7) despite mixed results such as: no exposure to mortgages and large holdings of BBB rated bonds but small junk bond holdings. Good overall profitability (5.5). Excellent expense controls.
Other Rating Factors: Good liquidity (6.9). Strong capitalization (10.0) based on excellent risk adjusted capital (severe loss scenario).
Principal Business: Individual health insurance (94%) and individual life insurance (6%).
Principal Investments: NonCMO investment grade bonds (75%), CMOs and structured securities (11%), noninv. grade bonds (6%), and policy loans (3%).
Investments in Affiliates: None
Group Affiliation: Sun Life Assurance Group
Licensed in: All states except AK, DE, ME, NH, NJ, NY, RI, VT, PR
Commenced Business: September 1937
Address: 1999 Bryan St Suite 900, Dallas, TX 75201
Phone: (781) 237-6030 **Domicile State:** TX **NAIC Code:** 68047

Data Date	Rating	RACR #1	RACR #2	Total Assets ($mil)	Capital ($mil)	Net Premium ($mil)	Net Income ($mil)
6-16	D-	4.54	3.62	110.2	40.5	12.4	1.9
6-15	C	4.23	3.09	110.0	37.8	14.0	1.7
2015	C	4.32	3.34	109.2	38.6	27.7	2.7
2014	C	4.02	2.88	108.9	35.9	31.6	1.8
2013	C-	3.16	2.21	105.1	29.5	37.1	3.4
2012	D	2.61	1.84	108.6	28.6	44.6	1.1
2011	D	1.52	1.09	104.5	20.8	53.8	-9.2

Sun Life Assurance Group Composite Group Rating: E Largest Group Members	Assets ($mil)	Rating
SUN LIFE ASR CO OF CANADA	18222	E
INDEPENDENCE LIFE ANNUITY CO	2863	D-
SUN LIFE HEALTH INS CO	448	D-
PROFESSIONAL INS CO	109	D-

PROFESSIONAL LIFE & CASUALTY COMPANY   C   Fair

Major Rating Factors: Fair quality investment portfolio (3.3 on a scale of 0 to 10) with large holdings of BBB rated bonds in addition to moderate junk bond exposure. Fair overall results on stability tests (4.3). Good liquidity (5.7) with sufficient resources to cover a large increase in policy surrenders.
Other Rating Factors: Strong capitalization (7.9) based on excellent risk adjusted capital (severe loss scenario). Excellent profitability (8.9).
Principal Business: Individual annuities (99%) and individual life insurance (1%).
Principal Investments: NonCMO investment grade bonds (63%), common & preferred stock (24%), noninv. grade bonds (12%), and cash (1%).
Investments in Affiliates: None
Group Affiliation: None
Licensed in: IL, IN, MT, ND, OK
Commenced Business: September 1957
Address: 20 N Wacker Dr Ste 3110, Chicago, IL 60606
Phone: (312) 220-0655 **Domicile State:** IL **NAIC Code:** 68063

Data Date	Rating	RACR #1	RACR #2	Total Assets ($mil)	Capital ($mil)	Net Premium ($mil)	Net Income ($mil)
6-16	C	3.00	1.58	163.7	46.6	5.1	1.6
6-15	C	2.78	1.50	156.7	42.4	4.5	3.9
2015	C	2.96	1.58	158.2	42.8	7.5	4.3
2014	C	2.68	1.45	154.2	41.8	0.4	5.1
2013	C	2.66	1.39	144.3	33.3	9.6	6.5
2012	C	2.39	1.18	129.2	25.1	13.0	3.2
2011	C	2.53	1.23	116.4	22.5	15.6	3.3

Rating Indexes

Ranges | Cap. | Stab. | Inv. | Prof. | Liq.
■ Weak ■ Fair ☐ Good ☐ Strong

PROTECTIVE LIFE & ANNUITY INSURANCE COMPANY   B   Good

Major Rating Factors: Good overall results on stability tests (5.9 on a scale of 0 to 10) despite negative cash flow from operations for 2015 and excessive premium growth. Other stability subfactors include good operational trends and excellent risk diversification. Good quality investment portfolio (5.6) despite mixed results such as: large holdings of BBB rated bonds but moderate junk bond exposure. Good overall profitability (5.9) although investment income, in comparison to reserve requirements, is below regulatory standards.
Other Rating Factors: Fair liquidity (4.5). Strong capitalization (7.4) based on excellent risk adjusted capital (severe loss scenario).
Principal Business: Individual annuities (48%), reinsurance (26%), and individual life insurance (26%).
Principal Investments: NonCMO investment grade bonds (73%), CMOs and structured securities (14%), mortgages in good standing (6%), noninv. grade bonds (4%), and misc. investments (4%).
Investments in Affiliates: None
Group Affiliation: Protective Life Group
Licensed in: All states except MN, PR
Commenced Business: December 1978
Address: 2801 Highway 280 South, Birmingham, AL 35223
Phone: (205) 268-1000 **Domicile State:** AL **NAIC Code:** 88536

Data Date	Rating	RACR #1	RACR #2	Total Assets ($mil)	Capital ($mil)	Net Premium ($mil)	Net Income ($mil)
6-16	B	2.45	1.24	1,999.6	162.0	30.8	25.9
6-15	B	2.35	1.21	2,059.7	159.3	22.7	15.0
2015	B	2.62	1.34	2,007.6	173.6	47.5	26.7
2014	B	2.70	1.39	2,093.7	183.4	49.0	33.6
2013	B	2.79	1.44	2,162.7	193.6	156.6	27.7
2012	B	2.86	1.45	2,133.9	206.3	290.1	27.9
2011	B	2.20	1.11	1,278.2	94.4	253.0	17.7

Adverse Trends in Operations

Decrease in asset base during 2015 (4%)
Decrease in capital during 2015 (5%)
Decrease in premium volume from 2013 to 2014 (69%)
Decrease in premium volume from 2012 to 2013 (46%)
Increase in policy surrenders from 2011 to 2012 (71%)

PROTECTIVE LIFE INSURANCE COMPANY — B — Good

Major Rating Factors: Good quality investment portfolio (5.7 on a scale of 0 to 10) despite significant exposure to mortgages . Mortgage default rate has been low. large holdings of BBB rated bonds in addition to small junk bond holdings. Good overall profitability (5.6) despite operating losses during the first six months of 2016. Good liquidity (6.0).

Other Rating Factors: Good overall results on stability tests (5.8) good operational trends, good risk adjusted capital for prior years and excellent risk diversification. Strong capitalization (7.3) based on excellent risk adjusted capital (severe loss scenario).

Principal Business: Individual annuities (45%), individual life insurance (41%), reinsurance (12%), and group life insurance (1%).

Principal Investments: NonCMO investment grade bonds (58%), mortgages in good standing (13%), CMOs and structured securities (13%), common & preferred stock (8%), and misc. investments (7%).

Investments in Affiliates: 9%

Group Affiliation: Protective Life Group

Licensed in: All states except NY

Commenced Business: September 1907

Address: 1620 Westgate Cir Suite 200, Brentwood, TN 37027-8035

Phone: (205) 879-9230 **Domicile State:** TN **NAIC Code:** 68136

Data Date	Rating	RACR #1	RACR #2	Total Assets ($mil)	Capital ($mil)	Net Premium ($mil)	Net Income ($mil)
6-16	B	1.64	1.21	43,425.8	4,265.6	1,215.7	-731.6
6-15	B	1.33	1.00	41,606.9	3,319.6	1,247.3	153.7
2015	B	1.27	1.01	41,809.7	3,781.9	2,682.3	440.0
2014	B	1.20	0.98	41,231.7	3,498.9	2,359.8	554.2
2013	B	1.03	0.83	41,027.0	2,917.7	4,589.6	165.5
2012	B	1.31	1.01	36,355.3	2,983.9	3,963.6	376.3
2011	B	1.18	0.92	32,250.9	2,625.9	5,637.9	259.2

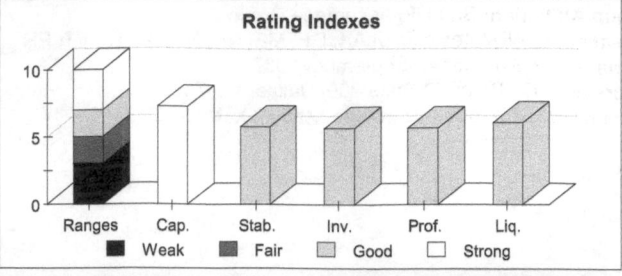

Rating Indexes

PROVIDENT LIFE & ACCIDENT INSURANCE COMPANY — C+ — Fair

Major Rating Factors: Fair quality investment portfolio (4.7 on a scale of 0 to 10) with large holdings of BBB rated bonds in addition to junk bond exposure equal to 72% of capital. Fair overall results on stability tests (4.4). Good overall profitability (6.6). Excellent expense controls.

Other Rating Factors: Strong capitalization (7.6) based on excellent risk adjusted capital (severe loss scenario). Excellent liquidity (7.5).

Principal Business: Individual health insurance (68%), individual life insurance (30%), and reinsurance (1%).

Principal Investments: NonCMO investment grade bonds (74%), CMOs and structured securities (7%), noninv. grade bonds (7%), mortgages in good standing (6%), and misc. investments (6%).

Investments in Affiliates: None

Group Affiliation: Unum Group

Licensed in: All states except NY

Commenced Business: May 1887

Address: 1 Fountain Square, Chattanooga, TN 37402

Phone: (423) 755-1373 **Domicile State:** TN **NAIC Code:** 68195

Data Date	Rating	RACR #1	RACR #2	Total Assets ($mil)	Capital ($mil)	Net Premium ($mil)	Net Income ($mil)
6-16	C+	2.74	1.37	8,342.6	738.9	465.9	96.4
6-15	C+	2.68	1.35	8,363.7	717.3	462.3	90.0
2015	C+	2.74	1.38	8,325.3	727.5	869.4	178.9
2014	C+	2.72	1.37	8,297.3	720.0	889.8	187.1
2013	C+	2.55	1.28	8,347.6	699.7	898.5	166.4
2012	C+	2.30	1.16	8,452.0	642.8	960.1	168.9
2011	C+	2.35	1.19	8,417.2	653.0	924.9	170.4

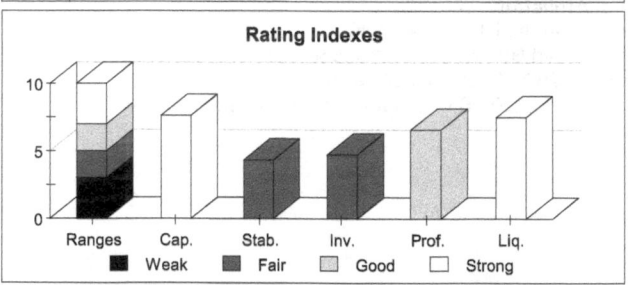

Rating Indexes

PROVIDENT LIFE & CASUALTY INSURANCE COMPANY — B- — Good

Major Rating Factors: Good overall results on stability tests (5.3 on a scale of 0 to 10) despite fair financial strength of affiliated Unum Group. Other stability subfactors include excellent operational trends and excellent risk diversification. Fair quality investment portfolio (4.6) with large holdings of BBB rated bonds in addition to moderate junk bond exposure. Strong capitalization (9.1) based on excellent risk adjusted capital (severe loss scenario).

Other Rating Factors: Excellent profitability (7.4). Excellent liquidity (7.1).

Principal Business: Individual health insurance (92%), reinsurance (5%), and individual life insurance (3%).

Principal Investments: NonCMO investment grade bonds (79%), noninv. grade bonds (9%), CMOs and structured securities (7%), and mortgages in good standing (4%).

Investments in Affiliates: None

Group Affiliation: Unum Group

Licensed in: AK, AR, CO, CT, DC, DE, GA, HI, ID, IL, IA, KY, LA, MA, MS, MO, NE, NH, NJ, NM, NY, NC, ND, OH, OK, PA, RI, SC, SD, TN, VA, WA

Commenced Business: January 1952

Address: 1 Fountain Square, Chattanooga, TN 37402

Phone: (423) 755-1373 **Domicile State:** TN **NAIC Code:** 68209

Data Date	Rating	RACR #1	RACR #2	Total Assets ($mil)	Capital ($mil)	Net Premium ($mil)	Net Income ($mil)
6-16	B-	4.54	2.43	767.5	152.4	46.3	5.6
6-15	B-	4.56	2.44	765.3	150.1	44.1	10.5
2015	B-	4.65	2.50	755.8	147.2	87.0	21.3
2014	B-	4.38	2.32	767.2	139.4	84.5	6.8
2013	B-	4.65	2.46	764.1	150.9	86.2	18.3
2012	B-	4.43	2.33	777.6	145.9	87.8	17.8
2011	B-	4.45	2.37	768.3	142.0	85.3	14.5

Unum Group
Composite Group Rating: C+

Largest Group Members	Assets ($mil)	Rating
UNUM LIFE INS CO OF AMERICA	20552	C+
PROVIDENT LIFE ACCIDENT INS CO	8325	C+
PAUL REVERE LIFE INS CO	3977	C+
FIRST UNUM LIFE INS CO	3130	C+
COLONIAL LIFE ACCIDENT INS CO	3019	C+

PRUCO LIFE INSURANCE COMPANY C+ Fair

Major Rating Factors: Fair overall results on stability tests (4.6 on a scale of 0 to 10). Good capitalization (5.1) based on good risk adjusted capital (moderate loss scenario). Good quality investment portfolio (5.7) despite substantial holdings of BBB bonds in addition to moderate junk bond exposure. Exposure to mortgages is significant, but the mortgage default rate has been low.

Other Rating Factors: Weak profitability (2.9) with investment income below regulatory standards in relation to interest assumptions of reserves. Excellent liquidity (9.4).

Principal Business: Individual annuities (68%), individual life insurance (27%), and reinsurance (4%).

Principal Investments: NonCMO investment grade bonds (45%), mortgages in good standing (15%), CMOs and structured securities (15%), policy loans (11%), and misc. investments (12%).

Investments in Affiliates: 7%

Group Affiliation: Prudential of America

Licensed in: All states except NY, PR

Commenced Business: December 1971

Address: 2999 N 44th St Suite 250, Phoenix, AZ 85018

Phone: (877) 301-1212 **Domicile State:** AZ **NAIC Code:** 79227

Data Date	Rating	RACR #1	RACR #2	Total Assets ($mil)	Capital ($mil)	Net Premium ($mil)	Net Income ($mil)
6-16	C+	1.05	0.63	107,972	1,249.1	-1,256.0	715.7
6-15	C+	2.31	1.36	109,420	2,707.0	3,987.6	331.0
2015	C+	2.27	1.36	107,815	2,795.6	7,918.6	530.9
2014	C+	2.33	1.38	106,838	2,656.5	8,744.8	108.9
2013	C+	2.18	1.32	98,541.3	2,386.9	11,307.7	553.1
2012	C+	2.09	1.34	81,002.0	2,210.6	18,196.4	591.4
2011	C+	2.03	1.23	59,524.8	1,496.0	18,292.6	-588.6

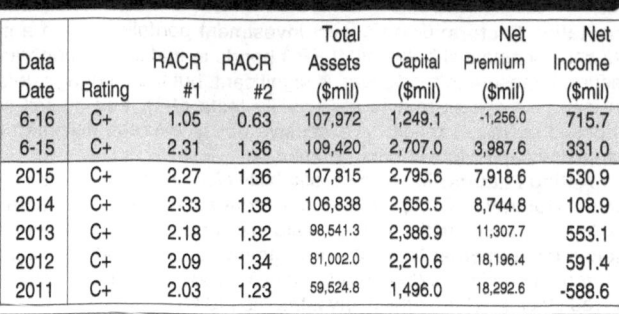

Rating Indexes

PRUCO LIFE INSURANCE COMPANY OF NEW JERSEY B- Good

Major Rating Factors: Good overall results on stability tests (5.2 on a scale of 0 to 10). Stability strengths include good operational trends, excellent risk adjusted capital for prior years and excellent risk diversification. Good current capitalization (6.7) based on good risk adjusted capital (severe loss scenario), although results have slipped from the excellent range during the last year. Good quality investment portfolio (5.5).

Other Rating Factors: Fair profitability (3.2) with investment income below regulatory standards in relation to interest assumptions of reserves. Excellent liquidity (9.0).

Principal Business: Individual annuities (57%) and individual life insurance (43%).

Principal Investments: NonCMO investment grade bonds (49%), CMOs and structured securities (17%), mortgages in good standing (14%), policy loans (11%), and misc. investments (9%).

Investments in Affiliates: 2%

Group Affiliation: Prudential of America

Licensed in: NJ, NY

Commenced Business: December 1982

Address: 213 Washington St, Newark, NJ 07102

Phone: (877) 301-1212 **Domicile State:** NJ **NAIC Code:** 97195

Data Date	Rating	RACR #1	RACR #2	Total Assets ($mil)	Capital ($mil)	Net Premium ($mil)	Net Income ($mil)
6-16	B-	1.90	0.96	13,931.4	299.9	33.8	60.9
6-15	B-	2.73	1.37	13,507.8	388.4	540.6	38.9
2015	B-	2.87	1.44	13,487.2	409.6	1,087.4	61.7
2014	B-	2.60	1.32	13,037.5	352.4	1,143.5	58.7
2013	B-	3.11	1.57	11,810.8	379.7	1,078.5	81.2
2012	B-	4.33	2.18	9,960.2	465.3	1,696.3	65.6
2011	B	2.60	1.30	7,960.6	260.3	1,663.3	12.6

Adverse Trends in Operations

Decrease in premium volume from 2014 to 2015 (5%)
Increase in policy surrenders from 2014 to 2015 (36%)
Increase in policy surrenders from 2012 to 2013 (27%)
Decrease in capital during 2013 (18%)
Decrease in premium volume from 2012 to 2013 (36%)

PRUDENTIAL ANNUITIES LIFE ASSURANCE CORPORATION C Fair

Major Rating Factors: Fair current capitalization (4.0 on a scale of 0 to 10) based on mixed results -- excessive policy leverage mitigated by excellent risk adjusted capital (severe loss scenario) reflecting improvement over results in 2012. Fair overall results on stability tests (4.1). Good quality investment portfolio (6.4).

Other Rating Factors: Weak profitability (1.2) with operating losses during the first six months of 2016. Excellent liquidity (7.0).

Principal Business: Individual annuities (98%) and individual life insurance (2%).

Principal Investments: NonCMO investment grade bonds (49%), CMOs and structured securities (19%), mortgages in good standing (17%), noninv. grade bonds (7%), and misc. investments (2%).

Investments in Affiliates: 3%

Group Affiliation: Prudential of America

Licensed in: All states except NY

Commenced Business: May 1988

Address: One Corporate Dr, 10th Floor, Shelton, CT 06484

Phone: (800) 628-6039 **Domicile State:** AZ **NAIC Code:** 86630

Data Date	Rating	RACR #1	RACR #2	Total Assets ($mil)	Capital ($mil)	Net Premium ($mil)	Net Income ($mil)
6-16	C	4.00	1.88	75,234.8	2,233.9	12,157.7	-10,075.0
6-15	C+	1.17	0.93	45,900.3	486.3	-81.9	174.1
2015	C+	1.29	0.98	42,821.4	482.1	-230.8	340.0
2014	C	1.44	1.11	47,706.6	605.7	-145.1	392.6
2013	C	1.01	0.81	50,649.1	443.5	-127.6	406.1
2012	C+	1.04	0.79	49,555.9	447.7	558.8	217.4
2011	C+	1.55	1.18	49,168.3	671.6	837.4	177.0

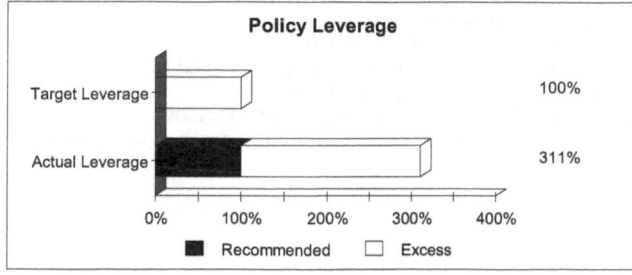

Policy Leverage

PRUDENTIAL INSURANCE COMPANY OF AMERICA — B — Good

Major Rating Factors: Good quality investment portfolio (6.0 on a scale of 0 to 10) despite substantial holdings of BBB bonds in addition to moderate junk bond exposure. Exposure to mortgages is significant, but the mortgage default rate has been low. Fair overall results on stability tests (4.1). Fair overall capitalization (4.0) based on mixed results -- excessive policy leverage mitigated by excellent risk adjusted capital (severe loss scenario).

Other Rating Factors: Excellent profitability (7.2). Excellent liquidity (8.0).

Principal Business: Group retirement contracts (44%), reinsurance (23%), group life insurance (16%), individual life insurance (11%), and other lines (5%).

Principal Investments: NonCMO investment grade bonds (47%), CMOs and structured securities (17%), mortgages in good standing (16%), common & preferred stock (7%), and misc. investments (10%).

Investments in Affiliates: 11%

Group Affiliation: Prudential of America

Licensed in: All states, the District of Columbia and Puerto Rico

Commenced Business: October 1875

Address: 751 Broad St, Newark, NJ 07102-3777

Phone: (973) 802-6000 **Domicile State:** NJ **NAIC Code:** 68241

Data Date	Rating	RACR #1	RACR #2	Total Assets ($mil)	Capital ($mil)	Net Premium ($mil)	Net Income ($mil)
6-16	B	1.34	1.00	253,157	9,430.1	10,255.6	1,661.6
6-15	B	1.41	1.02	249,946	10,563.6	-41,401.3	4,080.0
2015	B	1.53	1.15	244,996	11,543.7	-29,033.9	5,252.8
2014	B	1.35	0.93	309,102	10,331.0	22,557.6	901.1
2013	B	1.29	0.88	296,637	9,382.6	21,059.8	1,357.8
2012	B	1.21	0.83	285,087	8,698.9	52,479.2	1,382.4
2011	B	1.28	0.86	246,842	8,159.7	17,275.9	825.6

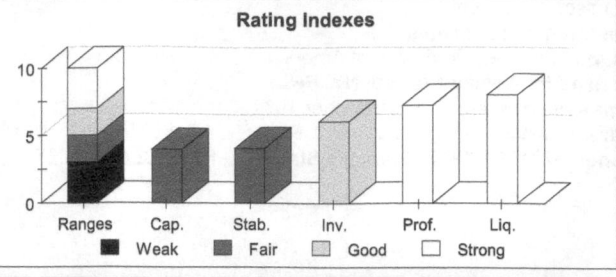

Rating Indexes

Ranges · Cap. · Stab. · Inv. · Prof. · Liq.

■ Weak ■ Fair ▨ Good □ Strong

PRUDENTIAL LEGACY INS CO OF NJ — C — Fair

Major Rating Factors: Fair current capitalization (3.2 on a scale of 0 to 10) based on mixed results -- excessive policy leverage mitigated by fair risk adjusted capital (severe loss scenario), although results have slipped from the excellent range over the last year. Good overall profitability (6.5). Despite its volitility, return on equity has been excellent over the last five years averaging 81.6%. Weak liquidity (0.7).

Other Rating Factors: Weak overall results on stability tests (2.8) including weak results on operational trends and negative cash flow from operations for 2015. High quality investment portfolio (9.4).

Principal Business: Reinsurance (100%).

Principal Investments: NonCMO investment grade bonds (100%).

Investments in Affiliates: None

Group Affiliation: Prudential of America

Licensed in: (No states)

Commenced Business: October 2010

Address: 751 Broad St, Newark, NJ 07102-3777

Phone: (800) 286-7754 **Domicile State:** NJ **NAIC Code:** 13809

Data Date	Rating	RACR #1	RACR #2	Total Assets ($mil)	Capital ($mil)	Net Premium ($mil)	Net Income ($mil)
2015	C	0.64	0.53	61,222.1	359.2	55,309.0	1,468.5
2014	U	3.50	3.15	6.0	6.0	0.0	0.0
2013	U	3.49	3.14	6.0	6.0	0.0	0.0
2012	U	3.48	3.14	6.0	5.9	0.0	0.0
2011	U	3.49	3.14	6.0	6.0	0.0	-0.1

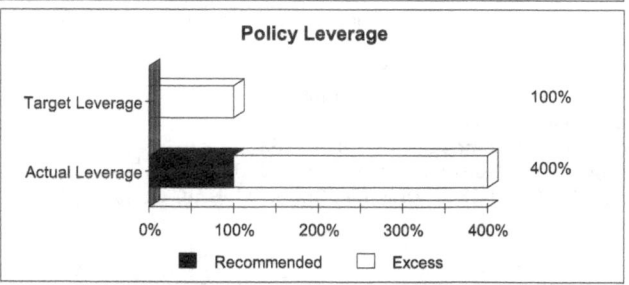

Policy Leverage

Target Leverage — 100%

Actual Leverage — 400%

0% 100% 200% 300% 400%

■ Recommended □ Excess

PRUDENTIAL RETIREMENT INSURANCE & ANNUITY — B- — Good

Major Rating Factors: Good overall results on stability tests (5.1 on a scale of 0 to 10) despite excessive premium growth. Other stability subfactors include good operational trends and excellent risk diversification. Good overall capitalization (6.0) based on good risk adjusted capital (moderate loss scenario). However, capital levels have fluctuated somewhat during past years. Good overall profitability (6.2).

Other Rating Factors: Fair quality investment portfolio (3.1). Excellent liquidity (7.3).

Principal Business: Reinsurance (60%) and group retirement contracts (40%).

Principal Investments: NonCMO investment grade bonds (49%), CMOs and structured securities (22%), mortgages in good standing (20%), and noninv. grade bonds (7%).

Investments in Affiliates: None

Group Affiliation: Prudential of America

Licensed in: All states, the District of Columbia and Puerto Rico

Commenced Business: October 1981

Address: 280 Trumbull St, Hartford, CT 06103-3509

Phone: (860) 534-2000 **Domicile State:** CT **NAIC Code:** 93629

Data Date	Rating	RACR #1	RACR #2	Total Assets ($mil)	Capital ($mil)	Net Premium ($mil)	Net Income ($mil)
6-16	B-	1.66	0.77	70,736.0	941.9	457.4	35.4
6-15	B-	1.80	0.82	78,233.0	1,069.6	324.4	93.0
2015	B-	1.89	0.86	75,576.9	1,080.4	749.7	114.9
2014	B-	1.60	0.76	78,877.5	932.7	568.4	191.0
2013	B-	1.66	0.79	78,046.5	941.0	583.1	313.0
2012	B-	2.04	0.91	69,265.3	1,072.0	451.6	231.4
2011	B-	2.10	0.90	63,442.9	1,079.4	233.1	168.4

Adverse Trends in Operations

Increase in policy surrenders from 2014 to 2015 (42%)
Decrease in asset base during 2015 (4%)
Increase in policy surrenders from 2013 to 2014 (27%)
Decrease in capital during 2013 (12%)
Increase in policy surrenders from 2011 to 2012 (140%)

REINSURANCE COMPANY OF MISSOURI INCORPORATED   C   Fair

Major Rating Factors: Good capitalization (6.5 on a scale of 0 to 10) based on good risk adjusted capital (severe loss scenario). Low quality investment portfolio (1.4). Weak overall results on stability tests (2.8) including weak results on operational trends.
Other Rating Factors: Excellent profitability (7.3). Excellent liquidity (8.6).
Principal Business: Reinsurance (100%).
Principal Investments: Common & preferred stock (91%), nonCMO investment grade bonds (7%), and CMOs and structured securities (2%).
Investments in Affiliates: 91%
Group Affiliation: Reinsurance Group of America Inc
Licensed in: MO
Commenced Business: December 1998
Address: 1370 Timberlake Manor Pkwy, Chesterfield, MO 63017-6039
Phone: (636) 736-7368 **Domicile State:** MO **NAIC Code:** 89004

Data Date	Rating	RACR #1	RACR #2	Total Assets ($mil)	Capital ($mil)	Net Premium ($mil)	Net Income ($mil)
6-16	C	1.01	0.94	1,640.4	1,603.4	-22.5	89.3
6-15	C+	0.96	0.89	1,553.0	1,544.5	2.1	7.1
2015	C	1.01	0.94	1,761.0	1,598.3	65.2	51.0
2014	C+	1.02	0.95	1,773.1	1,625.3	5.7	126.3
2013	C+	1.04	0.94	1,746.6	1,633.4	30.9	109.1
2012	C+	1.08	0.96	1,748.7	1,692.2	83.6	58.5
2011	C+	1.08	0.96	1,655.4	1,478.9	93.1	37.1

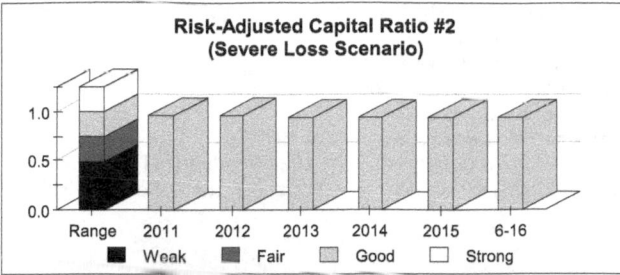

Risk-Adjusted Capital Ratio #2 (Severe Loss Scenario)

RELIANCE STANDARD LIFE INSURANCE COMPANY   B   Good

Major Rating Factors: Good overall results on stability tests (5.9 on a scale of 0 to 10). Stability strengths include excellent operational trends and excellent risk diversification. Good capitalization (6.0) based on good risk adjusted capital (severe loss scenario). Moreover, capital levels have been consistent over the last five years. Good liquidity (6.5).
Other Rating Factors: Fair quality investment portfolio (4.0) Excellent profitability (8.4).
Principal Business: Group health insurance (41%), individual annuities (25%), group life insurance (23%), group retirement contracts (7%), and reinsurance (3%).
Principal Investments: CMOs and structured securities (43%), nonCMO investment grade bonds (30%), noninv. grade bonds (10%), mortgages in good standing (10%), and common & preferred stock (4%).
Investments in Affiliates: 2%
Group Affiliation: Tokio Marine Holdings Inc
Licensed in: All states, the District of Columbia and Puerto Rico
Commenced Business: April 1907
Address: 111 S Wacker Dr Suite 4400, Chicago, IL 60606-4410
Phone: (215) 787-4000 **Domicile State:** IL **NAIC Code:** 68381

Data Date	Rating	RACR #1	RACR #2	Total Assets ($mil)	Capital ($mil)	Net Premium ($mil)	Net Income ($mil)
6-16	B	1.64	0.88	10,156.8	968.0	867.3	70.0
6-15	B	1.54	0.79	8,757.2	709.6	704.1	71.5
2015	B	1.64	0.89	9,580.8	923.9	1,536.0	124.5
2014	B	1.70	0.92	7,583.8	713.3	1,787.2	166.9
2013	B	1.78	1.06	5,980.4	598.4	1,642.5	134.6
2012	B	1.74	1.02	5,186.9	561.5	1,386.6	88.4
2011	B-	1.72	1.04	4,618.0	522.3	1,320.9	76.9

Adverse Trends In Operations

Decrease in premium volume from 2014 to 2015 (14%)
Increase in policy surrenders from 2012 to 2013 (50%)

RELIASTAR LIFE INSURANCE COMPANY   C+   Fair

Major Rating Factors: Fair profitability (3.9 on a scale of 0 to 10). Fair overall results on stability tests (3.6) including negative cash flow from operations for 2015. Good quality investment portfolio (6.1) despite large holdings of BBB rated bonds in addition to moderate junk bond exposure. Exposure to mortgages is significant, but the mortgage default rate has been low.
Other Rating Factors: Good liquidity (5.1). Strong capitalization (7.4) based on excellent risk adjusted capital (severe loss scenario).
Principal Business: Individual life insurance (37%), group health insurance (31%), group life insurance (16%), individual annuities (10%), and other lines (6%).
Principal Investments: NonCMO investment grade bonds (62%), mortgages in good standing (13%), CMOs and structured securities (11%), noninv. grade bonds (4%), and misc. investments (9%).
Investments in Affiliates: 3%
Group Affiliation: Voya Financial Inc
Licensed in: All states, the District of Columbia and Puerto Rico
Commenced Business: September 1885
Address: 20 Washington Ave S, Minneapolis, MN 55401
Phone: (770) 980-5100 **Domicile State:** MN **NAIC Code:** 67105

Data Date	Rating	RACR #1	RACR #2	Total Assets ($mil)	Capital ($mil)	Net Premium ($mil)	Net Income ($mil)
6-16	C+	2.06	1.24	19,884.7	1,645.8	394.9	55.7
6-15	C+	2.32	1.37	20,813.8	1,811.5	357.8	74.2
2015	C+	2.03	1.23	19,805.1	1,609.2	740.9	74.2
2014	C+	2.40	1.42	21,468.7	1,944.7	-149.0	103.9
2013	C	2.29	1.38	21,621.2	1,942.5	840.3	215.9
2012	C-	2.57	1.54	21,526.1	2,284.6	858.8	-155.3
2011	C-	2.48	1.44	20,779.6	2,104.3	886.1	-83.0

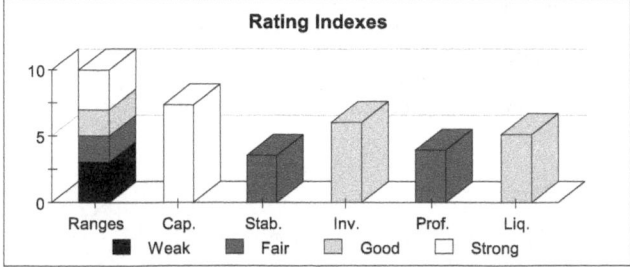

Rating Indexes

RELIASTAR LIFE INSURANCE COMPANY OF NEW YORK | B | Good

Major Rating Factors: Good overall results on stability tests (5.8 on a scale of 0 to 10). Stability strengths include excellent operational trends and excellent risk diversification. Good quality investment portfolio (6.5) despite mixed results such as: minimal exposure to mortgages and large holdings of BBB rated bonds but small junk bond holdings. Good liquidity (5.9).

Other Rating Factors: Fair profitability (4.6) with operating losses during the first six months of 2016. Strong capitalization (8.2) based on excellent risk adjusted capital (severe loss scenario).

Principal Business: Individual life insurance (74%), group health insurance (18%), group life insurance (5%), individual annuities (2%), and individual health insurance (1%).

Principal Investments: NonCMO investment grade bonds (72%), CMOs and structured securities (8%), mortgages in good standing (7%), policy loans (5%), and misc. investments (5%).

Investments in Affiliates: None

Group Affiliation: Voya Financial Inc

Licensed in: All states except PR

Commenced Business: September 1917

Address: 1000 Woodbury Rd Suite 102, Woodbury, NY 11797

Phone: (516) 682-8700 **Domicile State:** NY **NAIC Code:** 61360

Data Date	Rating	RACR #1	RACR #2	Total Assets ($mil)	Capital ($mil)	Net Premium ($mil)	Net Income ($mil)
6-16	B	3.41	1.83	3,067.1	304.7	79.1	-14.1
6-15	B	3.45	1.85	3,123.8	313.5	76.5	8.8
2015	B	3.52	1.89	3,053.7	314.9	146.6	16.6
2014	B	3.33	1.79	3,201.6	298.8	139.9	-40.7
2013	B-	3.86	2.04	3,208.8	329.5	139.2	20.5
2012	B-	3.69	1.98	3,232.4	340.6	157.4	40.1
2011	C	3.31	1.77	3,307.9	281.5	114.3	-49.1

Adverse Trends in Operations

Decrease in asset base during 2015 (5%)
Decrease in capital during 2014 (9%)
Decrease in premium volume from 2012 to 2013 (12%)
Decrease in capital during 2013 (3%)
Decrease in asset base during 2012 (2%)

RESERVE NATIONAL INSURANCE COMPANY * | A- | Excellent

Major Rating Factors: Good overall results on stability tests (6.2 on a scale of 0 to 10). Strengths that enhance stability include excellent operational trends and excellent risk diversification. Good liquidity (6.1) with sufficient resources to handle a spike in claims. Fair profitability (4.1) with operating losses during the first six months of 2016.

Other Rating Factors: Strong capitalization (7.8) based on excellent risk adjusted capital (severe loss scenario). High quality investment portfolio (8.0).

Principal Business: Individual health insurance (80%), individual life insurance (13%), reinsurance (4%), and group health insurance (3%).

Principal Investments: NonCMO investment grade bonds (90%), cash (4%), and CMOs and structured securities (3%).

Investments in Affiliates: None

Group Affiliation: Kemper Corporation

Licensed in: All states except CA, NY, PR

Commenced Business: September 1956

Address: 601 E Britton Rd, Oklahoma City, OK 73114

Phone: (405) 848-7931 **Domicile State:** OK **NAIC Code:** 68462

Data Date	Rating	RACR #1	RACR #2	Total Assets ($mil)	Capital ($mil)	Net Premium ($mil)	Net Income ($mil)
6-16	A-	2.01	1.53	123.3	40.1	70.4	-2.3
6-15	A	2.59	1.98	119.6	51.9	66.0	0.5
2015	A	2.18	1.66	122.8	45.1	132.7	-0.5
2014	A	2.44	1.88	118.2	51.0	131.8	1.7
2013	A	2.27	1.76	111.2	52.4	143.6	4.9
2012	A	2.66	2.04	116.0	58.4	135.2	8.8
2011	B	2.63	1.95	118.6	60.6	135.2	9.9

Adverse Trends in Operations

Increase in policy surrenders from 2014 to 2015 (46%)
Decrease in capital during 2015 (11%)
Decrease in premium volume from 2013 to 2014 (8%)
Decrease in asset base during 2013 (4%)
Decrease in capital during 2013 (10%)

RGA REINSURANCE COMPANY | B- | Good

Major Rating Factors: Good overall capitalization (5.6 on a scale of 0 to 10) based on good risk adjusted capital (moderate loss scenario). Nevertheless, capital levels have fluctuated during prior years. Good overall profitability (6.1) despite operating losses during the first six months of 2016. Good liquidity (5.8).

Other Rating Factors: Good overall results on stability tests (5.3) good operational trends and excellent risk diversification. Fair quality investment portfolio (4.7).

Principal Business: Reinsurance (100%).

Principal Investments: NonCMO investment grade bonds (44%), mortgages in good standing (16%), CMOs and structured securities (16%), noninv. grade bonds (9%), and misc. investments (15%).

Investments in Affiliates: 4%

Group Affiliation: Reinsurance Group of America Inc

Licensed in: All states, the District of Columbia and Puerto Rico

Commenced Business: October 1982

Address: 660 Mason Ridge Center Dr, St Louis, MO 63141

Phone: (314) 453-7368 **Domicile State:** MO **NAIC Code:** 93572

Data Date	Rating	RACR #1	RACR #2	Total Assets ($mil)	Capital ($mil)	Net Premium ($mil)	Net Income ($mil)
6-16	B-	1.41	0.80	25,223.7	1,483.5	1,190.6	-34.5
6-15	B-	1.54	0.80	23,784.8	1,440.5	1,198.5	-90.0
2015	B-	1.42	0.81	24,593.0	1,503.4	3,364.2	-23.6
2014	B	1.69	0.88	24,178.4	1,528.3	3,494.2	17.1
2013	B	1.70	0.90	23,259.8	1,550.1	2,305.6	115.8
2012	B	1.75	0.95	22,835.1	1,644.6	5,213.8	3.5
2011	B	1.97	1.13	16,913.0	1,515.9	3,176.5	129.7

Junk Bonds as a % of Capital

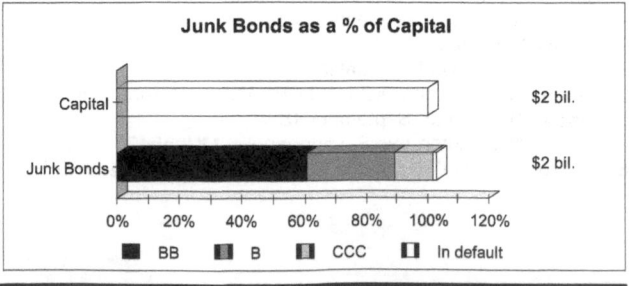

RIVERMONT LIFE INSURANCE COMPANY I   C   Fair

Major Rating Factors: Fair overall results on stability tests (3.9 on a scale of 0 to 10). Weak profitability (1.5) with investment income below regulatory standards in relation to interest assumptions of reserves. Strong overall capitalization (9.2) based on excellent risk adjusted capital (severe loss scenario). Nevertheless, capital levels have fluctuated during prior years.

Other Rating Factors: High quality investment portfolio (7.2). Excellent liquidity (7.9).

Principal Business: Reinsurance (100%).

Principal Investments: NonCMO investment grade bonds (78%) and CMOs and structured securities (21%).

Investments in Affiliates: None

Group Affiliation: Genworth Financial

Licensed in: SC

Commenced Business: October 2006

Address: 151 Meeting St Suite 301, Charleston, SC 29401

Phone: (843) 577-1026 **Domicile State:** SC **NAIC Code:** 13219

Data Date	Rating	RACR #1	RACR #2	Total Assets ($mil)	Capital ($mil)	Net Premium ($mil)	Net Income ($mil)
6-16	C	4.38	2.48	577.1	147.6	12.4	12.0
6-15	C	4.14	2.30	546.7	139.4	13.4	-7.7
2015	C	3.90	2.22	544.0	129.8	28.5	-12.4
2014	C	4.93	2.75	533.2	145.0	26.9	-13.1
2013	C	4.64	2.54	502.6	153.8	29.1	-12.5
2012	C	5.06	2.72	496.1	165.4	54.4	7.2
2011	C	5.01	2.58	460.8	163.1	19.4	-19.6

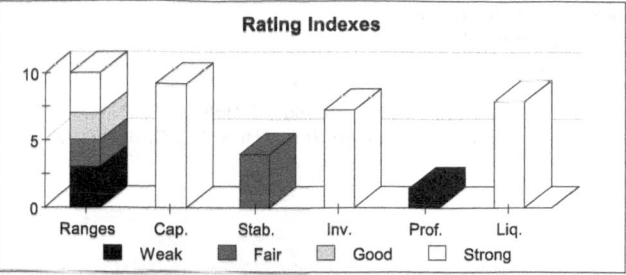

Rating Indexes

RIVERSOURCE LIFE INSURANCE COMPANY   C   Fair

Major Rating Factors: Fair overall results on stability tests (4.1 on a scale of 0 to 10). Good quality investment portfolio (5.9) despite large holdings of BBB rated bonds in addition to junk bond exposure equal to 50% of capital. Exposure to mortgages is significant, but the mortgage default rate has been low. Good profitability (5.0) despite operating losses during the first six months of 2016.

Other Rating Factors: Strong capitalization (7.4) based on excellent risk adjusted capital (severe loss scenario). Excellent liquidity (7.8).

Principal Business: Individual annuities (77%), individual life insurance (17%), individual health insurance (5%), and group retirement contracts (1%).

Principal Investments: NonCMO investment grade bonds (44%), CMOs and structured securities (21%), mortgages in good standing (11%), noninv. grade bonds (6%), and misc. investments (6%).

Investments in Affiliates: 3%

Group Affiliation: Ameriprise Financial Inc

Licensed in: All states except NY, PR

Commenced Business: October 1957

Address: 227 AXP Financial Center, Minneapolis, MN 55474

Phone: (612) 671-3131 **Domicile State:** MN **NAIC Code:** 65005

Data Date	Rating	RACR #1	RACR #2	Total Assets ($mil)	Capital ($mil)	Net Premium ($mil)	Net Income ($mil)
6-16	C	2.03	1.25	102,927	3,504.4	2,858.3	-641.1
6-15	C	1.85	1.12	103,923	3,242.9	3,020.9	341.1
2015	C	2.05	1.27	100,564	3,650.1	6,222.2	632.7
2014	C	2.00	1.22	104,763	3,332.3	5,872.3	1,153.9
2013	C-	1.59	0.95	104,356	2,685.9	6,187.8	1,336.8
2012	C-	1.94	1.14	96,669.1	3,112.6	6,323.6	1,975.9
2011	C-	1.90	1.10	91,266.4	2,681.3	7,638.7	-599.3

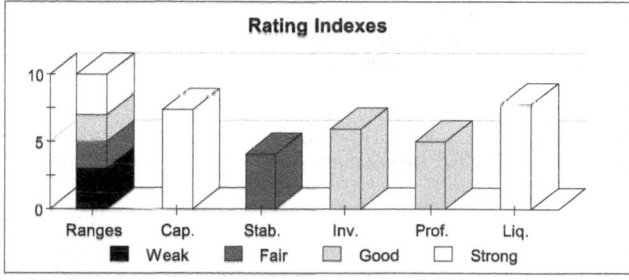

Rating Indexes

RIVERSOURCE LIFE INSURANCE COMPANY OF NEW YORK   C   Fair

Major Rating Factors: Fair overall results on stability tests (4.3 on a scale of 0 to 10) including fair financial strength of affiliated Ameriprise Financial Inc. Fair profitability (3.0) with operating losses during the first six months of 2016. Good quality investment portfolio (6.0) despite mixed results such as: minimal exposure to mortgages and large holdings of BBB rated bonds but small junk bond holdings.

Other Rating Factors: Strong capitalization (8.2) based on excellent risk adjusted capital (severe loss scenario). Excellent liquidity (7.5).

Principal Business: Individual annuities (77%), individual life insurance (16%), individual health insurance (4%), and group retirement contracts (3%).

Principal Investments: NonCMO investment grade bonds (60%), CMOs and structured securities (22%), mortgages in good standing (7%), noninv. grade bonds (4%), and policy loans (2%).

Investments in Affiliates: None

Group Affiliation: Ameriprise Financial Inc

Licensed in: NY

Commenced Business: October 1972

Address: 20 Madison Avenue Extension, Albany, NY 12203

Phone: (518) 869-8613 **Domicile State:** NY **NAIC Code:** 80594

Data Date	Rating	RACR #1	RACR #2	Total Assets ($mil)	Capital ($mil)	Net Premium ($mil)	Net Income ($mil)
6-16	C	3.59	1.79	6,638.3	330.6	176.9	-9.6
6-15	C	3.05	1.54	6,611.1	293.9	205.1	18.3
2015	C	3.50	1.76	6,497.2	325.5	412.4	48.9
2014	C	3.21	1.61	6,607.2	297.6	414.6	42.6
2013	C	2.67	1.34	6,315.7	250.3	428.1	90.4
2012	C	2.74	1.38	5,821.9	252.8	417.2	82.4
2011	B	2.70	1.36	5,503.6	235.5	482.2	-6.2

Ameriprise Financial Inc Composite Group Rating: C Largest Group Members	Assets ($mil)	Rating
RIVERSOURCE LIFE INS CO	100564	C
RIVERSOURCE LIFE INS CO OF NY	6497	C
IDS PROPERTY CASUALTY INS CO	1662	B-
AMERIPRISE INS CO	48	B

ROYAL STATE NATIONAL INSURANCE COMPANY LIMITED

C   **Fair**

Major Rating Factors: Fair profitability (3.8 on a scale of 0 to 10). Fair overall results on stability tests (4.2) including negative cash flow from operations for 2015. Good quality investment portfolio (5.9) despite mixed results such as: no exposure to mortgages and large holdings of BBB rated bonds but minimal holdings in junk bonds.

Other Rating Factors: Good liquidity (6.9). Strong capitalization (10.0) based on excellent risk adjusted capital (severe loss scenario).

Principal Business: Group life insurance (50%), group health insurance (39%), individual life insurance (8%), and reinsurance (2%).

Principal Investments: NonCMO investment grade bonds (67%), common & preferred stock (17%), CMOs and structured securities (14%), policy loans (1%), and misc. investments (2%).

Investments in Affiliates: 3%

Group Affiliation: Royal State Group

Licensed in: HI

Commenced Business: August 1961

Address: 819 S Beretania St, Honolulu, HI 96813

Phone: (808) 539-1600   **Domicile State:** HI   **NAIC Code:** 68551

Data Date	Rating	RACR #1	RACR #2	Total Assets ($mil)	Capital ($mil)	Net Premium ($mil)	Net Income ($mil)
6-16	C	4.70	3.13	45.7	28.8	2.7	0.2
6-15	C+	3.14	2.19	46.2	29.3	4.3	0.1
2015	C	4.91	3.29	45.2	28.5	7.0	-0.4
2014	B-	3.27	2.29	47.1	29.3	10.8	0.7
2013	B-	3.29	2.33	45.6	28.9	10.6	0.4
2012	B-	3.29	2.38	44.6	28.9	10.5	-0.1
2011	B-	4.44	3.08	43.3	28.6	5.8	0.8

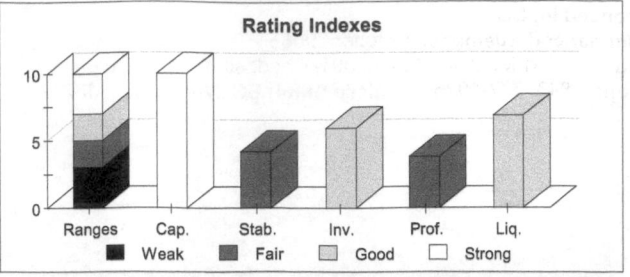

Rating Indexes

SAGICOR LIFE INSURANCE COMPANY

C-   **Fair**

Major Rating Factors: Fair liquidity (4.5 on a scale of 0 to 10) due, in part, to cash value policies that are subject to withdrawals with minimal or no penalty. Fair overall results on stability tests (3.1) including fair risk adjusted capital in prior years. Low quality investment portfolio (2.4) containing large holdings of BBB rated bonds in addition to moderate junk bond exposure.

Other Rating Factors: Weak profitability (2.0) with operating losses during the first six months of 2016. Good capitalization (5.2) based on good risk adjusted capital (moderate loss scenario).

Principal Business: Individual annuities (84%), individual life insurance (15%), and reinsurance (1%).

Principal Investments: NonCMO investment grade bonds (67%), CMOs and structured securities (21%), policy loans (3%), common & preferred stock (2%), and misc. investments (4%).

Investments in Affiliates: None

Group Affiliation: Sagicor Financial Corp

Licensed in: All states except AK, CT, NY, PR

Commenced Business: April 1954

Address: 2720 E Camelback Rd, Phoenix, AZ 85016

Phone: (800) 531-5067   **Domicile State:** TX   **NAIC Code:** 60445

Data Date	Rating	RACR #1	RACR #2	Total Assets ($mil)	Capital ($mil)	Net Premium ($mil)	Net Income ($mil)
6-16	C-	1.14	0.57	1,128.2	74.4	34.2	-14.4
6-15	C-	1.20	0.61	1,258.7	70.5	44.2	-3.3
2015	C-	1.49	0.75	1,193.5	78.7	80.8	3.4
2014	C-	1.33	0.69	1,214.9	74.2	74.2	0.2
2013	C-	1.43	0.74	1,176.2	75.8	87.4	1.1
2012	C-	1.26	0.66	1,099.9	60.1	148.8	-9.5
2011	C-	1.62	0.82	870.0	52.8	101.8	-3.8

Exposure to Withdrawals Without Penalty (as a % of capital)

SAVINGS BANK LIFE INSURANCE COMPANY OF MASSACHUSE

B+   **Good**

Major Rating Factors: Good quality investment portfolio (6.2 on a scale of 0 to 10) despite mixed results such as: large holdings of BBB rated bonds but junk bond exposure equal to 51% of capital. Good overall profitability (6.5). Excellent expense controls. Good liquidity (6.0) with sufficient resources to handle a spike in claims as well as a significant increase in policy surrenders.

Other Rating Factors: Good overall results on stability tests (6.4) excellent operational trends and excellent risk diversification. Strong capitalization (7.1) based on excellent risk adjusted capital (severe loss scenario).

Principal Business: Individual life insurance (98%) and individual annuities (2%).

Principal Investments: NonCMO investment grade bonds (67%), CMOs and structured securities (20%), common & preferred stock (5%), noninv. grade bonds (4%), and policy loans (3%).

Investments in Affiliates: 3%

Group Affiliation: Savings Bank Life Group

Licensed in: All states except NY, PR

Commenced Business: January 1992

Address: One Linscott Rd, Woburn, MA 01801

Phone: (781) 938-3500   **Domicile State:** MA   **NAIC Code:** 70435

Data Date	Rating	RACR #1	RACR #2	Total Assets ($mil)	Capital ($mil)	Net Premium ($mil)	Net Income ($mil)
6-16	B+	1.66	1.07	2,957.5	218.7	81.3	12.6
6-15	B+	1.67	1.13	2,870.9	239.2	125.8	-9.3
2015	B+	1.70	1.11	2,919.1	224.0	215.7	11.7
2014	B+	1.77	1.21	2,795.6	256.8	198.7	12.9
2013	B+	2.90	1.60	2,534.4	213.6	169.1	17.9
2012	B+	2.93	1.65	2,406.5	202.8	207.9	22.6
2011	B+	2.92	1.65	2,396.0	193.5	187.8	17.7

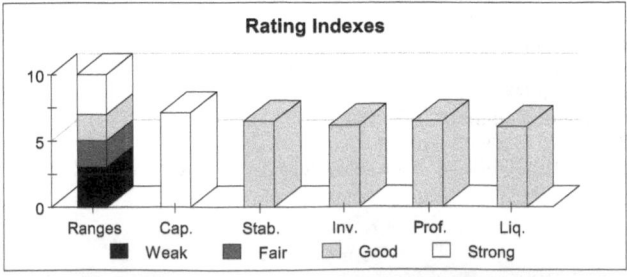

Rating Indexes

SBLI USA MUTUAL LIFE INSURANCE COMPANY INCORPORATE   B   Good

Major Rating Factors: Good quality investment portfolio (6.0 on a scale of 0 to 10) despite mixed results such as: no exposure to mortgages and large holdings of BBB rated bonds but minimal holdings in junk bonds. Good overall results on stability tests (5.6) despite negative cash flow from operations for 2015, fair risk adjusted capital in prior years. Other stability subfactors include excellent operational trends and excellent risk diversification. Fair liquidity (3.6).

Other Rating Factors: Strong capitalization (7.2) based on excellent risk adjusted capital (severe loss scenario). Excellent profitability (7.8).

Principal Business: Individual life insurance (71%), group life insurance (24%), reinsurance (5%), and individual health insurance (1%).

Principal Investments: NonCMO investment grade bonds (64%), CMOs and structured securities (26%), policy loans (7%), common & preferred stock (1%), and noninv. grade bonds (1%).

Investments in Affiliates: 1%

Group Affiliation: Reservoir Capital Group LLC

Licensed in: IL, IA, MI, MS, NH, NJ, NY, NC, OH, PA, SD, VT, PR

Commenced Business: January 2000

Address: 460 W 34th St Suite 800, New York, NY 10001-2320

Phone: (212) 356-0346 **Domicile State:** NY **NAIC Code:** 60176

Data Date	Rating	RACR #1	RACR #2	Total Assets ($mil)	Capital ($mil)	Net Premium ($mil)	Net Income ($mil)
6-16	B	1.98	1.11	1,533.2	118.5	28.8	8.3
6-15	B	1.74	0.97	1,515.8	104.4	29.0	3.3
2015	B	2.06	1.15	1,518.8	121.5	59.4	15.7
2014	B-	1.69	0.94	1,530.9	102.2	62.3	-1.4
2013	B-	1.44	0.79	1,479.1	89.0	65.6	-2.2
2012	C	1.22	0.65	1,486.5	81.3	68.4	-16.9
2011	C	1.11	0.59	1,486.1	76.4	72.5	-2.1

Adverse Trends in Operations
Decrease in premium volume from 2014 to 2015 (5%)
Decrease in premium volume from 2013 to 2014 (5%)
Decrease in premium volume from 2012 to 2013 (4%)
Decrease in premium volume from 2011 to 2012 (6%)

SCOR GLOBAL LIFE AMERICAS REINSURANCE COMPANY   C-   Fair

Major Rating Factors: Fair overall results on stability tests (3.3 on a scale of 0 to 10) including fair financial strength of affiliated SCOR Reinsurance Group and negative cash flow from operations for 2015, fair risk adjusted capital in prior years. Weak profitability (2.4) with operating losses during the first six months of 2016. Good capitalization (5.7) based on good risk adjusted capital (severe loss scenario).

Other Rating Factors: Good quality investment portfolio (6.6). Excellent liquidity (7.9).

Principal Business: Reinsurance (100%).

Principal Investments: NonCMO investment grade bonds (66%), CMOs and structured securities (17%), common & preferred stock (8%), noninv. grade bonds (7%), and misc. investments (3%).

Investments in Affiliates: 8%

Group Affiliation: SCOR Reinsurance Group

Licensed in: All states except NY, PR

Commenced Business: April 1945

Address: 2711 Centerville Rd Suite 400, Wilmington, DE 19808

Phone: (704) 344-2700 **Domicile State:** DE **NAIC Code:** 64688

Data Date	Rating	RACR #1	RACR #2	Total Assets ($mil)	Capital ($mil)	Net Premium ($mil)	Net Income ($mil)
6-16	C-	1.19	0.84	1,286.8	193.4	52.5	-3.7
6-15	C-	1.36	0.87	1,197.9	186.7	50.9	11.6
2015	C-	1.19	0.83	1,262.0	192.1	112.8	0.7
2014	C-	1.21	0.74	1,480.0	151.7	110.0	15.1
2013	C-	1.11	0.71	1,355.3	151.8	98.1	-40.6
2012	C-	1.93	1.17	1,378.6	157.8	90.0	6.6
2011	C-	1.44	0.95	1,453.0	175.3	-852.3	-2.8

SCOR Reinsurance Group Composite Group Rating: C- Largest Group Members	Assets ($mil)	Rating
SCOR REINS CO	2749	C-
SCOR GLOBAL LIFE AMERICAS REIN CO	1262	C-
SCOR GLOBAL LIFE USA RE CO	737	C
SCOR GLOBAL LIFE REINS CO OF DE	368	C
GENERAL SECURITY NATIONAL INS CO	334	C-

SCOR GLOBAL LIFE REINSURANCE COMPANY OF DELAWARE   C   Fair

Major Rating Factors: Fair overall results on stability tests (3.7 on a scale of 0 to 10) including fair financial strength of affiliated SCOR Reinsurance Group. Weak profitability (2.0) with investment income below regulatory standards in relation to interest assumptions of reserves. Strong capitalization (8.2) based on excellent risk adjusted capital (severe loss scenario).

Other Rating Factors: High quality investment portfolio (8.7). Excellent liquidity (7.7).

Principal Business: Reinsurance (100%).

Principal Investments: NonCMO investment grade bonds (76%), CMOs and structured securities (18%), policy loans (5%), and cash (1%).

Investments in Affiliates: None

Group Affiliation: SCOR Reinsurance Group

Licensed in: All states except AL, PR

Commenced Business: May 1977

Address: 2711 Centerville Rd Suite 400, Wilmington, DE 19808

Phone: (704) 344-2700 **Domicile State:** DE **NAIC Code:** 87017

Data Date	Rating	RACR #1	RACR #2	Total Assets ($mil)	Capital ($mil)	Net Premium ($mil)	Net Income ($mil)
6-16	C	2.88	1.77	381.4	83.3	33.6	5.1
6-15	C	2.17	1.34	355.1	65.6	29.4	16.5
2015	C	2.71	1.68	368.3	78.1	65.7	16.2
2014	C	1.52	0.93	456.5	46.5	51.3	-4.5
2013	C-	1.70	1.04	470.0	51.3	37.9	-3.7
2012	D+	1.66	1.03	450.6	25.5	33.0	-17.4
2011	D	1.19	0.75	409.0	32.1	109.8	-39.4

SCOR Reinsurance Group Composite Group Rating: C- Largest Group Members	Assets ($mil)	Rating
SCOR REINS CO	2749	C-
SCOR GLOBAL LIFE AMERICAS REIN CO	1262	C-
SCOR GLOBAL LIFE USA RE CO	737	C
SCOR GLOBAL LIFE REINS CO OF DE	368	C
GENERAL SECURITY NATIONAL INS CO	334	C-

SCOR GLOBAL LIFE USA RE CO

C **Fair**

Major Rating Factors: Fair overall results on stability tests (3.3 on a scale of 0 to 10) including fair financial strength of affiliated SCOR Reinsurance Group and negative cash flow from operations for 2015. Good overall profitability (6.8). Excellent expense controls. Strong capitalization (10.0) based on excellent risk adjusted capital (severe loss scenario).

Other Rating Factors: High quality investment portfolio (8.7). Excellent liquidity (8.0).

Principal Business: Reinsurance (100%).

Principal Investments: NonCMO investment grade bonds (86%), CMOs and structured securities (10%), and cash (1%).

Investments in Affiliates: None

Group Affiliation: SCOR Reinsurance Group

Licensed in: All states except PR

Commenced Business: October 1982

Address: 150 King St W 11th Fl, Toronto Ontario, CN M5H 1J9

Phone: (416) 979-6266 **Domicile State:** DE **NAIC Code:** 97071

Data Date	Rating	RACR #1	RACR #2	Total Assets ($mil)	Capital ($mil)	Net Premium ($mil)	Net Income ($mil)
6-16	C	5.71	3.59	718.4	339.4	87.0	16.4
6-15	C	5.30	3.42	787.2	378.4	75.6	3.1
2015	C	6.10	3.84	736.8	360.3	160.8	18.4
2014	C	5.37	3.48	812.3	377.6	184.3	22.3
2013	C	8.20	5.04	949.3	422.6	908.2	61.6
2012	B-	2.66	1.72	1,109.1	364.0	370.0	18.7
2011	B-	2.64	1.71	1,033.1	346.8	355.4	32.2

SCOR Reinsurance Group Composite Group Rating: C- Largest Group Members	Assets ($mil)	Rating
SCOR REINS CO	2749	C-
SCOR GLOBAL LIFE AMERICAS REIN CO	1262	C-
SCOR GLOBAL LIFE USA RE CO	737	C
SCOR GLOBAL LIFE REINS CO OF DE	368	C
GENERAL SECURITY NATIONAL INS CO	334	C-

SCOTTISH RE US INCORPORATED

D+ **Weak**

Major Rating Factors: Weak profitability (1.2 on a scale of 0 to 10) with operating losses during the first six months of 2016. Weak overall results on stability tests (2.4) including weak results on operational trends and negative cash flow from operations for 2015. Fair quality investment portfolio (3.5) with large holdings of BBB rated bonds in addition to moderate junk bond exposure.

Other Rating Factors: Fair liquidity (4.7). Good capitalization (5.0) based on good risk adjusted capital (moderate loss scenario).

Principal Business: Reinsurance (100%).

Principal Investments: CMOs and structured securities (50%), nonCMO investment grade bonds (47%), and noninv. grade bonds (3%).

Investments in Affiliates: None

Group Affiliation: Scottish Annuity & Life Holdings Ltd

Licensed in: All states except PR

Commenced Business: September 1977

Address: 160 Greentree Dr Suite 101, Dover, DE 19904-7620

Phone: (704) 542-9192 **Domicile State:** DE **NAIC Code:** 87572

Data Date	Rating	RACR #1	RACR #2	Total Assets ($mil)	Capital ($mil)	Net Premium ($mil)	Net Income ($mil)
6-16	D+	1.03	0.54	1,510.9	75.0	68.8	-1.9
6-15	C-	1.53	0.84	1,651.1	142.2	78.8	-24.3
2015	D+	1.08	0.57	1,570.3	80.9	13.8	-83.8
2014	C-	1.80	0.98	1,735.1	169.9	259.0	-1.3
2013	C-	1.73	0.95	1,808.2	171.7	251.2	-24.2
2012	F	1.84	1.11	1,556.9	193.5	135.5	-28.5
2011	F	2.10	1.32	1,722.6	328.6	114.1	-199.7

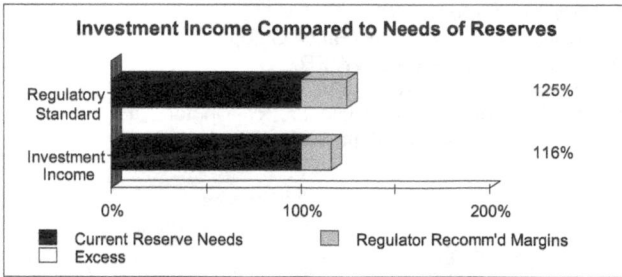

Investment Income Compared to Needs of Reserves

Regulatory Standard 125%
Investment Income 116%

0% 100% 200%

■ Current Reserve Needs ☐ Excess ▨ Regulator Recomm'd Margins

SECU LIFE INS CO

C **Fair**

Major Rating Factors: Fair overall results on stability tests (3.5 on a scale of 0 to 10) including lack of operational experience. Good overall profitability (5.9). Excellent expense controls. Strong overall capitalization (10.0) based on excellent risk adjusted capital (severe loss scenario). However, capital levels have fluctuated somewhat during past years.

Other Rating Factors: High quality investment portfolio (8.6). Excellent liquidity (9.5).

Principal Business: Individual annuities (58%), group life insurance (25%), and individual life insurance (17%).

Principal Investments: NonCMO investment grade bonds (40%), mortgages in good standing (37%), and cash (23%).

Investments in Affiliates: None

Group Affiliation: State Employees Credit Union

Licensed in: NC

Commenced Business: January 2013

Address: 1000 Wade Ave, Raleigh, NC 27605

Phone: (919) 839-5084 **Domicile State:** NC **NAIC Code:** 14924

Data Date	Rating	RACR #1	RACR #2	Total Assets ($mil)	Capital ($mil)	Net Premium ($mil)	Net Income ($mil)
6-16	C	5.42	4.88	34.4	25.7	3.6	0.3
6-15	D+	5.99	5.39	28.8	25.0	3.0	0.5
2015	C	5.37	4.83	31.6	25.5	6.3	0.9
2014	D+	5.89	5.30	26.3	24.6	2.1	0.3
2013	D	6.09	5.48	24.6	24.4	0.6	-0.7
2012	N/A	N/A	N/A	0.0	0.0	0.0	0.0
2011	N/A	N/A	N/A	0.0	0.0	0.0	0.0

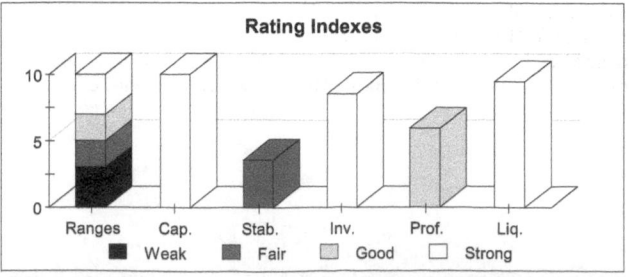

Rating Indexes

10

5

0
Ranges Cap. Stab. Inv. Prof. Liq.

■ Weak ▨ Fair ▨ Good ☐ Strong

SECURIAN LIFE INSURANCE COMPANY * A- Excellent

Major Rating Factors: Good overall profitability (6.9 on a scale of 0 to 10). Excellent expense controls. Good liquidity (6.9) with sufficient resources to handle a spike in claims. Excellent overall results on stability tests (7.2). Strengths that enhance stability include excellent operational trends and excellent risk diversification.

Other Rating Factors: Strong capitalization (10.0) based on excellent risk adjusted capital (severe loss scenario). High quality investment portfolio (7.5).

Principal Business: Group life insurance (73%), individual life insurance (11%), group health insurance (10%), reinsurance (3%), and other lines (2%).

Principal Investments: NonCMO investment grade bonds (80%), CMOs and structured securities (13%), noninv. grade bonds (3%), common & preferred stock (2%), and cash (2%).

Investments in Affiliates: None

Group Affiliation: Securian Financial Group

Licensed in: All states except PR

Commenced Business: December 1981

Address: 400 Robert St N, St Paul, MN 55101

Phone: (651) 665-3500 **Domicile State:** MN **NAIC Code:** 93742

Data Date	Rating	RACR #1	RACR #2	Total Assets ($mil)	Capital ($mil)	Net Premium ($mil)	Net Income ($mil)
6-16	A-	5.84	3.80	478.9	204.4	83.3	1.4
6-15	A-	5.42	3.78	362.6	198.2	109.8	-0.8
2015	A-	5.93	3.95	438.6	205.4	199.1	2.0
2014	A-	6.13	4.30	325.4	202.1	111.3	6.5
2013	B	6.47	4.56	207.8	131.5	83.2	-3.0
2012	A-	8.20	5.79	190.1	134.9	72.0	0.3
2011	B+	8.60	6.17	167.6	134.2	65.5	4.7

Adverse Trends in Operations

Change in premium mix from 2014 to 2015 (4.3%)
Decrease in capital during 2013 (2%)
Change in premium mix from 2012 to 2013 (4.2%)
Increase in policy surrenders from 2012 to 2013 (291%)

SECURITY BENEFIT LIFE INSURANCE COMPANY B Good

Major Rating Factors: Good overall results on stability tests (5.8 on a scale of 0 to 10). Stability strengths include good operational trends and excellent risk diversification. Good capitalization (6.1) based on good risk adjusted capital (moderate loss scenario). Capital levels have been relatively consistent over the last five years. Fair quality investment portfolio (3.8).

Other Rating Factors: Excellent profitability (7.5). Excellent liquidity (7.6).

Principal Business: Individual annuities (95%), group retirement contracts (4%), individual life insurance (1%), and reinsurance (1%).

Principal Investments: CMOs and structured securities (41%), nonCMO investment grade bonds (22%), mortgages in good standing (6%), noninv. grade bonds (5%), and policy loans (2%).

Investments in Affiliates: 15%

Group Affiliation: Sammons Enterprises Inc

Licensed in: All states except NY, PR

Commenced Business: February 1892

Address: One Security Benefit Place, Topeka, KS 66636-0001

Phone: (785) 431-3000 **Domicile State:** KS **NAIC Code:** 68675

Data Date	Rating	RACR #1	RACR #2	Total Assets ($mil)	Capital ($mil)	Net Premium ($mil)	Net Income ($mil)
6-16	B	1.73	0.80	28,075.4	1,227.3	1,452.5	3.0
6-15	B	2.31	1.08	26,527.7	1,300.2	1,508.8	53.5
2015	B	1.93	0.90	27,787.4	1,286.4	2,270.7	75.4
2014	B	2.42	1.14	24,987.4	1,301.5	5,061.3	122.1
2013	B	2.31	1.12	20,702.3	1,044.8	6,191.9	163.6
2012	B	2.19	1.06	15,392.6	774.0	2,478.2	156.9
2011	B-	2.22	1.09	10,507.8	612.8	1,629.1	1.2

Adverse Trends in Operations

Decrease in premium volume from 2014 to 2015 (55%)
Decrease in capital during 2015 (1%)
Decrease in premium volume from 2013 to 2014 (18%)
Increase in policy surrenders from 2013 to 2014 (29%)

SECURITY LIFE OF DENVER INSURANCE COMPANY C+ Fair

Major Rating Factors: Fair profitability (3.2 on a scale of 0 to 10) with operating losses during the first six months of 2016. Fair overall results on stability tests (3.3). Good quality investment portfolio (5.5) despite mixed results such as: large holdings of BBB rated bonds but junk bond exposure equal to 53% of capital.

Other Rating Factors: Good liquidity (5.5). Poor capitalization (2.6) based on weak risk adjusted capital (moderate loss scenario).

Principal Business: Reinsurance (62%) and individual life insurance (38%).

Principal Investments: NonCMO investment grade bonds (57%), CMOs and structured securities (13%), mortgages in good standing (10%), policy loans (9%), and misc. investments (10%).

Investments in Affiliates: 3%

Group Affiliation: Voya Financial Inc

Licensed in: All states, the District of Columbia and Puerto Rico

Commenced Business: May 1950

Address: 1290 Broadway, Denver, CO 80203-0000

Phone: (303) 860-1290 **Domicile State:** CO **NAIC Code:** 68713

Data Date	Rating	RACR #1	RACR #2	Total Assets ($mil)	Capital ($mil)	Net Premium ($mil)	Net Income ($mil)
6-16	C+	0.69	0.47	13,328.9	770.6	303.4	-2.6
6-15	C+	1.99	1.07	14,027.1	973.9	304.6	1.6
2015	C+	1.48	0.86	13,249.1	858.3	13.6	-244.5
2014	C+	1.91	1.11	14,228.3	1,128.8	-61.3	141.6
2013	C+	1.80	1.04	15,066.6	1,034.0	910.8	-0.1
2012	B-	2.25	1.27	16,427.4	1,459.9	7,104.5	-129.8
2011	C+	2.29	1.27	17,271.3	1,519.5	5,684.7	175.2

Rating Indexes

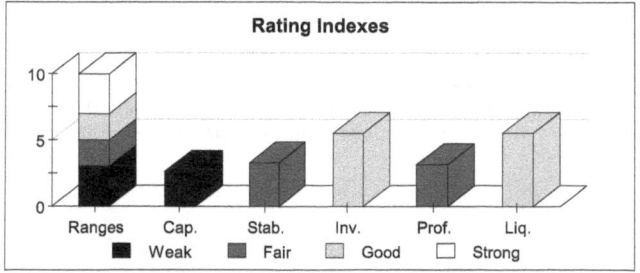

SECURITY MUTUAL LIFE INSURANCE CO OF NEW YORK   B   Good

Major Rating Factors: Good capitalization (5.7 on a scale of 0 to 10) based on good risk adjusted capital (moderate loss scenario). Capital levels have been relatively consistent over the last five years. Good quality investment portfolio (6.0) despite mixed results such as: minimal exposure to mortgages and large holdings of BBB rated bonds but minimal holdings in junk bonds. Good overall profitability (6.2).

Other Rating Factors: Fair overall results on stability tests (4.0). Weak liquidity (1.9).

Principal Business: Individual life insurance (90%), individual annuities (4%), group health insurance (3%), and group life insurance (3%).

Principal Investments: NonCMO investment grade bonds (75%), policy loans (13%), mortgages in good standing (7%), and CMOs and structured securities (4%).

Investments in Affiliates: None

Group Affiliation: None

Licensed in: All states except PR

Commenced Business: January 1887

Address: 100 Court St, Bimghamton, NY 13901-3479

Phone: (607) 723-3551   **Domicile State:** NY   **NAIC Code:** 68772

Data Date	Rating	RACR #1	RACR #2	Total Assets ($mil)	Capital ($mil)	Net Premium ($mil)	Net Income ($mil)
6-16	B	1.49	0.80	2,679.1	127.7	93.7	0.8
6-15	B	1.50	0.81	2,680.9	131.5	85.1	0.0
2015	B	1.55	0.84	2,667.8	136.5	174.6	6.9
2014	B	1.57	0.85	2,672.0	138.6	165.7	6.7
2013	B	1.52	0.83	2,676.4	133.6	170.7	8.4
2012	B	1.35	0.76	2,625.0	120.1	170.9	5.7
2011	B	1.33	0.75	2,557.5	120.4	159.8	10.0

Risk-Adjusted Capital Ratio #1 (Moderate Loss Scenario)

SECURITY NATIONAL LIFE INSURANCE COMPANY   D-   Weak

Major Rating Factors: Low quality investment portfolio (1.9 on a scale of 0 to 10) containing substantial holdings of BBB bonds in addition to moderate junk bond exposure. Exposure to mortgages is large, but the mortgage default rate has been low. Weak overall results on stability tests (1.3) including weak risk adjusted capital in prior years. Fair capitalization (3.6) based on fair risk adjusted capital (moderate loss scenario).

Other Rating Factors: Excellent profitability (7.4). Excellent liquidity (7.7).

Principal Business: Individual life insurance (83%), individual annuities (12%), and reinsurance (5%).

Principal Investments: NonCMO investment grade bonds (29%), mortgages in good standing (25%), real estate (8%), common & preferred stock (4%), and misc. investments (7%).

Investments in Affiliates: 2%

Group Affiliation: Security National Life

Licensed in: AL, AK, AZ, AR, CA, CO, DC, DE, FL, GA, HI, ID, IL, IN, IA, KS, KY, LA, MD, MI, MN, MS, MO, MT, NE, NV, NM, ND, OK, OR, SC, SD, TN, TX, UT, VA, WI, WY

Commenced Business: July 1967

Address: 5300 S 360 West Ste 310, Salt Lake City, UT 84132-1047

Phone: (801) 264-1060   **Domicile State:** UT   **NAIC Code:** 69485

Data Date	Rating	RACR #1	RACR #2	Total Assets ($mil)	Capital ($mil)	Net Premium ($mil)	Net Income ($mil)
6-16	D-	0.83	0.49	551.0	33.5	35.7	1.1
6-15	D-	0.60	0.37	539.9	33.2	33.5	0.6
2015	D-	0.85	0.51	544.1	32.8	67.0	3.5
2014	D-	0.62	0.38	507.8	34.4	61.5	5.1
2013	D	0.51	0.35	477.6	29.6	59.3	1.3
2012	D	0.67	0.43	464.3	29.8	55.8	0.4
2011	D	0.59	0.37	422.7	24.3	55.1	0.0

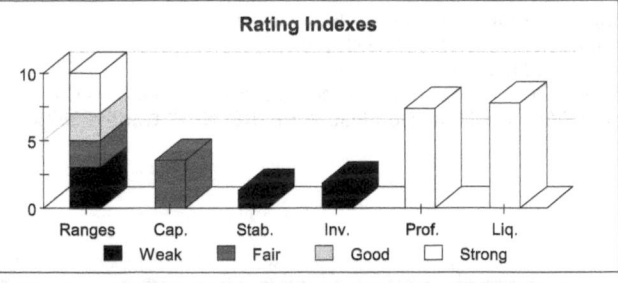

Rating Indexes

SECURITY PLAN INSURANCE COMPANY   C   Fair

Major Rating Factors: Fair overall results on stability tests (3.4 on a scale of 0 to 10) including potential financial drain due to affiliation with Citizens Inc. Fair profitability (4.3) with operating losses during the first six months of 2016. Good quality investment portfolio (6.1) despite mixed results such as: substantial holdings of BBB bonds but moderate junk bond exposure.

Other Rating Factors: Good liquidity (6.7). Strong capitalization (7.4) based on excellent risk adjusted capital (severe loss scenario).

Principal Business: Individual life insurance (93%), individual annuities (5%), and individual health insurance (1%).

Principal Investments: NonCMO investment grade bonds (78%), common & preferred stock (9%), noninv. grade bonds (4%), cash (4%), and misc. investments (5%).

Investments in Affiliates: 4%

Group Affiliation: Citizens Inc

Licensed in: AR, LA, MS

Commenced Business: March 1996

Address: 110 Railroad Ave, Donaldsonville, LA 70346-2520

Phone: (504) 473-8654   **Domicile State:** LA   **NAIC Code:** 60076

Data Date	Rating	RACR #1	RACR #2	Total Assets ($mil)	Capital ($mil)	Net Premium ($mil)	Net Income ($mil)
6-16	C	1.85	1.26	325.2	46.3	22.8	-1.4
6-15	C	1.99	1.37	326.2	48.0	22.8	-5.0
2015	C	1.91	1.32	322.1	47.0	41.7	-2.3
2014	C+	2.18	1.49	323.9	53.5	41.2	1.7
2013	C+	3.10	1.95	320.5	54.1	41.0	2.2
2012	C+	2.94	1.87	318.5	52.4	41.3	1.7
2011	C+	3.20	2.05	313.6	53.0	41.0	2.2

Citizens Inc Composite Group Rating: D+ Largest Group Members	Assets ($mil)	Rating
CICA LIFE INS CO OF AMERICA	841	D
SECURITY PLAN LIFE INS CO	322	C
CITIZENS NATIONAL LIFE INS CO	13	C
MAGNOLIA GUARANTY LIFE INS CO	11	C+
SECURITY PLAN FIRE INS CO	8	D

SENIOR HEALTH INSURANCE COMPANY OF PENNSYLVANIA   E   Very Weak

Major Rating Factors: Poor capitalization (1.1 on a scale of 0 to 10) based on weak risk adjusted capital (moderate loss scenario). Low quality investment portfolio (0.0) containing large holdings of BBB rated bonds in addition to significant exposure to junk bonds. Weak profitability (1.1) with operating losses during the first six months of 2016.

Other Rating Factors: Weak overall results on stability tests (1.1) including weak risk adjusted capital in prior years, negative cash flow from operations for 2015. Good liquidity (6.3).

Principal Business: Individual health insurance (91%), reinsurance (8%), and group health insurance (1%).

Principal Investments: NonCMO investment grade bonds (63%), CMOs and structured securities (14%), noninv. grade bonds (7%), common & preferred stock (3%), and mortgages in good standing (2%).

Investments in Affiliates: None

Group Affiliation: Senior Health Care Oversight Trust

Licensed in: All states except CT, NY, RI, VT, PR

Commenced Business: February 1965

Address: 11815 N Pennsylvania St, Carmel, IN 46032

Phone: (317) 817-3700 **Domicile State:** PA **NAIC Code:** 76325

Data Date	Rating	RACR #1	RACR #2	Total Assets ($mil)	Capital ($mil)	Net Premium ($mil)	Net Income ($mil)
6-16	E	0.51	0.25	2,794.8	35.0	65.1	-20.5
6-15	D+	0.78	0.39	2,894.3	77.8	70.7	7.7
2015	D	0.59	0.29	2,879.8	55.8	136.7	-9.0
2014	D+	0.87	0.42	2,907.0	80.0	155.2	-56.1
2013	D+	1.25	0.62	2,985.9	98.2	173.7	-3.4
2012	D+	1.22	0.60	3,080.7	105.5	194.0	-4.0
2011	D+	1.22	0.60	3,161.1	114.4	213.8	-57.2

Junk Bonds as a % of Capital

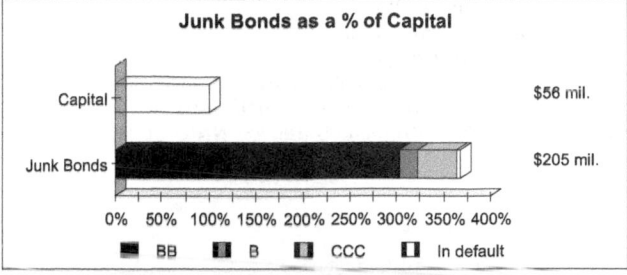

Capital $56 mil.

Junk Bonds $205 mil.

0% 50% 100% 150% 200% 250% 300% 350% 400%

■ BB   ▨ B   ▦ CCC   ▢ In default

SENTINEL SECURITY LIFE INSURANCE COMPANY   D+   Weak

Major Rating Factors: Low quality investment portfolio (2.8 on a scale of 0 to 10) containing large holdings of BBB rated bonds in addition to junk bond exposure equal to 63% of capital. Weak profitability (2.7) with investment income below regulatory standards in relation to interest assumptions of reserves. Weak overall results on stability tests (2.7).

Other Rating Factors: Good capitalization (5.7) based on good risk adjusted capital (moderate loss scenario). Excellent liquidity (8.8).

Principal Business: Individual annuities (79%), individual health insurance (17%), and individual life insurance (4%).

Principal Investments: CMOs and structured securities (49%), nonCMO investment grade bonds (37%), noninv. grade bonds (5%), mortgages in good standing (5%), and misc. investments (4%).

Investments in Affiliates: None

Group Affiliation: None

Licensed in: AZ, AR, CA, CO, FL, GA, HI, ID, IL, IA, KS, LA, MN, MT, NE, NV, NM, NC, ND, OK, OR, PA, SD, TX, UT, WA, WY

Commenced Business: September 1948

Address: 1405 West 2200 South, Salt Lake City, UT 84119-1485

Phone: (801) 484-8514 **Domicile State:** UT **NAIC Code:** 68802

Data Date	Rating	RACR #1	RACR #2	Total Assets ($mil)	Capital ($mil)	Net Premium ($mil)	Net Income ($mil)
6-16	D+	1.45	0.68	553.1	37.5	23.5	1.5
6-15	D	0.88	0.40	523.8	23.7	22.9	-0.4
2015	D	1.56	0.73	499.2	38.7	23.6	1.9
2014	D	1.10	0.50	479.5	25.7	31.6	-1.6
2013	D	1.13	0.54	403.7	15.2	17.1	-2.8
2012	C	1.52	0.75	384.9	19.7	70.3	0.0
2011	C	2.04	1.73	148.3	17.5	29.3	0.2

Rating Indexes

10

5

0

Ranges Cap. Stab. Inv. Prof. Liq.

■ Weak   ■ Fair   ▢ Good   ▢ Strong

SENTRY LIFE INSURANCE COMPANY *   A   Excellent

Major Rating Factors: Good overall profitability (6.2 on a scale of 0 to 10). Excellent overall results on stability tests (7.4). Strengths that enhance stability include excellent operational trends and excellent risk diversification. Strong capitalization (8.5) based on excellent risk adjusted capital (severe loss scenario). Furthermore, this high level of risk adjusted capital has been consistently maintained over the last five years.

Other Rating Factors: High quality investment portfolio (7.2). Excellent liquidity (7.8).

Principal Business: Group retirement contracts (93%), individual life insurance (4%), individual annuities (1%), group health insurance (1%), and group life insurance (1%).

Principal Investments: NonCMO investment grade bonds (90%), CMOs and structured securities (7%), and noninv. grade bonds (2%).

Investments in Affiliates: None

Group Affiliation: Sentry Ins Group

Licensed in: All states except NY, PR

Commenced Business: November 1958

Address: 1800 North Point Dr, Stevens Point, WI 54481

Phone: (715) 346-6000 **Domicile State:** WI **NAIC Code:** 68810

Data Date	Rating	RACR #1	RACR #2	Total Assets ($mil)	Capital ($mil)	Net Premium ($mil)	Net Income ($mil)
6-16	A	3.50	2.01	5,800.9	279.8	317.5	11.7
6-15	A	3.78	2.17	5,429.8	281.8	256.4	8.0
2015	A	3.50	2.07	5,560.2	268.8	660.9	13.6
2014	A	3.71	2.15	5,333.6	271.4	557.3	26.7
2013	A	3.77	2.16	4,909.7	272.5	502.1	26.2
2012	A	3.90	2.26	4,364.9	269.8	466.9	20.5
2011	A	4.15	2.40	3,873.5	274.8	400.3	22.9

Adverse Trends in Operations

Increase in policy surrenders from 2013 to 2014 (33%)
Decrease in capital during 2012 (2%)

SETTLERS LIFE INSURANCE COMPANY

B   **Good**

Major Rating Factors: Good overall results on stability tests (6.2 on a scale of 0 to 10). Stability strengths include good operational trends and good risk diversification. Good quality investment portfolio (5.9) despite mixed results such as: large holdings of BBB rated bonds but moderate junk bond exposure. Good overall profitability (5.4).

Other Rating Factors: Good liquidity (6.3). Strong capitalization (7.6) based on excellent risk adjusted capital (severe loss scenario).

Principal Business: Individual life insurance (88%), group life insurance (11%), and individual health insurance (1%).

Principal Investments: NonCMO investment grade bonds (84%), CMOs and structured securities (6%), noninv. grade bonds (3%), common & preferred stock (3%), and misc. investments (4%).

Investments in Affiliates: None

Group Affiliation: NGL Ins Group

Licensed in: All states except NY, PR

Commenced Business: September 1982

Address: 2 E Gilman St, Madison, WI 53703-1494

Phone: (608) 257-5611   **Domicile State:** WI   **NAIC Code:** 97241

Data Date	Rating	RACR #1	RACR #2	Total Assets ($mil)	Capital ($mil)	Net Premium ($mil)	Net Income ($mil)
6-16	B	2.62	1.40	392.9	40.2	25.3	1.1
6-15	B	3.42	1.83	399.2	53.4	23.3	1.3
2015	B	2.62	1.41	388.0	39.5	47.7	2.8
2014	B	3.40	1.83	394.2	52.6	44.8	7.1
2013	B	3.41	1.84	385.6	51.5	44.0	6.9
2012	B	3.45	1.83	378.3	49.6	43.1	4.7
2011	B	3.78	1.99	378.3	55.6	42.2	6.5

Adverse Trends in Operations

Increase in policy surrenders from 2014 to 2015 (44%)
Decrease in asset base during 2015 (2%)
Decrease in capital during 2015 (25%)
Decrease in capital during 2012 (11%)

SHELTER LIFE INSURANCE COMPANY *

A-   **Excellent**

Major Rating Factors: Good overall profitability (5.1 on a scale of 0 to 10) although investment income, in comparison to reserve requirements, is below regulatory standards. Good liquidity (5.8) with sufficient resources to handle a spike in claims as well as a significant increase in policy surrenders. Excellent overall results on stability tests (7.3) excellent operational trends and excellent risk diversification.

Other Rating Factors: Strong capitalization (8.9) based on excellent risk adjusted capital (severe loss scenario). High quality investment portfolio (7.9).

Principal Business: Individual life insurance (87%), group health insurance (6%), individual annuities (5%), group life insurance (1%), and individual health insurance (1%).

Principal Investments: NonCMO investment grade bonds (72%), CMOs and structured securities (19%), policy loans (2%), common & preferred stock (1%), and misc. investments (6%).

Investments in Affiliates: 2%

Group Affiliation: Shelter Ins Companies

Licensed in: AR, CO, IL, IN, IA, KS, KY, LA, MS, MO, NE, NV, OK, TN

Commenced Business: March 1959

Address: 1817 W Broadway, Columbia, MO 65218

Phone: (573) 445-8441   **Domicile State:** MO   **NAIC Code:** 65757

Data Date	Rating	RACR #1	RACR #2	Total Assets ($mil)	Capital ($mil)	Net Premium ($mil)	Net Income ($mil)
6-16	A-	3.48	2.28	1,180.1	191.9	64.1	9.0
6-15	A-	3.53	2.28	1,145.2	183.4	60.6	5.8
2015	A-	3.34	2.19	1,157.4	184.1	119.9	7.5
2014	A-	3.45	2.23	1,118.2	178.0	115.3	-4.9
2013	A-	3.60	2.37	1,078.4	181.6	113.0	14.6
2012	A-	3.34	2.19	1,044.8	165.4	128.4	15.5
2011	A-	3.39	2.20	1,012.8	162.3	147.0	11.8

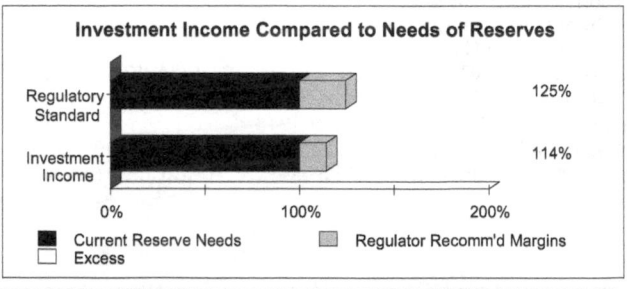

Investment Income Compared to Needs of Reserves

Regulatory Standard — 125%
Investment Income — 114%

Current Reserve Needs / Excess   Regulator Recomm'd Margins

SHELTERPOINT LIFE INSURANCE COMPANY *

A   **Excellent**

Major Rating Factors: Good overall results on stability tests (6.7 on a scale of 0 to 10). Strengths that enhance stability include excellent operational trends and good risk diversification. Strong capitalization (8.5) based on excellent risk adjusted capital (severe loss scenario). Furthermore, this high level of risk adjusted capital has been consistently maintained over the last five years. High quality investment portfolio (7.5).

Other Rating Factors: Excellent profitability (7.9). Excellent liquidity (7.0).

Principal Business: Group health insurance (98%) and group life insurance (2%).

Principal Investments: NonCMO investment grade bonds (71%), CMOs and structured securities (16%), common & preferred stock (10%), noninv. grade bonds (2%), and cash (1%).

Investments in Affiliates: 10%

Group Affiliation: ShelterPoint Group Inc

Licensed in: CA, CO, CT, DC, DE, FL, IL, MD, MA, MI, MN, NJ, NY, NC, PA, RI, SC, TN

Commenced Business: November 1972

Address: 600 Northern Blvd, Great Neck, NY 11021-5202

Phone: (516) 829-8100   **Domicile State:** NY   **NAIC Code:** 81434

Data Date	Rating	RACR #1	RACR #2	Total Assets ($mil)	Capital ($mil)	Net Premium ($mil)	Net Income ($mil)
6-16	A	2.36	1.99	105.4	56.0	50.0	1.4
6-15	A	2.35	1.98	105.3	55.7	49.1	1.2
2015	A	2.38	2.01	107.5	54.9	88.6	5.6
2014	A	2.40	2.03	104.4	54.9	86.7	10.0
2013	A	3.82	2.91	100.4	48.2	82.4	5.7
2012	A-	4.13	3.18	93.5	47.3	71.9	4.5
2011	B	3.87	3.01	87.2	43.4	69.2	4.5

Rating Indexes

Ranges   Cap.   Stab.   Inv.   Prof.   Liq.

Weak   Fair   Good   Strong

SHENANDOAH LIFE INS CO
B-   Good

Major Rating Factors: Good quality investment portfolio (5.8 on a scale of 0 to 10) despite mixed results such as: minimal exposure to mortgages and large holdings of BBB rated bonds but small junk bond holdings. Good overall profitability (6.0). Good overall results on stability tests (5.2) despite negative cash flow from operations for 2015 good operational trends, good risk adjusted capital for prior years and excellent risk diversification.
Other Rating Factors: Fair liquidity (3.9). Strong capitalization (7.2) based on excellent risk adjusted capital (severe loss scenario).
Principal Business: Individual life insurance (87%), individual health insurance (11%), and individual annuities (1%).
Principal Investments: NonCMO investment grade bonds (64%), CMOs and structured securities (23%), mortgages in good standing (7%), policy loans (2%), and misc. investments (4%).
Investments in Affiliates: None
Group Affiliation: Reservoir Capital Group LLC
Licensed in: AL, AZ, AR, CO, DC, DE, GA, IL, IN, IA, KS, KY, LA, MD, MI, MN, MS, MO, NE, NJ, NM, NC, OH, OK, PA, SC, TN, TX, VA, WV, WI
Commenced Business: February 1916
Address: 2301 Brambleton Ave SW, Roanoke, VA 24015
Phone: (540) 985-4400 **Domicile State:** VA **NAIC Code:** 68845

Data Date	Rating	RACR #1	RACR #2	Total Assets ($mil)	Capital ($mil)	Net Premium ($mil)	Net Income ($mil)
6-16	B-	2.09	1.10	1,128.1	87.1	21.1	7.9
6-15	C	1.75	0.92	1,153.3	76.4	22.6	9.4
2015	B-	2.11	1.11	1,131.8	87.9	44.8	21.0
2014	C	1.92	1.00	1,204.4	85.5	49.8	18.3
2013	C	1.74	0.93	1,278.8	81.1	54.7	12.6
2012	D	1.45	0.78	1,379.9	87.2	61.6	28.1
2011	N/A	N/A	N/A	1,432.1	15.6	65.7	8.3

Adverse Trends in Operations

Decrease in asset base during 2015 (6%)
Decrease in premium volume from 2014 to 2015 (10%)
Decrease in premium volume from 2012 to 2013 (11%)
Decrease in premium volume from 2011 to 2012 (6%)
Increase in policy surrenders from 2011 to 2012 (796%)

SOUTHERN FARM BUREAU LIFE INSURANCE COMPANY *
A   Excellent

Major Rating Factors: Good quality investment portfolio (6.0 on a scale of 0 to 10) despite significant exposure to mortgages . Mortgage default rate has been low. large holdings of BBB rated bonds in addition to small junk bond holdings. Good liquidity (6.3) with sufficient resources to handle a spike in claims as well as a significant increase in policy surrenders. Strong capitalization (9.1) based on excellent risk adjusted capital (severe loss scenario).
Other Rating Factors: Excellent profitability (7.9). Excellent overall results on stability tests (7.4) excellent operational trends and excellent risk diversification.
Principal Business: Individual life insurance (77%), individual annuities (19%), individual health insurance (3%), and group life insurance (1%).
Principal Investments: NonCMO investment grade bonds (57%), CMOs and structured securities (15%), mortgages in good standing (11%), common & preferred stock (5%), and misc. investments (11%).
Investments in Affiliates: 1%
Group Affiliation: Southern Farm Bureau Group
Licensed in: AL, AR, CO, FL, GA, KY, LA, MS, NC, SC, TN, TX, VA, PR
Commenced Business: December 1946
Address: 1401 Livingston Lane, Jackson, MS 39213
Phone: (601) 981-7422 **Domicile State:** MS **NAIC Code:** 68896

Data Date	Rating	RACR #1	RACR #2	Total Assets ($mil)	Capital ($mil)	Net Premium ($mil)	Net Income ($mil)
6-16	A	4.50	2.40	13,583.7	2,453.9	502.7	15.0
6-15	A	4.46	2.41	13,194.9	2,442.9	464.7	33.2
2015	A	4.55	2.45	13,307.9	2,456.8	904.7	77.0
2014	A	4.52	2.45	12,995.5	2,436.4	799.8	167.9
2013	A	4.42	2.42	12,679.3	2,327.2	785.7	149.8
2012	A	4.17	2.26	12,254.5	2,082.3	852.2	148.8
2011	A	3.92	2.14	11,673.2	1,904.2	906.9	150.0

Rating Indexes

Ranges · Cap. · Stab. · Inv. · Prof. · Liq.
■ Weak · ■ Fair · □ Good · □ Strong

SOUTHERN FINANCIAL LIFE INSURANCE COMPANY
D+   Weak

Major Rating Factors: Low quality investment portfolio (2.9 on a scale of 0 to 10) containing large holdings of BBB rated bonds in addition to junk bond exposure equal to 57% of capital. Weak overall results on stability tests (2.8). Good liquidity (6.6) with sufficient resources to handle a spike in claims.
Other Rating Factors: Strong capitalization (7.7) based on excellent risk adjusted capital (severe loss scenario). Excellent profitability (8.8).
Principal Business: Reinsurance (99%) and individual life insurance (1%).
Principal Investments: NonCMO investment grade bonds (47%), common & preferred stock (30%), noninv. grade bonds (17%), and cash (1%).
Investments in Affiliates: None
Group Affiliation: None
Licensed in: LA, TX
Commenced Business: June 1984
Address: 111 Matrix Loop, Lafayette, LA 70507
Phone: (727) 442-4084 **Domicile State:** LA **NAIC Code:** 69418

Data Date	Rating	RACR #1	RACR #2	Total Assets ($mil)	Capital ($mil)	Net Premium ($mil)	Net Income ($mil)
6-16	D+	2.72	1.48	106.6	29.7	8.3	1.1
6-15	D+	2.60	1.43	105.6	28.3	7.7	1.0
2015	D+	2.67	1.46	106.2	29.0	17.8	2.0
2014	D+	2.63	1.45	104.7	27.8	12.8	1.9
2013	D+	2.43	1.33	102.4	24.7	9.9	3.6
2012	D+	2.23	1.20	93.1	18.0	20.5	1.2
2011	D+	2.30	1.21	73.9	17.6	7.7	3.1

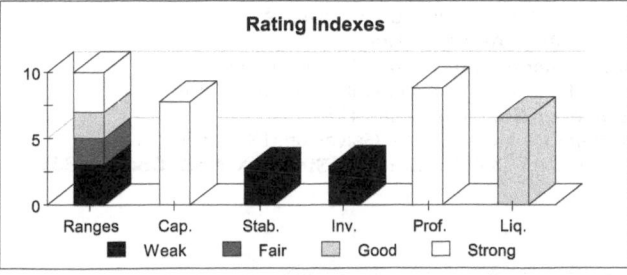

Rating Indexes

Ranges · Cap. · Stab. · Inv. · Prof. · Liq.
■ Weak · ■ Fair · □ Good · □ Strong

SOUTHLAND NATIONAL INSURANCE CORPORATION — C- — Fair

Major Rating Factors: Fair current capitalization (4.0 on a scale of 0 to 10) based on mixed results -- excessive policy leverage mitigated by excellent risk adjusted capital (severe loss scenario) reflecting significant improvement over results in 2011. Fair profitability (4.6) with operating losses during the first six months of 2016. Fair overall results on stability tests (3.3) including negative cash flow from operations for 2015, fair risk adjusted capital in prior years.

Other Rating Factors: Low quality investment portfolio (1.7). Excellent liquidity (9.1).

Principal Business: Reinsurance (49%), group health insurance (31%), individual life insurance (11%), and group life insurance (9%).

Principal Investments: Noninv. grade bonds (39%), cash (28%), nonCMO investment grade bonds (21%), and common & preferred stock (9%).

Investments in Affiliates: 60%

Group Affiliation: SNA Capital LLC

Licensed in: AL, AZ, AR, CO, FL, GA, IN, KY, LA, MS, NM, NC, OH, OK, SC, TN, TX, VA

Commenced Business: January 1969

Address: 2015 Ayrsley Town Blvd #150, Charlotte, NC 28273

Phone: (205) 345-7410 **Domicile State:** NC **NAIC Code:** 79057

Data Date	Rating	RACR #1	RACR #2	Total Assets ($mil)	Capital ($mil)	Net Premium ($mil)	Net Income ($mil)
6-16	C-	2.56	1.23	301.0	36.0	2.6	-1.5
6-15	C-	1.82	0.77	314.9	29.6	-155.3	10.9
2015	C-	2.18	0.93	307.4	34.0	-152.4	16.4
2014	D	1.83	0.89	318.1	22.9	145.2	-7.2
2013	C	0.96	0.82	167.1	9.5	6.5	0.2
2012	C	0.98	0.72	176.6	9.7	7.8	0.2
2011	C	1.04	0.71	187.6	10.8	27.4	0.9

Junk Bonds as a % of Capital

Capital — $34 mil.
Junk Bonds — $115 mil.

0% 40% 80% 120% 160% 200% 240% 280% 320% 360%

■ BB ■ B ▣ CCC ▢ In default

STANDARD INSURANCE COMPANY * — B+ — Good

Major Rating Factors: Good quality investment portfolio (5.3 on a scale of 0 to 10) despite substantial holdings of BBB bonds in addition to moderate junk bond exposure. Exposure to mortgages is large, but the mortgage default rate has been low. Good overall profitability (5.9). Good liquidity (6.8).

Other Rating Factors: Good overall results on stability tests (6.5) excellent operational trends and excellent risk diversification. Strong capitalization (7.2) based on excellent risk adjusted capital (severe loss scenario).

Principal Business: Group retirement contracts (41%), group health insurance (26%), group life insurance (17%), individual annuities (9%), and other lines (8%).

Principal Investments: NonCMO investment grade bonds (51%), mortgages in good standing (40%), noninv. grade bonds (4%), CMOs and structured securities (2%), and cash (1%).

Investments in Affiliates: None

Group Affiliation: Meiji Yasuda Life Ins Company

Licensed in: All states except NY

Commenced Business: April 1906

Address: 1100 SW Sixth Ave, Portland, OR 97204

Phone: (503) 321-7000 **Domicile State:** OR **NAIC Code:** 69019

Data Date	Rating	RACR #1	RACR #2	Total Assets ($mil)	Capital ($mil)	Net Premium ($mil)	Net Income ($mil)
6-16	B+	2.12	1.10	21,220.5	1,092.3	1,906.5	67.1
6-15	B+	2.32	1.21	20,991.2	1,138.2	1,734.1	104.2
2015	B+	2.21	1.16	20,781.6	1,085.0	3,528.4	160.1
2014	B+	2.38	1.26	20,361.1	1,151.8	4,019.8	209.4
2013	B+	2.37	1.32	19,118.7	1,287.3	3,489.3	195.8
2012	B+	2.36	1.33	17,250.3	1,190.3	3,506.4	125.4
2011	B+	2.44	1.42	16,014.1	1,139.2	3,547.4	127.2

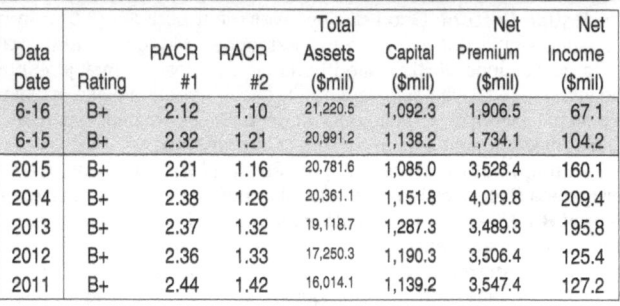

Rating Indexes

Ranges Cap. Stab. Inv. Prof. Liq.

■ Weak ■ Fair ▣ Good ▢ Strong

STANDARD LIFE & ACCIDENT INSURANCE COMPANY * — A- — Excellent

Major Rating Factors: Good overall results on stability tests (6.9 on a scale of 0 to 10) despite negative cash flow from operations for 2015. Strengths that enhance stability include excellent operational trends and excellent risk diversification. Good liquidity (6.9) with sufficient resources to handle a spike in claims as well as a significant increase in policy surrenders. Fair quality investment portfolio (4.9).

Other Rating Factors: Strong capitalization (10.0) based on excellent risk adjusted capital (severe loss scenario). Excellent profitability (8.6).

Principal Business: Individual health insurance (43%), reinsurance (32%), group health insurance (19%), and individual life insurance (6%).

Principal Investments: NonCMO investment grade bonds (73%), common & preferred stock (17%), mortgages in good standing (6%), noninv. grade bonds (2%), and CMOs and structured securities (1%).

Investments in Affiliates: None

Group Affiliation: American National Group Inc

Licensed in: All states except ME, NH, NJ, NY, PR

Commenced Business: June 1976

Address: One Moody Plaza, Galveston, TX 77550

Phone: (409) 763-4661 **Domicile State:** TX **NAIC Code:** 86355

Data Date	Rating	RACR #1	RACR #2	Total Assets ($mil)	Capital ($mil)	Net Premium ($mil)	Net Income ($mil)
6-16	A-	5.87	3.61	511.2	275.1	46.6	6.2
6-15	A-	5.43	3.38	522.4	274.2	56.0	10.0
2015	A-	5.93	3.68	514.5	278.1	105.2	8.6
2014	A-	5.09	3.17	530.2	259.1	120.7	20.6
2013	A-	5.22	3.20	527.6	252.2	108.7	18.0
2012	A-	5.88	3.59	527.8	255.8	106.2	22.4
2011	A-	5.71	3.50	515.1	235.5	105.2	26.5

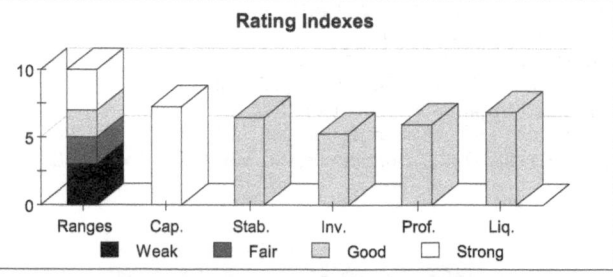

Adverse Trends in Operations

Decrease in asset base during 2015 (3%)
Decrease in premium volume from 2014 to 2015 (13%)
Decrease in capital during 2013 (1%)

STANDARD LIFE INSURANCE COMPANY OF NEW YORK *　　　A-　　Excellent

Major Rating Factors: Excellent overall results on stability tests (7.2 on a scale of 0 to 10). Strengths that enhance stability include excellent operational trends and excellent risk diversification. Strong capitalization (9.6) based on excellent risk adjusted capital (severe loss scenario). Furthermore, this high level of risk adjusted capital has been consistently maintained over the last five years. High quality investment portfolio (7.4).

Other Rating Factors: Excellent profitability (7.6) despite modest operating losses during 2011. Excellent liquidity (7.3).

Principal Business: Group health insurance (60%), group life insurance (38%), and individual health insurance (2%).

Principal Investments: NonCMO investment grade bonds (51%), mortgages in good standing (44%), cash (5%), and noninv. grade bonds (1%).

Investments in Affiliates: None

Group Affiliation: Meiji Yasuda Life Ins Company

Licensed in: NY

Commenced Business: January 2001

Address: 360 Hamilton Ave Suite 210, White Plains, NY 10601-1871

Phone: (503) 321-7859　**Domicile State:** NY　**NAIC Code:** 89009

Data Date	Rating	RACR #1	RACR #2	Total Assets ($mil)	Capital ($mil)	Net Premium ($mil)	Net Income ($mil)
6-16	A-	4.21	2.74	283.1	83.2	42.5	2.5
6-15	A-	3.88	2.56	279.8	83.6	45.7	7.7
2015	A-	4.14	2.73	282.7	80.9	89.4	6.3
2014	A-	3.57	2.37	275.3	76.6	95.2	4.0
2013	A-	3.28	2.19	265.6	71.6	98.0	2.7
2012	A-	3.07	2.10	251.1	69.3	100.1	6.1
2011	A-	3.34	2.21	231.3	53.8	65.9	-1.3

Adverse Trends in Operations

Decrease in premium volume from 2014 to 2015 (6%)
Decrease in premium volume from 2013 to 2014 (3%)
Decrease in premium volume from 2012 to 2013 (2%)
Increase in policy surrenders from 2012 to 2013 (771%)

STANDARD SECURITY LIFE INSURANCE CO OF NEW YORK *　　　A-　　Excellent

Major Rating Factors: Good overall results on stability tests (5.5 on a scale of 0 to 10). Strengths that enhance stability include good operational trends and excellent risk diversification. Good liquidity (6.7) with sufficient resources to handle a spike in claims. Strong capitalization (10.0) based on excellent risk adjusted capital (severe loss scenario).

Other Rating Factors: High quality investment portfolio (7.7). Excellent profitability (8.1).

Principal Business: Group health insurance (95%), reinsurance (4%), and individual health insurance (1%).

Principal Investments: NonCMO investment grade bonds (72%), common & preferred stock (12%), cash (2%), and CMOs and structured securities (1%).

Investments in Affiliates: 13%

Group Affiliation: Genove Holdings Inc

Licensed in: All states, the District of Columbia and Puerto Rico

Commenced Business: December 1958

Address: 485 Madison Ave, New York, NY 10022-5872

Phone: (212) 355-4141　**Domicile State:** NY　**NAIC Code:** 69078

Data Date	Rating	RACR #1	RACR #2	Total Assets ($mil)	Capital ($mil)	Net Premium ($mil)	Net Income ($mil)
6-16	A-	5.06	4.10	245.0	124.7	42.7	8.3
6-15	A-	3.66	2.89	267.1	120.4	105.2	7.1
2015	A-	3.95	3.20	269.9	125.1	211.0	13.2
2014	B	3.55	2.81	252.4	116.5	207.3	12.1
2013	B	3.29	2.67	249.5	114.0	214.4	9.2
2012	B	4.05	3.25	239.5	116.3	148.4	15.8
2011	A-	3.38	2.63	371.6	106.5	151.6	7.7

Adverse Trends in Operations

Decrease in premium volume from 2013 to 2014 (3%)
Decrease in capital during 2013 (2%)
Decrease in premium volume from 2011 to 2012 (2%)
Increase in policy surrenders from 2011 to 2012 (50%)
Decrease in asset base during 2012 (36%)

STARMOUNT LIFE INSURANCE COMPANY　　　　　　B　　Good

Major Rating Factors: Good capitalization (6.6 on a scale of 0 to 10) based on good risk adjusted capital (severe loss scenario). Moreover, capital levels have been consistently high over the last five years. Good overall profitability (5.2) although investment income, in comparison to reserve requirements, is below regulatory standards. Good liquidity (6.0).

Other Rating Factors: Good overall results on stability tests (5.4) despite excessive premium growth excellent operational trends, excellent risk adjusted capital for prior years and good risk diversification. High quality investment portfolio (7.3).

Principal Business: Group health insurance (50%), reinsurance (36%), individual life insurance (9%), and individual health insurance (5%).

Principal Investments: NonCMO investment grade bonds (68%), cash (19%), real estate (8%), common & preferred stock (2%), and misc. investments (3%).

Investments in Affiliates: None

Group Affiliation: H & J Capital LLC

Licensed in: All states except NY, PR

Commenced Business: August 1983

Address: 8485 Goodwood Blvd, Baton Rouge, LA 70806-7

Phone: (225) 926-2888　**Domicile State:** LA　**NAIC Code:** 68985

Data Date	Rating	RACR #1	RACR #2	Total Assets ($mil)	Capital ($mil)	Net Premium ($mil)	Net Income ($mil)
9-15	B	1.25	0.95	62.6	26.8	89.6	2.7
9-14	B	1.41	1.06	56.6	24.2	70.4	2.6
2014	B	1.35	1.02	59.1	25.0	95.2	3.8
2013	B	1.46	1.08	51.1	22.3	79.7	4.2
2012	B	1.52	1.12	45.3	19.5	66.1	2.2
2011	B	1.49	1.09	42.0	18.3	63.7	2.3
2010	B	1.51	1.10	37.5	16.8	57.4	2.4

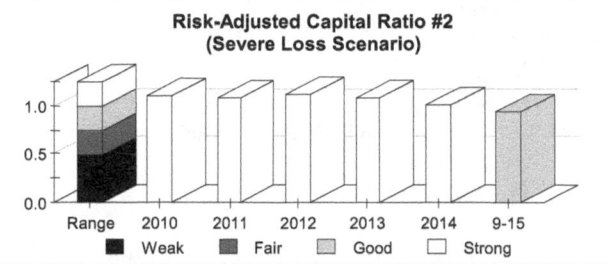

Risk-Adjusted Capital Ratio #2 (Severe Loss Scenario)

Range　2010　2011　2012　2013　2014　9-15
■ Weak　■ Fair　□ Good　□ Strong

STATE FARM LIFE & ACCIDENT ASSURANCE COMPANY *   A+   Excellent

Major Rating Factors: Good overall profitability (6.0 on a scale of 0 to 10) although investment income, in comparison to reserve requirements, is below regulatory standards. Good liquidity (6.3) with sufficient resources to handle a spike in claims as well as a significant increase in policy surrenders. Excellent overall results on stability tests (7.9) excellent operational trends and excellent risk diversification.

Other Rating Factors: Strong capitalization (10.0) based on excellent risk adjusted capital (severe loss scenario). High quality investment portfolio (7.8).

Principal Business: Individual life insurance (86%) and individual annuities (14%).

Principal Investments: NonCMO investment grade bonds (70%), CMOs and structured securities (22%), policy loans (7%), and noninv. grade bonds (1%).

Investments in Affiliates: 1%

Group Affiliation: State Farm Group

Licensed in: CT, IL, NY, WI

Commenced Business: July 1961

Address: One State Farm Plaza, Bloomington, IL 61710

Phone: (309) 766-2311 **Domicile State:** IL **NAIC Code:** 69094

Data Date	Rating	RACR #1	RACR #2	Total Assets ($mil)	Capital ($mil)	Net Premium ($mil)	Net Income ($mil)
6-16	A+	5.58	3.15	2,692.7	476.8	124.0	11.7
6-15	A+	5.62	3.22	2,540.7	448.2	115.0	9.7
2015	A+	5.53	3.16	2,614.1	464.6	231.6	23.2
2014	A+	5.57	3.21	2,469.9	438.3	220.4	24.3
2013	A+	5.61	3.25	2,334.1	417.4	210.1	21.5
2012	A+	5.70	3.29	2,198.3	403.5	195.7	31.6
2011	A+	5.23	3.03	2,048.4	364.7	188.8	28.1

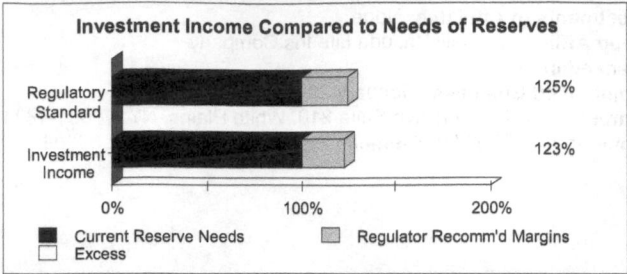

Investment Income Compared to Needs of Reserves

Regulatory Standard — 125%
Investment Income — 123%

■ Current Reserve Needs   ▨ Regulator Recomm'd Margins
□ Excess

STATE FARM LIFE INSURANCE COMPANY *   A+   Excellent

Major Rating Factors: Good quality investment portfolio (6.6 on a scale of 0 to 10) despite mixed results such as: minimal exposure to mortgages and substantial holdings of BBB bonds but minimal holdings in junk bonds. Good overall profitability (6.5). Excellent expense controls. Good liquidity (6.1).

Other Rating Factors: Excellent overall results on stability tests (7.9) excellent operational trends and excellent risk diversification. Strong capitalization (9.3) based on excellent risk adjusted capital (severe loss scenario).

Principal Business: Individual life insurance (81%), individual annuities (18%), and group life insurance (1%).

Principal Investments: NonCMO investment grade bonds (56%), CMOs and structured securities (19%), mortgages in good standing (9%), policy loans (7%), and common & preferred stock (5%).

Investments in Affiliates: 3%

Group Affiliation: State Farm Group

Licensed in: All states except MA, NY, WI, PR

Commenced Business: April 1929

Address: One State Farm Plaza, Bloomington, IL 61710

Phone: (309) 766-2311 **Domicile State:** IL **NAIC Code:** 69108

Data Date	Rating	RACR #1	RACR #2	Total Assets ($mil)	Capital ($mil)	Net Premium ($mil)	Net Income ($mil)
6-16	A+	4.45	2.50	68,156.4	9,873.7	2,715.9	202.9
6-15	A+	4.40	2.50	65,049.0	9,341.5	2,523.5	333.7
2015	A+	4.46	2.53	66,498.2	9,559.9	5,224.3	644.2
2014	A+	4.32	2.47	63,530.5	9,001.1	5,002.1	497.5
2013	A+	4.30	2.46	60,442.0	8,444.7	4,750.7	433.6
2012	A+	4.25	2.43	56,865.4	7,538.2	4,433.4	475.1
2011	A+	4.04	2.30	53,597.5	6,798.4	4,350.3	572.4

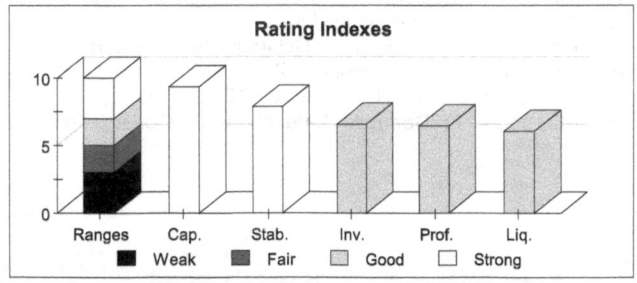

Rating Indexes

Ranges   Cap.   Stab.   Inv.   Prof.   Liq.

■ Weak   ▨ Fair   ▧ Good   □ Strong

STATE LIFE INSURANCE COMPANY   B   Good

Major Rating Factors: Good quality investment portfolio (5.4 on a scale of 0 to 10) despite mixed results such as: large holdings of BBB rated bonds but moderate junk bond exposure. Good overall results on stability tests (6.3). Stability strengths include excellent operational trends and excellent risk diversification. Fair liquidity (4.3).

Other Rating Factors: Strong capitalization (7.1) based on excellent risk adjusted capital (severe loss scenario). Excellent profitability (8.2).

Principal Business: Individual life insurance (49%), individual annuities (42%), reinsurance (5%), and individual health insurance (3%).

Principal Investments: NonCMO investment grade bonds (69%), CMOs and structured securities (20%), mortgages in good standing (7%), noninv. grade bonds (3%), and common & preferred stock (1%).

Investments in Affiliates: None

Group Affiliation: American United Life Group

Licensed in: All states except NY, PR

Commenced Business: September 1894

Address: 141 E Washington St, Indianapolis, IN 46204

Phone: (317) 285-1877 **Domicile State:** IN **NAIC Code:** 69116

Data Date	Rating	RACR #1	RACR #2	Total Assets ($mil)	Capital ($mil)	Net Premium ($mil)	Net Income ($mil)
6-16	B	2.10	1.08	6,448.0	437.6	362.0	11.3
6-15	B	2.17	1.12	5,857.5	403.7	298.6	14.1
2015	B	2.14	1.12	6,119.3	426.9	643.7	37.3
2014	B	1.97	1.02	5,522.2	354.2	599.3	23.5
2013	B	2.02	1.05	5,010.6	332.0	524.0	29.5
2012	B	2.00	1.03	4,597.5	306.2	531.9	35.0
2011	B	1.98	1.02	4,089.8	279.7	550.5	59.4

Adverse Trends in Operations

Decrease in premium volume from 2012 to 2013 (1%)
Decrease in premium volume from 2011 to 2012 (3%)

STATE MUTUAL INSURANCE COMPANY   C-   Fair

Major Rating Factors: Fair quality investment portfolio (4.4 on a scale of 0 to 10) with significant exposure to mortgages . Mortgage default rate has been low. Fair profitability (4.2) with operating losses during the first six months of 2016. Fair overall results on stability tests (3.0) including excessive premium growth.
Other Rating Factors: Good liquidity (6.4). Strong capitalization (7.0) based on excellent risk adjusted capital (severe loss scenario).
Principal Business: Individual life insurance (41%), individual health insurance (36%), and reinsurance (23%).
Principal Investments: NonCMO investment grade bonds (52%), CMOs and structured securities (18%), mortgages in good standing (10%), policy loans (5%), and misc. investments (14%).
Investments in Affiliates: 5%
Group Affiliation: None
Licensed in: All states except AK, CA, CT, ME, MA, MI, NH, NJ, NY, PR
Commenced Business: October 1890
Address: 210 E Second Ave Suite 301, Rome, GA 30161-1714
Phone: (706) 291-1054 **Domicile State:** GA **NAIC Code:** 69132

Data Date	Rating	RACR #1	RACR #2	Total Assets ($mil)	Capital ($mil)	Net Premium ($mil)	Net Income ($mil)
6-16	C-	1.96	1.02	281.2	30.1	11.0	-2.1
6-15	C	0.83	0.58	290.6	36.1	8.4	2.2
2015	D+	2.31	1.27	286.7	33.7	18.7	1.0
2014	C	1.64	1.02	292.5	33.9	0.4	0.2
2013	C	1.73	1.04	296.8	30.0	21.5	0.8
2012	C	1.93	1.11	298.0	29.4	16.3	1.4
2011	C-	2.04	1.18	304.6	32.7	-134.3	-0.5

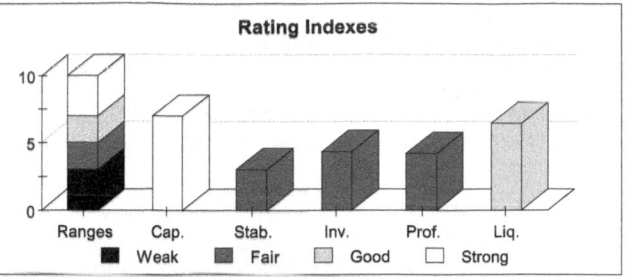

Rating Indexes

SUN LIFE & HEALTH INSURANCE COMPANY   D-   Weak

Major Rating Factors: Weak overall results on stability tests (1.1 on a scale of 0 to 10) including potential financial drain due to affiliation with Sun Life Assurance Group and excessive premium growth. Weak profitability (2.0) with operating losses during the first six months of 2016. Strong capitalization (9.6) based on excellent risk adjusted capital (severe loss scenario).
Other Rating Factors: High quality investment portfolio (7.2). Excellent liquidity (7.1).
Principal Business: N/A
Principal Investments: NonCMO investment grade bonds (47%), CMOs and structured securities (38%), mortgages in good standing (12%), and noninv. grade bonds (1%).
Investments in Affiliates: None
Group Affiliation: Sun Life Assurance Group
Licensed in: All states, the District of Columbia and Puerto Rico
Commenced Business: January 1975
Address: 100 Bright Meadow Blvd, Enfield, CT 06083-1900
Phone: (860) 403-1179 **Domicile State:** MI **NAIC Code:** 80926

Data Date	Rating	RACR #1	RACR #2	Total Assets ($mil)	Capital ($mil)	Net Premium ($mil)	Net Income ($mil)
6-16	D-	4.10	2.70	494.0	199.2	167.6	-45.9
6-15	C-	4.80	3.11	384.2	178.9	85.5	3.4
2015	C	6.46	4.17	447.7	241.5	173.5	17.2
2014	C-	4.77	3.13	371.8	175.5	168.0	-1.4
2013	C-	5.38	3.67	353.7	182.0	166.8	-35.8
2012	C-	6.10	2.98	64.6	48.1	0.0	1.8
2011	C	5.80	2.84	65.1	44.3	0.0	1.6

Sun Life Assurance Group Composite Group Rating: E Largest Group Members	Assets ($mil)	Rating
SUN LIFE ASR CO OF CANADA	18222	E
INDEPENDENCE LIFE ANNUITY CO	2863	D-
SUN LIFE HEALTH INS CO	448	D-
PROFESSIONAL INS CO	109	D-

SUN LIFE ASSURANCE COMPANY OF CANADA   E   Very Weak

Major Rating Factors: Poor current capitalization (2.0 on a scale of 0 to 10) based on weak risk adjusted capital (moderate loss scenario), although results have slipped from the good range during the last year. Low quality investment portfolio (2.2) containing large holdings of BBB rated bonds in addition to moderate junk bond exposure. Exposure to mortgages is significant, but the mortgage default rate has been low. Weak profitability (1.8) with operating losses during the first six months of 2016.
Other Rating Factors: Weak overall results on stability tests (0.1) including weak risk adjusted capital in prior years. Good liquidity (6.4).
Principal Business: Group health insurance (57%), individual life insurance (21%), group life insurance (19%), and reinsurance (3%).
Principal Investments: NonCMO investment grade bonds (57%), mortgages in good standing (16%), real estate (7%), CMOs and structured securities (7%), and misc. investments (11%).
Investments in Affiliates: 2%
Group Affiliation: Sun Life Assurance Group
Licensed in: All states except NY
Commenced Business: May 1871
Address: One Sun Life Executive Park, Wellesley Hills, MA 02481
Phone: (781) 237-6030 **Domicile State:** MI **NAIC Code:** 80802

Data Date	Rating	RACR #1	RACR #2	Total Assets ($mil)	Capital ($mil)	Net Premium ($mil)	Net Income ($mil)
6-16	E	0.63	0.37	20,273.9	1,087.2	2,605.6	-973.0
6-15	D	0.75	0.43	17,012.6	994.8	1,163.4	162.1
2015	D	1.27	0.74	18,222.4	1,925.8	2,207.2	86.4
2014	D	0.75	0.43	17,090.5	940.3	2,349.1	-64.3
2013	D	0.53	0.30	15,368.9	766.7	-919.7	234.8
2012	C-	0.79	0.45	17,403.4	1,037.6	2,283.3	119.1
2011	C-	0.77	0.44	17,348.7	1,017.6	2,397.5	-253.2

Risk-Adjusted Capital Ratio #1
(Moderate Loss Scenario)

SUNSET LIFE INSURANCE COMPANY OF AMERICA — B — Good

Major Rating Factors: Good quality investment portfolio (6.0 on a scale of 0 to 10) despite large holdings of BBB rated bonds in addition to moderate junk bond exposure. Exposure to mortgages is significant, but the mortgage default rate has been low. Good overall profitability (6.1). Fair liquidity (4.9).

Other Rating Factors: Fair overall results on stability tests (4.7) including negative cash flow from operations for 2015. Strong capitalization (7.6) based on excellent risk adjusted capital (severe loss scenario).

Principal Business: Individual life insurance (78%) and individual annuities (22%).

Principal Investments: NonCMO investment grade bonds (68%), mortgages in good standing (16%), CMOs and structured securities (11%), policy loans (2%), and misc. investments (3%).

Investments in Affiliates: None

Group Affiliation: Kansas City Life Group

Licensed in: All states except AL, NH, NJ, NY, TN, VT, WI, PR

Commenced Business: May 1937

Address: 3520 Broadway, Kansas City, MO 64121-9532

Phone: (816) 753-7000 **Domicile State:** MO **NAIC Code:** 69272

Data Date	Rating	RACR #1	RACR #2	Total Assets ($mil)	Capital ($mil)	Net Premium ($mil)	Net Income ($mil)
6-16	B	2.70	1.38	333.0	30.4	3.6	1.3
6-15	B	2.87	1.48	348.7	33.5	4.9	1.9
2015	B	2.66	1.38	338.7	29.4	8.3	2.8
2014	B-	2.75	1.41	354.1	32.0	16.0	4.4
2013	B-	2.61	1.34	355.7	31.2	15.3	4.8
2012	B	2.58	1.30	368.1	32.6	10.0	6.3
2011	B	2.54	1.26	379.2	33.7	12.4	5.4

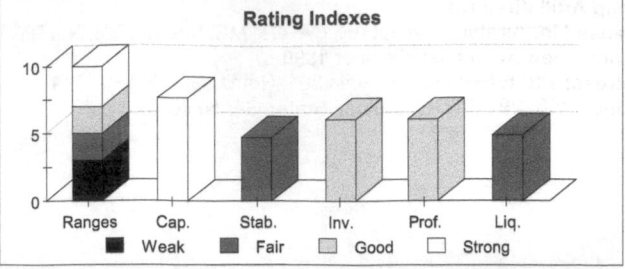

Rating Indexes

SWISS RE LIFE & HEALTH AMERICA INCORPORATED — C — Fair

Major Rating Factors: Fair overall results on stability tests (3.8 on a scale of 0 to 10) including excessive premium growth. Good current capitalization (6.7) based on good risk adjusted capital (severe loss scenario), although results have slipped from the excellent range during the last year. Good quality investment portfolio (5.7) despite mixed results such as: large holdings of BBB rated bonds but moderate junk bond exposure.

Other Rating Factors: Good liquidity (5.9). Weak profitability (2.0).

Principal Business: Reinsurance (100%).

Principal Investments: NonCMO investment grade bonds (69%), CMOs and structured securities (15%), mortgages in good standing (7%), noninv. grade bonds (4%), and policy loans (1%).

Investments in Affiliates: 6%

Group Affiliation: Swiss Reinsurance Group

Licensed in: All states, the District of Columbia and Puerto Rico

Commenced Business: September 1967

Address: 237 East High Street, Jefferson City, MO 65101

Phone: (877) 794-7773 **Domicile State:** MO **NAIC Code:** 82627

Data Date	Rating	RACR #1	RACR #2	Total Assets ($mil)	Capital ($mil)	Net Premium ($mil)	Net Income ($mil)
6-16	C	1.65	0.96	13,844.0	1,308.5	1,145.8	26.8
6-15	C	1.68	1.11	11,093.2	1,459.0	873.6	107.1
2015	C	1.83	1.08	12,264.0	1,318.3	2,983.5	85.8
2014	C	1.69	1.12	11,247.5	1,461.0	2,107.9	-924.1
2013	C	1.86	1.31	9,994.7	1,644.0	1,644.4	95.4
2012	D+	1.35	0.97	9,138.9	1,185.3	1,557.8	95.4
2011	D	4.69	2.13	9,006.5	1,050.2	315.6	-889.9

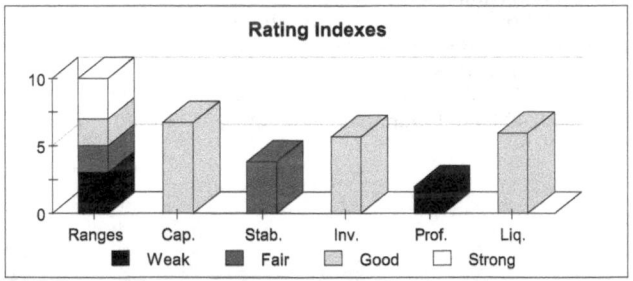

Rating Indexes

SYMETRA LIFE INSURANCE COMPANY * — B+ — Good

Major Rating Factors: Good quality investment portfolio (5.3 on a scale of 0 to 10) despite large holdings of BBB rated bonds in addition to moderate junk bond exposure. Exposure to mortgages is significant, but the mortgage default rate has been low. Good liquidity (6.6) with sufficient resources to cover a large increase in policy surrenders. Good overall results on stability tests (6.7) excellent operational trends and excellent risk diversification.

Other Rating Factors: Strong capitalization (7.2) based on excellent risk adjusted capital (severe loss scenario). Excellent profitability (8.2).

Principal Business: Individual annuities (76%), group health insurance (14%), individual life insurance (8%), group life insurance (1%), and group retirement contracts (1%).

Principal Investments: NonCMO investment grade bonds (62%), mortgages in good standing (17%), CMOs and structured securities (12%), noninv. grade bonds (4%), and common & preferred stock (3%).

Investments in Affiliates: 1%

Group Affiliation: Sumitomo Life Ins Company

Licensed in: All states except NY, PR

Commenced Business: April 1957

Address: 4125 Westown Pkwy Ste 102, West Des Moines, IA 50266

Phone: (425) 376-8000 **Domicile State:** IA **NAIC Code:** 68608

Data Date	Rating	RACR #1	RACR #2	Total Assets ($mil)	Capital ($mil)	Net Premium ($mil)	Net Income ($mil)
6-16	B+	2.08	1.13	33,273.1	2,064.9	2,480.0	2.7
6-15	B+	2.18	1.19	30,417.8	2,070.1	1,999.1	88.4
2015	B+	2.13	1.16	31,806.9	2,081.5	4,587.1	205.5
2014	B+	2.24	1.23	29,151.7	2,078.3	3,254.2	241.0
2013	B+	2.18	1.19	27,220.0	1,869.7	2,995.6	183.6
2012	B+	2.32	1.28	25,467.8	1,912.6	1,955.3	252.3
2011	B+	2.33	1.23	24,771.5	1,822.8	2,626.7	155.8

Adverse Trends in Operations

Decrease in capital during 2013 (2%)
Decrease in premium volume from 2011 to 2012 (26%)

TEACHERS INSURANCE & ANNUITY ASSOCIATION OF AMERIC/   A+   Excellent

Major Rating Factors: Good quality investment portfolio (6.6 on a scale of 0 to 10) despite mixed results such as: substantial holdings of BBB bonds but moderate junk bond exposure. Good liquidity (6.9) with sufficient resources to handle a spike in claims as well as a significant increase in policy surrenders. Strong capitalization (9.5) based on excellent risk adjusted capital (severe loss scenario).

Other Rating Factors: Excellent profitability (8.6). Excellent overall results on stability tests (7.9) excellent operational trends and excellent risk diversification.

Principal Business: Group retirement contracts (49%), individual annuities (49%), and individual life insurance (2%).

Principal Investments: NonCMO investment grade bonds (42%), CMOs and structured securities (29%), mortgages in good standing (8%), noninv. grade bonds (6%), and misc. investments (14%).

Investments In Affiliates: 9%
Group Affiliation: TIAA
Licensed in: All states, the District of Columbia and Puerto Rico
Commenced Business: May 1918
Address: 730 Third Ave 7th Floor, New York, NY 10017
Phone: (212) 490-9000   **Domicile State:** NY   **NAIC Code:** 69345

Data Date	Rating	RACR #1	RACR #2	Total Assets ($mil)	Capital ($mil)	Net Premium ($mil)	Net Income ($mil)
6-16	A+	5.10	2.69	276,045	35,070.3	7,304.9	760.9
6-15	A+	5.59	2.92	266,931	34,419.1	5,695.1	579.5
2015	A+	5.24	2.80	270,094	34,735.5	11,950.9	1,254.0
2014	A+	5.63	2.96	262,634	33,919.9	11,185.7	984.3
2013	A+	5.68	3.00	250,494	30,779.1	12,580.2	1,751.5
2012	A+	5.25	2.82	237,038	29,309.0	10,431.7	2,041.8
2011	A+	4.85	2.66	225,932	27,130.9	11,084.6	2,358.9

Rating Indexes (Ranges, Cap., Stab., Inv., Prof., Liq. — Weak, Fair, Good, Strong)

TENNESSEE FARMERS LIFE INSURANCE COMPANY *   A   Excellent

Major Rating Factors: Good quality investment portfolio (5.9 on a scale of 0 to 10) despite mixed results such as: large holdings of BBB rated bonds but moderate junk bond exposure. Good overall profitability (6.6). Excellent expense controls. Good liquidity (6.2) with sufficient resources to handle a spike in claims as well as a significant increase in policy surrenders.

Other Rating Factors: Excellent overall results on stability tests (7.4) excellent operational trends and excellent risk diversification. Strong capitalization (7.7) based on excellent risk adjusted capital (severe loss scenario).

Principal Business: Individual life insurance (73%), individual annuities (25%), and reinsurance (2%).

Principal Investments: NonCMO investment grade bonds (61%), common & preferred stock (28%), noninv. grade bonds (8%), policy loans (1%), and real estate (1%).

Investments In Affiliates: 23%
Group Affiliation: Tennessee Farmers Ins Companies
Licensed in: TN
Commenced Business: September 1973
Address: 147 Bear Creek Pike, Columbia, TN 38401-2266
Phone: (931) 388-7872   **Domicile State:** TN   **NAIC Code:** 82759

Data Date	Rating	RACR #1	RACR #2	Total Assets ($mil)	Capital ($mil)	Net Premium ($mil)	Net Income ($mil)
6-16	A	2.25	1.49	2,151.3	389.7	104.4	14.6
6-15	A	2.30	1.47	2,055.0	373.5	92.6	18.6
2015	A	2.25	1.48	2,090.6	375.6	184.5	25.2
2014	A	2.29	1.50	2,003.7	357.0	170.6	35.2
2013	A	2.24	1.46	1,913.6	328.1	185.5	34.5
2012	A	2.33	1.56	1,790.6	292.7	194.5	31.9
2011	A	2.46	1.62	1,665.4	267.0	207.8	16.1

Rating Indexes (Ranges, Cap., Stab., Inv., Prof., Liq. — Weak, Fair, Good, Strong)

TEXAS LIFE INSURANCE COMPANY   B   Good

Major Rating Factors: Good overall results on stability tests (5.4 on a scale of 0 to 10) despite fair financial strength of affiliated Wilton Re Holdings Ltd. Other stability subfactors include excellent operational trends, good risk adjusted capital for prior years and excellent risk diversification. Good quality investment portfolio (5.8) despite mixed results such as: large holdings of BBB rated bonds but moderate junk bond exposure. Good overall profitability (5.2) although investment income, in comparison to reserve requirements, is below regulatory standards.

Other Rating Factors: Good liquidity (6.5). Strong capitalization (7.0) based on excellent risk adjusted capital (severe loss scenario).

Principal Business: Individual life insurance (100%).

Principal Investments: NonCMO investment grade bonds (51%), CMOs and structured securities (37%), policy loans (4%), noninv. grade bonds (3%), and misc. investments (4%).

Investments in Affiliates: None
Group Affiliation: Wilton Re Holdings Ltd
Licensed in: All states except NY, PR
Commenced Business: April 1901
Address: 900 Washington Ave, Waco, TX 76701
Phone: (254) 752-6521   **Domicile State:** TX   **NAIC Code:** 69396

Data Date	Rating	RACR #1	RACR #2	Total Assets ($mil)	Capital ($mil)	Net Premium ($mil)	Net Income ($mil)
6-16	B	1.82	1.01	1,078.6	82.2	120.6	14.6
6-15	B	1.91	1.04	1,041.4	83.3	109.2	15.4
2015	B	2.12	1.17	1,076.3	98.4	218.4	50.0
2014	B	1.68	0.92	1,016.6	68.9	208.1	25.6
2013	B	1.96	1.07	952.9	80.4	197.7	33.2
2012	B	1.84	1.01	878.4	69.6	148.8	1.1
2011	C+	1.71	0.93	816.5	52.3	135.5	27.6

Wilton Re Holdings Ltd
Composite Group Rating: C+
Largest Group Members

	Assets ($mil)	Rating
WILCO LIFE INS CO	3486	C
WILTON REASSURANCE CO	3039	C+
WILCAC LIFE INS CO	2480	C
TEXAS LIFE INS CO	1076	B
WILTON REASSURANCE LIFE CO OF NY	902	B-

THRIVENT LIFE INSURANCE COMPANY

B **Good**

Major Rating Factors: Good overall capitalization (6.6 on a scale of 0 to 10) based on good risk adjusted capital (severe loss scenario). Nevertheless, capital levels have fluctuated during prior years. Good liquidity (6.3) with sufficient resources to cover a large increase in policy surrenders. Good overall results on stability tests (6.1) excellent operational trends and excellent risk diversification.
Other Rating Factors: Fair quality investment portfolio (4.5). Fair profitability (4.6) with investment income below regulatory standards in relation to interest assumptions of reserves.
Principal Business: Individual annuities (94%) and individual life insurance (6%).
Principal Investments: NonCMO investment grade bonds (61%), CMOs and structured securities (28%), noninv. grade bonds (8%), cash (2%), and policy loans (1%).
Investments in Affiliates: 1%
Group Affiliation: Thrivent Financial for Lutherans Grp
Licensed in: All states except GA, ME, MA, NH, NY, NC, RI, VT, WY, PR
Commenced Business: December 1982
Address: 625 Fourth Ave S, Minneapolis, MN 55415
Phone: (612) 340-7214 **Domicile State:** MN **NAIC Code:** 97721

Data Date	Rating	RACR #1	RACR #2	Total Assets ($mil)	Capital ($mil)	Net Premium ($mil)	Net Income ($mil)
6-16	B	1.94	0.95	3,541.4	154.0	76.3	5.5
6-15	B+	2.20	1.08	3,566.4	167.8	65.1	6.6
2015	B	1.91	0.94	3,519.4	149.5	144.9	13.6
2014	B+	2.13	1.05	3,500.4	159.7	115.4	23.3
2013	B+	2.35	1.13	3,468.2	162.6	147.9	25.2
2012	B+	2.53	1.20	3,283.8	167.8	145.7	26.0
2011	B+	2.63	1.23	3,132.3	169.5	157.0	21.3

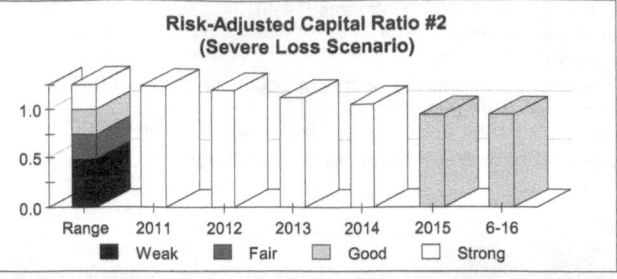

Risk-Adjusted Capital Ratio #2 (Severe Loss Scenario)

TIAA-CREF LIFE INSURANCE COMPANY

B **Good**

Major Rating Factors: Good quality investment portfolio (5.9 on a scale of 0 to 10) despite mixed results such as: no exposure to mortgages and large holdings of BBB rated bonds but small junk bond holdings. Good liquidity (5.6) with sufficient resources to cover a large increase in policy surrenders. Good overall results on stability tests (6.3) excellent operational trends and excellent risk diversification.
Other Rating Factors: Weak profitability (2.0) with operating losses during the first six months of 2016. Strong capitalization (7.2) based on excellent risk adjusted capital (severe loss scenario).
Principal Business: Individual life insurance (43%), individual annuities (41%), group life insurance (16%), and individual health insurance (1%).
Principal Investments: NonCMO investment grade bonds (90%), CMOs and structured securities (8%), and noninv. grade bonds (1%).
Investments in Affiliates: None
Group Affiliation: TIAA
Licensed in: All states except PR
Commenced Business: December 1996
Address: 730 Third Ave, New York, NY 10017
Phone: (212) 916-4900 **Domicile State:** NY **NAIC Code:** 60142

Data Date	Rating	RACR #1	RACR #2	Total Assets ($mil)	Capital ($mil)	Net Premium ($mil)	Net Income ($mil)
6-16	B	2.14	1.12	11,505.5	400.8	309.9	-13.6
6-15	B	2.00	1.05	10,711.2	347.4	336.9	-12.1
2015	B	1.93	1.02	10,774.2	362.5	713.4	-39.8
2014	B	2.13	1.13	9,803.2	354.6	675.5	-17.5
2013	B	2.49	1.32	7,988.6	373.8	480.9	-29.3
2012	A-	3.18	1.69	5,656.3	412.9	282.5	18.1
2011	A-	3.50	1.85	4,250.1	398.4	223.8	29.5

Adverse Trends in Operations

Decrease in capital during 2014 (5%)
Increase in policy surrenders from 2013 to 2014 (59%)
Decrease in capital during 2013 (9%)

TIME INSURANCE COMPANY

C+ **Fair**

Major Rating Factors: Fair overall results on stability tests (3.0 on a scale of 0 to 10) including negative cash flow from operations for 2015. Good current capitalization (5.9) based on mixed results -- excessive policy leverage mitigated by excellent risk adjusted capital (severe loss scenario) reflecting improvement over results in 2013. Good quality investment portfolio (6.6).
Other Rating Factors: Weak profitability (2.8). Weak liquidity (0.1).
Principal Business: Individual health insurance (70%), group health insurance (28%), and individual life insurance (2%).
Principal Investments: NonCMO investment grade bonds (95%), CMOs and structured securities (13%), common & preferred stock (5%), real estate (2%), and noninv. grade bonds (1%).
Investments in Affiliates: None
Group Affiliation: Assurant Inc
Licensed in: All states except NY, PR
Commenced Business: March 1910
Address: 501 W Michigan, Milwaukee, WI 53201
Phone: (612) 738-4449 **Domicile State:** WI **NAIC Code:** 69477

Data Date	Rating	RACR #1	RACR #2	Total Assets ($mil)	Capital ($mil)	Net Premium ($mil)	Net Income ($mil)
6-16	C+	2.15	1.74	613.4	355.9	9.8	2.8
6-15	C+	1.08	0.86	1,129.6	319.8	1,149.2	-267.7
2015	C+	1.44	1.16	1,157.9	471.7	2,031.9	-389.3
2014	C+	1.46	1.15	991.0	389.7	1,755.5	-64.6
2013	B-	1.14	0.88	691.5	212.0	1,269.5	5.6
2012	B-	1.20	0.92	645.4	205.8	1,164.5	48.7
2011	B-	1.51	1.16	748.7	273.0	1,215.0	34.5

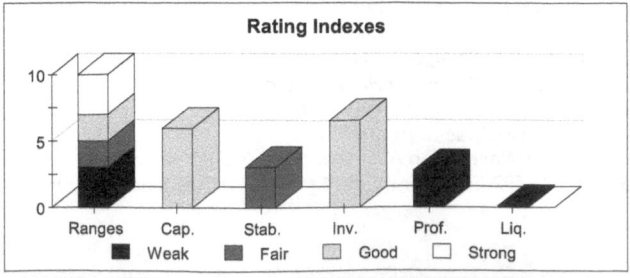

Rating Indexes

TRANS OCEANIC LIFE INSURANCE COMPANY *   A   Excellent

Major Rating Factors: Good quality investment portfolio (5.2 on a scale of 0 to 10) with no exposure to mortgages and no exposure to junk bonds. Good overall results on stability tests (6.4). Strengths that enhance stability include excellent operational trends and good risk diversification. Strong capitalization (8.4) based on excellent risk adjusted capital (severe loss scenario).
Other Rating Factors: Excellent profitability (9.1). Excellent liquidity (8.9).
Principal Business: Individual health insurance (92%) and individual life insurance (8%).
Principal Investments: Cash (33%), nonCMO investment grade bonds (28%), CMOs and structured securities (23%), real estate (10%), and misc. investments (6%).
Investments in Affiliates: None
Group Affiliation: Trans-Oceanic Group Inc
Licensed in: FL, PR
Commenced Business: December 1959
Address: 3 Munet Court, Guaynabo, PR 00936-3467
Phone: (787) 782-2680 **Domicile State:** PR **NAIC Code:** 69523

Data Date	Rating	RACR #1	RACR #2	Total Assets ($mil)	Capital ($mil)	Net Premium ($mil)	Net Income ($mil)
2015	A	3.12	1.95	68.3	36.2	30.4	5.0
2014	A	3.09	2.06	65.1	33.7	29.8	4.6
2013	B+	2.67	1.83	58.9	29.5	29.8	6.0
2012	B+	2.11	1.46	49.6	22.5	28.5	3.7
2011	B+	1.80	1.26	42.9	17.3	26.1	3.3

Adverse Trends in Operations

Increase in policy surrenders from 2012 to 2013 (257%)

TRANS WORLD ASSURANCE COMPANY   B   Good

Major Rating Factors: Good quality investment portfolio (5.9 on a scale of 0 to 10) despite mixed results such as: minimal exposure to mortgages and large holdings of BBB rated bonds but minimal holdings in junk bonds. Good liquidity (6.5) with sufficient resources to cover a large increase in policy surrenders. Good overall results on stability tests (6.1) excellent operational trends and good risk diversification.
Other Rating Factors: Strong capitalization (8.2) based on excellent risk adjusted capital (severe loss scenario). Excellent profitability (8.3).
Principal Business: Individual life insurance (76%), reinsurance (13%), and individual annuities (11%).
Principal Investments: NonCMO investment grade bonds (74%), common & preferred stock (8%), mortgages in good standing (7%), real estate (4%), and misc. investments (6%).
Investments in Affiliates: 15%
Group Affiliation: TWA Corp
Licensed in: All states except NH, NY, VT, PR
Commenced Business: December 1963
Address: 885 South El Camino Real, San Mateo, CA 94402
Phone: (850) 456-7401 **Domicile State:** CA **NAIC Code:** 69566

Data Date	Rating	RACR #1	RACR #2	Total Assets ($mil)	Capital ($mil)	Net Premium ($mil)	Net Income ($mil)
6-16	B	2.36	1.80	350.2	82.6	5.7	0.5
6-15	B	2.25	1.77	350.2	83.0	5.6	1.9
2015	B	2.38	1.83	350.8	83.0	10.1	6.4
2014	B	2.20	1.73	350.1	81.4	11.0	4.6
2013	B	2.06	1.62	347.8	77.1	11.0	4.9
2012	B	1.75	1.43	346.3	73.2	11.2	5.9
2011	B	1.70	1.41	345.1	72.0	11.9	2.1

Adverse Trends in Operations

Decrease in premium volume from 2014 to 2015 (8%)
Increase in policy surrenders from 2013 to 2014 (26%)
Decrease in premium volume from 2012 to 2013 (2%)
Decrease in premium volume from 2011 to 2012 (6%)

TRANSAMERICA ADVISORS LIFE INSURANCE COMPANY   B-   Good

Major Rating Factors: Good liquidity (6.8 on a scale of 0 to 10) with sufficient resources to handle a spike in claims as well as a significant increase in policy surrenders. Fair profitability (4.6) with operating losses during the first six months of 2016. Fair overall results on stability tests (3.9).
Other Rating Factors: Strong capitalization (10.0) based on excellent risk adjusted capital (severe loss scenario). High quality investment portfolio (7.4).
Principal Business: Individual life insurance (64%) and individual annuities (36%).
Principal Investments: NonCMO investment grade bonds (50%), policy loans (25%), CMOs and structured securities (7%), noninv. grade bonds (3%), and mortgages in good standing (3%).
Investments in Affiliates: 1%
Group Affiliation: AEGON USA Group
Licensed in: All states except NY, PR
Commenced Business: December 1986
Address: 425 W Capital Ave Suite 1800, Little Rock, AR 72201
Phone: (800) 535-5549 **Domicile State:** AR **NAIC Code:** 79022

Data Date	Rating	RACR #1	RACR #2	Total Assets ($mil)	Capital ($mil)	Net Premium ($mil)	Net Income ($mil)
6-16	B-	8.35	4.17	8,535.9	680.4	3.4	-53.3
6-15	B-	11.13	5.60	9,398.4	975.0	7.6	62.3
2015	B-	9.52	4.77	8,752.6	790.3	11.1	-24.1
2014	B-	10.27	5.14	9,692.5	912.1	9.3	201.5
2013	B-	8.73	4.45	10,135.2	733.4	18.0	196.6
2012	D	7.41	3.78	10,031.8	636.2	17.9	178.2
2011	D	5.34	2.75	10,050.8	438.0	16.2	-340.2

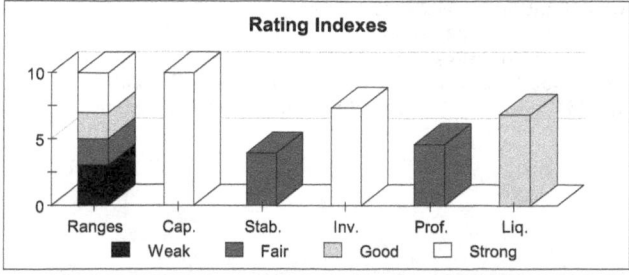

Rating Indexes

TRANSAMERICA FINANCIAL LIFE INSURANCE COMPANY — B — Good

Major Rating Factors: Good overall results on stability tests (6.1 on a scale of 0 to 10). Stability strengths include excellent operational trends, good risk adjusted capital for prior years and excellent risk diversification. Good quality investment portfolio (5.3) despite large holdings of BBB rated bonds in addition to moderate junk bond exposure. Exposure to mortgages is significant, but the mortgage default rate has been low. Good overall profitability (6.1).

Other Rating Factors: Strong capitalization (7.8) based on excellent risk adjusted capital (severe loss scenario). Excellent liquidity (9.3).

Principal Business: Group retirement contracts (77%), individual annuities (10%), reinsurance (8%), individual life insurance (2%), and other lines (2%).

Principal Investments: NonCMO investment grade bonds (57%), CMOs and structured securities (15%), mortgages in good standing (11%), noninv. grade bonds (6%), and policy loans (1%).

Investments in Affiliates: 4%

Group Affiliation: AEGON USA Group

Licensed in: All states except PR

Commenced Business: October 1947

Address: 440 Mamaroneck Ave, Harrison, NY 10528

Phone: (914) 697-8000 **Domicile State:** NY **NAIC Code:** 70688

Data Date	Rating	RACR #1	RACR #2	Total Assets ($mil)	Capital ($mil)	Net Premium ($mil)	Net Income ($mil)
6-16	B	3.10	1.50	32,355.4	1,168.1	2,975.5	0.7
6-15	B	2.76	1.34	31,593.7	1,016.3	2,990.0	110.6
2015	B	3.15	1.54	31,535.3	1,167.4	5,807.6	259.9
2014	B	2.69	1.31	31,099.3	957.7	5,434.3	23.9
2013	B	2.71	1.32	29,402.4	934.6	5,239.6	226.1
2012	C+	2.43	1.19	26,958.7	836.0	4,935.8	198.0
2011	C+	2.04	0.99	25,478.4	692.1	4,424.7	-266.8

Adverse Trends in Operations

Increase in policy surrenders from 2013 to 2014 (29%)

TRANSAMERICA LIFE INSURANCE COMPANY — B — Good

Major Rating Factors: Good quality investment portfolio (6.1 on a scale of 0 to 10) despite large holdings of BBB rated bonds in addition to moderate junk bond exposure. Exposure to mortgages is significant, but the mortgage default rate has been low. Fair profitability (4.7). Fair overall results on stability tests (4.5) including negative cash flow from operations for 2015.

Other Rating Factors: Strong capitalization (7.2) based on excellent risk adjusted capital (severe loss scenario). Excellent liquidity (7.3).

Principal Business: Group retirement contracts (37%), individual annuities (34%), individual life insurance (12%), reinsurance (8%), and other lines (8%).

Principal Investments: NonCMO investment grade bonds (54%), CMOs and structured securities (12%), mortgages in good standing (10%), noninv. grade bonds (4%), and misc. investments (10%).

Investments in Affiliates: 8%

Group Affiliation: AEGON USA Group

Licensed in: All states except NY

Commenced Business: March 1962

Address: 4333 Edgewood Rd NE, Cedar Rapids, IA 52499

Phone: (319) 398-8511 **Domicile State:** IA **NAIC Code:** 86231

Data Date	Rating	RACR #1	RACR #2	Total Assets ($mil)	Capital ($mil)	Net Premium ($mil)	Net Income ($mil)
6-16	B	1.68	1.11	129,413	5,862.9	6,249.0	229.4
6-15	B	1.71	1.14	122,306	5,162.7	8,268.4	-56.7
2015	B	1.58	1.06	126,036	5,458.6	14,777.9	-250.9
2014	B-	2.09	1.34	124,486	5,835.3	15,782.9	233.6
2013	B-	1.63	1.02	115,276	4,717.9	15,446.5	57.5
2012	C	1.83	1.13	105,497	5,470.6	11,782.0	791.6
2011	C	1.69	1.02	102,718	5,121.6	9,845.0	-2,459.3

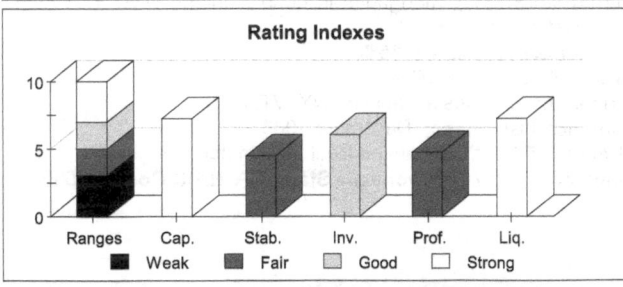

Rating Indexes

TRANSAMERICA PREMIER LIFE INSURANCE COMPANY — C+ — Fair

Major Rating Factors: Fair quality investment portfolio (4.4 on a scale of 0 to 10) with large holdings of BBB rated bonds in addition to junk bond exposure equal to 66% of capital. Fair overall results on stability tests (3.3) including fair risk adjusted capital in prior years. Good capitalization (5.4) based on good risk adjusted capital (moderate loss scenario).

Other Rating Factors: Good overall profitability (6.6). Good liquidity (6.4).

Principal Business: Individual life insurance (43%), individual annuities (18%), group health insurance (16%), reinsurance (14%), and other lines (9%).

Principal Investments: NonCMO investment grade bonds (57%), CMOs and structured securities (16%), mortgages in good standing (9%), policy loans (5%), and misc. investments (10%).

Investments in Affiliates: 4%

Group Affiliation: AEGON USA Group

Licensed in: All states except NY

Commenced Business: May 1860

Address: 4333 Edgewood Rd NE, Cedar Rapids, IA 52499

Phone: (319) 355-8511 **Domicile State:** IA **NAIC Code:** 66281

Data Date	Rating	RACR #1	RACR #2	Total Assets ($mil)	Capital ($mil)	Net Premium ($mil)	Net Income ($mil)
6-16	C+	1.28	0.74	43,239.2	1,436.1	1,587.1	49.5
6-15	C+	1.80	1.01	42,334.9	1,929.5	1,551.5	230.9
2015	C+	1.41	0.81	41,649.4	1,508.0	3,094.9	213.8
2014	C+	1.53	0.88	42,248.2	1,774.7	6,292.5	350.7
2013	C+	1.58	0.78	31,879.6	971.2	1,586.3	166.9
2012	C+	1.20	0.59	31,057.2	811.3	1,497.6	143.5
2011	C+	1.31	0.64	31,107.3	980.9	1,391.7	481.7

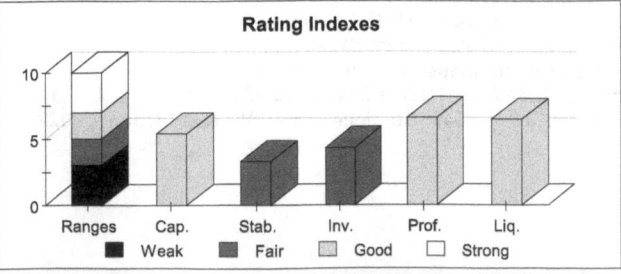

Rating Indexes

TRIPLE S VIDA INCORPORATED
B-   **Good**

Major Rating Factors: Good capitalization (5.2 on a scale of 0 to 10) based on good risk adjusted capital (moderate loss scenario). Good overall results on stability tests (5.2) despite fair risk adjusted capital in prior years. Strengths include good financial support from affiliation with Triple-S Management Corp, excellent operational trends and good risk diversification. Fair quality investment portfolio (4.7).

Other Rating Factors: Fair liquidity (3.9). Excellent profitability (7.8).

Principal Business: Individual life insurance (52%), individual health insurance (31%), individual annuities (6%), group health insurance (6%), and group life insurance (5%).

Principal Investments: NonCMO investment grade bonds (74%), common & preferred stock (12%), CMOs and structured securities (10%), noninv. grade bonds (2%), and misc. investments (2%).

Investments in Affiliates: 2%

Group Affiliation: Triple-S Management Corp

Licensed in: PR

Commenced Business: September 1964

Address: 1052 Munoz Rivera Ave, Rio Piedras, PR 00927

Phone: (787) 758-4888 **Domicile State:** PR **NAIC Code:** 73814

Data Date	Rating	RACR #1	RACR #2	Total Assets ($mil)	Capital ($mil)	Net Premium ($mil)	Net Income ($mil)
9-15	B-	1.12	0.74	572.3	64.9	120.2	6.2
9-14	B-	1.04	0.70	537.9	63.6	117.2	9.8
2014	B-	1.19	0.81	0.0	0.0	0.0	0.0
2013	B-	1.00	0.69	0.0	0.0	0.0	0.0
2012	B-	1.16	0.75	0.0	0.0	0.0	0.0
2011	B-	1.21	0.78	0.0	0.0	0.0	0.0
2010	C+	1.48	0.98	0.0	0.0	0.0	0.0

Risk-Adjusted Capital Ratio #1
(Moderate Loss Scenario)

Weak ■   Fair ▨   Good ☐

TRUSTMARK INSURANCE COMPANY *
B+   **Good**

Major Rating Factors: Good overall profitability (5.8 on a scale of 0 to 10). Good overall results on stability tests (6.8). Stability strengths include excellent operational trends and excellent risk diversification. Fair quality investment portfolio (4.9) with substantial holdings of BBB bonds in addition to moderate junk bond exposure.

Other Rating Factors: Strong capitalization (7.9) based on excellent risk adjusted capital (severe loss scenario). Excellent liquidity (7.2).

Principal Business: Group life insurance (41%), group health insurance (24%), individual health insurance (24%), individual life insurance (9%), and reinsurance (1%).

Principal Investments: NonCMO investment grade bonds (44%), CMOs and structured securities (29%), common & preferred stock (10%), noninv. grade bonds (8%), and misc. investments (9%).

Investments in Affiliates: None

Group Affiliation: Trustmark Group Inc

Licensed in: All states, the District of Columbia and Puerto Rico

Commenced Business: January 1913

Address: 400 Field Dr, Lake Forest, IL 60045-2581

Phone: (847) 615-1500 **Domicile State:** IL **NAIC Code:** 61425

Data Date	Rating	RACR #1	RACR #2	Total Assets ($mil)	Capital ($mil)	Net Premium ($mil)	Net Income ($mil)
6-16	B+	2.82	1.58	1,430.6	290.6	159.3	10.0
6-15	B+	2.87	1.63	1,424.2	312.4	139.1	12.4
2015	B+	3.15	1.77	1,406.8	286.7	293.6	16.3
2014	B+	3.02	1.75	1,393.5	287.7	312.2	18.9
2013	B+	3.24	1.89	1,369.8	297.8	294.0	30.0
2012	B+	3.00	1.78	1,320.0	266.5	307.6	22.3
2011	B	3.19	1.85	1,264.8	256.4	283.3	22.7

Adverse Trends in Operations

Decrease in premium volume from 2014 to 2015 (6%)
Decrease in capital during 2014 (3%)
Decrease in premium volume from 2012 to 2013 (4%)

TRUSTMARK LIFE INSURANCE COMPANY *
B+   **Good**

Major Rating Factors: Good quality investment portfolio (6.4 on a scale of 0 to 10) despite mixed results such as: no exposure to mortgages and substantial holdings of BBB bonds but small junk bond holdings. Good liquidity (6.9) with sufficient resources to handle a spike in claims. Good overall results on stability tests (5.4) despite negative cash flow from operations for 2015 good operational trends and excellent risk diversification.

Other Rating Factors: Strong capitalization (10.0) based on excellent risk adjusted capital (severe loss scenario). Excellent profitability (7.3).

Principal Business: Group health insurance (95%) and group life insurance (5%).

Principal Investments: NonCMO investment grade bonds (72%), CMOs and structured securities (11%), noninv. grade bonds (9%), and common & preferred stock (8%).

Investments in Affiliates: None

Group Affiliation: Trustmark Group Inc

Licensed in: All states except PR

Commenced Business: February 1925

Address: 400 Field Dr, Lake Forest, IL 60045-2581

Phone: (847) 615-1500 **Domicile State:** IL **NAIC Code:** 62863

Data Date	Rating	RACR #1	RACR #2	Total Assets ($mil)	Capital ($mil)	Net Premium ($mil)	Net Income ($mil)
6-16	B+	6.29	4.24	325.4	169.5	80.2	8.7
6-15	B+	5.10	3.42	347.5	171.6	84.6	10.3
2015	B+	5.62	3.77	321.3	159.8	163.7	8.4
2014	B+	4.41	3.01	353.2	162.6	206.9	14.0
2013	B+	3.61	2.53	365.5	160.6	264.5	13.9
2012	B+	3.28	2.34	367.8	165.8	320.1	15.1
2011	B+	2.99	2.25	370.2	168.2	383.3	13.2

Adverse Trends in Operations

Decrease in asset base during 2015 (9%)
Decrease in premium volume from 2014 to 2015 (21%)
Decrease in premium volume from 2013 to 2014 (22%)
Decrease in premium volume from 2012 to 2013 (17%)
Decrease in premium volume from 2011 to 2012 (16%)

UNICARE LIFE & HEALTH INSURANCE COMPANY   B-   Good

Major Rating Factors: Good overall profitability (6.2 on a scale of 0 to 10). Excellent expense controls. Good liquidity (6.7) with sufficient resources to handle a spike in claims. Fair quality investment portfolio (3.8).
Other Rating Factors: Fair overall results on stability tests (4.1). Strong capitalization (7.8) based on excellent risk adjusted capital (severe loss scenario).
Principal Business: Reinsurance (44%), group life insurance (35%), group health insurance (13%), and individual health insurance (8%).
Principal Investments: NonCMO investment grade bonds (80%), noninv. grade bonds (14%), CMOs and structured securities (1%), and cash (1%).
Investments in Affiliates: None
Group Affiliation: Anthem Inc
Licensed in: All states, the District of Columbia and Puerto Rico
Commenced Business: December 1980
Address: 1209 Orange St, Wilmington, DE 19801
Phone: (877) 864-2273 **Domicile State:** IN **NAIC Code:** 80314

Data Date	Rating	RACR #1	RACR #2	Total Assets ($mil)	Capital ($mil)	Net Premium ($mil)	Net Income ($mil)
6-16	B-	2.10	1.55	300.3	78.2	131.7	18.1
6-15	B-	1.86	1.37	324.3	70.8	127.3	15.6
2015	B-	3.06	2.27	373.8	108.4	291.9	21.5
2014	B-	1.77	1.32	413.3	63.8	329.6	25.0
2013	B	3.13	2.32	469.1	126.3	321.7	43.7
2012	B	2.83	2.05	554.2	158.8	439.4	74.4
2011	B	2.27	1.66	642.9	149.3	632.5	51.2

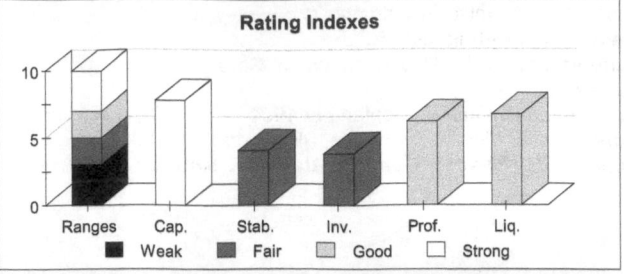

Rating Indexes

(Ranges, Cap., Stab., Inv., Prof., Liq.)
■ Weak ■ Fair ▨ Good ☐ Strong

UNIMERICA INSURANCE COMPANY   B   Good

Major Rating Factors: Good overall results on stability tests (5.6 on a scale of 0 to 10) despite fair financial strength of affiliated UnitedHealth Group Inc. Other stability subfactors include excellent operational trends, excellent risk adjusted capital for prior years and excellent risk diversification. Good overall capitalization (6.2) based on excellent risk adjusted capital (severe loss scenario). However, capital levels have fluctuated somewhat during past years. Good liquidity (6.6).
Other Rating Factors: High quality investment portfolio (8.4). Excellent profitability (8.3).
Principal Business: Reinsurance (53%), group health insurance (45%), and group life insurance (2%).
Principal Investments: NonCMO investment grade bonds (84%) and CMOs and structured securities (17%).
Investments in Affiliates: None
Group Affiliation: UnitedHealth Group Inc
Licensed in: All states except NY, PR
Commenced Business: December 1980
Address: 711 High St, Des Moines, IA 50392
Phone: (877) 832-7734 **Domicile State:** WI **NAIC Code:** 91529

Data Date	Rating	RACR #1	RACR #2	Total Assets ($mil)	Capital ($mil)	Net Premium ($mil)	Net Income ($mil)
6-16	B	1.94	1.55	443.4	159.5	367.0	26.2
6-15	B	2.21	1.76	422.1	157.8	313.9	31.0
2015	B	1.99	1.59	435.9	167.7	669.4	65.7
2014	B	2.54	2.02	415.0	187.8	582.4	76.9
2013	B	2.82	2.24	410.1	181.1	489.2	43.3
2012	B	3.17	2.48	326.6	153.2	319.8	32.2
2011	B	3.07	2.37	289.0	129.9	228.4	9.5

UnitedHealth Group Inc Composite Group Rating: C+ Largest Group Members	Assets ($mil)	Rating
UNITED HEALTHCARE INS CO	15791	C
OXFORD HEALTH INS INC	2195	B
SIERRA HEALTH AND LIFE INS CO INC	1677	B
UNITED HEALTHCARE INS CO OF NY	1223	B-
UNITEDHEALTHCARE PLAN RIVER VALLEY	1131	B-

UNION FIDELITY LIFE INSURANCE COMPANY   D+   Weak

Major Rating Factors: Low quality investment portfolio (2.7 on a scale of 0 to 10) containing large holdings of BBB rated bonds in addition to significant exposure to junk bonds. Weak profitability (1.7) with operating losses during the first six months of 2016. Weak overall results on stability tests (2.7) including weak risk adjusted capital in prior years, negative cash flow from operations for 2015.
Other Rating Factors: Fair capitalization (4.8) based on fair risk adjusted capital (moderate loss scenario). Excellent liquidity (8.3).
Principal Business: Reinsurance (88%), group health insurance (5%), group life insurance (4%), individual life insurance (2%), and individual health insurance (1%).
Principal Investments: NonCMO investment grade bonds (76%), CMOs and structured securities (13%), mortgages in good standing (4%), and noninv. grade bonds (3%).
Investments in Affiliates: 1%
Group Affiliation: General Electric Corp Group
Licensed in: All states except NY, PR
Commenced Business: February 1926
Address: 7101 College Blvd Suite 1400, Overland Park, KS 66210
Phone: (913) 982-3700 **Domicile State:** KS **NAIC Code:** 62596

Data Date	Rating	RACR #1	RACR #2	Total Assets ($mil)	Capital ($mil)	Net Premium ($mil)	Net Income ($mil)
6-16	D+	0.98	0.50	19,529.4	495.1	132.7	-107.8
6-15	D+	0.99	0.52	19,498.2	491.5	135.6	-26.6
2015	D+	0.89	0.46	19,365.0	428.3	276.3	-60.9
2014	D+	1.04	0.54	19,673.7	518.4	285.9	-280.8
2013	D+	1.07	0.55	19,510.6	569.3	305.7	6.3
2012	D	1.01	0.52	19,585.3	560.1	316.1	-430.4
2011	D+	0.80	0.42	19,089.5	445.2	320.2	-598.5

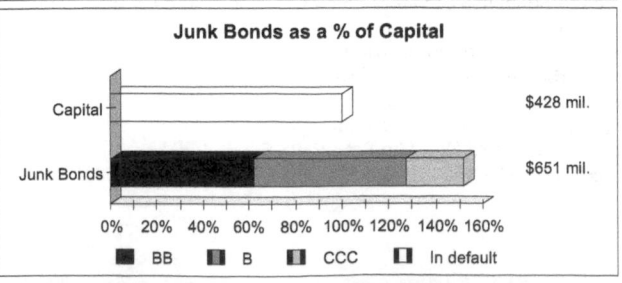

Junk Bonds as a % of Capital

Capital — $428 mil.
Junk Bonds — $651 mil.

(0% 20% 40% 60% 80% 100% 120% 140% 160%)
■ BB ▨ B ☐ CCC ☐ In default

UNION LABOR LIFE INSURANCE COMPANY · B- · Good

Major Rating Factors: Good quality investment portfolio (6.4 on a scale of 0 to 10) despite mixed results such as: minimal exposure to mortgages and substantial holdings of BBB bonds but no exposure to junk bonds. Good overall results on stability tests (5.0) despite negative cash flow from operations for 2015. Other stability subfactors include excellent operational trends and excellent risk diversification. Fair profitability (3.1).

Other Rating Factors: Strong capitalization (7.2) based on excellent risk adjusted capital (severe loss scenario). Excellent liquidity (7.0).

Principal Business: Group health insurance (53%), group life insurance (29%), reinsurance (13%), group retirement contracts (4%), and individual life insurance (1%).

Principal Investments: NonCMO investment grade bonds (61%), CMOs and structured securities (24%), common & preferred stock (7%), and mortgages in good standing (6%).

Investments in Affiliates: 7%
Group Affiliation: ULLICO Inc
Licensed in: All states except PR
Commenced Business: May 1927
Address: 111 Massachusetts Ave NW, Washington, DC 20001-1625
Phone: (202) 682-6690 **Domicile State:** MD **NAIC Code:** 69744

Data Date	Rating	RACR #1	RACR #2	Total Assets ($mil)	Capital ($mil)	Net Premium ($mil)	Net Income ($mil)
6-16	B-	1.58	1.10	3,272.1	82.1	68.3	5.2
6-15	B-	1.45	1.02	3,262.4	77.3	70.7	1.8
2015	B-	1.52	1.07	3,238.8	79.6	138.3	3.5
2014	B-	1.42	1.00	3,337.5	76.4	142.1	1.4
2013	B-	1.66	1.20	2,813.7	87.7	139.5	-11.1
2012	B-	2.22	1.50	2,905.9	96.9	148.8	7.9
2011	C+	1.82	1.15	3,495.0	91.0	156.3	2.7

Adverse Trends in Operations

Decrease in asset base during 2015 (3%)
Decrease in capital during 2014 (13%)
Decrease in asset base during 2013 (3%)
Decrease in premium volume from 2011 to 2012 (5%)
Decrease in asset base during 2012 (17%)

UNION SECURITY INSURANCE COMPANY · B · Good

Major Rating Factors: Good quality investment portfolio (5.4 on a scale of 0 to 10) despite significant exposure to mortgages . Mortgage default rate has been low. large holdings of BBB rated bonds in addition to small junk bond holdings. Good overall profitability (6.3). Good liquidity (5.5).

Other Rating Factors: Fair overall results on stability tests (4.8) including negative cash flow from operations for 2015. Strong capitalization (10.0) based on excellent risk adjusted capital (severe loss scenario).

Principal Business: Group health insurance (57%), group life insurance (17%), reinsurance (13%), individual health insurance (7%), and other lines (6%).

Principal Investments: NonCMO investment grade bonds (71%), mortgages in good standing (14%), common & preferred stock (5%), CMOs and structured securities (4%), and misc. investments (5%).

Investments in Affiliates: 1%
Group Affiliation: Assurant Inc
Licensed in: All states except NY, PR
Commenced Business: September 1910
Address: 500 Bielenberg Dr, Woodbury, MN 55125
Phone: (612) 738-5063 **Domicile State:** KS **NAIC Code:** 70408

Data Date	Rating	RACR #1	RACR #2	Total Assets ($mil)	Capital ($mil)	Net Premium ($mil)	Net Income ($mil)
6-16	B	5.03	2.97	3,119.7	415.0	-1,470.5	358.1
6-15	B	1.80	1.18	4,911.1	413.9	517.0	25.0
2015	B	1.91	1.26	4,711.8	428.4	1,028.4	71.5
2014	B	1.82	1.18	4,937.1	415.7	1,016.0	67.3
2013	B	1.88	1.21	5,085.8	434.7	986.2	85.4
2012	B	2.10	1.28	5,015.5	438.8	986.8	95.3
2011	B	2.02	1.24	5,139.5	455.8	1,050.4	69.1

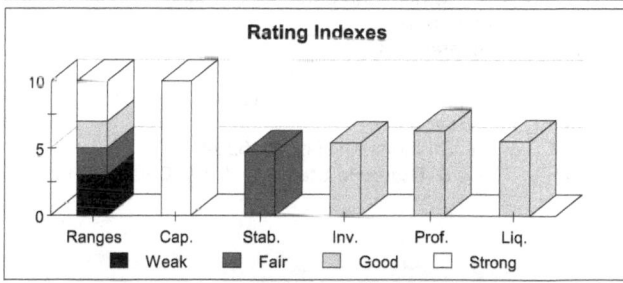

Rating Indexes

UNION SECURITY LIFE INSURANCE COMPANY OF NEW YORK * · B+ · Good

Major Rating Factors: Good overall results on stability tests (5.0 on a scale of 0 to 10) despite negative cash flow from operations for 2015. Other stability subfactors include excellent risk diversification. Good overall profitability (5.9). Strong capitalization (10.0) based on excellent risk adjusted capital (severe loss scenario).

Other Rating Factors: High quality investment portfolio (7.5). Excellent liquidity (7.3).

Principal Business: Group health insurance (39%), individual health insurance (28%), reinsurance (17%), group life insurance (9%), and other lines (6%).

Principal Investments: NonCMO investment grade bonds (72%), mortgages in good standing (14%), CMOs and structured securities (7%), common & preferred stock (5%), and misc. investments (1%).

Investments in Affiliates: None
Group Affiliation: Assurant Inc
Licensed in: NY
Commenced Business: April 1974
Address: 220 Salina Meadows Pkwy #255, Syracuse, NY 13212
Phone: (315) 451-0066 **Domicile State:** NY **NAIC Code:** 81477

Data Date	Rating	RACR #1	RACR #2	Total Assets ($mil)	Capital ($mil)	Net Premium ($mil)	Net Income ($mil)
6-16	B+	7.09	6.38	88.0	65.4	-72.5	13.7
6-15	B+	4.31	3.88	132.7	39.5	11.1	0.4
2015	B+	4.34	3.91	128.3	39.5	21.6	3.3
2014	B+	4.66	4.19	138.7	42.8	23.8	5.6
2013	B+	4.44	4.00	147.7	40.9	27.4	5.4
2012	B	5.02	4.21	160.6	46.9	30.1	5.5
2011	B	4.32	3.39	168.1	40.7	35.2	-0.1

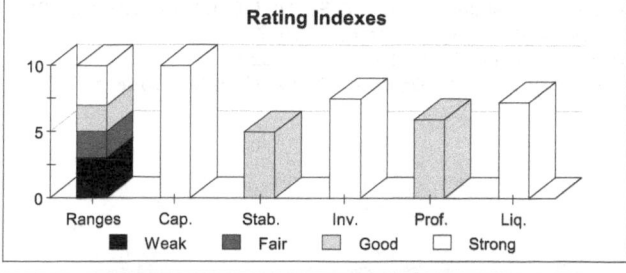

Rating Indexes

UNITED AMERICAN INSURANCE COMPANY

B-   **Good**

Major Rating Factors: Good overall capitalization (5.7 on a scale of 0 to 10) based on good risk adjusted capital (severe loss scenario). Nevertheless, capital levels have fluctuated during prior years. Good quality investment portfolio (6.2) despite mixed results such as: large holdings of BBB rated bonds but moderate junk bond exposure. Good overall profitability (6.0) despite operating losses during the first six months of 2016.

Other Rating Factors: Good liquidity (5.8). Fair overall results on stability tests (4.9).

Principal Business: Individual health insurance (56%), group health insurance (27%), reinsurance (11%), individual annuities (3%), and individual life insurance (2%).

Principal Investments: NonCMO investment grade bonds (81%), noninv. grade bonds (5%), common & preferred stock (4%), CMOs and structured securities (3%), and misc. investments (4%).

Investments in Affiliates: 6%

Group Affiliation: Torchmark Corp

Licensed in: All states except NY, PR

Commenced Business: August 1981

Address: 10306 Regency Parkway Dr, Omaha, NE 68114

Phone: (972) 529-5085 **Domicile State:** NE **NAIC Code:** 92916

Data Date	Rating	RACR #1	RACR #2	Total Assets ($mil)	Capital ($mil)	Net Premium ($mil)	Net Income ($mil)
6-16	B-	1.16	0.84	1,598.2	159.3	357.8	-3.2
6-15	B-	0.87	0.64	1,674.2	152.0	459.6	-13.0
2015	B-	1.24	0.90	1,559.7	192.7	815.3	80.1
2014	B-	1.01	0.74	1,694.9	178.4	870.9	29.5
2013	B	1.27	0.91	1,683.4	211.6	745.1	58.1
2012	B	1.47	1.05	1,722.8	256.1	779.2	78.8
2011	B	1.54	1.07	1,703.5	243.9	692.2	75.0

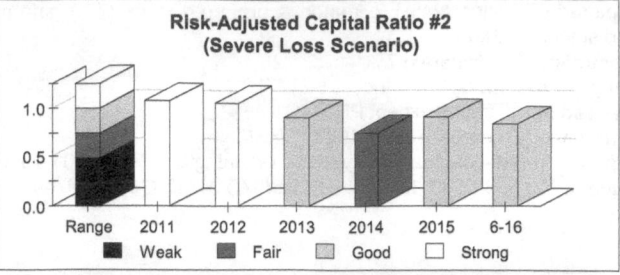

Risk-Adjusted Capital Ratio #2
(Severe Loss Scenario)

UNITED FARM FAMILY LIFE INSURANCE COMPANY *

A   **Excellent**

Major Rating Factors: Good quality investment portfolio (6.9 on a scale of 0 to 10) despite significant exposure to mortgages . Mortgage default rate has been low. substantial holdings of BBB bonds in addition to no exposure to junk bonds. Good overall profitability (6.0) although investment income, in comparison to reserve requirements, is below regulatory standards. Good liquidity (5.8).

Other Rating Factors: Strong capitalization (8.4) based on excellent risk adjusted capital (severe loss scenario). Excellent overall results on stability tests (7.4) excellent operational trends and excellent risk diversification.

Principal Business: Individual life insurance (79%), reinsurance (12%), and individual annuities (9%).

Principal Investments: NonCMO investment grade bonds (64%), mortgages in good standing (17%), CMOs and structured securities (10%), policy loans (5%), and misc. investments (5%).

Investments in Affiliates: 2%

Group Affiliation: Indiana Farm Bureau

Licensed in: AZ, CA, IL, IN, MD, MA, NH, NJ, NC, ND, OH, PA

Commenced Business: May 1964

Address: 225 S East St, Indianapolis, IN 46202

Phone: (317) 692-7200 **Domicile State:** IN **NAIC Code:** 69892

Data Date	Rating	RACR #1	RACR #2	Total Assets ($mil)	Capital ($mil)	Net Premium ($mil)	Net Income ($mil)
6-16	A	3.25	1.93	2,234.9	310.9	68.5	7.8
6-15	A	3.15	1.88	2,176.6	294.5	69.8	9.1
2015	A	3.21	1.92	2,203.5	301.5	136.5	16.6
2014	A	3.12	1.88	2,145.3	286.6	141.8	16.9
2013	A	3.07	1.84	2,087.0	275.2	144.3	12.8
2012	A	2.97	1.77	2,006.6	242.4	145.3	14.6
2011	A	2.97	1.77	1,923.8	235.8	155.0	12.1

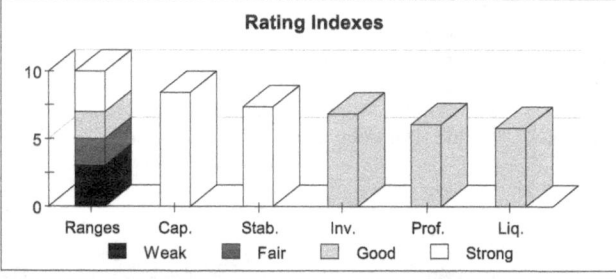

Rating Indexes

UNITED FIDELITY LIFE INSURANCE COMPANY

C   **Fair**

Major Rating Factors: Fair capitalization (4.7 on a scale of 0 to 10) based on fair risk adjusted capital (severe loss scenario). Fair quality investment portfolio (3.4). Fair overall results on stability tests (4.4) including fair risk adjusted capital in prior years.

Other Rating Factors: Good overall profitability (6.9). Good liquidity (6.8).

Principal Business: Individual life insurance (91%), individual annuities (4%), individual health insurance (3%), and reinsurance (2%).

Principal Investments: Common & preferred stock (77%), CMOs and structured securities (8%), nonCMO investment grade bonds (7%), policy loans (2%), and misc. investments (6%).

Investments in Affiliates: 75%

Group Affiliation: Americo Life Inc

Licensed in: All states except CT, FL, HI, ME, MI, MN, NH, NJ, NY, VT, PR

Commenced Business: September 1977

Address: 500 North Akard, Dallas, TX 75201

Phone: (816) 391-2000 **Domicile State:** TX **NAIC Code:** 87645

Data Date	Rating	RACR #1	RACR #2	Total Assets ($mil)	Capital ($mil)	Net Premium ($mil)	Net Income ($mil)
6-16	C	0.73	0.71	741.5	441.0	3.6	34.8
6-15	C	0.72	0.70	760.5	448.4	3.9	53.9
2015	C	0.75	0.73	755.3	450.6	7.5	52.5
2014	C	0.74	0.72	779.6	464.2	7.9	44.2
2013	C	0.74	0.72	778.2	450.2	8.6	44.2
2012	C	0.70	0.68	730.1	396.9	9.3	24.2
2011	C	0.70	0.68	717.4	376.9	10.1	27.7

Risk-Adjusted Capital Ratio #2
(Severe Loss Scenario)

UNITED HEALTHCARE INSURANCE COMPANY   C   Fair

Major Rating Factors: Fair overall capitalization (4.4 on a scale of 0 to 10) based on mixed results -- excessive policy leverage mitigated by fair risk adjusted capital (moderate loss scenario). Fair overall results on stability tests (3.8) including fair risk adjusted capital in prior years. Good quality investment portfolio (6.6).

Other Rating Factors: Weak liquidity (1.8). Excellent profitability (8.7).

Principal Business: Group health insurance (81%), individual health insurance (14%), and reinsurance (5%).

Principal Investments: NonCMO investment grade bonds (54%), common & preferred stock (23%), CMOs and structured securities (16%), noninv. grade bonds (6%), and misc. investments (1%).

Investments in Affiliates: 20%

Group Affiliation: UnitedHealth Group Inc

Licensed in: All states except NY

Commenced Business: April 1972

Address: 185 Asylum St, Hartford, CT 06103-3408

Phone: (877) 832-7734   **Domicile State:** CT   **NAIC Code:** 79413

Data Date	Rating	RACR #1	RACR #2	Total Assets ($mil)	Capital ($mil)	Net Premium ($mil)	Net Income ($mil)
6-16	C	0.81	0.68	15,432.2	4,212.0	22,650.4	575.7
6-15	C	0.86	0.73	15,113.4	4,870.9	20,705.1	358.2
2015	C	0.89	0.75	15,791.2	5,589.7	41,950.2	1,930.3
2014	C	0.82	0.69	15,113.4	5,595.8	43,936.4	2,658.1
2013	C	0.76	0.64	14,512.6	5,039.5	44,680.4	2,384.0
2012	C	0.76	0.64	14,118.3	4,711.9	42,602.9	2,531.0
2011	C	0.73	0.62	15,022.1	4,421.6	41,956.3	2,430.1

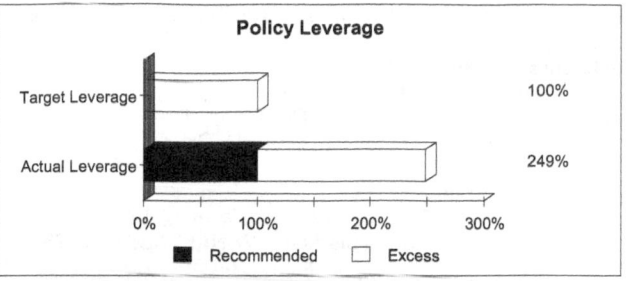

Policy Leverage

Target Leverage — 100%

Actual Leverage — 249%

0%   100%   200%   300%

■ Recommended   □ Excess

UNITED HERITAGE LIFE INSURANCE COMPANY   B   Good

Major Rating Factors: Good liquidity (5.0 on a scale of 0 to 10) with sufficient resources to cover a large increase in policy surrenders. Good overall results on stability tests (5.7). Stability strengths include excellent operational trends and excellent risk diversification. Fair quality investment portfolio (4.6).

Other Rating Factors: Strong capitalization (7.4) based on excellent risk adjusted capital (severe loss scenario). Excellent profitability (8.1).

Principal Business: Individual life insurance (59%), individual annuities (32%), group life insurance (4%), group health insurance (4%), and group retirement contracts (1%).

Principal Investments: NonCMO investment grade bonds (76%), CMOs and structured securities (8%), noninv. grade bonds (8%), common & preferred stock (2%), and misc. investments (5%).

Investments in Affiliates: None

Group Affiliation: United Heritage Mutual Holding Co

Licensed in: AK, AZ, AR, CA, CO, DC, DE, FL, GA, HI, ID, IL, IN, IA, KS, KY, LA, MI, MN, MO, MT, NE, NV, NM, NC, ND, OH, OK, OR, PA, SC, SD, TN, TX, UT, VA, WA, WI, WY

Commenced Business: September 1935

Address: 707 East United Heritage Ct, Meridian, ID 83642-3527

Phone: (208) 466-7856   **Domicile State:** ID   **NAIC Code:** 63983

Data Date	Rating	RACR #1	RACR #2	Total Assets ($mil)	Capital ($mil)	Net Premium ($mil)	Net Income ($mil)
6-16	B	2.53	1.25	549.7	60.4	36.0	1.7
6-15	B	2.54	1.29	542.2	58.3	48.9	2.1
2015	B	2.52	1.27	541.6	59.3	83.1	4.6
2014	B	2.69	1.38	522.6	58.0	63.0	6.3
2013	B-	2.71	1.40	520.1	55.4	68.1	5.9
2012	B-	2.64	1.36	504.2	52.4	65.4	6.0
2011	B	2.57	1.35	486.6	49.1	58.0	5.3

Exposure to Withdrawals Without Penalty
(as a % of capital)

Capital — $59 mil.

Withdrawals w/o Penalty — $148 mil.

0%   100%   200%   300%

UNITED INSURANCE COMPANY OF AMERICA   B-   Good

Major Rating Factors: Good overall capitalization (6.7 on a scale of 0 to 10) based on good risk adjusted capital (severe loss scenario). Nevertheless, capital levels have fluctuated during prior years. Good overall profitability (6.2). Good liquidity (5.6) with sufficient resources to handle a spike in claims as well as a significant increase in policy surrenders.

Other Rating Factors: Good overall results on stability tests (5.3) excellent operational trends and excellent risk diversification. Fair quality investment portfolio (4.4).

Principal Business: Reinsurance (52%), individual life insurance (46%), and individual health insurance (2%).

Principal Investments: NonCMO investment grade bonds (61%), noninv. grade bonds (9%), policy loans (8%), common & preferred stock (6%), and misc. investments (14%).

Investments in Affiliates: 4%

Group Affiliation: Kemper Corporation

Licensed in: All states except AK, NY, PR

Commenced Business: April 1928

Address: 12115 Lackland Rd, St Louis, MO 63146-4003

Phone: (312) 661-4681   **Domicile State:** IL   **NAIC Code:** 69930

Data Date	Rating	RACR #1	RACR #2	Total Assets ($mil)	Capital ($mil)	Net Premium ($mil)	Net Income ($mil)
6-16	B-	1.64	0.96	3,704.1	423.4	183.8	38.7
6-15	B-	1.61	0.95	3,662.0	424.2	189.2	29.0
2015	B-	1.59	0.93	3,675.8	405.4	364.2	64.8
2014	B-	1.67	1.00	3,644.8	439.4	362.7	122.5
2013	B-	1.53	0.95	3,591.7	436.1	375.0	79.0
2012	B-	1.58	1.00	3,550.3	464.1	383.6	95.9
2011	B-	1.63	1.05	3,493.3	480.6	386.6	95.4

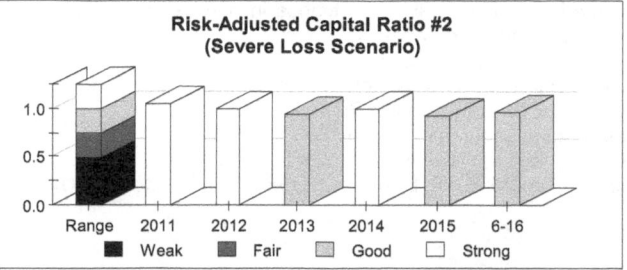

Risk-Adjusted Capital Ratio #2
(Severe Loss Scenario)

Range 2011 2012 2013 2014 2015 6-16

■ Weak   ■ Fair   □ Good   □ Strong

UNITED LIFE INSURANCE COMPANY   B   Good

Major Rating Factors: Good quality investment portfolio (6.2 on a scale of 0 to 10) despite mixed results such as: minimal exposure to mortgages and large holdings of BBB rated bonds but small junk bond holdings. Good liquidity (5.6) with sufficient resources to cover a large increase in policy surrenders. Fair overall results on stability tests (4.9) including negative cash flow from operations for 2015.

Other Rating Factors: Fair profitability (4.7) with operating losses during the first six months of 2016. Strong capitalization (7.6) based on excellent risk adjusted capital (severe loss scenario).

Principal Business: Individual annuities (49%), individual life insurance (49%), individual health insurance (1%), and group life insurance (1%).

Principal Investments: NonCMO investment grade bonds (77%), CMOs and structured securities (18%), noninv. grade bonds (2%), common & preferred stock (1%), and cash (1%).

Investments in Affiliates: None

Group Affiliation: United Fire & Casualty Group

Licensed in: AL, AZ, AR, CA, CO, DE, FL, ID, IL, IN, IA, KS, KY, LA, MD, MI, MN, MS, MO, MT, NE, NV, NJ, NM, NC, ND, OH, OK, PA, SD, TN, TX, UT, VA, WV, WI, WY

Commenced Business: October 1962

Address: 118 Second Ave SE, Cedar Rapids, IA 52401

Phone: (800) 553-7937 **Domicile State:** IA **NAIC Code:** 69973

Data Date	Rating	RACR #1	RACR #2	Total Assets ($mil)	Capital ($mil)	Net Premium ($mil)	Net Income ($mil)
6-16	B	2.71	1.43	1,532.7	138.7	71.2	-0.7
6-15	B	2.86	1.52	1,591.1	156.7	71.8	0.4
2015	B	2.76	1.47	1,535.9	138.9	143.0	-1.5
2014	B	2.83	1.50	1,635.4	155.7	198.8	3.5
2013	B	2.74	1.42	1,648.0	158.0	164.3	5.9
2012	B	2.72	1.39	1,675.7	158.7	154.2	7.4
2011	B	2.86	1.44	1,651.1	167.2	170.0	6.2

Rating Indexes

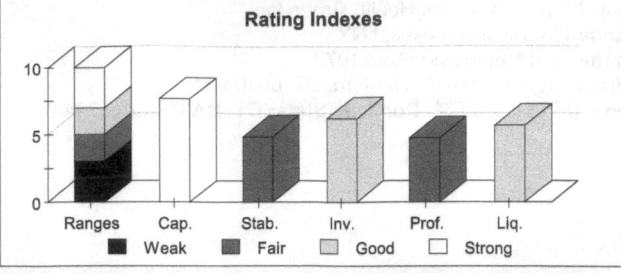

UNITED OF OMAHA LIFE INSURANCE COMPANY   B   Good

Major Rating Factors: Good current capitalization (6.9 on a scale of 0 to 10) based on good risk adjusted capital (severe loss scenario), although results have slipped from the excellent range during the last year. Good quality investment portfolio (5.1) despite large holdings of BBB rated bonds in addition to moderate junk bond exposure. Exposure to mortgages is significant, but the mortgage default rate has been low. Good overall profitability (5.6) despite operating losses during the first six months of 2016.

Other Rating Factors: Good liquidity (6.4). Good overall results on stability tests (5.4) good operational trends and excellent risk diversification.

Principal Business: Individual life insurance (33%), individual health insurance (28%), group health insurance (12%), group retirement contracts (12%), and other lines (15%).

Principal Investments: NonCMO investment grade bonds (54%), CMOs and structured securities (22%), mortgages in good standing (12%), noninv. grade bonds (4%), and misc. investments (7%).

Investments in Affiliates: 1%

Group Affiliation: Mutual Of Omaha Group

Licensed in: All states except NY

Commenced Business: November 1926

Address: Mutual Of Omaha Plaza, Omaha, NE 68175

Phone: (402) 342-7600 **Domicile State:** NE **NAIC Code:** 69868

Data Date	Rating	RACR #1	RACR #2	Total Assets ($mil)	Capital ($mil)	Net Premium ($mil)	Net Income ($mil)
6-16	B	1.71	0.99	20,032.6	1,300.3	1,930.9	-1.8
6-15	B	1.92	1.13	19,078.4	1,503.2	1,720.6	152.1
2015	B	1.90	1.11	19,622.5	1,441.7	3,572.3	153.6
2014	B	1.95	1.15	18,786.7	1,422.7	2,712.4	164.4
2013	B	1.71	1.00	18,122.5	1,226.9	3,428.2	69.9
2012	B	1.42	0.83	16,698.1	1,027.2	3,464.0	-31.5
2011	B	1.46	0.86	15,737.8	1,036.1	3,162.9	-207.0

Risk-Adjusted Capital Ratio #2 (Severe Loss Scenario)

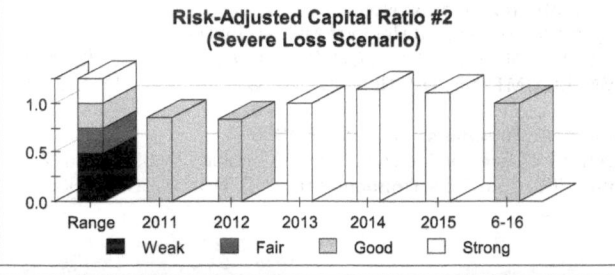

UNITED STATES LIFE INSURANCE COMPANY IN NYC   B   Good

Major Rating Factors: Good overall results on stability tests (5.8 on a scale of 0 to 10) despite excessive premium growth. Other stability subfactors include excellent operational trends and excellent risk diversification. Good quality investment portfolio (5.1) despite large holdings of BBB rated bonds in addition to junk bond exposure equal to 55% of capital. Exposure to mortgages is significant, but the mortgage default rate has been low. Good liquidity (6.0).

Other Rating Factors: Strong capitalization (7.4) based on excellent risk adjusted capital (severe loss scenario). Excellent profitability (7.9).

Principal Business: Individual annuities (68%), individual life insurance (12%), group health insurance (8%), group life insurance (8%), and group retirement contracts (5%).

Principal Investments: NonCMO investment grade bonds (50%), CMOs and structured securities (28%), mortgages in good standing (10%), noninv. grade bonds (5%), and policy loans (1%).

Investments in Affiliates: 1%

Group Affiliation: American International Group

Licensed in: All states except PR

Commenced Business: March 1850

Address: 390 Park Ave, New York, NY 10022-4684

Phone: (212) 709-6000 **Domicile State:** NY **NAIC Code:** 70106

Data Date	Rating	RACR #1	RACR #2	Total Assets ($mil)	Capital ($mil)	Net Premium ($mil)	Net Income ($mil)
6-16	B	2.59	1.27	29,018.5	1,988.5	1,107.1	1.7
6-15	B-	2.78	1.35	27,918.0	2,052.1	872.6	193.2
2015	B	2.62	1.30	28,404.0	2,090.4	1,984.7	365.0
2014	B-	2.63	1.29	27,985.4	2,000.8	1,918.6	319.8
2013	B-	2.32	1.15	25,538.0	1,765.2	1,772.8	420.1
2012	B-	2.58	1.27	24,541.6	1,878.3	1,458.3	269.6
2011	B-	2.59	1.28	23,095.9	1,842.3	2,429.6	107.2

Adverse Trends in Operations

Change in premium mix from 2012 to 2013 (5.6%)
Decrease in capital during 2013 (6%)
Change in premium mix from 2011 to 2012 (6.6%)
Decrease in premium volume from 2011 to 2012 (40%)

UNITED TEACHER ASSOCIATES INSURANCE COMPANY   C   Fair

Major Rating Factors: Fair quality investment portfolio (4.0 on a scale of 0 to 10) with large holdings of BBB rated bonds in addition to junk bond exposure equal to 63% of capital. Fair profitability (4.2) with operating losses during the first six months of 2016. Fair overall results on stability tests (4.1).
Other Rating Factors: Good capitalization (5.3) based on good risk adjusted capital (moderate loss scenario). Excellent liquidity (7.2).
Principal Business: Individual health insurance (80%), group health insurance (12%), individual life insurance (3%), reinsurance (3%), and group retirement contracts (2%).
Principal Investments: NonCMO investment grade bonds (65%), CMOs and structured securities (22%), common & preferred stock (5%), noninv. grade bonds (4%), and misc. investments (5%).
Investments in Affiliates: 2%
Group Affiliation: HC2 Holdings Inc
Licensed in: All states except NH, NY, RI, VT
Commenced Business: January 1959
Address: 5508 Parkcrest Dr, Austin, TX 78731
Phone: (512) 451-2224 **Domicile State:** TX **NAIC Code:** 63479

Data Date	Rating	RACR #1	RACR #2	Total Assets ($mil)	Capital ($mil)	Net Premium ($mil)	Net Income ($mil)
6-16	C	1.17	0.73	1,071.3	57.7	34.7	-10.1
6-15	C	1.45	0.80	1,048.0	59.2	37.6	4.0
2015	C	1.44	0.91	1,044.6	61.0	36.6	67.5
2014	C-	1.36	0.75	1,018.1	56.1	83.8	-36.6
2013	C	2.13	1.16	940.0	84.4	77.7	3.5
2012	C	1.69	0.84	839.3	47.9	52.8	-14.7
2011	B-	1.51	0.92	847.1	66.9	205.7	7.2

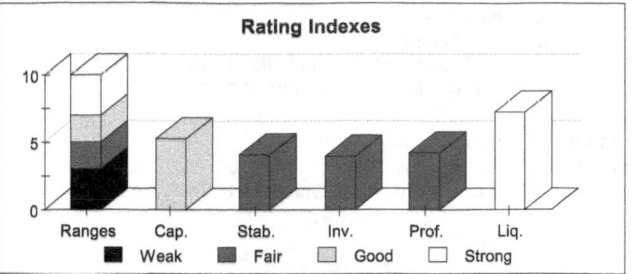

Rating Indexes

Ranges Cap. Stab. Inv. Prof. Liq.
■ Weak ■ Fair □ Good □ Strong

UNITED WORLD LIFE INSURANCE COMPANY *   B+   Good

Major Rating Factors: Good overall results on stability tests (6.7 on a scale of 0 to 10). Stability strengths include good operational trends and excellent risk diversification. Good overall profitability (5.3). Strong capitalization (8.6) based on excellent risk adjusted capital (severe loss scenario).
Other Rating Factors: High quality investment portfolio (7.6). Excellent liquidity (7.0).
Principal Business: Individual health insurance (100%).
Principal Investments: NonCMO investment grade bonds (63%), CMOs and structured securities (24%), cash (7%), noninv. grade bonds (1%), and policy loans (1%).
Investments in Affiliates: None
Group Affiliation: Mutual Of Omaha Group
Licensed in: All states except CT, NY, PR
Commenced Business: April 1970
Address: Mutual Of Omaha Plaza, Omaha, NE 68175
Phone: (402) 342-7600 **Domicile State:** NE **NAIC Code:** 72850

Data Date	Rating	RACR #1	RACR #2	Total Assets ($mil)	Capital ($mil)	Net Premium ($mil)	Net Income ($mil)
6-16	B+	4.84	2.05	122.6	50.0	0.6	1.2
6-15	B+	4.48	1.89	116.7	50.1	0.6	0.7
2015	B+	4.92	2.09	123.7	48.9	1.4	-0.5
2014	B+	4.62	1.95	119.4	49.4	1.5	1.6
2013	B+	4.19	1.76	114.9	48.6	1.6	1.2
2012	B+	3.89	1.63	103.1	47.3	1.7	0.1
2011	B+	3.67	1.53	106.1	47.3	1.9	1.9

Adverse Trends in Operations

Decrease in premium volume from 2014 to 2015 (5%)
Increase in policy surrenders from 2014 to 2015 (38%)
Change in asset mix during 2013 (4.1%)
Decrease in premium volume from 2011 to 2012 (8%)
Decrease in asset base during 2012 (3%)

UNITEDHEALTHCARE LIFE INSURANCE COMPANY   C   Fair

Major Rating Factors: Fair overall results on stability tests (3.8 on a scale of 0 to 10) including excessive premium growth and negative cash flow from operations for 2015. Good overall capitalization (5.6) based on mixed results -- excessive policy leverage mitigated by excellent risk adjusted capital (severe loss scenario). Capital levels have been relatively consistent over the last five years. Good liquidity (5.5).
Other Rating Factors: Weak profitability (2.6) with operating losses during the first six months of 2016. High quality investment portfolio (8.3).
Principal Business: Individual health insurance (59%) and group health insurance (41%).
Principal Investments: NonCMO investment grade bonds (85%), CMOs and structured securities (8%), and cash (7%).
Investments in Affiliates: None
Group Affiliation: UnitedHealth Group Inc
Licensed in: All states except MA, NY, PR
Commenced Business: December 1982
Address: 3100 AMS Blvd, Green Bay, WI 54313
Phone: (800) 232-5432 **Domicile State:** WI **NAIC Code:** 97179

Data Date	Rating	RACR #1	RACR #2	Total Assets ($mil)	Capital ($mil)	Net Premium ($mil)	Net Income ($mil)
6-16	C	1.26	1.00	560.0	130.7	486.6	-42.7
6-15	C	1.38	1.11	330.5	75.4	327.7	-72.6
2015	C	1.61	1.28	488.4	137.1	700.9	-143.0
2014	B	1.51	1.23	132.6	41.4	245.0	-15.4
2013	B	2.11	1.69	57.0	29.3	84.8	7.3
2012	B	1.50	1.21	49.0	23.8	99.9	8.9
2011	B	1.74	1.40	65.7	32.3	119.4	10.3

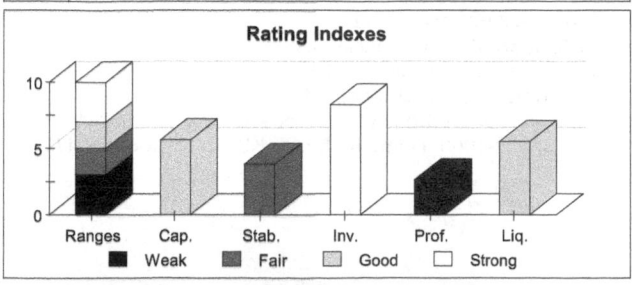

Rating Indexes

Ranges Cap. Stab. Inv. Prof. Liq.
■ Weak ■ Fair □ Good □ Strong

UNIVERSAL GUARANTY LIFE INSURANCE COMPANY   C+   Fair

Major Rating Factors: Fair overall results on stability tests (4.8 on a scale of 0 to 10) including negative cash flow from operations for 2015, fair risk adjusted capital in prior years. Good current capitalization (5.7) based on good risk adjusted capital (moderate loss scenario) reflecting some improvement over results in 2012. Good liquidity (5.3).
Other Rating Factors: Low quality investment portfolio (2.9). Excellent profitability (7.1).
Principal Business: Individual life insurance (95%), individual annuities (3%), and group life insurance (2%).
Principal Investments: NonCMO investment grade bonds (53%), common & preferred stock (14%), real estate (7%), noninv. grade bonds (5%), and misc. investments (21%).
Investments in Affiliates: 6%
Group Affiliation: UTG Inc
Licensed in: AL, AZ, AR, CO, DE, GA, ID, IL, IN, IA, KS, KY, LA, MA, MN, MS, MO, MT, NE, NV, NM, NC, ND, OH, OK, OR, PA, RI, SC, SD, TN, TX, UT, VA, WA, WV, WI
Commenced Business: December 1966
Address: 65 E State St Suite 2100, Columbus, OH 43215-4260
Phone: (217) 241-6300 **Domicile State:** OH **NAIC Code:** 70130

Data Date	Rating	RACR #1	RACR #2	Total Assets ($mil)	Capital ($mil)	Net Premium ($mil)	Net Income ($mil)
6-16	C+	1.45	0.83	338.1	41.2	3.6	2.3
6-15	C+	1.55	0.92	341.9	42.2	3.7	4.5
2015	C+	1.39	0.79	334.8	39.8	6.8	0.3
2014	C+	1.44	0.89	343.2	41.1	7.3	12.2
2013	C	1.16	0.72	348.1	34.9	8.2	4.8
2012	C	1.06	0.68	360.6	32.2	9.0	6.9
2011	C	1.14	0.80	263.2	33.2	7.4	0.6

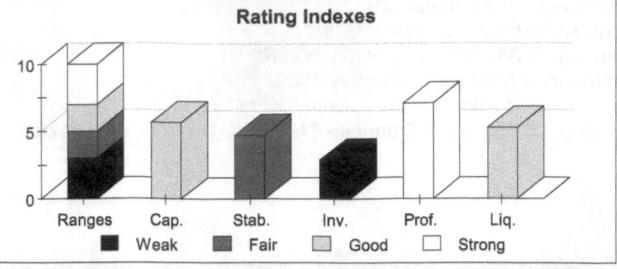

Rating Indexes

Ranges | Cap. | Stab. | Inv. | Prof. | Liq.
■ Weak   ■ Fair   ▨ Good   □ Strong

UNIVERSAL LIFE INSURANCE COMPANY   B   Good

Major Rating Factors: Good overall results on stability tests (5.4 on a scale of 0 to 10). Stability strengths include excellent operational trends, good risk adjusted capital for prior years and excellent risk diversification. Fair quality investment portfolio (4.6). Strong capitalization (7.4) based on excellent risk adjusted capital (severe loss scenario).
Other Rating Factors: Excellent profitability (9.0). Excellent liquidity (9.6).
Principal Business: Individual annuities (95%), group life insurance (2%), group health insurance (1%), and credit life insurance (1%).
Principal Investments: NonCMO investment grade bonds (71%), CMOs and structured securities (12%), noninv. grade bonds (4%), common & preferred stock (4%), and cash (3%).
Investments in Affiliates: None
Group Affiliation: Universal Ins Co Group
Licensed in: PR
Commenced Business: September 1994
Address: 16 Calle Mejico, San Juan, PR 00919-1899
Phone: (787) 706-7337 **Domicile State:** PR **NAIC Code:** 60041

Data Date	Rating	RACR #1	RACR #2	Total Assets ($mil)	Capital ($mil)	Net Premium ($mil)	Net Income ($mil)
6-16	B	2.45	1.28	1,017.4	61.4	52.0	11.6
6-15	B	1.88	0.96	945.1	43.2	58.9	12.7
2015	B	2.19	1.13	981.8	54.0	109.0	19.0
2014	B	2.03	1.07	814.2	42.8	132.2	16.0
2013	C+	1.34	0.77	773.5	29.4	140.7	3.6
2012	C+	1.58	0.91	592.0	27.6	140.2	3.8
2011	C+	2.01	1.16	429.7	23.9	137.4	1.7

Adverse Trends in Operations

Decrease in premium volume from 2014 to 2015 (18%)
Decrease in premium volume from 2013 to 2014 (6%)
Increase in policy surrenders from 2012 to 2013 (40%)
Increase in policy surrenders from 2011 to 2012 (34%)

UNIVERSAL UNDERWRITERS LIFE INSURANCE COMPANY   B-   Good

Major Rating Factors: Good overall results on stability tests (5.1 on a scale of 0 to 10) despite fair financial strength of affiliated Zurich Financial Services Group. Other stability subfactors include good operational trends and excellent risk diversification. Good liquidity (6.1) with sufficient resources to handle a spike in claims as well as a significant increase in policy surrenders. Fair profitability (3.0) with investment income below regulatory standards in relation to interest assumptions of reserves.
Other Rating Factors: Strong capitalization (9.5) based on excellent risk adjusted capital (severe loss scenario). High quality investment portfolio (7.8).
Principal Business: Individual life insurance (98%) and reinsurance (2%).
Principal Investments: NonCMO investment grade bonds (55%), CMOs and structured securities (40%), and policy loans (5%).
Investments in Affiliates: None
Group Affiliation: Zurich Financial Services Group
Licensed in: All states except NY, PR
Commenced Business: October 1965
Address: 7045 College Boulevard, Overland Park, KS 66211-1523
Phone: (913) 339-1000 **Domicile State:** KS **NAIC Code:** 70173

Data Date	Rating	RACR #1	RACR #2	Total Assets ($mil)	Capital ($mil)	Net Premium ($mil)	Net Income ($mil)
6-16	B-	2.95	2.65	156.6	27.7	3.1	1.6
6-15	B-	2.56	2.30	161.7	24.0	3.2	1.1
2015	B-	2.63	2.36	160.6	24.6	5.6	1.6
2014	B-	2.47	2.22	160.6	23.2	6.5	2.0
2013	B-	2.35	2.11	155.9	22.0	6.4	1.8
2012	B-	2.18	1.96	150.3	20.4	6.9	4.8
2011	C+	1.78	1.60	148.0	16.6	8.1	5.0

Zurich Financial Services Group
Composite Group Rating: C+
Largest Group Members

	Assets ($mil)	Rating
ZURICH AMERICAN INS CO	30471	B-
ZURICH AMERICAN LIFE INS CO	12271	C
FARMERS NEW WORLD LIFE INS CO	7049	B-
RURAL COMMUNITY INS CO	3680	B
CENTRE LIFE INS CO	1884	B-

UNUM INSURANCE COMPANY   C   Fair

Major Rating Factors: Fair overall results on stability tests (3.8 on a scale of 0 to 10). Good quality investment portfolio (5.7) despite mixed results such as: no exposure to mortgages and large holdings of BBB rated bonds but no exposure to junk bonds. Weak profitability (2.2) with investment income below regulatory standards in relation to interest assumptions of reserves.

Other Rating Factors: Strong capitalization (8.0) based on excellent risk adjusted capital (severe loss scenario). Excellent liquidity (10.0).
Principal Business: Individual life insurance (100%).
Principal Investments: NonCMO investment grade bonds (77%), CMOs and structured securities (18%), and cash (3%).
Investments in Affiliates: None
Group Affiliation: Unum Group
Licensed in: All states except AK, NY, PR
Commenced Business: February 1966
Address: 2211 Congress St, Portland, ME 04122
Phone: (423) 294-1011 **Domicile State:** ME **NAIC Code:** 67601

Data Date	Rating	RACR #1	RACR #2	Total Assets ($mil)	Capital ($mil)	Net Premium ($mil)	Net Income ($mil)
6-16	C	6.80	4.49	57.9	44.3	0.0	0.9
6-15	C	6.64	4.24	56.7	42.9	0.0	1.5
2015	C	6.71	4.19	57.0	43.7	0.0	2.5
2014	C	6.46	3.96	56.2	41.6	0.0	2.3
2013	C	6.30	3.80	54.8	40.1	0.0	2.2
2012	C	6.13	3.52	53.6	38.5	0.0	2.3
2011	C	5.81	3.59	55.8	36.9	0.0	2.5

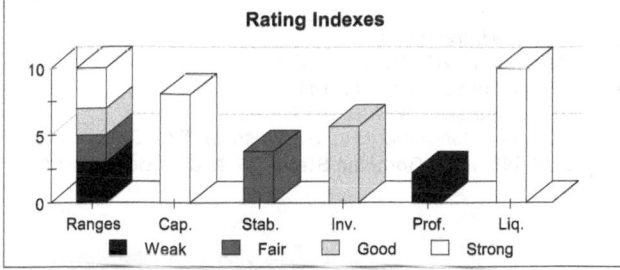

Rating Indexes

UNUM LIFE INSURANCE COMPANY OF AMERICA   C+   Fair

Major Rating Factors: Fair quality investment portfolio (3.6 on a scale of 0 to 10) with large holdings of BBB rated bonds in addition to significant exposure to junk bonds. Fair overall results on stability tests (4.8). Good overall profitability (6.7).
Other Rating Factors: Strong capitalization (7.2) based on excellent risk adjusted capital (severe loss scenario). Excellent liquidity (7.0).
Principal Business: Group health insurance (61%), group life insurance (29%), individual health insurance (7%), and reinsurance (2%).
Principal Investments: NonCMO investment grade bonds (73%), noninv. grade bonds (11%), CMOs and structured securities (9%), and mortgages in good standing (4%).
Investments in Affiliates: None
Group Affiliation: Unum Group
Licensed in: All states except NY
Commenced Business: September 1966
Address: 2211 Congress St, Portland, ME 04122
Phone: (207) 770-9306 **Domicile State:** ME **NAIC Code:** 62235

Data Date	Rating	RACR #1	RACR #2	Total Assets ($mil)	Capital ($mil)	Net Premium ($mil)	Net Income ($mil)
6-16	C+	2.19	1.15	20,748.9	1,559.4	1,674.4	163.5
6-15	C+	2.27	1.21	20,188.3	1,496.1	1,568.6	101.4
2015	C+	2.28	1.22	20,552.3	1,567.3	3,168.1	203.5
2014	C+	2.42	1.29	19,701.4	1,546.1	2,914.6	195.0
2013	C+	2.49	1.34	19,078.5	1,557.9	2,794.2	176.2
2012	C+	2.57	1.38	18,879.8	1,573.5	2,702.0	202.9
2011	C+	2.65	1.42	18,303.5	1,548.8	2,603.1	199.0

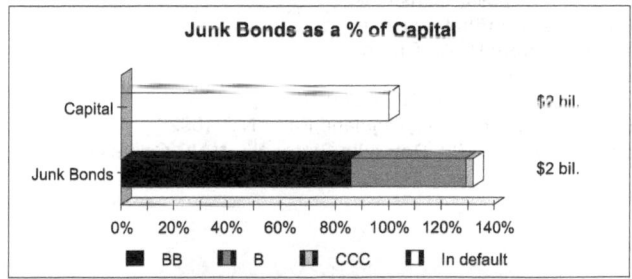

Junk Bonds as a % of Capital

US FINANCIAL LIFE INSURANCE COMPANY   B   Good

Major Rating Factors: Good overall profitability (6.2 on a scale of 0 to 10). Excellent expense controls. Good liquidity (6.2) with sufficient resources to handle a spike in claims as well as a significant increase in policy surrenders. Good overall results on stability tests (6.3) despite negative cash flow from operations for 2015 good operational trends and excellent risk diversification.
Other Rating Factors: Strong capitalization (8.4) based on excellent risk adjusted capital (severe loss scenario). High quality investment portfolio (7.4).
Principal Business: Individual life insurance (100%).
Principal Investments: NonCMO investment grade bonds (94%), policy loans (5%), noninv. grade bonds (2%), and common & preferred stock (1%).
Investments in Affiliates: None
Group Affiliation: AXA Financial Inc
Licensed in: All states except NY, PR
Commenced Business: September 1974
Address: 6 East Fourth St, Cincinnati, OH 45202
Phone: (201) 743-5073 **Domicile State:** OH **NAIC Code:** 84530

Data Date	Rating	RACR #1	RACR #2	Total Assets ($mil)	Capital ($mil)	Net Premium ($mil)	Net Income ($mil)
6-16	B	3.56	1.92	600.5	93.5	17.9	0.1
6-15	B	3.02	1.62	609.7	86.4	14.9	9.3
2015	B	3.53	1.90	597.3	93.7	35.1	14.9
2014	B	3.60	1.92	642.9	102.2	38.1	35.1
2013	B	2.08	1.10	638.1	62.5	43.3	8.0
2012	B	2.08	1.11	628.9	63.2	46.2	30.2
2011	B	1.98	1.05	628.4	61.9	52.5	-6.6

Adverse Trends in Operations

Decrease in capital during 2015 (8%)
Decrease in asset base during 2015 (7%)
Increase in policy surrenders from 2014 to 2015 (74%)
Decrease in premium volume from 2013 to 2014 (12%)
Decrease in premium volume from 2011 to 2012 (12%)

USAA LIFE INSURANCE COMPANY *   A   Excellent

Major Rating Factors: Good quality investment portfolio (6.7 on a scale of 0 to 10) despite mixed results such as: large holdings of BBB rated bonds but moderate junk bond exposure. Good liquidity (5.7) with sufficient resources to handle a spike in claims as well as a significant increase in policy surrenders. Excellent overall results on stability tests (7.4) excellent operational trends and excellent risk diversification.

Other Rating Factors: Strong capitalization (8.5) based on excellent risk adjusted capital (severe loss scenario). Excellent profitability (8.9).

Principal Business: Individual life insurance (45%), individual annuities (43%), and individual health insurance (12%).

Principal Investments: NonCMO investment grade bonds (72%), CMOs and structured securities (21%), noninv. grade bonds (3%), mortgages in good standing (2%), and misc. investments (2%).

Investments in Affiliates: None

Group Affiliation: USAA Group

Licensed in: All states except NY, PR

Commenced Business: August 1963

Address: 9800 Fredericksburg Rd, San Antonio, TX 78288

Phone: (210) 498-8000 **Domicile State:** TX **NAIC Code:** 69663

Data Date	Rating	RACR #1	RACR #2	Total Assets ($mil)	Capital ($mil)	Net Premium ($mil)	Net Income ($mil)
6-16	A	3.80	2.02	23,536.5	2,295.0	864.3	100.0
6-15	A	4.02	2.15	22,526.7	2,191.5	720.3	126.1
2015	A	3.87	2.11	22,777.1	2,256.2	1,423.7	218.7
2014	A	4.01	2.17	21,985.4	2,140.7	1,486.7	279.2
2013	A	3.83	2.05	21,114.0	1,973.4	1,786.6	244.5
2012	A	3.92	2.17	19,647.1	1,834.3	1,612.0	211.0
2011	A	3.70	1.94	18,240.3	1,703.4	1,788.0	283.8

Adverse Trends in Operations

Decrease in premium volume from 2014 to 2015 (4%)
Decrease in premium volume from 2013 to 2014 (17%)
Decrease in premium volume from 2011 to 2012 (10%)

USAA LIFE INSURANCE COMPANY OF NEW YORK *   B+   Good

Major Rating Factors: Good quality investment portfolio (5.2 on a scale of 0 to 10) despite mixed results such as: large holdings of BBB rated bonds but moderate junk bond exposure. Good overall results on stability tests (6.6). Strengths include good financial support from affiliation with USAA Group, excellent operational trends and excellent risk diversification. Fair liquidity (4.8).

Other Rating Factors: Strong capitalization (7.4) based on excellent risk adjusted capital (severe loss scenario). Excellent profitability (8.5).

Principal Business: Individual life insurance (63%) and individual annuities (37%).

Principal Investments: NonCMO investment grade bonds (78%), CMOs and structured securities (17%), noninv. grade bonds (4%), common & preferred stock (1%), and policy loans (1%).

Investments in Affiliates: None

Group Affiliation: USAA Group

Licensed in: NY

Commenced Business: November 1997

Address: 529 Main Street, Highland Falls, NY 10928

Phone: (210) 498-8000 **Domicile State:** NY **NAIC Code:** 60228

Data Date	Rating	RACR #1	RACR #2	Total Assets ($mil)	Capital ($mil)	Net Premium ($mil)	Net Income ($mil)
6-16	B+	2.48	1.28	720.8	73.3	22.0	2.2
6-15	B+	2.59	1.34	689.0	71.6	18.5	3.9
2015	B+	2.51	1.32	699.4	72.5	35.1	3.6
2014	B+	2.50	1.31	665.4	68.0	36.9	5.7
2013	B+	2.41	1.25	641.1	62.9	39.3	3.8
2012	B+	2.60	1.37	599.6	59.6	46.8	5.1
2011	B+	2.31	1.17	554.7	54.5	66.3	8.8

USAA Group
Composite Group Rating: B+
Largest Group Members

	Assets ($mil)	Rating
UNITED SERVICES AUTOMOBILE ASN	32549	B+
USAA LIFE INS CO	22777	A
USAA CASUALTY INS CO	9669	A-
USAA GENERAL INDEMNITY CO	3504	B+
CATASTROPHE REINS CO	1775	D

USABLE LIFE *   B+   Good

Major Rating Factors: Good quality investment portfolio (6.3 on a scale of 0 to 10) despite mixed results such as: minimal exposure to mortgages and large holdings of BBB rated bonds but minimal holdings in junk bonds. Good liquidity (6.5) with sufficient resources to handle a spike in claims. Good overall results on stability tests (6.4) excellent operational trends and excellent risk diversification.

Other Rating Factors: Strong capitalization (7.9) based on excellent risk adjusted capital (severe loss scenario). Excellent profitability (8.6).

Principal Business: Reinsurance (60%), group life insurance (19%), group health insurance (15%), individual health insurance (5%), and individual life insurance (1%).

Principal Investments: NonCMO investment grade bonds (69%), CMOs and structured securities (12%), common & preferred stock (10%), mortgages in good standing (3%), and misc. investments (6%).

Investments in Affiliates: 1%

Group Affiliation: Arkansas Bl Cross Bl Shield Group

Licensed in: All states except NY, PR

Commenced Business: December 1980

Address: 320 W Capitol Suite 700, Little Rock, AR 72201

Phone: (501) 375-7200 **Domicile State:** AR **NAIC Code:** 94358

Data Date	Rating	RACR #1	RACR #2	Total Assets ($mil)	Capital ($mil)	Net Premium ($mil)	Net Income ($mil)
6-16	B+	2.13	1.57	482.3	224.6	301.2	9.1
6-15	B+	1.94	1.42	457.6	205.7	294.2	11.7
2015	B+	2.07	1.52	467.9	215.3	580.2	27.3
2014	B+	1.83	1.34	446.0	194.3	591.7	24.6
2013	B+	1.60	1.17	408.3	166.3	570.0	11.5
2012	B+	1.64	1.21	381.2	156.3	505.7	15.4
2011	B+	1.72	1.28	346.8	144.0	454.4	8.2

Adverse Trends in Operations

Decrease in premium volume from 2014 to 2015 (2%)
Change in asset mix during 2012 (8.1%)

VANTIS LIFE INSURANCE COMPANY   B-   Good

Major Rating Factors: Fair current capitalization (4.0 on a scale of 0 to 10) based on mixed results -- excessive policy leverage mitigated by excellent risk adjusted capital (severe loss scenario) reflecting improvement over results in 2011. Fair quality investment portfolio (4.9). Fair overall results on stability tests (4.6) including negative cash flow from operations for 2015 and excessive premium growth.

Other Rating Factors: Good overall profitability (5.5) despite operating losses during the first six months of 2016. Good liquidity (6.6).

Principal Business: Individual life insurance (66%), individual annuities (26%), and group life insurance (8%).

Principal Investments: NonCMO investment grade bonds (66%), CMOs and structured securities (13%), noninv. grade bonds (8%), common & preferred stock (5%), and misc. investments (7%).

Investments in Affiliates: 3%
Group Affiliation: VantisLife Group
Licensed in: All states except NY, PR
Commenced Business: January 1964
Address: 200 Day Hill Rd, Windsor, CT 06095
Phone: (860) 298-5400 **Domicile State:** CT **NAIC Code:** 68632

Data Date	Rating	RACR #1	RACR #2	Total Assets ($mil)	Capital ($mil)	Net Premium ($mil)	Net Income ($mil)
6-16	B-	5.10	3.07	252.8	83.5	13.3	-0.9
6-15	B-	3.05	1.86	267.4	91.2	9.8	0.0
2015	B-	5.07	3.02	251.6	87.3	-605.1	-0.5
2014	B-	1.89	1.04	874.4	69.6	33.3	3.0
2013	B-	1.89	1.04	896.3	71.7	34.4	1.8
2012	B-	1.85	1.03	899.7	70.3	33.9	2.0
2011	C+	1.76	0.97	903.0	70.5	33.4	1.3

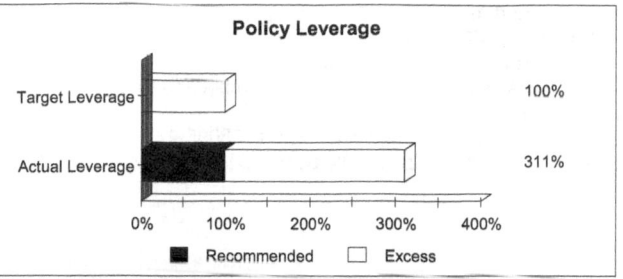

Policy Leverage

Target Leverage — 100%
Actual Leverage — 311%

■ Recommended □ Excess

VARIABLE ANNUITY LIFE INSURANCE COMPANY   B   Good

Major Rating Factors: Good overall results on stability tests (5.8 on a scale of 0 to 10). Stability strengths include good operational trends and excellent risk diversification. Good quality investment portfolio (5.2) despite large holdings of BBB rated bonds in addition to junk bond exposure equal to 63% of capital. Exposure to mortgages is significant, but the mortgage default rate has been low. Good overall profitability (6.1).

Other Rating Factors: Good liquidity (5.8). Strong capitalization (7.3) based on excellent risk adjusted capital (severe loss scenario).

Principal Business: Group retirement contracts (51%) and individual annuities (49%).

Principal Investments: CMOs and structured securities (39%), nonCMO investment grade bonds (37%), mortgages in good standing (10%), noninv. grade bonds (5%), and policy loans (2%).

Investments in Affiliates: 10%
Group Affiliation: American International Group
Licensed in: All states except PR
Commenced Business: May 1969
Address: 2929 Allen Parkway, Houston, TX 77019
Phone: (713) 522-1111 **Domicile State:** TX **NAIC Code:** 70238

Data Date	Rating	RACR #1	RACR #2	Total Assets ($mil)	Capital ($mil)	Net Premium ($mil)	Net Income ($mil)
6-16	B	2.46	1.21	75,558.9	3,043.9	2,194.3	447.9
6-15	B	2.92	1.40	76,252.0	3,492.7	2,155.1	411.8
2015	B	2.36	1.17	74,140.6	2,722.6	5,118.7	757.0
2014	B	3.03	1.45	77,095.2	3,618.1	4,830.3	1,024.6
2013	B	4.01	1.90	77,174.4	4,811.9	5,616.9	1,271.0
2012	B	4.02	1.95	70,614.3	4,235.5	5,409.8	703.0
2011	B	3.48	1.73	65,226.4	4,238.8	5,972.2	832.1

Adverse Trends in Operations

Decrease in asset base during 2015 (4%)
Decrease in capital during 2015 (25%)
Decrease in premium volume from 2013 to 2014 (14%)
Decrease in capital during 2014 (25%)
Decrease in premium volume from 2011 to 2012 (9%)

VOYA INSURANCE & ANNUITY COMPANY   B-   Good

Major Rating Factors: Good capitalization (6.0 on a scale of 0 to 10) based on good risk adjusted capital (moderate loss scenario). Good overall profitability (6.2). Fair quality investment portfolio (4.4) with large holdings of BBB rated bonds in addition to junk bond exposure equal to 52% of capital. Exposure to mortgages is significant, but the mortgage default rate has been low.

Other Rating Factors: Fair overall results on stability tests (4.8) including excessive premium growth. Excellent liquidity (7.5).

Principal Business: Individual annuities (78%), reinsurance (18%), group retirement contracts (3%), and individual life insurance (1%).

Principal Investments: NonCMO investment grade bonds (67%), CMOs and structured securities (12%), mortgages in good standing (11%), noninv. grade bonds (3%), and cash (2%).

Investments in Affiliates: None
Group Affiliation: Voya Financial Inc
Licensed in: All states except NY, PR
Commenced Business: October 1973
Address: 909 Locust St, Des Moines, IA 50309
Phone: (770) 980-5100 **Domicile State:** IA **NAIC Code:** 80942

Data Date	Rating	RACR #1	RACR #2	Total Assets ($mil)	Capital ($mil)	Net Premium ($mil)	Net Income ($mil)
6-16	B-	1.64	0.82	64,700.6	1,773.5	1,149.4	127.1
6-15	B+	1.70	0.85	64,576.0	1,772.5	839.9	253.2
2015	B-	1.95	0.97	63,981.2	2,074.8	2,654.4	553.3
2014	B	2.06	1.03	66,778.8	2,119.4	2,419.5	335.6
2013	B	1.86	0.93	69,266.0	1,941.6	6,164.9	-55.8
2012	C	1.99	1.00	68,101.4	2,174.1	3,344.2	-9.1
2011	C	1.91	0.95	71,509.0	2,222.0	3,859.9	386.0

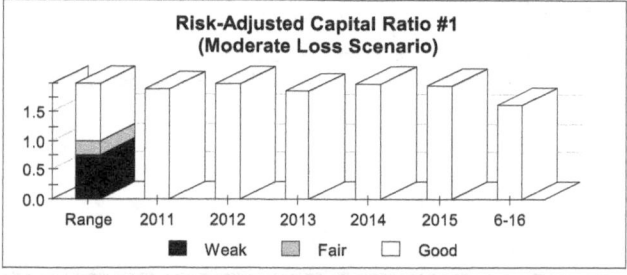

Risk-Adjusted Capital Ratio #1 (Moderate Loss Scenario)

■ Weak ▨ Fair □ Good

VOYA RETIREMENT INSURANCE & ANNUITY COMPANY *   B+   Good

Major Rating Factors: Good overall results on stability tests (6.5 on a scale of 0 to 10). Stability strengths include excellent operational trends and excellent risk diversification. Good quality investment portfolio (5.6) despite large holdings of BBB rated bonds in addition to junk bond exposure equal to 56% of capital. Exposure to mortgages is significant, but the mortgage default rate has been low. Good overall profitability (6.4).

Other Rating Factors: Strong capitalization (7.3) based on excellent risk adjusted capital (severe loss scenario). Excellent liquidity (9.1).

Principal Business: Group retirement contracts (98%), individual life insurance (1%), and individual annuities (1%).

Principal Investments: NonCMO investment grade bonds (62%), mortgages in good standing (14%), CMOs and structured securities (12%), noninv. grade bonds (4%), and misc. investments (5%).

Investments in Affiliates: 1%

Group Affiliation: Voya Financial Inc

Licensed in: All states, the District of Columbia and Puerto Rico

Commenced Business: April 1976

Address: One Orange Way, Windsor, CT 06095-4774

Phone: (866) 723-4646 **Domicile State:** CT **NAIC Code:** 86509

Data Date	Rating	RACR #1	RACR #2	Total Assets ($mil)	Capital ($mil)	Net Premium ($mil)	Net Income ($mil)
6-16	B+	2.49	1.21	89,930.9	1,969.4	5,822.1	141.4
6-15	B+	2.40	1.18	91,931.3	1,902.9	5,763.9	88.8
2015	B+	2.62	1.29	87,214.1	2,030.2	12,041.8	317.5
2014	B	2.63	1.30	89,253.5	2,007.9	9,826.8	321.7
2013	B	2.65	1.30	85,670.1	2,010.8	9,439.7	175.2
2012	B-	2.62	1.28	78,660.1	1,921.8	8,592.0	261.6
2011	B-	2.62	1.28	69,340.0	1,931.9	9,060.2	194.4

Adverse Trends in Operations

Decrease in asset base during 2015 (2%)
Increase in policy surrenders from 2012 to 2013 (26%)
Decrease in premium volume from 2011 to 2012 (5%)

WASHINGTON NATIONAL INSURANCE COMPANY   D+   Weak

Major Rating Factors: Weak overall results on stability tests (2.7 on a scale of 0 to 10) including potential financial drain due to affiliation with CNO Financial Group Inc. Fair quality investment portfolio (4.7) with large holdings of BBB rated bonds in addition to junk bond exposure equal to 58% of capital. Good capitalization (6.4) based on good risk adjusted capital (severe loss scenario).

Other Rating Factors: Good overall profitability (6.5). Good liquidity (6.4).

Principal Business: Individual health insurance (61%), group health insurance (25%), individual life insurance (7%), reinsurance (5%), and individual annuities (1%).

Principal Investments: NonCMO investment grade bonds (60%), CMOs and structured securities (23%), mortgages in good standing (6%), noninv. grade bonds (4%), and misc. investments (7%).

Investments in Affiliates: 1%

Group Affiliation: CNO Financial Group Inc

Licensed in: All states except NY

Commenced Business: September 1923

Address: 11825 N Pennsylvania St, Carmel, IN 60069

Phone: (847) 793-3379 **Domicile State:** IN **NAIC Code:** 70319

Data Date	Rating	RACR #1	RACR #2	Total Assets ($mil)	Capital ($mil)	Net Premium ($mil)	Net Income ($mil)
6-16	D+	1.70	0.92	4,870.3	329.2	328.8	54.9
6-15	D+	1.68	0.90	4,789.5	329.5	322.9	27.3
2015	D+	1.70	0.93	4,807.8	333.1	649.7	60.9
2014	D+	1.67	0.90	4,775.3	327.0	610.0	50.8
2013	D+	2.20	1.15	5,286.1	431.9	540.7	59.6
2012	D+	2.28	1.23	5,247.6	469.4	522.4	58.6
2011	D+	2.22	1.20	5,335.9	500.9	523.9	71.3

CNO Financial Group Inc Composite Group Rating: D+ Largest Group Members	Assets ($mil)	Rating
BANKERS LIFE CAS CO	16905	D+
WASHINGTON NATIONAL INS CO	4808	D+
COLONIAL PENN LIFE INS CO	816	D+
BANKERS CONSECO LIFE INS CO	218	D

WEA INSURANCE CORPORATION   C   Fair

Major Rating Factors: Fair quality investment portfolio (4.5 on a scale of 0 to 10). Fair overall results on stability tests (3.7) including negative cash flow from operations for 2015. Good liquidity (6.3) with sufficient resources to handle a spike in claims.

Other Rating Factors: Weak profitability (1.4) with operating losses during the first six months of 2016. Strong capitalization (7.2) based on excellent risk adjusted capital (severe loss scenario).

Principal Business: Group health insurance (100%).

Principal Investments: NonCMO investment grade bonds (55%), CMOs and structured securities (24%), common & preferred stock (20%), and cash (1%).

Investments in Affiliates: None

Group Affiliation: Wisconsin Education Assn Ins Trust

Licensed in: WI

Commenced Business: July 1985

Address: 45 Nob Hill Rd, Madison, WI 53713

Phone: (608) 276-4000 **Domicile State:** WI **NAIC Code:** 72273

Data Date	Rating	RACR #1	RACR #2	Total Assets ($mil)	Capital ($mil)	Net Premium ($mil)	Net Income ($mil)
6-16	C	1.63	1.14	635.3	149.4	248.4	-8.9
6-15	C	1.85	1.31	676.5	182.8	280.9	-14.8
2015	C	1.70	1.20	644.2	160.7	550.6	-34.2
2014	C	1.97	1.40	683.9	200.2	593.3	-28.0
2013	C	2.28	1.61	720.9	243.0	594.6	-15.1
2012	B-	2.19	1.59	686.8	232.1	635.9	19.1
2011	B	1.88	1.39	643.7	221.5	770.3	-0.5

Rating Indexes

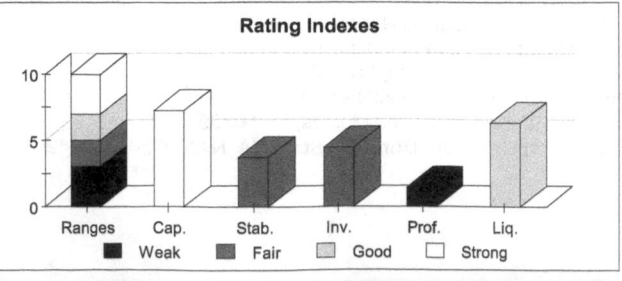

WEST COAST LIFE INSURANCE COMPANY

C+   **Fair**

Major Rating Factors: Fair quality investment portfolio (4.9 on a scale of 0 to 10) with large holdings of BBB rated bonds in addition to moderate junk bond exposure. Exposure to mortgages is significant, but the mortgage default rate has been low. Fair overall results on stability tests (4.6). Good liquidity (5.8).

Other Rating Factors: Weak profitability (2.6) with operating losses during the first six months of 2016. Strong capitalization (7.2) based on excellent risk adjusted capital (severe loss scenario).

Principal Business: Individual life insurance (86%) and reinsurance (14%).

Principal Investments: NonCMO investment grade bonds (75%), mortgages in good standing (11%), CMOs and structured securities (5%), noninv. grade bonds (4%), and misc. investments (5%).

Investments in Affiliates: None

Group Affiliation: Protective Life Group

Licensed in: All states except NY, PR

Commenced Business: February 1915

Address: 9140 W Dodge Rd, Omaha, NE 68114

Phone: (415) 591-8200 **Domicile State:** NE **NAIC Code:** 70335

Data Date	Rating	RACR #1	RACR #2	Total Assets ($mil)	Capital ($mil)	Net Premium ($mil)	Net Income ($mil)
6-16	C+	2.38	1.16	5,058.3	376.2	7.3	-3.8
6-15	C+	2.28	1.13	4,939.6	346.7	12.3	-21.5
2015	C+	2.83	1.40	4,985.3	419.4	10.1	58.5
2014	C+	2.85	1.43	4,810.1	412.3	3.3	-89.2
2013	C+	3.24	1.62	4,516.1	450.0	24.6	12.5
2012	C+	3.47	1.72	4,210.3	471.8	-574.3	-67.0
2011	C+	2.03	1.29	4,085.2	488.3	273.7	8.2

Rating Indexes

Ranges, Cap., Stab., Inv., Prof., Liq.
Weak, Fair, Good, Strong

WESTERN & SOUTHERN LIFE INSURANCE COMPANY

B   **Good**

Major Rating Factors: Good overall results on stability tests (5.7 on a scale of 0 to 10). Stability strengths include excellent operational trends and excellent risk diversification. Fair quality investment portfolio (3.4). Strong capitalization (8.0) based on excellent risk adjusted capital (severe loss scenario). Moreover, capital levels have been consistently high over the last five years.

Other Rating Factors: Excellent profitability (7.8). Excellent liquidity (7.0).

Principal Business: Individual life insurance (87%), individual health insurance (10%), group life insurance (1%), and reinsurance (1%).

Principal Investments: Common & preferred stock (38%), nonCMO investment grade bonds (31%), CMOs and structured securities (10%), noninv. grade bonds (3%), and policy loans (2%).

Investments in Affiliates: 35%

Group Affiliation: Western & Southern Group

Licensed in: All states except AK, CT, ME, MA, NH, NY, VT, PR

Commenced Business: April 1888

Address: 400 Broadway, Cincinnati, OH 45202

Phone: (513) 357-4000 **Domicile State:** OH **NAIC Code:** 70483

Data Date	Rating	RACR #1	RACR #2	Total Assets ($mil)	Capital ($mil)	Net Premium ($mil)	Net Income ($mil)
6-16	B	2.02	1.68	9,959.3	4,623.0	121.6	18.8
6-15	B	1.93	1.60	10,021.9	4,504.0	122.2	-17.0
2015	B	2.01	1.69	9,792.3	4,548.3	256.2	268.1
2014	B	1.87	1.56	9,918.3	4,294.2	263.2	519.5
2013	B	1.75	1.49	9,405.3	4,211.0	266.8	90.6
2012	B	1.79	1.53	8,612.3	3,728.5	279.2	11.2
2011	B	1.81	1.54	8,316.2	3,554.6	280.4	276.6

Adverse Trends in Operations

Decrease in asset base during 2015 (1%)
Decrease in premium volume from 2014 to 2015 (3%)
Decrease in premium volume from 2013 to 2014 (1%)
Decrease in premium volume from 2012 to 2013 (4%)

WESTERN UNITED LIFE ASSURANCE COMPANY

B-   **Good**

Major Rating Factors: Good capitalization (6.0 on a scale of 0 to 10) based on good risk adjusted capital (moderate loss scenario). Capital levels have been relatively consistent over the last five years. Fair quality investment portfolio (3.2) with large holdings of BBB rated bonds in addition to moderate junk bond exposure. Fair liquidity (4.3).

Other Rating Factors: Fair overall results on stability tests (4.8). Excellent profitability (8.5).

Principal Business: Individual annuities (100%).

Principal Investments: NonCMO investment grade bonds (67%), CMOs and structured securities (27%), noninv. grade bonds (3%), common & preferred stock (1%), and misc. investments (2%).

Investments in Affiliates: None

Group Affiliation: Manhattan Life Group Inc

Licensed in: All states except CA, MN, NJ, NY, WI, PR

Commenced Business: February 1975

Address: 1058 W Club Blvd Ste 658, Durham, NC 27701

Phone: (919) 286-3116 **Domicile State:** WA **NAIC Code:** 85189

Data Date	Rating	RACR #1	RACR #2	Total Assets ($mil)	Capital ($mil)	Net Premium ($mil)	Net Income ($mil)
6-16	B-	1.64	0.78	1,142.3	71.8	88.5	4.2
6-15	B-	1.60	0.78	1,062.3	63.6	108.2	4.6
2015	B-	1.68	0.81	1,096.3	70.5	191.6	12.5
2014	B-	1.61	0.79	990.7	61.8	239.8	11.5
2013	B-	2.59	2.33	14.8	7.4	0.6	0.2
2012	C	2.56	2.30	15.3	7.4	0.9	0.3
2011	C	2.49	2.24	15.5	7.3	0.9	0.2

Risk-Adjusted Capital Ratio #1
(Moderate Loss Scenario)

Range, 2011, 2012, 2013, 2014, 2015, 6-16
Weak, Fair, Good

WESTERN-SOUTHERN LIFE ASSURANCE COMPANY — B — Good

Major Rating Factors: Good overall results on stability tests (5.1 on a scale of 0 to 10) despite negative cash flow from operations for 2015. Other stability subfactors include good operational trends and excellent risk diversification. Good quality investment portfolio (5.2) despite mixed results such as: large holdings of BBB rated bonds but junk bond exposure equal to 82% of capital. Good overall profitability (6.6).

Other Rating Factors: Good liquidity (5.5). Strong capitalization (7.3) based on excellent risk adjusted capital (severe loss scenario).

Principal Business: Individual annuities (41%), individual life insurance (38%), reinsurance (18%), and group retirement contracts (3%).

Principal Investments: NonCMO investment grade bonds (48%), CMOs and structured securities (32%), noninv. grade bonds (7%), mortgages in good standing (7%), and common & preferred stock (2%).

Investments in Affiliates: 2%

Group Affiliation: Western & Southern Group

Licensed in: All states except AK, ME, NH, NY, RI, PR

Commenced Business: March 1981

Address: 400 Broadway, Cincinnati, OH 45202

Phone: (513) 357-4000 **Domicile State:** OH **NAIC Code:** 92622

Data Date	Rating	RACR #1	RACR #2	Total Assets ($mil)	Capital ($mil)	Net Premium ($mil)	Net Income ($mil)
6-16	B	2.22	1.17	12,485.6	1,038.4	330.5	29.7
6-15	B	2.35	1.23	13,175.5	1,151.8	275.4	42.4
2015	B	2.18	1.15	12,553.4	995.2	578.6	68.0
2014	B	2.20	1.15	13,147.0	1,051.3	801.5	179.6
2013	B	2.44	1.25	13,146.8	1,176.7	935.7	108.8
2012	B-	2.30	1.17	12,387.9	1,025.7	1,553.3	34.3
2011	B-	2.32	1.13	11,394.9	986.9	887.8	104.3

Adverse Trends in Operations

Decrease in asset base during 2015 (5%)
Decrease in premium volume from 2014 to 2015 (28%)
Decrease in premium volume from 2013 to 2014 (14%)
Decrease in capital during 2014 (11%)
Decrease in premium volume from 2012 to 2013 (40%)

WILCAC LIFE INSURANCE COMPANY — C — Fair

Major Rating Factors: Good quality investment portfolio (6.2 on a scale of 0 to 10) despite mixed results such as: large holdings of BBB rated bonds but moderate junk bond exposure. Good overall profitability (5.2) although investment income, in comparison to reserve requirements, is below regulatory standards. Weak overall results on stability tests (2.6) including weak results on operational trends, negative cash flow from operations for 2015.

Other Rating Factors: Strong capitalization (8.0) based on excellent risk adjusted capital (severe loss scenario). Excellent liquidity (10.0).

Principal Business: Individual life insurance (91%), group retirement contracts (4%), and individual health insurance (4%).

Principal Investments: NonCMO investment grade bonds (73%), CMOs and structured securities (20%), noninv. grade bonds (3%), common & preferred stock (3%), and cash (1%).

Investments in Affiliates: None

Group Affiliation: Wilton Re Holdings Ltd

Licensed in: All states, the District of Columbia and Puerto Rico

Commenced Business: August 1911

Address: 333 S Wabash Ave, Chicago, IL 60604

Phone: (312) 822-5000 **Domicile State:** IL **NAIC Code:** 62413

Data Date	Rating	RACR #1	RACR #2	Total Assets ($mil)	Capital ($mil)	Net Premium ($mil)	Net Income ($mil)
6-16	C	3.11	1.69	2,331.2	146.2	0.0	5.0
6-15	C	4.91	2.56	2,491.3	249.5	0.3	9.3
2015	C	3.19	1.71	2,479.9	139.4	0.3	25.2
2014	C	5.20	2.64	2,450.4	250.3	0.2	34.0
2013	C	7.87	3.84	2,937.9	597.3	0.5	47.7
2012	C	5.81	3.10	3,094.6	556.2	0.4	43.8
2011	C	5.73	3.04	3,210.0	519.4	0.5	29.0

Adverse Trends in Operations

Decrease in capital during 2015 (44%)
Decrease in capital during 2014 (58%)
Decrease in premium volume from 2013 to 2014 (50%)
Increase in policy surrenders from 2013 to 2014 (735%)
Increase in policy surrenders from 2011 to 2012 (555%)

WILCO LIFE INSURANCE COMPANY — C — Fair

Major Rating Factors: Fair quality investment portfolio (3.7 on a scale of 0 to 10) with large holdings of BBB rated bonds in addition to moderate junk bond exposure. Fair profitability (4.7) with operating losses during the first six months of 2016. Fair liquidity (4.6) as cash from operations and sale of marketable assets may not be adequate to cover a spike in claims or a run on policy withdrawals.

Other Rating Factors: Fair overall results on stability tests (3.6) including weak risk adjusted capital in prior years, negative cash flow from operations for 2015. Good capitalization (5.5) based on good risk adjusted capital (moderate loss scenario).

Principal Business: Individual life insurance (86%), individual health insurance (13%), and reinsurance (1%).

Principal Investments: NonCMO investment grade bonds (59%), CMOs and structured securities (31%), policy loans (5%), noninv. grade bonds (2%), and misc. investments (3%).

Investments in Affiliates: None

Group Affiliation: Wilton Re Holdings Ltd

Licensed in: All states except NY

Commenced Business: May 1962

Address: 12821 E New Market St Ste 250, Carmel, IN 46032

Phone: (317) 817-6400 **Domicile State:** IN **NAIC Code:** 65900

Data Date	Rating	RACR #1	RACR #2	Total Assets ($mil)	Capital ($mil)	Net Premium ($mil)	Net Income ($mil)
6-16	C	1.30	0.68	3,299.2	139.5	48.6	-3.2
6-15	C	1.81	0.96	3,642.4	228.7	65.9	23.0
2015	C	1.78	0.93	3,485.6	200.6	128.4	56.2
2014	C-	1.76	0.93	3,732.0	225.3	155.6	62.6
2013	D	1.00	0.53	3,825.5	129.7	237.1	49.7
2012	D	0.55	0.29	3,957.2	51.4	257.2	-34.5
2011	D	0.78	0.42	4,151.6	117.4	278.0	22.1

Rating Indexes

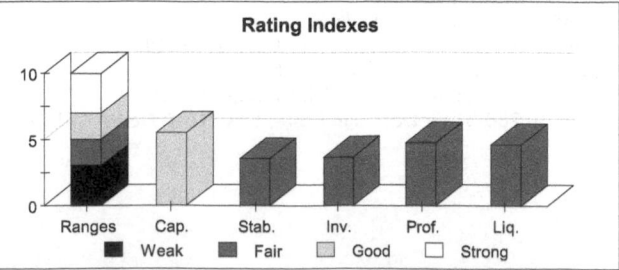

WILLIAM PENN LIFE INSURANCE COMPANY OF NEW YORK — C- — Fair

Major Rating Factors: Fair quality investment portfolio (3.8 on a scale of 0 to 10) with large holdings of BBB rated bonds in addition to junk bond exposure equal to 92% of capital. Exposure to mortgages is significant, but the mortgage default rate has been low. Fair overall results on stability tests (3.1) including excessive premium growth. Weak profitability (1.7).

Other Rating Factors: Good liquidity (6.4). Strong capitalization (7.8) based on excellent risk adjusted capital (severe loss scenario).

Principal Business: Individual life insurance (100%).

Principal Investments: NonCMO investment grade bonds (56%), mortgages in good standing (21%), noninv. grade bonds (13%), CMOs and structured securities (9%), and misc. investments (2%).

Investments in Affiliates: None

Group Affiliation: Legal & General America Inc

Licensed in: AZ, CT, DC, FL, ID, IA, KS, KY, MD, MS, MT, NJ, NY, OK, OR, PA, RI, SC, SD, TX, VT

Commenced Business: February 1963

Address: 100 Quentin Roosevelt Blvd, Garden City, NY 11530

Phone: (516) 794-3700 **Domicile State:** NY **NAIC Code:** 66230

Data Date	Rating	RACR #1	RACR #2	Total Assets ($mil)	Capital ($mil)	Net Premium ($mil)	Net Income ($mil)
6-16	C-	3.24	1.52	1,167.3	154.6	43.5	25.6
6-15	C-	3.25	1.54	1,154.1	153.9	23.2	-14.3
2015	C-	2.80	1.32	1,158.7	133.2	24.8	-30.5
2014	C-	3.73	1.77	1,146.4	176.6	34.6	-15.1
2013	C-	4.50	2.19	1,134.1	195.9	47.2	-15.2
2012	C	5.59	2.93	1,121.3	206.4	3.4	-13.4
2011	C	4.73	2.45	1,140.7	190.2	49.2	-1.3

Rating Indexes

Ranges, Cap., Stab., Inv., Prof., Liq.
■ Weak ■ Fair □ Good □ Strong

WILTON REASSURANCE COMPANY — C+ — Fair

Major Rating Factors: Fair overall results on stability tests (4.2 on a scale of 0 to 10) including fair financial strength of affiliated Wilton Re Holdings Ltd. Fair current capitalization (4.3) based on fair risk adjusted capital (moderate loss scenario), although results have slipped from the good range during the last year. Fair quality investment portfolio (4.3).

Other Rating Factors: Good liquidity (6.7). Excellent profitability (7.9) despite modest operating losses during 2011.

Principal Business: Reinsurance (100%).

Principal Investments: NonCMO investment grade bonds (41%), CMOs and structured securities (25%), common & preferred stock (24%), policy loans (4%), and misc. investments (6%).

Investments in Affiliates: 23%

Group Affiliation: Wilton Re Holdings Ltd

Licensed in: All states except PR

Commenced Business: February 1901

Address: 100 S 5th St Ste 1075, Minneapolis, MN 55402

Phone: (201) 802-5807 **Domicile State:** MN **NAIC Code:** 66133

Data Date	Rating	RACR #1	RACR #2	Total Assets ($mil)	Capital ($mil)	Net Premium ($mil)	Net Income ($mil)
6-16	C+	0.75	0.66	2,860.6	676.5	87.7	33.0
6-15	B-	0.97	0.86	2,988.5	820.4	81.6	106.4
2015	B-	1.03	0.90	3,039.3	866.4	183.0	184.1
2014	B-	1.00	0.89	3,095.5	842.0	000.0	150.6
2013	B	1.52	1.13	3,470.8	608.8	345.1	67.1
2012	B	1.12	0.87	3,260.0	427.2	691.9	141.7
2011	C	1.01	0.80	2,678.8	328.9	897.0	-5.6

Wilton Re Holdings Ltd
Composite Group Rating: C+
Largest Group Members

	Assets ($mil)	Rating
WILCO LIFE INS CO	3486	C
WILTON REASSURANCE CO	3039	C+
WILCAC LIFE INS CO	2480	C
TEXAS LIFE INS CO	1076	B
WILTON REASSURANCE LIFE CO OF NY	902	B-

WILTON REASSURANCE LIFE COMPANY OF NEW YORK — B- — Good

Major Rating Factors: Good overall results on stability tests (5.3 on a scale of 0 to 10) despite fair financial strength of affiliated Wilton Re Holdings Ltd and negative cash flow from operations for 2015. Other stability subfactors include good operational trends, good risk adjusted capital for prior years and excellent risk diversification. Good quality investment portfolio (6.1) despite mixed results such as: no exposure to mortgages and large holdings of BBB rated bonds but small junk bond holdings. Good liquidity (5.6).

Other Rating Factors: Fair profitability (3.7). Strong capitalization (7.6) based on excellent risk adjusted capital (severe loss scenario).

Principal Business: Individual life insurance (86%), individual annuities (12%), and reinsurance (2%).

Principal Investments: NonCMO investment grade bonds (54%), CMOs and structured securities (38%), noninv. grade bonds (3%), policy loans (2%), and misc. investments (2%).

Investments in Affiliates: None

Group Affiliation: Wilton Re Holdings Ltd

Licensed in: All states except PR

Commenced Business: November 1956

Address: 800 Westchester Ave 641 N, Rye Brook, NY 10573

Phone: (212) 224-1879 **Domicile State:** NY **NAIC Code:** 60704

Data Date	Rating	RACR #1	RACR #2	Total Assets ($mil)	Capital ($mil)	Net Premium ($mil)	Net Income ($mil)
6-16	B-	2.77	1.40	899.2	96.1	8.5	4.2
6-15	B-	3.00	1.51	901.4	104.4	9.8	0.1
2015	B-	2.62	1.31	902.2	90.8	17.9	-12.1
2014	B-	3.02	1.52	910.8	106.6	17.3	-1.7
2013	C+	3.18	1.59	901.3	113.1	-32.5	13.7
2012	C+	3.30	1.65	884.0	118.3	-375.6	36.3
2011	C+	1.68	0.85	1,195.1	87.0	48.0	-0.7

Wilton Re Holdings Ltd
Composite Group Rating: C+
Largest Group Members

	Assets ($mil)	Rating
WILCO LIFE INS CO	3486	C
WILTON REASSURANCE CO	3039	C+
WILCAC LIFE INS CO	2480	C
TEXAS LIFE INS CO	1076	B
WILTON REASSURANCE LIFE CO OF NY	902	B-

ZURICH AMERICAN LIFE INSURANCE COMPANY   C   Fair

Major Rating Factors: Fair overall capitalization (3.0 on a scale of 0 to 10) based on mixed results -- excessive policy leverage mitigated by excellent risk adjusted capital (severe loss scenario). Nevertheless, capital levels have fluctuated during prior years. Fair overall results on stability tests (3.7) including negative cash flow from operations for 2015. Weak profitability (1.6) with operating losses during the first six months of 2016.

Other Rating Factors: High quality investment portfolio (8.0). Excellent liquidity (7.1).

Principal Business: Individual annuities (38%), individual life insurance (35%), group life insurance (26%), and group health insurance (1%).

Principal Investments: NonCMO investment grade bonds (55%), CMOs and structured securities (29%), policy loans (10%), common & preferred stock (4%), and cash (1%).

Investments in Affiliates: 4%

Group Affiliation: Zurich Financial Services Group

Licensed in: All states except NY, PR

Commenced Business: September 1947

Address: 1400 American Lane, Schaumburg, IL 60196-5452

Phone: (877) 301-5376 **Domicile State:** IL **NAIC Code:** 90557

Data Date	Rating	RACR #1	RACR #2	Total Assets ($mil)	Capital ($mil)	Net Premium ($mil)	Net Income ($mil)
6-16	C	1.78	1.00	12,103.8	112.7	12.5	-12.6
6-15	C	0.19	0.15	12,829.5	138.4	-27.9	-11.2
2015	C	1.87	1.05	12,270.8	125.6	17.1	-23.2
2014	C	2.02	1.18	12,689.3	146.9	0.0	3.9
2013	C	1.86	1.08	12,968.6	132.1	-295.0	-49.5
2012	C	2.19	1.25	12,767.4	168.6	-103.5	-5.2
2011	C	2.19	1.26	12,697.1	168.4	-137.2	-6.6

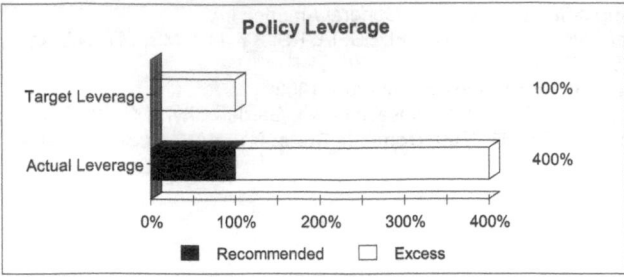

Policy Leverage

Target Leverage — 100%

Actual Leverage — 400%

0% 100% 200% 300% 400%

■ Recommended ☐ Excess

Section III

Weiss Ratings
Recommended Companies

A compilation of those

U.S. Life and Annuity Insurers

receiving a Weiss Safety Rating
of A+, A, A- or B+.

Companies are listed in alphabetical order.

Section III Contents

This section provides a list of recommended carriers along with additional information you should have when shopping for insurance. It contains all insurers receiving a Weiss Safety Rating of A+, A, A-, or B+. If an insurer is not on this list, it should not be automatically assumed that the firm is weak. Indeed, there are many firms that have not achieved a B+ or better rating but are in relatively good condition with adequate resources to cover their risk during an average recession. Not being included in this list should not be construed as a recommendation to surrender policies.

Left Pages

1. **Safety Rating**   Our rating is measured on a scale from A to F and considers a wide range of factors. Highly-rated companies are, in our opinion, less likely to experience financial difficulties than lower rated firms. See *About Weiss Safety Ratings* for more information.

2. **Insurance Company Name**   The legally registered name, which can sometimes differ from the name that the company uses for advertising. An insurer's name can be very similar to the name of other companies which may not be on our Recommended List, so make sure you note the exact name before contacting your agent.

3. **Address**   The address of the main office where you can contact the firm for additional financial data or for the location of local branches and/or registered agents.

4. **Telephone Number**   The number to call for additional financial data or for the phone numbers of local branches and/or registered agents.

Right Pages

The right-side pages present the percentage of the company's business that is involved in each type of insurance. Specifically, the numbers shown are the amounts of premium (including certain annuity payments and other deposit funds not technically called premiums) for each line of business as a percent of total premiums. The amounts shown are net premiums and, therefore, include only policies for which the company carries risk.

1. **Domicile State**   The state which has primary regulatory responsibility for the company. It may differ from the location of the company's corporate headquarters. You do not have to be living in the domicile state to purchase insurance from this firm, provided it is licensed to do business in your state.

2. **Individual Life**   Life insurance policies for individual customers, as opposed to group policies.

3. **Individual Health**   Health insurance policies for individual customers, as opposed to group policies.

4. **Individual**   Annuity contracts for individual customers which may be fixed and/or

Annuities   variable annuity contracts.

5. **Group Life**   Life insurance policies for groups such as the employees of a corporation, public institution, or union.

6. **Group Health**   Health insurance policies for groups such as the employees of a corporation, public institution or union.

7. **Group Annuities**   Annuity contracts for groups such as the employees of a corporation, public institution or union. These include Guaranteed Interest Contracts (GICs) and other pension products.

8. **Credit Life**   Life insurance policies designed to protect lenders against the eventual death of the borrower. Typically, if the borrower dies, the policy guarantees repayment of the loan balance.

9. **Credit Health**   Health insurance policies designed to protect lenders against the sickness of the borrower. Typically, if the borrower becomes ill, the policy guarantees repayment of the loan balance.

10. **Supplemental Contracts**   Policies in which the premium is paid from the benefits of another contract.

Weiss Safety Ratings are not deemed to be a recommendation concerning the purchase or sale of the securities of any insurance company that is publicly owned.

RATING	INSURANCE COMPANY NAME	ADDRESS	CITY	STATE	ZIP	PHONE
A	4 EVER LIFE INS CO	2 MID AMERICA PLAZA SUITE 200	OAKBROOK TERRACE	IL	60181	(888) 923-4227
B+	ADVANCE INS CO OF KS	1133 SW TOPEKA BLVD.	TOPEKA	KS	66629	(800) 530-5989
B+	AETNA HEALTH & LIFE INS CO	151 FARMINGTON AVENUE	HARTFORD	IL	06156	(800) 872-3862
A-	ALLIANZ LIFE INS CO OF NY	ONE CHASE MANHATTAN PLZ 38 FL	NEW YORK	NY	10005	(800) 950-5872
A-	AMALGAMATED LIFE INS CO	333 WESTCHESTER AVE	WHITE PLAINS	NY	10604	(914) 367-5000
B+	AMERICAN FAMILY LIFE ASR CO OF COLUM	1932 WYNNTON RD	COLUMBUS	GA	31999	(800) 992-3522
A-	AMERICAN FAMILY LIFE ASR CO OF NY	22 CORPORATE WOODS BLVD #2	ALBANY	NY	12211	(800) 992-3522
A+	AMERICAN FAMILY LIFE INS CO	6000 AMERICAN PARKWAY	MADISON	WI	53783	(800) 692-6326
B+	AMERICAN FIDELITY ASR CO	2000 N CLASSEN BLVD	OKLAHOMA CITY	OK	73106	(800) 654-8489
A-	AMERICAN HEALTH & LIFE INS CO	307 WEST 7TH STREET, STE 400	FORT WORTH	TX	76102	(817) 348-7500
A-	AMERICAN REPUBLIC INS CO	601 SIXTH AVE	DES MOINES	IA	50309	(800) 247-2190
B+	AMERICAN UNITED LIFE INS CO	ONE AMERICAN SQUARE	INDIANAPOLIS	IN	46204	(317) 285-1877
A-	ANNUITY INVESTORS LIFE INS CO	250 E FIFTH ST	CINCINNATI	OH	45202	(888) 497-8556
A-	ANTHEM LIFE INS CO	6740 N HIGH ST SUITE 200	WORTHINGTON	OH	43085	(800) 551-7265
B+	ASSURITY LIFE INS CO	2000 Q STREET	LINCOLN	NE	68503	(800) 869-0355
A-	AUTO-OWNERS LIFE INS CO	6101 ANACAPRI BLVD	LANSING	MI	48917	(517) 323-1200
B+	AXA EQUITABLE LIFE INS CO	1290 AVENUE OF THE AMERICAS	NEW YORK	NY	10104	(800) 777-6510
B+	BLUEBONNET LIFE INS CO	3545 LAKELAND DRIVE	FLOWOOD	MS	39232	(800) 222-8046
B+	BOSTON MUTUAL LIFE INS CO	120 ROYALL ST	CANTON	MA	02021	(800) 669-2668
A-	CENTRAL STATES H & L CO OF OMAHA	1212 N 96TH ST	OMAHA	NE	68114	(800) 826-6587
A-	CIGNA LIFE INS CO OF NEW YORK	140 E 45TH ST	NEW YORK	NY	10017	(212) 618-5757
A-	COMPANION LIFE INS CO	2501 FARAWAY DR	COLUMBIA	SC	29219	(800) 753-0404
A-	COTTON STATES LIFE INS CO	13560 MORRIS RD SUITE 4000	ALPHARETTA	GA	30004	(866) 714-6902
A-	COUNTRY INVESTORS LIFE ASR CO	1701 N TOWANDA AVE	BLOOMINGTON	IL	61701	(866) 268-6879
A+	COUNTRY LIFE INS CO	1701 N TOWANDA AVE	BLOOMINGTON	IL	61701	(866) 268-6879
B+	DEARBORN NATIONAL LIFE INS CO	300 EAST RANDOLPH STREET	CHICAGO	IL	60601	(800) 348-4512
B+	DEARBORN NATIONAL LIFE INS CO OF NY	1250 PITTSFORD VICTOR RD # 116	PITTSFORD	NY	14534	(888) 851-9156
A-	DELAWARE AMERICAN LIFE INS CO	600 KING ST	WILMINGTON	DE	19801	(302) 594-2000
B+	EMPIRE FIDELITY INVESTMENTS L I C	200 LIBERTY ST 1 WORLD FINANCL	NEW YORK	NY	10281	(800) 634-9361
A-	ERIE FAMILY LIFE INS CO	100 ERIE INSURANCE PL	ERIE	PA	16530	(800) 458-0811
A-	FAMILY HERITAGE LIFE INS CO OF AMER	6001 E ROYALTON RD SUITE 200	CLEVELAND	OH	44147	(440) 922-5200
B+	FARM BUREAU LIFE INS CO	5400 UNIVERSITY AVE	WEST DES MOINES	IA	50266	(800) 247-4170
A-	FARM BUREAU LIFE INS CO OF MICHIGAN	7373 WEST SAGINAW HWY	LANSING	MI	48909	(800) 292-2680
A-	FARM BUREAU LIFE INS CO OF MISSOURI	701 S COUNTRY CLUB DR	JEFFERSON CITY	MO	65109	(800) 778-6452
A	FEDERATED LIFE INS CO	121 E PARK SQUARE	OWATONNA	MN	55060	(888) 333-4949
A-	FIDELITY INVESTMENTS LIFE INS CO	175 E 400 S 8TH FLOOR	SALT LAKE CITY	UT	84111	(800) 634-9361
A	FIRST RELIANCE STANDARD LIFE INS CO	590 MADISON AVE 29TH FLOOR	NEW YORK	NY	10022	(800) 353-3986
A	FIRST SYMETRA NATL LIFE INS CO OF NY	260 MADISON AVE 8TH FLOOR	NEW YORK	NY	10016	(800) 796-3872
B+	FIRST UNITED AMERICAN LIFE INS CO	1020 7TH NORTH ST	LIVERPOOL	NY	13088	(315) 451-2544
A	FRANDISCO LIFE INS CO	135 E TUGALO ST	TOCCOA	GA	30577	(706) 886-7571
A-	GARDEN STATE LIFE INS CO	2450 S SHORE BLVD SUITE 301	LEAGUE CITY	TX	77573	(800) 638-8565
B+	GERBER LIFE INS CO	1311 MAMARONECK AVE	WHITE PLAINS	NY	10605	(800) 704-2180
B+	GOVERNMENT PERSONNEL MUTUAL L I C	2211 NE LOOP 410	SAN ANTONIO	TX	78217	(800) 938-4765
B+	GREAT SOUTHERN LIFE INS CO	500 N AKARD	DALLAS	TX	75201	(800) 231-0801
B+	GREATER GEORGIA LIFE INS CO	THREE RAVINIA DR SUITE 1700	ATLANTA	GA	30346	(888) 208-2183
A	GUARDIAN LIFE INS CO OF AMERICA	7 HANOVER SQUARE	NEW YORK	NY	10004	(800) 441-6455
A-	ILLINOIS MUTUAL LIFE INS CO	300 SW ADAMS	PEORIA	IL	61634	(800) 437-7355
B+	JOHN HANCOCK LIFE INS CO OF NY	100 SUMMIT LAKE DR 2ND FLOOR	VALHALLA	NY	10595	(800) 743-5542
A-	LIFE INS CO OF ALABAMA	302 BROAD ST	GADSDEN	AL	35901	(800) 226-2371
A-	LIFE INS CO OF BOSTON & NEW YORK	277 NORTH AVE SUITE 200	NEW ROCHELLE	NY	10801	(800) 645-2317
A	LIFEWISE ASR CO	7007 220TH SW	MOUNTLAKE TERRACE	WA	98043	(800) 258-0394
B+	LOCOMOTIVE ENGRS&COND MUT PROT ASSN	4000 TOWN CENTER SUITE 1250	SOUTHFIELD	MI	48075	(800) 514-0010
A-	MASSACHUSETTS MUTUAL LIFE INS CO	1295 STATE ST	SPRINGFIELD	MA	01111	(800) 272-2216
B+	MEDICO CORP LIFE INS CO	11808 GRANT ST	OMAHA	NE	68164	(800) 822-9993
B+	MIDLAND NATIONAL LIFE INS CO	ONE MIDLAND PLAZA	SIOUX FALLS	SD	57193	(800) 923-3223
A	MIDWESTERN UNITED LIFE INS CO	8605 KINGS MILL PL	FORT WAYNE	IN	46804	(800) 333-6965

DOM. STATE	IND. LIFE	IND. HEALTH	IND. ANNU.	GROUP LIFE	GROUP HEALTH	GROUP ANNU	CREDIT LIFE	CREDIT HEALTH	SUP. CONTR.	OTHER	INSURANCE COMPANY NAME
IL	0	0	0	6	94	0	0	0	0	0	4 EVER LIFE INS CO
KS	13	0	0	58	28	0	0	0	0	0	ADVANCE INS CO OF KS
CT	0	9	0	0	91	0	0	0	0	0	AETNA HEALTH & LIFE INS CO
NY	0	1	99	0	0	0	0	0	0	0	ALLIANZ LIFE INS CO OF NY
NY	2	2	0	74	22	0	0	0	0	0	AMALGAMATED LIFE INS CO
NE	24	71	4	0	1	0	0	0	0	0	AMERICAN FAMILY LIFE ASR CO OF COLUM
NY	4	95	0	0	2	0	0	0	0	0	AMERICAN FAMILY LIFE ASR CO OF NY
WI	95	0	4	1	0	0	0	0	0	0	AMERICAN FAMILY LIFE INS CO
OK	10	27	25	0	36	2	0	0	0	0	AMERICAN FIDELITY ASR CO
TX	16	0	0	11	4	0	33	35	0	0	AMERICAN HEALTH & LIFE INS CO
IA	3	75	0	0	22	0	0	0	0	0	AMERICAN REPUBLIC INS CO
IN	6	0	4	3	2	85	0	0	0	0	AMERICAN UNITED LIFE INS CO
OH	0	0	88	0	0	12	0	0	0	0	ANNUITY INVESTORS LIFE INS CO
IN	1	0	0	74	25	0	0	0	0	0	ANTHEM LIFE INS CO
NE	57	33	6	3	1	0	0	0	0	0	ASSURITY LIFE INS CO
MI	41	5	36	1	1	16	0	0	0	0	AUTO-OWNERS LIFE INS CO
NY	18	0	61	0	0	21	0	0	0	0	AXA EQUITABLE LIFE INS CO
MS	3	0	0	96	0	0	0	0	0	0	BLUEBONNET LIFE INS CO
MA	67	5	0	15	13	0	0	0	0	0	BOSTON MUTUAL LIFE INS CO
NE	3	0	0	0	0	0	60	37	0	0	CENTRAL STATES H & L CO OF OMAHA
NY	0	0	0	33	67	0	0	0	0	0	CIGNA LIFE INS CO OF NEW YORK
SC	0	0	0	12	88	0	0	0	0	0	COMPANION LIFE INS CO
GA	100	0	0	0	0	0	0	0	0	0	COTTON STATES LIFE INS CO
IL	0	0	0	0	0	0	0	0	0	0	COUNTRY INVESTORS LIFE ASR CO
IL	60	14	17	1	8	0	0	0	0	0	COUNTRY LIFE INS CO
IL	3	0	1	66	30	0	0	0	0	0	DEARBORN NATIONAL LIFE INS CO
NY	0	0	0	51	48	0	0	0	0	0	DEARBORN NATIONAL LIFE INS CO OF NY
DE	9	16	0	12	63	0	0	0	0	0	DELAWARE AMERICAN LIFE INS CO
NY	0	0	100	0	0	0	0	0	0	0	EMPIRE FIDELITY INVESTMENTS L I C
PA	76	0	23	0	0	0	0	0	0	0	ERIE FAMILY LIFE INS CO
OH	13	84	0	0	3	0	0	0	0	0	FAMILY HERITAGE LIFE INS CO OF AMER
IA	47	0	52	0	0	1	0	0	0	0	FARM BUREAU LIFE INS CO
MI	63	0	34	1	0	2	0	0	0	0	FARM BUREAU LIFE INS CO OF MICHIGAN
MO	77	0	22	1	0	0	0	0	0	0	FARM BUREAU LIFE INS CO OF MISSOURI
MN	68	14	15	3	0	0	0	0	0	0	FEDERATED LIFE INS CO
UT	0	0	100	0	0	0	0	0	0	0	FIDELITY INVESTMENTS LIFE INS CO
NY	0	0	0	22	78	0	0	0	0	0	FIRST RELIANCE STANDARD LIFE INS CO
NY	1	0	96	0	4	0	0	0	0	0	FIRST SYMETRA NATL LIFE INS CO OF NY
NY	35	55	7	0	3	0	0	0	0	0	FIRST UNITED AMERICAN LIFE INS CO
GA	0	0	0	0	0	0	25	75	0	0	FRANDISCO LIFE INS CO
TX	100	0	0	0	0	0	0	0	0	0	GARDEN STATE LIFE INS CO
NY	65	2	0	0	32	0	0	0	0	0	GERBER LIFE INS CO
TX	91	7	2	0	0	0	0	0	0	0	GOVERNMENT PERSONNEL MUTUAL L I C
TX	100	0	0	0	0	0	0	0	0	0	GREAT SOUTHERN LIFE INS CO
GA	2	0	0	57	41	0	0	0	0	0	GREATER GEORGIA LIFE INS CO
NY	50	6	0	7	37	0	0	0	0	0	GUARDIAN LIFE INS CO OF AMERICA
IL	45	52	1	0	2	0	0	0	0	0	ILLINOIS MUTUAL LIFE INS CO
NY	60	0	1	0	0	39	0	0	0	0	JOHN HANCOCK LIFE INS CO OF NY
AL	17	76	0	0	7	0	0	0	0	0	LIFE INS CO OF ALABAMA
NY	68	29	0	0	3	0	0	0	0	0	LIFE INS CO OF BOSTON & NEW YORK
WA	0	0	0	0	100	0	0	0	0	0	LIFEWISE ASR CO
MI	100	0	0	0	0	0	0	0	0	0	LOCOMOTIVE ENGRS&COND MUT PROT ASSN
MA	25	3	10	6	0	56	0	0	0	0	MASSACHUSETTS MUTUAL LIFE INS CO
NE	0	0	0	0	0	0	0	0	0	0	MEDICO CORP LIFE INS CO
IA	25	0	66	1	0	8	0	0	0	0	MIDLAND NATIONAL LIFE INS CO
IN	100	0	0	0	0	0	0	0	0	0	MIDWESTERN UNITED LIFE INS CO

RATING	INSURANCE COMPANY NAME	ADDRESS	CITY	STATE	ZIP	PHONE
B+	MINNESOTA LIFE INS CO	400 N ROBERT ST	ST PAUL	MN	55101	(651) 665-3500
A	MML BAY STATE LIFE INS CO	100 BRIGHT MEADOW BLVD	ENFIELD	CT	06082	(800) 272-2216
A-	MUTUAL OF AMERICA LIFE INS CO	320 PARK AVE	NEW YORK	NY	10022	(800) 468-3785
B+	MUTUAL OF OMAHA INS CO	3300 MUTUAL OF OMAHA PLAZA	OMAHA	NE	68175	(800) 228-7104
B+	NATIONAL FARMERS UNION LIFE INS CO	500 NORTH AKARD	DALLAS	TX	75201	(800) 366-6565
B+	NATIONAL INCOME LIFE INS CO	1020 SEVENTH N ST SUITE 130	LIVERPOOL	NY	13088	(315) 451-2544
A	NATIONAL WESTERN LIFE INS CO	850 EAST ANDERSON LANE	AUSTIN	TX	78752	(800) 531-5442
B+	NEW YORK LIFE INS & ANNUITY CORP	200 CONTINENTAL DR	NEWARK	DE	19713	(212) 576-7000
A-	NEW YORK LIFE INS CO	51 MADISON AVE	NEW YORK	NY	10010	(212) 576-7000
A-	NIPPON LIFE INS CO OF AMERICA	650 8TH ST	DES MOINES	IA	50309	(800) 374-1835
A-	NORTHWESTERN MUTUAL LIFE INS CO	720 E WISCONSIN AVE	MILWAUKEE	WI	53202	(414) 271-1444
B+	OHIO NATIONAL LIFE ASR CORP	ONE FINANCIAL WAY	CINCINNATI	OH	45242	(800) 366-6654
A-	PACIFIC GUARDIAN LIFE INS CO LTD	1440 KAPIOLANI BLVD STE 1700	HONOLULU	HI	96814	(800) 432-3306
B+	PACIFIC LIFE & ANNUITY CO	3800 N CENTRAL AVE SUITE 460	PHOENIX	AZ	85012	(800) 800-7646
A-	PACIFIC LIFE INS CO	1299 FARNAM ST	OMAHA	NE	68102	(800) 800-7646
B+	PAN AMERICAN ASR CO	PAN AMERICAN LIFE CENTER	NEW ORLEANS	LA	70130	(877) 939-4550
A	PARKER CENTENNIAL ASR CO	2345 WAUKEGAN RD #5210	BANNOCKBURN	IL	60015	(800) 373-6879
A-	PHYSICIANS LIFE INS CO	2600 DODGE ST	OMAHA	NE	68131	(800) 228-9100
A+	PHYSICIANS MUTUAL INS CO	2600 DODGE ST	OMAHA	NE	68131	(800) 228-9100
B+	PRINCIPAL LIFE INS CO	711 HIGH ST	DES MOINES	IA	50392	(800) 986-3343
A-	RESERVE NATIONAL INS CO	601 E BRITTON RD	OKLAHOMA CITY	OK	73114	(800) 654-9106
B+	SAVINGS BANK LIFE INS CO OF MA	ONE LINSCOTT RD	WOBURN	MA	01801	(888) 438-7254
A-	SECURIAN LIFE INS CO	400 ROBERT ST N	ST PAUL	MN	55101	(651) 665-3500
A	SENTRY LIFE INS CO	1800 NORTH POINT DR	STEVENS POINT	WI	54481	(800) 373-6879
A-	SHELTER LIFE INS CO	1817 W BROADWAY	COLUMBIA	MO	65218	(800) 743-5837
A	SHELTERPOINT LIFE INS CO	600 NORTHERN BLVD	GREAT NECK	NY	11021	(800) 365-4999
A	SOUTHERN FARM BUREAU LIFE INS CO	1401 LIVINGSTON LANE	JACKSON	MS	39213	(800) 457-9611
B+	SOUTHERN PIONEER LIFE INS CO	400 ROBERT ST N	ST PAUL	MN	55101	(866) 884-6167
B+	STANDARD INS CO	1100 SW SIXTH AVE	PORTLAND	OR	97204	(503) 321-7000
A-	STANDARD LIFE & ACCIDENT INS CO	ONE MOODY PLAZA	GALVESTON	TX	77550	(888) 290-1085
A-	STANDARD LIFE INS CO OF NY	360 HAMILTON AVE SUITE 210	WHITE PLAINS	NY	10601	(503) 321-7859
A-	STANDARD SECURITY LIFE INS CO OF NY	485 MADISON AVE	NEW YORK	NY	10022	(212) 355-4141
A+	STATE FARM LIFE & ACCIDENT ASR CO	ONE STATE FARM PLAZA	BLOOMINGTON	IL	61710	(855) 733-7333
A+	STATE FARM LIFE INS CO	ONE STATE FARM PLAZA	BLOOMINGTON	IL	61710	(855) 733-7333
B+	SYMETRA LIFE INS CO	4125 WESTOWN PKWY STE 102	WEST DES MOINES	IA	50266	(800) 796-3872
A+	TEACHERS INS & ANNUITY ASN OF AM	730 THIRD AVE 7TH FLOOR	NEW YORK	NY	10017	(800) 842-2252
A	TENNESSEE FARMERS LIFE INS CO	147 BEAR CREEK PIKE	COLUMBIA	TN	38401	(931) 388-7872
A	TRANS OCEANIC LIFE INS CO	3 MUNET COURT	GUAYNABO	PR	00936	(787) 620-2680
B+	TRUSTMARK INS CO	400 FIELD DR	LAKE FOREST	IL	60045	(800) 366-6663
B+	TRUSTMARK LIFE INS CO	400 FIELD DR	LAKE FOREST	IL	60045	(800) 366-6663
B+	UNION SECURITY LIFE INS CO OF NY	220 SALINA MEADOWS PKWY #255	SYRACUSE	NY	13212	(800) 852-2244
A	UNITED FARM FAMILY LIFE INS CO	225 S EAST ST	INDIANAPOLIS	IN	46202	(800) 723-3276
B+	UNITED WORLD LIFE INS CO	MUTUAL OF OMAHA PLAZA	OMAHA	NE	68175	(800) 228-7104
A	USAA LIFE INS CO	9800 FREDERICKSBURG RD	SAN ANTONIO	TX	78288	(210) 498-8000
B+	USAA LIFE INS CO OF NEW YORK	529 MAIN STREET	HIGHLAND FALLS	NY	10928	(210) 498-8000
B+	USABLE LIFE	320 W CAPITOL SUITE 700	LITTLE ROCK	AR	72201	(800) 370-5856
B+	VOYA RETIREMENT INS & ANNUITY CO	ONE ORANGE WAY	WINDSOR	CT	06095	(877) 886-5050

DOM. STATE	IND. LIFE	IND. HEALTH	IND. ANNU.	GROUP LIFE	GROUP HEALTH	GROUP ANNU	CREDIT LIFE	CREDIT HEALTH	SUP. CONTR.	OTHER	INSURANCE COMPANY NAME
MN	22	0	13	28	4	31	1	1	0	0	MINNESOTA LIFE INS CO
CT	91	0	0	9	0	0	0	0	0	0	MML BAY STATE LIFE INS CO
NY	0	0	25	0	0	75	0	0	0	0	MUTUAL OF AMERICA LIFE INS CO
NE	0	90	0	0	10	0	0	0	0	0	MUTUAL OF OMAHA INS CO
TX	97	0	1	2	0	0	0	0	0	0	NATIONAL FARMERS UNION LIFE INS CO
NY	90	10	0	0	0	0	0	0	0	0	NATIONAL INCOME LIFE INS CO
CO	27	0	73	0	0	0	0	0	0	0	NATIONAL WESTERN LIFE INS CO
DE	14	0	84	1	0	1	0	0	0	0	NEW YORK LIFE INS & ANNUITY CORP
NY	64	1	0	10	1	24	0	0	0	0	NEW YORK LIFE INS CO
IA	0	0	0	1	99	0	0	0	0	0	NIPPON LIFE INS CO OF AMERICA
WI	76	9	13	0	0	1	0	0	0	0	NORTHWESTERN MUTUAL LIFE INS CO
OH	96	4	0	0	0	0	0	0	0	0	OHIO NATIONAL LIFE ASR CORP
HI	37	0	0	11	52	0	0	0	0	0	PACIFIC GUARDIAN LIFE INS CO LTD
AZ	7	0	93	0	0	0	0	0	0	0	PACIFIC LIFE & ANNUITY CO
NE	31	0	64	0	0	5	0	0	0	0	PACIFIC LIFE INS CO
LA	100	0	0	0	0	0	0	0	0	0	PAN AMERICAN ASR CO
WI	0	0	0	0	0	100	0	0	0	0	PARKER CENTENNIAL ASR CO
NE	58	0	23	19	0	0	0	0	0	0	PHYSICIANS LIFE INS CO
NE	0	80	0	0	20	0	0	0	0	0	PHYSICIANS MUTUAL INS CO
IA	13	4	41	5	13	24	0	0	0	0	PRINCIPAL LIFE INS CO
OK	13	80	0	0	7	0	0	0	0	0	RESERVE NATIONAL INS CO
MA	97	0	3	0	0	0	0	0	0	0	SAVINGS BANK LIFE INS CO OF MA
MN	21	0	1	59	16	0	1	1	0	0	SECURIAN LIFE INS CO
WI	3	0	1	1	0	95	0	0	0	0	SENTRY LIFE INS CO
MO	85	1	5	1	7	0	0	0	0	0	SHELTER LIFE INS CO
NY	0	0	0	2	98	0	0	0	0	0	SHELTERPOINT LIFE INS CO
MS	78	1	20	1	0	0	0	0	0	0	SOUTHERN FARM BUREAU LIFE INS CO
AR	5	0	0	0	0	0	70	26	0	0	SOUTHERN PIONEER LIFE INS CO
OR	0	5	11	3	30	51	0	0	0	0	STANDARD INS CO
TX	11	78	0	0	11	0	0	0	0	0	STANDARD LIFE & ACCIDENT INS CO
NY	0	1	0	38	60	0	0	0	0	0	STANDARD LIFE INS CO OF NY
NY	0	2	0	1	97	0	0	0	0	0	STANDARD SECURITY LIFE INS CO OF NY
IL	86	0	14	0	0	0	0	0	0	0	STATE FARM LIFE & ACCIDENT ASR CO
IL	81	0	18	1	0	0	0	0	0	0	STATE FARM LIFE INS CO
IA	7	0	78	1	13	1	0	0	0	0	SYMETRA LIFE INS CO
NY	2	0	49	0	0	49	0	0	0	0	TEACHERS INS & ANNUITY ASN OF AM
TN	71	0	27	0	2	0	0	0	0	0	TENNESSEE FARMERS LIFE INS CO
PR	7	93	0	0	0	0	0	0	0	0	TRANS OCEANIC LIFE INS CO
IL	9	15	0	47	28	0	0	0	0	0	TRUSTMARK INS CO
IL	0	0	0	5	95	0	0	0	0	0	TRUSTMARK LIFE INS CO
NY	1	2	0	14	81	0	1	2	0	0	UNION SECURITY LIFE INS CO OF NY
IN	89	0	11	0	0	0	0	0	0	0	UNITED FARM FAMILY LIFE INS CO
NE	100	0	0	0	0	0	0	0	0	0	UNITED WORLD LIFE INS CO
TX	37	17	46	0	0	0	0	0	0	0	USAA LIFE INS CO
NY	49	0	51	0	0	0	0	0	0	0	USAA LIFE INS CO OF NEW YORK
AR	1	17	0	24	58	0	0	0	0	0	USABLE LIFE
CT	0	0	1	0	0	99	0	0	0	0	VOYA RETIREMENT INS & ANNUITY CO

Section IV

Weiss Ratings Recommended Companies by State

A compilation of those

U.S. Life and Annuity Insurers

receiving a Weiss Safety Rating
of A+, A, A- or B+.

Companies are ranked by Safety Rating
in each state where they are licensed to do business.

Section IV Contents

This section provides a list of the recommended carriers licensed to do business in each state. It contains all insurers receiving a Weiss Safety Rating of A+, A, A-, or B+. If an insurer is not on this list, it should not be automatically assumed that the firm is weak. Indeed, there are many firms that have not achieved a B+ or better rating but are in relatively good condition with adequate resources to cover their risk during an average recession. Not being included in this list should not be construed as a recommendation to surrender policies.

Companies are ranked within each state by their Safety Rating. However, companies with the same rating should be viewed as having the same relative strength regardless of their ranking in this table. While the specific order in which they appear on the page is based upon differences in our underlying indexes, you can assume that companies with the same rating have differences that are only minor and relatively inconsequential.

1. **Safety Rating**   Our rating is measured on a scale from A to F and considers a wide range of factors. Highly-rated companies are, in our opinion, less likely to experience financial difficulties than lower rated firms. See *About Weiss Safety Ratings* for more information.

2. **Insurance Company Name**   The legally registered name, which can sometimes differ from the name that the company uses for advertising. An insurer's name can be very similar to the name of other companies which may not be on our Recommended List, so make sure you note the exact name before contacting your agent.

3. **Domicile State**   The state which has primary regulatory responsibility for the company. It may differ from the location of the company's corporate headquarters. You do not have to be living in the domicile state to purchase insurance from this firm, provided it is licensed to do business in your state.

4. **Total Assets**   All assets admitted by state insurance regulators in millions of dollars. This includes investments, current business assets, and separate accounts.

Weiss Safety Ratings are not deemed to be a recommendation concerning the purchase or sale of the securities of any insurance company that is publicly owned.

Alabama

INSURANCE COMPANY NAME	DOM. STATE	TOTAL ASSETS ($MIL)
Rating: A+		
AMERICAN FAMILY LIFE INS CO	WI	5,407.4
COUNTRY LIFE INS CO	IL	10,264.7
PHYSICIANS MUTUAL INS CO	NE	2,153.3
STATE FARM LIFE INS CO	IL	68,156.4
TEACHERS INS & ANNUITY ASN OF AM	NY	276,045.0
Rating: A		
4 EVER LIFE INS CO	IL	211.4
FEDERATED LIFE INS CO	MN	1,710.7
GUARDIAN LIFE INS CO OF AMERICA	NY	50,389.3
MIDWESTERN UNITED LIFE INS CO	IN	235.0
MML BAY STATE LIFE INS CO	CT	4,737.2
NATIONAL WESTERN LIFE INS CO	CO	10,673.8
PARKER CENTENNIAL ASR CO	WI	92.2
SENTRY LIFE INS CO	WI	5,800.9
SOUTHERN FARM BUREAU LIFE INS CO	MS	13,583.7
USAA LIFE INS CO	TX	23,536.5
Rating: A-		
AMALGAMATED LIFE INS CO	NY	122.5
AMERICAN HEALTH & LIFE INS CO	TX	907.2
AMERICAN REPUBLIC INS CO	IA	909.7
ANNUITY INVESTORS LIFE INS CO	OH	3,041.6
ANTHEM LIFE INS CO	IN	630.6
AUTO-OWNERS LIFE INS CO	MI	3,832.7
CENTRAL STATES H & L CO OF OMAHA	NE	421.1
CIGNA LIFE INS CO OF NEW YORK	NY	380.3
COMPANION LIFE INS CO	SC	329.6
COTTON STATES LIFE INS CO	GA	334.6
COUNTRY INVESTORS LIFE ASR CO	IL	297.1
DELAWARE AMERICAN LIFE INS CO	DE	145.9
FAMILY HERITAGE LIFE INS CO OF AMER	OH	1,004.9
FIDELITY INVESTMENTS LIFE INS CO	UT	25,080.7
GARDEN STATE LIFE INS CO	TX	126.5
ILLINOIS MUTUAL LIFE INS CO	IL	1,434.6
LIFE INS CO OF ALABAMA	AL	118.6
MASSACHUSETTS MUTUAL LIFE INS CO	MA	226,444.0
MUTUAL OF AMERICA LIFE INS CO	NY	18,135.8
NEW YORK LIFE INS CO	NY	167,828.0
NIPPON LIFE INS CO OF AMERICA	IA	217.7
NORTHWESTERN MUTUAL LIFE INS CO	WI	244,873.0
PACIFIC LIFE INS CO	NE	115,113.0
PHYSICIANS LIFE INS CO	NE	1,549.0
RESERVE NATIONAL INS CO	OK	123.3
SECURIAN LIFE INS CO	MN	478.9
STANDARD LIFE & ACCIDENT INS CO	TX	511.2
STANDARD SECURITY LIFE INS CO OF NY	NY	245.0
Rating: B+		
AETNA HEALTH & LIFE INS CO	CT	2,349.9
AMERICAN FAMILY LIFE ASR CO OF COLUM	NE	117,278.0
AMERICAN FIDELITY ASR CO	OK	5,305.5
AMERICAN UNITED LIFE INS CO	IN	23,906.8
ASSURITY LIFE INS CO	NE	2,550.8
AXA EQUITABLE LIFE INS CO	NY	171,038.0

INSURANCE COMPANY NAME	DOM. STATE	TOTAL ASSETS ($MIL)
BLUEBONNET LIFE INS CO	MS	58.9
BOSTON MUTUAL LIFE INS CO	MA	1,317.6
DEARBORN NATIONAL LIFE INS CO	IL	1,969.6
GERBER LIFE INS CO	NY	3,240.4
GOVERNMENT PERSONNEL MUTUAL L I C	TX	834.7
GREAT SOUTHERN LIFE INS CO	TX	218.2
GREATER GEORGIA LIFE INS CO	GA	58.6
MEDICO CORP LIFE INS CO	NE	45.2
MIDLAND NATIONAL LIFE INS CO	IA	47,985.0
MINNESOTA LIFE INS CO	MN	38,458.7
MUTUAL OF OMAHA INS CO	NE	7,112.9
NEW YORK LIFE INS & ANNUITY CORP	DE	137,896.0
OHIO NATIONAL LIFE ASR CORP	OH	3,833.0
PACIFIC LIFE & ANNUITY CO	AZ	6,374.0
PAN AMERICAN ASR CO	LA	25.4
PRINCIPAL LIFE INS CO	IA	165,432.0
SAVINGS BANK LIFE INS CO OF MA	MA	2,957.5
SOUTHERN PIONEER LIFE INS CO	AR	16.8
STANDARD INS CO	OR	21,220.5
SYMETRA LIFE INS CO	IA	33,273.1
TRUSTMARK INS CO	IL	1,430.6
TRUSTMARK LIFE INS CO	IL	325.4
UNITED WORLD LIFE INS CO	NE	122.6
USABLE LIFE	AR	482.3
VOYA RETIREMENT INS & ANNUITY CO	CT	89,930.9

Alaska

INSURANCE COMPANY NAME	DOM. STATE	TOTAL ASSETS ($MIL)
Rating: A+		
AMERICAN FAMILY LIFE INS CO	WI	5,407.4
COUNTRY LIFE INS CO	IL	10,264.7
PHYSICIANS MUTUAL INS CO	NE	2,153.3
STATE FARM LIFE INS CO	IL	68,156.4
TEACHERS INS & ANNUITY ASN OF AM	NY	276,045.0
Rating: A		
4 EVER LIFE INS CO	IL	211.4
GUARDIAN LIFE INS CO OF AMERICA	NY	50,389.3
LIFEWISE ASR CO	WA	143.3
MIDWESTERN UNITED LIFE INS CO	IN	235.0
MML BAY STATE LIFE INS CO	CT	4,737.2
NATIONAL WESTERN LIFE INS CO	CO	10,673.8
PARKER CENTENNIAL ASR CO	WI	92.2
SENTRY LIFE INS CO	WI	5,800.9
USAA LIFE INS CO	TX	23,536.5
Rating: A-		
AMALGAMATED LIFE INS CO	NY	122.5
AMERICAN HEALTH & LIFE INS CO	TX	907.2
AMERICAN REPUBLIC INS CO	IA	909.7
ANNUITY INVESTORS LIFE INS CO	OH	3,041.6
ANTHEM LIFE INS CO	IN	630.6
CENTRAL STATES H & L CO OF OMAHA	NE	421.1
COMPANION LIFE INS CO	SC	329.6
COUNTRY INVESTORS LIFE ASR CO	IL	297.1
DELAWARE AMERICAN LIFE INS CO	DE	145.9
FAMILY HERITAGE LIFE INS CO OF AMER	OH	1,004.9
FIDELITY INVESTMENTS LIFE INS CO	UT	25,080.7
GARDEN STATE LIFE INS CO	TX	126.5
MASSACHUSETTS MUTUAL LIFE INS CO	MA	226,444.0
MUTUAL OF AMERICA LIFE INS CO	NY	18,135.8
NEW YORK LIFE INS CO	NY	167,828.0
NIPPON LIFE INS CO OF AMERICA	IA	217.7
NORTHWESTERN MUTUAL LIFE INS CO	WI	244,873.0
PACIFIC GUARDIAN LIFE INS CO LTD	HI	544.4
PACIFIC LIFE INS CO	NE	115,113.0
PHYSICIANS LIFE INS CO	NE	1,549.0
RESERVE NATIONAL INS CO	OK	123.3
SECURIAN LIFE INS CO	MN	478.9
STANDARD LIFE & ACCIDENT INS CO	TX	511.2
STANDARD SECURITY LIFE INS CO OF NY	NY	245.0
Rating: B+		
AETNA HEALTH & LIFE INS CO	CT	2,349.9
AMERICAN FAMILY LIFE ASR CO OF COLUM	NE	117,278.0
AMERICAN FIDELITY ASR CO	OK	5,305.5
AMERICAN UNITED LIFE INS CO	IN	23,906.8
ASSURITY LIFE INS CO	NE	2,550.8
AXA EQUITABLE LIFE INS CO	NY	171,038.0
BOSTON MUTUAL LIFE INS CO	MA	1,317.6
DEARBORN NATIONAL LIFE INS CO	IL	1,969.6
GERBER LIFE INS CO	NY	3,240.4
GOVERNMENT PERSONNEL MUTUAL L I C	TX	834.7
GREAT SOUTHERN LIFE INS CO	TX	218.2

INSURANCE COMPANY NAME	DOM. STATE	TOTAL ASSETS ($MIL)
MEDICO CORP LIFE INS CO	NE	45.2
MIDLAND NATIONAL LIFE INS CO	IA	47,985.0
MINNESOTA LIFE INS CO	MN	38,458.7
MUTUAL OF OMAHA INS CO	NE	7,112.9
NATIONAL FARMERS UNION LIFE INS CO	TX	206.0
NEW YORK LIFE INS & ANNUITY CORP	DE	137,896.0
OHIO NATIONAL LIFE ASR CORP	OH	3,833.0
PACIFIC LIFE & ANNUITY CO	AZ	6,374.0
PRINCIPAL LIFE INS CO	IA	165,432.0
SAVINGS BANK LIFE INS CO OF MA	MA	2,957.5
STANDARD INS CO	OR	21,220.5
SYMETRA LIFE INS CO	IA	33,273.1
TRUSTMARK INS CO	IL	1,430.6
TRUSTMARK LIFE INS CO	IL	325.4
UNITED WORLD LIFE INS CO	NE	122.6
USABLE LIFE	AR	482.3
VOYA RETIREMENT INS & ANNUITY CO	CT	89,930.9

Arizona

INSURANCE COMPANY NAME	DOM. STATE	TOTAL ASSETS ($MIL)

Rating: A+

INSURANCE COMPANY NAME	DOM. STATE	TOTAL ASSETS ($MIL)
AMERICAN FAMILY LIFE INS CO	WI	5,407.4
COUNTRY LIFE INS CO	IL	10,264.7
PHYSICIANS MUTUAL INS CO	NE	2,153.3
STATE FARM LIFE INS CO	IL	68,156.4
TEACHERS INS & ANNUITY ASN OF AM	NY	276,045.0

Rating: A

INSURANCE COMPANY NAME	DOM. STATE	TOTAL ASSETS ($MIL)
4 EVER LIFE INS CO	IL	211.4
FEDERATED LIFE INS CO	MN	1,710.7
GUARDIAN LIFE INS CO OF AMERICA	NY	50,389.3
LIFEWISE ASR CO	WA	143.3
MIDWESTERN UNITED LIFE INS CO	IN	235.0
MML BAY STATE LIFE INS CO	CT	4,737.2
NATIONAL WESTERN LIFE INS CO	CO	10,673.8
PARKER CENTENNIAL ASR CO	WI	92.2
SENTRY LIFE INS CO	WI	5,800.9
UNITED FARM FAMILY LIFE INS CO	IN	2,234.9
USAA LIFE INS CO	TX	23,536.5

Rating: A-

INSURANCE COMPANY NAME	DOM. STATE	TOTAL ASSETS ($MIL)
AMALGAMATED LIFE INS CO	NY	122.5
AMERICAN HEALTH & LIFE INS CO	TX	907.2
AMERICAN REPUBLIC INS CO	IA	909.7
ANNUITY INVESTORS LIFE INS CO	OH	3,041.6
ANTHEM LIFE INS CO	IN	630.6
AUTO-OWNERS LIFE INS CO	MI	3,832.7
CENTRAL STATES H & L CO OF OMAHA	NE	421.1
COMPANION LIFE INS CO	SC	329.6
COUNTRY INVESTORS LIFE ASR CO	IL	297.1
DELAWARE AMERICAN LIFE INS CO	DE	145.9
FAMILY HERITAGE LIFE INS CO OF AMER	OH	1,004.9
FIDELITY INVESTMENTS LIFE INS CO	UT	25,080.7
GARDEN STATE LIFE INS CO	TX	126.5
ILLINOIS MUTUAL LIFE INS CO	IL	1,434.6
MASSACHUSETTS MUTUAL LIFE INS CO	MA	226,444.0
MUTUAL OF AMERICA LIFE INS CO	NY	18,135.8
NEW YORK LIFE INS CO	NY	167,828.0
NIPPON LIFE INS CO OF AMERICA	IA	217.7
NORTHWESTERN MUTUAL LIFE INS CO	WI	244,873.0
PACIFIC GUARDIAN LIFE INS CO LTD	HI	544.4
PACIFIC LIFE INS CO	NE	115,113.0
PHYSICIANS LIFE INS CO	NE	1,549.0
RESERVE NATIONAL INS CO	OK	123.3
SECURIAN LIFE INS CO	MN	478.9
STANDARD LIFE & ACCIDENT INS CO	TX	511.2
STANDARD SECURITY LIFE INS CO OF NY	NY	245.0

Rating: B+

INSURANCE COMPANY NAME	DOM. STATE	TOTAL ASSETS ($MIL)
AETNA HEALTH & LIFE INS CO	CT	2,349.9
AMERICAN FAMILY LIFE ASR CO OF COLUM	NE	117,278.0
AMERICAN FIDELITY ASR CO	OK	5,305.5
AMERICAN UNITED LIFE INS CO	IN	23,906.8
ASSURITY LIFE INS CO	NE	2,550.8
AXA EQUITABLE LIFE INS CO	NY	171,038.0
BOSTON MUTUAL LIFE INS CO	MA	1,317.6

INSURANCE COMPANY NAME	DOM. STATE	TOTAL ASSETS ($MIL)
DEARBORN NATIONAL LIFE INS CO	IL	1,969.6
FARM BUREAU LIFE INS CO	IA	8,582.6
GERBER LIFE INS CO	NY	3,240.4
GOVERNMENT PERSONNEL MUTUAL L I C	TX	834.7
GREAT SOUTHERN LIFE INS CO	TX	218.2
MEDICO CORP LIFE INS CO	NE	45.2
MIDLAND NATIONAL LIFE INS CO	IA	47,985.0
MINNESOTA LIFE INS CO	MN	38,458.7
MUTUAL OF OMAHA INS CO	NE	7,112.9
NATIONAL FARMERS UNION LIFE INS CO	TX	206.0
NEW YORK LIFE INS & ANNUITY CORP	DE	137,896.0
OHIO NATIONAL LIFE ASR CORP	OH	3,833.0
PACIFIC LIFE & ANNUITY CO	AZ	6,374.0
PAN AMERICAN ASR CO	LA	25.4
PRINCIPAL LIFE INS CO	IA	165,432.0
SAVINGS BANK LIFE INS CO OF MA	MA	2,957.5
STANDARD INS CO	OR	21,220.5
SYMETRA LIFE INS CO	IA	33,273.1
TRUSTMARK INS CO	IL	1,430.6
TRUSTMARK LIFE INS CO	IL	325.4
UNITED WORLD LIFE INS CO	NE	122.6
USABLE LIFE	AR	482.3
VOYA RETIREMENT INS & ANNUITY CO	CT	89,930.9

Arkansas

INSURANCE COMPANY NAME	DOM. STATE	TOTAL ASSETS ($MIL)

Rating: A+

INSURANCE COMPANY NAME	DOM. STATE	TOTAL ASSETS ($MIL)
AMERICAN FAMILY LIFE INS CO	WI	5,407.4
COUNTRY LIFE INS CO	IL	10,264.7
PHYSICIANS MUTUAL INS CO	NE	2,153.3
STATE FARM LIFE INS CO	IL	68,156.4
TEACHERS INS & ANNUITY ASN OF AM	NY	276,045.0

Rating: A

INSURANCE COMPANY NAME	DOM. STATE	TOTAL ASSETS ($MIL)
4 EVER LIFE INS CO	IL	211.4
FEDERATED LIFE INS CO	MN	1,710.7
GUARDIAN LIFE INS CO OF AMERICA	NY	50,389.3
MIDWESTERN UNITED LIFE INS CO	IN	235.0
MML BAY STATE LIFE INS CO	CT	4,737.2
NATIONAL WESTERN LIFE INS CO	CO	10,673.8
PARKER CENTENNIAL ASR CO	WI	02.2
SENTRY LIFE INS CO	WI	5,800.9
SOUTHERN FARM BUREAU LIFE INS CO	MS	13,583.7
USAA LIFE INS CO	TX	23,536.5

Rating: A-

INSURANCE COMPANY NAME	DOM. STATE	TOTAL ASSETS ($MIL)
AMALGAMATED LIFE INS CO	NY	122.5
AMERICAN HEALTH & LIFE INS CO	TX	907.2
AMERICAN REPUBLIC INS CO	IA	909.7
ANNUITY INVESTORS LIFE INS CO	OH	3,041.6
ANTHEM LIFE INS CO	IN	630.6
AUTO-OWNERS LIFE INS CO	MI	3,832.7
CENTRAL STATES H & L CO OF OMAHA	NE	421.1
COMPANION LIFE INS CO	SC	329.6
COUNTRY INVESTORS LIFE ASR CO	IL	297.1
DELAWARE AMERICAN LIFE INS CO	DE	145.9
FAMILY HERITAGE LIFE INS CO OF AMER	OH	1,004.9
FIDELITY INVESTMENTS LIFE INS CO	UT	25,080.7
GARDEN STATE LIFE INS CO	TX	126.5
ILLINOIS MUTUAL LIFE INS CO	IL	1,434.6
LIFE INS CO OF ALABAMA	AL	118.6
MASSACHUSETTS MUTUAL LIFE INS CO	MA	226,444.0
MUTUAL OF AMERICA LIFE INS CO	NY	18,135.8
NEW YORK LIFE INS CO	NY	167,828.0
NIPPON LIFE INS CO OF AMERICA	IA	217.7
NORTHWESTERN MUTUAL LIFE INS CO	WI	244,873.0
PACIFIC LIFE INS CO	NE	115,113.0
PHYSICIANS LIFE INS CO	NE	1,549.0
RESERVE NATIONAL INS CO	OK	123.3
SECURIAN LIFE INS CO	MN	478.9
SHELTER LIFE INS CO	MO	1,180.1
STANDARD LIFE & ACCIDENT INS CO	TX	511.2
STANDARD SECURITY LIFE INS CO OF NY	NY	245.0

Rating: B+

INSURANCE COMPANY NAME	DOM. STATE	TOTAL ASSETS ($MIL)
AETNA HEALTH & LIFE INS CO	CT	2,349.9
AMERICAN FAMILY LIFE ASR CO OF COLUM	NE	117,278.0
AMERICAN FIDELITY ASR CO	OK	5,305.5
AMERICAN UNITED LIFE INS CO	IN	23,906.8
ASSURITY LIFE INS CO	NE	2,550.8
AXA EQUITABLE LIFE INS CO	NY	171,038.0
BLUEBONNET LIFE INS CO	MS	58.9
BOSTON MUTUAL LIFE INS CO	MA	1,317.6
DEARBORN NATIONAL LIFE INS CO	IL	1,969.6
GERBER LIFE INS CO	NY	3,240.4
GOVERNMENT PERSONNEL MUTUAL L I C	TX	834.7
GREAT SOUTHERN LIFE INS CO	TX	218.2
MEDICO CORP LIFE INS CO	NE	45.2
MIDLAND NATIONAL LIFE INS CO	IA	47,985.0
MINNESOTA LIFE INS CO	MN	38,458.7
MUTUAL OF OMAHA INS CO	NE	7,112.9
NATIONAL FARMERS UNION LIFE INS CO	TX	206.0
NEW YORK LIFE INS & ANNUITY CORP	DE	137,896.0
OHIO NATIONAL LIFE ASR CORP	OH	3,833.0
PACIFIC LIFE & ANNUITY CO	AZ	6,374.0
PAN AMERICAN ASR CO	LA	25.4
PRINCIPAL LIFE INS CO	IA	165,432.0
SAVINGS BANK LIFE INS CO OF MA	MA	2,957.5
SOUTHERN PIONEER LIFE INS CO	AR	16.8
STANDARD INS CO	OR	21,220.5
SYMETRA LIFE INS CO	IA	33,273.1
TRUSTMARK INS CO	IL	1,430.6
TRUSTMARK LIFE INS CO	IL	325.4
UNITED WORLD LIFE INS CO	NE	122.6
USABLE LIFE	AR	482.3
VOYA RETIREMENT INS & ANNUITY CO	CT	89,930.9

California

INSURANCE COMPANY NAME	DOM. STATE	TOTAL ASSETS ($MIL)
Rating: A+		
AMERICAN FAMILY LIFE INS CO	WI	5,407.4
PHYSICIANS MUTUAL INS CO	NE	2,153.3
STATE FARM LIFE INS CO	IL	68,156.4
TEACHERS INS & ANNUITY ASN OF AM	NY	276,045.0
Rating: A		
4 EVER LIFE INS CO	IL	211.4
FEDERATED LIFE INS CO	MN	1,710.7
GUARDIAN LIFE INS CO OF AMERICA	NY	50,389.3
LIFEWISE ASR CO	WA	143.3
MIDWESTERN UNITED LIFE INS CO	IN	235.0
MML BAY STATE LIFE INS CO	CT	4,737.2
NATIONAL WESTERN LIFE INS CO	CO	10,673.8
PARKER CENTENNIAL ASR CO	WI	92.2
SENTRY LIFE INS CO	WI	5,800.9
SHELTERPOINT LIFE INS CO	NY	105.4
UNITED FARM FAMILY LIFE INS CO	IN	2,234.9
USAA LIFE INS CO	TX	23,536.5
Rating: A-		
AMALGAMATED LIFE INS CO	NY	122.5
AMERICAN HEALTH & LIFE INS CO	TX	907.2
AMERICAN REPUBLIC INS CO	IA	909.7
ANNUITY INVESTORS LIFE INS CO	OH	3,041.6
ANTHEM LIFE INS CO	IN	630.6
CENTRAL STATES H & L CO OF OMAHA	NE	421.1
DELAWARE AMERICAN LIFE INS CO	DE	145.9
FAMILY HERITAGE LIFE INS CO OF AMER	OH	1,004.9
FIDELITY INVESTMENTS LIFE INS CO	UT	25,080.7
GARDEN STATE LIFE INS CO	TX	126.5
ILLINOIS MUTUAL LIFE INS CO	IL	1,434.6
MASSACHUSETTS MUTUAL LIFE INS CO	MA	226,444.0
MUTUAL OF AMERICA LIFE INS CO	NY	18,135.8
NEW YORK LIFE INS CO	NY	167,828.0
NIPPON LIFE INS CO OF AMERICA	IA	217.7
NORTHWESTERN MUTUAL LIFE INS CO	WI	244,873.0
PACIFIC GUARDIAN LIFE INS CO LTD	HI	544.4
PACIFIC LIFE INS CO	NE	115,113.0
PHYSICIANS LIFE INS CO	NE	1,549.0
SECURIAN LIFE INS CO	MN	478.9
STANDARD LIFE & ACCIDENT INS CO	TX	511.2
STANDARD SECURITY LIFE INS CO OF NY	NY	245.0
Rating: B+		
AETNA HEALTH & LIFE INS CO	CT	2,349.9
AMERICAN FAMILY LIFE ASR CO OF COLUM	NE	117,278.0
AMERICAN FIDELITY ASR CO	OK	5,305.5
AMERICAN UNITED LIFE INS CO	IN	23,906.8
ASSURITY LIFE INS CO	NE	2,550.8
AXA EQUITABLE LIFE INS CO	NY	171,038.0
BOSTON MUTUAL LIFE INS CO	MA	1,317.6
DEARBORN NATIONAL LIFE INS CO	IL	1,969.6
GERBER LIFE INS CO	NY	3,240.4
GOVERNMENT PERSONNEL MUTUAL L I C	TX	834.7
GREAT SOUTHERN LIFE INS CO	TX	218.2

INSURANCE COMPANY NAME	DOM. STATE	TOTAL ASSETS ($MIL)
MIDLAND NATIONAL LIFE INS CO	IA	47,985.0
MINNESOTA LIFE INS CO	MN	38,458.7
MUTUAL OF OMAHA INS CO	NE	7,112.9
NATIONAL FARMERS UNION LIFE INS CO	TX	206.0
NEW YORK LIFE INS & ANNUITY CORP	DE	137,896.0
OHIO NATIONAL LIFE ASR CORP	OH	3,833.0
PACIFIC LIFE & ANNUITY CO	AZ	6,374.0
PAN AMERICAN ASR CO	LA	25.4
PRINCIPAL LIFE INS CO	IA	165,432.0
SAVINGS BANK LIFE INS CO OF MA	MA	2,957.5
STANDARD INS CO	OR	21,220.5
SYMETRA LIFE INS CO	IA	33,273.1
TRUSTMARK INS CO	IL	1,430.6
TRUSTMARK LIFE INS CO	IL	325.4
UNITED WORLD LIFE INS CO	NE	122.6
USABLE LIFE	AR	482.3
VOYA RETIREMENT INS & ANNUITY CO	CT	89,930.9

Colorado

INSURANCE COMPANY NAME	DOM. STATE	TOTAL ASSETS ($MIL)

Rating: A+

INSURANCE COMPANY NAME	DOM. STATE	TOTAL ASSETS ($MIL)
AMERICAN FAMILY LIFE INS CO	WI	5,407.4
COUNTRY LIFE INS CO	IL	10,264.7
PHYSICIANS MUTUAL INS CO	NE	2,153.3
STATE FARM LIFE INS CO	IL	68,156.4
TEACHERS INS & ANNUITY ASN OF AM	NY	276,045.0

Rating: A

INSURANCE COMPANY NAME	DOM. STATE	TOTAL ASSETS ($MIL)
4 EVER LIFE INS CO	IL	211.4
FEDERATED LIFE INS CO	MN	1,710.7
GUARDIAN LIFE INS CO OF AMERICA	NY	50,389.3
LIFEWISE ASR CO	WA	143.3
MIDWESTERN UNITED LIFE INS CO	IN	235.0
MML BAY STATE LIFE INS CO	CT	4,737.2
NATIONAL WESTERN LIFE INS CO	CO	10,673.8
PARKER CENTENNIAL ASR CO	WI	92.2
SENTRY LIFE INS CO	WI	5,800.9
SHELTERPOINT LIFE INS CO	NY	105.4
SOUTHERN FARM BUREAU LIFE INS CO	MS	13,583.7
USAA LIFE INS CO	TX	23,536.5

Rating: A-

INSURANCE COMPANY NAME	DOM. STATE	TOTAL ASSETS ($MIL)
AMALGAMATED LIFE INS CO	NY	122.5
AMERICAN HEALTH & LIFE INS CO	TX	907.2
AMERICAN REPUBLIC INS CO	IA	909.7
ANNUITY INVESTORS LIFE INS CO	OH	3,041.6
ANTHEM LIFE INS CO	IN	630.6
AUTO-OWNERS LIFE INS CO	MI	3,832.7
CENTRAL STATES H & L CO OF OMAHA	NE	421.1
COMPANION LIFE INS CO	SC	329.6
COUNTRY INVESTORS LIFE ASR CO	IL	297.1
DELAWARE AMERICAN LIFE INS CO	DE	145.9
FAMILY HERITAGE LIFE INS CO OF AMER	OH	1,004.9
FIDELITY INVESTMENTS LIFE INS CO	UT	25,080.7
GARDEN STATE LIFE INS CO	TX	126.5
ILLINOIS MUTUAL LIFE INS CO	IL	1,434.6
MASSACHUSETTS MUTUAL LIFE INS CO	MA	226,444.0
MUTUAL OF AMERICA LIFE INS CO	NY	18,135.8
NEW YORK LIFE INS CO	NY	167,828.0
NIPPON LIFE INS CO OF AMERICA	IA	217.7
NORTHWESTERN MUTUAL LIFE INS CO	WI	244,873.0
PACIFIC GUARDIAN LIFE INS CO LTD	HI	544.4
PACIFIC LIFE INS CO	NE	115,113.0
PHYSICIANS LIFE INS CO	NE	1,549.0
RESERVE NATIONAL INS CO	OK	123.3
SECURIAN LIFE INS CO	MN	478.9
SHELTER LIFE INS CO	MO	1,180.1
STANDARD LIFE & ACCIDENT INS CO	TX	511.2
STANDARD SECURITY LIFE INS CO OF NY	NY	245.0

Rating: B+

INSURANCE COMPANY NAME	DOM. STATE	TOTAL ASSETS ($MIL)
AETNA HEALTH & LIFE INS CO	CT	2,349.9
AMERICAN FAMILY LIFE ASR CO OF COLUM	NE	117,278.0
AMERICAN FIDELITY ASR CO	OK	5,305.5
AMERICAN UNITED LIFE INS CO	IN	23,906.8
ASSURITY LIFE INS CO	NE	2,550.8

INSURANCE COMPANY NAME	DOM. STATE	TOTAL ASSETS ($MIL)
AXA EQUITABLE LIFE INS CO	NY	171,038.0
BOSTON MUTUAL LIFE INS CO	MA	1,317.6
DEARBORN NATIONAL LIFE INS CO	IL	1,969.6
FARM BUREAU LIFE INS CO	IA	8,582.6
GERBER LIFE INS CO	NY	3,240.4
GOVERNMENT PERSONNEL MUTUAL L I C	TX	834.7
GREAT SOUTHERN LIFE INS CO	TX	218.2
MEDICO CORP LIFE INS CO	NE	45.2
MIDLAND NATIONAL LIFE INS CO	IA	47,985.0
MINNESOTA LIFE INS CO	MN	38,458.7
MUTUAL OF OMAHA INS CO	NE	7,112.9
NATIONAL FARMERS UNION LIFE INS CO	TX	206.0
NEW YORK LIFE INS & ANNUITY CORP	DE	137,896.0
OHIO NATIONAL LIFE ASR CORP	OH	3,833.0
PACIFIC LIFE & ANNUITY CO	AZ	6,374.0
PAN AMERICAN ASR CO	LA	25.4
PRINCIPAL LIFE INS CO	IA	165,432.0
SAVINGS BANK LIFE INS CO OF MA	MA	2,957.5
STANDARD INS CO	OR	21,220.5
SYMETRA LIFE INS CO	IA	33,273.1
TRUSTMARK INS CO	IL	1,430.6
TRUSTMARK LIFE INS CO	IL	325.4
UNITED WORLD LIFE INS CO	NE	122.6
USABLE LIFE	AR	482.3
VOYA RETIREMENT INS & ANNUITY CO	CT	89,930.9

Connecticut

INSURANCE COMPANY NAME	DOM. STATE	TOTAL ASSETS ($MIL)

Rating: A+

INSURANCE COMPANY NAME	DOM. STATE	TOTAL ASSETS ($MIL)
AMERICAN FAMILY LIFE INS CO	WI	5,407.4
COUNTRY LIFE INS CO	IL	10,264.7
PHYSICIANS MUTUAL INS CO	NE	2,153.3
STATE FARM LIFE & ACCIDENT ASR CO	IL	2,692.7
STATE FARM LIFE INS CO	IL	68,156.4
TEACHERS INS & ANNUITY ASN OF AM	NY	276,045.0

Rating: A

INSURANCE COMPANY NAME	DOM. STATE	TOTAL ASSETS ($MIL)
4 EVER LIFE INS CO	IL	211.4
FEDERATED LIFE INS CO	MN	1,710.7
GUARDIAN LIFE INS CO OF AMERICA	NY	50,389.3
MIDWESTERN UNITED LIFE INS CO	IN	235.0
MML BAY STATE LIFE INS CO	CT	4,737.2
NATIONAL WESTERN LIFE INS CO	CO	10,673.8
PARKER CENTENNIAL ASR CO	WI	92.2
SENTRY LIFE INS CO	WI	5,800.9
SHELTERPOINT LIFE INS CO	NY	105.4
USAA LIFE INS CO	TX	23,536.5

Rating: A-

INSURANCE COMPANY NAME	DOM. STATE	TOTAL ASSETS ($MIL)
ALLIANZ LIFE INS CO OF NY	NY	3,131.2
AMALGAMATED LIFE INS CO	NY	122.5
AMERICAN FAMILY LIFE ASR CO OF NY	NY	885.2
AMERICAN HEALTH & LIFE INS CO	TX	907.2
AMERICAN REPUBLIC INS CO	IA	909.7
ANNUITY INVESTORS LIFE INS CO	OH	3,041.6
ANTHEM LIFE INS CO	IN	630.6
CENTRAL STATES H & L CO OF OMAHA	NE	421.1
COMPANION LIFE INS CO	SC	329.6
COUNTRY INVESTORS LIFE ASR CO	IL	297.1
DELAWARE AMERICAN LIFE INS CO	DE	145.9
FAMILY HERITAGE LIFE INS CO OF AMER	OH	1,004.9
FIDELITY INVESTMENTS LIFE INS CO	UT	25,080.7
GARDEN STATE LIFE INS CO	TX	126.5
ILLINOIS MUTUAL LIFE INS CO	IL	1,434.6
MASSACHUSETTS MUTUAL LIFE INS CO	MA	226,444.0
MUTUAL OF AMERICA LIFE INS CO	NY	18,135.8
NEW YORK LIFE INS CO	NY	167,828.0
NIPPON LIFE INS CO OF AMERICA	IA	217.7
NORTHWESTERN MUTUAL LIFE INS CO	WI	244,873.0
PACIFIC LIFE INS CO	NE	115,113.0
PHYSICIANS LIFE INS CO	NE	1,549.0
RESERVE NATIONAL INS CO	OK	123.3
SECURIAN LIFE INS CO	MN	478.9
STANDARD LIFE & ACCIDENT INS CO	TX	511.2
STANDARD SECURITY LIFE INS CO OF NY	NY	245.0

Rating: B+

INSURANCE COMPANY NAME	DOM. STATE	TOTAL ASSETS ($MIL)
AETNA HEALTH & LIFE INS CO	CT	2,349.9
AMERICAN FAMILY LIFE ASR CO OF COLUM	NE	117,278.0
AMERICAN FIDELITY ASR CO	OK	5,305.5
AMERICAN UNITED LIFE INS CO	IN	23,906.8
ASSURITY LIFE INS CO	NE	2,550.8
AXA EQUITABLE LIFE INS CO	NY	171,038.0
BOSTON MUTUAL LIFE INS CO	MA	1,317.6

INSURANCE COMPANY NAME	DOM. STATE	TOTAL ASSETS ($MIL)
DEARBORN NATIONAL LIFE INS CO	IL	1,969.6
GERBER LIFE INS CO	NY	3,240.4
GOVERNMENT PERSONNEL MUTUAL L I C	TX	834.7
GREAT SOUTHERN LIFE INS CO	TX	218.2
MIDLAND NATIONAL LIFE INS CO	IA	47,985.0
MINNESOTA LIFE INS CO	MN	38,458.7
MUTUAL OF OMAHA INS CO	NE	7,112.9
NEW YORK LIFE INS & ANNUITY CORP	DE	137,896.0
OHIO NATIONAL LIFE ASR CORP	OH	3,833.0
PACIFIC LIFE & ANNUITY CO	AZ	6,374.0
PAN AMERICAN ASR CO	LA	25.4
PRINCIPAL LIFE INS CO	IA	165,432.0
SAVINGS BANK LIFE INS CO OF MA	MA	2,957.5
STANDARD INS CO	OR	21,220.5
SYMETRA LIFE INS CO	IA	33,273.1
TRUSTMARK INS CO	IL	1,430.6
TRUSTMARK LIFE INS CO	IL	325.4
USABLE LIFE	AR	482.3
VOYA RETIREMENT INS & ANNUITY CO	CT	89,930.9

Delaware

INSURANCE COMPANY NAME	DOM. STATE	TOTAL ASSETS ($MIL)

Rating: A+

INSURANCE COMPANY NAME	DOM. STATE	TOTAL ASSETS ($MIL)
AMERICAN FAMILY LIFE INS CO	WI	5,407.4
COUNTRY LIFE INS CO	IL	10,264.7
PHYSICIANS MUTUAL INS CO	NE	2,153.3
STATE FARM LIFE INS CO	IL	68,156.4
TEACHERS INS & ANNUITY ASN OF AM	NY	276,045.0

Rating: A

INSURANCE COMPANY NAME	DOM. STATE	TOTAL ASSETS ($MIL)
4 EVER LIFE INS CO	IL	211.4
FEDERATED LIFE INS CO	MN	1,710.7
FIRST RELIANCE STANDARD LIFE INS CO	NY	190.3
GUARDIAN LIFE INS CO OF AMERICA	NY	50,389.3
MIDWESTERN UNITED LIFE INS CO	IN	235.0
MML BAY STATE LIFE INS CO	CT	4,737.2
NATIONAL WESTERN LIFE INS CO	CO	10,673.8
PARKER CENTENNIAL ASR CO	WI	92.2
SENTRY LIFE INS CO	WI	5,800.9
SHELTERPOINT LIFE INS CO	NY	105.4
USAA LIFE INS CO	TX	23,536.5

Rating: A-

INSURANCE COMPANY NAME	DOM. STATE	TOTAL ASSETS ($MIL)
AMALGAMATED LIFE INS CO	NY	122.5
AMERICAN HEALTH & LIFE INS CO	TX	907.2
AMERICAN REPUBLIC INS CO	IA	909.7
ANNUITY INVESTORS LIFE INS CO	OH	3,041.6
ANTHEM LIFE INS CO	IN	630.6
CENTRAL STATES H & L CO OF OMAHA	NE	421.1
COMPANION LIFE INS CO	SC	329.6
COUNTRY INVESTORS LIFE ASR CO	IL	297.1
DELAWARE AMERICAN LIFE INS CO	DE	145.9
FAMILY HERITAGE LIFE INS CO OF AMER	OH	1,004.9
FIDELITY INVESTMENTS LIFE INS CO	UT	25,080.7
GARDEN STATE LIFE INS CO	TX	126.5
ILLINOIS MUTUAL LIFE INS CO	IL	1,434.6
MASSACHUSETTS MUTUAL LIFE INS CO	MA	226,444.0
MUTUAL OF AMERICA LIFE INS CO	NY	18,135.8
NEW YORK LIFE INS CO	NY	167,828.0
NIPPON LIFE INS CO OF AMERICA	IA	217.7
NORTHWESTERN MUTUAL LIFE INS CO	WI	244,873.0
PACIFIC LIFE INS CO	NE	115,113.0
PHYSICIANS LIFE INS CO	NE	1,549.0
RESERVE NATIONAL INS CO	OK	123.3
SECURIAN LIFE INS CO	MN	478.9
STANDARD LIFE & ACCIDENT INS CO	TX	511.2
STANDARD SECURITY LIFE INS CO OF NY	NY	245.0

Rating: B+

INSURANCE COMPANY NAME	DOM. STATE	TOTAL ASSETS ($MIL)
AETNA HEALTH & LIFE INS CO	CT	2,349.9
AMERICAN FAMILY LIFE ASR CO OF COLUM	NE	117,278.0
AMERICAN FIDELITY ASR CO	OK	5,305.5
AMERICAN UNITED LIFE INS CO	IN	23,906.8
ASSURITY LIFE INS CO	NE	2,550.8
AXA EQUITABLE LIFE INS CO	NY	171,038.0
BOSTON MUTUAL LIFE INS CO	MA	1,317.6
DEARBORN NATIONAL LIFE INS CO	IL	1,969.6
GERBER LIFE INS CO	NY	3,240.4

INSURANCE COMPANY NAME	DOM. STATE	TOTAL ASSETS ($MIL)
GOVERNMENT PERSONNEL MUTUAL L I C	TX	834.7
GREAT SOUTHERN LIFE INS CO	TX	218.2
MEDICO CORP LIFE INS CO	NE	45.2
MIDLAND NATIONAL LIFE INS CO	IA	47,985.0
MINNESOTA LIFE INS CO	MN	38,458.7
MUTUAL OF OMAHA INS CO	NE	7,112.9
NEW YORK LIFE INS & ANNUITY CORP	DE	137,896.0
OHIO NATIONAL LIFE ASR CORP	OH	3,833.0
PACIFIC LIFE & ANNUITY CO	AZ	6,374.0
PAN AMERICAN ASR CO	LA	25.4
PRINCIPAL LIFE INS CO	IA	165,432.0
SAVINGS BANK LIFE INS CO OF MA	MA	2,957.5
STANDARD INS CO	OR	21,220.5
SYMETRA LIFE INS CO	IA	33,273.1
TRUSTMARK INS CO	IL	1,430.6
TRUSTMARK LIFE INS CO	IL	325.4
UNITED WORLD LIFE INS CO	NE	122.6
USABLE LIFE	AR	482.3
VOYA RETIREMENT INS & ANNUITY CO	CT	89,930.9

District Of Columbia

INSURANCE COMPANY NAME	DOM. STATE	TOTAL ASSETS ($MIL)

Rating: A+

INSURANCE COMPANY NAME	DOM. STATE	TOTAL ASSETS ($MIL)
AMERICAN FAMILY LIFE INS CO	WI	5,407.4
PHYSICIANS MUTUAL INS CO	NE	2,153.3
STATE FARM LIFE INS CO	IL	68,156.4
TEACHERS INS & ANNUITY ASN OF AM	NY	276,045.0

Rating: A

INSURANCE COMPANY NAME	DOM. STATE	TOTAL ASSETS ($MIL)
4 EVER LIFE INS CO	IL	211.4
FIRST RELIANCE STANDARD LIFE INS CO	NY	190.3
GUARDIAN LIFE INS CO OF AMERICA	NY	50,389.3
MIDWESTERN UNITED LIFE INS CO	IN	235.0
MML BAY STATE LIFE INS CO	CT	4,737.2
NATIONAL WESTERN LIFE INS CO	CO	10,673.8
PARKER CENTENNIAL ASR CO	WI	92.2
SENTRY LIFE INS CO	WI	5,800.9
SHELTERPOINT LIFE INS CO	NY	105.4
USAA LIFE INS CO	TX	23,536.5

Rating: A-

INSURANCE COMPANY NAME	DOM. STATE	TOTAL ASSETS ($MIL)
ALLIANZ LIFE INS CO OF NY	NY	3,131.2
AMALGAMATED LIFE INS CO	NY	122.5
AMERICAN HEALTH & LIFE INS CO	TX	907.2
AMERICAN REPUBLIC INS CO	IA	909.7
ANNUITY INVESTORS LIFE INS CO	OH	3,041.6
ANTHEM LIFE INS CO	IN	630.6
CENTRAL STATES H & L CO OF OMAHA	NE	421.1
CIGNA LIFE INS CO OF NEW YORK	NY	380.3
COMPANION LIFE INS CO	SC	329.6
DELAWARE AMERICAN LIFE INS CO	DE	145.9
ERIE FAMILY LIFE INS CO	PA	2,217.2
FAMILY HERITAGE LIFE INS CO OF AMER	OH	1,004.9
FIDELITY INVESTMENTS LIFE INS CO	UT	25,080.7
GARDEN STATE LIFE INS CO	TX	126.5
MASSACHUSETTS MUTUAL LIFE INS CO	MA	226,444.0
MUTUAL OF AMERICA LIFE INS CO	NY	18,135.8
NEW YORK LIFE INS CO	NY	167,828.0
NIPPON LIFE INS CO OF AMERICA	IA	217.7
NORTHWESTERN MUTUAL LIFE INS CO	WI	244,873.0
PACIFIC LIFE INS CO	NE	115,113.0
PHYSICIANS LIFE INS CO	NE	1,549.0
RESERVE NATIONAL INS CO	OK	123.3
SECURIAN LIFE INS CO	MN	478.9
STANDARD LIFE & ACCIDENT INS CO	TX	511.2
STANDARD SECURITY LIFE INS CO OF NY	NY	245.0

Rating: B+

INSURANCE COMPANY NAME	DOM. STATE	TOTAL ASSETS ($MIL)
AETNA HEALTH & LIFE INS CO	CT	2,349.9
AMERICAN FAMILY LIFE ASR CO OF COLUM	NE	117,278.0
AMERICAN FIDELITY ASR CO	OK	5,305.5
AMERICAN UNITED LIFE INS CO	IN	23,906.8
ASSURITY LIFE INS CO	NE	2,550.8
AXA EQUITABLE LIFE INS CO	NY	171,038.0
BOSTON MUTUAL LIFE INS CO	MA	1,317.6
DEARBORN NATIONAL LIFE INS CO	IL	1,969.6
GERBER LIFE INS CO	NY	3,240.4
GOVERNMENT PERSONNEL MUTUAL L I C	TX	834.7

INSURANCE COMPANY NAME	DOM. STATE	TOTAL ASSETS ($MIL)
GREAT SOUTHERN LIFE INS CO	TX	218.2
MEDICO CORP LIFE INS CO	NE	45.2
MIDLAND NATIONAL LIFE INS CO	IA	47,985.0
MINNESOTA LIFE INS CO	MN	38,458.7
MUTUAL OF OMAHA INS CO	NE	7,112.9
NATIONAL FARMERS UNION LIFE INS CO	TX	206.0
NEW YORK LIFE INS & ANNUITY CORP	DE	137,896.0
OHIO NATIONAL LIFE ASR CORP	OH	3,833.0
PACIFIC LIFE & ANNUITY CO	AZ	6,374.0
PAN AMERICAN ASR CO	LA	25.4
PRINCIPAL LIFE INS CO	IA	165,432.0
SAVINGS BANK LIFE INS CO OF MA	MA	2,957.5
STANDARD INS CO	OR	21,220.5
SYMETRA LIFE INS CO	IA	33,273.1
TRUSTMARK INS CO	IL	1,430.6
TRUSTMARK LIFE INS CO	IL	325.4
UNITED WORLD LIFE INS CO	NE	122.6
USABLE LIFE	AR	482.3
VOYA RETIREMENT INS & ANNUITY CO	CT	89,930.9

Florida

INSURANCE COMPANY NAME	DOM. STATE	TOTAL ASSETS ($MIL)

Rating: A+

INSURANCE COMPANY NAME	DOM. STATE	TOTAL ASSETS ($MIL)
AMERICAN FAMILY LIFE INS CO	WI	5,407.4
COUNTRY LIFE INS CO	IL	10,264.7
PHYSICIANS MUTUAL INS CO	NE	2,153.3
STATE FARM LIFE INS CO	IL	68,156.4
TEACHERS INS & ANNUITY ASN OF AM	NY	276,045.0

Rating: A

INSURANCE COMPANY NAME	DOM. STATE	TOTAL ASSETS ($MIL)
4 EVER LIFE INS CO	IL	211.4
FEDERATED LIFE INS CO	MN	1,710.7
GUARDIAN LIFE INS CO OF AMERICA	NY	50,389.3
MIDWESTERN UNITED LIFE INS CO	IN	235.0
MML BAY STATE LIFE INS CO	CT	4,737.2
NATIONAL WESTERN LIFE INS CO	CO	10,673.8
PARKER CENTENNIAL ASR CO	WI	92.2
SENTRY LIFE INS CO	WI	5,800.9
SHELTERPOINT LIFE INS CO	NY	105.4
SOUTHERN FARM BUREAU LIFE INS CO	MS	13,583.7
TRANS OCEANIC LIFE INS CO	PR	68.3
USAA LIFE INS CO	TX	23,536.5

Rating: A-

INSURANCE COMPANY NAME	DOM. STATE	TOTAL ASSETS ($MIL)
AMALGAMATED LIFE INS CO	NY	122.5
AMERICAN HEALTH & LIFE INS CO	TX	907.2
AMERICAN REPUBLIC INS CO	IA	909.7
ANNUITY INVESTORS LIFE INS CO	OH	3,041.6
ANTHEM LIFE INS CO	IN	630.6
AUTO-OWNERS LIFE INS CO	MI	3,832.7
CENTRAL STATES H & L CO OF OMAHA	NE	421.1
COMPANION LIFE INS CO	SC	329.6
COTTON STATES LIFE INS CO	GA	334.6
COUNTRY INVESTORS LIFE ASR CO	IL	297.1
DELAWARE AMERICAN LIFE INS CO	DE	145.9
FAMILY HERITAGE LIFE INS CO OF AMER	OH	1,004.9
FIDELITY INVESTMENTS LIFE INS CO	UT	25,080.7
GARDEN STATE LIFE INS CO	TX	126.5
ILLINOIS MUTUAL LIFE INS CO	IL	1,434.6
LIFE INS CO OF ALABAMA	AL	118.6
MASSACHUSETTS MUTUAL LIFE INS CO	MA	226,444.0
MUTUAL OF AMERICA LIFE INS CO	NY	18,135.8
NEW YORK LIFE INS CO	NY	167,828.0
NIPPON LIFE INS CO OF AMERICA	IA	217.7
NORTHWESTERN MUTUAL LIFE INS CO	WI	244,873.0
PACIFIC LIFE INS CO	NE	115,113.0
PHYSICIANS LIFE INS CO	NE	1,549.0
RESERVE NATIONAL INS CO	OK	123.3
SECURIAN LIFE INS CO	MN	478.9
STANDARD LIFE & ACCIDENT INS CO	TX	511.2
STANDARD SECURITY LIFE INS CO OF NY	NY	245.0

Rating: B+

INSURANCE COMPANY NAME	DOM. STATE	TOTAL ASSETS ($MIL)
AETNA HEALTH & LIFE INS CO	CT	2,349.9
AMERICAN FAMILY LIFE ASR CO OF COLUM	NE	117,278.0
AMERICAN FIDELITY ASR CO	OK	5,305.5
AMERICAN UNITED LIFE INS CO	IN	23,906.8
ASSURITY LIFE INS CO	NE	2,550.8

INSURANCE COMPANY NAME	DOM. STATE	TOTAL ASSETS ($MIL)
AXA EQUITABLE LIFE INS CO	NY	171,038.0
BOSTON MUTUAL LIFE INS CO	MA	1,317.6
DEARBORN NATIONAL LIFE INS CO	IL	1,969.6
GERBER LIFE INS CO	NY	3,240.4
GOVERNMENT PERSONNEL MUTUAL L I C	TX	834.7
GREAT SOUTHERN LIFE INS CO	TX	218.2
MEDICO CORP LIFE INS CO	NE	45.2
MIDLAND NATIONAL LIFE INS CO	IA	47,985.0
MINNESOTA LIFE INS CO	MN	38,458.7
MUTUAL OF OMAHA INS CO	NE	7,112.9
NEW YORK LIFE INS & ANNUITY CORP	DE	137,896.0
OHIO NATIONAL LIFE ASR CORP	OH	3,833.0
PACIFIC LIFE & ANNUITY CO	AZ	6,374.0
PAN AMERICAN ASR CO	LA	25.4
PRINCIPAL LIFE INS CO	IA	165,432.0
SAVINGS BANK LIFE INS CO OF MA	MA	2,957.5
STANDARD INS CO	OR	21,220.5
SYMETRA LIFE INS CO	IA	33,273.1
TRUSTMARK INS CO	IL	1,430.6
TRUSTMARK LIFE INS CO	IL	325.4
UNITED WORLD LIFE INS CO	NE	122.6
USABLE LIFE	AR	482.3
VOYA RETIREMENT INS & ANNUITY CO	CT	89,930.9

Georgia

INSURANCE COMPANY NAME	DOM. STATE	TOTAL ASSETS ($MIL)

Rating: A+

INSURANCE COMPANY NAME	DOM. STATE	TOTAL ASSETS ($MIL)
AMERICAN FAMILY LIFE INS CO	WI	5,407.4
COUNTRY LIFE INS CO	IL	10,264.7
PHYSICIANS MUTUAL INS CO	NE	2,153.3
STATE FARM LIFE INS CO	IL	68,156.4
TEACHERS INS & ANNUITY ASN OF AM	NY	276,045.0

Rating: A

INSURANCE COMPANY NAME	DOM. STATE	TOTAL ASSETS ($MIL)
4 EVER LIFE INS CO	IL	211.4
FEDERATED LIFE INS CO	MN	1,710.7
FRANDISCO LIFE INS CO	GA	78.5
GUARDIAN LIFE INS CO OF AMERICA	NY	50,389.3
MIDWESTERN UNITED LIFE INS CO	IN	235.0
MML BAY STATE LIFE INS CO	CT	4,737.2
NATIONAL WESTERN LIFE INS CO	CO	10,673.8
PARKER CENTENNIAL ASR CO	WI	92.2
SENTRY LIFE INS CO	WI	5,800.9
SOUTHERN FARM BUREAU LIFE INS CO	MS	13,583.7
USAA LIFE INS CO	TX	23,536.5

Rating: A-

INSURANCE COMPANY NAME	DOM. STATE	TOTAL ASSETS ($MIL)
AMALGAMATED LIFE INS CO	NY	122.5
AMERICAN HEALTH & LIFE INS CO	TX	907.2
AMERICAN REPUBLIC INS CO	IA	909.7
ANNUITY INVESTORS LIFE INS CO	OH	3,041.6
ANTHEM LIFE INS CO	IN	630.6
AUTO-OWNERS LIFE INS CO	MI	3,832.7
CENTRAL STATES H & L CO OF OMAHA	NE	421.1
COMPANION LIFE INS CO	SC	329.6
COTTON STATES LIFE INS CO	GA	334.6
COUNTRY INVESTORS LIFE ASR CO	IL	297.1
DELAWARE AMERICAN LIFE INS CO	DE	145.9
FAMILY HERITAGE LIFE INS CO OF AMER	OH	1,004.9
FIDELITY INVESTMENTS LIFE INS CO	UT	25,080.7
GARDEN STATE LIFE INS CO	TX	126.5
ILLINOIS MUTUAL LIFE INS CO	IL	1,434.6
LIFE INS CO OF ALABAMA	AL	118.6
MASSACHUSETTS MUTUAL LIFE INS CO	MA	226,444.0
MUTUAL OF AMERICA LIFE INS CO	NY	18,135.8
NEW YORK LIFE INS CO	NY	167,828.0
NIPPON LIFE INS CO OF AMERICA	IA	217.7
NORTHWESTERN MUTUAL LIFE INS CO	WI	244,873.0
PACIFIC LIFE INS CO	NE	115,113.0
PHYSICIANS LIFE INS CO	NE	1,549.0
RESERVE NATIONAL INS CO	OK	123.3
SECURIAN LIFE INS CO	MN	478.9
STANDARD LIFE & ACCIDENT INS CO	TX	511.2
STANDARD SECURITY LIFE INS CO OF NY	NY	245.0

Rating: B+

INSURANCE COMPANY NAME	DOM. STATE	TOTAL ASSETS ($MIL)
AETNA HEALTH & LIFE INS CO	CT	2,349.9
AMERICAN FAMILY LIFE ASR CO OF COLUM	NE	117,278.0
AMERICAN FIDELITY ASR CO	OK	5,305.5
AMERICAN UNITED LIFE INS CO	IN	23,906.8
ASSURITY LIFE INS CO	NE	2,550.8
AXA EQUITABLE LIFE INS CO	NY	171,038.0

INSURANCE COMPANY NAME	DOM. STATE	TOTAL ASSETS ($MIL)
BOSTON MUTUAL LIFE INS CO	MA	1,317.6
DEARBORN NATIONAL LIFE INS CO	IL	1,969.6
GERBER LIFE INS CO	NY	3,240.4
GOVERNMENT PERSONNEL MUTUAL L I C	TX	834.7
GREAT SOUTHERN LIFE INS CO	TX	218.2
GREATER GEORGIA LIFE INS CO	GA	58.6
MEDICO CORP LIFE INS CO	NE	45.2
MIDLAND NATIONAL LIFE INS CO	IA	47,985.0
MINNESOTA LIFE INS CO	MN	38,458.7
MUTUAL OF OMAHA INS CO	NE	7,112.9
NEW YORK LIFE INS & ANNUITY CORP	DE	137,896.0
OHIO NATIONAL LIFE ASR CORP	OH	3,833.0
PACIFIC LIFE & ANNUITY CO	AZ	6,374.0
PAN AMERICAN ASR CO	LA	25.4
PRINCIPAL LIFE INS CO	IA	165,432.0
SAVINGS BANK LIFE INS CO OF MA	MA	2,957.5
SOUTHERN PIONEER LIFE INS CO	AR	16.8
STANDARD INS CO	OR	21,220.5
SYMETRA LIFE INS CO	IA	33,273.1
TRUSTMARK INS CO	IL	1,430.6
TRUSTMARK LIFE INS CO	IL	325.4
UNITED WORLD LIFE INS CO	NE	122.6
USABLE LIFE	AR	482.3
VOYA RETIREMENT INS & ANNUITY CO	CT	89,930.9

Hawaii

INSURANCE COMPANY NAME	DOM. STATE	TOTAL ASSETS ($MIL)
Rating: A+		
AMERICAN FAMILY LIFE INS CO	WI	5,407.4
PHYSICIANS MUTUAL INS CO	NE	2,153.3
STATE FARM LIFE INS CO	IL	68,156.4
TEACHERS INS & ANNUITY ASN OF AM	NY	276,045.0
Rating: A		
4 EVER LIFE INS CO	IL	211.4
GUARDIAN LIFE INS CO OF AMERICA	NY	50,389.3
MIDWESTERN UNITED LIFE INS CO	IN	235.0
MML BAY STATE LIFE INS CO	CT	4,737.2
NATIONAL WESTERN LIFE INS CO	CO	10,673.8
PARKER CENTENNIAL ASR CO	WI	92.2
SENTRY LIFE INS CO	WI	5,800.9
USAA LIFE INS CO	TX	23,536.5
Rating: A-		
AMALGAMATED LIFE INS CO	NY	122.5
AMERICAN HEALTH & LIFE INS CO	TX	907.2
AMERICAN REPUBLIC INS CO	IA	909.7
ANNUITY INVESTORS LIFE INS CO	OH	3,041.6
ANTHEM LIFE INS CO	IN	630.6
CENTRAL STATES H & L CO OF OMAHA	NE	421.1
DELAWARE AMERICAN LIFE INS CO	DE	145.9
FAMILY HERITAGE LIFE INS CO OF AMER	OH	1,004.9
FIDELITY INVESTMENTS LIFE INS CO	UT	25,080.7
GARDEN STATE LIFE INS CO	TX	126.5
MASSACHUSETTS MUTUAL LIFE INS CO	MA	226,444.0
MUTUAL OF AMERICA LIFE INS CO	NY	18,135.8
NEW YORK LIFE INS CO	NY	167,828.0
NIPPON LIFE INS CO OF AMERICA	IA	217.7
NORTHWESTERN MUTUAL LIFE INS CO	WI	244,873.0
PACIFIC GUARDIAN LIFE INS CO LTD	HI	544.4
PACIFIC LIFE INS CO	NE	115,113.0
PHYSICIANS LIFE INS CO	NE	1,549.0
RESERVE NATIONAL INS CO	OK	123.3
SECURIAN LIFE INS CO	MN	478.9
STANDARD LIFE & ACCIDENT INS CO	TX	511.2
STANDARD SECURITY LIFE INS CO OF NY	NY	245.0
Rating: B+		
AETNA HEALTH & LIFE INS CO	CT	2,349.9
AMERICAN FAMILY LIFE ASR CO OF COLUM	NE	117,278.0
AMERICAN FIDELITY ASR CO	OK	5,305.5
AMERICAN UNITED LIFE INS CO	IN	23,906.8
ASSURITY LIFE INS CO	NE	2,550.8
AXA EQUITABLE LIFE INS CO	NY	171,038.0
BOSTON MUTUAL LIFE INS CO	MA	1,317.6
DEARBORN NATIONAL LIFE INS CO	IL	1,969.6
GERBER LIFE INS CO	NY	3,240.4
GOVERNMENT PERSONNEL MUTUAL L I C	TX	834.7
GREAT SOUTHERN LIFE INS CO	TX	218.2
MEDICO CORP LIFE INS CO	NE	45.2
MIDLAND NATIONAL LIFE INS CO	IA	47,985.0
MINNESOTA LIFE INS CO	MN	38,458.7
MUTUAL OF OMAHA INS CO	NE	7,112.9

INSURANCE COMPANY NAME	DOM. STATE	TOTAL ASSETS ($MIL)
NEW YORK LIFE INS & ANNUITY CORP	DE	137,896.0
OHIO NATIONAL LIFE ASR CORP	OH	3,833.0
PACIFIC LIFE & ANNUITY CO	AZ	6,374.0
PAN AMERICAN ASR CO	LA	25.4
PRINCIPAL LIFE INS CO	IA	165,432.0
SAVINGS BANK LIFE INS CO OF MA	MA	2,957.5
STANDARD INS CO	OR	21,220.5
SYMETRA LIFE INS CO	IA	33,273.1
TRUSTMARK INS CO	IL	1,430.6
TRUSTMARK LIFE INS CO	IL	325.4
UNITED WORLD LIFE INS CO	NE	122.6
USABLE LIFE	AR	482.3
VOYA RETIREMENT INS & ANNUITY CO	CT	89,930.9

Idaho

INSURANCE COMPANY NAME	DOM. STATE	TOTAL ASSETS ($MIL)
Rating: A+		
AMERICAN FAMILY LIFE INS CO	WI	5,407.4
COUNTRY LIFE INS CO	IL	10,264.7
PHYSICIANS MUTUAL INS CO	NE	2,153.3
STATE FARM LIFE INS CO	IL	68,156.4
TEACHERS INS & ANNUITY ASN OF AM	NY	276,045.0
Rating: A		
4 EVER LIFE INS CO	IL	211.4
FEDERATED LIFE INS CO	MN	1,710.7
GUARDIAN LIFE INS CO OF AMERICA	NY	50,389.3
LIFEWISE ASR CO	WA	143.3
MIDWESTERN UNITED LIFE INS CO	IN	235.0
MML BAY STATE LIFE INS CO	CT	4,737.2
NATIONAL WESTERN LIFE INS CO	CO	10,673.8
PARKER CENTENNIAL ASR CO	WI	92.2
SENTRY LIFE INS CO	WI	5,800.9
USAA LIFE INS CO	TX	23,536.5
Rating: A-		
AMALGAMATED LIFE INS CO	NY	122.5
AMERICAN HEALTH & LIFE INS CO	TX	907.2
AMERICAN REPUBLIC INS CO	IA	909.7
ANNUITY INVESTORS LIFE INS CO	OH	3,041.6
ANTHEM LIFE INS CO	IN	630.6
AUTO-OWNERS LIFE INS CO	MI	3,832.7
CENTRAL STATES H & L CO OF OMAHA	NE	421.1
COMPANION LIFE INS CO	SC	329.6
COUNTRY INVESTORS LIFE ASR CO	IL	297.1
DELAWARE AMERICAN LIFE INS CO	DE	145.9
FAMILY HERITAGE LIFE INS CO OF AMER	OH	1,004.9
FIDELITY INVESTMENTS LIFE INS CO	UT	25,080.7
GARDEN STATE LIFE INS CO	TX	126.5
ILLINOIS MUTUAL LIFE INS CO	IL	1,434.6
MASSACHUSETTS MUTUAL LIFE INS CO	MA	226,444.0
MUTUAL OF AMERICA LIFE INS CO	NY	18,135.8
NEW YORK LIFE INS CO	NY	167,828.0
NIPPON LIFE INS CO OF AMERICA	IA	217.7
NORTHWESTERN MUTUAL LIFE INS CO	WI	244,873.0
PACIFIC GUARDIAN LIFE INS CO LTD	HI	544.4
PACIFIC LIFE INS CO	NE	115,113.0
PHYSICIANS LIFE INS CO	NE	1,549.0
RESERVE NATIONAL INS CO	OK	123.3
SECURIAN LIFE INS CO	MN	478.9
STANDARD LIFE & ACCIDENT INS CO	TX	511.2
STANDARD SECURITY LIFE INS CO OF NY	NY	245.0
Rating: B+		
AETNA HEALTH & LIFE INS CO	CT	2,349.9
AMERICAN FAMILY LIFE ASR CO OF COLUM	NE	117,278.0
AMERICAN FIDELITY ASR CO	OK	5,305.5
AMERICAN UNITED LIFE INS CO	IN	23,906.8
ASSURITY LIFE INS CO	NE	2,550.8
AXA EQUITABLE LIFE INS CO	NY	171,038.0
BOSTON MUTUAL LIFE INS CO	MA	1,317.6
DEARBORN NATIONAL LIFE INS CO	IL	1,969.6

INSURANCE COMPANY NAME	DOM. STATE	TOTAL ASSETS ($MIL)
FARM BUREAU LIFE INS CO	IA	8,582.6
GERBER LIFE INS CO	NY	3,240.4
GOVERNMENT PERSONNEL MUTUAL L I C	TX	834.7
GREAT SOUTHERN LIFE INS CO	TX	218.2
MEDICO CORP LIFE INS CO	NE	45.2
MIDLAND NATIONAL LIFE INS CO	IA	47,985.0
MINNESOTA LIFE INS CO	MN	38,458.7
MUTUAL OF OMAHA INS CO	NE	7,112.9
NATIONAL FARMERS UNION LIFE INS CO	TX	206.0
NEW YORK LIFE INS & ANNUITY CORP	DE	137,896.0
OHIO NATIONAL LIFE ASR CORP	OH	3,833.0
PACIFIC LIFE & ANNUITY CO	AZ	6,374.0
PAN AMERICAN ASR CO	LA	25.4
PRINCIPAL LIFE INS CO	IA	165,432.0
SAVINGS BANK LIFE INS CO OF MA	MA	2,957.5
STANDARD INS CO	OR	21,220.5
SYMETRA LIFE INS CO	IA	33,273.1
TRUSTMARK INS CO	IL	1,430.6
TRUSTMARK LIFE INS CO	IL	325.4
UNITED WORLD LIFE INS CO	NE	122.6
USABLE LIFE	AR	482.3
VOYA RETIREMENT INS & ANNUITY CO	CT	89,930.9

Illinois

INSURANCE COMPANY NAME	DOM. STATE	TOTAL ASSETS ($MIL)	INSURANCE COMPANY NAME	DOM. STATE	TOTAL ASSETS ($MIL)
Rating: A+			ASSURITY LIFE INS CO	NE	2,550.8
			AXA EQUITABLE LIFE INS CO	NY	171,038.0
AMERICAN FAMILY LIFE INS CO	WI	5,407.4	BOSTON MUTUAL LIFE INS CO	MA	1,317.6
COUNTRY LIFE INS CO	IL	10,264.7	DEARBORN NATIONAL LIFE INS CO	IL	1,969.6
PHYSICIANS MUTUAL INS CO	NE	2,153.3	GERBER LIFE INS CO	NY	3,240.4
STATE FARM LIFE & ACCIDENT ASR CO	IL	2,692.7	GOVERNMENT PERSONNEL MUTUAL L I C	TX	834.7
STATE FARM LIFE INS CO	IL	68,156.4	GREAT SOUTHERN LIFE INS CO	TX	218.2
TEACHERS INS & ANNUITY ASN OF AM	NY	276,045.0	MEDICO CORP LIFE INS CO	NE	45.2
			MIDLAND NATIONAL LIFE INS CO	IA	47,985.0
Rating: A			MINNESOTA LIFE INS CO	MN	38,458.7
			MUTUAL OF OMAHA INS CO	NE	7,112.9
4 EVER LIFE INS CO	IL	211.4	NATIONAL FARMERS UNION LIFE INS CO	TX	206.0
FEDERATED LIFE INS CO	MN	1,710.7	NEW YORK LIFE INS & ANNUITY CORP	DE	137,896.0
GUARDIAN LIFE INS CO OF AMERICA	NY	50,389.3	OHIO NATIONAL LIFE ASR CORP	OH	3,833.0
MIDWESTERN UNITED LIFE INS CO	IN	235.0	PACIFIC LIFE & ANNUITY CO	AZ	6,374.0
MML BAY STATE LIFE INS CO	CT	4,737.2	PAN AMERICAN ASR CO	LA	25.4
NATIONAL WESTERN LIFE INS CO	CO	10,673.8	PRINCIPAL LIFE INS CO	IA	165,432.0
PARKER CENTENNIAL ASR CO	WI	92.2	SAVINGS BANK LIFE INS CO OF MA	MA	2,957.5
SENTRY LIFE INS CO	WI	5,800.9	STANDARD INS CO	OR	21,220.5
SHELTERPOINT LIFE INS CO	NY	105.4	SYMETRA LIFE INS CO	IA	33,273.1
UNITED FARM FAMILY LIFE INS CO	IN	2,234.9	TRUSTMARK INS CO	IL	1,430.6
USAA LIFE INS CO	TX	23,536.5	TRUSTMARK LIFE INS CO	IL	325.4
			UNITED WORLD LIFE INS CO	NE	122.6
Rating: A-			USABLE LIFE	AR	482.3
			VOYA RETIREMENT INS & ANNUITY CO	CT	89,930.9
ALLIANZ LIFE INS CO OF NY	NY	3,131.2			
AMALGAMATED LIFE INS CO	NY	122.5			
AMERICAN HEALTH & LIFE INS CO	TX	907.2			
AMERICAN REPUBLIC INS CO	IA	909.7			
ANNUITY INVESTORS LIFE INS CO	OH	3,041.6			
ANTHEM LIFE INS CO	IN	630.6			
AUTO-OWNERS LIFE INS CO	MI	3,832.7			
CENTRAL STATES H & L CO OF OMAHA	NE	421.1			
COMPANION LIFE INS CO	SC	329.6			
COUNTRY INVESTORS LIFE ASR CO	IL	297.1			
DELAWARE AMERICAN LIFE INS CO	DE	145.9			
ERIE FAMILY LIFE INS CO	PA	2,217.2			
FAMILY HERITAGE LIFE INS CO OF AMER	OH	1,004.9			
FIDELITY INVESTMENTS LIFE INS CO	UT	25,080.7			
GARDEN STATE LIFE INS CO	TX	126.5			
ILLINOIS MUTUAL LIFE INS CO	IL	1,434.6			
MASSACHUSETTS MUTUAL LIFE INS CO	MA	220,444.0			
MUTUAL OF AMERICA LIFE INS CO	NY	18,135.8			
NEW YORK LIFE INS CO	NY	167,828.0			
NIPPON LIFE INS CO OF AMERICA	IA	217.7			
NORTHWESTERN MUTUAL LIFE INS CO	WI	244,873.0			
PACIFIC LIFE INS CO	NE	115,113.0			
PHYSICIANS LIFE INS CO	NE	1,549.0			
RESERVE NATIONAL INS CO	OK	123.3			
SECURIAN LIFE INS CO	MN	478.9			
SHELTER LIFE INS CO	MO	1,180.1			
STANDARD LIFE & ACCIDENT INS CO	TX	511.2			
STANDARD SECURITY LIFE INS CO OF NY	NY	245.0			
Rating: B+					
AETNA HEALTH & LIFE INS CO	CT	2,349.9			
AMERICAN FAMILY LIFE ASR CO OF COLUM	NE	117,278.0			
AMERICAN FIDELITY ASR CO	OK	5,305.5			
AMERICAN UNITED LIFE INS CO	IN	23,906.8			

Indiana

INSURANCE COMPANY NAME	DOM. STATE	TOTAL ASSETS ($MIL)

Rating: A+

INSURANCE COMPANY NAME	DOM. STATE	TOTAL ASSETS ($MIL)
AMERICAN FAMILY LIFE INS CO	WI	5,407.4
COUNTRY LIFE INS CO	IL	10,264.7
PHYSICIANS MUTUAL INS CO	NE	2,153.3
STATE FARM LIFE INS CO	IL	68,156.4
TEACHERS INS & ANNUITY ASN OF AM	NY	276,045.0

Rating: A

INSURANCE COMPANY NAME	DOM. STATE	TOTAL ASSETS ($MIL)
4 EVER LIFE INS CO	IL	211.4
FEDERATED LIFE INS CO	MN	1,710.7
GUARDIAN LIFE INS CO OF AMERICA	NY	50,389.3
MIDWESTERN UNITED LIFE INS CO	IN	235.0
MML BAY STATE LIFE INS CO	CT	4,737.2
NATIONAL WESTERN LIFE INS CO	CO	10,673.8
PARKER CENTENNIAL ASR CO	WI	92.2
SENTRY LIFE INS CO	WI	5,800.9
UNITED FARM FAMILY LIFE INS CO	IN	2,234.9
USAA LIFE INS CO	TX	23,536.5

Rating: A-

INSURANCE COMPANY NAME	DOM. STATE	TOTAL ASSETS ($MIL)
AMALGAMATED LIFE INS CO	NY	122.5
AMERICAN HEALTH & LIFE INS CO	TX	907.2
AMERICAN REPUBLIC INS CO	IA	909.7
ANNUITY INVESTORS LIFE INS CO	OH	3,041.6
ANTHEM LIFE INS CO	IN	630.6
AUTO-OWNERS LIFE INS CO	MI	3,832.7
CENTRAL STATES H & L CO OF OMAHA	NE	421.1
COMPANION LIFE INS CO	SC	329.6
COUNTRY INVESTORS LIFE ASR CO	IL	297.1
DELAWARE AMERICAN LIFE INS CO	DE	145.9
ERIE FAMILY LIFE INS CO	PA	2,217.2
FAMILY HERITAGE LIFE INS CO OF AMER	OH	1,004.9
FIDELITY INVESTMENTS LIFE INS CO	UT	25,080.7
GARDEN STATE LIFE INS CO	TX	126.5
ILLINOIS MUTUAL LIFE INS CO	IL	1,434.6
MASSACHUSETTS MUTUAL LIFE INS CO	MA	226,444.0
MUTUAL OF AMERICA LIFE INS CO	NY	18,135.8
NEW YORK LIFE INS CO	NY	167,828.0
NIPPON LIFE INS CO OF AMERICA	IA	217.7
NORTHWESTERN MUTUAL LIFE INS CO	WI	244,873.0
PACIFIC LIFE INS CO	NE	115,113.0
PHYSICIANS LIFE INS CO	NE	1,549.0
RESERVE NATIONAL INS CO	OK	123.3
SECURIAN LIFE INS CO	MN	478.9
SHELTER LIFE INS CO	MO	1,180.1
STANDARD LIFE & ACCIDENT INS CO	TX	511.2
STANDARD SECURITY LIFE INS CO OF NY	NY	245.0

Rating: B+

INSURANCE COMPANY NAME	DOM. STATE	TOTAL ASSETS ($MIL)
AETNA HEALTH & LIFE INS CO	CT	2,349.9
AMERICAN FAMILY LIFE ASR CO OF COLUM	NE	117,278.0
AMERICAN FIDELITY ASR CO	OK	5,305.5
AMERICAN UNITED LIFE INS CO	IN	23,906.8
ASSURITY LIFE INS CO	NE	2,550.8
AXA EQUITABLE LIFE INS CO	NY	171,038.0
BOSTON MUTUAL LIFE INS CO	MA	1,317.6

INSURANCE COMPANY NAME	DOM. STATE	TOTAL ASSETS ($MIL)
DEARBORN NATIONAL LIFE INS CO	IL	1,969.6
GERBER LIFE INS CO	NY	3,240.4
GOVERNMENT PERSONNEL MUTUAL L I C	TX	834.7
GREAT SOUTHERN LIFE INS CO	TX	218.2
MEDICO CORP LIFE INS CO	NE	45.2
MIDLAND NATIONAL LIFE INS CO	IA	47,985.0
MINNESOTA LIFE INS CO	MN	38,458.7
MUTUAL OF OMAHA INS CO	NE	7,112.9
NATIONAL FARMERS UNION LIFE INS CO	TX	206.0
NEW YORK LIFE INS & ANNUITY CORP	DE	137,896.0
OHIO NATIONAL LIFE ASR CORP	OH	3,833.0
PACIFIC LIFE & ANNUITY CO	AZ	6,374.0
PAN AMERICAN ASR CO	LA	25.4
PRINCIPAL LIFE INS CO	IA	165,432.0
SAVINGS BANK LIFE INS CO OF MA	MA	2,957.5
SOUTHERN PIONEER LIFE INS CO	AR	16.8
STANDARD INS CO	OR	21,220.5
SYMETRA LIFE INS CO	IA	33,273.1
TRUSTMARK INS CO	IL	1,430.6
TRUSTMARK LIFE INS CO	IL	325.4
UNITED WORLD LIFE INS CO	NE	122.6
USABLE LIFE	AR	482.3
VOYA RETIREMENT INS & ANNUITY CO	CT	89,930.9

Iowa

INSURANCE COMPANY NAME	DOM. STATE	TOTAL ASSETS ($MIL)

Rating: A+

INSURANCE COMPANY NAME	DOM. STATE	TOTAL ASSETS ($MIL)
AMERICAN FAMILY LIFE INS CO	WI	5,407.4
COUNTRY LIFE INS CO	IL	10,264.7
PHYSICIANS MUTUAL INS CO	NE	2,153.3
STATE FARM LIFE INS CO	IL	68,156.4
TEACHERS INS & ANNUITY ASN OF AM	NY	276,045.0

Rating: A

INSURANCE COMPANY NAME	DOM. STATE	TOTAL ASSETS ($MIL)
4 EVER LIFE INS CO	IL	211.4
FEDERATED LIFE INS CO	MN	1,710.7
GUARDIAN LIFE INS CO OF AMERICA	NY	50,389.3
MIDWESTERN UNITED LIFE INS CO	IN	235.0
MML BAY STATE LIFE INS CO	CT	4,737.2
NATIONAL WESTERN LIFE INS CO	CO	10,673.8
PARKER CENTENNIAL ASR CO	WI	92.2
SENTRY LIFE INS CO	WI	5,800.9
USAA LIFE INS CO	TX	23,536.5

Rating: A-

INSURANCE COMPANY NAME	DOM. STATE	TOTAL ASSETS ($MIL)
AMALGAMATED LIFE INS CO	NY	122.5
AMERICAN HEALTH & LIFE INS CO	TX	907.2
AMERICAN REPUBLIC INS CO	IA	909.7
ANNUITY INVESTORS LIFE INS CO	OH	3,041.6
ANTHEM LIFE INS CO	IN	630.6
AUTO-OWNERS LIFE INS CO	MI	3,832.7
CENTRAL STATES H & L CO OF OMAHA	NE	421.1
COMPANION LIFE INS CO	SC	329.6
COUNTRY INVESTORS LIFE ASR CO	IL	297.1
DELAWARE AMERICAN LIFE INS CO	DE	145.9
FAMILY HERITAGE LIFE INS CO OF AMER	OH	1,004.9
FIDELITY INVESTMENTS LIFE INS CO	UT	25,080.7
GARDEN STATE LIFE INS CO	TX	126.5
ILLINOIS MUTUAL LIFE INS CO	IL	1,434.6
MASSACHUSETTS MUTUAL LIFE INS CO	MA	226,444.0
MUTUAL OF AMERICA LIFE INS CO	NY	18,135.8
NEW YORK LIFE INS CO	NY	167,828.0
NIPPON LIFE INS CO OF AMERICA	IA	217.7
NORTHWESTERN MUTUAL LIFE INS CO	WI	244,873.0
PACIFIC GUARDIAN LIFE INS CO LTD	HI	544.4
PACIFIC LIFE INS CO	NE	115,113.0
PHYSICIANS LIFE INS CO	NE	1,549.0
RESERVE NATIONAL INS CO	OK	123.3
SECURIAN LIFE INS CO	MN	478.9
SHELTER LIFE INS CO	MO	1,180.1
STANDARD LIFE & ACCIDENT INS CO	TX	511.2
STANDARD SECURITY LIFE INS CO OF NY	NY	245.0

Rating: B+

INSURANCE COMPANY NAME	DOM. STATE	TOTAL ASSETS ($MIL)
AETNA HEALTH & LIFE INS CO	CT	2,349.9
AMERICAN FAMILY LIFE ASR CO OF COLUM	NE	117,278.0
AMERICAN FIDELITY ASR CO	OK	5,305.5
AMERICAN UNITED LIFE INS CO	IN	23,906.8
ASSURITY LIFE INS CO	NE	2,550.8
AXA EQUITABLE LIFE INS CO	NY	171,038.0
BOSTON MUTUAL LIFE INS CO	MA	1,317.6
DEARBORN NATIONAL LIFE INS CO	IL	1,969.6

INSURANCE COMPANY NAME	DOM. STATE	TOTAL ASSETS ($MIL)
FARM BUREAU LIFE INS CO	IA	8,582.6
GERBER LIFE INS CO	NY	3,240.4
GOVERNMENT PERSONNEL MUTUAL L I C	TX	834.7
GREAT SOUTHERN LIFE INS CO	TX	218.2
MEDICO CORP LIFE INS CO	NE	45.2
MIDLAND NATIONAL LIFE INS CO	IA	47,985.0
MINNESOTA LIFE INS CO	MN	38,458.7
MUTUAL OF OMAHA INS CO	NE	7,112.9
NATIONAL FARMERS UNION LIFE INS CO	TX	206.0
NEW YORK LIFE INS & ANNUITY CORP	DE	137,896.0
OHIO NATIONAL LIFE ASR CORP	OH	3,833.0
PACIFIC LIFE & ANNUITY CO	AZ	6,374.0
PRINCIPAL LIFE INS CO	IA	165,432.0
SAVINGS BANK LIFE INS CO OF MA	MA	2,957.5
STANDARD INS CO	OR	21,220.5
SYMETRA LIFE INS CO	IA	33,273.1
TRUSTMARK INS CO	IL	1,430.6
TRUSTMARK LIFE INS CO	IL	325.4
UNITED WORLD LIFE INS CO	NE	122.6
USABLE LIFE	AR	482.3
VOYA RETIREMENT INS & ANNUITY CO	CT	89,930.9

Kansas

INSURANCE COMPANY NAME	DOM. STATE	TOTAL ASSETS ($MIL)

Rating: A+

INSURANCE COMPANY NAME	DOM. STATE	TOTAL ASSETS ($MIL)
AMERICAN FAMILY LIFE INS CO	WI	5,407.4
COUNTRY LIFE INS CO	IL	10,264.7
PHYSICIANS MUTUAL INS CO	NE	2,153.3
STATE FARM LIFE INS CO	IL	68,156.4
TEACHERS INS & ANNUITY ASN OF AM	NY	276,045.0

Rating: A

INSURANCE COMPANY NAME	DOM. STATE	TOTAL ASSETS ($MIL)
4 EVER LIFE INS CO	IL	211.4
FEDERATED LIFE INS CO	MN	1,710.7
GUARDIAN LIFE INS CO OF AMERICA	NY	50,389.3
LIFEWISE ASR CO	WA	143.3
MIDWESTERN UNITED LIFE INS CO	IN	235.0
MML BAY STATE LIFE INS CO	CT	4,737.2
NATIONAL WESTERN LIFE INS CO	CO	10,673.8
PARKER CENTENNIAL ASR CO	WI	92.2
SENTRY LIFE INS CO	WI	5,800.9
USAA LIFE INS CO	TX	23,536.5

Rating: A-

INSURANCE COMPANY NAME	DOM. STATE	TOTAL ASSETS ($MIL)
AMALGAMATED LIFE INS CO	NY	122.5
AMERICAN HEALTH & LIFE INS CO	TX	907.2
AMERICAN REPUBLIC INS CO	IA	909.7
ANNUITY INVESTORS LIFE INS CO	OH	3,041.6
ANTHEM LIFE INS CO	IN	630.6
AUTO-OWNERS LIFE INS CO	MI	3,832.7
CENTRAL STATES H & L CO OF OMAHA	NE	421.1
COMPANION LIFE INS CO	SC	329.6
COUNTRY INVESTORS LIFE ASR CO	IL	297.1
DELAWARE AMERICAN LIFE INS CO	DE	145.9
FAMILY HERITAGE LIFE INS CO OF AMER	OH	1,004.9
FIDELITY INVESTMENTS LIFE INS CO	UT	25,080.7
GARDEN STATE LIFE INS CO	TX	126.5
ILLINOIS MUTUAL LIFE INS CO	IL	1,434.6
MASSACHUSETTS MUTUAL LIFE INS CO	MA	226,444.0
MUTUAL OF AMERICA LIFE INS CO	NY	18,135.8
NEW YORK LIFE INS CO	NY	167,828.0
NIPPON LIFE INS CO OF AMERICA	IA	217.7
NORTHWESTERN MUTUAL LIFE INS CO	WI	244,873.0
PACIFIC LIFE INS CO	NE	115,113.0
PHYSICIANS LIFE INS CO	NE	1,549.0
RESERVE NATIONAL INS CO	OK	123.3
SECURIAN LIFE INS CO	MN	478.9
SHELTER LIFE INS CO	MO	1,180.1
STANDARD LIFE & ACCIDENT INS CO	TX	511.2
STANDARD SECURITY LIFE INS CO OF NY	NY	245.0

Rating: B+

INSURANCE COMPANY NAME	DOM. STATE	TOTAL ASSETS ($MIL)
ADVANCE INS CO OF KS	KS	54.9
AETNA HEALTH & LIFE INS CO	CT	2,349.9
AMERICAN FAMILY LIFE ASR CO OF COLUM	NE	117,278.0
AMERICAN FIDELITY ASR CO	OK	5,305.5
AMERICAN UNITED LIFE INS CO	IN	23,906.8
ASSURITY LIFE INS CO	NE	2,550.8
AXA EQUITABLE LIFE INS CO	NY	171,038.0
BOSTON MUTUAL LIFE INS CO	MA	1,317.6

INSURANCE COMPANY NAME	DOM. STATE	TOTAL ASSETS ($MIL)
DEARBORN NATIONAL LIFE INS CO	IL	1,969.6
FARM BUREAU LIFE INS CO	IA	8,582.6
GERBER LIFE INS CO	NY	3,240.4
GOVERNMENT PERSONNEL MUTUAL L I C	TX	834.7
GREAT SOUTHERN LIFE INS CO	TX	218.2
MEDICO CORP LIFE INS CO	NE	45.2
MIDLAND NATIONAL LIFE INS CO	IA	47,985.0
MINNESOTA LIFE INS CO	MN	38,458.7
MUTUAL OF OMAHA INS CO	NE	7,112.9
NATIONAL FARMERS UNION LIFE INS CO	TX	206.0
NEW YORK LIFE INS & ANNUITY CORP	DE	137,896.0
OHIO NATIONAL LIFE ASR CORP	OH	3,833.0
PACIFIC LIFE & ANNUITY CO	AZ	6,374.0
PAN AMERICAN ASR CO	LA	25.4
PRINCIPAL LIFE INS CO	IA	165,432.0
SAVINGS BANK LIFE INS CO OF MA	MA	2,957.5
SOUTHERN PIONEER LIFE INS CO	AR	16.8
STANDARD INS CO	OR	21,220.5
SYMETRA LIFE INS CO	IA	33,273.1
TRUSTMARK INS CO	IL	1,430.6
TRUSTMARK LIFE INS CO	IL	325.4
UNITED WORLD LIFE INS CO	NE	122.6
USABLE LIFE	AR	482.3
VOYA RETIREMENT INS & ANNUITY CO	CT	89,930.9

Kentucky

INSURANCE COMPANY NAME	DOM. STATE	TOTAL ASSETS ($MIL)
Rating: A+		
AMERICAN FAMILY LIFE INS CO	WI	5,407.4
COUNTRY LIFE INS CO	IL	10,264.7
PHYSICIANS MUTUAL INS CO	NE	2,153.3
STATE FARM LIFE INS CO	IL	68,156.4
TEACHERS INS & ANNUITY ASN OF AM	NY	276,045.0
Rating: A		
4 EVER LIFE INS CO	IL	211.4
FEDERATED LIFE INS CO	MN	1,710.7
GUARDIAN LIFE INS CO OF AMERICA	NY	50,389.3
MIDWESTERN UNITED LIFE INS CO	IN	235.0
MML BAY STATE LIFE INS CO	CT	4,737.2
NATIONAL WESTERN LIFE INS CO	CO	10,673.8
PARKER CENTENNIAL ASR CO	WI	92.2
SENTRY LIFE INS CO	WI	5,800.9
SOUTHERN FARM BUREAU LIFE INS CO	MS	13,583.7
USAA LIFE INS CO	TX	23,536.5
Rating: A-		
AMALGAMATED LIFE INS CO	NY	122.5
AMERICAN HEALTH & LIFE INS CO	TX	907.2
AMERICAN REPUBLIC INS CO	IA	909.7
ANNUITY INVESTORS LIFE INS CO	OH	3,041.6
ANTHEM LIFE INS CO	IN	630.6
AUTO-OWNERS LIFE INS CO	MI	3,832.7
CENTRAL STATES H & L CO OF OMAHA	NE	421.1
COMPANION LIFE INS CO	SC	329.6
COTTON STATES LIFE INS CO	GA	334.6
COUNTRY INVESTORS LIFE ASR CO	IL	297.1
DELAWARE AMERICAN LIFE INS CO	DE	145.9
ERIE FAMILY LIFE INS CO	PA	2,217.2
FAMILY HERITAGE LIFE INS CO OF AMER	OH	1,004.9
FIDELITY INVESTMENTS LIFE INS CO	UT	25,080.7
GARDEN STATE LIFE INS CO	TX	126.5
ILLINOIS MUTUAL LIFE INS CO	IL	1,434.6
LIFE INS CO OF ALABAMA	AL	118.6
MASSACHUSETTS MUTUAL LIFE INS CO	MA	226,444.0
MUTUAL OF AMERICA LIFE INS CO	NY	18,135.8
NEW YORK LIFE INS CO	NY	167,828.0
NIPPON LIFE INS CO OF AMERICA	IA	217.7
NORTHWESTERN MUTUAL LIFE INS CO	WI	244,873.0
PACIFIC LIFE INS CO	NE	115,113.0
PHYSICIANS LIFE INS CO	NE	1,549.0
RESERVE NATIONAL INS CO	OK	123.3
SECURIAN LIFE INS CO	MN	478.9
SHELTER LIFE INS CO	MO	1,180.1
STANDARD LIFE & ACCIDENT INS CO	TX	511.2
STANDARD SECURITY LIFE INS CO OF NY	NY	245.0
Rating: B+		
AETNA HEALTH & LIFE INS CO	CT	2,349.9
AMERICAN FAMILY LIFE ASR CO OF COLUM	NE	117,278.0
AMERICAN FIDELITY ASR CO	OK	5,305.5
AMERICAN UNITED LIFE INS CO	IN	23,906.8
ASSURITY LIFE INS CO	NE	2,550.8

INSURANCE COMPANY NAME	DOM. STATE	TOTAL ASSETS ($MIL)
AXA EQUITABLE LIFE INS CO	NY	171,038.0
BOSTON MUTUAL LIFE INS CO	MA	1,317.6
DEARBORN NATIONAL LIFE INS CO	IL	1,969.6
GERBER LIFE INS CO	NY	3,240.4
GOVERNMENT PERSONNEL MUTUAL L I C	TX	834.7
GREAT SOUTHERN LIFE INS CO	TX	218.2
MEDICO CORP LIFE INS CO	NE	45.2
MIDLAND NATIONAL LIFE INS CO	IA	47,985.0
MINNESOTA LIFE INS CO	MN	38,458.7
MUTUAL OF OMAHA INS CO	NE	7,112.9
NATIONAL FARMERS UNION LIFE INS CO	TX	206.0
NEW YORK LIFE INS & ANNUITY CORP	DE	137,896.0
OHIO NATIONAL LIFE ASR CORP	OH	3,833.0
PACIFIC LIFE & ANNUITY CO	AZ	6,374.0
PAN AMERICAN ASR CO	LA	25.4
PRINCIPAL LIFE INS CO	IA	165,432.0
SAVINGS BANK LIFE INS CO OF MA	MA	2,957.5
SOUTHERN PIONEER LIFE INS CO	AR	16.8
STANDARD INS CO	OR	21,220.5
SYMETRA LIFE INS CO	IA	33,273.1
TRUSTMARK INS CO	IL	1,430.6
TRUSTMARK LIFE INS CO	IL	325.4
UNITED WORLD LIFE INS CO	NE	122.6
USABLE LIFE	AR	482.3
VOYA RETIREMENT INS & ANNUITY CO	CT	89,930.9

Louisiana

INSURANCE COMPANY NAME	DOM. STATE	TOTAL ASSETS ($MIL)

Rating: A+

INSURANCE COMPANY NAME	DOM. STATE	TOTAL ASSETS ($MIL)
AMERICAN FAMILY LIFE INS CO	WI	5,407.4
COUNTRY LIFE INS CO	IL	10,264.7
PHYSICIANS MUTUAL INS CO	NE	2,153.3
STATE FARM LIFE INS CO	IL	68,156.4
TEACHERS INS & ANNUITY ASN OF AM	NY	276,045.0

Rating: A

INSURANCE COMPANY NAME	DOM. STATE	TOTAL ASSETS ($MIL)
4 EVER LIFE INS CO	IL	211.4
FEDERATED LIFE INS CO	MN	1,710.7
GUARDIAN LIFE INS CO OF AMERICA	NY	50,389.3
MIDWESTERN UNITED LIFE INS CO	IN	235.0
MML BAY STATE LIFE INS CO	CT	4,737.2
NATIONAL WESTERN LIFE INS CO	CO	10,673.8
PARKER CENTENNIAL ASR CO	WI	92.2
SENTRY LIFE INS CO	WI	5,800.9
SOUTHERN FARM BUREAU LIFE INS CO	MS	13,583.7
USAA LIFE INS CO	TX	23,536.5

Rating: A-

INSURANCE COMPANY NAME	DOM. STATE	TOTAL ASSETS ($MIL)
AMALGAMATED LIFE INS CO	NY	122.5
AMERICAN HEALTH & LIFE INS CO	TX	907.2
AMERICAN REPUBLIC INS CO	IA	909.7
ANNUITY INVESTORS LIFE INS CO	OH	3,041.6
ANTHEM LIFE INS CO	IN	630.6
CENTRAL STATES H & L CO OF OMAHA	NE	421.1
COMPANION LIFE INS CO	SC	329.6
COTTON STATES LIFE INS CO	GA	334.6
COUNTRY INVESTORS LIFE ASR CO	IL	297.1
DELAWARE AMERICAN LIFE INS CO	DE	145.9
FAMILY HERITAGE LIFE INS CO OF AMER	OH	1,004.9
FIDELITY INVESTMENTS LIFE INS CO	UT	25,080.7
GARDEN STATE LIFE INS CO	TX	126.5
ILLINOIS MUTUAL LIFE INS CO	IL	1,434.6
LIFE INS CO OF ALABAMA	AL	118.6
MASSACHUSETTS MUTUAL LIFE INS CO	MA	226,444.0
MUTUAL OF AMERICA LIFE INS CO	NY	18,135.8
NEW YORK LIFE INS CO	NY	167,828.0
NIPPON LIFE INS CO OF AMERICA	IA	217.7
NORTHWESTERN MUTUAL LIFE INS CO	WI	244,873.0
PACIFIC GUARDIAN LIFE INS CO LTD	HI	544.4
PACIFIC LIFE INS CO	NE	115,113.0
PHYSICIANS LIFE INS CO	NE	1,549.0
RESERVE NATIONAL INS CO	OK	123.3
SECURIAN LIFE INS CO	MN	478.9
SHELTER LIFE INS CO	MO	1,180.1
STANDARD LIFE & ACCIDENT INS CO	TX	511.2
STANDARD SECURITY LIFE INS CO OF NY	NY	245.0

Rating: B+

INSURANCE COMPANY NAME	DOM. STATE	TOTAL ASSETS ($MIL)
AETNA HEALTH & LIFE INS CO	CT	2,349.9
AMERICAN FAMILY LIFE ASR CO OF COLUM	NE	117,278.0
AMERICAN FIDELITY ASR CO	OK	5,305.5
AMERICAN UNITED LIFE INS CO	IN	23,906.8
ASSURITY LIFE INS CO	NE	2,550.8
AXA EQUITABLE LIFE INS CO	NY	171,038.0

INSURANCE COMPANY NAME	DOM. STATE	TOTAL ASSETS ($MIL)
BLUEBONNET LIFE INS CO	MS	58.9
BOSTON MUTUAL LIFE INS CO	MA	1,317.6
DEARBORN NATIONAL LIFE INS CO	IL	1,969.6
GERBER LIFE INS CO	NY	3,240.4
GOVERNMENT PERSONNEL MUTUAL L I C	TX	834.7
GREAT SOUTHERN LIFE INS CO	TX	218.2
MEDICO CORP LIFE INS CO	NE	45.2
MIDLAND NATIONAL LIFE INS CO	IA	47,985.0
MINNESOTA LIFE INS CO	MN	38,458.7
MUTUAL OF OMAHA INS CO	NE	7,112.9
NEW YORK LIFE INS & ANNUITY CORP	DE	137,896.0
OHIO NATIONAL LIFE ASR CORP	OH	3,833.0
PACIFIC LIFE & ANNUITY CO	AZ	6,374.0
PAN AMERICAN ASR CO	LA	25.4
PRINCIPAL LIFE INS CO	IA	165,432.0
SAVINGS BANK LIFE INS CO OF MA	MA	2,957.5
SOUTHERN PIONEER LIFE INS CO	AR	16.8
STANDARD INS CO	OR	21,220.5
SYMETRA LIFE INS CO	IA	33,273.1
TRUSTMARK INS CO	IL	1,430.6
TRUSTMARK LIFE INS CO	IL	325.4
UNITED WORLD LIFE INS CO	NE	122.6
USABLE LIFE	AR	482.3
VOYA RETIREMENT INS & ANNUITY CO	CT	89,930.9

Maine

INSURANCE COMPANY NAME	DOM. STATE	TOTAL ASSETS ($MIL)

Rating: A+

INSURANCE COMPANY NAME	DOM. STATE	TOTAL ASSETS ($MIL)
AMERICAN FAMILY LIFE INS CO	WI	5,407.4
COUNTRY LIFE INS CO	IL	10,264.7
PHYSICIANS MUTUAL INS CO	NE	2,153.3
STATE FARM LIFE INS CO	IL	68,156.4
TEACHERS INS & ANNUITY ASN OF AM	NY	276,045.0

Rating: A

INSURANCE COMPANY NAME	DOM. STATE	TOTAL ASSETS ($MIL)
4 EVER LIFE INS CO	IL	211.4
FEDERATED LIFE INS CO	MN	1,710.7
GUARDIAN LIFE INS CO OF AMERICA	NY	50,389.3
MIDWESTERN UNITED LIFE INS CO	IN	235.0
MML BAY STATE LIFE INS CO	CT	4,737.2
NATIONAL WESTERN LIFE INS CO	CO	10,673.8
PARKER CENTENNIAL ASR CO	WI	92.2
SENTRY LIFE INS CO	WI	5,800.9
USAA LIFE INS CO	TX	23,536.5

Rating: A-

INSURANCE COMPANY NAME	DOM. STATE	TOTAL ASSETS ($MIL)
AMALGAMATED LIFE INS CO	NY	122.5
AMERICAN HEALTH & LIFE INS CO	TX	907.2
AMERICAN REPUBLIC INS CO	IA	909.7
ANNUITY INVESTORS LIFE INS CO	OH	3,041.6
ANTHEM LIFE INS CO	IN	630.6
CENTRAL STATES H & L CO OF OMAHA	NE	421.1
COMPANION LIFE INS CO	SC	329.6
COUNTRY INVESTORS LIFE ASR CO	IL	297.1
DELAWARE AMERICAN LIFE INS CO	DE	145.9
FAMILY HERITAGE LIFE INS CO OF AMER	OH	1,004.9
FIDELITY INVESTMENTS LIFE INS CO	UT	25,080.7
GARDEN STATE LIFE INS CO	TX	126.5
ILLINOIS MUTUAL LIFE INS CO	IL	1,434.6
MASSACHUSETTS MUTUAL LIFE INS CO	MA	226,444.0
MUTUAL OF AMERICA LIFE INS CO	NY	18,135.8
NEW YORK LIFE INS CO	NY	167,828.0
NORTHWESTERN MUTUAL LIFE INS CO	WI	244,873.0
PACIFIC LIFE INS CO	NE	115,113.0
PHYSICIANS LIFE INS CO	NE	1,549.0
RESERVE NATIONAL INS CO	OK	123.3
SECURIAN LIFE INS CO	MN	478.9
STANDARD SECURITY LIFE INS CO OF NY	NY	245.0

Rating: B+

INSURANCE COMPANY NAME	DOM. STATE	TOTAL ASSETS ($MIL)
AETNA HEALTH & LIFE INS CO	CT	2,349.9
AMERICAN FAMILY LIFE ASR CO OF COLUM	NE	117,278.0
AMERICAN FIDELITY ASR CO	OK	5,305.5
AMERICAN UNITED LIFE INS CO	IN	23,906.8
ASSURITY LIFE INS CO	NE	2,550.8
AXA EQUITABLE LIFE INS CO	NY	171,038.0
BOSTON MUTUAL LIFE INS CO	MA	1,317.6
DEARBORN NATIONAL LIFE INS CO	IL	1,969.6
GERBER LIFE INS CO	NY	3,240.4
GOVERNMENT PERSONNEL MUTUAL L I C	TX	834.7
GREAT SOUTHERN LIFE INS CO	TX	218.2
MEDICO CORP LIFE INS CO	NE	45.2
MIDLAND NATIONAL LIFE INS CO	IA	47,985.0

INSURANCE COMPANY NAME	DOM. STATE	TOTAL ASSETS ($MIL)
MINNESOTA LIFE INS CO	MN	38,458.7
MUTUAL OF OMAHA INS CO	NE	7,112.9
NEW YORK LIFE INS & ANNUITY CORP	DE	137,896.0
OHIO NATIONAL LIFE ASR CORP	OH	3,833.0
PACIFIC LIFE & ANNUITY CO	AZ	6,374.0
PRINCIPAL LIFE INS CO	IA	165,432.0
SAVINGS BANK LIFE INS CO OF MA	MA	2,957.5
STANDARD INS CO	OR	21,220.5
SYMETRA LIFE INS CO	IA	33,273.1
TRUSTMARK INS CO	IL	1,430.6
TRUSTMARK LIFE INS CO	IL	325.4
UNITED WORLD LIFE INS CO	NE	122.6
USABLE LIFE	AR	482.3
VOYA RETIREMENT INS & ANNUITY CO	CT	89,930.9

Maryland

INSURANCE COMPANY NAME	DOM. STATE	TOTAL ASSETS ($MIL)
Rating: A+		
AMERICAN FAMILY LIFE INS CO	WI	5,407.4
COUNTRY LIFE INS CO	IL	10,264.7
PHYSICIANS MUTUAL INS CO	NE	2,153.3
STATE FARM LIFE INS CO	IL	68,156.4
TEACHERS INS & ANNUITY ASN OF AM	NY	276,045.0
Rating: A		
4 EVER LIFE INS CO	IL	211.4
FEDERATED LIFE INS CO	MN	1,710.7
GUARDIAN LIFE INS CO OF AMERICA	NY	50,389.3
LIFEWISE ASR CO	WA	143.3
MIDWESTERN UNITED LIFE INS CO	IN	235.0
MML BAY STATE LIFE INS CO	CT	4,737.2
NATIONAL WESTERN LIFE INS CO	CO	10,673.8
PARKER CENTENNIAL ASR CO	WI	92.2
SENTRY LIFE INS CO	WI	5,800.9
SHELTERPOINT LIFE INS CO	NY	105.4
UNITED FARM FAMILY LIFE INS CO	IN	2,234.9
USAA LIFE INS CO	TX	23,536.5
Rating: A-		
AMALGAMATED LIFE INS CO	NY	122.5
AMERICAN HEALTH & LIFE INS CO	TX	907.2
AMERICAN REPUBLIC INS CO	IA	909.7
ANNUITY INVESTORS LIFE INS CO	OH	3,041.6
ANTHEM LIFE INS CO	IN	630.6
CENTRAL STATES H & L CO OF OMAHA	NE	421.1
COMPANION LIFE INS CO	SC	329.6
COUNTRY INVESTORS LIFE ASR CO	IL	297.1
DELAWARE AMERICAN LIFE INS CO	DE	145.9
ERIE FAMILY LIFE INS CO	PA	2,217.2
FAMILY HERITAGE LIFE INS CO OF AMER	OH	1,004.9
FIDELITY INVESTMENTS LIFE INS CO	UT	25,080.7
GARDEN STATE LIFE INS CO	TX	126.5
ILLINOIS MUTUAL LIFE INS CO	IL	1,434.6
MASSACHUSETTS MUTUAL LIFE INS CO	MA	226,444.0
MUTUAL OF AMERICA LIFE INS CO	NY	18,135.8
NEW YORK LIFE INS CO	NY	167,828.0
NIPPON LIFE INS CO OF AMERICA	IA	217.7
NORTHWESTERN MUTUAL LIFE INS CO	WI	244,873.0
PACIFIC LIFE INS CO	NE	115,113.0
PHYSICIANS LIFE INS CO	NE	1,549.0
RESERVE NATIONAL INS CO	OK	123.3
SECURIAN LIFE INS CO	MN	478.9
STANDARD LIFE & ACCIDENT INS CO	TX	511.2
STANDARD SECURITY LIFE INS CO OF NY	NY	245.0
Rating: B+		
AETNA HEALTH & LIFE INS CO	CT	2,349.9
AMERICAN FAMILY LIFE ASR CO OF COLUM	NE	117,278.0
AMERICAN FIDELITY ASR CO	OK	5,305.5
AMERICAN UNITED LIFE INS CO	IN	23,906.8
ASSURITY LIFE INS CO	NE	2,550.8
AXA EQUITABLE LIFE INS CO	NY	171,038.0
BOSTON MUTUAL LIFE INS CO	MA	1,317.6

INSURANCE COMPANY NAME	DOM. STATE	TOTAL ASSETS ($MIL)
DEARBORN NATIONAL LIFE INS CO	IL	1,969.6
GERBER LIFE INS CO	NY	3,240.4
GOVERNMENT PERSONNEL MUTUAL L I C	TX	834.7
GREAT SOUTHERN LIFE INS CO	TX	218.2
MEDICO CORP LIFE INS CO	NE	45.2
MIDLAND NATIONAL LIFE INS CO	IA	47,985.0
MINNESOTA LIFE INS CO	MN	38,458.7
MUTUAL OF OMAHA INS CO	NE	7,112.9
NEW YORK LIFE INS & ANNUITY CORP	DE	137,896.0
OHIO NATIONAL LIFE ASR CORP	OH	3,833.0
PACIFIC LIFE & ANNUITY CO	AZ	6,374.0
PAN AMERICAN ASR CO	LA	25.4
PRINCIPAL LIFE INS CO	IA	165,432.0
SAVINGS BANK LIFE INS CO OF MA	MA	2,957.5
STANDARD INS CO	OR	21,220.5
SYMETRA LIFE INS CO	IA	33,273.1
TRUSTMARK INS CO	IL	1,430.6
TRUSTMARK LIFE INS CO	IL	325.4
UNITED WORLD LIFE INS CO	NE	122.6
USABLE LIFE	AR	482.3
VOYA RETIREMENT INS & ANNUITY CO	CT	89,930.9

Massachusetts

INSURANCE COMPANY NAME	DOM. STATE	TOTAL ASSETS ($MIL)

Rating: A+

INSURANCE COMPANY NAME	DOM. STATE	TOTAL ASSETS ($MIL)
AMERICAN FAMILY LIFE INS CO	WI	5,407.4
COUNTRY LIFE INS CO	IL	10,264.7
PHYSICIANS MUTUAL INS CO	NE	2,153.3
TEACHERS INS & ANNUITY ASN OF AM	NY	276,045.0

Rating: A

INSURANCE COMPANY NAME	DOM. STATE	TOTAL ASSETS ($MIL)
4 EVER LIFE INS CO	IL	211.4
FEDERATED LIFE INS CO	MN	1,710.7
GUARDIAN LIFE INS CO OF AMERICA	NY	50,389.3
MIDWESTERN UNITED LIFE INS CO	IN	235.0
MML BAY STATE LIFE INS CO	CT	4,737.2
NATIONAL WESTERN LIFE INS CO	CO	10,673.8
PARKER CENTENNIAL ASR CO	WI	92.2
SENTRY LIFE INS CO	WI	5,800.9
SHELTERPOINT LIFE INS CO	NY	105.4
UNITED FARM FAMILY LIFE INS CO	IN	2,234.9
USAA LIFE INS CO	TX	23,536.5

Rating: A-

INSURANCE COMPANY NAME	DOM. STATE	TOTAL ASSETS ($MIL)
AMALGAMATED LIFE INS CO	NY	122.5
AMERICAN FAMILY LIFE ASR CO OF NY	NY	885.2
AMERICAN HEALTH & LIFE INS CO	TX	907.2
AMERICAN REPUBLIC INS CO	IA	909.7
ANNUITY INVESTORS LIFE INS CO	OH	3,041.6
ANTHEM LIFE INS CO	IN	630.6
CENTRAL STATES H & L CO OF OMAHA	NE	421.1
COMPANION LIFE INS CO	SC	329.6
COUNTRY INVESTORS LIFE ASR CO	IL	297.1
DELAWARE AMERICAN LIFE INS CO	DE	145.9
FAMILY HERITAGE LIFE INS CO OF AMER	OH	1,004.9
FIDELITY INVESTMENTS LIFE INS CO	UT	25,080.7
GARDEN STATE LIFE INS CO	TX	126.5
ILLINOIS MUTUAL LIFE INS CO	IL	1,434.6
MASSACHUSETTS MUTUAL LIFE INS CO	MA	226,444.0
MUTUAL OF AMERICA LIFE INS CO	NY	18,135.8
NEW YORK LIFE INS CO	NY	167,828.0
NIPPON LIFE INS CO OF AMERICA	IA	217.7
NORTHWESTERN MUTUAL LIFE INS CO	WI	244,873.0
PACIFIC LIFE INS CO	NE	115,113.0
PHYSICIANS LIFE INS CO	NE	1,549.0
RESERVE NATIONAL INS CO	OK	123.3
SECURIAN LIFE INS CO	MN	478.9
STANDARD LIFE & ACCIDENT INS CO	TX	511.2
STANDARD SECURITY LIFE INS CO OF NY	NY	245.0

Rating: B+

INSURANCE COMPANY NAME	DOM. STATE	TOTAL ASSETS ($MIL)
AETNA HEALTH & LIFE INS CO	CT	2,349.9
AMERICAN FAMILY LIFE ASR CO OF COLUM	NE	117,278.0
AMERICAN FIDELITY ASR CO	OK	5,305.5
AMERICAN UNITED LIFE INS CO	IN	23,906.8
ASSURITY LIFE INS CO	NE	2,550.8
AXA EQUITABLE LIFE INS CO	NY	171,038.0
BOSTON MUTUAL LIFE INS CO	MA	1,317.6
DEARBORN NATIONAL LIFE INS CO	IL	1,969.6
GERBER LIFE INS CO	NY	3,240.4

INSURANCE COMPANY NAME	DOM. STATE	TOTAL ASSETS ($MIL)
GOVERNMENT PERSONNEL MUTUAL L I C	TX	834.7
GREAT SOUTHERN LIFE INS CO	TX	218.2
MIDLAND NATIONAL LIFE INS CO	IA	47,985.0
MINNESOTA LIFE INS CO	MN	38,458.7
MUTUAL OF OMAHA INS CO	NE	7,112.9
NEW YORK LIFE INS & ANNUITY CORP	DE	137,896.0
OHIO NATIONAL LIFE ASR CORP	OH	3,833.0
PACIFIC LIFE & ANNUITY CO	AZ	6,374.0
PRINCIPAL LIFE INS CO	IA	165,432.0
SAVINGS BANK LIFE INS CO OF MA	MA	2,957.5
STANDARD INS CO	OR	21,220.5
SYMETRA LIFE INS CO	IA	33,273.1
TRUSTMARK INS CO	IL	1,430.6
TRUSTMARK LIFE INS CO	IL	325.4
UNITED WORLD LIFE INS CO	NE	122.6
USABLE LIFE	AR	482.3
VOYA RETIREMENT INS & ANNUITY CO	CT	89,900.9

Michigan

INSURANCE COMPANY NAME	DOM. STATE	TOTAL ASSETS ($MIL)

Rating: A+

INSURANCE COMPANY NAME	DOM. STATE	TOTAL ASSETS ($MIL)
AMERICAN FAMILY LIFE INS CO	WI	5,407.4
COUNTRY LIFE INS CO	IL	10,264.7
PHYSICIANS MUTUAL INS CO	NE	2,153.3
STATE FARM LIFE INS CO	IL	68,156.4
TEACHERS INS & ANNUITY ASN OF AM	NY	276,045.0

Rating: A

INSURANCE COMPANY NAME	DOM. STATE	TOTAL ASSETS ($MIL)
4 EVER LIFE INS CO	IL	211.4
FEDERATED LIFE INS CO	MN	1,710.7
GUARDIAN LIFE INS CO OF AMERICA	NY	50,389.3
MIDWESTERN UNITED LIFE INS CO	IN	235.0
MML BAY STATE LIFE INS CO	CT	4,737.2
NATIONAL WESTERN LIFE INS CO	CO	10,673.8
PARKER CENTENNIAL ASR CO	WI	92.2
SENTRY LIFE INS CO	WI	5,800.9
SHELTERPOINT LIFE INS CO	NY	105.4
USAA LIFE INS CO	TX	23,536.5

Rating: A-

INSURANCE COMPANY NAME	DOM. STATE	TOTAL ASSETS ($MIL)
AMALGAMATED LIFE INS CO	NY	122.5
AMERICAN HEALTH & LIFE INS CO	TX	907.2
AMERICAN REPUBLIC INS CO	IA	909.7
ANNUITY INVESTORS LIFE INS CO	OH	3,041.6
ANTHEM LIFE INS CO	IN	630.6
AUTO-OWNERS LIFE INS CO	MI	3,832.7
CENTRAL STATES H & L CO OF OMAHA	NE	421.1
COMPANION LIFE INS CO	SC	329.6
COUNTRY INVESTORS LIFE ASR CO	IL	297.1
DELAWARE AMERICAN LIFE INS CO	DE	145.9
FAMILY HERITAGE LIFE INS CO OF AMER	OH	1,004.9
FARM BUREAU LIFE INS CO OF MICHIGAN	MI	2,361.9
FIDELITY INVESTMENTS LIFE INS CO	UT	25,080.7
GARDEN STATE LIFE INS CO	TX	126.5
ILLINOIS MUTUAL LIFE INS CO	IL	1,434.6
MASSACHUSETTS MUTUAL LIFE INS CO	MA	226,444.0
MUTUAL OF AMERICA LIFE INS CO	NY	18,135.8
NEW YORK LIFE INS CO	NY	167,828.0
NIPPON LIFE INS CO OF AMERICA	IA	217.7
NORTHWESTERN MUTUAL LIFE INS CO	WI	244,873.0
PACIFIC LIFE INS CO	NE	115,113.0
PHYSICIANS LIFE INS CO	NE	1,549.0
RESERVE NATIONAL INS CO	OK	123.3
SECURIAN LIFE INS CO	MN	478.9
STANDARD LIFE & ACCIDENT INS CO	TX	511.2
STANDARD SECURITY LIFE INS CO OF NY	NY	245.0

Rating: B+

INSURANCE COMPANY NAME	DOM. STATE	TOTAL ASSETS ($MIL)
AETNA HEALTH & LIFE INS CO	CT	2,349.9
AMERICAN FAMILY LIFE ASR CO OF COLUM	NE	117,278.0
AMERICAN FIDELITY ASR CO	OK	5,305.5
AMERICAN UNITED LIFE INS CO	IN	23,906.8
ASSURITY LIFE INS CO	NE	2,550.8
AXA EQUITABLE LIFE INS CO	NY	171,038.0
BOSTON MUTUAL LIFE INS CO	MA	1,317.6
DEARBORN NATIONAL LIFE INS CO	IL	1,969.6

INSURANCE COMPANY NAME	DOM. STATE	TOTAL ASSETS ($MIL)
GERBER LIFE INS CO	NY	3,240.4
GOVERNMENT PERSONNEL MUTUAL L I C	TX	834.7
GREAT SOUTHERN LIFE INS CO	TX	218.2
JOHN HANCOCK LIFE INS CO OF NY	NY	17,005.3
LOCOMOTIVE ENGRS&COND MUT PROT ASSN	MI	63.0
MEDICO CORP LIFE INS CO	NE	45.2
MIDLAND NATIONAL LIFE INS CO	IA	47,985.0
MINNESOTA LIFE INS CO	MN	38,458.7
MUTUAL OF OMAHA INS CO	NE	7,112.9
NATIONAL FARMERS UNION LIFE INS CO	TX	206.0
NEW YORK LIFE INS & ANNUITY CORP	DE	137,896.0
OHIO NATIONAL LIFE ASR CORP	OH	3,833.0
PACIFIC LIFE & ANNUITY CO	AZ	6,374.0
PAN AMERICAN ASR CO	LA	25.4
PRINCIPAL LIFE INS CO	IA	165,432.0
SAVINGS BANK LIFE INS CO OF MA	MA	2,957.5
STANDARD INS CO	OR	21,220.5
SYMETRA LIFE INS CO	IA	33,273.1
TRUSTMARK INS CO	IL	1,430.6
TRUSTMARK LIFE INS CO	IL	325.4
UNITED WORLD LIFE INS CO	NE	122.6
USABLE LIFE	AR	482.3
VOYA RETIREMENT INS & ANNUITY CO	CT	89,930.9

Minnesota

INSURANCE COMPANY NAME	DOM. STATE	TOTAL ASSETS ($MIL)

Rating: A+

INSURANCE COMPANY NAME	DOM. STATE	TOTAL ASSETS ($MIL)
AMERICAN FAMILY LIFE INS CO	WI	5,407.4
COUNTRY LIFE INS CO	IL	10,264.7
PHYSICIANS MUTUAL INS CO	NE	2,153.3
STATE FARM LIFE INS CO	IL	68,156.4
TEACHERS INS & ANNUITY ASN OF AM	NY	276,045.0

Rating: A

INSURANCE COMPANY NAME	DOM. STATE	TOTAL ASSETS ($MIL)
4 EVER LIFE INS CO	IL	211.4
FEDERATED LIFE INS CO	MN	1,710.7
GUARDIAN LIFE INS CO OF AMERICA	NY	50,389.3
MIDWESTERN UNITED LIFE INS CO	IN	235.0
MML BAY STATE LIFE INS CO	CT	4,737.2
NATIONAL WESTERN LIFE INS CO	CO	10,673.8
PARKER CENTENNIAL ASR CO	WI	92.2
SENTRY LIFE INS CO	WI	5,800.9
SHELTERPOINT LIFE INS CO	NY	105.4
USAA LIFE INS CO	TX	23,536.5

Rating: A-

INSURANCE COMPANY NAME	DOM. STATE	TOTAL ASSETS ($MIL)
ALLIANZ LIFE INS CO OF NY	NY	3,131.2
AMALGAMATED LIFE INS CO	NY	122.5
AMERICAN HEALTH & LIFE INS CO	TX	907.2
AMERICAN REPUBLIC INS CO	IA	909.7
ANNUITY INVESTORS LIFE INS CO	OH	3,041.6
ANTHEM LIFE INS CO	IN	630.6
AUTO-OWNERS LIFE INS CO	MI	3,832.7
CENTRAL STATES H & I CO OF OMAHA	NE	421.1
COMPANION LIFE INS CO	SC	329.6
COUNTRY INVESTORS LIFE ASR CO	IL	297.1
DELAWARE AMERICAN LIFE INS CO	DE	145.9
ERIE FAMILY LIFE INS CO	PA	2,217.2
FAMILY HERITAGE LIFE INS CO OF AMER	OH	1,004.9
FIDELITY INVESTMENTS LIFE INS CO	UT	25,080.7
GARDEN STATE LIFE INS CO	TX	126.5
ILLINOIS MUTUAL LIFE INS CO	IL	1,434.6
MASSACHUSETTS MUTUAL LIFE INS CO	MA	226,444.0
MUTUAL OF AMERICA LIFE INS CO	NY	18,135.8
NEW YORK LIFE INS CO	NY	167,828.0
NIPPON LIFE INS CO OF AMERICA	IA	217.7
NORTHWESTERN MUTUAL LIFE INS CO	WI	244,873.0
PACIFIC LIFE INS CO	NE	115,113.0
PHYSICIANS LIFE INS CO	NE	1,549.0
RESERVE NATIONAL INS CO	OK	123.3
SECURIAN LIFE INS CO	MN	478.9
STANDARD LIFE & ACCIDENT INS CO	TX	511.2
STANDARD SECURITY LIFE INS CO OF NY	NY	245.0

Rating: B+

INSURANCE COMPANY NAME	DOM. STATE	TOTAL ASSETS ($MIL)
AETNA HEALTH & LIFE INS CO	CT	2,349.9
AMERICAN FAMILY LIFE ASR CO OF COLUM	NE	117,278.0
AMERICAN FIDELITY ASR CO	OK	5,305.5
AMERICAN UNITED LIFE INS CO	IN	23,906.8
ASSURITY LIFE INS CO	NE	2,550.8
AXA EQUITABLE LIFE INS CO	NY	171,038.0
BOSTON MUTUAL LIFE INS CO	MA	1,317.6

INSURANCE COMPANY NAME	DOM. STATE	TOTAL ASSETS ($MIL)
DEARBORN NATIONAL LIFE INS CO	IL	1,969.6
FARM BUREAU LIFE INS CO	IA	8,582.6
GERBER LIFE INS CO	NY	3,240.4
GOVERNMENT PERSONNEL MUTUAL L I C	TX	834.7
GREAT SOUTHERN LIFE INS CO	TX	218.2
MEDICO CORP LIFE INS CO	NE	45.2
MIDLAND NATIONAL LIFE INS CO	IA	47,985.0
MINNESOTA LIFE INS CO	MN	38,458.7
MUTUAL OF OMAHA INS CO	NE	7,112.9
NATIONAL FARMERS UNION LIFE INS CO	TX	206.0
NEW YORK LIFE INS & ANNUITY CORP	DE	137,896.0
OHIO NATIONAL LIFE ASR CORP	OH	3,833.0
PACIFIC LIFE & ANNUITY CO	AZ	6,374.0
PAN AMERICAN ASR CO	LA	25.4
PRINCIPAL LIFE INS CO	IA	165,432.0
SAVINGS BANK LIFE INS CO OF MA	MA	2,957.5
STANDARD INS CO	OR	21,220.5
SYMETRA LIFE INS CO	IA	33,273.1
TRUSTMARK INS CO	IL	1,430.6
TRUSTMARK LIFE INS CO	IL	325.4
UNITED WORLD LIFE INS CO	NE	122.6
USABLE LIFE	AR	482.3
VOYA RETIREMENT INS & ANNUITY CO	CT	89,930.9

Mississippi

INSURANCE COMPANY NAME	DOM. STATE	TOTAL ASSETS ($MIL)

Rating: A+

INSURANCE COMPANY NAME	DOM. STATE	TOTAL ASSETS ($MIL)
AMERICAN FAMILY LIFE INS CO	WI	5,407.4
COUNTRY LIFE INS CO	IL	10,264.7
PHYSICIANS MUTUAL INS CO	NE	2,153.3
STATE FARM LIFE INS CO	IL	68,156.4
TEACHERS INS & ANNUITY ASN OF AM	NY	276,045.0

Rating: A

INSURANCE COMPANY NAME	DOM. STATE	TOTAL ASSETS ($MIL)
4 EVER LIFE INS CO	IL	211.4
FEDERATED LIFE INS CO	MN	1,710.7
GUARDIAN LIFE INS CO OF AMERICA	NY	50,389.3
MIDWESTERN UNITED LIFE INS CO	IN	235.0
MML BAY STATE LIFE INS CO	CT	4,737.2
NATIONAL WESTERN LIFE INS CO	CO	10,673.8
PARKER CENTENNIAL ASR CO	WI	92.2
SENTRY LIFE INS CO	WI	5,800.9
SOUTHERN FARM BUREAU LIFE INS CO	MS	13,583.7
USAA LIFE INS CO	TX	23,536.5

Rating: A-

INSURANCE COMPANY NAME	DOM. STATE	TOTAL ASSETS ($MIL)
AMALGAMATED LIFE INS CO	NY	122.5
AMERICAN HEALTH & LIFE INS CO	TX	907.2
AMERICAN REPUBLIC INS CO	IA	909.7
ANNUITY INVESTORS LIFE INS CO	OH	3,041.6
ANTHEM LIFE INS CO	IN	630.6
AUTO-OWNERS LIFE INS CO	MI	3,832.7
CENTRAL STATES H & L CO OF OMAHA	NE	421.1
COMPANION LIFE INS CO	SC	329.6
COTTON STATES LIFE INS CO	GA	334.6
COUNTRY INVESTORS LIFE ASR CO	IL	297.1
DELAWARE AMERICAN LIFE INS CO	DE	145.9
FAMILY HERITAGE LIFE INS CO OF AMER	OH	1,004.9
FIDELITY INVESTMENTS LIFE INS CO	UT	25,080.7
GARDEN STATE LIFE INS CO	TX	126.5
ILLINOIS MUTUAL LIFE INS CO	IL	1,434.6
LIFE INS CO OF ALABAMA	AL	118.6
MASSACHUSETTS MUTUAL LIFE INS CO	MA	226,444.0
MUTUAL OF AMERICA LIFE INS CO	NY	18,135.8
NEW YORK LIFE INS CO	NY	167,828.0
NIPPON LIFE INS CO OF AMERICA	IA	217.7
NORTHWESTERN MUTUAL LIFE INS CO	WI	244,873.0
PACIFIC LIFE INS CO	NE	115,113.0
PHYSICIANS LIFE INS CO	NE	1,549.0
RESERVE NATIONAL INS CO	OK	123.3
SECURIAN LIFE INS CO	MN	478.9
SHELTER LIFE INS CO	MO	1,180.1
STANDARD LIFE & ACCIDENT INS CO	TX	511.2
STANDARD SECURITY LIFE INS CO OF NY	NY	245.0

Rating: B+

INSURANCE COMPANY NAME	DOM. STATE	TOTAL ASSETS ($MIL)
AETNA HEALTH & LIFE INS CO	CT	2,349.9
AMERICAN FAMILY LIFE ASR CO OF COLUM	NE	117,278.0
AMERICAN FIDELITY ASR CO	OK	5,305.5
AMERICAN UNITED LIFE INS CO	IN	23,906.8
ASSURITY LIFE INS CO	NE	2,550.8
AXA EQUITABLE LIFE INS CO	NY	171,038.0

INSURANCE COMPANY NAME	DOM. STATE	TOTAL ASSETS ($MIL)
BLUEBONNET LIFE INS CO	MS	58.9
BOSTON MUTUAL LIFE INS CO	MA	1,317.6
DEARBORN NATIONAL LIFE INS CO	IL	1,969.6
GERBER LIFE INS CO	NY	3,240.4
GOVERNMENT PERSONNEL MUTUAL L I C	TX	834.7
GREAT SOUTHERN LIFE INS CO	TX	218.2
GREATER GEORGIA LIFE INS CO	GA	58.6
MEDICO CORP LIFE INS CO	NE	45.2
MIDLAND NATIONAL LIFE INS CO	IA	47,985.0
MINNESOTA LIFE INS CO	MN	38,458.7
MUTUAL OF OMAHA INS CO	NE	7,112.9
NATIONAL FARMERS UNION LIFE INS CO	TX	206.0
NEW YORK LIFE INS & ANNUITY CORP	DE	137,896.0
OHIO NATIONAL LIFE ASR CORP	OH	3,833.0
PACIFIC LIFE & ANNUITY CO	AZ	6,374.0
PAN AMERICAN ASR CO	LA	25.4
PRINCIPAL LIFE INS CO	IA	165,432.0
SAVINGS BANK LIFE INS CO OF MA	MA	2,957.5
SOUTHERN PIONEER LIFE INS CO	AR	16.8
STANDARD INS CO	OR	21,220.5
SYMETRA LIFE INS CO	IA	33,273.1
TRUSTMARK INS CO	IL	1,430.6
TRUSTMARK LIFE INS CO	IL	325.4
UNITED WORLD LIFE INS CO	NE	122.6
USABLE LIFE	AR	482.3
VOYA RETIREMENT INS & ANNUITY CO	CT	89,930.9

Missouri

INSURANCE COMPANY NAME	DOM. STATE	TOTAL ASSETS ($MIL)	INSURANCE COMPANY NAME	DOM. STATE	TOTAL ASSETS ($MIL)
			AXA EQUITABLE LIFE INS CO	NY	171,038.0
			BOSTON MUTUAL LIFE INS CO	MA	1,317.6
Rating: A+			DEARBORN NATIONAL LIFE INS CO	IL	1,969.6
			GERBER LIFE INS CO	NY	3,240.4
AMERICAN FAMILY LIFE INS CO	WI	5,407.4	GOVERNMENT PERSONNEL MUTUAL L I C	TX	834.7
COUNTRY LIFE INS CO	IL	10,264.7	GREAT SOUTHERN LIFE INS CO	TX	218.2
PHYSICIANS MUTUAL INS CO	NE	2,153.3	MEDICO CORP LIFE INS CO	NE	45.2
STATE FARM LIFE INS CO	IL	68,156.4	MIDLAND NATIONAL LIFE INS CO	IA	47,985.0
TEACHERS INS & ANNUITY ASN OF AM	NY	276,045.0	MINNESOTA LIFE INS CO	MN	38,458.7
			MUTUAL OF OMAHA INS CO	NE	7,112.9
Rating: A			NATIONAL FARMERS UNION LIFE INS CO	TX	206.0
			NEW YORK LIFE INS & ANNUITY CORP	DE	137,896.0
4 EVER LIFE INS CO	IL	211.4	OHIO NATIONAL LIFE ASR CORP	OH	3,833.0
FEDERATED LIFE INS CO	MN	1,710.7	PACIFIC LIFE & ANNUITY CO	AZ	6,374.0
GUARDIAN LIFE INS CO OF AMERICA	NY	50,389.3	PAN AMERICAN ASR CO	LA	25.4
MIDWESTERN UNITED LIFE INS CO	IN	235.0	PRINCIPAL LIFE INS CO	IA	165,432.0
MML BAY STATE LIFE INS CO	CT	4,737.2	SAVINGS BANK LIFE INS CO OF MA	MA	2,957.5
NATIONAL WESTERN LIFE INS CO	CO	10,673.8	SOUTHERN PIONEER LIFE INS CO	AR	16.8
PARKER CENTENNIAL ASR CO	WI	92.2	STANDARD INS CO	OR	21,220.5
SENTRY LIFE INS CO	WI	5,800.9	SYMETRA LIFE INS CO	IA	33,273.1
USAA LIFE INS CO	TX	23,536.5	TRUSTMARK INS CO	IL	1,430.6
			TRUSTMARK LIFE INS CO	IL	325.4
Rating: A-			UNITED WORLD LIFE INS CO	NE	122.6
			USABLE LIFE	AR	482.3
ALLIANZ LIFE INS CO OF NY	NY	3,131.2	VOYA RETIREMENT INS & ANNUITY CO	CT	89,930.9
AMALGAMATED LIFE INS CO	NY	122.5			
AMERICAN HEALTH & LIFE INS CO	TX	907.2			
AMERICAN REPUBLIC INS CO	IA	909.7			
ANNUITY INVESTORS LIFE INS CO	OH	3,041.6			
ANTHEM LIFE INS CO	IN	630.6			
AUTO-OWNERS LIFE INS CO	MI	3,832.7			
CENTRAL STATES H & L CO OF OMAHA	NE	421.1			
CIGNA LIFE INS CO OF NEW YORK	NY	380.3			
COMPANION LIFE INS CO	SC	329.6			
COUNTRY INVESTORS LIFE ASR CO	IL	297.1			
DELAWARE AMERICAN LIFE INS CO	DE	145.9			
FAMILY HERITAGE LIFE INS CO OF AMER	OH	1,004.9			
FARM BUREAU LIFE INS CO OF MISSOURI	MO	558.9			
FIDELITY INVESTMENTS LIFE INS CO	UT	25,080.7			
GARDEN STATE LIFE INS CO	TX	126.5			
ILLINOIS MUTUAL LIFE INS CO	IL	1,434.6			
MASSACHUSETTS MUTUAL LIFE INS CO	MA	226,444.0			
MUTUAL OF AMERICA LIFE INS CO	NY	18,135.8			
NEW YORK LIFE INS CO	NY	107,020.0			
NIPPON LIFE INS CO OF AMERICA	IA	217.7			
NORTHWESTERN MUTUAL LIFE INS CO	WI	244,873.0			
PACIFIC GUARDIAN LIFE INS CO LTD	HI	544.4			
PACIFIC LIFE INS CO	NE	115,113.0			
PHYSICIANS LIFE INS CO	NE	1,549.0			
RESERVE NATIONAL INS CO	OK	123.3			
SECURIAN LIFE INS CO	MN	478.9			
SHELTER LIFE INS CO	MO	1,180.1			
STANDARD LIFE & ACCIDENT INS CO	TX	511.2			
STANDARD SECURITY LIFE INS CO OF NY	NY	245.0			

Rating: B+

INSURANCE COMPANY NAME	DOM. STATE	TOTAL ASSETS ($MIL)
AETNA HEALTH & LIFE INS CO	CT	2,349.9
AMERICAN FAMILY LIFE ASR CO OF COLUM	NE	117,278.0
AMERICAN FIDELITY ASR CO	OK	5,305.5
AMERICAN UNITED LIFE INS CO	IN	23,906.8
ASSURITY LIFE INS CO	NE	2,550.8

Montana

INSURANCE COMPANY NAME	DOM. STATE	TOTAL ASSETS ($MIL)
Rating: A+		
AMERICAN FAMILY LIFE INS CO	WI	5,407.4
COUNTRY LIFE INS CO	IL	10,264.7
PHYSICIANS MUTUAL INS CO	NE	2,153.3
STATE FARM LIFE INS CO	IL	68,156.4
TEACHERS INS & ANNUITY ASN OF AM	NY	276,045.0
Rating: A		
4 EVER LIFE INS CO	IL	211.4
FEDERATED LIFE INS CO	MN	1,710.7
GUARDIAN LIFE INS CO OF AMERICA	NY	50,389.3
LIFEWISE ASR CO	WA	143.3
MIDWESTERN UNITED LIFE INS CO	IN	235.0
MML BAY STATE LIFE INS CO	CT	4,737.2
NATIONAL WESTERN LIFE INS CO	CO	10,673.8
PARKER CENTENNIAL ASR CO	WI	92.2
SENTRY LIFE INS CO	WI	5,800.9
USAA LIFE INS CO	TX	23,536.5
Rating: A-		
AMALGAMATED LIFE INS CO	NY	122.5
AMERICAN HEALTH & LIFE INS CO	TX	907.2
AMERICAN REPUBLIC INS CO	IA	909.7
ANNUITY INVESTORS LIFE INS CO	OH	3,041.6
ANTHEM LIFE INS CO	IN	630.6
CENTRAL STATES H & L CO OF OMAHA	NE	421.1
COMPANION LIFE INS CO	SC	329.6
COUNTRY INVESTORS LIFE ASR CO	IL	297.1
DELAWARE AMERICAN LIFE INS CO	DE	145.9
FAMILY HERITAGE LIFE INS CO OF AMER	OH	1,004.9
FIDELITY INVESTMENTS LIFE INS CO	UT	25,080.7
GARDEN STATE LIFE INS CO	TX	126.5
ILLINOIS MUTUAL LIFE INS CO	IL	1,434.6
MASSACHUSETTS MUTUAL LIFE INS CO	MA	226,444.0
MUTUAL OF AMERICA LIFE INS CO	NY	18,135.8
NEW YORK LIFE INS CO	NY	167,828.0
NIPPON LIFE INS CO OF AMERICA	IA	217.7
NORTHWESTERN MUTUAL LIFE INS CO	WI	244,873.0
PACIFIC GUARDIAN LIFE INS CO LTD	HI	544.4
PACIFIC LIFE INS CO	NE	115,113.0
PHYSICIANS LIFE INS CO	NE	1,549.0
RESERVE NATIONAL INS CO	OK	123.3
SECURIAN LIFE INS CO	MN	478.9
STANDARD LIFE & ACCIDENT INS CO	TX	511.2
STANDARD SECURITY LIFE INS CO OF NY	NY	245.0
Rating: B+		
AETNA HEALTH & LIFE INS CO	CT	2,349.9
AMERICAN FAMILY LIFE ASR CO OF COLUM	NE	117,278.0
AMERICAN FIDELITY ASR CO	OK	5,305.5
AMERICAN UNITED LIFE INS CO	IN	23,906.8
ASSURITY LIFE INS CO	NE	2,550.8
AXA EQUITABLE LIFE INS CO	NY	171,038.0
BOSTON MUTUAL LIFE INS CO	MA	1,317.6
DEARBORN NATIONAL LIFE INS CO	IL	1,969.6
FARM BUREAU LIFE INS CO	IA	8,582.6

INSURANCE COMPANY NAME	DOM. STATE	TOTAL ASSETS ($MIL)
GERBER LIFE INS CO	NY	3,240.4
GOVERNMENT PERSONNEL MUTUAL L I C	TX	834.7
GREAT SOUTHERN LIFE INS CO	TX	218.2
MEDICO CORP LIFE INS CO	NE	45.2
MIDLAND NATIONAL LIFE INS CO	IA	47,985.0
MINNESOTA LIFE INS CO	MN	38,458.7
MUTUAL OF OMAHA INS CO	NE	7,112.9
NATIONAL FARMERS UNION LIFE INS CO	TX	206.0
NEW YORK LIFE INS & ANNUITY CORP	DE	137,896.0
OHIO NATIONAL LIFE ASR CORP	OH	3,833.0
PACIFIC LIFE & ANNUITY CO	AZ	6,374.0
PAN AMERICAN ASR CO	LA	25.4
PRINCIPAL LIFE INS CO	IA	165,432.0
SAVINGS BANK LIFE INS CO OF MA	MA	2,957.5
STANDARD INS CO	OR	21,220.5
SYMETRA LIFE INS CO	IA	33,273.1
TRUSTMARK INS CO	IL	1,430.6
TRUSTMARK LIFE INS CO	IL	325.4
UNITED WORLD LIFE INS CO	NE	122.6
USABLE LIFE	AR	482.3
VOYA RETIREMENT INS & ANNUITY CO	CT	89,930.9

Nebraska

INSURANCE COMPANY NAME	DOM. STATE	TOTAL ASSETS ($MIL)

Rating: A+

INSURANCE COMPANY NAME	DOM. STATE	TOTAL ASSETS ($MIL)
AMERICAN FAMILY LIFE INS CO	WI	5,407.4
COUNTRY LIFE INS CO	IL	10,264.7
PHYSICIANS MUTUAL INS CO	NE	2,153.3
STATE FARM LIFE INS CO	IL	68,156.4
TEACHERS INS & ANNUITY ASN OF AM	NY	276,045.0

Rating: A

INSURANCE COMPANY NAME	DOM. STATE	TOTAL ASSETS ($MIL)
4 EVER LIFE INS CO	IL	211.4
FEDERATED LIFE INS CO	MN	1,710.7
GUARDIAN LIFE INS CO OF AMERICA	NY	50,389.3
MIDWESTERN UNITED LIFE INS CO	IN	235.0
MML BAY STATE LIFE INS CO	CT	4,737.2
NATIONAL WESTERN LIFE INS CO	CO	10,673.8
PARKER CENTENNIAL ASR CO	WI	92.2
SENTRY LIFE INS CO	WI	5,800.9
USAA LIFE INS CO	TX	23,536.5

Rating: A-

INSURANCE COMPANY NAME	DOM. STATE	TOTAL ASSETS ($MIL)
AMALGAMATED LIFE INS CO	NY	122.5
AMERICAN HEALTH & LIFE INS CO	TX	907.2
AMERICAN REPUBLIC INS CO	IA	909.7
ANNUITY INVESTORS LIFE INS CO	OH	3,041.6
ANTHEM LIFE INS CO	IN	630.6
AUTO-OWNERS LIFE INS CO	MI	3,832.7
CENTRAL STATES H & L CO OF OMAHA	NE	421.1
COMPANION LIFE INS CO	SC	329.6
COUNTRY INVESTORS LIFE ASR CO	IL	297.1
DELAWARE AMERICAN LIFE INS CO	DE	145.9
FAMILY HERITAGE LIFE INS CO OF AMER	OH	1,004.9
FIDELITY INVESTMENTS LIFE INS CO	UT	25,080.7
GARDEN STATE LIFE INS CO	TX	126.5
ILLINOIS MUTUAL LIFE INS CO	IL	1,434.6
MASSACHUSETTS MUTUAL LIFE INS CO	MA	226,444.0
MUTUAL OF AMERICA LIFE INS CO	NY	18,135.8
NEW YORK LIFE INS CO	NY	167,828.0
NIPPON LIFE INS CO OF AMERICA	IA	217.7
NORTHWESTERN MUTUAL LIFE INS CO	WI	244,873.0
PACIFIC GUARDIAN LIFE INS CO LTD	HI	544.4
PACIFIC LIFE INS CO	NE	115,113.0
PHYSICIANS LIFE INS CO	NE	1,549.0
RESERVE NATIONAL INS CO	OK	123.3
SECURIAN LIFE INS CO	MN	478.9
SHELTER LIFE INS CO	MO	1,180.1
STANDARD LIFE & ACCIDENT INS CO	TX	511.2
STANDARD SECURITY LIFE INS CO OF NY	NY	245.0

Rating: B+

INSURANCE COMPANY NAME	DOM. STATE	TOTAL ASSETS ($MIL)
AETNA HEALTH & LIFE INS CO	CT	2,349.9
AMERICAN FAMILY LIFE ASR CO OF COLUM	NE	117,278.0
AMERICAN FIDELITY ASR CO	OK	5,305.5
AMERICAN UNITED LIFE INS CO	IN	23,906.8
ASSURITY LIFE INS CO	NE	2,550.8
AXA EQUITABLE LIFE INS CO	NY	171,038.0
BOSTON MUTUAL LIFE INS CO	MA	1,317.6
DEARBORN NATIONAL LIFE INS CO	IL	1,969.6

INSURANCE COMPANY NAME	DOM. STATE	TOTAL ASSETS ($MIL)
FARM BUREAU LIFE INS CO	IA	8,582.6
GERBER LIFE INS CO	NY	3,240.4
GOVERNMENT PERSONNEL MUTUAL L I C	TX	834.7
GREAT SOUTHERN LIFE INS CO	TX	218.2
LOCOMOTIVE ENGRS&COND MUT PROT ASSN	MI	63.0
MEDICO CORP LIFE INS CO	NE	45.2
MIDLAND NATIONAL LIFE INS CO	IA	47,985.0
MINNESOTA LIFE INS CO	MN	38,458.7
MUTUAL OF OMAHA INS CO	NE	7,112.9
NATIONAL FARMERS UNION LIFE INS CO	TX	206.0
NEW YORK LIFE INS & ANNUITY CORP	DE	137,896.0
OHIO NATIONAL LIFE ASR CORP	OH	3,833.0
PACIFIC LIFE & ANNUITY CO	AZ	6,374.0
PAN AMERICAN ASR CO	LA	25.4
PRINCIPAL LIFE INS CO	IA	165,432.0
SAVINGS BANK LIFE INS CO OF MA	MA	2,957.5
STANDARD INS CO	OR	21,220.5
SYMETRA LIFE INS CO	IA	33,273.1
TRUSTMARK INS CO	IL	1,430.6
TRUSTMARK LIFE INS CO	IL	325.4
UNITED WORLD LIFE INS CO	NE	122.6
USABLE LIFE	AR	482.3
VOYA RETIREMENT INS & ANNUITY CO	CT	89,930.9

Nevada

INSURANCE COMPANY NAME	DOM. STATE	TOTAL ASSETS ($MIL)

Rating: A+

INSURANCE COMPANY NAME	DOM. STATE	TOTAL ASSETS ($MIL)
AMERICAN FAMILY LIFE INS CO	WI	5,407.4
COUNTRY LIFE INS CO	IL	10,264.7
PHYSICIANS MUTUAL INS CO	NE	2,153.3
STATE FARM LIFE INS CO	IL	68,156.4
TEACHERS INS & ANNUITY ASN OF AM	NY	276,045.0

Rating: A

INSURANCE COMPANY NAME	DOM. STATE	TOTAL ASSETS ($MIL)
4 EVER LIFE INS CO	IL	211.4
FEDERATED LIFE INS CO	MN	1,710.7
GUARDIAN LIFE INS CO OF AMERICA	NY	50,389.3
LIFEWISE ASR CO	WA	143.3
MIDWESTERN UNITED LIFE INS CO	IN	235.0
MML BAY STATE LIFE INS CO	CT	4,737.2
NATIONAL WESTERN LIFE INS CO	CO	10,673.8
PARKER CENTENNIAL ASR CO	WI	92.2
SENTRY LIFE INS CO	WI	5,800.9
USAA LIFE INS CO	TX	23,536.5

Rating: A-

INSURANCE COMPANY NAME	DOM. STATE	TOTAL ASSETS ($MIL)
AMALGAMATED LIFE INS CO	NY	122.5
AMERICAN HEALTH & LIFE INS CO	TX	907.2
AMERICAN REPUBLIC INS CO	IA	909.7
ANNUITY INVESTORS LIFE INS CO	OH	3,041.6
ANTHEM LIFE INS CO	IN	630.6
AUTO-OWNERS LIFE INS CO	MI	3,832.7
CENTRAL STATES H & L CO OF OMAHA	NE	421.1
COMPANION LIFE INS CO	SC	329.6
COUNTRY INVESTORS LIFE ASR CO	IL	297.1
DELAWARE AMERICAN LIFE INS CO	DE	145.9
FAMILY HERITAGE LIFE INS CO OF AMER	OH	1,004.9
FIDELITY INVESTMENTS LIFE INS CO	UT	25,080.7
GARDEN STATE LIFE INS CO	TX	126.5
ILLINOIS MUTUAL LIFE INS CO	IL	1,434.6
MASSACHUSETTS MUTUAL LIFE INS CO	MA	226,444.0
MUTUAL OF AMERICA LIFE INS CO	NY	18,135.8
NEW YORK LIFE INS CO	NY	167,828.0
NIPPON LIFE INS CO OF AMERICA	IA	217.7
NORTHWESTERN MUTUAL LIFE INS CO	WI	244,873.0
PACIFIC GUARDIAN LIFE INS CO LTD	HI	544.4
PACIFIC LIFE INS CO	NE	115,113.0
PHYSICIANS LIFE INS CO	NE	1,549.0
RESERVE NATIONAL INS CO	OK	123.3
SECURIAN LIFE INS CO	MN	478.9
SHELTER LIFE INS CO	MO	1,180.1
STANDARD LIFE & ACCIDENT INS CO	TX	511.2
STANDARD SECURITY LIFE INS CO OF NY	NY	245.0

Rating: B+

INSURANCE COMPANY NAME	DOM. STATE	TOTAL ASSETS ($MIL)
AETNA HEALTH & LIFE INS CO	CT	2,349.9
AMERICAN FAMILY LIFE ASR CO OF COLUM	NE	117,278.0
AMERICAN FIDELITY ASR CO	OK	5,305.5
AMERICAN UNITED LIFE INS CO	IN	23,906.8
ASSURITY LIFE INS CO	NE	2,550.8
AXA EQUITABLE LIFE INS CO	NY	171,038.0
BOSTON MUTUAL LIFE INS CO	MA	1,317.6

INSURANCE COMPANY NAME	DOM. STATE	TOTAL ASSETS ($MIL)
DEARBORN NATIONAL LIFE INS CO	IL	1,969.6
FARM BUREAU LIFE INS CO	IA	8,582.6
GERBER LIFE INS CO	NY	3,240.4
GOVERNMENT PERSONNEL MUTUAL L I C	TX	834.7
GREAT SOUTHERN LIFE INS CO	TX	218.2
MEDICO CORP LIFE INS CO	NE	45.2
MIDLAND NATIONAL LIFE INS CO	IA	47,985.0
MINNESOTA LIFE INS CO	MN	38,458.7
MUTUAL OF OMAHA INS CO	NE	7,112.9
NATIONAL FARMERS UNION LIFE INS CO	TX	206.0
NEW YORK LIFE INS & ANNUITY CORP	DE	137,896.0
OHIO NATIONAL LIFE ASR CORP	OH	3,833.0
PACIFIC LIFE & ANNUITY CO	AZ	6,374.0
PAN AMERICAN ASR CO	LA	25.4
PRINCIPAL LIFE INS CO	IA	165,432.0
SAVINGS BANK LIFE INS CO OF MA	MA	2,957.5
STANDARD INS CO	OR	21,220.5
SYMETRA LIFE INS CO	IA	33,273.1
TRUSTMARK INS CO	IL	1,430.6
TRUSTMARK LIFE INS CO	IL	325.4
UNITED WORLD LIFE INS CO	NE	122.6
USABLE LIFE	AR	482.3
VOYA RETIREMENT INS & ANNUITY CO	CT	89,930.9

New Hampshire

INSURANCE COMPANY NAME	DOM. STATE	TOTAL ASSETS ($MIL)
Rating: A+		
AMERICAN FAMILY LIFE INS CO	WI	5,407.4
PHYSICIANS MUTUAL INS CO	NE	2,153.3
STATE FARM LIFE INS CO	IL	68,156.4
TEACHERS INS & ANNUITY ASN OF AM	NY	276,045.0
Rating: A		
4 EVER LIFE INS CO	IL	211.4
FEDERATED LIFE INS CO	MN	1,710.7
GUARDIAN LIFE INS CO OF AMERICA	NY	50,389.3
MIDWESTERN UNITED LIFE INS CO	IN	235.0
MML BAY STATE LIFE INS CO	CT	4,737.2
NATIONAL WESTERN LIFE INS CO	CO	10,673.8
PARKER CENTENNIAL ASR CO	WI	92.2
SENTRY LIFE INS CO	WI	5,800.9
UNITED FARM FAMILY LIFE INS CO	IN	2,234.9
USAA LIFE INS CO	TX	23,536.5
Rating: A-		
AMALGAMATED LIFE INS CO	NY	122.5
AMERICAN HEALTH & LIFE INS CO	TX	907.2
AMERICAN REPUBLIC INS CO	IA	909.7
ANNUITY INVESTORS LIFE INS CO	OH	3,041.6
ANTHEM LIFE INS CO	IN	630.6
CENTRAL STATES H & L CO OF OMAHA	NE	421.1
COMPANION LIFE INS CO	SC	329.6
DELAWARE AMERICAN LIFE INS CO	DE	145.9
FAMILY HERITAGE LIFE INS CO OF AMER	OH	1,004.9
FIDELITY INVESTMENTS LIFE INS CO	UT	25,080.7
GARDEN STATE LIFE INS CO	TX	126.5
ILLINOIS MUTUAL LIFE INS CO	IL	1,434.6
MASSACHUSETTS MUTUAL LIFE INS CO	MA	226,444.0
MUTUAL OF AMERICA LIFE INS CO	NY	18,135.8
NEW YORK LIFE INS CO	NY	167,828.0
NORTHWESTERN MUTUAL LIFE INS CO	WI	244,873.0
PACIFIC LIFE INS CO	NE	115,113.0
PHYSICIANS LIFE INS CO	NE	1,549.0
RESERVE NATIONAL INS CO	OK	123.3
SECURIAN LIFE INS CO	MN	478.9
STANDARD SECURITY LIFE INS CO OF NY	NY	245.0
Rating: B+		
AETNA HEALTH & LIFE INS CO	CT	2,349.9
AMERICAN FAMILY LIFE ASR CO OF COLUM	NE	117,278.0
AMERICAN FIDELITY ASR CO	OK	5,305.5
AMERICAN UNITED LIFE INS CO	IN	23,906.8
ASSURITY LIFE INS CO	NE	2,550.8
AXA EQUITABLE LIFE INS CO	NY	171,038.0
BOSTON MUTUAL LIFE INS CO	MA	1,317.6
DEARBORN NATIONAL LIFE INS CO	IL	1,969.6
GERBER LIFE INS CO	NY	3,240.4
GOVERNMENT PERSONNEL MUTUAL L I C	TX	834.7
MIDLAND NATIONAL LIFE INS CO	IA	47,985.0
MINNESOTA LIFE INS CO	MN	38,458.7
MUTUAL OF OMAHA INS CO	NE	7,112.9
NEW YORK LIFE INS & ANNUITY CORP	DE	137,896.0

INSURANCE COMPANY NAME	DOM. STATE	TOTAL ASSETS ($MIL)
OHIO NATIONAL LIFE ASR CORP	OH	3,833.0
PACIFIC LIFE & ANNUITY CO	AZ	6,374.0
PRINCIPAL LIFE INS CO	IA	165,432.0
SAVINGS BANK LIFE INS CO OF MA	MA	2,957.5
STANDARD INS CO	OR	21,220.5
SYMETRA LIFE INS CO	IA	33,273.1
TRUSTMARK INS CO	IL	1,430.6
TRUSTMARK LIFE INS CO	IL	325.4
UNITED WORLD LIFE INS CO	NE	122.6
USABLE LIFE	AR	482.3
VOYA RETIREMENT INS & ANNUITY CO	CT	89,930.9

New Jersey

INSURANCE COMPANY NAME	DOM. STATE	TOTAL ASSETS ($MIL)

Rating: A+

INSURANCE COMPANY NAME	DOM. STATE	TOTAL ASSETS ($MIL)
AMERICAN FAMILY LIFE INS CO	WI	5,407.4
PHYSICIANS MUTUAL INS CO	NE	2,153.3
STATE FARM LIFE INS CO	IL	68,156.4
TEACHERS INS & ANNUITY ASN OF AM	NY	276,045.0

Rating: A

INSURANCE COMPANY NAME	DOM. STATE	TOTAL ASSETS ($MIL)
4 EVER LIFE INS CO	IL	211.4
FEDERATED LIFE INS CO	MN	1,710.7
GUARDIAN LIFE INS CO OF AMERICA	NY	50,389.3
MIDWESTERN UNITED LIFE INS CO	IN	235.0
MML BAY STATE LIFE INS CO	CT	4,737.2
NATIONAL WESTERN LIFE INS CO	CO	10,673.8
PARKER CENTENNIAL ASR CO	WI	92.2
SENTRY LIFE INS CO	WI	5,800.9
SHELTERPOINT LIFE INS CO	NY	105.4
UNITED FARM FAMILY LIFE INS CO	IN	2,234.9
USAA LIFE INS CO	TX	23,536.5

Rating: A-

INSURANCE COMPANY NAME	DOM. STATE	TOTAL ASSETS ($MIL)
AMALGAMATED LIFE INS CO	NY	122.5
AMERICAN FAMILY LIFE ASR CO OF NY	NY	885.2
AMERICAN HEALTH & LIFE INS CO	TX	907.2
AMERICAN REPUBLIC INS CO	IA	909.7
ANNUITY INVESTORS LIFE INS CO	OH	3,041.6
ANTHEM LIFE INS CO	IN	630.6
CENTRAL STATES H & L CO OF OMAHA	NE	421.1
DELAWARE AMERICAN LIFE INS CO	DE	145.9
FAMILY HERITAGE LIFE INS CO OF AMER	OH	1,004.9
FIDELITY INVESTMENTS LIFE INS CO	UT	25,080.7
GARDEN STATE LIFE INS CO	TX	126.5
ILLINOIS MUTUAL LIFE INS CO	IL	1,434.6
MASSACHUSETTS MUTUAL LIFE INS CO	MA	226,444.0
MUTUAL OF AMERICA LIFE INS CO	NY	18,135.8
NEW YORK LIFE INS CO	NY	167,828.0
NIPPON LIFE INS CO OF AMERICA	IA	217.7
NORTHWESTERN MUTUAL LIFE INS CO	WI	244,873.0
PACIFIC LIFE INS CO	NE	115,113.0
PHYSICIANS LIFE INS CO	NE	1,549.0
RESERVE NATIONAL INS CO	OK	123.3
SECURIAN LIFE INS CO	MN	478.9
STANDARD SECURITY LIFE INS CO OF NY	NY	245.0

Rating: B+

INSURANCE COMPANY NAME	DOM. STATE	TOTAL ASSETS ($MIL)
AETNA HEALTH & LIFE INS CO	CT	2,349.9
AMERICAN FAMILY LIFE ASR CO OF COLUM	NE	117,278.0
AMERICAN FIDELITY ASR CO	OK	5,305.5
AMERICAN UNITED LIFE INS CO	IN	23,906.8
ASSURITY LIFE INS CO	NE	2,550.8
AXA EQUITABLE LIFE INS CO	NY	171,038.0
BOSTON MUTUAL LIFE INS CO	MA	1,317.6
DEARBORN NATIONAL LIFE INS CO	IL	1,969.6
GERBER LIFE INS CO	NY	3,240.4
GREAT SOUTHERN LIFE INS CO	TX	218.2
MIDLAND NATIONAL LIFE INS CO	IA	47,985.0
MINNESOTA LIFE INS CO	MN	38,458.7

INSURANCE COMPANY NAME	DOM. STATE	TOTAL ASSETS ($MIL)
MUTUAL OF OMAHA INS CO	NE	7,112.9
NEW YORK LIFE INS & ANNUITY CORP	DE	137,896.0
OHIO NATIONAL LIFE ASR CORP	OH	3,833.0
PACIFIC LIFE & ANNUITY CO	AZ	6,374.0
PAN AMERICAN ASR CO	LA	25.4
PRINCIPAL LIFE INS CO	IA	165,432.0
SAVINGS BANK LIFE INS CO OF MA	MA	2,957.5
STANDARD INS CO	OR	21,220.5
SYMETRA LIFE INS CO	IA	33,273.1
TRUSTMARK INS CO	IL	1,430.6
TRUSTMARK LIFE INS CO	IL	325.4
UNITED WORLD LIFE INS CO	NE	122.6
USABLE LIFE	AR	482.3
VOYA RETIREMENT INS & ANNUITY CO	CT	89,930.9

New Mexico

INSURANCE COMPANY NAME	DOM. STATE	TOTAL ASSETS ($MIL)
Rating: A+		
AMERICAN FAMILY LIFE INS CO	WI	5,407.4
COUNTRY LIFE INS CO	IL	10,264.7
PHYSICIANS MUTUAL INS CO	NE	2,153.3
STATE FARM LIFE INS CO	IL	68,156.4
TEACHERS INS & ANNUITY ASN OF AM	NY	276,045.0
Rating: A		
4 EVER LIFE INS CO	IL	211.4
FEDERATED LIFE INS CO	MN	1,710.7
GUARDIAN LIFE INS CO OF AMERICA	NY	50,389.3
LIFEWISE ASR CO	WA	143.3
MIDWESTERN UNITED LIFE INS CO	IN	235.0
MML BAY STATE LIFE INS CO	CT	4,737.2
NATIONAL WESTERN LIFE INS CO	CO	10,073.8
PARKER CENTENNIAL ASR CO	WI	92.2
SENTRY LIFE INS CO	WI	5,800.9
USAA LIFE INS CO	TX	23,536.5
Rating: A-		
AMALGAMATED LIFE INS CO	NY	122.5
AMERICAN HEALTH & LIFE INS CO	TX	907.2
AMERICAN REPUBLIC INS CO	IA	909.7
ANNUITY INVESTORS LIFE INS CO	OH	3,041.6
ANTHEM LIFE INS CO	IN	630.6
AUTO-OWNERS LIFE INS CO	MI	3,832.7
CENTRAL STATES H & L CO OF OMAHA	NE	421.1
COMPANION LIFE INS CO	SC	329.6
COUNTRY INVESTORS LIFE ASR CO	IL	297.1
DELAWARE AMERICAN LIFE INS CO	DE	145.9
FAMILY HERITAGE LIFE INS CO OF AMER	OH	1,004.9
FIDELITY INVESTMENTS LIFE INS CO	UT	25,080.7
GARDEN STATE LIFE INS CO	TX	126.5
ILLINOIS MUTUAL LIFE INS CO	IL	1,434.6
MASSACHUSETTS MUTUAL LIFE INS CO	MA	226,444.0
MUTUAL OF AMERICA LIFE INS CO	NY	18,135.8
NEW YORK LIFE INS CO	NY	167,828.0
NIPPON LIFE INS CO OF AMERICA	IA	217.7
NORTHWESTERN MUTUAL LIFE INS CO	WI	244,873.0
PACIFIC GUARDIAN LIFE INS CO LTD	HI	544.4
PACIFIC LIFE INS CO	NE	115,113.0
PHYSICIANS LIFE INS CO	NE	1,549.0
RESERVE NATIONAL INS CO	OK	123.3
SECURIAN LIFE INS CO	MN	478.9
STANDARD LIFE & ACCIDENT INS CO	TX	511.2
STANDARD SECURITY LIFE INS CO OF NY	NY	245.0
Rating: B+		
AETNA HEALTH & LIFE INS CO	CT	2,349.9
AMERICAN FAMILY LIFE ASR CO OF COLUM	NE	117,278.0
AMERICAN FIDELITY ASR CO	OK	5,305.5
AMERICAN UNITED LIFE INS CO	IN	23,906.8
ASSURITY LIFE INS CO	NE	2,550.8
AXA EQUITABLE LIFE INS CO	NY	171,038.0
BOSTON MUTUAL LIFE INS CO	MA	1,317.6
DEARBORN NATIONAL LIFE INS CO	IL	1,969.6

INSURANCE COMPANY NAME	DOM. STATE	TOTAL ASSETS ($MIL)
FARM BUREAU LIFE INS CO	IA	8,582.6
GERBER LIFE INS CO	NY	3,240.4
GOVERNMENT PERSONNEL MUTUAL L I C	TX	834.7
GREAT SOUTHERN LIFE INS CO	TX	218.2
LOCOMOTIVE ENGRS&COND MUT PROT ASSN	MI	63.0
MEDICO CORP LIFE INS CO	NE	45.2
MIDLAND NATIONAL LIFE INS CO	IA	47,985.0
MINNESOTA LIFE INS CO	MN	38,458.7
MUTUAL OF OMAHA INS CO	NE	7,112.9
NATIONAL FARMERS UNION LIFE INS CO	TX	206.0
NEW YORK LIFE INS & ANNUITY CORP	DE	137,896.0
OHIO NATIONAL LIFE ASR CORP	OH	3,833.0
PACIFIC LIFE & ANNUITY CO	AZ	6,374.0
PAN AMERICAN ASR CO	LA	25.4
PRINCIPAL LIFE INS CO	IA	165,432.0
SAVINGS BANK LIFE INS CO OF MA	MA	2,957.5
SOUTHERN PIONEER LIFE INS CO	AR	16.8
STANDARD INS CO	OR	21,220.5
SYMETRA LIFE INS CO	IA	33,273.1
TRUSTMARK INS CO	IL	1,430.6
TRUSTMARK LIFE INS CO	IL	325.4
UNITED WORLD LIFE INS CO	NE	122.6
USABLE LIFE	AR	482.3
VOYA RETIREMENT INS & ANNUITY CO	CT	89,930.9

New York

INSURANCE COMPANY NAME	DOM. STATE	TOTAL ASSETS ($MIL)
Rating: A+		
PHYSICIANS MUTUAL INS CO	NE	2,153.3
STATE FARM LIFE & ACCIDENT ASR CO	IL	2,692.7
TEACHERS INS & ANNUITY ASN OF AM	NY	276,045.0
Rating: A		
4 EVER LIFE INS CO	IL	211.4
FEDERATED LIFE INS CO	MN	1,710.7
FIRST RELIANCE STANDARD LIFE INS CO	NY	190.3
FIRST SYMETRA NATL LIFE INS CO OF NY	NY	1,467.2
GUARDIAN LIFE INS CO OF AMERICA	NY	50,389.3
SHELTERPOINT LIFE INS CO	NY	105.4
Rating: A-		
ALLIANZ LIFE INS CO OF NY	NY	3,131.2
AMALGAMATED LIFE INS CO	NY	122.5
AMERICAN FAMILY LIFE ASR CO OF NY	NY	885.2
CIGNA LIFE INS CO OF NEW YORK	NY	380.3
DELAWARE AMERICAN LIFE INS CO	DE	145.9
GARDEN STATE LIFE INS CO	TX	126.5
LIFE INS CO OF BOSTON & NEW YORK	NY	135.2
MASSACHUSETTS MUTUAL LIFE INS CO	MA	226,444.0
MUTUAL OF AMERICA LIFE INS CO	NY	18,135.8
NEW YORK LIFE INS CO	NY	167,828.0
NIPPON LIFE INS CO OF AMERICA	IA	217.7
NORTHWESTERN MUTUAL LIFE INS CO	WI	244,873.0
SECURIAN LIFE INS CO	MN	478.9
STANDARD LIFE INS CO OF NY	NY	283.1
STANDARD SECURITY LIFE INS CO OF NY	NY	245.0
Rating: B+		
AETNA HEALTH & LIFE INS CO	CT	2,349.9
AMERICAN UNITED LIFE INS CO	IN	23,906.8
AXA EQUITABLE LIFE INS CO	NY	171,038.0
BOSTON MUTUAL LIFE INS CO	MA	1,317.6
DEARBORN NATIONAL LIFE INS CO OF NY	NY	38.7
EMPIRE FIDELITY INVESTMENTS L I C	NY	2,497.9
FIRST UNITED AMERICAN LIFE INS CO	NY	219.9
GERBER LIFE INS CO	NY	3,240.4
JOHN HANCOCK LIFE INS CO OF NY	NY	17,005.3
MUTUAL OF OMAHA INS CO	NE	7,112.9
NATIONAL INCOME LIFE INS CO	NY	185.3
NEW YORK LIFE INS & ANNUITY CORP	DE	137,896.0
PACIFIC LIFE & ANNUITY CO	AZ	6,374.0
PRINCIPAL LIFE INS CO	IA	165,432.0
TRUSTMARK INS CO	IL	1,430.6
TRUSTMARK LIFE INS CO	IL	325.4
UNION SECURITY LIFE INS CO OF NY	NY	88.0
USAA LIFE INS CO OF NEW YORK	NY	720.8
VOYA RETIREMENT INS & ANNUITY CO	CT	89,930.9

North Carolina

INSURANCE COMPANY NAME	DOM. STATE	TOTAL ASSETS ($MIL)

Rating: A+

INSURANCE COMPANY NAME	DOM. STATE	TOTAL ASSETS ($MIL)
AMERICAN FAMILY LIFE INS CO	WI	5,407.4
COUNTRY LIFE INS CO	IL	10,264.7
PHYSICIANS MUTUAL INS CO	NE	2,153.3
STATE FARM LIFE INS CO	IL	68,156.4
TEACHERS INS & ANNUITY ASN OF AM	NY	276,045.0

Rating: A

INSURANCE COMPANY NAME	DOM. STATE	TOTAL ASSETS ($MIL)
4 EVER LIFE INS CO	IL	211.4
FEDERATED LIFE INS CO	MN	1,710.7
GUARDIAN LIFE INS CO OF AMERICA	NY	50,389.3
MIDWESTERN UNITED LIFE INS CO	IN	235.0
MML BAY STATE LIFE INS CO	CT	4,737.2
NATIONAL WESTERN LIFE INS CO	CO	10,673.8
PARKER CENTENNIAL ASR CO	WI	92.2
SENTRY LIFE INS CO	WI	5,800.9
SHELTERPOINT LIFE INS CO	NY	105.4
SOUTHERN FARM BUREAU LIFE INS CO	MS	13,583.7
UNITED FARM FAMILY LIFE INS CO	IN	2,234.9
USAA LIFE INS CO	TX	23,536.5

Rating: A-

INSURANCE COMPANY NAME	DOM. STATE	TOTAL ASSETS ($MIL)
AMALGAMATED LIFE INS CO	NY	122.5
AMERICAN HEALTH & LIFE INS CO	TX	907.2
AMERICAN REPUBLIC INS CO	IA	909.7
ANNUITY INVESTORS LIFE INS CO	OH	3,041.6
ANTHEM LIFE INS CO	IN	630.6
AUTO-OWNERS LIFE INS CO	MI	3,832.7
CENTRAL STATES H & L CO OF OMAHA	NE	421.1
COMPANION LIFE INS CO	SC	329.6
COTTON STATES LIFE INS CO	GA	334.6
COUNTRY INVESTORS LIFE ASR CO	IL	297.1
DELAWARE AMERICAN LIFE INS CO	DE	145.9
ERIE FAMILY LIFE INS CO	PA	2,217.2
FAMILY HERITAGE LIFE INS CO OF AMER	OH	1,004.9
FIDELITY INVESTMENTS LIFE INS CO	UT	25,080.7
GARDEN STATE LIFE INS CO	TX	126.5
ILLINOIS MUTUAL LIFE INS CO	IL	1,434.6
LIFE INS CO OF ALABAMA	AL	118.6
MASSACHUSETTS MUTUAL LIFE INS CO	MA	226,444.0
MUTUAL OF AMERICA LIFE INS CO	NY	18,135.8
NEW YORK LIFE INS CO	NY	167,828.0
NIPPON LIFE INS CO OF AMERICA	IA	217.7
NORTHWESTERN MUTUAL LIFE INS CO	WI	244,873.0
PACIFIC LIFE INS CO	NE	115,113.0
PHYSICIANS LIFE INS CO	NE	1,549.0
RESERVE NATIONAL INS CO	OK	123.3
SECURIAN LIFE INS CO	MN	478.9
STANDARD LIFE & ACCIDENT INS CO	TX	511.2
STANDARD SECURITY LIFE INS CO OF NY	NY	245.0

Rating: B+

INSURANCE COMPANY NAME	DOM. STATE	TOTAL ASSETS ($MIL)
AETNA HEALTH & LIFE INS CO	CT	2,349.9
AMERICAN FAMILY LIFE ASR CO OF COLUM	NE	117,278.0
AMERICAN FIDELITY ASR CO	OK	5,305.5
AMERICAN UNITED LIFE INS CO	IN	23,906.8

INSURANCE COMPANY NAME	DOM. STATE	TOTAL ASSETS ($MIL)
ASSURITY LIFE INS CO	NE	2,550.8
AXA EQUITABLE LIFE INS CO	NY	171,038.0
BOSTON MUTUAL LIFE INS CO	MA	1,317.6
DEARBORN NATIONAL LIFE INS CO	IL	1,969.6
GERBER LIFE INS CO	NY	3,240.4
GOVERNMENT PERSONNEL MUTUAL L I C	TX	834.7
GREAT SOUTHERN LIFE INS CO	TX	218.2
GREATER GEORGIA LIFE INS CO	GA	58.6
MEDICO CORP LIFE INS CO	NE	45.2
MIDLAND NATIONAL LIFE INS CO	IA	47,985.0
MINNESOTA LIFE INS CO	MN	38,458.7
MUTUAL OF OMAHA INS CO	NE	7,112.9
NEW YORK LIFE INS & ANNUITY CORP	DE	137,896.0
OHIO NATIONAL LIFE ASR CORP	OH	3,833.0
PACIFIC LIFE & ANNUITY CO	AZ	6,374.0
PAN AMERICAN ASR CO	LA	25.4
PRINCIPAL LIFE INS CO	IA	165,432.0
SAVINGS BANK LIFE INS CO OF MA	MA	2,957.5
STANDARD INS CO	OR	21,220.5
SYMETRA LIFE INS CO	IA	33,273.1
TRUSTMARK INS CO	IL	1,430.6
TRUSTMARK LIFE INS CO	IL	325.4
UNITED WORLD LIFE INS CO	NE	122.6
USABLE LIFE	AR	482.3
VOYA RETIREMENT INS & ANNUITY CO	CT	89,930.9

North Dakota

INSURANCE COMPANY NAME	DOM. STATE	TOTAL ASSETS ($MIL)

Rating: A+

INSURANCE COMPANY NAME	DOM. STATE	TOTAL ASSETS ($MIL)
AMERICAN FAMILY LIFE INS CO	WI	5,407.4
COUNTRY LIFE INS CO	IL	10,264.7
PHYSICIANS MUTUAL INS CO	NE	2,153.3
STATE FARM LIFE INS CO	IL	68,156.4
TEACHERS INS & ANNUITY ASN OF AM	NY	276,045.0

Rating: A

INSURANCE COMPANY NAME	DOM. STATE	TOTAL ASSETS ($MIL)
4 EVER LIFE INS CO	IL	211.4
FEDERATED LIFE INS CO	MN	1,710.7
GUARDIAN LIFE INS CO OF AMERICA	NY	50,389.3
LIFEWISE ASR CO	WA	143.3
MIDWESTERN UNITED LIFE INS CO	IN	235.0
MML BAY STATE LIFE INS CO	CT	4,737.2
NATIONAL WESTERN LIFE INS CO	CO	10,673.8
PARKER CENTENNIAL ASR CO	WI	92.2
SENTRY LIFE INS CO	WI	5,800.9
UNITED FARM FAMILY LIFE INS CO	IN	2,234.9
USAA LIFE INS CO	TX	23,536.5

Rating: A-

INSURANCE COMPANY NAME	DOM. STATE	TOTAL ASSETS ($MIL)
ALLIANZ LIFE INS CO OF NY	NY	3,131.2
AMALGAMATED LIFE INS CO	NY	122.5
AMERICAN FAMILY LIFE ASR CO OF NY	NY	885.2
AMERICAN HEALTH & LIFE INS CO	TX	907.2
AMERICAN REPUBLIC INS CO	IA	909.7
ANNUITY INVESTORS LIFE INS CO	OH	3,041.6
ANTHEM LIFE INS CO	IN	630.6
AUTO-OWNERS LIFE INS CO	MI	3,832.7
CENTRAL STATES H & L CO OF OMAHA	NE	421.1
COMPANION LIFE INS CO	SC	329.6
COUNTRY INVESTORS LIFE ASR CO	IL	297.1
DELAWARE AMERICAN LIFE INS CO	DE	145.9
FAMILY HERITAGE LIFE INS CO OF AMER	OH	1,004.9
FIDELITY INVESTMENTS LIFE INS CO	UT	25,080.7
GARDEN STATE LIFE INS CO	TX	126.5
ILLINOIS MUTUAL LIFE INS CO	IL	1,434.6
MASSACHUSETTS MUTUAL LIFE INS CO	MA	226,444.0
MUTUAL OF AMERICA LIFE INS CO	NY	18,135.8
NEW YORK LIFE INS CO	NY	167,828.0
NIPPON LIFE INS CO OF AMERICA	IA	217.7
NORTHWESTERN MUTUAL LIFE INS CO	WI	244,873.0
PACIFIC LIFE INS CO	NE	115,113.0
PHYSICIANS LIFE INS CO	NE	1,549.0
RESERVE NATIONAL INS CO	OK	123.3
SECURIAN LIFE INS CO	MN	478.9
STANDARD LIFE & ACCIDENT INS CO	TX	511.2
STANDARD SECURITY LIFE INS CO OF NY	NY	245.0

Rating: B+

INSURANCE COMPANY NAME	DOM. STATE	TOTAL ASSETS ($MIL)
AETNA HEALTH & LIFE INS CO	CT	2,349.9
AMERICAN FAMILY LIFE ASR CO OF COLUM	NE	117,278.0
AMERICAN FIDELITY ASR CO	OK	5,305.5
AMERICAN UNITED LIFE INS CO	IN	23,906.8
ASSURITY LIFE INS CO	NE	2,550.8
AXA EQUITABLE LIFE INS CO	NY	171,038.0
BOSTON MUTUAL LIFE INS CO	MA	1,317.6
DEARBORN NATIONAL LIFE INS CO	IL	1,969.6
FARM BUREAU LIFE INS CO	IA	8,582.6
GERBER LIFE INS CO	NY	3,240.4
GOVERNMENT PERSONNEL MUTUAL L I C	TX	834.7
GREAT SOUTHERN LIFE INS CO	TX	218.2
MEDICO CORP LIFE INS CO	NE	45.2
MIDLAND NATIONAL LIFE INS CO	IA	47,985.0
MINNESOTA LIFE INS CO	MN	38,458.7
MUTUAL OF OMAHA INS CO	NE	7,112.9
NATIONAL FARMERS UNION LIFE INS CO	TX	206.0
NEW YORK LIFE INS & ANNUITY CORP	DE	137,896.0
OHIO NATIONAL LIFE ASR CORP	OH	3,833.0
PACIFIC LIFE & ANNUITY CO	AZ	6,374.0
PAN AMERICAN ASR CO	LA	25.4
PRINCIPAL LIFE INS CO	IA	165,432.0
SAVINGS BANK LIFE INS CO OF MA	MA	2,957.5
STANDARD INS CO	OR	21,220.5
SYMETRA LIFE INS CO	IA	33,273.1
TRUSTMARK INS CO	IL	1,430.6
TRUSTMARK LIFE INS CO	IL	325.4
UNITED WORLD LIFE INS CO	NE	122.6
USABLE LIFE	AR	482.3
VOYA RETIREMENT INS & ANNUITY CO	CT	89,930.9

Ohio

INSURANCE COMPANY NAME	DOM. STATE	TOTAL ASSETS ($MIL)
Rating: A+		
AMERICAN FAMILY LIFE INS CO	WI	5,407.4
COUNTRY LIFE INS CO	IL	10,264.7
PHYSICIANS MUTUAL INS CO	NE	2,153.3
STATE FARM LIFE INS CO	IL	68,156.4
TEACHERS INS & ANNUITY ASN OF AM	NY	276,045.0
Rating: A		
4 EVER LIFE INS CO	IL	211.4
FEDERATED LIFE INS CO	MN	1,710.7
GUARDIAN LIFE INS CO OF AMERICA	NY	50,389.3
MIDWESTERN UNITED LIFE INS CO	IN	235.0
MML BAY STATE LIFE INS CO	CT	4,737.2
NATIONAL WESTERN LIFE INS CO	CO	10,673.8
PARKER CENTENNIAL ASR CO	WI	92.2
SENTRY LIFE INS CO	WI	5,800.9
UNITED FARM FAMILY LIFE INS CO	IN	2,234.9
USAA LIFE INS CO	TX	23,536.5
Rating: A-		
AMALGAMATED LIFE INS CO	NY	122.5
AMERICAN HEALTH & LIFE INS CO	TX	907.2
AMERICAN REPUBLIC INS CO	IA	909.7
ANNUITY INVESTORS LIFE INS CO	OH	3,041.6
ANTHEM LIFE INS CO	IN	630.6
AUTO-OWNERS LIFE INS CO	MI	3,832.7
CENTRAL STATES H & L CO OF OMAHA	NE	421.1
COMPANION LIFE INS CO	SC	329.6
COUNTRY INVESTORS LIFE ASR CO	IL	297.1
DELAWARE AMERICAN LIFE INS CO	DE	145.9
ERIE FAMILY LIFE INS CO	PA	2,217.2
FAMILY HERITAGE LIFE INS CO OF AMER	OH	1,004.9
FIDELITY INVESTMENTS LIFE INS CO	UT	25,080.7
GARDEN STATE LIFE INS CO	TX	126.5
ILLINOIS MUTUAL LIFE INS CO	IL	1,434.6
MASSACHUSETTS MUTUAL LIFE INS CO	MA	226,444.0
MUTUAL OF AMERICA LIFE INS CO	NY	18,135.8
NEW YORK LIFE INS CO	NY	167,828.0
NIPPON LIFE INS CO OF AMERICA	IA	217.7
NORTHWESTERN MUTUAL LIFE INS CO	WI	244,873.0
PACIFIC LIFE INS CO	NE	115,113.0
PHYSICIANS LIFE INS CO	NE	1,549.0
RESERVE NATIONAL INS CO	OK	123.3
SECURIAN LIFE INS CO	MN	478.9
STANDARD LIFE & ACCIDENT INS CO	TX	511.2
STANDARD SECURITY LIFE INS CO OF NY	NY	245.0
Rating: B+		
AETNA HEALTH & LIFE INS CO	CT	2,349.9
AMERICAN FAMILY LIFE ASR CO OF COLUM	NE	117,278.0
AMERICAN FIDELITY ASR CO	OK	5,305.5
AMERICAN UNITED LIFE INS CO	IN	23,906.8
ASSURITY LIFE INS CO	NE	2,550.8
AXA EQUITABLE LIFE INS CO	NY	171,038.0
BOSTON MUTUAL LIFE INS CO	MA	1,317.6
DEARBORN NATIONAL LIFE INS CO	IL	1,969.6

INSURANCE COMPANY NAME	DOM. STATE	TOTAL ASSETS ($MIL)
GERBER LIFE INS CO	NY	3,240.4
GOVERNMENT PERSONNEL MUTUAL L I C	TX	834.7
GREAT SOUTHERN LIFE INS CO	TX	218.2
MEDICO CORP LIFE INS CO	NE	45.2
MIDLAND NATIONAL LIFE INS CO	IA	47,985.0
MINNESOTA LIFE INS CO	MN	38,458.7
MUTUAL OF OMAHA INS CO	NE	7,112.9
NATIONAL FARMERS UNION LIFE INS CO	TX	206.0
NEW YORK LIFE INS & ANNUITY CORP	DE	137,896.0
OHIO NATIONAL LIFE ASR CORP	OH	3,833.0
PACIFIC LIFE & ANNUITY CO	AZ	6,374.0
PAN AMERICAN ASR CO	LA	25.4
PRINCIPAL LIFE INS CO	IA	165,432.0
SAVINGS BANK LIFE INS CO OF MA	MA	2,957.5
STANDARD INS CO	OR	21,220.5
SYMETRA LIFE INS CO	IA	33,273.1
TRUSTMARK INS CO	IL	1,430.6
TRUSTMARK LIFE INS CO	IL	325.4
UNITED WORLD LIFE INS CO	NE	122.6
USABLE LIFE	AR	482.3
VOYA RETIREMENT INS & ANNUITY CO	CT	89,930.9

Oklahoma

INSURANCE COMPANY NAME	DOM. STATE	TOTAL ASSETS ($MIL)	INSURANCE COMPANY NAME	DOM. STATE	TOTAL ASSETS ($MIL)
### Rating: A+			DEARBORN NATIONAL LIFE INS CO	IL	1,969.6
			FARM BUREAU LIFE INS CO	IA	8,582.6
AMERICAN FAMILY LIFE INS CO	WI	5,407.4	GERBER LIFE INS CO	NY	3,240.4
COUNTRY LIFE INS CO	IL	10,264.7	GOVERNMENT PERSONNEL MUTUAL L I C	TX	834.7
PHYSICIANS MUTUAL INS CO	NE	2,153.3	GREAT SOUTHERN LIFE INS CO	TX	218.2
STATE FARM LIFE INS CO	IL	68,156.4	MEDICO CORP LIFE INS CO	NE	45.2
TEACHERS INS & ANNUITY ASN OF AM	NY	276,045.0	MIDLAND NATIONAL LIFE INS CO	IA	47,985.0
			MINNESOTA LIFE INS CO	MN	38,458.7
### Rating: A			MUTUAL OF OMAHA INS CO	NE	7,112.9
			NATIONAL FARMERS UNION LIFE INS CO	TX	206.0
4 EVER LIFE INS CO	IL	211.4	NEW YORK LIFE INS & ANNUITY CORP	DE	137,896.0
FEDERATED LIFE INS CO	MN	1,710.7	OHIO NATIONAL LIFE ASR CORP	OH	3,833.0
GUARDIAN LIFE INS CO OF AMERICA	NY	50,389.3	PACIFIC LIFE & ANNUITY CO	AZ	6,374.0
LIFEWISE ASR CO	WA	143.3	PAN AMERICAN ASR CO	LA	25.4
MIDWESTERN UNITED LIFE INS CO	IN	235.0	PRINCIPAL LIFE INS CO	IA	165,432.0
MML BAY STATE LIFE INS CO	CT	4,737.2	SAVINGS BANK LIFE INS CO OF MA	MA	2,957.5
NATIONAL WESTERN LIFE INS CO	CO	10,673.8	SOUTHERN PIONEER LIFE INS CO	AR	16.8
PARKER CENTENNIAL ASR CO	WI	92.2	STANDARD INS CO	OR	21,220.5
SENTRY LIFE INS CO	WI	5,800.9	SYMETRA LIFE INS CO	IA	33,273.1
USAA LIFE INS CO	TX	23,536.5	TRUSTMARK INS CO	IL	1,430.6
			TRUSTMARK LIFE INS CO	IL	325.4
### Rating: A-			UNITED WORLD LIFE INS CO	NE	122.6
			USABLE LIFE	AR	482.3
AMALGAMATED LIFE INS CO	NY	122.5	VOYA RETIREMENT INS & ANNUITY CO	CT	89,930.9
AMERICAN HEALTH & LIFE INS CO	TX	907.2			
AMERICAN REPUBLIC INS CO	IA	909.7			
ANNUITY INVESTORS LIFE INS CO	OH	3,041.6			
ANTHEM LIFE INS CO	IN	630.6			
CENTRAL STATES H & L CO OF OMAHA	NE	421.1			
COMPANION LIFE INS CO	SC	329.6			
COUNTRY INVESTORS LIFE ASR CO	IL	297.1			
DELAWARE AMERICAN LIFE INS CO	DE	145.9			
FAMILY HERITAGE LIFE INS CO OF AMER	OH	1,004.9			
FIDELITY INVESTMENTS LIFE INS CO	UT	25,080.7			
GARDEN STATE LIFE INS CO	TX	126.5			
ILLINOIS MUTUAL LIFE INS CO	IL	1,434.6			
LIFE INS CO OF ALABAMA	AL	118.6			
MASSACHUSETTS MUTUAL LIFE INS CO	MA	226,444.0			
MUTUAL OF AMERICA LIFE INS CO	NY	18,135.8			
NEW YORK LIFE INS CO	NY	167,828.0			
NIPPON LIFE INS CO OF AMERICA	IA	217.7			
NORTHWESTERN MUTUAL LIFE INS CO	WI	244,873.0			
PACIFIC GUARDIAN LIFE INS CO LTD	HI	544.4			
PACIFIC LIFE INS CO	NE	115,113.0			
PHYSICIANS LIFE INS CO	NE	1,549.0			
RESERVE NATIONAL INS CO	OK	123.3			
SECURIAN LIFE INS CO	MN	478.9			
SHELTER LIFE INS CO	MO	1,180.1			
STANDARD LIFE & ACCIDENT INS CO	TX	511.2			
STANDARD SECURITY LIFE INS CO OF NY	NY	245.0			
### Rating: B+					
AETNA HEALTH & LIFE INS CO	CT	2,349.9			
AMERICAN FAMILY LIFE ASR CO OF COLUM	NE	117,278.0			
AMERICAN FIDELITY ASR CO	OK	5,305.5			
AMERICAN UNITED LIFE INS CO	IN	23,906.8			
ASSURITY LIFE INS CO	NE	2,550.8			
AXA EQUITABLE LIFE INS CO	NY	171,038.0			
BOSTON MUTUAL LIFE INS CO	MA	1,317.6			

Oregon

INSURANCE COMPANY NAME	DOM. STATE	TOTAL ASSETS ($MIL)

Rating: A+

INSURANCE COMPANY NAME	DOM. STATE	TOTAL ASSETS ($MIL)
AMERICAN FAMILY LIFE INS CO	WI	5,407.4
COUNTRY LIFE INS CO	IL	10,264.7
PHYSICIANS MUTUAL INS CO	NE	2,153.3
STATE FARM LIFE INS CO	IL	68,156.4
TEACHERS INS & ANNUITY ASN OF AM	NY	276,045.0

Rating: A

INSURANCE COMPANY NAME	DOM. STATE	TOTAL ASSETS ($MIL)
4 EVER LIFE INS CO	IL	211.4
FEDERATED LIFE INS CO	MN	1,710.7
GUARDIAN LIFE INS CO OF AMERICA	NY	50,389.3
LIFEWISE ASR CO	WA	143.3
MIDWESTERN UNITED LIFE INS CO	IN	235.0
MML BAY STATE LIFE INS CO	CT	4,737.2
NATIONAL WESTERN LIFE INS CO	CO	10,673.8
PARKER CENTENNIAL ASR CO	WI	92.2
SENTRY LIFE INS CO	WI	5,800.9
USAA LIFE INS CO	TX	23,536.5

Rating: A-

INSURANCE COMPANY NAME	DOM. STATE	TOTAL ASSETS ($MIL)
AMALGAMATED LIFE INS CO	NY	122.5
AMERICAN HEALTH & LIFE INS CO	TX	907.2
AMERICAN REPUBLIC INS CO	IA	909.7
ANNUITY INVESTORS LIFE INS CO	OH	3,041.6
ANTHEM LIFE INS CO	IN	630.6
AUTO-OWNERS LIFE INS CO	MI	3,832.7
CENTRAL STATES H & L CO OF OMAHA	NE	421.1
COMPANION LIFE INS CO	SC	329.6
COUNTRY INVESTORS LIFE ASR CO	IL	297.1
DELAWARE AMERICAN LIFE INS CO	DE	145.9
FAMILY HERITAGE LIFE INS CO OF AMER	OH	1,004.9
FIDELITY INVESTMENTS LIFE INS CO	UT	25,080.7
GARDEN STATE LIFE INS CO	TX	126.5
ILLINOIS MUTUAL LIFE INS CO	IL	1,434.6
MASSACHUSETTS MUTUAL LIFE INS CO	MA	226,444.0
MUTUAL OF AMERICA LIFE INS CO	NY	18,135.8
NEW YORK LIFE INS CO	NY	167,828.0
NIPPON LIFE INS CO OF AMERICA	IA	217.7
NORTHWESTERN MUTUAL LIFE INS CO	WI	244,873.0
PACIFIC GUARDIAN LIFE INS CO LTD	HI	544.4
PACIFIC LIFE INS CO	NE	115,113.0
PHYSICIANS LIFE INS CO	NE	1,549.0
RESERVE NATIONAL INS CO	OK	123.3
SECURIAN LIFE INS CO	MN	478.9
STANDARD LIFE & ACCIDENT INS CO	TX	511.2
STANDARD SECURITY LIFE INS CO OF NY	NY	245.0

Rating: B+

INSURANCE COMPANY NAME	DOM. STATE	TOTAL ASSETS ($MIL)
AETNA HEALTH & LIFE INS CO	CT	2,349.9
AMERICAN FAMILY LIFE ASR CO OF COLUM	NE	117,278.0
AMERICAN FIDELITY ASR CO	OK	5,305.5
AMERICAN UNITED LIFE INS CO	IN	23,906.8
ASSURITY LIFE INS CO	NE	2,550.8
AXA EQUITABLE LIFE INS CO	NY	171,038.0
BOSTON MUTUAL LIFE INS CO	MA	1,317.6
DEARBORN NATIONAL LIFE INS CO	IL	1,969.6

INSURANCE COMPANY NAME	DOM. STATE	TOTAL ASSETS ($MIL)
FARM BUREAU LIFE INS CO	IA	8,582.6
GERBER LIFE INS CO	NY	3,240.4
GOVERNMENT PERSONNEL MUTUAL L I C	TX	834.7
GREAT SOUTHERN LIFE INS CO	TX	218.2
MEDICO CORP LIFE INS CO	NE	45.2
MIDLAND NATIONAL LIFE INS CO	IA	47,985.0
MINNESOTA LIFE INS CO	MN	38,458.7
MUTUAL OF OMAHA INS CO	NE	7,112.9
NATIONAL FARMERS UNION LIFE INS CO	TX	206.0
NEW YORK LIFE INS & ANNUITY CORP	DE	137,896.0
OHIO NATIONAL LIFE ASR CORP	OH	3,833.0
PACIFIC LIFE & ANNUITY CO	AZ	6,374.0
PAN AMERICAN ASR CO	LA	25.4
PRINCIPAL LIFE INS CO	IA	165,432.0
SAVINGS BANK LIFE INS CO OF MA	MA	2,957.5
STANDARD INS CO	OR	21,220.5
SYMETRA LIFE INS CO	IA	33,273.1
TRUSTMARK INS CO	IL	1,430.6
TRUSTMARK LIFE INS CO	IL	325.4
UNITED WORLD LIFE INS CO	NE	122.6
USABLE LIFE	AR	482.3
VOYA RETIREMENT INS & ANNUITY CO	CT	89,930.9

Pennsylvania

INSURANCE COMPANY NAME	DOM. STATE	TOTAL ASSETS ($MIL)
Rating: A+		
AMERICAN FAMILY LIFE INS CO	WI	5,407.4
COUNTRY LIFE INS CO	IL	10,264.7
PHYSICIANS MUTUAL INS CO	NE	2,153.3
STATE FARM LIFE INS CO	IL	68,156.4
TEACHERS INS & ANNUITY ASN OF AM	NY	276,045.0
Rating: A		
4 EVER LIFE INS CO	IL	211.4
FEDERATED LIFE INS CO	MN	1,710.7
GUARDIAN LIFE INS CO OF AMERICA	NY	50,389.3
MIDWESTERN UNITED LIFE INS CO	IN	235.0
MML BAY STATE LIFE INS CO	CT	4,737.2
NATIONAL WESTERN LIFE INS CO	CO	10,673.8
PARKER CENTENNIAL ASR CO	WI	92.2
SENTRY LIFE INS CO	WI	5,800.9
SHELTERPOINT LIFE INS CO	NY	105.4
UNITED FARM FAMILY LIFE INS CO	IN	2,234.9
USAA LIFE INS CO	TX	23,536.5
Rating: A-		
AMALGAMATED LIFE INS CO	NY	122.5
AMERICAN HEALTH & LIFE INS CO	TX	907.2
AMERICAN REPUBLIC INS CO	IA	909.7
ANNUITY INVESTORS LIFE INS CO	OH	3,041.6
ANTHEM LIFE INS CO	IN	630.6
AUTO-OWNERS LIFE INS CO	MI	3,832.7
CENTRAL STATES H & L CO OF OMAHA	NE	421.1
CIGNA LIFE INS CO OF NEW YORK	NY	380.3
COMPANION LIFE INS CO	SC	329.6
COUNTRY INVESTORS LIFE ASR CO	IL	297.1
DELAWARE AMERICAN LIFE INS CO	DE	145.9
ERIE FAMILY LIFE INS CO	PA	2,217.2
FAMILY HERITAGE LIFE INS CO OF AMER	OH	1,004.9
FIDELITY INVESTMENTS LIFE INS CO	UT	25,080.7
GARDEN STATE LIFE INS CO	TX	126.5
ILLINOIS MUTUAL LIFE INS CO	IL	1,434.6
MASSACHUSETTS MUTUAL LIFE INS CO	MA	226,444.0
MUTUAL OF AMERICA LIFE INS CO	NY	18,135.8
NEW YORK LIFE INS CO	NY	167,828.0
NIPPON LIFE INS CO OF AMERICA	IA	217.7
NORTHWESTERN MUTUAL LIFE INS CO	WI	244,873.0
PACIFIC LIFE INS CO	NE	115,113.0
PHYSICIANS LIFE INS CO	NE	1,549.0
RESERVE NATIONAL INS CO	OK	123.3
SECURIAN LIFE INS CO	MN	478.9
STANDARD LIFE & ACCIDENT INS CO	TX	511.2
STANDARD SECURITY LIFE INS CO OF NY	NY	245.0
Rating: B+		
AETNA HEALTH & LIFE INS CO	CT	2,349.9
AMERICAN FAMILY LIFE ASR CO OF COLUM	NE	117,278.0
AMERICAN FIDELITY ASR CO	OK	5,305.5
AMERICAN UNITED LIFE INS CO	IN	23,906.8
ASSURITY LIFE INS CO	NE	2,550.8
AXA EQUITABLE LIFE INS CO	NY	171,038.0

INSURANCE COMPANY NAME	DOM. STATE	TOTAL ASSETS ($MIL)
BOSTON MUTUAL LIFE INS CO	MA	1,317.6
DEARBORN NATIONAL LIFE INS CO	IL	1,969.6
GERBER LIFE INS CO	NY	3,240.4
GOVERNMENT PERSONNEL MUTUAL L I C	TX	834.7
GREAT SOUTHERN LIFE INS CO	TX	218.2
MEDICO CORP LIFE INS CO	NE	45.2
MIDLAND NATIONAL LIFE INS CO	IA	47,985.0
MINNESOTA LIFE INS CO	MN	38,458.7
MUTUAL OF OMAHA INS CO	NE	7,112.9
NATIONAL FARMERS UNION LIFE INS CO	TX	206.0
NEW YORK LIFE INS & ANNUITY CORP	DE	137,896.0
OHIO NATIONAL LIFE ASR CORP	OH	3,833.0
PACIFIC LIFE & ANNUITY CO	AZ	6,374.0
PAN AMERICAN ASR CO	LA	25.4
PRINCIPAL LIFE INS CO	IA	165,432.0
SAVINGS BANK LIFE INS CO OF MA	MA	2,957.5
STANDARD INS CO	OR	21,220.5
SYMETRA LIFE INS CO	IA	33,273.1
TRUSTMARK INS CO	IL	1,430.6
TRUSTMARK LIFE INS CO	IL	325.4
UNITED WORLD LIFE INS CO	NE	122.6
USABLE LIFE	AR	482.3
VOYA RETIREMENT INS & ANNUITY CO	CT	89,930.9

Puerto Rico

INSURANCE COMPANY NAME	DOM. STATE	TOTAL ASSETS ($MIL)
Rating: A+		
TEACHERS INS & ANNUITY ASN OF AM	NY	276,045.0
Rating: A		
4 EVER LIFE INS CO	IL	211.4
NATIONAL WESTERN LIFE INS CO	CO	10,673.8
SOUTHERN FARM BUREAU LIFE INS CO	MS	13,583.7
TRANS OCEANIC LIFE INS CO	PR	68.3
Rating: A-		
FAMILY HERITAGE LIFE INS CO OF AMER	OH	1,004.9
MASSACHUSETTS MUTUAL LIFE INS CO	MA	226,444.0
NEW YORK LIFE INS CO	NY	167,828.0
STANDARD SECURITY LIFE INS CO OF NY	NY	245.0
Rating: B+		
AMERICAN FAMILY LIFE ASR CO OF COLUM	NE	117,278.0
AMERICAN FIDELITY ASR CO	OK	5,305.5
AXA EQUITABLE LIFE INS CO	NY	171,038.0
BOSTON MUTUAL LIFE INS CO	MA	1,317.6
DEARBORN NATIONAL LIFE INS CO	IL	1,969.6
GERBER LIFE INS CO	NY	3,240.4
MIDLAND NATIONAL LIFE INS CO	IA	47,985.0
MINNESOTA LIFE INS CO	MN	38,458.7
MUTUAL OF OMAHA INS CO	NE	7,112.9
OHIO NATIONAL LIFE ASR CORP	OH	3,833.0
PAN AMERICAN ASR CO	LA	25.4
PRINCIPAL LIFE INS CO	IA	165,432.0
STANDARD INS CO	OR	21,220.5
TRUSTMARK INS CO	IL	1,430.6
VOYA RETIREMENT INS & ANNUITY CO	CT	89,930.9

Rhode Island

INSURANCE COMPANY NAME	DOM. STATE	TOTAL ASSETS ($MIL)

Rating: A+

INSURANCE COMPANY NAME	DOM. STATE	TOTAL ASSETS ($MIL)
AMERICAN FAMILY LIFE INS CO	WI	5,407.4
COUNTRY LIFE INS CO	IL	10,264.7
PHYSICIANS MUTUAL INS CO	NE	2,153.3
STATE FARM LIFE INS CO	IL	68,156.4
TEACHERS INS & ANNUITY ASN OF AM	NY	276,045.0

Rating: A

INSURANCE COMPANY NAME	DOM. STATE	TOTAL ASSETS ($MIL)
4 EVER LIFE INS CO	IL	211.4
FEDERATED LIFE INS CO	MN	1,710.7
GUARDIAN LIFE INS CO OF AMERICA	NY	50,389.3
MIDWESTERN UNITED LIFE INS CO	IN	235.0
MML BAY STATE LIFE INS CO	CT	4,737.2
NATIONAL WESTERN LIFE INS CO	CO	10,673.8
PARKER CENTENNIAL ASR CO	WI	92.2
SENTRY LIFE INS CO	WI	5,800.9
SHELTERPOINT LIFE INS CO	NY	105.4
USAA LIFE INS CO	TX	23,536.5

Rating: A-

INSURANCE COMPANY NAME	DOM. STATE	TOTAL ASSETS ($MIL)
AMALGAMATED LIFE INS CO	NY	122.5
AMERICAN HEALTH & LIFE INS CO	TX	907.2
AMERICAN REPUBLIC INS CO	IA	909.7
ANNUITY INVESTORS LIFE INS CO	OH	3,041.6
CENTRAL STATES H & L CO OF OMAHA	NE	421.1
COMPANION LIFE INS CO	SC	329.6
COUNTRY INVESTORS LIFE ASR CO	IL	297.1
DELAWARE AMERICAN LIFE INS CO	DE	145.9
FAMILY HERITAGE LIFE INS CO OF AMER	OH	1,004.9
FIDELITY INVESTMENTS LIFE INS CO	UT	25,080.7
GARDEN STATE LIFE INS CO	TX	126.5
ILLINOIS MUTUAL LIFE INS CO	IL	1,434.6
MASSACHUSETTS MUTUAL LIFE INS CO	MA	226,444.0
MUTUAL OF AMERICA LIFE INS CO	NY	18,135.8
NEW YORK LIFE INS CO	NY	167,828.0
NIPPON LIFE INS CO OF AMERICA	IA	217.7
NORTHWESTERN MUTUAL LIFE INS CO	WI	244,873.0
PACIFIC LIFE INS CO	NE	115,113.0
PHYSICIANS LIFE INS CO	NE	1,549.0
RESERVE NATIONAL INS CO	OK	123.3
SECURIAN LIFE INS CO	MN	478.9
STANDARD LIFE & ACCIDENT INS CO	TX	511.2
STANDARD SECURITY LIFE INS CO OF NY	NY	245.0

Rating: B+

INSURANCE COMPANY NAME	DOM. STATE	TOTAL ASSETS ($MIL)
AETNA HEALTH & LIFE INS CO	CT	2,349.9
AMERICAN FAMILY LIFE ASR CO OF COLUM	NE	117,278.0
AMERICAN FIDELITY ASR CO	OK	5,305.5
AMERICAN UNITED LIFE INS CO	IN	23,906.8
ASSURITY LIFE INS CO	NE	2,550.8
AXA EQUITABLE LIFE INS CO	NY	171,038.0
BOSTON MUTUAL LIFE INS CO	MA	1,317.6
DEARBORN NATIONAL LIFE INS CO	IL	1,969.6
GERBER LIFE INS CO	NY	3,240.4
GOVERNMENT PERSONNEL MUTUAL L I C	TX	834.7
MEDICO CORP LIFE INS CO	NE	45.2

INSURANCE COMPANY NAME	DOM. STATE	TOTAL ASSETS ($MIL)
MIDLAND NATIONAL LIFE INS CO	IA	47,985.0
MINNESOTA LIFE INS CO	MN	38,458.7
MUTUAL OF OMAHA INS CO	NE	7,112.9
NEW YORK LIFE INS & ANNUITY CORP	DE	137,896.0
OHIO NATIONAL LIFE ASR CORP	OH	3,833.0
PACIFIC LIFE & ANNUITY CO	AZ	6,374.0
PRINCIPAL LIFE INS CO	IA	165,432.0
SAVINGS BANK LIFE INS CO OF MA	MA	2,957.5
STANDARD INS CO	OR	21,220.5
SYMETRA LIFE INS CO	IA	33,273.1
TRUSTMARK INS CO	IL	1,430.6
TRUSTMARK LIFE INS CO	IL	325.4
UNITED WORLD LIFE INS CO	NE	122.6
USABLE LIFE	AR	482.3
VOYA RETIREMENT INS & ANNUITY CO	CT	89,930.9

South Carolina

INSURANCE COMPANY NAME	DOM. STATE	TOTAL ASSETS ($MIL)

Rating: A+

INSURANCE COMPANY NAME	DOM. STATE	TOTAL ASSETS ($MIL)
AMERICAN FAMILY LIFE INS CO	WI	5,407.4
COUNTRY LIFE INS CO	IL	10,264.7
PHYSICIANS MUTUAL INS CO	NE	2,153.3
STATE FARM LIFE INS CO	IL	68,156.4
TEACHERS INS & ANNUITY ASN OF AM	NY	276,045.0

Rating: A

INSURANCE COMPANY NAME	DOM. STATE	TOTAL ASSETS ($MIL)
4 EVER LIFE INS CO	IL	211.4
FEDERATED LIFE INS CO	MN	1,710.7
GUARDIAN LIFE INS CO OF AMERICA	NY	50,389.3
MIDWESTERN UNITED LIFE INS CO	IN	235.0
MML BAY STATE LIFE INS CO	CT	4,737.2
NATIONAL WESTERN LIFE INS CO	CO	10,673.8
PARKER CENTENNIAL ASR CO	WI	92.2
SENTRY LIFE INS CO	WI	5,800.9
SHELTERPOINT LIFE INS CO	NY	105.4
SOUTHERN FARM BUREAU LIFE INS CO	MS	13,583.7
USAA LIFE INS CO	TX	23,536.5

Rating: A-

INSURANCE COMPANY NAME	DOM. STATE	TOTAL ASSETS ($MIL)
AMALGAMATED LIFE INS CO	NY	122.5
AMERICAN HEALTH & LIFE INS CO	TX	907.2
AMERICAN REPUBLIC INS CO	IA	909.7
ANNUITY INVESTORS LIFE INS CO	OH	3,041.6
ANTHEM LIFE INS CO	IN	630.6
AUTO-OWNERS LIFE INS CO	MI	3,832.7
CENTRAL STATES H & L CO OF OMAHA	NE	421.1
COMPANION LIFE INS CO	SC	329.6
COTTON STATES LIFE INS CO	GA	334.6
COUNTRY INVESTORS LIFE ASR CO	IL	297.1
DELAWARE AMERICAN LIFE INS CO	DE	145.9
FAMILY HERITAGE LIFE INS CO OF AMER	OH	1,004.9
FIDELITY INVESTMENTS LIFE INS CO	UT	25,080.7
GARDEN STATE LIFE INS CO	TX	126.5
ILLINOIS MUTUAL LIFE INS CO	IL	1,434.6
LIFE INS CO OF ALABAMA	AL	118.6
MASSACHUSETTS MUTUAL LIFE INS CO	MA	226,444.0
MUTUAL OF AMERICA LIFE INS CO	NY	18,135.8
NEW YORK LIFE INS CO	NY	167,828.0
NIPPON LIFE INS CO OF AMERICA	IA	217.7
NORTHWESTERN MUTUAL LIFE INS CO	WI	244,873.0
PACIFIC LIFE INS CO	NE	115,113.0
PHYSICIANS LIFE INS CO	NE	1,549.0
RESERVE NATIONAL INS CO	OK	123.3
SECURIAN LIFE INS CO	MN	478.9
STANDARD LIFE & ACCIDENT INS CO	TX	511.2
STANDARD SECURITY LIFE INS CO OF NY	NY	245.0

Rating: B+

INSURANCE COMPANY NAME	DOM. STATE	TOTAL ASSETS ($MIL)
AETNA HEALTH & LIFE INS CO	CT	2,349.9
AMERICAN FAMILY LIFE ASR CO OF COLUM	NE	117,278.0
AMERICAN FIDELITY ASR CO	OK	5,305.5
AMERICAN UNITED LIFE INS CO	IN	23,906.8
ASSURITY LIFE INS CO	NE	2,550.8
AXA EQUITABLE LIFE INS CO	NY	171,038.0

INSURANCE COMPANY NAME	DOM. STATE	TOTAL ASSETS ($MIL)
BOSTON MUTUAL LIFE INS CO	MA	1,317.6
DEARBORN NATIONAL LIFE INS CO	IL	1,969.6
GERBER LIFE INS CO	NY	3,240.4
GOVERNMENT PERSONNEL MUTUAL L I C	TX	834.7
GREAT SOUTHERN LIFE INS CO	TX	218.2
GREATER GEORGIA LIFE INS CO	GA	58.6
MEDICO CORP LIFE INS CO	NE	45.2
MIDLAND NATIONAL LIFE INS CO	IA	47,985.0
MINNESOTA LIFE INS CO	MN	38,458.7
MUTUAL OF OMAHA INS CO	NE	7,112.9
NEW YORK LIFE INS & ANNUITY CORP	DE	137,896.0
OHIO NATIONAL LIFE ASR CORP	OH	3,833.0
PACIFIC LIFE & ANNUITY CO	AZ	6,374.0
PAN AMERICAN ASR CO	LA	25.4
PRINCIPAL LIFE INS CO	IA	165,432.0
SAVINGS BANK LIFE INS CO OF MA	MA	2,957.5
SOUTHERN PIONEER LIFE INS CO	AR	16.8
STANDARD INS CO	OR	21,220.5
SYMETRA LIFE INS CO	IA	33,273.1
TRUSTMARK INS CO	IL	1,430.6
TRUSTMARK LIFE INS CO	IL	325.4
UNITED WORLD LIFE INS CO	NE	122.6
USABLE LIFE	AR	482.3
VOYA RETIREMENT INS & ANNUITY CO	CT	89,930.9

South Dakota

INSURANCE COMPANY NAME	DOM. STATE	TOTAL ASSETS ($MIL)

Rating: A+

INSURANCE COMPANY NAME	DOM. STATE	TOTAL ASSETS ($MIL)
AMERICAN FAMILY LIFE INS CO	WI	5,407.4
COUNTRY LIFE INS CO	IL	10,264.7
PHYSICIANS MUTUAL INS CO	NE	2,153.3
STATE FARM LIFE INS CO	IL	68,156.4
TEACHERS INS & ANNUITY ASN OF AM	NY	276,045.0

Rating: A

INSURANCE COMPANY NAME	DOM. STATE	TOTAL ASSETS ($MIL)
4 EVER LIFE INS CO	IL	211.4
FEDERATED LIFE INS CO	MN	1,710.7
GUARDIAN LIFE INS CO OF AMERICA	NY	50,389.3
MIDWESTERN UNITED LIFE INS CO	IN	235.0
MML BAY STATE LIFE INS CO	CT	4,737.2
NATIONAL WESTERN LIFE INS CO	CO	10,673.8
PARKER CENTENNIAL ASR CO	WI	92.2
SENTRY LIFE INS CO	WI	5,800.9
USAA LIFE INS CO	TX	23,536.5

Rating: A-

INSURANCE COMPANY NAME	DOM. STATE	TOTAL ASSETS ($MIL)
AMALGAMATED LIFE INS CO	NY	122.5
AMERICAN HEALTH & LIFE INS CO	TX	907.2
AMERICAN REPUBLIC INS CO	IA	909.7
ANNUITY INVESTORS LIFE INS CO	OH	3,041.6
ANTHEM LIFE INS CO	IN	630.6
AUTO-OWNERS LIFE INS CO	MI	3,832.7
CENTRAL STATES H & L CO OF OMAHA	NE	421.1
COMPANION LIFE INS CO	SC	329.6
COUNTRY INVESTORS LIFE ASR CO	IL	297.1
DELAWARE AMERICAN LIFE INS CO	DE	145.9
FAMILY HERITAGE LIFE INS CO OF AMER	OH	1,004.9
FIDELITY INVESTMENTS LIFE INS CO	UT	25,080.7
GARDEN STATE LIFE INS CO	TX	126.5
ILLINOIS MUTUAL LIFE INS CO	IL	1,434.6
MASSACHUSETTS MUTUAL LIFE INS CO	MA	226,444.0
MUTUAL OF AMERICA LIFE INS CO	NY	18,135.8
NEW YORK LIFE INS CO	NY	167,828.0
NIPPON LIFE INS CO OF AMERICA	IA	217.7
NORTHWESTERN MUTUAL LIFE INS CO	WI	244,873.0
PACIFIC GUARDIAN LIFE INS CO LTD	HI	544.4
PACIFIC LIFE INS CO	NE	115,113.0
PHYSICIANS LIFE INS CO	NE	1,549.0
RESERVE NATIONAL INS CO	OK	123.3
SECURIAN LIFE INS CO	MN	478.9
STANDARD LIFE & ACCIDENT INS CO	TX	511.2
STANDARD SECURITY LIFE INS CO OF NY	NY	245.0

Rating: B+

INSURANCE COMPANY NAME	DOM. STATE	TOTAL ASSETS ($MIL)
AETNA HEALTH & LIFE INS CO	CT	2,349.9
AMERICAN FAMILY LIFE ASR CO OF COLUM	NE	117,278.0
AMERICAN FIDELITY ASR CO	OK	5,305.5
AMERICAN UNITED LIFE INS CO	IN	23,906.8
ASSURITY LIFE INS CO	NE	2,550.8
AXA EQUITABLE LIFE INS CO	NY	171,038.0
BOSTON MUTUAL LIFE INS CO	MA	1,317.6
DEARBORN NATIONAL LIFE INS CO	IL	1,969.6
FARM BUREAU LIFE INS CO	IA	8,582.6

INSURANCE COMPANY NAME	DOM. STATE	TOTAL ASSETS ($MIL)
GERBER LIFE INS CO	NY	3,240.4
GOVERNMENT PERSONNEL MUTUAL L I C	TX	834.7
GREAT SOUTHERN LIFE INS CO	TX	218.2
MEDICO CORP LIFE INS CO	NE	45.2
MIDLAND NATIONAL LIFE INS CO	IA	47,985.0
MINNESOTA LIFE INS CO	MN	38,458.7
MUTUAL OF OMAHA INS CO	NE	7,112.9
NATIONAL FARMERS UNION LIFE INS CO	TX	206.0
NEW YORK LIFE INS & ANNUITY CORP	DE	137,896.0
OHIO NATIONAL LIFE ASR CORP	OH	3,833.0
PACIFIC LIFE & ANNUITY CO	AZ	6,374.0
PRINCIPAL LIFE INS CO	IA	165,432.0
SAVINGS BANK LIFE INS CO OF MA	MA	2,957.5
STANDARD INS CO	OR	21,220.5
SYMETRA LIFE INS CO	IA	33,273.1
TRUSTMARK INS CO	IL	1,430.6
TRUSTMARK LIFE INS CO	IL	325.4
UNITED WORLD LIFE INS CO	NE	122.6
USABLE LIFE	AR	482.3
VOYA RETIREMENT INS & ANNUITY CO	CT	89,930.9

Tennessee

INSURANCE COMPANY NAME	DOM. STATE	TOTAL ASSETS ($MIL)
Rating: A+		
AMERICAN FAMILY LIFE INS CO	WI	5,407.4
COUNTRY LIFE INS CO	IL	10,264.7
PHYSICIANS MUTUAL INS CO	NE	2,153.3
STATE FARM LIFE INS CO	IL	68,156.4
TEACHERS INS & ANNUITY ASN OF AM	NY	276,045.0
Rating: A		
4 EVER LIFE INS CO	IL	211.4
FEDERATED LIFE INS CO	MN	1,710.7
GUARDIAN LIFE INS CO OF AMERICA	NY	50,389.3
MIDWESTERN UNITED LIFE INS CO	IN	235.0
MML BAY STATE LIFE INS CO	CT	4,737.2
NATIONAL WESTERN LIFE INS CO	CO	10,673.8
PARKER CENTENNIAL ASR CO	WI	92.2
SENTRY LIFE INS CO	WI	5,800.9
SHELTERPOINT LIFE INS CO	NY	105.4
SOUTHERN FARM BUREAU LIFE INS CO	MS	13,583.7
TENNESSEE FARMERS LIFE INS CO	TN	2,151.3
USAA LIFE INS CO	TX	23,536.5
Rating: A-		
AMALGAMATED LIFE INS CO	NY	122.5
AMERICAN HEALTH & LIFE INS CO	TX	907.2
AMERICAN REPUBLIC INS CO	IA	909.7
ANNUITY INVESTORS LIFE INS CO	OH	3,041.6
ANTHEM LIFE INS CO	IN	630.6
AUTO-OWNERS LIFE INS CO	MI	3,832.7
CENTRAL STATES H & L CO OF OMAHA	NE	421.1
CIGNA LIFE INS CO OF NEW YORK	NY	300.3
COMPANION LIFE INS CO	SC	329.6
COTTON STATES LIFE INS CO	GA	334.6
COUNTRY INVESTORS LIFE ASR CO	IL	297.1
DELAWARE AMERICAN LIFE INS CO	DE	145.9
ERIE FAMILY LIFE INS CO	PA	2,217.2
FAMILY HERITAGE LIFE INS CO OF AMER	OH	1,004.9
FIDELITY INVESTMENTS LIFE INS CO	UT	25,080.7
GARDEN STATE LIFE INS CO	TX	126.5
ILLINOIS MUTUAL LIFE INS CO	IL	1,434.6
LIFE INS CO OF ALABAMA	AL	118.6
MASSACHUSETTS MUTUAL LIFE INS CO	MA	226,444.0
MUTUAL OF AMERICA LIFE INS CO	NY	18,135.8
NEW YORK LIFE INS CO	NY	167,828.0
NIPPON LIFE INS CO OF AMERICA	IA	217.7
NORTHWESTERN MUTUAL LIFE INS CO	WI	244,873.0
PACIFIC LIFE INS CO	NE	115,113.0
PHYSICIANS LIFE INS CO	NE	1,549.0
RESERVE NATIONAL INS CO	OK	123.3
SECURIAN LIFE INS CO	MN	478.9
SHELTER LIFE INS CO	MO	1,180.1
STANDARD LIFE & ACCIDENT INS CO	TX	511.2
STANDARD SECURITY LIFE INS CO OF NY	NY	245.0
Rating: B+		
AETNA HEALTH & LIFE INS CO	CT	2,349.9
AMERICAN FAMILY LIFE ASR CO OF COLUM	NE	117,278.0

INSURANCE COMPANY NAME	DOM. STATE	TOTAL ASSETS ($MIL)
AMERICAN FIDELITY ASR CO	OK	5,305.5
AMERICAN UNITED LIFE INS CO	IN	23,906.8
ASSURITY LIFE INS CO	NE	2,550.8
AXA EQUITABLE LIFE INS CO	NY	171,038.0
BLUEBONNET LIFE INS CO	MS	58.9
BOSTON MUTUAL LIFE INS CO	MA	1,317.6
DEARBORN NATIONAL LIFE INS CO	IL	1,969.6
GERBER LIFE INS CO	NY	3,240.4
GOVERNMENT PERSONNEL MUTUAL L I C	TX	834.7
GREAT SOUTHERN LIFE INS CO	TX	218.2
GREATER GEORGIA LIFE INS CO	GA	58.6
MEDICO CORP LIFE INS CO	NE	45.2
MIDLAND NATIONAL LIFE INS CO	IA	47,985.0
MINNESOTA LIFE INS CO	MN	38,458.7
MUTUAL OF OMAHA INS CO	NE	7,112.9
NEW YORK LIFE INS & ANNUITY CORP	DE	137,896.0
OHIO NATIONAL LIFE ASR CORP	OH	3,833.0
PACIFIC LIFE & ANNUITY CO	AZ	6,374.0
PAN AMERICAN ASR CO	LA	25.4
PRINCIPAL LIFE INS CO	IA	165,432.0
SAVINGS BANK LIFE INS CO OF MA	MA	2,957.5
SOUTHERN PIONEER LIFE INS CO	AR	16.8
STANDARD INS CO	OR	21,220.5
SYMETRA LIFE INS CO	IA	33,273.1
TRUSTMARK INS CO	IL	1,430.6
TRUSTMARK LIFE INS CO	IL	325.4
UNITED WORLD LIFE INS CO	NE	122.6
USABLE LIFE	AR	482.3
VOYA RETIREMENT INS & ANNUITY CO	CT	89,930.9

Texas

INSURANCE COMPANY NAME	DOM. STATE	TOTAL ASSETS ($MIL)

Rating: A+

INSURANCE COMPANY NAME	DOM. STATE	TOTAL ASSETS ($MIL)
AMERICAN FAMILY LIFE INS CO	WI	5,407.4
COUNTRY LIFE INS CO	IL	10,264.7
PHYSICIANS MUTUAL INS CO	NE	2,153.3
STATE FARM LIFE INS CO	IL	68,156.4
TEACHERS INS & ANNUITY ASN OF AM	NY	276,045.0

Rating: A

INSURANCE COMPANY NAME	DOM. STATE	TOTAL ASSETS ($MIL)
4 EVER LIFE INS CO	IL	211.4
FEDERATED LIFE INS CO	MN	1,710.7
GUARDIAN LIFE INS CO OF AMERICA	NY	50,389.3
LIFEWISE ASR CO	WA	143.3
MIDWESTERN UNITED LIFE INS CO	IN	235.0
MML BAY STATE LIFE INS CO	CT	4,737.2
NATIONAL WESTERN LIFE INS CO	CO	10,673.8
PARKER CENTENNIAL ASR CO	WI	92.2
SENTRY LIFE INS CO	WI	5,800.9
SOUTHERN FARM BUREAU LIFE INS CO	MS	13,583.7
USAA LIFE INS CO	TX	23,536.5

Rating: A-

INSURANCE COMPANY NAME	DOM. STATE	TOTAL ASSETS ($MIL)
AMALGAMATED LIFE INS CO	NY	122.5
AMERICAN HEALTH & LIFE INS CO	TX	907.2
AMERICAN REPUBLIC INS CO	IA	909.7
ANNUITY INVESTORS LIFE INS CO	OH	3,041.6
ANTHEM LIFE INS CO	IN	630.6
CENTRAL STATES H & L CO OF OMAHA	NE	421.1
COMPANION LIFE INS CO	SC	329.6
COUNTRY INVESTORS LIFE ASR CO	IL	297.1
DELAWARE AMERICAN LIFE INS CO	DE	145.9
FAMILY HERITAGE LIFE INS CO OF AMER	OH	1,004.9
FIDELITY INVESTMENTS LIFE INS CO	UT	25,080.7
GARDEN STATE LIFE INS CO	TX	126.5
ILLINOIS MUTUAL LIFE INS CO	IL	1,434.6
MASSACHUSETTS MUTUAL LIFE INS CO	MA	226,444.0
MUTUAL OF AMERICA LIFE INS CO	NY	18,135.8
NEW YORK LIFE INS CO	NY	167,828.0
NIPPON LIFE INS CO OF AMERICA	IA	217.7
NORTHWESTERN MUTUAL LIFE INS CO	WI	244,873.0
PACIFIC GUARDIAN LIFE INS CO LTD	HI	544.4
PACIFIC LIFE INS CO	NE	115,113.0
PHYSICIANS LIFE INS CO	NE	1,549.0
RESERVE NATIONAL INS CO	OK	123.3
SECURIAN LIFE INS CO	MN	478.9
STANDARD LIFE & ACCIDENT INS CO	TX	511.2
STANDARD SECURITY LIFE INS CO OF NY	NY	245.0

Rating: B+

INSURANCE COMPANY NAME	DOM. STATE	TOTAL ASSETS ($MIL)
AETNA HEALTH & LIFE INS CO	CT	2,349.9
AMERICAN FAMILY LIFE ASR CO OF COLUM	NE	117,278.0
AMERICAN FIDELITY ASR CO	OK	5,305.5
AMERICAN UNITED LIFE INS CO	IN	23,906.8
ASSURITY LIFE INS CO	NE	2,550.8
AXA EQUITABLE LIFE INS CO	NY	171,038.0
BOSTON MUTUAL LIFE INS CO	MA	1,317.6
DEARBORN NATIONAL LIFE INS CO	IL	1,969.6

INSURANCE COMPANY NAME	DOM. STATE	TOTAL ASSETS ($MIL)
GERBER LIFE INS CO	NY	3,240.4
GOVERNMENT PERSONNEL MUTUAL L I C	TX	834.7
GREAT SOUTHERN LIFE INS CO	TX	218.2
LOCOMOTIVE ENGRS&COND MUT PROT ASSN	MI	63.0
MEDICO CORP LIFE INS CO	NE	45.2
MIDLAND NATIONAL LIFE INS CO	IA	47,985.0
MINNESOTA LIFE INS CO	MN	38,458.7
MUTUAL OF OMAHA INS CO	NE	7,112.9
NATIONAL FARMERS UNION LIFE INS CO	TX	206.0
NEW YORK LIFE INS & ANNUITY CORP	DE	137,896.0
OHIO NATIONAL LIFE ASR CORP	OH	3,833.0
PACIFIC LIFE & ANNUITY CO	AZ	6,374.0
PAN AMERICAN ASR CO	LA	25.4
PRINCIPAL LIFE INS CO	IA	165,432.0
SAVINGS BANK LIFE INS CO OF MA	MA	2,957.5
SOUTHERN PIONEER LIFE INS CO	AR	16.8
STANDARD INS CO	OR	21,220.5
SYMETRA LIFE INS CO	IA	33,273.1
TRUSTMARK INS CO	IL	1,430.6
TRUSTMARK LIFE INS CO	IL	325.4
UNITED WORLD LIFE INS CO	NE	122.6
USABLE LIFE	AR	482.3
VOYA RETIREMENT INS & ANNUITY CO	CT	89,930.9

Utah

INSURANCE COMPANY NAME	DOM. STATE	TOTAL ASSETS ($MIL)

Rating: A+

INSURANCE COMPANY NAME	DOM. STATE	TOTAL ASSETS ($MIL)
AMERICAN FAMILY LIFE INS CO	WI	5,407.4
COUNTRY LIFE INS CO	IL	10,264.7
PHYSICIANS MUTUAL INS CO	NE	2,153.3
STATE FARM LIFE INS CO	IL	68,156.4
TEACHERS INS & ANNUITY ASN OF AM	NY	276,045.0

Rating: A

INSURANCE COMPANY NAME	DOM. STATE	TOTAL ASSETS ($MIL)
4 EVER LIFE INS CO	IL	211.4
FEDERATED LIFE INS CO	MN	1,710.7
GUARDIAN LIFE INS CO OF AMERICA	NY	50,389.3
LIFEWISE ASR CO	WA	143.3
MIDWESTERN UNITED LIFE INS CO	IN	235.0
MML BAY STATE LIFE INS CO	CT	4,737.2
NATIONAL WESTERN LIFE INS CO	CO	10,673.8
PARKER CENTENNIAL ASR CO	WI	92.2
SENTRY LIFE INS CO	WI	5,800.9
USAA LIFE INS CO	TX	23,536.5

Rating: A-

INSURANCE COMPANY NAME	DOM. STATE	TOTAL ASSETS ($MIL)
AMALGAMATED LIFE INS CO	NY	122.5
AMERICAN HEALTH & LIFE INS CO	TX	907.2
AMERICAN REPUBLIC INS CO	IA	909.7
ANNUITY INVESTORS LIFE INS CO	OH	3,041.6
ANTHEM LIFE INS CO	IN	630.6
AUTO-OWNERS LIFE INS CO	MI	3,832.7
CENTRAL STATES H & L CO OF OMAHA	NE	421.1
COMPANION LIFE INS CO	SC	329.6
DELAWARE AMERICAN LIFE INS CO	DE	145.9
FAMILY HERITAGE LIFE INS CO OF AMER	OH	1,004.9
FIDELITY INVESTMENTS LIFE INS CO	UT	25,080.7
GARDEN STATE LIFE INS CO	TX	126.5
ILLINOIS MUTUAL LIFE INS CO	IL	1,434.6
MASSACHUSETTS MUTUAL LIFE INS CO	MA	226,444.0
MUTUAL OF AMERICA LIFE INS CO	NY	18,135.8
NEW YORK LIFE INS CO	NY	167,828.0
NIPPON LIFE INS CO OF AMERICA	IA	217.7
NORTHWESTERN MUTUAL LIFE INS CO	WI	244,873.0
PACIFIC GUARDIAN LIFE INS CO LTD	HI	544.4
PACIFIC LIFE INS CO	NE	115,113.0
PHYSICIANS LIFE INS CO	NE	1,549.0
RESERVE NATIONAL INS CO	OK	123.3
SECURIAN LIFE INS CO	MN	478.9
STANDARD LIFE & ACCIDENT INS CO	TX	511.2
STANDARD SECURITY LIFE INS CO OF NY	NY	245.0

Rating: B+

INSURANCE COMPANY NAME	DOM. STATE	TOTAL ASSETS ($MIL)
AETNA HEALTH & LIFE INS CO	CT	2,349.9
AMERICAN FAMILY LIFE ASR CO OF COLUM	NE	117,278.0
AMERICAN FIDELITY ASR CO	OK	5,305.5
AMERICAN UNITED LIFE INS CO	IN	23,906.8
ASSURITY LIFE INS CO	NE	2,550.8
AXA EQUITABLE LIFE INS CO	NY	171,038.0
BOSTON MUTUAL LIFE INS CO	MA	1,317.6
DEARBORN NATIONAL LIFE INS CO	IL	1,969.6
FARM BUREAU LIFE INS CO	IA	8,582.6

INSURANCE COMPANY NAME	DOM. STATE	TOTAL ASSETS ($MIL)
GERBER LIFE INS CO	NY	3,240.4
GOVERNMENT PERSONNEL MUTUAL L I C	TX	834.7
GREAT SOUTHERN LIFE INS CO	TX	218.2
MEDICO CORP LIFE INS CO	NE	45.2
MIDLAND NATIONAL LIFE INS CO	IA	47,985.0
MINNESOTA LIFE INS CO	MN	38,458.7
MUTUAL OF OMAHA INS CO	NE	7,112.9
NATIONAL FARMERS UNION LIFE INS CO	TX	206.0
NEW YORK LIFE INS & ANNUITY CORP	DE	137,896.0
OHIO NATIONAL LIFE ASR CORP	OH	3,833.0
PACIFIC LIFE & ANNUITY CO	AZ	6,374.0
PAN AMERICAN ASR CO	LA	25.4
PRINCIPAL LIFE INS CO	IA	165,432.0
SAVINGS BANK LIFE INS CO OF MA	MA	2,957.5
STANDARD INS CO	OR	21,220.5
SYMETRA LIFE INS CO	IA	33,273.1
TRUSTMARK INS CO	IL	1,430.6
TRUSTMARK LIFE INS CO	IL	325.4
UNITED WORLD LIFE INS CO	NE	122.6
USABLE LIFE	AR	482.3
VOYA RETIREMENT INS & ANNUITY CO	CT	89,930.9

Vermont

INSURANCE COMPANY NAME	DOM. STATE	TOTAL ASSETS ($MIL)
Rating: A+		
AMERICAN FAMILY LIFE INS CO	WI	5,407.4
PHYSICIANS MUTUAL INS CO	NE	2,153.3
STATE FARM LIFE INS CO	IL	68,156.4
TEACHERS INS & ANNUITY ASN OF AM	NY	276,045.0
Rating: A		
4 EVER LIFE INS CO	IL	211.4
FEDERATED LIFE INS CO	MN	1,710.7
GUARDIAN LIFE INS CO OF AMERICA	NY	50,389.3
MIDWESTERN UNITED LIFE INS CO	IN	235.0
MML BAY STATE LIFE INS CO	CT	4,737.2
NATIONAL WESTERN LIFE INS CO	CO	10,673.8
PARKER CENTENNIAL ASR CO	WI	92.2
SENTRY LIFE INS CO	WI	5,800.9
USAA LIFE INS CO	TX	23,536.5
Rating: A-		
AMALGAMATED LIFE INS CO	NY	122.5
AMERICAN FAMILY LIFE ASR CO OF NY	NY	885.2
AMERICAN HEALTH & LIFE INS CO	TX	907.2
AMERICAN REPUBLIC INS CO	IA	909.7
CENTRAL STATES H & L CO OF OMAHA	NE	421.1
COMPANION LIFE INS CO	SC	329.6
DELAWARE AMERICAN LIFE INS CO	DE	145.9
FAMILY HERITAGE LIFE INS CO OF AMER	OH	1,004.9
FIDELITY INVESTMENTS LIFE INS CO	UT	25,080.7
GARDEN STATE LIFE INS CO	TX	126.5
ILLINOIS MUTUAL LIFE INS CO	IL	1,434.6
MASSACHUSETTS MUTUAL LIFE INS CO	MA	226,444.0
MUTUAL OF AMERICA LIFE INS CO	NY	18,135.8
NEW YORK LIFE INS CO	NY	167,828.0
NIPPON LIFE INS CO OF AMERICA	IA	217.7
NORTHWESTERN MUTUAL LIFE INS CO	WI	244,873.0
PACIFIC LIFE INS CO	NE	115,113.0
PHYSICIANS LIFE INS CO	NE	1,549.0
RESERVE NATIONAL INS CO	OK	123.3
SECURIAN LIFE INS CO	MN	478.9
STANDARD LIFE & ACCIDENT INS CO	TX	511.2
STANDARD SECURITY LIFE INS CO OF NY	NY	245.0
Rating: B+		
AETNA HEALTH & LIFE INS CO	CT	2,349.9
AMERICAN FAMILY LIFE ASR CO OF COLUM	NE	117,278.0
AMERICAN FIDELITY ASR CO	OK	5,305.5
AMERICAN UNITED LIFE INS CO	IN	23,906.8
ASSURITY LIFE INS CO	NE	2,550.8
AXA EQUITABLE LIFE INS CO	NY	171,038.0
BOSTON MUTUAL LIFE INS CO	MA	1,317.6
DEARBORN NATIONAL LIFE INS CO	IL	1,969.6
GERBER LIFE INS CO	NY	3,240.4
GOVERNMENT PERSONNEL MUTUAL L I C	TX	834.7
MEDICO CORP LIFE INS CO	NE	45.2
MIDLAND NATIONAL LIFE INS CO	IA	47,985.0
MINNESOTA LIFE INS CO	MN	38,458.7
MUTUAL OF OMAHA INS CO	NE	7,112.9

INSURANCE COMPANY NAME	DOM. STATE	TOTAL ASSETS ($MIL)
NEW YORK LIFE INS & ANNUITY CORP	DE	137,896.0
OHIO NATIONAL LIFE ASR CORP	OH	3,833.0
PACIFIC LIFE & ANNUITY CO	AZ	6,374.0
PRINCIPAL LIFE INS CO	IA	165,432.0
SAVINGS BANK LIFE INS CO OF MA	MA	2,957.5
STANDARD INS CO	OR	21,220.5
SYMETRA LIFE INS CO	IA	33,273.1
TRUSTMARK INS CO	IL	1,430.6
TRUSTMARK LIFE INS CO	IL	325.4
UNITED WORLD LIFE INS CO	NE	122.6
USABLE LIFE	AR	482.3
VOYA RETIREMENT INS & ANNUITY CO	CT	89,930.9

Virginia

INSURANCE COMPANY NAME	DOM. STATE	TOTAL ASSETS ($MIL)	INSURANCE COMPANY NAME	DOM. STATE	TOTAL ASSETS ($MIL)
			DEARBORN NATIONAL LIFE INS CO	IL	1,969.6
			GERBER LIFE INS CO	NY	3,240.4
Rating: A+			GOVERNMENT PERSONNEL MUTUAL L I C	TX	834.7
			GREAT SOUTHERN LIFE INS CO	TX	218.2
AMERICAN FAMILY LIFE INS CO	WI	5,407.4	GREATER GEORGIA LIFE INS CO	GA	58.6
COUNTRY LIFE INS CO	IL	10,264.7	MEDICO CORP LIFE INS CO	NE	45.2
PHYSICIANS MUTUAL INS CO	NE	2,153.3	MIDLAND NATIONAL LIFE INS CO	IA	47,985.0
STATE FARM LIFE INS CO	IL	68,156.4	MINNESOTA LIFE INS CO	MN	38,458.7
TEACHERS INS & ANNUITY ASN OF AM	NY	276,045.0	MUTUAL OF OMAHA INS CO	NE	7,112.9
			NATIONAL FARMERS UNION LIFE INS CO	TX	206.0
Rating: A			NEW YORK LIFE INS & ANNUITY CORP	DE	137,896.0
			OHIO NATIONAL LIFE ASR CORP	OH	3,833.0
4 EVER LIFE INS CO	IL	211.4	PACIFIC LIFE & ANNUITY CO	AZ	6,374.0
FEDERATED LIFE INS CO	MN	1,710.7	PAN AMERICAN ASR CO	LA	25.4
GUARDIAN LIFE INS CO OF AMERICA	NY	50,389.3	PRINCIPAL LIFE INS CO	IA	165,432.0
MIDWESTERN UNITED LIFE INS CO	IN	235.0	SAVINGS BANK LIFE INS CO OF MA	MA	2,957.5
MML BAY STATE LIFE INS CO	CT	4,737.2	STANDARD INS CO	OR	21,220.5
NATIONAL WESTERN LIFE INS CO	CO	10,673.8	SYMETRA LIFE INS CO	IA	33,273.1
PARKER CENTENNIAL ASR CO	WI	92.2	TRUSTMARK INS CO	IL	1,430.6
SENTRY LIFE INS CO	WI	5,800.9	TRUSTMARK LIFE INS CO	IL	325.4
SOUTHERN FARM BUREAU LIFE INS CO	MS	13,583.7	UNITED WORLD LIFE INS CO	NE	122.6
USAA LIFE INS CO	TX	23,536.5	USABLE LIFE	AR	482.3
			VOYA RETIREMENT INS & ANNUITY CO	CT	89,930.9
Rating: A-					
AMALGAMATED LIFE INS CO	NY	122.5			
AMERICAN HEALTH & LIFE INS CO	TX	907.2			
AMERICAN REPUBLIC INS CO	IA	909.7			
ANNUITY INVESTORS LIFE INS CO	OH	3,041.6			
ANTHEM LIFE INS CO	IN	630.6			
AUTO-OWNERS LIFE INS CO	MI	3,832.7			
CENTRAL STATES H & L CO OF OMAHA	NE	421.1			
COMPANION LIFE INS CO	SC	329.6			
COTTON STATES LIFE INS CO	GA	334.6			
COUNTRY INVESTORS LIFE ASR CO	IL	207.1			
DELAWARE AMERICAN LIFE INS CO	DE	145.9			
ERIE FAMILY LIFE INS CO	PA	2,217.2			
FAMILY HERITAGE LIFE INS CO OF AMER	OH	1,004.9			
FIDELITY INVESTMENTS LIFE INS CO	UT	25,080.7			
GARDEN STATE LIFE INS CO	TX	126.5			
ILLINOIS MUTUAL LIFE INS CO	IL	1,434.6			
MASSACHUSETTS MUTUAL LIFE INS CO	MA	226,444.0			
MUTUAL OF AMERICA LIFE INS CO	NY	18,135.8			
NEW YORK LIFE INS CO	NY	167,828.0			
NIPPON LIFE INS CO OF AMERICA	IA	217.7			
NORTHWESTERN MUTUAL LIFE INS CO	WI	244,873.0			
PACIFIC LIFE INS CO	NE	115,113.0			
PHYSICIANS LIFE INS CO	NE	1,549.0			
RESERVE NATIONAL INS CO	OK	123.3			
SECURIAN LIFE INS CO	MN	478.9			
STANDARD LIFE & ACCIDENT INS CO	TX	511.2			
STANDARD SECURITY LIFE INS CO OF NY	NY	245.0			
Rating: B+					
AETNA HEALTH & LIFE INS CO	CT	2,349.9			
AMERICAN FAMILY LIFE ASR CO OF COLUM	NE	117,278.0			
AMERICAN FIDELITY ASR CO	OK	5,305.5			
AMERICAN UNITED LIFE INS CO	IN	23,906.8			
ASSURITY LIFE INS CO	NE	2,550.8			
AXA EQUITABLE LIFE INS CO	NY	171,038.0			
BOSTON MUTUAL LIFE INS CO	MA	1,317.6			

Washington

INSURANCE COMPANY NAME	DOM. STATE	TOTAL ASSETS ($MIL)	INSURANCE COMPANY NAME	DOM. STATE	TOTAL ASSETS ($MIL)
Rating: A+			FARM BUREAU LIFE INS CO	IA	8,582.6
			GERBER LIFE INS CO	NY	3,240.4
AMERICAN FAMILY LIFE INS CO	WI	5,407.4	GOVERNMENT PERSONNEL MUTUAL L I C	TX	834.7
COUNTRY LIFE INS CO	IL	10,264.7	GREAT SOUTHERN LIFE INS CO	TX	218.2
PHYSICIANS MUTUAL INS CO	NE	2,153.3	MEDICO CORP LIFE INS CO	NE	45.2
STATE FARM LIFE INS CO	IL	68,156.4	MIDLAND NATIONAL LIFE INS CO	IA	47,985.0
TEACHERS INS & ANNUITY ASN OF AM	NY	276,045.0	MINNESOTA LIFE INS CO	MN	38,458.7
			MUTUAL OF OMAHA INS CO	NE	7,112.9
Rating: A			NATIONAL FARMERS UNION LIFE INS CO	TX	206.0
			NEW YORK LIFE INS & ANNUITY CORP	DE	137,896.0
4 EVER LIFE INS CO	IL	211.4	OHIO NATIONAL LIFE ASR CORP	OH	3,833.0
FEDERATED LIFE INS CO	MN	1,710.7	PACIFIC LIFE & ANNUITY CO	AZ	6,374.0
GUARDIAN LIFE INS CO OF AMERICA	NY	50,389.3	PAN AMERICAN ASR CO	LA	25.4
LIFEWISE ASR CO	WA	143.3	PRINCIPAL LIFE INS CO	IA	165,432.0
MIDWESTERN UNITED LIFE INS CO	IN	235.0	SAVINGS BANK LIFE INS CO OF MA	MA	2,957.5
MML BAY STATE LIFE INS CO	CT	4,737.2	STANDARD INS CO	OR	21,220.5
NATIONAL WESTERN LIFE INS CO	CO	10,673.8	SYMETRA LIFE INS CO	IA	33,273.1
PARKER CENTENNIAL ASR CO	WI	92.2	TRUSTMARK INS CO	IL	1,430.6
SENTRY LIFE INS CO	WI	5,800.9	TRUSTMARK LIFE INS CO	IL	325.4
USAA LIFE INS CO	TX	23,536.5	UNITED WORLD LIFE INS CO	NE	122.6
			USABLE LIFE	AR	482.3
Rating: A-			VOYA RETIREMENT INS & ANNUITY CO	CT	89,930.9
AMALGAMATED LIFE INS CO	NY	122.5			
AMERICAN HEALTH & LIFE INS CO	TX	907.2			
AMERICAN REPUBLIC INS CO	IA	909.7			
ANNUITY INVESTORS LIFE INS CO	OH	3,041.6			
ANTHEM LIFE INS CO	IN	630.6			
AUTO-OWNERS LIFE INS CO	MI	3,832.7			
CENTRAL STATES H & L CO OF OMAHA	NE	421.1			
COMPANION LIFE INS CO	SC	329.6			
COUNTRY INVESTORS LIFE ASR CO	IL	297.1			
DELAWARE AMERICAN LIFE INS CO	DE	145.9			
FAMILY HERITAGE LIFE INS CO OF AMER	OH	1,004.9			
FIDELITY INVESTMENTS LIFE INS CO	UT	25,080.7			
GARDEN STATE LIFE INS CO	TX	126.5			
ILLINOIS MUTUAL LIFE INS CO	IL	1,434.6			
MASSACHUSETTS MUTUAL LIFE INS CO	MA	226,444.0			
MUTUAL OF AMERICA LIFE INS CO	NY	18,135.8			
NEW YORK LIFE INS CO	NY	167,828.0			
NIPPON LIFE INS CO OF AMERICA	IA	217.7			
NORTHWESTERN MUTUAL LIFE INS CO	WI	244,873.0			
PACIFIC GUARDIAN LIFE INS CO LTD	HI	544.4			
PACIFIC LIFE INS CO	NE	115,113.0			
PHYSICIANS LIFE INS CO	NE	1,549.0			
RESERVE NATIONAL INS CO	OK	123.3			
SECURIAN LIFE INS CO	MN	478.9			
STANDARD LIFE & ACCIDENT INS CO	TX	511.2			
STANDARD SECURITY LIFE INS CO OF NY	NY	245.0			
Rating: B+					
AETNA HEALTH & LIFE INS CO	CT	2,349.9			
AMERICAN FAMILY LIFE ASR CO OF COLUM	NE	117,278.0			
AMERICAN FIDELITY ASR CO	OK	5,305.5			
AMERICAN UNITED LIFE INS CO	IN	23,906.8			
ASSURITY LIFE INS CO	NE	2,550.8			
AXA EQUITABLE LIFE INS CO	NY	171,038.0			
BOSTON MUTUAL LIFE INS CO	MA	1,317.6			
DEARBORN NATIONAL LIFE INS CO	IL	1,969.6			

West Virginia

INSURANCE COMPANY NAME	DOM. STATE	TOTAL ASSETS ($MIL)

Rating: A+

INSURANCE COMPANY NAME	DOM. STATE	TOTAL ASSETS ($MIL)
AMERICAN FAMILY LIFE INS CO	WI	5,407.4
COUNTRY LIFE INS CO	IL	10,264.7
PHYSICIANS MUTUAL INS CO	NE	2,153.3
STATE FARM LIFE INS CO	IL	68,156.4
TEACHERS INS & ANNUITY ASN OF AM	NY	276,045.0

Rating: A

INSURANCE COMPANY NAME	DOM. STATE	TOTAL ASSETS ($MIL)
4 EVER LIFE INS CO	IL	211.4
FEDERATED LIFE INS CO	MN	1,710.7
GUARDIAN LIFE INS CO OF AMERICA	NY	50,389.3
MIDWESTERN UNITED LIFE INS CO	IN	235.0
MML BAY STATE LIFE INS CO	CT	4,737.2
NATIONAL WESTERN LIFE INS CO	CO	10,673.8
PARKER CENTENNIAL ASR CO	WI	92.2
SENTRY LIFE INS CO	WI	5,800.9
USAA LIFE INS CO	TX	23,536.5

Rating: A-

INSURANCE COMPANY NAME	DOM. STATE	TOTAL ASSETS ($MIL)
AMALGAMATED LIFE INS CO	NY	122.5
AMERICAN HEALTH & LIFE INS CO	TX	907.2
AMERICAN REPUBLIC INS CO	IA	909.7
ANNUITY INVESTORS LIFE INS CO	OH	3,041.6
ANTHEM LIFE INS CO	IN	630.6
CENTRAL STATES H & L CO OF OMAHA	NE	421.1
COMPANION LIFE INS CO	SC	329.6
COUNTRY INVESTORS LIFE ASR CO	IL	297.1
DELAWARE AMERICAN LIFE INS CO	DE	145.9
ERIE FAMILY LIFE INS CO	PA	2,217.2
FAMILY HERITAGE LIFE INS CO OF AMER	OH	1,004.8
FIDELITY INVESTMENTS LIFE INS CO	UT	25,080.7
GARDEN STATE LIFE INS CO	TX	126.5
ILLINOIS MUTUAL LIFE INS CO	IL	1,434.6
MASSACHUSETTS MUTUAL LIFE INS CO	MA	226,444.0
MUTUAL OF AMERICA LIFE INS CO	NY	18,135.8
NEW YORK LIFE INS CO	NY	167,828.0
NIPPON LIFE INS CO OF AMERICA	IA	217.7
NORTHWESTERN MUTUAL LIFE INS CO	WI	244,873.0
PACIFIC LIFE INS CO	NE	116,113.0
PHYSICIANS LIFE INS CO	NE	1,549.0
RESERVE NATIONAL INS CO	OK	123.3
SECURIAN LIFE INS CO	MN	478.9
STANDARD LIFE & ACCIDENT INS CO	TX	511.2
STANDARD SECURITY LIFE INS CO OF NY	NY	245.0

Rating: B+

INSURANCE COMPANY NAME	DOM. STATE	TOTAL ASSETS ($MIL)
AETNA HEALTH & LIFE INS CO	CT	2,349.9
AMERICAN FAMILY LIFE ASR CO OF COLUM	NE	117,278.0
AMERICAN FIDELITY ASR CO	OK	5,305.5
AMERICAN UNITED LIFE INS CO	IN	23,906.8
ASSURITY LIFE INS CO	NE	2,550.8
AXA EQUITABLE LIFE INS CO	NY	171,038.0
BOSTON MUTUAL LIFE INS CO	MA	1,317.6
DEARBORN NATIONAL LIFE INS CO	IL	1,969.6
GERBER LIFE INS CO	NY	3,240.4
GOVERNMENT PERSONNEL MUTUAL L I C	TX	834.7

INSURANCE COMPANY NAME	DOM. STATE	TOTAL ASSETS ($MIL)
GREAT SOUTHERN LIFE INS CO	TX	218.2
MEDICO CORP LIFE INS CO	NE	45.2
MIDLAND NATIONAL LIFE INS CO	IA	47,985.0
MINNESOTA LIFE INS CO	MN	38,458.7
MUTUAL OF OMAHA INS CO	NE	7,112.9
NEW YORK LIFE INS & ANNUITY CORP	DE	137,896.0
OHIO NATIONAL LIFE ASR CORP	OH	3,833.0
PACIFIC LIFE & ANNUITY CO	AZ	6,374.0
PAN AMERICAN ASR CO	LA	25.4
PRINCIPAL LIFE INS CO	IA	165,432.0
SAVINGS BANK LIFE INS CO OF MA	MA	2,957.5
STANDARD INS CO	OR	21,220.5
SYMETRA LIFE INS CO	IA	33,273.1
TRUSTMARK INS CO	IL	1,430.6
TRUSTMARK LIFE INS CO	IL	325.4
UNITED WORLD LIFE INS CO	NE	122.6
USABLE LIFE	AR	482.3
VOYA RETIREMENT INS & ANNUITY CO	CT	89,930.9

Wisconsin

INSURANCE COMPANY NAME	DOM. STATE	TOTAL ASSETS ($MIL)

Rating: A+

INSURANCE COMPANY NAME	DOM. STATE	TOTAL ASSETS ($MIL)
AMERICAN FAMILY LIFE INS CO	WI	5,407.4
COUNTRY LIFE INS CO	IL	10,264.7
PHYSICIANS MUTUAL INS CO	NE	2,153.3
STATE FARM LIFE & ACCIDENT ASR CO	IL	2,692.7
TEACHERS INS & ANNUITY ASN OF AM	NY	276,045.0

Rating: A

INSURANCE COMPANY NAME	DOM. STATE	TOTAL ASSETS ($MIL)
4 EVER LIFE INS CO	IL	211.4
FEDERATED LIFE INS CO	MN	1,710.7
GUARDIAN LIFE INS CO OF AMERICA	NY	50,389.3
MIDWESTERN UNITED LIFE INS CO	IN	235.0
MML BAY STATE LIFE INS CO	CT	4,737.2
NATIONAL WESTERN LIFE INS CO	CO	10,673.8
PARKER CENTENNIAL ASR CO	WI	92.2
SENTRY LIFE INS CO	WI	5,800.9
USAA LIFE INS CO	TX	23,536.5

Rating: A-

INSURANCE COMPANY NAME	DOM. STATE	TOTAL ASSETS ($MIL)
AMALGAMATED LIFE INS CO	NY	122.5
AMERICAN HEALTH & LIFE INS CO	TX	907.2
AMERICAN REPUBLIC INS CO	IA	909.7
ANNUITY INVESTORS LIFE INS CO	OH	3,041.6
ANTHEM LIFE INS CO	IN	630.6
AUTO-OWNERS LIFE INS CO	MI	3,832.7
CENTRAL STATES H & L CO OF OMAHA	NE	421.1
COMPANION LIFE INS CO	SC	329.6
COUNTRY INVESTORS LIFE ASR CO	IL	297.1
DELAWARE AMERICAN LIFE INS CO	DE	145.9
ERIE FAMILY LIFE INS CO	PA	2,217.2
FAMILY HERITAGE LIFE INS CO OF AMER	OH	1,004.9
FIDELITY INVESTMENTS LIFE INS CO	UT	25,080.7
GARDEN STATE LIFE INS CO	TX	126.5
ILLINOIS MUTUAL LIFE INS CO	IL	1,434.6
MASSACHUSETTS MUTUAL LIFE INS CO	MA	226,444.0
MUTUAL OF AMERICA LIFE INS CO	NY	18,135.8
NEW YORK LIFE INS CO	NY	167,828.0
NIPPON LIFE INS CO OF AMERICA	IA	217.7
NORTHWESTERN MUTUAL LIFE INS CO	WI	244,873.0
PACIFIC LIFE INS CO	NE	115,113.0
PHYSICIANS LIFE INS CO	NE	1,549.0
RESERVE NATIONAL INS CO	OK	123.3
SECURIAN LIFE INS CO	MN	478.9
STANDARD LIFE & ACCIDENT INS CO	TX	511.2
STANDARD SECURITY LIFE INS CO OF NY	NY	245.0

Rating: B+

INSURANCE COMPANY NAME	DOM. STATE	TOTAL ASSETS ($MIL)
AETNA HEALTH & LIFE INS CO	CT	2,349.9
AMERICAN FAMILY LIFE ASR CO OF COLUM	NE	117,278.0
AMERICAN FIDELITY ASR CO	OK	5,305.5
AMERICAN UNITED LIFE INS CO	IN	23,906.8
ASSURITY LIFE INS CO	NE	2,550.8
AXA EQUITABLE LIFE INS CO	NY	171,038.0
BOSTON MUTUAL LIFE INS CO	MA	1,317.6
DEARBORN NATIONAL LIFE INS CO	IL	1,969.6
FARM BUREAU LIFE INS CO	IA	8,582.6

INSURANCE COMPANY NAME	DOM. STATE	TOTAL ASSETS ($MIL)
GERBER LIFE INS CO	NY	3,240.4
GOVERNMENT PERSONNEL MUTUAL L I C	TX	834.7
GREAT SOUTHERN LIFE INS CO	TX	218.2
MEDICO CORP LIFE INS CO	NE	45.2
MIDLAND NATIONAL LIFE INS CO	IA	47,985.0
MINNESOTA LIFE INS CO	MN	38,458.7
MUTUAL OF OMAHA INS CO	NE	7,112.9
NATIONAL FARMERS UNION LIFE INS CO	TX	206.0
NEW YORK LIFE INS & ANNUITY CORP	DE	137,896.0
OHIO NATIONAL LIFE ASR CORP	OH	3,833.0
PACIFIC LIFE & ANNUITY CO	AZ	6,374.0
PAN AMERICAN ASR CO	LA	25.4
PRINCIPAL LIFE INS CO	IA	165,432.0
SAVINGS BANK LIFE INS CO OF MA	MA	2,957.5
STANDARD INS CO	OR	21,220.5
SYMETRA LIFE INS CO	IA	33,273.1
TRUSTMARK INS CO	IL	1,430.6
TRUSTMARK LIFE INS CO	IL	325.4
UNITED WORLD LIFE INS CO	NE	122.6
USABLE LIFE	AR	482.3
VOYA RETIREMENT INS & ANNUITY CO	CT	89,930.9

Wyoming

INSURANCE COMPANY NAME	DOM. STATE	TOTAL ASSETS ($MIL)

Rating: A+

INSURANCE COMPANY NAME	DOM. STATE	TOTAL ASSETS ($MIL)
AMERICAN FAMILY LIFE INS CO	WI	5,407.4
COUNTRY LIFE INS CO	IL	10,264.7
PHYSICIANS MUTUAL INS CO	NE	2,153.3
STATE FARM LIFE INS CO	IL	68,156.4
TEACHERS INS & ANNUITY ASN OF AM	NY	276,045.0

Rating: A

INSURANCE COMPANY NAME	DOM. STATE	TOTAL ASSETS ($MIL)
4 EVER LIFE INS CO	IL	211.4
FEDERATED LIFE INS CO	MN	1,710.7
GUARDIAN LIFE INS CO OF AMERICA	NY	50,389.3
LIFEWISE ASR CO	WA	143.3
MIDWESTERN UNITED LIFE INS CO	IN	235.0
MML BAY STATE LIFE INS CO	CT	4,737.2
NATIONAL WESTERN LIFE INS CO	CO	10,673.8
PARKER CENTENNIAL ASR CO	WI	92.2
SENTRY LIFE INS CO	WI	5,800.9
USAA LIFE INS CO	TX	23,536.5

Rating: A-

INSURANCE COMPANY NAME	DOM. STATE	TOTAL ASSETS ($MIL)
AMALGAMATED LIFE INS CO	NY	122.5
AMERICAN HEALTH & LIFE INS CO	TX	907.2
AMERICAN REPUBLIC INS CO	IA	909.7
ANNUITY INVESTORS LIFE INS CO	OH	3,041.6
ANTHEM LIFE INS CO	IN	630.6
CENTRAL STATES H & L CO OF OMAHA	NE	421.1
COMPANION LIFE INS CO	SC	329.6
COUNTRY INVESTORS LIFE ASR CO	IL	297.1
DELAWARE AMERICAN LIFE INS CO	DE	145.9
FAMILY HERITAGE LIFE INS CO OF AMER	OH	1,004.0
FIDELITY INVESTMENTS LIFE INS CO	UT	25,080.7
GARDEN STATE LIFE INS CO	TX	126.5
ILLINOIS MUTUAL LIFE INS CO	IL	1,434.6
MASSACHUSETTS MUTUAL LIFE INS CO	MA	226,444.0
MUTUAL OF AMERICA LIFE INS CO	NY	18,135.8
NEW YORK LIFE INS CO	NY	167,828.0
NORTHWESTERN MUTUAL LIFE INS CO	WI	244,873.0
PACIFIC GUARDIAN LIFE INS CO LTD	HI	544.4
PACIFIC LIFE INS CO	NE	115,113.0
PHYSICIANS LIFE INS CO	NE	1,549.0
RESERVE NATIONAL INS CO	OK	123.3
SECURIAN LIFE INS CO	MN	478.9
STANDARD LIFE & ACCIDENT INS CO	TX	511.2
STANDARD SECURITY LIFE INS CO OF NY	NY	245.0

Rating: B+

INSURANCE COMPANY NAME	DOM. STATE	TOTAL ASSETS ($MIL)
AETNA HEALTH & LIFE INS CO	CT	2,349.9
AMERICAN FAMILY LIFE ASR CO OF COLUM	NE	117,278.0
AMERICAN FIDELITY ASR CO	OK	5,305.5
AMERICAN UNITED LIFE INS CO	IN	23,906.8
ASSURITY LIFE INS CO	NE	2,550.8
AXA EQUITABLE LIFE INS CO	NY	171,038.0
BOSTON MUTUAL LIFE INS CO	MA	1,317.6
DEARBORN NATIONAL LIFE INS CO	IL	1,969.6
FARM BUREAU LIFE INS CO	IA	8,582.6
GERBER LIFE INS CO	NY	3,240.4

INSURANCE COMPANY NAME	DOM. STATE	TOTAL ASSETS ($MIL)
GOVERNMENT PERSONNEL MUTUAL L I C	TX	834.7
GREAT SOUTHERN LIFE INS CO	TX	218.2
MEDICO CORP LIFE INS CO	NE	45.2
MIDLAND NATIONAL LIFE INS CO	IA	47,985.0
MINNESOTA LIFE INS CO	MN	38,458.7
MUTUAL OF OMAHA INS CO	NE	7,112.9
NATIONAL FARMERS UNION LIFE INS CO	TX	206.0
NEW YORK LIFE INS & ANNUITY CORP	DE	137,896.0
OHIO NATIONAL LIFE ASR CORP	OH	3,833.0
PACIFIC LIFE & ANNUITY CO	AZ	6,374.0
PRINCIPAL LIFE INS CO	IA	165,432.0
SAVINGS BANK LIFE INS CO OF MA	MA	2,957.5
STANDARD INS CO	OR	21,220.5
SYMETRA LIFE INS CO	IA	33,273.1
TRUSTMARK INS CO	IL	1,430.6
TRUSTMARK LIFE INS CO	IL	325.4
UNITED WORLD LIFE INS CO	NE	122.6
USABLE LIFE	AR	482.3
VOYA RETIREMENT INS & ANNUITY CO	CT	89,930.9

Section V

All Companies
Listed by Rating

A list of all rated and unrated

U.S. Life and Annuity Insurers

Companies are ranked by Weiss Safety Rating
and then listed alphabetically within each rating category.

Section V Contents

This section sorts all companies by their Weiss Safety Rating and then lists them alphabetically within each rating category. The purpose of this section is to provide in one place all of those companies receiving a given rating. Companies with the same rating should be viewed as having the same relative risk regardless of their order in this table.

1. **Safety Rating**   Our rating is measured on a scale from A to F and considers a wide range of factors. Highly rated companies are, in our opinion, less likely to experience financial difficulties than lower rated firms. See *About Weiss Safety Ratings* for more information.

2. **Insurance Company Name**   The legally registered name, which can sometimes differ from the name that the company uses for advertising. An insurer's name can be very similar to that of another, so verify the company's exact name and state of domicile to make sure you are looking at the correct company.

3. **Domicile State**   The state which has primary regulatory responsibility for the company. It may differ from the location of the company's corporate headquarters. You do not have to be living in the domicile state to purchase insurance from this firm, provided it is licensed to do business in your state.

4. **Total Assets**   All assets admitted by state insurance regulators in millions of dollars. This includes investments, current business assets and separate accounts.

INSURANCE COMPANY NAME	DOM. STATE	TOTAL ASSETS ($MIL)

Rating: A+

INSURANCE COMPANY NAME	DOM. STATE	TOTAL ASSETS ($MIL)
AMERICAN FAMILY LIFE INS CO	WI	5,407.4
COUNTRY LIFE INS CO	IL	10,264.7
PHYSICIANS MUTUAL INS CO	NE	2,153.3
STATE FARM LIFE & ACCIDENT ASR CO	IL	2,692.7
STATE FARM LIFE INS CO	IL	68,156.4
TEACHERS INS & ANNUITY ASN OF AM	NY	276,045.0

Rating: A

INSURANCE COMPANY NAME	DOM. STATE	TOTAL ASSETS ($MIL)
4 EVER LIFE INS CO	IL	211.4
FEDERATED LIFE INS CO	MN	1,710.7
FIRST RELIANCE STANDARD LIFE INS CO	NY	190.3
FIRST SYMETRA NATL LIFE INS CO OF NY	NY	1,467.2
FRANDISCO LIFE INS CO	GA	78.5
GUARDIAN LIFE INS CO OF AMERICA	NY	50,389.3
LIFEWISE ASR CO	WA	143.3
MIDWESTERN UNITED LIFE INS CO	IN	235.0
MML BAY STATE LIFE INS CO	CT	4,737.2
NATIONAL WESTERN LIFE INS CO	CO	10,673.8
PARKER CENTENNIAL ASR CO	WI	92.2
SENTRY LIFE INS CO	WI	5,800.9
SHELTERPOINT LIFE INS CO	NY	105.4
SOUTHERN FARM BUREAU LIFE INS CO	MS	13,583.7
TENNESSEE FARMERS LIFE INS CO	TN	2,151.3
TRANS OCEANIC LIFE INS CO	PR	68.3
UNITED FARM FAMILY LIFE INS CO	IN	2,234.9
USAA LIFE INS CO	TX	23,536.5

Rating: A-

INSURANCE COMPANY NAME	DOM. STATE	TOTAL ASSETS ($MIL)
ALLIANZ LIFE INS CO OF NY	NY	3,131.2
AMALGAMATED LIFE INS CO	NY	122.5
AMERICAN FAMILY LIFE ASR CO OF NY	NY	885.2
AMERICAN HEALTH & LIFE INS CO	TX	907.2
AMERICAN REPUBLIC INS CO	IA	909.7
ANNUITY INVESTORS LIFE INS CO	OH	3,041.6
ANTHEM LIFE INS CO	IN	630.6
AUTO-OWNERS LIFE INS CO	MI	3,832.7
CENTRAL STATES H & L CO OF OMAHA	NE	421.1
CIGNA LIFE INS CO OF NEW YORK	NY	380.3
COMPANION LIFE INS CO	SC	329.6
COTTON STATES LIFE INS CO	GA	334.6
COUNTRY INVESTORS LIFE ASR CO	IL	297.1
DELAWARE AMERICAN LIFE INS CO	DE	145.9
ERIE FAMILY LIFE INS CO	PA	2,217.2
FAMILY HERITAGE LIFE INS CO OF AMER	OH	1,004.9
FARM BUREAU LIFE INS CO OF MICHIGAN	MI	2,361.9
FARM BUREAU LIFE INS CO OF MISSOURI	MO	558.9
FIDELITY INVESTMENTS LIFE INS CO	UT	25,080.7
GARDEN STATE LIFE INS CO	TX	126.5
ILLINOIS MUTUAL LIFE INS CO	IL	1,434.6
LIFE INS CO OF ALABAMA	AL	118.6
LIFE INS CO OF BOSTON & NEW YORK	NY	135.2
MASSACHUSETTS MUTUAL LIFE INS CO	MA	226,444.0
MUTUAL OF AMERICA LIFE INS CO	NY	18,135.8

INSURANCE COMPANY NAME	DOM. STATE	TOTAL ASSETS ($MIL)
NEW YORK LIFE INS CO	NY	167,828.0
NIPPON LIFE INS CO OF AMERICA	IA	217.7
NORTHWESTERN MUTUAL LIFE INS CO	WI	244,873.0
PACIFIC GUARDIAN LIFE INS CO LTD	HI	544.4
PACIFIC LIFE INS CO	NE	115,113.0
PHYSICIANS LIFE INS CO	NE	1,549.0
RESERVE NATIONAL INS CO	OK	123.3
SECURIAN LIFE INS CO	MN	478.9
SHELTER LIFE INS CO	MO	1,180.1
STANDARD LIFE & ACCIDENT INS CO	TX	511.2
STANDARD LIFE INS CO OF NY	NY	283.1
STANDARD SECURITY LIFE INS CO OF NY	NY	245.0

Rating: B+

INSURANCE COMPANY NAME	DOM. STATE	TOTAL ASSETS ($MIL)
ADVANCE INS CO OF KS	KS	54.9
AETNA HEALTH & LIFE INS CO	CT	2,349.9
AMERICAN FAMILY LIFE ASR CO OF COLUM	NE	117,278.0
AMERICAN FIDELITY ASR CO	OK	5,305.5
AMERICAN UNITED LIFE INS CO	IN	23,906.8
ASSURITY LIFE INS CO	NE	2,550.8
AXA EQUITABLE LIFE INS CO	NY	171,038.0
BLUEBONNET LIFE INS CO	MS	58.9
BOSTON MUTUAL LIFE INS CO	MA	1,317.6
DEARBORN NATIONAL LIFE INS CO	IL	1,969.6
DEARBORN NATIONAL LIFE INS CO OF NY	NY	38.7
EMPIRE FIDELITY INVESTMENTS L I C	NY	2,497.9
FARM BUREAU LIFE INS CO	IA	8,582.6
FIRST UNITED AMERICAN LIFE INS CO	NY	219.9
GERBER LIFE INS CO	NY	3,240.4
GOVERNMENT PERSONNEL MUTUAL L I C	TX	834.7
GREAT SOUTHERN LIFE INS CO	TX	218.2
GREATER GEORGIA LIFE INS CO	GA	58.6
JOHN HANCOCK LIFE INS CO OF NY	NY	17,005.3
LOCOMOTIVE ENGRS&COND MUT PROT ASSN	MI	63.0
MEDICO CORP LIFE INS CO	NE	45.2
MIDLAND NATIONAL LIFE INS CO	IA	47,985.0
MINNESOTA LIFE INS CO	MN	38,458.7
MUTUAL OF OMAHA INS CO	NE	7,112.9
NATIONAL FARMERS UNION LIFE INS CO	TX	206.0
NATIONAL INCOME LIFE INS CO	NY	185.3
NEW YORK LIFE INS & ANNUITY CORP	DE	137,896.0
OHIO NATIONAL LIFE ASR CORP	OH	3,833.0
PACIFIC LIFE & ANNUITY CO	AZ	6,374.0
PAN AMERICAN ASR CO	LA	25.4
PRINCIPAL LIFE INS CO	IA	165,432.0
SAVINGS BANK LIFE INS CO OF MA	MA	2,957.5
SOUTHERN PIONEER LIFE INS CO	AR	16.8
STANDARD INS CO	OR	21,220.5
SYMETRA LIFE INS CO	IA	33,273.1
TRUSTMARK INS CO	IL	1,430.6
TRUSTMARK LIFE INS CO	IL	325.4
UNION SECURITY LIFE INS CO OF NY	NY	88.0
UNITED WORLD LIFE INS CO	NE	122.6
USAA LIFE INS CO OF NEW YORK	NY	720.8

INSURANCE COMPANY NAME	DOM. STATE	TOTAL ASSETS ($MIL)	INSURANCE COMPANY NAME	DOM. STATE	TOTAL ASSETS ($MIL)
Rating: B+ (Continued)			FIDELITY SECURITY LIFE INS CO	MO	864.4
USABLE LIFE	AR	482.3	FIDELITY SECURITY LIFE INS CO OF NY	NY	39.4
VOYA RETIREMENT INS & ANNUITY CO	CT	89,930.9	FIRST ASR LIFE OF AMERICA	LA	39.4
Rating: B			FIRST PENN-PACIFIC LIFE INS CO	IN	1,568.0
			FIRST SECURITY BENEFIT LIFE & ANN	NY	683.1
AAA LIFE INS CO	MI	612.8	FORETHOUGHT LIFE INS CO	IN	22,257.6
AAA LIFE INS CO OF NY	NY	7.9	GENERAL AMERICAN LIFE INS CO	MO	12,497.0
ACE LIFE INS CO	CT	46.0	GENERAL RE LIFE CORP	CT	3,389.4
AETNA LIFE INS CO	CT	22,194.2	GENERATION LIFE INS CO	AZ	32.9
ALLIANZ LIFE INS CO OF NORTH AMERICA	MN	125,342.0	GOLDEN RULE INS CO	IN	618.1
ALLSTATE LIFE INS CO	IL	32,095.1	GPM HEALTH & LIFE INS CO	WA	141.0
AMERICAN EQUITY INVEST LIFE INS CO	IA	44,851.9	GREAT WESTERN INS CO	UT	1,149.2
AMERICAN FARM LIFE INS CO	TX	3.9	GREAT-WEST LIFE & ANNUITY INS OF NY	NY	1,801.4
AMERICAN GENERAL LIFE INS CO	TX	171,739.0	GREENFIELDS LIFE INS CO	CO	8.9
AMERICAN HERITAGE LIFE INS CO	FL	1,846.7	GUARANTEE TRUST LIFE INS CO	IL	515.0
AMERICAN MATURITY LIFE INS CO	CT	60.5	GUARDIAN INS & ANNUITY CO INC	DE	16,278.3
AMERICAN MODERN LIFE INS CO	OH	45.9	HARLEYSVILLE LIFE INS CO	PA	408.4
AMERICAN NATIONAL INS CO	TX	18,521.1	HCC LIFE INS CO	IN	1,001.7
AMERICAN NATIONAL LIFE INS CO OF NY	NY	401.1	HM LIFE INS CO	PA	646.6
AMERICAN PUBLIC LIFE INS CO	OK	91.4	HM LIFE INS CO OF NEW YORK	NY	69.9
AMERICAN REPUBLIC CORP INS CO	NE	23.5	HOMESTEADERS LIFE CO	IA	2,693.3
AMERITAS LIFE INS CORP	NE	18,307.1	HORACE MANN LIFE INS CO	IL	8,506.0
AMICA LIFE INS CO	RI	1,239.5	INTRAMERICA LIFE INS CO	NY	32.3
ANTHEM LIFE & DISABILITY INS CO	NY	25.1	INVESTORS LIFE INS CO NORTH AMERICA	TX	643.0
AURORA NATIONAL LIFE ASR CO	CA	2,899.3	JACKSON NATIONAL LIFE INS CO	MI	195,328.0
AXA CORPORATE SOLUTIONS LIFE REINS	DE	258.3	JACKSON NATIONAL LIFE INS CO OF NY	NY	10,960.4
AXA EQUITABLE LIFE & ANNUITY CO	CO	448.0	JAMESTOWN LIFE INS CO	VA	124.6
BALTIMORE LIFE INS CO	MD	1,216.4	JOHN HANCOCK LIFE & HEALTH INS CO	MA	11,960.9
BANKERS FIDELITY LIFE INS CO	GA	141.3	JOHN HANCOCK LIFE INS CO (USA)	MI	238,670.0
BENEFICIAL LIFE INS CO	UT	2,339.7	KANSAS CITY LIFE INS CO	MO	3,337.0
BERKLEY LIFE & HEALTH INS CO	IA	243.3	LAFAYETTE LIFE INS CO	OH	4,702.8
BERKSHIRE LIFE INS CO OF AMERICA	MA	3,436.0	LIBERTY LIFE ASR CO OF BOSTON	NH	16,655.8
BEST LIFE & HEALTH INS CO	TX	18.4	LIBERTY NATIONAL LIFE INS CO	NE	7,686.0
BLUE CROSS BLUE SHIELD OF KANSAS INC	KS	1,497.5	LIFE INS CO OF NORTH AMERICA	PA	8,452.1
BLUE SHIELD OF CALIFORNIA L&H INS CO	CA	483.6	LIFE INS CO OF THE SOUTHWEST	TX	15,767.3
CARIBBEAN AMERICAN LIFE ASR CO	PR	39.0	LINCOLN LIFE & ANNUITY CO OF NY	NY	13,414.4
CHRISTIAN FIDELITY LIFE INS CO	TX	70.6	LINCOLN NATIONAL LIFE INS CO	IN	219,393.0
CHURCH LIFE INS CORP	NY	298.1	LONGEVITY INS CO	TX	7.8
CIGNA HEALTH & LIFE INS CO	CT	6,742.1	MANHATTAN LIFE INS CO	NY	487.7
CIGNA WORLDWIDE INS CO	DE	51.5	MANHATTAN NATIONAL LIFE INS CO	OH	168.8
CINCINNATI LIFE INS CO	OH	4,214.2	MEDICO INS CO	NE	77.2
CM LIFE INS CO	CT	9,489.1	MEDICO LIFE & HEALTH INS CO	IA	14.2
COLORADO BANKERS LIFE INS CO	NC	333.4	MERIT LIFE INS CO	IN	559.3
COLUMBIAN MUTUAL LIFE INS CO	NY	1,377.6	METLIFE INS CO USA	DE	184,071.0
CONSUMERS LIFE INS CO	OH	41.7	MONITOR LIFE INS CO OF NEW YORK	NY	21.9
CONTINENTAL AMERICAN INS CO	SC	582.5	MONY LIFE INS CO OF AMERICA	AZ	2,984.8
CONTINENTAL LIFE INS CO OF BRENTWOOD	TN	283.3	MOTORISTS LIFE INS CO	OH	455.4
CSI LIFE INS CO	NE	18.9	MUTUAL SAVINGS LIFE INS CO	AL	455.6
DESERET MUTUAL INS CO	UT	39.6	MUTUAL TRUST LIFE INS CO	IL	1,933.2
EAGLE LIFE INS CO	IA	393.4	NATIONAL BENEFIT LIFE INS CO	NY	495.1
EMC NATIONAL LIFE CO	IA	965.4	NATIONAL FARM LIFE INS CO	TX	395.2
EQUITABLE LIFE & CASUALTY INS CO	UT	317.1	NATIONAL LIFE INS CO	VT	9,158.4
FARM FAMILY LIFE INS CO	NY	1,327.5	NATIONAL SECURITY INS CO	AL	54.4
			NATIONAL SECURITY LIFE & ANNUITY CO	NY	442.8

INSURANCE COMPANY NAME	DOM. STATE	TOTAL ASSETS ($MIL)	INSURANCE COMPANY NAME	DOM. STATE	TOTAL ASSETS ($MIL)
			TRANSAMERICA LIFE INS CO	IA	129,413.0
			TRUSTMARK LIFE INS CO OF NEW YORK	NY	8.5

Rating: B   (Continued)

INSURANCE COMPANY NAME	DOM. STATE	TOTAL ASSETS ($MIL)
NATIONAL TEACHERS ASSOCIATES L I C	TX	452.4
NEW ENGLAND LIFE INS CO	MA	10,003.1
NIAGARA LIFE & HEALTH INS CO	NY	16.9
NORTH AMERICAN CO FOR LIFE & H INS	IA	20,376.2
NORTHWESTERN LONG TERM CARE INS CO	WI	166.0
NTA LIFE INS CO OF NEW YORK	NY	7.0
NYLIFE INS CO OF ARIZONA	AZ	199.0
OHIO MOTORISTS LIFE INSURANCE CO	OH	10.5
OHIO NATIONAL LIFE INS CO	OH	28,044.7
OLD AMERICAN INS CO	MO	253.5
OLD UNITED LIFE INS CO	AZ	81.3
OPTUM INS OF OHIO INC	OH	113.1
OXFORD LIFE INS CO	AZ	1,599.4
PACIFIC CENTURY LIFE INS CORP	AZ	354.6
PAN AMERICAN LIFE INS CO OF PR	PR	8.4
PAN-AMERICAN LIFE INS CO	LA	1,275.4
PARK AVENUE LIFE INS CO	DE	269.0
PATRIOT LIFE INS CO	MI	16.7
PEKIN LIFE INS CO	IL	1,426.6
PENN MUTUAL LIFE INS CO	PA	18,813.7
PHARMACISTS LIFE INS CO	IA	99.3
PHILADELPHIA AMERICAN LIFE INS CO	TX	253.2
PIONEER MUTUAL LIFE INS CO	ND	515.2
PRENEED REINS CO OF AMERICA	AZ	40.6
PRIMERICA LIFE INS CO	MA	1,315.9
PRINCIPAL NATIONAL LIFE INS CO	IA	214.1
PROTECTIVE LIFE & ANNUITY INS CO	AL	1,999.6
PROTECTIVE LIFE INS CO	TN	43,425.8
PROVIDENT AMER LIFE & HEALTH INS CO	OH	18.6
PRUDENTIAL INS CO OF AMERICA	NJ	253,157.0
RELIANCE STANDARD LIFE INS CO	IL	10,156.8
RELIASTAR LIFE INS CO OF NEW YORK	NY	3,067.1
S USA LIFE INS CO INC	AZ	13.3
SBLI USA MUT LIFE INS CO INC	NY	1,533.2
SECURITY BENEFIT LIFE INS CO	KS	28,075.4
SECURITY LIFE INS CO OF AMERICA	MN	67.1
SECURITY MUTUAL LIFE INS CO OF NY	NY	2,679.1
SENTRY LIFE INS CO OF NEW YORK	NY	78.6
SETTLERS LIFE INS CO	WI	392.9
SOUTHERN NATL LIFE INS CO INC	LA	15.0
STARMOUNT LIFE INS CO	LA	62.6
STATE LIFE INS CO	IN	6,448.0
STATE LIFE INS FUND	WI	--
SUNSET LIFE INS CO OF AMERICA	MO	333.0
SWBC LIFE INS CO	TX	24.1
SYMETRA NATIONAL LIFE INS CO	IA	16.9
TEXAS LIFE INS CO	TX	1,078.6
THRIVENT LIFE INS CO	MN	3,541.4
TIAA-CREF LIFE INS CO	NY	11,505.5
TPM LIFE INS CO	PA	7.0
TRANS WORLD ASR CO	CA	350.2
TRANSAMERICA FINANCIAL LIFE INS CO	NY	32,355.4

INSURANCE COMPANY NAME	DOM. STATE	TOTAL ASSETS ($MIL)
UNIFIED LIFE INS CO	TX	184.2
UNIMERICA INS CO	WI	443.4
UNIMERICA LIFE INS CO OF NY	NY	39.1
UNION NATIONAL LIFE INS CO	LA	19.6
UNION SECURITY INS CO	KS	3,119.7
UNITED HERITAGE LIFE INS CO	ID	549.7
UNITED HOME LIFE INS CO	IN	86.1
UNITED LIFE INS CO	IA	1,532.7
UNITED OF OMAHA LIFE INS CO	NE	20,032.6
UNITED STATES LIFE INS CO IN NYC	NY	29,018.5
UNIVERSAL LIFE INS CO	PR	1,017.4
US FINANCIAL LIFE INS CO	OH	600.5
USIC LIFE INS CO	PR	9.8
UTIC INS CO	AL	79.1
VARIABLE ANNUITY LIFE INS CO	TX	75,558.9
WESTERN & SOUTHERN LIFE INS CO	OH	9,959.3
WESTERN-SOUTHERN LIFE ASR CO	OH	12,485.6

Rating: B-

INSURANCE COMPANY NAME	DOM. STATE	TOTAL ASSETS ($MIL)
ALFA LIFE INS CORP	AL	1,412.5
AMERICAN CONTINENTAL INS CO	TN	208.7
AMERICAN EQUITY INVESTMENT LIFE NY	NY	215.2
AMERICAN FEDERATED LIFE INS CO	MS	32.1
AMERICAN FIDELITY LIFE INS CO	FL	421.6
AMERICAN INCOME LIFE INS CO	IN	3,234.8
AMERICAN MEMORIAL LIFE INS CO	SD	2,876.1
AMERICAN NATIONAL LIFE INS CO OF TX	TX	123.5
AMERICO FINANCIAL LIFE & ANNUITY INS	TX	4,250.1
AMERITAS LIFE INS CORP OF NY	NY	1,188.8
ATLANTIC COAST LIFE INS CO	SC	205.2
AUTOMOBILE CLUB OF SOUTHERN CA INS	CA	1,031.3
BANKERS FIDELITY ASR CO	GA	9.7
BEST MERIDIAN INS CO	FL	309.9
CENTRE LIFE INS CO	MA	1,850.7
CLOVER INS CO	TX	11.7
CMFG LIFE INS CO	IA	15,969.4
COMMONWEALTH ANNUITY & LIFE INS CO	MA	12,253.5
CONNECTICUT GENERAL LIFE INS CO	CT	17,491.2
ENTERPRISE LIFE INS CO	TX	30.3
EQUITRUST LIFE INS CO	IL	16,791.6
FARMERS NEW WORLD LIFE INS CO	WA	7,148.3
FIDELITY & GUARANTY LIFE INS CO NY	NY	526.8
FIRST COMMAND LIFE INS CO	TX	36.6
FIRST HEALTH LIFE & HEALTH INS CO	TX	650.1
FUNERAL DIRECTORS LIFE INS CO	TX	1,199.9
GENWORTH LIFE & ANNUITY INS CO	VA	23,144.6
GENWORTH LIFE INS CO	DE	39,497.6
GLOBE LIFE & ACCIDENT INS CO	NE	3,889.6
GREAT AMERICAN LIFE INS CO	OH	27,716.3
GREAT-WEST LIFE & ANNUITY INS CO	CO	58,321.7
GUGGENHEIM LIFE & ANNUITY CO	DE	13,900.3
HANNOVER LIFE REASSUR CO OF AMERICA	FL	4,177.5

INSURANCE COMPANY NAME	DOM. STATE	TOTAL ASSETS ($MIL)
Rating: B- (Continued)		
HARTFORD LIFE & ANNUITY INS CO	CT	38,138.2
HEARTLAND NATIONAL LIFE INS CO	IN	11.1
IA AMERICAN LIFE INS CO	TX	225.3
INTEGRITY LIFE INS CO	OH	7,432.8
INVESTORS GROWTH LIFE INS CO	AZ	14.7
JOHN ALDEN LIFE INS CO	WI	253.8
KENTUCKY FUNERAL DIRECTORS LIFE INS	KY	19.3
LIFECARE ASSURANCE CO	AZ	2,206.6
LIFEMAP ASR CO	OR	80.3
LIFESHIELD NATIONAL INS CO	OK	69.2
LINCOLN HERITAGE LIFE INS CO	IL	901.6
LONDON LIFE INS CO	MI	23.4
M LIFE INS CO	CO	302.0
METROPOLITAN LIFE INS CO	NY	401,502.0
METROPOLITAN TOWER LIFE INS CO	DE	4,588.5
MONY LIFE INS CO	NY	7,390.6
NATIONAL FOUNDATION LIFE INS CO	TX	32.4
NATIONAL GUARDIAN LIFE INS CO	WI	3,502.2
NATIONAL INTEGRITY LIFE INS CO	NY	4,718.8
NATIONWIDE LIFE INS CO	OH	129,443.0
OHIO STATE LIFE INS CO	TX	13.8
OLD REPUBLIC LIFE INS CO	IL	125.5
OZARK NATIONAL LIFE INS CO	MO	793.4
PARAGON LIFE INS CO OF INDIANA	IN	1,782.6
PENN INS & ANNUITY CO	DE	4,022.4
PERFORMANCE LIFE OF AMERICA	LA	31.6
PROVIDENT LIFE & CAS INS CO	TN	767.5
PRUCO LIFE INS CO OF NEW JERSEY	NJ	13,931.4
PRUDENTIAL RETIREMENT INS & ANNUITY	CT	70,736.0
RELIABLE LIFE INS CO	MO	22.6
RGA REINSURANCE CO	MO	25,223.7
SHENANDOAH LIFE INS CO	VA	1,128.1
TEXAS DIRECTORS LIFE INS CO	TX	5.8
TRANSAMERICA ADVISORS LIFE INS CO	AR	8,535.9
TRIPLE S VIDA INC	PR	572.3
UNICARE LIFE & HEALTH INS CO	IN	300.3
UNION LABOR LIFE INS CO	MD	3,272.1
UNITED AMERICAN INS CO	NE	1,598.2
UNITED INS CO OF AMERICA	IL	3,704.1
UNIVERSAL UNDERWRITERS LIFE INS CO	KS	156.6
VANTIS LIFE INS CO	CT	252.8
VANTISLIFE INS CO OF NEW YORK	NY	11.8
VERSANT LIFE INS CO	MS	6.0
VOYA INS & ANNUITY CO	IA	64,700.6
WESTERN UNITED LIFE ASR CO	WA	1,142.3
WILTON REASSURANCE LIFE CO OF NY	NY	899.2
WINDSOR LIFE INS CO	TX	3.2
ZALE LIFE INS CO	AZ	12.0
Rating: C+		
ALL SAVERS LIFE INS CO OF CA	CA	6.8
ALLSTATE ASR CO	IL	654.6

INSURANCE COMPANY NAME	DOM. STATE	TOTAL ASSETS ($MIL)
ALLSTATE LIFE INS CO OF NEW YORK	NY	6,366.6
AMERICAN BANKERS LIFE ASR CO OF FL	FL	392.8
AMERICAN RETIREMENT LIFE INS CO	OH	77.1
ATHENE ANNUITY & LIFE CO	IA	45,056.3
AUTO CLUB LIFE INS CO	MI	681.0
BANNER LIFE INS CO	MD	2,469.4
BERKSHIRE HATHAWAY LIFE INS CO OF NE	NE	16,826.7
BROOKE LIFE INS CO	MI	3,935.4
CENTRAL RESERVE LIFE INS CO	OH	29.2
CHESAPEAKE LIFE INS CO	OK	118.2
CITIZENS FIDELITY INS CO	AR	70.0
COLONIAL LIFE & ACCIDENT INS CO	SC	3,091.7
COLUMBUS LIFE INS CO	OH	3,642.9
COMBINED INS CO OF AMERICA	IL	1,364.1
COMBINED LIFE INS CO OF NEW YORK	NY	407.6
COMPANION LIFE INS CO	NY	1,037.2
CONSTITUTION LIFE INS CO	TX	393.9
CONTINENTAL GENERAL INS CO	OH	247.5
DELAWARE LIFE INS CO OF NEW YORK	NY	2,815.6
DIRECT GENERAL LIFE INS CO	SC	29.3
FIDELITY & GUARANTY LIFE INS CO	IA	20,647.2
FIRST METLIFE INVESTORS INS CO	NY	6,131.2
FIRST UNUM LIFE INS CO	NY	3,181.3
FIVE STAR LIFE INS CO	LA	270.7
FORESTERS LIFE INS & ANNUITY CO	NY	2,002.0
FREEDOM LIFE INS CO OF AMERICA	TX	83.9
GENWORTH LIFE INS CO OF NEW YORK	NY	8,470.8
GRANGE LIFE INS CO	OH	401.8
GREAT WEST LIFE ASR CO	MI	77.4
HARTFORD INTL LIFE REASR CORP	CT	10.9
HARTFORD LIFE & ACCIDENT INS CO	CT	9,024.5
HARTFORD LIFE INS CO	CT	113,812.0
HEALTHMARKETS INS CO	OK	24.9
HUMANA INS CO OF PUERTO RICO INC	PR	69.6
IDEALIFE INS CO	CT	19.7
KANAWHA INS CO	SC	1,788.6
LANDCAR LIFE INS CO	UT	21.7
LINCOLN BENEFIT LIFE CO	NE	11,496.8
LONDON LIFE REINSURANCE CO	PA	289.3
LOYAL AMERICAN LIFE INS CO	OH	270.0
MADISON NATIONAL LIFE INS CO INC	WI	329.6
MAGNOLIA GUARANTY LIFE INS CO	MS	11.1
MEDAMERICA INS CO	PA	914.3
MEDAMERICA INS CO OF FL	FL	33.7
MID-WEST NATIONAL LIFE INS CO OF TN	TX	167.2
MISSOURI VALLEY LIFE AND HLTH INS CO	MO	19.9
MUNICH AMERICAN LIFE REINS CO	GA	--
NORTH AMERICAN INS CO	WI	20.4
OMAHA INS CO	NE	83.9
OPTIMUM RE INS CO	TX	153.8
PACIFICARE LIFE & HEALTH INS CO	IN	207.0
PAUL REVERE LIFE INS CO	MA	3,903.5
PIONEER SECURITY LIFE INS CO	TX	124.2
PLATEAU INS CO	TN	25.8

INSURANCE COMPANY NAME	DOM. STATE	TOTAL ASSETS ($MIL)
Rating: C+ (Continued)		
POPULAR LIFE RE	PR	60.7
PROVIDENT LIFE & ACCIDENT INS CO	TN	8,342.6
PRUCO LIFE INS CO	AZ	107,972.0
PYRAMID LIFE INS CO	KS	73.5
RELIASTAR LIFE INS CO	MN	19,884.7
SECURITY LIFE OF DENVER INS CO	CO	13,328.9
STERLING LIFE INS CO	IL	--
SUPERIOR FUNERAL & LIFE INS CO	AR	173.0
TIME INS CO	WI	613.4
TRANSAMERICA PREMIER LIFE INS CO	IA	43,239.2
UNIVERSAL GUARANTY LIFE INS CO	OH	338.1
UNUM LIFE INS CO OF AMERICA	ME	20,748.9
WEST COAST LIFE INS CO	NE	5,058.3
WILTON REASSURANCE CO	MN	2,860.6
ZURICH AMERICAN LIFE INS CO OF NY	NY	82.8
Rating: C		
ACCORDIA LIFE & ANNUITY CO	IA	7,633.4
AGC LIFE INS CO	MO	15,561.0
ALL SAVERS INS CO	IN	1,437.0
AMALGAMATED LIFE & HEALTH INS CO	IL	5.8
AMERICAN CENTURY LIFE INS CO	OK	71.9
AMERICAN FARMERS & RANCHERS LIFE INS	OK	27.2
AMERICAN LIFE & ACC INS CO OF KY	KY	207.9
AMERICAN LIFE INS CO	DE	11,974.0
AMERICAN PROGRESSIVE L&H I C OF NY	NY	222.7
AMERICAN SAVINGS LIFE INS CO	AZ	57.8
AMERICAN-AMICABLE LIFE INS CO OF TX	TX	292.4
ATHENE ANNUITY & LIFE ASR CO	DE	10,581.5
ATHENE ANNUITY & LIFE ASR CO OF NY	NY	3,274.1
ATHENE LIFE INS CO OF NEW YORK	NY	944.2
BANKERS LIFE INS CO	FL	426.3
BANKERS LIFE OF LOUISIANA	LA	14.0
CANADA LIFE ASSURANCE CO-US BRANCH	MI	4,463.0
CAPITOL LIFE INS CO	TX	229.5
CENTRAL UNITED LIFE INS CO	AR	381.6
CHESTERFIELD REINS CO	MO	325.4
CITIZENS NATIONAL LIFE INS CO	TX	12.6
CITIZENS SECURITY LIFE INS CO	KY	23.6
COLUMBIAN LIFE INS CO	IL	318.3
DELAWARE LIFE INS CO	DE	40,645.8
EMPLOYERS REASSURANCE CORP	KS	10,616.1
EPIC LIFE INSURANCE CO	WI	44.1
FAMILY BENEFIT LIFE INS CO	MO	104.3
FAMILY LIFE INS CO	TX	158.6
FAMILY SECURITY LIFE INS CO INC	MS	6.7
FIDELITY LIFE ASSN A LEGAL RESERVE	IL	405.4
FIRST ALLMERICA FINANCIAL LIFE INS	MA	3,403.1
FIRST BERKSHIRE HATHAWAY LIFE INS CO	NY	162.7
FLORIDA COMBINED LIFE INS CO INC	FL	51.7
GERMANIA LIFE INS CO	TX	82.5
GREAT CENTRAL LIFE INS CO	LA	--

INSURANCE COMPANY NAME	DOM. STATE	TOTAL ASSETS ($MIL)
GUARANTY INCOME LIFE INS CO	LA	491.3
HALLMARK LIFE INS CO	AZ	18.4
HAWKEYE LIFE INS GROUP INC	IA	11.5
HEALTH NET LIFE INS CO	CA	634.2
HERITAGE LIFE INS CO	AZ	4,496.3
HUMANA INS CO OF KENTUCKY	KY	195.7
INVESTORS HERITAGE LIFE INS CO	KY	488.1
LANDMARK LIFE INS CO	TX	45.7
LEADERS LIFE INS CO	OK	6.4
LIFE OF AMERICA INS CO	TX	12.6
LIFE OF THE SOUTH INS CO	GA	91.8
MAJESTIC LIFE INS CO	LA	--
MAPFRE LIFE INS CO	DE	30.2
MEMBERS LIFE INS CO	IA	38.3
MOLINA HEALTHCARE OF TEXAS INS CO	TX	6.5
MUNICH AMERICAN REASSURANCE CO	GA	7,687.5
NATIONAL FAMILY CARE LIFE INS CO	TX	16.4
NATIONAL HEALTH INS CO	TX	31.5
NATIONWIDE LIFE & ANNUITY INS CO	OH	12,581.2
NEW ERA LIFE INS CO	TX	472.4
NEW ERA LIFE INS CO OF THE MIDWEST	TX	107.0
NORTH AMERICAN NATIONAL RE INS CO	AZ	32.8
OCCIDENTAL LIFE INS CO OF NC	TX	254.7
OLD SPARTAN LIFE INS CO INC	SC	21.8
OLD SURETY LIFE INS CO	OK	25.6
PAVONIA LIFE INS CO OF MICHIGAN	MI	1,074.0
PAVONIA LIFE INS CO OF NEW YORK	NY	31.9
PHYSICIANS BENEFITS TRUST LIFE INS	IL	8.5
PIONEER AMERICAN INS CO	TX	61.0
PRESIDENTIAL LIFE INS CO	TX	4.2
PROFESSIONAL LIFE & CAS CO	IL	163.7
PROTEC INS CO	IL	3.6
PRUDENTIAL ANNUITIES LIFE ASR CORP	AZ	75,234.8
PRUDENTIAL LEGACY INS CO OF NJ	NJ	61,222.1
REINSURANCE CO OF MO INC	MO	1,640.4
RIVERMONT LIFE INS CO I	SC	577.1
RIVERSOURCE LIFE INS CO	MN	102,927.0
RIVERSOURCE LIFE INS CO OF NY	NY	6,638.3
ROYAL STATE NATIONAL INS CO LTD	HI	45.7
SCOR GLOBAL LIFE REINS CO OF DE	DE	381.4
SCOR GLOBAL LIFE USA RE CO	DE	718.4
SECU LIFE INS CO	NC	34.4
SECURITY PLAN LIFE INS CO	LA	325.2
SOUTHERN FINANCIAL LIFE INS CO	KY	4.9
SURENCY LIFE & HEALTH INS CO	KS	9.4
SWISS RE LIFE & HEALTH AMER INC	MO	13,844.0
UNITED FIDELITY LIFE INS CO	TX	741.5
UNITED HEALTHCARE INS CO	CT	15,432.2
UNITED NATIONAL LIFE INS CO OF AM	IL	21.7
UNITED TEACHER ASSOCIATES INS CO	TX	1,071.3
UNITEDHEALTHCARE LIFE INS CO	WI	560.0
UNUM INS CO	ME	57.9
WEA INS CORP	WI	635.3
WILCAC LIFE INS CO	IL	2,331.2

INSURANCE COMPANY NAME	DOM. STATE	TOTAL ASSETS ($MIL)
Rating: C (Continued)		
WILCO LIFE INS CO	IN	3,299.2
ZURICH AMERICAN LIFE INS CO	IL	12,103.8
Rating: C-		
AMERICAN BENEFIT LIFE INS CO	OK	117.9
AMERICAN HOME LIFE INS CO	KS	250.5
AMERICAN LIFE & ANNUITY CO	AR	51.1
AURIGEN REINS CO OF AMERICA	AR	42.5
CINCINNATI EQUITABLE LIFE INS CO	OH	113.7
COLONIAL LIFE INS CO OF TX	TX	18.2
COOPERATIVA DE SEGUROS DE VIDA DE PR	PR	516.9
ELCO MUTUAL LIFE & ANNUITY	IL	680.2
FEDERAL LIFE INS CO	IL	226.4
FIRST NATIONAL LIFE INS CO OF USA	NE	5.6
FRINGE BENEFIT LIFE INS CO	TX	42.0
GULF GUARANTY LIFE INS CO	MS	16.2
INDUSTRIAL ALLIANCE INS & FIN SERV	TX	213.3
JEFFERSON NATIONAL LIFE INS CO	TX	4,281.9
JEFFERSON NATIONAL LIFE INS CO OF NY	NY	37.5
LIFE ASR CO OF AMERICA	IL	6.2
LIFE ASSURANCE CO INC	OK	4.7
MEMORIAL LIFE INS CO	LA	--
MOUNTAIN LIFE INS CO	TN	10.8
MULTINATIONAL LIFE INS CO	PR	113.3
PROVIDENT AMERICAN INS CO	TX	20.5
RABENHORST LIFE INS CO	LA	29.3
SAGICOR LIFE INS CO	TX	1,128.2
SCOR GLOBAL LIFE AMERICAS REIN CO	DE	1,286.8
SENIOR LIFE INS CO	GA	48.8
SOUTHLAND NATIONAL INS CORP	NC	301.0
STANDARD LIFE & CAS INS CO	UT	30.7
STATE MUTUAL INS CO	GA	281.2
SURETY LIFE & CASUALTY INS CO	ND	11.1
TEXAS SERVICE LIFE INS CO	TX	62.8
TOWN & COUNTRY LIFE INS CO	UT	7.0
TRANS CITY LIFE INS CO	AZ	19.5
UNITY FINANCIAL LIFE INS CO	OH	217.3
USA INS CO	MS	3.4
WICHITA NATIONAL LIFE INS CO	OK	17.1
WILLIAM PENN LIFE INS CO OF NEW YORK	NY	1,167.3
Rating: D+		
BANKERS LIFE & CAS CO	IL	17,123.8
COLONIAL PENN LIFE INS CO	PA	845.9
COLONIAL SECURITY LIFE INS CO	TX	2.6
CONTINENTAL LIFE INS CO	PA	24.9
FINANCIAL AMERICAN LIFE INS CO	KS	7.9
FUTURAL LIFE CO	AZ	6.3
GENERAL FIDELITY LIFE INS CO	SC	25.3
LEWER LIFE INS CO	MO	30.0
LIBERTY BANKERS LIFE INS CO	OK	1,433.2
MARQUETTE INDEMNITY & LIFE INS CO	AZ	6.4
SCOTTISH RE US INC	DE	1,510.9

INSURANCE COMPANY NAME	DOM. STATE	TOTAL ASSETS ($MIL)
SENTINEL SECURITY LIFE INS CO	UT	553.1
SOUTHERN FINANCIAL LIFE INS CO	LA	106.6
SOUTHERN SECURITY LIFE INS CO INC	MS	1.6
STERLING INVESTORS LIFE INS CO	IN	20.3
SURETY LIFE INS CO	NE	20.5
T J M LIFE INS CO	TX	16.1
UNION FIDELITY LIFE INS CO	KS	19,529.4
USA LIFE ONE INS CO OF INDIANA	IN	36.4
WASHINGTON NATIONAL INS CO	IN	4,870.3
Rating: D		
AMERICAN FINANCIAL SECURITY L I C	MO	7.5
AMERICAN LABOR LIFE INS CO	AZ	9.4
AMERICAN UNDERWRITERS LIFE INS CO	AZ	70.6
ARKANSAS BANKERS LIFE INS CO	AR	3.1
ASSOCIATED MUTUAL	MI	8.6
ATLANTA LIFE INS CO	GA	47.1
BANKERS CONSECO LIFE INS CO	NY	226.5
BANKERS LIFE INS CO OF AMERICA	TX	5.3
BENEVOLENT LIFE INS CO INC	LA	2.1
CENTRAL SECURITY LIFE INS CO	TX	93.1
CENTURION LIFE INS CO	IA	1,275.3
CENTURY LIFE ASR CO	OK	12.0
CICA LIFE INS CO OF AMERICA	CO	878.2
COMMERCIAL TRAVELERS MUTUAL INS CO	NY	15.4
COOPERATIVE LIFE INS CO	AR	6.6
DAKOTA CAPITAL LIFE INS CO	ND	4.1
FAMILY LIBERTY LIFE INS CO	TX	32.2
FIDELITY STANDARD LIFE INS CO	AR	3.1
FIRST CONTINENTAL LIFE & ACC INS CO	TX	8.0
FIRST GUARANTY INS CO	LA	55.4
FOUNDATION LIFE INS CO OF AR	AR	4.9
GREAT FIDELITY LIFE INS CO	IN	3.2
HAWTHORN LIFE INS CO	TX	10.4
INDIVIDUAL ASR CO LIFE HEALTH & ACC	OK	21.5
JEFF DAVIS MORTUARY BENEFIT ASSOC	LA	5.4
JEFFERSON LIFE INS CO	TX	2.4
KENTUCKY HOME LIFE INS CO	KY	5.8
LIFE INS CO OF LOUISIANA	LA	8.3
LIFESECURE INS CO	MI	292.9
MAPFRE LIFE INS CO OF PR	PR	57.4
MEDICAL BENEFITS MUTUAL LIFE INS CO	OH	16.2
MEMORIAL INS CO OF AMERICA	AR	1.2
MULHEARN PROTECTIVE INS CO	LA	11.9
PELLERIN LIFE INS CO	LA	10.9
PURITAN LIFE INS CO	TX	14.4
PURITAN LIFE INS CO OF AMERICA	TX	37.2
UNITED FUNERAL BENEFIT LIFE INS CO	OK	46.9
UNIVERSAL FIDELITY LIFE INS CO	OK	10.9
WESTERN AMERICAN LIFE INS CO	TX	29.0
Rating: D-		
ABILITY INS CO	NE	1,299.9
CAPITOL SECURITY LIFE INS CO	TX	4.5

INSURANCE COMPANY NAME	DOM. STATE	TOTAL ASSETS ($MIL)

Rating: D- (Continued)

INSURANCE COMPANY NAME	DOM. STATE	TOTAL ASSETS ($MIL)
DELTA LIFE INS CO	GA	62.6
FIRST WYOMING LIFE INS CO	NE	4.2
HAYMARKET INS CO	NE	435.1
INDEPENDENCE LIFE & ANNUITY CO	DE	2,972.8
INTERNATIONAL AMERICAN LIFE INS CO	TX	2.0
PHL VARIABLE INS CO	CT	6,555.1
PHOENIX LIFE & ANNUITY CO	CT	41.2
PINE BELT LIFE INS CO	MS	1.5
PROFESSIONAL INS CO	TX	110.2
REGAL LIFE OF AMERICA INS CO	TX	8.2
SECURITY NATIONAL LIFE INS CO	UT	551.0
SOUTHWEST SERVICE LIFE INS CO	TX	10.8
SUN LIFE & HEALTH INS CO	MI	494.0
TRINITY LIFE INS CO	OK	166.9
TRIPLE-S BLUE II	PR	--
UNITED ASR LIFE INS CO	TX	2.2
UNITED FUNERAL DIR BENEFIT LIC	TX	116.9
US ALLIANCE LIFE & SECURITY CO	KS	8.8

Rating: E+

INSURANCE COMPANY NAME	DOM. STATE	TOTAL ASSETS ($MIL)
ALABAMA LIFE REINS CO INC	AL	25.9
AMERICAN LIFE & SECURITY CORP	NE	20.1
CAPITAL RESERVE LIFE INS CO	MO	1.4
GREAT PLAINS LIFE ASR CO	SD	7.8
KILPATRICK LIFE INS CO	LA	188.8
LILY LIFE INS CO	TX	1.2
NETCARE LIFE & HEALTH INS CO	GU	26.9
NORTH CAROLINA MUTUAL LIFE INS CO	NC	36.2
RELIABLE LIFE INS CO	LA	7.1

Rating: E

INSURANCE COMPANY NAME	DOM. STATE	TOTAL ASSETS ($MIL)
AMERICAN HOME LIFE INS CO	AR	19.9
CROWN GLOBAL INS CO OF AMERICA	DE	417.0
DIRECTORS LIFE ASR CO	OK	32.2
INVESTORS PREFERRED LIFE INS CO	SD	162.9
JACKSON GRIFFIN INS CO	AR	11.7
LOMBARD INTL LIFE ASR CO	PA	5,610.7
MCS LIFE INS CO	PR	58.9
MEDAMERICA INS CO OF NEW YORK	NY	697.8
PHOENIX LIFE INS CO	NY	12,507.1
RHODES LIFE INS CO OF LA INC	LA	4.0
SENIOR HEALTH INS CO OF PENNSYLVANIA	PA	2,794.8
SMITH BURIAL & LIFE INS CO	AR	4.6
SUN LIFE ASR CO OF CANADA	MI	20,273.9
UNITED SECURITY ASR CO OF PA	PA	154.9
WILLIAMS PROGRESSIVE LIFE & ACC I C	LA	11.1

Rating: E-

INSURANCE COMPANY NAME	DOM. STATE	TOTAL ASSETS ($MIL)
AMERICAN INDEPENDENT NETWORK INS CO	NY	24.4

Rating: F

INSURANCE COMPANY NAME	DOM. STATE	TOTAL ASSETS ($MIL)
AMERICAN COMMUNITY MUT INS CO	MI	--
CONCERT HEALTH PLAN INS CO	IL	--

INSURANCE COMPANY NAME	DOM. STATE	TOTAL ASSETS ($MIL)
DLE LIFE INS CO	LA	--
FIDELITY MUTUAL LIFE INS CO	PA	--
FREMONT LIFE INS CO	CA	--
GERTRUDE GEDDES WILLIS LIFE INS CO	LA	--
GREAT REPUBLIC LIFE INS CO	WA	--
HIGGINBOTHAM BURIAL INS CO	AR	--
JORDAN FUNERAL & INS CO INC	AL	--
LONE STAR LIFE INS CO	TX	--
MONARCH LIFE INS CO	MA	693.0
MOTHE LIFE INS CO	LA	--

Rating: U

INSURANCE COMPANY NAME	DOM. STATE	TOTAL ASSETS ($MIL)
ACADEME INC	WA	5.7
ALLIANZ LIFE & ANNUITY CO	MN	9.4
ALLIED FINANCIAL INS CO	TX	--
AMERICAN CENTURY LIFE INS CO TX	TX	--
AMERICAN CREDITORS LIFE INS CO	DE	12.0
AMERICAN INTEGRITY LIFE INS CO	AR	0.9
AMERICAN MEDICAL & LIFE INS CO	NY	4.4
AMERICAN PHOENIX LIFE & REASSUR CO	CT	6.4
AMERICAN SERVICE LIFE INS CO	AR	0.9
ASSURED LIFE ASSOCIATION	CO	--
ATHENE LIFE INS CO	DE	227.8
BLUE SPIRIT INS CO	VT	--
CALPERS LONG-TERM CARE PROGRAM		--
CANYON STATE LIFE INS CO	AZ	--
CAREAMERICA LIFE INS CO	CA	28.7
CASS COUNTY LIFE INS CO	TX	3.1
CATERPILLAR LIFE INS CO	MO	147.4
CATHOLIC FINANCIAL LIFE	WI	--
CIGNA ARBOR LIFE INS CO	CT	8.4
CLEAR SPRING LIFE INS CO	TX	283.7
COMMENCEMENT BAY LIFE INS CO	WA	7.7
COMMONWEALTH DEALERS LIFE INS CO	VA	6.0
CONSECO LIFE INS CO OF TX	TX	1,264.6
CORVESTA LIFE INS CO	AZ	9.2
CSA FRATERNAL LIFE	IL	--
DESTINY HEALTH INS CO	IL	3.5
DL REINSURANCE CO	DE	1,363.2
DOCTORS LIFE INS CO	CA	15.6
EDUCATORS LIFE INS CO OF AMERICA	IL	441.3
EVERENCE ASSN INC	IN	--
EVERENCE INS CO	IN	22.5
EVERGREEN LIFE INS CO	TX	1.6
FAMILY SERVICE LIFE INS CO	TX	350.7
FINANCIAL ASSURANCE LIFE INS CO	TX	11.3
FIRST DIMENSION LIFE INS CO INC	OK	4.8
FIRST LANDMARK LIFE INS CO	NE	2.0
FORETHOUGHT NATIONAL LIFE INS CO	TX	199.4
GMHP HEALTH INS LMTD	GU	0.5
GREAT WESTERN LIFE INS CO	MT	--
GRIFFIN LEGGETT BURIAL INS CO	AR	0.1
GULF STATES LIFE INS CO INC	LA	2.7
IBC LIFE INS CO	TX	3.4

INSURANCE COMPANY NAME	DOM. STATE	TOTAL ASSETS ($MIL)	INSURANCE COMPANY NAME	DOM. STATE	TOTAL ASSETS ($MIL)

Rating: U (Continued)

INSURANCE COMPANY NAME	DOM. STATE	TOTAL ASSETS ($MIL)
INDEPENDENCE INS INC	DE	1.7
JRD LIFE INS CO	AZ	--
KNIGHTS OF COLUMBUS	CT	--
KSKJ LIFE	IL	--
LIFE PROTECTION INS CO	TX	7.7
LOMBARD INTL LIFE ASR CO OF NY	NY	4.7
LOYAL CHRISTIAN BENEFIT ASSN	PA	--
MELLON LIFE INS CO	DE	24.6
METLIFE INS LTD GUAM BRANCH	GU	3.1
MILILANI LIFE INS CO	HI	1.9
MINNETONKA LIFE INS CO	AZ	--
NEW FOUNDATION LIFE INS CO	AR	--
OMAHA LIFE INS CO	NE	10.8
ORDER UNITED COMM TRAVELERS OF AMER	OH	--
PAN AMERICAN ASR CO INTL INC	FL	5.0
PIONEER MILITARY INS CO	NV	1.6
PORT-O-CALL LIFE INS CO	AR	0.4
PREFERRED SECURITY LIFE INS CO	TX	2.9
PRINCIPAL LIFE INS CO IOWA	IA	331.4
REGAL REINSURANCE COMPANY	MA	6.1
RELIABLE SERVICE INS CO	LA	0.1
RELIANCE STANDARD LIFE INS CO OF TX	TX	876.4
RESOURCE LIFE INS CO	IL	7.0
ROYAL NEIGHBORS OF AMERICA	IL	--
SECURICO LIFE INS CO	TX	2.7
SECURITAS FINANCIAL LIFE INS CO	NC	5.8
SENTINEL AMERICAN LIFE INS CO	TX	30.5
SERVCO LIFE INS CO	TX	5.0
SERVICE LIFE & CAS INS CO	TX	22.0
SHELTERPOINT INS CO	FL	8.6
SHERIDAN LIFE INS CO	OK	2.2
SOUTHERN FIDELITY LIFE INS CO	AR	0.1
SOUTHERN LIFE & HEALTH INS CO	WI	85.5
SOUTHWEST CREDIT LIFE INC	NM	0.7
SPJST	TX	--
SQUIRE REASSURANCE CO LLC	MI	12.6
STARVED ROCK LIFE INS CO	AZ	--
STATE FARM HEALTH INS CO	IL	8.4
STRUCTURED ANNUITY RE CO	IA	1,421.9
THRIVENT FINANCIAL FOR LUTHERANS	WI	--
TIPPECANOE LIFE INS CO	AZ	--
TRANS-WESTERN LIFE INS CO	TX	0.5
UBS LIFE INS CO USA	CA	41.3
UNITED BENEFIT LIFE INS CO	OH	3.0
UNIVANTAGE INS CO	UT	1.9
WESTERN CATHOLIC UNION	IL	--
XL LIFE INS & ANNUITY CO	IL	16.7

Section VI

Rating Upgrades
and Downgrades

A list of all

U.S. Life and Annuity Insurers

receiving a rating upgrade or downgrade
during the current quarter.

Section VI Contents

This section identifies those companies receiving a rating change since the previous edition of this publication, whether it be a rating upgrade, rating downgrade, newly-rated company or the withdrawal of a rating. A rating may be withdrawn due to a merger, dissolution, liquidation or lack of information. A rating upgrade or downgrade may entail a change from one letter grade to another, or it may mean the addition or deletion of a plus or minus sign within the same letter grade previously assigned to the company. Each rating upgrade and downgrade is accompanied by a brief explanation of why the rating was changed. Ratings are normally updated once each quarter of the year. In some instances, however, a company's rating may be downgraded outside of the normal updates due to overriding circumstances. The tables for new and withdrawn ratings will contain some or all of the following information:

1. **Insurance Company Name**

   The legally registered name, which can sometimes differ from the name that the company uses for advertising. An insurer's name can be very similar to that of another, so verify the company's exact name and state of domicile to make sure you are looking at the correct company.

2. **Domicile State**

   The state which has primary regulatory responsibility for the company. It may differ from the location of the company's corporate headquarters. You do not have to be living in the domicile state to purchase insurance from this firm, provided it is licensed to do business in your state.

3. **Total Assets**

   All assets admitted by state insurance regulators in millions of dollars. This includes investments, current business assets, and separate accounts.

4. **New Safety Rating**

   The rating assigned to the company as of the date of this Guide's publication. Our rating is measured on a scale from A to F and considers a wide range of factors. Highly rated companies are, in our opinion, less likely to experience financial difficulties than lower-rated firms. See *About Weiss Safety Ratings* for more information.

5. **Previous Safety Rating**

   The rating assigned to the company prior to its most recent change.

6. **Date of Change**

   The date that the rating upgrade or downgrade officially occurred. Normally, all rating changes are put into effect on a single day each quarter of the year. In some instances, however, a rating may have been changed outside of this normal update.

New Ratings

INSURANCE COMPANY NAME	DOM. STATE	TOTAL ASSETS ($MIL)	NEW RATING	PREVIOUS RATING	DATE OF CHANGE

No new ratings are being released in this edition.

Withdrawn Ratings

INSURANCE COMPANY NAME	DOM. STATE	TOTAL ASSETS ($MIL)	NEW RATING	PREVIOUS RATING	DATE OF CHANGE
CENSTAT LIFE ASR CO	AZ	4.7	U	C	10/05/16
MELANCON LIFE INS CO	LA	6.6	U	D	10/05/16
PACIFIC BEACON LIFE REASSUR INC	HI	389.7	U	B	10/05/16
RIVER LAKE INS CO	SC	50.8	U	C	10/05/16
RIVER LAKE INS CO II	SC	72.2	U	C	10/05/16
WESTPORT LIFE INS CO	AZ	2.1	U	D	10/05/16

Rating Upgrades

AAA LIFE INS CO OF NY was upgraded to B from C in October 2016 based on a markedly improved stability index. composite rating for affiliated ACLI Acquisition Co Group rose to B from B-.

ACE LIFE INS CO was upgraded to B from C+ in October 2016 based on a markedly improved stability index. composite rating for affiliated Chubb Limited Group rose to B from C+, as exemplified by recent upgrade of affiliates: COMBINED INS CO OF AMERICA to C+ from C. COMBINED LIFE INS CO OF NEW YORK to C+ from C.

ANNUITY INVESTORS LIFE INS CO was upgraded to A- from B in October 2016 based on an improved capitalization index.

AXA CORPORATE SOLUTIONS LIFE REINS was upgraded to B from B- in October 2016 based on a markedly improved stability index. enhanced financial strength of affiliates in AXA Financial Inc Group, notably the recent upgrade of affiliated company AXA EQUITABLE LIFE & ANNUITY CO to B from B-.

AXA EQUITABLE LIFE & ANNUITY CO was upgraded to B from B- in October 2016 based on a higher stability index. enhanced financial strength of affiliates in AXA Financial Inc Group.

BANNER LIFE INS CO was upgraded to C+ from C in October 2016 based on a markedly improved capitalization index and a higher five-year profitability index.

COMBINED INS CO OF AMERICA was upgraded to C+ from C in October 2016 based on a greatly improved capitalization index, a markedly improved investment safety index and a greatly improved stability index. composite rating for affiliated Chubb Limited Group rose to B from C+.

COMBINED LIFE INS CO OF NEW YORK was upgraded to C+ from C in October 2016 based on a higher capitalization index, a higher investment safety index, an improved five-year profitability index and a higher stability index. composite rating for affiliated Chubb Limited Group rose to B from C+, notably the recent upgrade of affiliated company COMBINED INS CO OF AMERICA to C+ from C.

ENTERPRISE LIFE INS CO was upgraded to B- from C in October 2016 based on a markedly improved stability index.

LONGEVITY INS CO was upgraded to B from D in October 2016 based on a greatly improved stability index. composite rating for affiliated Penn Mutual Life Ins Company Group rose to B from E.

MAPFRE LIFE INS CO OF PR was upgraded to D from D- in October 2016 based on a higher stability index.

MIDWESTERN UNITED LIFE INS CO was upgraded to A from A- in October 2016 based on a markedly improved stability index.

SENTINEL SECURITY LIFE INS CO was upgraded to D+ from D in October 2016 based on a higher five-year profitability index.

SOUTHERN PIONEER LIFE INS CO was upgraded to B+ from B in October 2016 based on a markedly improved stability index.

TPM LIFE INS CO was upgraded to B from B- in October 2016 based on an improved capitalization index and an improved five-year profitability index. composite rating for affiliated Wheaton Management LLC Group rose to B from B-.

Rating Downgrades

DELTA LIFE INS CO was downgraded to D- from D in October 2016 due to a declining capitalization index, a declining investment safety index and a declining stability index.

FINANCIAL AMERICAN LIFE INS CO was downgraded to D+ from C- in October 2016 due to capitalization index and a declining five-year profitability index.

INDEPENDENCE LIFE & ANNUITY CO was downgraded to D- from C in October 2016 due to a substantially lower stability index. In addition, the composite rating for affiliated Sun Life Assurance Group fell to E from D+.

JACKSON NATIONAL LIFE INS CO was downgraded to B from B+ in October 2016 due to a substantially lower capitalization index, a substantially lower investment safety index, a substantially lower five-year profitability index and a significant decline in its stability index.

MEDAMERICA INS CO was downgraded to C+ from B in October 2016 due to a significant decline in its stability index. In addition, the composite rating for affiliated Lifetime Healthcare Inc Group fell to B from B+.

PROFESSIONAL INS CO was downgraded to D- from C in October 2016 due to a substantially lower stability index. In addition, the composite rating for affiliated Sun Life Assurance Group fell to E from D+.

PRUDENTIAL ANNUITIES LIFE ASR CORP was downgraded to C from C+ in October 2016 due to a substantially lower five-year profitability index.

PURITAN LIFE INS CO was downgraded to D from C in October 2016 due to a lower five-year profitability index. In addition, the composite rating for affiliated Verde Investments Inc Group fell to D from C.

SENIOR HEALTH INS CO OF PENNSYLVANIA was downgraded to E from D in October 2016 due to a declining capitalization index, a lower investment safety index, a lower five-year profitability index and a declining stability index.

SMITH BURIAL & LIFE INS CO was downgraded to E from D- in October 2016 due to a substantially lower capitalization index, a declining investment safety index, a declining five-year profitability index and a significant decline in its stability index.

STERLING INVESTORS LIFE INS CO was downgraded to D+ from C in October 2016 due to a significant decline in its capitalization index and a substantially lower five-year profitability index.

SUN LIFE & HEALTH INS CO was downgraded to D- from C in October 2016 due to a declining capitalization index. In addition, the composite rating for affiliated Sun Life Assurance Group fell to E from D+.

WESTERN AMERICAN LIFE INS CO was downgraded to D from D+ in October 2016 due to a declining capitalization index, a declining investment safety index and a significant decline in its stability index. In addition, the composite rating for affiliated Maximum Corporation Group fell to D from D+.

Appendix

State Guaranty Associations

The states have established insurance guaranty associations to help pay claims to policyholders of failed insurance companies. However, there are several cautions which you must be aware of with respect to this coverage:

1. Most of the guaranty associations do not set aside funds in advance. Rather, states assess contributions from other insurance companies after an insolvency occurs.

2. There can be an unacceptably long delay before claims are paid.

3. Each state is governed by its own legislation, providing a wide range of coverage and conditions that may apply. According to the National Organization of Life and Health Guaranty Associations (NOLHGA), the issues are extremely complex with unique variables for each individual state.

4. The table on the following page is designed to help you sort out these issues. However, it is not intended to handle all of them. If your carrier has failed and you need a complete answer, we recommend you contact your State Insurance Official or NOLHGA at 703-481-5206.

State guaranty associations are set up to cover policyholders residing in their own state. This essentially means that each individual state is responsible for policyholders residing in that state, no matter where the insolvent insurer is domiciled.

Non-resident coverage is provided only under certain circumstances listed in the state's statutes. The general conditions are typically as follows:

a) The insurer of the policyholder must be domiciled and licensed in the state in which the non-resident is seeking coverage;

b) When the contracts were sold, the insurers that issued the policies were not licensed in the state in which the policyholder resides;

c) The non-resident policyholder is not eligible for coverage from his or her state of residence;

d) The state where the policyholder resides must have a guaranty association similar to that of the state in which he or she is seeking non-resident coverage.

Warning: Be sure to contact the specific state guaranty association for information in that state's laws. Conditions and limitations are subject to individual state statutes and can change.

Following is a brief explanation of each of the columns in the table.

1. **Maximum Aggregate Benefits for All Lines of Insurance**

   The maximum amount payable by the State Guaranty Fund to cover all types of insurance including life insurance, health insurance, disability and annuities.

2. **Maximum Death Benefit with Respect to Any One Life**

   The maximum amount payable by the State Guaranty Fund for a death claim on a single life. If the policy benefits are higher than the Guaranty Fund's coverage limits, policyholders may typically be able to file a claim with the court-appointed Liquidator of the insolvent insurance company to try to recover the difference. But success is uncertain.

3. **Liability for Cash or Withdrawal Value of Life Insurance Policy**

   The maximum cash value or withdrawal value the Guaranty Fund will assume responsibility for related to an individual life insurance policy.

4. **Maximum Liability for Present Value of an Annuity Contract**

   The maximum cash value or withdrawal value the Guaranty Fund will assume responsibility for related to an individual annuity contract. The coverage may be higher if the annuity is in the payout phase.

Coverage of State Guaranty Funds

State	Max. Aggregate Benefits for All Lines of Insurance	Max. Death Benefit with Respect to Any One Life	Max. Liability for Cash or Withdrawal Value of Life Insurance Policy	Max. Liability for Present Value of an Annuity Contract	State Guaranty Association Phone Numbers	State Guaranty Web Address
Alabama	$300,000	$300,000	$100,000	$250,000	(205) 879-2202	www.allifega.org
Alaska	$300,000	$300,000	$100,000	$100,000	(907) 243-2311	www.aklifega.org
Arizona	$300,000	$300,000	$100,000	$250,000	(602) 364-3863	www.id.state.az.us
Arkansas	$300,000	$300,000	$300,000	$300,000	(501) 375-9151	www.arlifega.org
California	80% not to exceed $300,000	80% not to exceed $300,000	80% not to exceed $100,000	80% not to exceed $250,000	(323) 782-0182	www.califega.org
Colorado	$300,000	$300,000	$100,000	$250,000	(303) 292-5022	www.colifega.org
Connecticut	$500,000	$500,000	$500,000	$500,000	(860) 647-1054	www.ctlifega.org
Delaware	$300,000	$300,000	$100,000	$250,000	(302) 456-3656	www.delifega.org
Dist. of Col.	$300,000	$300,000	$100,000	$300,000	(202) 434-8771	www.dclifega.org
Florida	$300,000	$300,000	$100,000	$250,000	(904) 398-3644	www.flahiga.org
Georgia	$300,000	$300,000	$100,000	$250,000	(770) 621-9835	www.gaiga.org
Hawaii	$300,000	$300,000	$100,000	$100,000	(808) 528-5400	www.hilifega.org
Idaho	$300,000	$300,000	$100,000	$250,000	(208) 378-9510	www.idlifega.org
Illinois	$300,000	$300,000	$100,000	$250,000	(773) 714-8050	www.ilhiga.org
Indiana	$300,000	$300,000	$100,000	$100,000	(317) 692-0574	www.inlifega.org
Iowa	$300,000	$300,000	$100,000	$250,000	(515) 248-5712	www.ialifega.org
Kansas	$300,000	$300,000	$100,000	$250,000	(785) 271-1199	www.kslifega.org
Kentucky	$300,000	$300,000	$100,000	$250,000	(502) 895-5915	www.klhiga.org
Louisiana	$500,000	$300,000	$100,000	$250,000	(225) 381-0656	www.lalifega.org
Maine	$300,000	$300,000	$100,000	$250,000	(207) 633-1090	www.melifega.org
Maryland	$300,000	$300,000	$100,000	$250,000	(410) 248-0407	www.mdlifega.org
Massachusetts	$300,000	$300,000	$100,000	$250,000	(413) 744-8483	www.malifega.org
Michigan	$300,000	$300,000	$100,000	$250,000	(517) 339-1755	www.milifega.org
Minnesota	$500,000	$500,000	$130,000	$250,000	(651) 407-3149	www.mnlifega.org
Mississippi	$300,000	$300,000	$100,000	$100,000	(601) 981-0755	www.mslifega.org
Missouri	$300,000	$300,000	$100,000	$100,000	(573) 634-8455	www.mo-iga.org
Montana	$300,000	$300,000	$100,000	$250,000	(262) 965-5761	www.mtlifega.org
Nebraska	$300,000	$300,000	$100,000	$250,000	(402) 474-6900	www.nelifega.org
Nevada	$300,000	$300,000	$100,000	$250,000	(775) 329-8387	www.nvlifega.org
New Hampshire	$300,000	$300,000	$100,000	$100,000	(603) 472-3734	www.nhlifega.org
New Jersey	$500,000	$500,000	$100,000	$100,000	(732) 345-5200	www.njlifega.org
New Mexico	$300,000	$300,000	$100,000	$250,000	(505) 820-7355	www.nmlifega.org
New York	$500,000	$500,000	$500,000	$500,000	(212) 202-4243	www.nylifega.org
North Carolina	$300,000	$300,000	$300,000	$300,000	(919) 833-6838	www.nclifega.org
North Dakota	$300,000	$300,000	$100,000	$250,000	(701) 235-4108	www.ndlifega.org
Ohio	$300,000	$300,000	$100,000	$250,000	(614) 442-6601	www.olhiga.org
Oklahoma	$300,000	$300,000	$100,000	$300,000	(405) 272-9221	www.oklifega.org
Oregon	$300,000	$300,000	$100,000	$250,000	(855) 378-9510	www.orlifega.org
Pennsylvania	$300,000	$300,000	$100,000	$100,000	(610) 975-0572	www.palifega.org
Puerto Rico	$300,000	$300,000	$100,000	$100,000	(787) 765-2095	www.ocs.gobierno.pr
Rhode Island	$300,000	$300,000	$100,000	$250,000	(401) 273-2921	www.rilifega.org
South Carolina	$300,000	$300,000	$300,000	$300,000	(803) 783-4947	www.sclifega.org
South Dakota	$300,000	$300,000	$100,000	$250,000	(605) 336-0177	www.sdlifega.org
Tennessee	$300,000	$300,000	$100,000	$250,000	(615) 242-8758	www.tnlifega.org
Texas	$300,000	$300,000	$100,000	$250,000	(512) 476-5101	www.txlifega.org
Utah	$500,000	$500,000	$200,000	$200,000	(801) 302-9955	www.utlifega.org
Vermont	$300,000	$300,000	$100,000	$250,000	(802) 249-0284	www.vtlifega.org
Virginia	$350,000	$300,000	$100,000	$250,000	(804) 282-2240	www.valifega.org
Washington	$500,000	$500,000	$500,000	$500,000	(360) 426-6744	www.walifega.org
West Virginia	$300,000	$300,000	$100,000	$250,000	(304) 733-6904	www.wvlifega.org
Wisconsin	$300,000	$300,000	$300,000	$300,000	(608) 242-9473	www.wilifega.org
Wyoming	$300,000	$300,000	$100,000	$100,000	(303) 292-5022	www.wylifega.org

State Insurance Commissioners' Departmental Phone Numbers

State	Official's Title	Website Address	Phone Number
Alabama	Commissioner	www.aldoi.org	(334) 269-3550
Alaska	Director	https://www.commerce.alaska.gov/web/ins/	(800) 467-8725
Arizona	Director	https://insurance.az.gov/	(602) 364-2499
Arkansas	Commissioner	www.insurance.arkansas.gov	(800) 282-9134
California	Commissioner	www.insurance.ca.gov	(800) 927-4357
Colorado	Commissioner	https://www.colorado.gov/dora/division-insurance	(800) 886-7675
Connecticut	Commissioner	http://www.ct.gov/cid/site/default.asp	(800) 203-3447
Delaware	Commissioner	http://delawareinsurance.gov/	(800) 282-8611
Dist. of Columbia	Commissioner	http://disb.dc.gov/	(202) 727-8000
Florida	Commissioner	www.floir.com/	(850) 413-3140
Georgia	Commissioner	www.oci.ga.gov/	(800) 656-2298
Hawaii	Commissioner	http://cca.hawaii.gov/ins/	(808) 586-2790
Idaho	Director	www.doi.idaho.gov	(800) 721-3272
Illinois	Director	www.insurance.illinois.gov/	(866) 445-5364
Indiana	Commissioner	www.in.gov/idoi/	(317) 232-2385
Iowa	Commissioner	www.iid.state.ia.us	(877) 955-1212
Kansas	Commissioner	www.ksinsurance.org	(800) 432-2484
Kentucky	Commissioner	http://insurance.ky.gov/	(800) 595-6053
Louisiana	Commissioner	www.ldi.la.gov/	(800) 259-5300
Maine	Superintendent	www.maine.gov/pfr/insurance/	(800) 300-5000
Maryland	Commissioner	http://insurance.maryland.gov/Pages/default.aspx	(800) 492-6116
Massachusetts	Commissioner	www.mass.gov/ocabr/government/oca-agencies/doi-lp/	(877) 563-4467
Michigan	Director	http://www.michigan.gov/difs	(877) 999-6442
Minnesota	Commissioner	http://mn.gov/commerce/	(651) 539-1500
Mississippi	Commissioner	http://www.mid.ms.gov/	(601) 359-3569
Missouri	Director	www.insurance.mo.gov	(800) 726-7390
Montana	Commissioner	http://csimt.gov/	(800) 332-6148
Nebraska	Director	www.doi.nebraska.gov/	(402) 471-2201
Nevada	Commissioner	www.doi.nv.gov/	(888) 872-3234
New Hampshire	Commissioner	www.nh.gov/insurance/	(800) 852-3416
New Jersey	Commissioner	www.state.nj.us/dobi/	(800) 446-7467
New Mexico	Superintendent	www.osi.state.nm.us/	(855) 427-5674
New York	Superintendent	www.dfs.ny.gov/	(800) 342-3736
North Carolina	Commissioner	www.ncdoi.com	(800) 546-5664
North Dakota	Commissioner	www.nd.gov/ndins/	(800) 247-0560
Ohio	Lieutenant Governor	www.insurance.ohio.gov/	(800) 686-1526
Oklahoma	Commissioner	www.ok.gov/oid/	(800) 522-0071
Oregon	Insurance Commissioner	www.oregon.gov/dcbs/insurance/Pages/index.aspx	(888) 877-4894
Pennsylvania	Commissioner	www.insurance.pa.gov/	(877) 881-6388
Puerto Rico	Commissioner	www.ocs.gobierno.pr	(787) 304-8686
Rhode Island	Superintendent	www.dbr.state.ri.us/divisions/insurance/	(401) 462-9500
South Carolina	Director	www.doi.sc.gov	(803) 737-6160
South Dakota	Director	http://dlr.sd.gov/insurance/default.aspx	(605) 773-3563
Tennessee	Commissioner	www.tn.gov/insurance/	(615) 741-2241
Texas	Commissioner	www.tdi.texas.gov/	(800) 252-3439
Utah	Commissioner	www.insurance.utah.gov	(800) 439-3805
Vermont	Commissioner	www.dfr.vermont.gov/	(802) 828-3301
Virgin Islands	Lieutenant Governor	http://ltg.gov.vi/division-of-banking-and-insurance.html	(340) 774-7166
Virginia	Commissioner	www.scc.virginia.gov/boi/	(804) 371-9741
Washington	Commissioner	www.insurance.wa.gov	(800) 562-6900
West Virginia	Commissioner	www.wvinsurance.gov	(888) 879-9842
Wisconsin	Commissioner	oci.wi.gov	(800) 236-8517
Wyoming	Commissioner	http://doi.wyo.gov/	(800) 438-5768

Risk-Adjusted Capital for Life and Annuity Insurers in Weiss Rating Model

Among the most important indicators used in the analysis of an individual company are our two risk-adjusted capital ratios, which are useful tools in determining exposure to investment, liquidity and insurance risk in relation to the capital the company has to cover those risks.

The first risk-adjusted capital ratio evaluates the company's ability to withstand a moderate loss scenario. The second ratio evaluates the company's ability to withstand a severe loss scenario.

In order to calculate these risk-adjusted capital ratios, we follow these steps:

1. Capital Resources
First, we add up all of the company's resources which could be used to cover losses. These include capital, surplus, the Asset Valuation Reserve (AVR), and a portion of the provision for future policyholders' dividends, where appropriate. Additional credit may also be given for the use of conservative reserving assumptions and other "hidden capital" when applicable.

2. Target Capital
Next, we determine the company's target capital. This answers the question: Based upon the company's level of risk in both its insurance business and its investment portfolio, how much capital would it need to cover potential losses during a moderate loss scenario? In other words, we determine how much capital we believe this company *should* have.

3. Risk-Adjusted Capital Ratio #1
We compare the results of step 1 with those of step 2. Specifically, we divide the "capital resources" by the "target capital" and express it in terms of a ratio. This ratio is called RACR #1. (See next page for more detail on methodology.)

If a company has a Risk-Adjusted Capital Ratio of 1.0 or more, it means the company has all of the capital we believe it requires to withstand potential losses which could be inflicted by a moderate loss scenario. If the company has less than 1.0, it does not currently have all of the basic capital resources we think it needs. During times of financial distress, companies often have access to additional capital through contributions from a parent company, current profits or reductions in policyholder dividends. Therefore, an allowance is made in our rating system for firms with somewhat less than 1.0 Risk-Adjusted Capital Ratios.

4. Risk-Adjusted Capital Ratio #2
We repeat steps 2 and 3, but now assuming a severe loss scenario. This ratio is called RACR #2.

5. Capitalization Index
We convert RACR #1 and #2 into an index. It is measured on a scale of zero to ten, with ten being the best and seven or better considered strong. A company whose capital, surplus and AVR equal its target capital will have a Risk-Adjusted Capital Ratio of 1.0 and a Risk-Adjusted Capital Index of 7.0.

How We Determine Target Capital

The basic procedure for determining target capital is to ask these questions:

1.   What is the breakdown of the company's investment portfolio and types of business?

2.   For each category, what are the potential losses which could be incurred in the loss scenario?

3.   In order to cover those potential losses, how much in capital resources does the company need? It stands to reason that more capital is needed as a cushion for losses on high-risk investments, such as junk bonds, than would be necessary for low-risk investments, such as AAA-rated utility bonds.

     Unfortunately, the same questions we have raised about Wall Street rating systems with respect to how they rate insurance companies can be asked about the way they rate bonds. However, we do not rate bonds ourselves. Therefore, we must rely upon the bond ratings of other rating agencies. This is another reason why we have stricter capital requirements for the insurance companies. It accounts for the fact that they may need some extra protection in case an AAA-rated bond may not be quite as good as it appears to be.

     Finally, target capital is adjusted for the company's spread of risk in the diversification of its investment portfolio, the size and number of the policies it writes and the diversification of its business.

Table 1 on the next page shows target capital percentages used by the National Association of Insurance Commissioners (NAIC) in relation to Weiss Risk-Adjusted Capital Ratios #1 and #2 (RACR #1 and RACR #2).

The percentages shown in the table answer the question: How much should the firm hold in capital resources for every $100 it has committed to each category? Several of the items in Table 1 are expressed as ranges. The actual percentages used in the calculation of target capital for an individual company may vary due to the levels of risks in the operations, investments or policy obligations of that specific company.

Table 1. Target Capital Percentages

Asset Risk	Weiss Ratings RACR#1 (%)	Weiss Ratings RACR#2 (%)	NAIC	
Bonds				
Government guaranteed bonds	0	0	0	
Class 1	.5-.75	1-1.5	0.4	
Class 2	2	5	1.3	
Class 3	5	15	4.6	
Class 4	10	30	10	
Class 5	20	60	23	
Class 6	20	60	30	
Mortgages				
In good standing	0.5	1	0	
90 days overdue	1.7-20	3.8-25	0.1-18	
In process of foreclosure	25-33	33-50	1.4-23	
Real Estate				
Class 1	20	50	15	
Class 2	10	33	23	
Preferred Stock				
Class 1	3	5	1.1	
Class 2	4	6	3.0	
Class 3	7	9	7.2	
Class 4	12	15	15	
Class 5	22	29	20	
Class 6	30	39	15	
Class 7	3-30	5-39	22.5-45	
Common Stock				
Unaffiliated	25	33	22.5-45	
Affiliated	25-100	33-100	22.5-45	
Short-term investment	0.5	1	0.4	
Premium notes	2	5	6.8	
Collateral loans	2	5	6.8	
Separate account equity	25	33	11	**
Other invested assets	5	10	6.8	
Insurance Risk				
Individual life reserves*	.06-.15	.08-.21	.09-.23	
Group life reserves*	.05-.12	.06-.16	.08-.18	
Individual Health Premiums				
Class 1	12-20	15-25	10-16.5	
Class 2	9.6	12	6.7-12	
Class 3	6.4	8	3.5/$50,000	
Class 4	12-28	15-35	23.1-53.9	
Class 5	12-20	15-25	10.8-38.5	
Group Health Premiums				
Class 1	5.6-12	7-15	9-15	
Class 2	20	25	25	
Class 3	9.6	12	6.7-12	
Class 4	6.4	8	3.5/$50,000	
Class 5	12-20	15-25	4.6-23.1	
Managed care credit	5-40	6-50	NAIC calculation	
Premiums subject to rate guarantees	100-209	120-250	2.4-6.4	
Individual claim reserves	4	5	5-7.7	
Group claim reserves	4	5	5-7.7	
Reinsurance	0-2	0-5	0.8	
Interest Rate Risk				
Policy loans	0-2	0-5	1.1	
Life reserves	1-2	1-3	0.7-1.1	
Individual annuity reserves	1-3	1-5	0.7-1.1	
Group annuity reserves	1-2	1-3	0.7-1.1	
Guaranteed interest contract reserves	1-2	1-3	0.7-1.1	

All numbers are shown for illustrative purposes. Figures actually used in the formula vary annually based on industry experience.
*Based on net amount at risk.
**Risk-based capital for separate account assets that are not tied to an index = 100% of the risk-based capital of assets in the accounts.

Investment Class   ## Descriptions

Government guaranteed bonds		Guaranteed bonds issued by U.S. and other governments which receive the top rating of state insurance commissioners.
Bonds	Class 1	Investment grade bonds rated AAA, AA or A by Moody's or Standard & Poor's or deemed AAA - A equivalent by state insurance commissioners.
	Class 2	Investment grade bonds with some speculative elements, rated BBB or equivalent.
	Class 3	Noninvestment grade bonds, rated BB or equivalent.
	Class 4	Noninvestment grade bonds, rated B or equivalent.
	Class 5	Noninvestment grade bonds, rated CCC, CC or C or equivalent.
	Class 6	Noninvestment grade bonds, in or near default.
Mortgages		Mortgages in good standing
		Mortgages 90 days past due
		Mortgages in process of foreclosure
Real Estate	Class 1	Properties acquired in satisfaction of debt.
	Class 2	Company occupied and other investment properties.
Preferred stock	Class 1	Highest quality unaffiliated preferred stock.
	Class 2	High quality unaffiliated preferred stock.
	Class 3	Medium quality unaffiliated preferred stock.
	Class 4	Low quality unaffiliated preferred stock.
	Class 5	Lowest quality unaffiliated preferred stock.
	Class 6	Unaffiliated preferred stock, in or near default.
	Class 7	Affiliated preferred stock.
Common stock		Unaffiliated common stock.
		Affiliated common stock.
Short-term investments		All investments whose maturities at the time of acquisition were one year or less.
Premium Notes		Loans for payment of premiums.
Collateral loans		Loans made to a company or individual where the underlying security is in the form of bonds, stocks, or other marketable securities.
Separate account assets		Investments held in an account segregated from the general assets of the company, generally used to provide variable annuity benefits.
Other invested assets		Any invested assets that do not fit under the main categories above.
Individual life reserves		Funds set aside for payment of life insurance benefits under an individual contract rather than a company or group, underwriting based on individual profile.
Group life reserves		Funds set aside for payment of life insurance benefits under a contract with at least 10 people whereby all members have a common interest and are joined for a reason other than to obtain insurance.
Individual health premiums	Class 1	Usual and customary hospital and medical premiums which include traditional medical reimbursement plans that are subject to annual rate increases based on the company's claims experience.
	Class 2	Medicare supplement, dental, and other limited benefits anticipating rate increases.
	Class 3	Hospital indemnity plans, accidental death and dismemberment policies, and other limited benefits not anticipating rate increases.
	Class 4	Noncancellable disability income.
	Class 5	Guaranteed renewable disability income.

Group health premiums	Class 1	Usual and customary hospital and medical premiums which include traditional medical reimbursement plans that are subject to annual rate increases based on the company's claims experience.
	Class 2	Stop loss and minimum premium where a known claims liability is minimal or nonexistent.
	Class 3	Medicare supplement, dental, and other limited benefits anticipating rate increases.
	Class 4	Hospital indemnity plans, accidental death and dismemberment policies, and other limited benefits not anticipating rate increases.
	Class 5	Disability Income.
Managed care credit		Premiums for HMO and PPO business which carry less risk than traditional indemnity business. Included in this credit are provider compensation arrangements such as salary, capitation and fixed payment per service.
Premiums subject to rate guarantees		Health insurance premiums from policies where the rate paid by the policyholder is guaranteed for a period of time, such as one year, 15 months, 27 months or 37 months.
Individual claim reserves		Accident and health reserves for claims on individual policies.
Group claim reserves		Accident and health reserves for claims on group policies.
Reinsurance		Amounts recoverable on paid and unpaid losses for all reinsurance ceded; unearned premiums on accident and health reinsurance ceded; and funds held with unauthorized reinsurers.
Policy loans		Loans against the cash value of a life insurance policy.
Life reserves		Reserves for life insurance claims net of reinsurance and policy loans.
Individual annuity reserves		Reserves held in order to pay off maturing individual annuities or those surrendered before maturity.
Group annuity reserves		Reserves held in order to pay off maturing group annuities or those surrendered before maturity.
GIC reserves		Reserves held to pay off maturing guaranteed interest contracts.

Table 2. Bond Default Rates - potential losses as a percent of bond portfolio

Bond Rating	(1) Moody's 15 Yr Rate (%)	(2) Moody's 12 Yr Rate (%)	(3) Worst Year (%)	(4) 3 Cum. Recession Years (%)	(5) Weiss 15 Year Rate (%)	(6) Assumed Loss Rate (%)	(7) Losses as % of Holdings (%)	(8) RACR #2 Rate (%)
Aaa	2.80	1.60	0.10	0.30	1.89	50	0.95	1.00
Aa	2.00	1.60	0.20	0.60	2.19	50	1.09	1.00
A	3.30	2.50	0.40	1.20	3.67	55	2.02	1.00
Baa	7.20	5.50	1.10	3.26	8.58	60	5.15	5.00
Ba	20.10	17.90	8.40	23.08	36.47	65	23.71	15.00
B	33.70	32.50	21.60	50.80	62.24	70	43.57	30.00

Comments On Target Capital Percentages

The factors that are chiefly responsible for the conservative results of our Risk-Adjusted Capital Ratios are the investment risks of bond Classes 2 - 6, mortgages, real estate and affiliate common stock as well as the interest rate risk for annuities and GICs. Comments on the basis of these figures are found below. Additional comments address factors that vary, based on particular performance or risk characteristics of the individual company.

Bonds   Target capital percentages for bonds are derived from a model that factors in historical cumulative bond default rates from the last 20 years and the additional loss potential during a prolonged economic decline. The continuance of post-World War II prosperity is by no means certain. Realistic analysis of potential losses must factor in the possibility of severe economic reversal. **Table 2** shows how this was done for each bond rating classification. A 15-year cumulative default rate is used (column 1), due to the 15-year average maturity at issue of bonds held by life insurance companies. These are historical default rates for 1970-1990 for each bond class, taken from *Moody's Studies Loss Potential of Life Insurance Assets*.

To factor in the additional loss potential of a severe three-year-long economic decline, we reduced the base to Moody's 12-year rate (column 2), determined the worst single year experience (column 3), spread that experience over three years (column 4), and added the historical 12-year rate to the 3-year projection to derive Weiss Ratings 15-year default rate (column 5). Note: Due to the shrinking base of nondefaulted bonds in each year, column 4 may be somewhat less than three times column 3, and column 5 may be somewhat less than the sum of column 2 and column 4.

The next step was to determine the losses that could be expected from these defaults. This would be equivalent to the capital a company should have to cover those losses. Loss rates were assigned for each bond class (column 6), based on the fact that higher-rated issues generally carry less debt and the fact that the debt is also better secured, leading to higher recovery rates upon default. Column 7 shows losses as a percent of holdings for each bond class.

Column 8 shows the target capital percentages that are used in RACR #2 (Table 1, RACR #2 column, Bonds - classes 1 to 6).

Regulations limiting junk bond holdings of insurers to a set percent of assets are a tacit acknowledgement that the 10% and 20% maximum reserve requirements used by State Insurance Commissioners (Table 1, NAIC column, Bonds-classes 4, 5 and 6) are inadequate. If the figure adequately represented full loss potential, there would be no need to limit holdings through legislation since an adequate loss reserve would provide sufficient capital to absorb potential losses.

Mortgages

Mortgage default rates for the Risk-Adjusted Capital Ratios are derived from historical studies of mortgage and real estate losses in selected depressed markets. The rate for RACR #2 (Table 1, RACR #2 column, Mortgages – 90 days overdue) will vary between 3.8 and 25%, based on the performance of the company's mortgage portfolio in terms of mortgage loans 90 days or more past due, in process of foreclosure and foreclosed during the previous year.

Real Estate

The 33% rate (Table 1, RACR #2 column, Real Estate – Class 2) used for potential real estate losses in Weiss ratios is based on historical losses in depressed markets. It avoids the commonly made assumption that the continuous appreciation of property values experienced since World War II must inevitably continue.

Affiliate Common Stock

The target capital rate on affiliate common stock for RACR #2 can vary between 33% and 100% (Table 1, RACR #2 column, Common stock - Affiliate) depending on the financial strength of the affiliate and the prospects for obtaining capital from the affiliate should the need arise.

Insurance Risk

Calculations of target capital for insurance risk vary according to categories. For individual and group life insurance, target capital is a percentage of net amount at risk (total amount of insurance in force less reserves). Individual and group health insurance risk is calculated as a percentage of premium. Categories vary from "usual and customary hospital and medical premiums" where risk is relatively low, because losses from one year are recouped by annual rate increases to "noncancellable disability income" where the risk of loss is greater because disability benefits are paid in future years without the possibility of recovery.

Reinsurance

This factor varies with the quality of the reinsuring companies and the type of reinsurance being used (e.g. co-insurance, modified co-insurance, yearly renewable term, etc.).

Interest Rate Risk On Annuities

The 1 - 5% rate on individual annuities as a percentage of reserves (Table 1, RACR #2 column 3, Individual annuity reserves) and the 1 - 3% rate for group annuities as a percentage of reserves (Table 1, RACR #2 column 3, Group annuity reserves and GICs) are derived from studies of potential losses that can occur when assets and liabilities are not properly matched.

Companies are especially prone to losses in this area for one of two reasons: (1) They promise high interest rates on their annuities and have not locked in corresponding yields on their investments. If interest rates fall, the company will have difficulties earning the promised rate. (2) They lock in high returns on their investments but allow policy surrenders without market value adjustments. If market values decline and surrenders increase, liquidity problems can result in substantial losses.

The target capital figure used for each company is based on the surrender characteristics of its policies, the interest rate used in calculating reserves and the actuarial analysis found in New York Regulation 126 filing or similar studies where applicable.

RECENT INDUSTRY FAILURES
2016

Institution	Headquarters	Industry	Date of Failure	At Date of Failure Total Assets ($Mil)	At Date of Failure Safety Rating
Consumers Choice Health Ins. Co	S Carolina	Health	01/06/16	92.4	D- (Weak)
Moda Health Plan Inc	Oregon	Health	01/28/16	445.5	D+ (Weak)
Family Health Hawaii MBS	Hawaii	Health	04/07/16	5.5	D (Weak)
Health Republic Ins. of NY Corp	New York	Health	04/22/16	525.3	D+ (Weak)
HealthyCT Inc.	Connecticut	Health	07/01/16	112.3	D+ (Weak)
Land of Lincoln Mut Hlth Ins. Co	Illinois	Health	07/14/16	107.8	D+ (Weak)
Excalibur Reins Corp	Pennsylvania	P&C	07/18/16	9.0	U (Unrated)
Castlepoint National Ins. Co	California	P&C	07/28/16	355.2	C- (Fair)
Freelancers Consumer Operated	New Jersey	Health	09/12/16	135.3	D+ (Weak)

2015

Institution	Headquarters	Industry	Date of Failure	At Date of Failure	
				Total Assets ($Mil)	Safety Rating
Millers Classified Ins Co	Illinois	P&C	01/20/15	2.7	E (Very Weak)
Eveready Ins Co	New York	P&C	01/29/15	10.6	E- (Very Weak)
Jordan Funeral and Ins Co, Inc	Alabama	L&H	02/17/15	1.1	U (Unrated)
Drivers Insurance Co	New York	P&C	03/12/15	3.0	E- (Very Weak)
Lumbermens UW Alliance	Missouri	P&C	05/19/15	354.3	E- (Very Weak)
Pinelands Ins Co RRG, Inc	D. C.	P&C	08/25/15	4.9	E (Very Weak)
Louisiana Health Cooperative, Inc	Louisiana	Health	09/01/15	59.5	E (Very Weak)
Affirmative Ins Co	Illinois	P&C	09/16/15	181.2	E (Very Weak)
Affirmative Casualty Ins Co	Louisiana	P&C	10/05/15	32.6	D+ (Weak)
Affirmative Direct Ins Co	New York	P&C	10/05/15	5.3	U (Unrated)
Nevada Health Co-op	Nevada	Health	10/14/15	47.9	E- (Very Weak)
Winhealth Partners	Wyoming	Health	10/21/15	34.0	D (Weak)
Kentucky Health Cooperative Inc	Kentucky	Health	10/29/15	189.5	D+ (Weak)
Meritus Mutual Health Partners	Arizona	Health	10/30/15	45.8	D (Weak)
Meritus Health Partners	Arizona	Health	10/30/15	43.0	D+ (Weak)
Regis Ins Co	Pennsylvania	P&C	10/30/15	.6	E- (Very Weak)
Arches Mutual Ins Co	Utah	Health	11/02/15	77.2	D (Weak)
Lincoln General Ins Co	Pennsylvania	P&C	11/05/15	65.6	E- (Very Weak)
Advantage Health Solutions Inc	Indiana	Health	11/06/15	64.2	E (Very Weak)
Colorado Hlth Ins Cooperative Inc	Colorado	Health	11/10/15	108.7	D+ (Weak)
Consumers Mutual Ins of MI	Michigan	Health	11/13/15	60.4	E- (Very Weak)

2014

Institution	Headquarters	Industry	Date of Failure	Total Assets ($Mil)	Safety Rating
				At Date of Failure	
Union Mutual Ins Co	Oklahoma	P&C	01/24/14	5.1	E+ (Very Weak)
Commonwealth Ins Co	Pennsylvania	P&C	03/20/14	1.1	E (Very Weak)
LEMIC Ins Co	Louisiana	P&C	03/31/14	51.6	D (Weak)
Interstate Bankers Casualty Co	Illinois	P&C	04/16/14	16.2	D+ (Weak)
Freestone Ins Co	Delaware	P&C	04/28/14	421.2	D- (Weak)
Alameda Alliance For Health	California	Health	05/05/14	176.3	D (Weak)
Sunshine State Ins Co	Florida	P&C	06/03/14	22.9	E+ (Very Weak)
Physicians United Plan Inc	Florida	Health	06/09/14	110.7	E (Very Weak)
Red Rock Ins Co	Oklahoma	P&C	08/01/14	28.5	E+ (Very Weak)
DLE Life Ins Co	Louisiana	L&H	10/02/14	39.3	D- (Weak)
Mothe Life Ins Co	Louisiana	L&H	10/02/14	15.2	E- (Very Weak)
First Keystone RRG Inc	S. Carolina	P&C	10/21/14	13.6	E+ (Very Weak)
SeeChange Health Ins Co	California	Health	11/19/14	23.4	D (Weak)
PROAIR Risk Retention Grp Inc	Nevada	P&C	11/12/14	0.5	U (Unrated)
Florida Healthcare Plus, Inc	Florida	Health	12/10/14	11.1	U (Unrated)
CoOportunity Health, Inc	Iowa	Health	12/23/14	195.7	U (Unrated)

2013

Institution	Headquarters	Industry	Date of Failure	Total Assets ($Mil)	Safety Rating
				At Date of Failure	
Partnership Health Plan Inc	Wisconsin	Health	01/18/13	27.1	D (Weak)
Driver's Insurance Co	Oklahoma	P&C	02/21/13	33.1	D+ (Weak)
Lewis & Clark LTC RRG	Nevada	P&C	02/28/13	16.4	E (Very Weak)
Pride National Ins Co	Oklahoma	P&C	03/08/13	17.1	E+ (Very Weak)
Santa Fe Auto	Texas	P&C	03/08/13	22.9	E (Very Weak)
Ullico Casualty Co	Delaware	P&C	03/11/13	327.7	D (Weak)
Builders Ins Co Inc	Nevada	P&C	03/15/13	15.0	U (Unrated)
Nevada Contractors Ins Co Inc	Nevada	P&C	03/15/13	49.0	U (Unrated)
Universal Health Care Ins Co Inc	Florida	Health	03/22/13	106.1	C (Fair)
Universal Health Care Inc	Florida	Health	03/25/13	109.0	D (Weak)
Universal HMO of Texas	Texas	Health	04/18/13	15.3	C- (Fair)
Universal Health Care of NV Inc	Nevada	Health	06/03/13	1.9	D+ (Weak)
Liberty First RRG Ins Co	Utah	P&C	08/06/13	2.5	E (Very Weak)
United Contractors Ins Co Inc, RRG	Delaware	P&C	08/22/13	17.0	E (Very Weak)
Advance Physicians Ins RRG, Inc	Arizona	P&C	08/29/13	1.9	D (Weak)
Georgia Mutual Ins Co	Georgia	P&C	09/10/13	3.3	D (Weak)
Ocean Risk Retention Group	D. C.	P&C	09/6/13	7.9	E (Very Weak)
Gertrude Geddes Willis LIC	Louisiana	L&H	10/24/13	4.9	U (Unrated)
San Antonio Indemnity Co	Texas	P&C	10/31/13	2.8	E+ (Very Weak)
Higginbotham Burial Ins Co	Arkansas	L&H	11/04/13	1.3	U (Unrated)
Indemnity Ins Corp RRG	Delaware	P&C	11/07/13	83.2	D- (Weak)
Concert Health Plan Ins Co	Illinois	L&H	12/10/13	1.8	D- (Weak)
ICM Insurance Co	New York	P&C	12/23/13	5.0	E+ (Very Weak)

2012

Institution	Headquarters	Industry	Date of Failure	At Date of Failure Total Assets ($Mil)	Safety Rating
Autoglass Ins Co	New York	P&C	01/09/12	N/A	U (Unrated)
Health Facilities of CA Mut I C RRG	Nevada	P&C	01/10/12	1.9	U (Unrated)
Republic Mortgage Ins Co	N. Carolina	P&C	01/19/12	1.41	E (Very Weak)
CAGC Ins Co	N. Carolina	P&C	01/26/12	11.8	U (Unrated)
First Sealord Surety Inc.	Pennsylvania	P&C	02/08/12	15.2	U (Unrated)
Scaffold Industry Ins Co RRG, Inc	D. C.	P&C	05/01/12	5.1	E+ (Very Weak)
Financial Guaranty Ins Co	New York	P&C	06/11/12	2054.0	E- (Very Weak)
Global Health Plan & Ins Co	Puerto Rico	Health	06/13/12	1.1	U (Unrated)
Garden State Indemnity Co, Inc	New Jersey	P&C	06/22/12	2.93	E- (Very Weak)
AvaHealth Inc	Florida	HMO	06/27/12	3.3	E (Very Weak)
Lumbermens Mutual Casualty Co	Illinois	P&C	07/02/12	798.0	E (Very Weak)
American Manufacturers Mutual	Illinois	P&C	07/02/12	10.0	E+ (Very Weak)
Millers First Ins Co	Illinois	P&C	07/24/12	23.0	E (Very Weak)
American Motorists Ins Co	Illinois	P&C	08/16/12	19.7	D (Weak)
Home Value Ins Co	Ohio	P&C	08/31/12	3.5	U (Unrated)
Northern Plains Ins Co	S. Dakota	P&C	09/18/12	1.4	D (Weak)
Jamestown Ins Co RRG	S. Carolina	P&C	09/24/12	5.9	E+ (Very Weak)
Interstate Auto Ins Co	Maryland	P&C	10/11/12	4.6	D (Weak)
Regional Health Ins Co, RRG	D. C.	P&C	10/18/12	0.6	U (Unrated)
DC Chartered Health Plan Inc	D. C.	HMO	10/19/12	65.4	E- (Very Weak)
American Fellowship Mut Ins Co	Michigan	P&C	10/29/12	50.0	D (Weak)
Gramercy Ins Co	Texas	P&C	12/04/12	41.8	D (Weak)
Triad Guaranty ASR Corp	Illinois	P&C	12/11/12	16.1	B (Good)
Triad Guaranty Ins Corp	Illinois	P&C	12/11/12	766.7	E (Very Weak)

2011

Institution	Headquarters	Industry	Date of Failure	Total Assets ($Mil)	Safety Rating
Comm. Ins Alliance Reciprocal	Florida	P&C	01/26/11	N/A	N/A
Aequicap Ins Co	Florida	P&C	02/28/11	29.7	E+ (Very Weak)
US Rail Ins Co a RRG	Vermont	P&C	03/04/11	3.2	E (Very Weak)
Seminole Casualty Ins Co	Florida	P&C	03/15/11	35.6	D (Weak)
Qualicare Self-Insurance Trust	Georgia	HMO	4/21/11	N/A	U (Unrated)
Majestic Insurance Co	California	P&C	04/21/11	313.1	D- (Weak)
Reinsurance Co of America Inc	Illinois	P&C	04/27/11	7.1	D (Weak)
National Insurance Co	Puerto Rico	P&C	05/24/11	79.4	D+ (Weak)
Argus Fire & Casualty Ins Co	Florida	P&C	05/27/11	33.8	D (Weak)
Security Pacific Ins Co	Delaware	P&C	06/15/11	N/A	N/A
Great Republic Life Ins Co	Washington	L&H	07/07/11	16.9	E+ (Very Weak)
National Group Ins Co	Florida	P&C	08/01/11	9.53	E- (Very Weak)
Federal Motors Carriers RRG Inc	Delaware	P&C	08/18/11	11.9	E (Very Weak)
PMI Insurance Co	Arizona	P&C	08/19/11	436.9	D (Weak)
PMI Mortgage Ins Co	Arizona	P&C	08/19/11	2841.2	D (Weak)
Western Insurance Co	Utah	P&C	08/25/11	21.7	U (Unrated)
Homewise Preferred Ins Co	Florida	P&C	09/02/11	11.1	E (Very Weak)
American Sterling Ins Co	California	P&C	09/26/11	15.4	D (Weak)
Quality Health Plans Inc	Florida	HMO	10/17/11	45.0	E+ (Very Weak)
HomeWise Ins Co	Florida	P&C	11/18/11	84.7	D (Weak)
Southern Eagle Ins Co	Florida	P&C	12/06/11	18.6	D (Weak)
Minnesota Surety & Trust Co	Minnesota	P&C	12/02/11	1.5	E (Very Weak)

Glossary

This glossary contains the most important terms used in this publication.

Admitted Assets

The total of all investments and business interests that are acceptable under statutory accounting rules.

Asset/Liability Matching

The designation of particular investments (assets) to particular policy obligations (liabilities) so that investments mature at the appropriate times and with appropriate yields to meet policy obligations as they come due.

Asset Valuation Reserve (AVR)

A liability established under statutory accounting rules whose purpose is to protect the company's surplus from the effects of defaults and market value fluctuation on stocks, bonds, mortgages and real estate. This replaces the Mandatory Securities Valuation Reserve (MSVR) and is more comprehensive in that it includes a mortgage loss reserve, whereas the MSVR did not.

Average Recession

A recession involving a decline in real GDP which is approximately equivalent to the average of the postwar recessions of 1957-58, 1960, 1970, 1974-75, 1980 and 1981-82. It is assumed, however, that in today's market, the financial losses suffered from a recession of that magnitude would be greater than those experienced in previous decades. (See also "Severe Recession.")

Capital

Strictly speaking, capital refers to funds raised through the sale of common and preferred stock. Mutual companies have capital in the form of retained earnings. In a more general sense, the term capital is commonly used to refer to a company's equity or net worth, that is, the difference between assets and liabilities (i.e., capital and surplus as shown on the balance sheet).

Capital Resources

The sum of various resources which serve as a capital cushion to losses, including capital, surplus and Asset Valuation Reserve (AVR).

Capitalization Index

An index, expressed on a scale of zero to ten, with seven or higher considered excellent, that measures the adequacy of the company's capital resources to deal with a variety of business and economic scenarios. It combines Risk-Adjusted Capital Ratios #1 and #2 as well as a leverage test that examines pricing risk.

Cash and Demand Deposits

Includes cash on hand and on deposit. A negative figure indicates that the company has more checks outstanding than current funds to cover those checks. This is not an unusual situation for an insurance company.

Collateralized Mortgage Obligation (CMO)	Mortgage-backed bond that splits the payments from mortgage pools into different classes, called tranches. The investor may purchase a bond or tranche that passes through to him or her the principal and interest payments made by the mortgage holders in that specific maturity class (usually two, five, 10 or 20 years). The risk associated with a CMO is in the variation of the payment speed on the mortgage pool which, if different than originally assumed, can cause the total return to vary greatly.
Common and Preferred Stocks	See "Stocks".
Deposit Funds	Accumulated contributions of a group out of which immediate annuities are purchased as the individual members of the group retire.
Direct Premiums Written	Total gross premiums derived from policies issued directly by the company. This figure excludes the impact of reinsurance.
Safety Rating	Weiss Safety Ratings grade insurers on a scale from A (Excellent) to F (Failed). Ratings are based on five major factors: investment safety, policy leverage, capitalization, profitability and stability of operations.
Five-Year Profitability Index	See "Profitability Index."
Government Securities	Securities issued and/or guaranteed by U.S. and foreign governments which are rated as highest quality (Class 1) by state insurance commissioners. Included in this category are bonds issued by governmental agencies and guaranteed with the full faith and credit of the government. Regardless of the issuing entity, they are viewed as being relatively safer than the other investment categories. See "Investment Grade Bonds" to determine which items are excluded from this category.
Health Claims Reserve	Funds set aside from premiums for the eventual payment of health benefits after the end of the statement year.
Insurance Risk	The risk that the level of claims and related expenses will exceed current premiums plus reserves allocated for their payment.
Interest Rate Risk	The risk that, due to changes in interest rates, investment income will not meet the needs of policy commitments. This risk can be reduced by effective asset/liability matching.
Invested Assets	The total size of the firm's investment portfolio.
Investment Grade Bonds	This covers all investment grade bonds other than those listed in "Government Securities" (above). Specifically, this includes: (1) nonguaranteed obligations of governments; (2) obligations of governments rated as Class 2 by state insurance commissioners; (3) state and municipal bonds; plus (4) investment grade corporate bonds.

Investment Safety Index Measured on a scale of zero to ten, with ten being the best and seven or better considered strong. Each investment area is rated as to quality and vulnerability during an unfavorable economic environment (updated using quarterly data when available).

Investments in Affiliates Includes bonds, preferred stocks and common stocks, as well as other vehicles which many insurance companies use to invest in—and establish a corporate link with—affiliated companies

Life and Annuity Claims Reserve Funds set aside from premiums for the eventual payment of life and annuity claims.

Liquidity Index An index, expressed on a scale from zero to ten, with seven or higher considered excellent, which measures the company's ability to raise the necessary cash to meet policyholder obligations. This index includes a stress test which considers the consequences of a spike in claims or a run on policy surrenders. Sometimes a company may appear to have the necessary resources, but may be unable to sell its investments at the prices at which they are valued in the company's financial statements.

Mandatory Security Valuation Reserve (MSVR) Reserve for investment losses and asset value fluctuation mandated by the state insurance commissioners for companies registered as life and health insurers. As of December 31, 1992, this was replaced by the Asset Valuation Reserve.

Moderate Loss Scenario An economic decline from current levels approximately equivalent to that of the average postwar recession.

Mortgages in Good Standing Mortgages which are current in their payments (excludes mortgage-backed securities).

Net Premiums Written The total dollar volume of premiums retained by the company. This figure is equal to direct premiums written, plus reinsurance assumed less reinsurance ceded.

Noninvestment Grade Bonds Low-rated issues, commonly known as "junk bonds," which carry a high risk as defined by the state insurance commissioners. These include bond Classes 3 - 6.

Nonperforming Mortgages Mortgages which are (a) 90 days or more past due or (b) in process of foreclosure.

Other Investments Items not included in any of the other categories such as premium notes, collateral loans, short-term investments and other miscellaneous items.

Other Structured Securities Nonresidential mortgage related and other securitized loan-backed or asset-backed securities. This category also includes CMOs with noninvestment grade ratings.

Policy Leverage	A measure of insurance risk based on the relationship of net premiums to capital resources.
Policy Loans	Loans to policyholders under insurance contracts.
Profitability Index	Measured on a scale of zero to ten, with ten being the best and seven or better considered strong. A composite of five factors: (1) gain or loss on operations; (2) consistency of operating results; (3) impact of operating results on surplus; (4) adequacy of investment income as compared to the needs of policy reserves; and (5) expenses in relation to industry averages. Thus, the overall index is an indicator of the health of a company's current and past operations.
Purchase Money Mortgages	Mortgages written by an insurance company to facilitate the sale of property owned by the company.
Real Estate	Direct real estate investments including property (a) occupied by the company; (b) acquired through foreclosure and (c) purchased as an investment.
Reinsurance Assumed	Insurance risk acquired by taking on partial or full responsibility for claims on policies written by other companies. (See "Reinsurance Ceded.")
Reinsurance Ceded	Insurance risk sold to another company.
Risk-Adjusted Capital	The capital resources that would be needed in a worsening economic environment (same as "Target Capital").
Risk-Adjusted Capital Ratio #1	The capital resources which a company currently has, in relation to the resources that would be needed to deal with a moderate loss scenario. This scenario is based on historical experience during an average recession and adjusted to reflect current conditions and vulnerabilities (updated using quarterly data when available).
Risk-Adjusted Capital Ratio #2	The capital resources which a company currently has, in relation to the resources that would be needed to deal with a severe loss scenario. This scenario is based on historical experience of the postwar period and adjusted to reflect current conditions and the potential impact of a severe recession (updated using quarterly data when available).
Separate Accounts	Funds segregated from the general account and valued at market. Used to fund indexed products, such as variable life and variable annuity products.
Severe Loss Scenario	An economic decline from current levels in which the loss experience of the single worst year of the postwar period is extended for a period of three years. (See also "Moderate Loss Scenario".)
Severe Recession	A prolonged economic slowdown in which the single worst year of the postwar period is extended for a period of three years. (See also "Average Recession".)

Stability Index   Measured on a scale of zero to ten. This integrates a wide variety of factors that reflects the company's financial stability and diversification of risk.

State of Domicile   Although most insurance companies are licensed to do business in many states, they have only one state of domicile. This is the state which has primary regulatory responsibility for the company. Use the state of domicile to make absolutely sure that you have the correct company. Bear in mind, however, that this need not be the state where the company's main offices are located.

State Guaranty Funds   Funds that are designed to raise cash from existing insurance carriers to cover policy claims of bankrupt insurance companies.

Stocks   Common and preferred equities, including ownership in affiliates.

Surplus   The difference between assets and liabilities, including paid-in contributed surplus, plus the statutory equivalent of "retained earnings" in non-insurance business corporations.

Target Capital   See "Risk-Adjusted Capital."

Total Assets   Total admitted assets, including investments and other business assets. See "Admitted Assets."